Proceedings of the Institution of Mechanical Engineers

I Mech E

Flow Induced Vibrations

International Conference

20–22 May 1991
Bedford Hotel, Brighton

Sponsored by
Power Industries Division of the Institution of Mechanical Engineers

In association with
Japan Society of Mechanical Engineers
Société des Ingenieurs et Scientifiques de France
Verein Deutscher Ingenieure
Canadian Society for Mechanical Engineering

IMechE 1991–6

Published for IMechE by
Mechanical Engineering Publications Limited

The Publishers are not responsible for any statement made in this publication. Data, discussion and conclusions developed by authors are for information only and are not intended for use without independent substantiating investigation on the part of potential users.

Printed by Waveney Print Services Ltd, Beccles, Suffolk

Contents

Industrial implications of flow induced vibrations

L R WOOTTON, BSc, PhD, FEng, FICE, MRAeS
W S Atkins Engineering Sciences, Epsom, Surrey

1. The First Conference

The first International Conference on Flow induced vibrations in this series was held at Keswick in 1973 and, naturally, reports on work that in the main was carried out at that time. The industrial scene that provoked the organisation of this conference was quite different to the industrial scene now. In 1973, there was massive effort in the UK nuclear industry to resolve potential and actual flow-induced vibration problems in the AGR nuclear plant then being commissioned. During the late 1960's and early 1970's, the design, testing and commissioning of other, PWR, nuclear plant was at a peak worldwide and there was a concurrent interest in flow-induced vibration issues there. In civil engineering, the early 1970's marked the end of an era of major wind-sensitive structures such as, in the UK, the Severn, Forth, Humber, Erskine and Tamar bridges and, overseas, a number of exciting new cable stay bridges over the Rhine, new bridges in Norway and the new Bosphorous bridge. The development of the steel box section for suspension and cable stay bridges put great demands on those involved in aerodynamic stability. The rewards of their success were considerable with a reduction in the deck weight of more than a third in bridges initiated over the decade from about 1960. There had been a number of very tall chimney stacks built for coal fired power stations, following the contemporary environmental legislation. In London there were new tall offices under construction: in Germany, many town centres featured tall, elegant, concrete T.V. and micro-wave transmission towers often with restaurants. In the defence field, the UK was commissioning the new Polaris nuclear submarines and there was considerable activity in the design of heat exchangers. All of these were substantial industrial and infrastructure investments in major engineering activities, in which flow-induced vibration problems could, in the main, be readily identified if not so easily solved.

There was, clearly, a huge financial gearing on investment in flow-induced response R&D in terms of the elimination of risk of the projects not working.

At a less grand scale, there were parallel developments in manufacture and construction techniques that increased the risk of flow induced vibrations. The change of street lighting from cast iron and concrete to lightweight pre-fabricated welded steel poles reduced the structural damping and increased the sensitivity to dynamic wind loads. The change from all riveted skins and strengtheners on aircraft panels to integrally milled panels reduced damping in those structures. The drive for greater thermal efficiency resulted in thinner walled boiler tubes with associated effects on dynamic response and during the late 1960's there was a dramatic increase in dynamically-induced failures, the cause of which was far from obvious. Vibrations had been experienced in some process plants and pipelines due, it was thought, to instabilities in the internal flow and most notably where multi-phase flows could occur. Whilst such problems were of rare occurrence, they did indicate the need to carry out research of a fundamental nature to identify the parameters of the problem.

As further background, it should be noted that, in 1973, not a litre of oil had been produced from the North Sea and wave loading was analysed at the simplest level. The largest computers available for technical work in the early 1970's had the capacity equivalent to desk top machines of today. Compared with now, the tools and expertise for tackling the problems thrown up were much more limited. At the undergraduate level, structural dynamics had been taught in most engineering courses for many years but multi-mode analysis, even of simple mass-spring-damper models, and spectral analysis techniques would have only been mentioned. In industry, structural and fluid dynamics were treated as specialist topics, drawing as much as possible from equivalent static load assumptions or other simplifications.

In the aircraft industry, traditionally a leader in the application of advanced analytical, flutter calculations were carried out using experimentally derived derivatives in equations of motion in a style that had been in use since the Second World War. Finite element methods were being developed for the natural frequency and mode estimates in the early 1970's. The first forced-vibration and response calculations in industry were around 1973. The wider application of finite-element methods was just starting. In the UK, the Atomic Energy Authority had initiated the development of FE software, for static analysis, in the late 1960's.

In civil engineering the first applications were in static analysis, then in natural frequency and then, much later, in response calculations. On the fluid dynamic side, computational techniques were limited to potential and steady flow models. Experimental work dominated. Whilst the transducers were well developed (eg pietzo-electric accelerometers, constant temperature hot wires and high performance strain guages), data collection and analysis was still almost wholly analogue. A/D conversion, where available, would be off line. It was, therefore, commonly necessary to study the effect of parametric changes on response by implementing such changes on a physical model. In many cases there was strong pressure to use a full-scale or near full-scale model, or, alternatively, to use ingenious methods to overcome the problems of some degree of representation of all the necessary parameters. Effort tended to be put into the physical problems of modelling and data acquisition rather than in interpretation of the data in fundamental terms. A classic example of the investment then was the full-scale testing built by the Atomic Energy Authority to study the axial-flow induced motion of the nuclear fuel stringers for the Advanced Gas-cooled Reactors then under development in the UK. This huge facility operated for 20 years, closing last year. However, the failure to understand the cause of the problem and reduce its effects early and, most notably, the decision to design each AGR with distinctly different fuel stringer details meant that flow-induced vibrations cost the electricity authorities dearly.

In the area of acoustic-induced vibration, the late 1960's had seen the development of the use of the Miles equation for estimating the stress induced by broad band acoustic pressure uniformly distributed over a surface and design methods for sonic fatigue using one mode for the analysis of the plate.

The situation in the early 1970's was, therefore, one in which there were a number of flow-induced vibration issues which has significant economic implications. The techniques for solving these problems were understood, mainly in the academic or government research world, but were not established or proven in the industrial world.

As a consequence, the problems of flow-induced vibration were the province of the specialist, of whom there might be a few hundred worldwide. There was very little opportunity to leave general lessons from the testing work that constituted the activities in flow-induced vibrations. Most of this work was targeted to solve ad hoc problems or details of a wider issue. Perhaps, also, the 1973 conference was initiated as a result of some significant and dramatic failures. For example, the Emley moor television mast collapsed in March 1969, the fuel stringers of the UK's AGR reactors had problems of vibration, a number of heat exchangers (including one on a nuclear submarine) had failed in service, a new deep water jetty had experienced severe flow-induced motion, acoustic-induced vibration was identified as a cause of reduced life of components in nuclear reactors.

It was, therefore, in the hope that some general lessons might be learnt and that there might be value in interchange between workers in different industrial areas that the first conference was initiated. This paper is concerned with whether scientists and engineers made the progress that they might have hoped in the last twenty years and how lessons from history might help guide us in the future.

2. The Second, Third and Fourth Conference

Following the undoubted value of the first conference, second, third and fourth conferences were held (see Table 2) and now a fifth, though with several changes of organiser. The second and third conferences were, deliberately completely devoted to nuclear power issues and dominated by papers from the nuclear utilities and nuclear energy authorities, with a relatively small contribution (in quantity terms) from the academic world and from the private sector contractors. In retrospect, it is possible to view these two conferences as retrospective exhibitions of the flow-induced vibration problems that the nuclear industry had faced over the previous two decades. The Fourth conference reverted back to the style of the first: that is it brought together the activities of a number of different applications (nuclear, civil, process industry etc) with common technical threads of interest.

3. The Fifth Conference

The situation today is quite different in both industrial and technical terms and, as a result of both, the interest in flow-induced vibration has changed. On the industrial side, petrochemical and progress industries (including pharmaceuticals and food processing) have grown enormously. Much of the plant is assembled from standard or near standard components. Any flow-induced vibration problems that do occur in the first few components can be resolved. In any case, design checks can now be made.

There are probably fewer long span cable-stay or suspension bridges under construction now and, certainly, there has been a significant reduction of interest in very tall power station stacks. There will, of course, always be the record breakers: for example the new bridge in Japan that will soon be the longest in the world, and a 400m stack that is proposed for a power station in Hong Kong. Innovation such as the use of wind breaks to reduce wind loads on high sided vehicles produce new problems in the stability of long-span bridges also raises new problems.

The nuclear industry which was the centre of much of the expertise in this area in 1973 is now much more mature. It now has far less effort involved in design of new reactors and far more effort in reactor life extension. There are far greater demands on those concerned with acoustic-induced fatigue in reactors as a result. In heat exchangers, the pressure on designers is to improve operational and thermal efficiency and, at the same time, have a trouble free and very long life span.

The pressure to increase the energy efficiency of plant is now much stronger than 20 or so years ago. There has been at least a threefold in the real price of energy since 1973. This has been due to a number of factors such as increased oil prices (forced by OPEC countries), the more realistic costing of nuclear power (including enhanced safety requirements and the cost of decommissioning) and more stringent environmental legislation. In this context it should be rated that the major cause of the global greenhouse effect is energy and that the main use of energy is in moving fluids (table 3).

The most impressive industrial growth over the last two decades has, however, been in the exploitation of North Sea and other offshore oil and gas. In this area, we see huge technical developments some of which are reported at this conference. The need to exploit oil and gas from offshore reservoirs has been one of the most important stimulations for engineering in the last part of this century. Much of the offshore oil reserves are in politically stable parts of the world and, in any case, are well distributed geographically.

(Norwegian and British North Sea, Gulf of Mexico, West Africa, Brazil, Australia, SE Asia etc.). The challenge, well met by the engineers, is to produce oil and gas from these sources at a cost that is comparable with that of oil production from land based reservoirs in the Middle East. This exploitation started in water depths that are not regarded as modest (up to say 125m) but has now move into much deeper sites. Even at the shallower water depths, some interesting wave and current flow-induced vibration problems have had to be solved on the fixed platforms and drilling rigs. In deeper water, there is much economic benefit to be gained from the use of compliant structures and, de facto, this presents new challenges in the field of flow/structure interaction.

The last two decades have seen another important change that affects engineering style. Accidents such as Chernobyl, Piper Alpha, Swetso, Fixborough, Esso Valdives have made everyone aware of the consequences of failure in large nuclear or non-nuclear facilities. The need to reduce the risk of accidents is now fully apparent: there are positive attitudes to safety and environmental protection. A consequence of these pressures is the need for all engineering to be quality assured. Subjects such as flow-induced vibrations do not fit well into the new environment of codes of practice, quality management, quality assurance and audit trails.

4. What has been learnt

Over the last two decades, these conferences (including the 5th) have presented nearly 300 papers. Many of these report substantial pieces of work: the 5 largest experimental programmes described would, at today's prices, cost $50-$100 million. The whole programme of work described might, on the same basis, have cost around $250 million. More significant than the money, it represents the output from more than a thousand man years of key and high calibre technologists. Much of the effort described concerns the successful solution of specific problems but what have been the strategic developments in analysis, prediction and solution of flow-induced vibration problems in the past two decades.

First, dynamic structural analysis computational methods can now be used to give accurate modes and frequencies of almost all structural forms provided that they have linear elasticity and are of fixed mass. We are moving forward in the area of composite materials and other materials with non-linear elastic properties. There remains little or no progress in the estimation of structural damping. Indeed, the standard equation of motion in which damping is represented by a body velocity term has become so entrenched as the basis of all calculations that almost no attention is given to assessing the effect of other structural forms. Since analysis of vibration amplitudes is commonly strongly damping dependent, it is clear that the ommission of generic research in this area is important.

In the area of fluid forcing, computation of results from fundamental fluid dynamics simulations and interpretation of experimental data has developed enormously, particularly in the display of data, in spectral techniques and in the special properties of forces, acoustic pressures, structural response and so on. However, a subject such as the flow-induced dynamic forces of tube banks, is still far from the goal of being able to use analytical techniques as the basis of firm design practice. Significantly, an independent audit trail on many of the early research would show that the credibility gained through age and continued reference is, in practice, not deserved. Much of the early work would not stand up to the rigours of quality assurance procedures of the 1990's. Flow calculations have developed enormously but it is still questionable if they form the basis of reliable prediction methods.

5. Future Requirements

We are now in a situation where flow-induced vibration problems occur over a wide range of industries with relatively low frequency but commonly with serious effect when they do. Industries where this subject is of concern either for reasons of safety or in terms of operational efficiency include:

- Civil engineering - wind-induced motions.
- Power engineering - hydro power, aerogenerators.
- Offshore engineering - wave and current induced motions.
- Process engineering - single and multi-phase flows.
- Automotive - engine vibration.
- Nuclear engineering - heat exchangers and reactor flows.
- Aerospace - engine turbine blade vibration.

It is the diversity of these areas, the inherent technical complexity of the problems that make it difficult to build up expertise in any one centre. A common characteristic is the need to identify the cause of the vibration and to produce a solution that is efficient and effective in the shortest possible timescale. Taken across the industrial world and across many of these industries, however, it is possible to develop analytical techniques and verify their application. Many of the problems involve a wide range of complex technical disciplines such as fluid

dynamics (of internal flows, flow round bluff bodies and flutter), structural dynamics, materials technology, structural reliability and failure analysis. This breadth of expertise is seldom available in any single institution. It is also clear that the main benefit of conferences is not to educate attendees fully in the state of the art but, rather, it is to inform who knows how to deal with particular classes of problems. The end of this paper is therefore a proposal to carry out, at a European level first, an exercise with the following objectives:

- Identify the European centres of expertise and the direction of their current developments and research programmes. Some of these research activities are already part of CEC sponsored programmes.

- Develop improved framework for analysis and solution of problems.

- From this framework the relative merits of different techniques can be assessed. One of the key issues will be to assess the potential value of computational fluid dynamic techniques and the developments in other areas that are needed.

The overall objective is to reduce the cost of industry of maintaining expertise in flow-induced vibration problems by using the best available know how in their avoidance and solution. This will include development of methodologies (perhaps using Expert Systems) and techniques, training and education and the full use of previous experience.

Although the industrial challenges have changed since 1973 and much good work has been done in developing techniques since then, there remains the need to develop effective procedures for the control and elimination of flow induced vibration.

© IMechE 1991 C416/111

TABLE 1

Examples of flow-induced vibration issues in the early 1970's

Structure or facility	Potential Problem	Examples	Cost of failure in 1991 US dollars
Long span cable-staye suspension bridges	Deck motion Cable response Tower response	Forth, UK Severn, UK Lower Yar, Austral. Kniebruche, Germany Bosphorous, Turkey Humber, UK	$10 million plus possible loss due to closure
Television and communications towers	Vortex-induced motion of tower and aerials	Stuttgart, Germany Hanover, Germany Dusseldorf, Germany Emley Moor, UK Post Office Tower London, UK	$15 million plus loss of television and communications
Heat Exchanger, and pipes carrying flowing fluids	Cross-flow induced vibr. and failure. Internal flow induced motion	Process plant Coal-fired power stations Nuclear plant Nuclear submarines Industrial plant pipelines	$100 millions if major plant put out of action

TABLE 2

International Conferences on Flow-induced Vibration

Date and details	Papers		Author distribution	
1973, Keswick UK Atomic Energy Authority	Basic fluid dynamics Structural Respnse Acoustic vibration Heat exchanger and reactor problems Analysis & techniques	12 19 6 13 9	Nuclear utilities Civil Eng (wind) Other industry Academic	18 14 7 20 ── 59
1978, Keswick British Nuclear En. anad UKAEA	Nuclear fuel system Heat exchangers Acoustic excitation of nuclear core Seismic excitation Fluid dynamic excitation of nuclear core Plant and components Vibration monitoring	9 7 9 11 5 6 4	Nuclear Industry Academic	46 13 ── 59
1982, London British Nuclear Energy Society	Heat exchangers Nuclear core Seismic Acoustics Vibration monitoring	16 23 7 5 5	Nuclear industry Academic	48 8 ── 56

1987, Bowness-on-Windermere	Heat Exchangers	16	Nuclear utilities	7
	Hydraulics	11	Civil engineering	10
	Wind and vortex		Other industry	4
	shedding	14	Academic	22
	Analysis & simulation	7		
	Axial & annular flow	5		
				56

1991, Brighton Inst. of Mechanical Engineering	Offshore and marine	9	Nuclear utilities	14
	Heat exchangers	17	Civil Engineering	8
	Industrial valves etc	7	Other industry	22
	Damage	8		
	Theory	11		
	Wind	5		
	Experimental	8		
				65

TABLE 3

Examples of the movement of fluid in the creation of power and energy use

Fixed Power Sources

Coal-fired power stations	:	combustion process heat exchangers and turbines cooling circuit
Nuclear power	:	primary and secondary circuits, heat exchangers and turbines
Wind	:	aerodynamics of wind turbines
Hydro and tidal	:	hydraulic turbines

Transport

Road	:	internal combustion flows external aerodynamic flows over vehicles
Air	:	turbine engine combustion and flows aerodynamic flows
Rail	:	aerodynamics and domestic

Industrial, commercial

Process industries	:	production of hydrocarbon-based products, drinks, plastics, pharmaceuticals, gas compression, paints, concrete and other slurries.
Distribution	:	gas and oil pipelines and distribution.
Water supply	:	water purification, distribution and sewage disposal.
Domestic	:	refrigeration heating systems.
Commercial	:	heating and ventilation and air-conditioning food and drug refrigeration.

C146/106

A comparison of experimentally and theoretical determined lift coefficients for a transversely oscillating cylinder with rectangular cross-section

S DENIZ, MSc and T STAUBLI, PhD, MASME, MIAHR
ETH Zurich, Swiss Federal Institute of Technology, Zurich, Switzerland

SYNOPSIS

Fluid forces acting on an oscillating cylinder with rectangular cross-section (L/D = 2) were measured in a water channel. Experimentally determined force coefficients are compared with coefficients resulting from two different theoretical methods. The mathematical models employed are the classical quasi-steady theory of galloping and the unsteady aerofoil theory.

Comparison of experimental and theoretical values confirm that for high reduced velocities agreement is good. Furthermore, unsteady aerofoil theory predicts the magnitude of the lift force well for very low reduced velocities ($v_{red} > 6$) reflecting that unsteady aerofoil theory correctly models inertia effects. Phase predictions with unsteady aerofoil theory are qualitatively – for high reduced velocities also quantitatively – correct.

NOTATIONS

c_y coefficient of force acting normal to the side faces

c_L lift coefficient of force acting normal to the free-stream velocity

c_{Ls} $= c_L \sin\Theta$; lift component leading the displacement by $\pi/2$

$C(k)$ Theordorsen function

D thickness of cylinder

f_e frequency of oscillation

F_L lift force

$H_0^{(2)}$ Hankel function of second kind of order 0

$H_1^{(2)}$ Hankel function of second kind of order 1

L length of cylinder

Re $= V L/v$: Reynolds number

S $= f_e D/V$: Strouhal number

S_{NO} Strouhal number of non-oscillating cylinder

V free stream velocity

V_{red} $= V/f_e D$: reduced velocity

V_{rel} relative velocity

y displacement

α angle of incidence

η $= y/D$: amplitude of displacement

Θ phase angle between displacement and lift force

$\wedge$ amplitudes

1 INTRODUCTION

Recently Luo and Bearman (1) applied unsteady aerofoil theory for prediction of fluctuating lift on a transversely oscillating square-section cylinder. Unsteady aerofoil theory allows to give estimates of inertia and of shed vorticity. Accordingly, the unsteady aerofoil theory gives better estimates of lift especially for the lower range of reduced velocities where inertia and shed vorticity show increased influence.

On the other hand, the quasi-steady theory of Parkinson (2, 3) is based on the force curves measured on a stationary cylinder.

In contrast to unsteady aerofoil theory the quasi-steady model takes into account that force coefficients do not increase linearly for larger angles of incidence of the relative flow.

However, in the range of reduced velocities V_{red} where the flow field is dominated by resonance with the Kármán vortex street neither model accurately predicts lift coefficients. The limits up to which the models are applicable will be shown in the following by comparison with experimental data.

Unsteady aerofoil theory bases on potential flow and assumes a Kutta condition. Originally it was derived by Theodorsen (5) to describe fluid forces on thin aerofoils oscillating with small amplitudes. However, it also allows to give estimates of inertia and of shed vorticity for bluff bodies as demonstrated by Luo and Bearman (1).

The time dependent lift force for oscillations transversely to the free stream is given by

$$F_L = -c_{mo}\, \rho\, \frac{\pi L^2}{4}\, \ddot{y} - \frac{\partial c_L}{\partial \alpha}\, \rho\, V\, \frac{L}{2}\, C(k)\, \dot{y} \tag{1}$$

For the cylinder of rectangular cross-section with $L/D = 2$ as depicted on Fig. 1 the potential flow inertia coefficient c_{mo} was taken as 1.36. The slope determined from the lift-curve for $\alpha = 0°$ is $\partial c_L/\partial\alpha = -4.85$ and for $\alpha = 10°$ $\partial c_L/\partial\alpha = 6.32$. $C(k)$ is Theodorsen's function.

$$C(k) = H_1^{(2)}(k)\,/\,H_1^{(2)}(k) + i H_o^{(2)}(k) \tag{2}$$

with $k = \pi/V_{red}$

The Theodorsen function is a complex function and, therefore, a phase angle between lift F_L and displacement y results. This phase angle determines the ranges in reduced velocity of positive energy transfer from the fluid to the cylinder and thus the ranges of possible self-exited body oscillations. These ranges are explicitly shown on Fig. 7 and 8.

Quasi-steady theory, also reviewed by Luo and Bearman (1), assumes a fluid force

(side force coefficient c_y) on the cylinder which leads the displacement by $\pi/2$. Measurements of the force coefficient c_y for varying angles of incidence α on a stationary cylinder (Fig. 1) are represented by an odd power polynominal:

$$c_y(\alpha) = A(\alpha) - B(\alpha)^3 + C(\alpha)^5 - D(\alpha)^7 \tag{3}$$

where for the rectangular cylinder:

A = -4.75	B = 32.4
C = 11 000	D = 187 000

This polynomial is valid for a limited range of incidence: $-12° < \alpha < 12°$.

For quasi-steady oscillations with $\alpha = \text{atan}[(dy/dt)/V]$ follows from equation (3) for the lift coefficient in case of plunging oscillation:

$$c_y(\dot{y}/V) = A(\dot{y}/V) - B(\dot{y}/V)^3 + C(\dot{y}/V)^5 + D(\dot{y}/V)^7 \tag{4}$$

In contrast to unsteady aerofoil theory, force coefficients determined with this quasi-steady method will not increase linearly with oscillation amplitude (see Fig. 5).

2 EXPERIMENTS

Experiments were performed in a towing tank filled with water. The test-cylinder was externally forced to oscillate by an hydraulically driven shaker mechanism. Fluid forces acting on the cylinder were measured as well as their phase angle with respect to the cylinder displacement. The experimental arrangement and the applied measuring technique are described in detail by Staubli (4).

Fig. 1 shows the geometry (L = 60 mm and D = 30 mm) of the investigated profile and the force curves measured on a stationary cylinder for varying angle of incidence and for three different Reynolds numbers. Downward forces are found for angles of incidence between $\alpha = 0°$ and $10°$.

In case of cylinder oscillations, parameters varied in this experimental study were the amplitude ($\hat{\eta} = \hat{y}/D = 0.01 - 1.5$) and the frequency of oscillation ($S = f_e D/V = 0.01 - 0.3$).

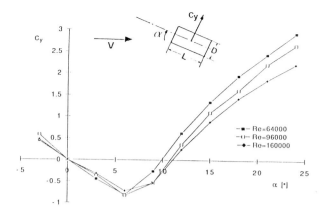

Fig. 1 Geometry of rectangular section (L/D = 2) and force curve of a stationary cylinder for three different Reynolds numbers.

The chosen frequency range allowed to investigate interaction of form induced flow separation effects with vortex shedding. Resonance and drastic changes of phase jumps are observed in the region of synchronization (see Fig. 6 to 8). The data presented in this paper only focus at the frequency component at the excitation frequency f_e. This component results from frequency decomposition of the measured signals. Force fluctuations due to the natural vortex shedding at a frequency different from the excitation frequency are not presented.

Data will be displayed as a function of reduced velocity V_{red}, since the comparison of experimental and theoretical values agree best for high reduced velocities, that is for low excitation frequencies ($V_{red} = V/f_e D$). For this reason it was prefered not to display data as a function of excitation frequency f_e.

It should be noted that coefficients displayed in the following represent amplitudes and not RMS-values ($\hat{c}_L = c_{Lrms} \sqrt{2}$)

3 RESULTS

Fig. 2 shows the lift coefficients $\hat{c}_{Ls}$ for oscillations of three different oscillation amplitudes $\hat{\eta}$. Experimental data are compared to the quasi-steady and the unsteady models.

The lift coefficient $\hat{c}_{Ls}$ is the component of the unsteady lift force responsible for energy transfer from the fluid to the body or from the body to the fluid, since it is the component which leads the displacement by $\pi/2$. $\hat{c}_{Ls}$ is computed from the magnitude of the lift force at the exitation frequency f_e and the phase Θ between diplacement and lift force: $\hat{c}_{Ls} = \hat{c}_L \sin\Theta$. Positive values of $\hat{c}_{Ls}$ indicate an energy transfer from the fluid to the body. Accordingly, an elastically mounted cylinder would undergo self-excited oscillations for the ranges of reduced velocity where $\hat{c}_{Ls}$ is positive.

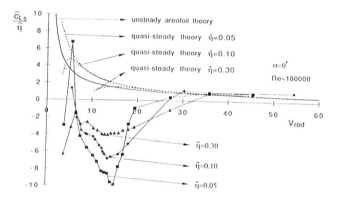

Fig. 2 Lift coefficient $\hat{c}_{Ls}$ (normalized with $\hat{\eta}$) as a function of reduced velocity V_{red}; comparison of experiment with quasi-steady theory and with unsteady aerofoil theory.

Theoretical results, displayed in Fig. 2 show always positive values of $\hat{c}_{Ls}/\hat{\eta}$, which is expected since $\partial c_y/\partial\alpha < 0$ for $\alpha = 0°$. Unsteady aerofoil theory and quasi-steady theory agree well with each other for reduced velocities $V_{red} > 20$. Theory and measurements start deviating for $V_{red} < 30$, since the effects of Kármán vortex shedding dominate the force coefficients. Above this range galloping oscillations will occur without interaction with the Kármán vortex shedding. It should be noted that, according to our measurements, both theories slightly underestimate for large reduced velocities the force coefficients. Unsteady aerofoil theory by Luo/Bearman assumes a linear relationship of lift force and amplitude of oscillation. Because of this linear relationship, curves for different amplitudes of oscillation collapse to one single curve in Fig. 2. Quasi-steady theory distinguishes three different curves for reduced velocities $V_{red} < 20$ according to the three different amplitudes of oscillation depicted on the graph of Fig. 2. However only at low reduced velocities these three curves deviate from each other. Comparison with experimental data demonstrates that neither theory is, of course, valid in the range where vortex interaction occurs.

More details on the dependence on amplitude of oscillation is given in Fig. 5 for $V_{red} = 35.8$.

Experimental data show that for $V_{red} \approx 5$ vortex induced forces may be cause of flow induced oscillation of limited amplitudes. These amplitudes are limited since $\hat{c}_{Ls}$ becomes negative for $\hat{\eta} > 0.2$ as shown on Fig. 2.

Measurements of the lift coefficient $\hat{c}_{Ls}$ for small amplitudes of oscillation ($\hat{\eta} = 0.05$) are displayed on Fig. 3. Results of measurements without incidence ($\alpha = 0°$) and with a mean incidence of $\alpha = 10°$ are compared with unsteady aerofoil theory. For high reduced velocities no galloping oscillations will be possible for the case with incidence ($\alpha = 10°$) due to the negative values of $\hat{c}_{Ls}$ (Theoretical values are negative for $\alpha = 10°$ since $\partial c_y / \partial \alpha > 0$).

Kármán vortex induced energy transfer from the fluid to the cylinder is observed for reduced velocities below the values of the reduced velocities which correspond to the natural vortex shedding of the non-oscillating cylinder; an observation which is also typical for cylinders of different shapes, including circular cylinders.

The Strouhal numbers of the non-oscillating cylinder with and without incidence were determined from experiment as: $S_{NO(\alpha=0°)} = 0.078$ and $S_{NO(\alpha=10°)} = 0.13$, and the corresponding reduced velocities as: $V_{red(\alpha=0°)} = 12.8$ and $V_{red(\alpha=10°)} = 8.0$.

The results of the comparison of measurements and unsteady aerofoil theory according Luo/Bearman show reasonable coincidence at high reduced velocities. Especially the case with incidence shows good agreement for reduced velocities down to $V_{red} = 15$.

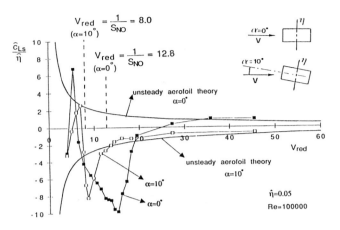

Fig. 3 Normalized lift coefficient $\hat{c}_{Ls}/\hat{\eta}$ for small amplitude of oscillation ($\hat{\eta} = 0.05$) without incidence ($\alpha = 0°$) and with incidence of $\alpha = 10°$; comparison of experiment with unsteady aerofoil theory.

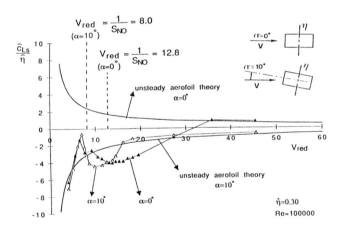

Fig. 4 Normalized lift coefficient $\hat{c}_{Ls}/\hat{\eta}$ for large amplitude of oscillation ($\hat{\eta} = 0.30$) without incidence ($\alpha = 0°$) and with incidence of $\alpha = 10°$; comparison of experiment with unsteady aerofoil theory.

Fig. 4, which shows $\hat{c}_{Ls}$ for larger amplitudes of oscillation ($\hat{\eta} = 0.3$), demonstrates that unsteady aerofoil theory overestimates the danger of flow induced vibrations for low reduced velocities in case of large amplitudes of oscillation (lightly damped mechanical systems).

The reason for the overestimation of the exciting forces is demonstrated on Fig. 5

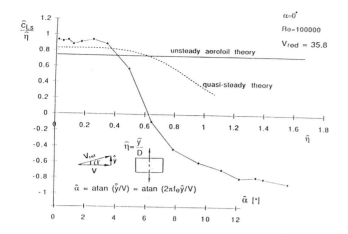

Fig. 5 Normalized lift coefficient $\hat{c}_{Ls}/\hat{\eta}$ as a function of the oscillation amplitude $\hat{\eta}$; comparison of experiment with quasi-steady theory and with unsteady aerofoil theory.

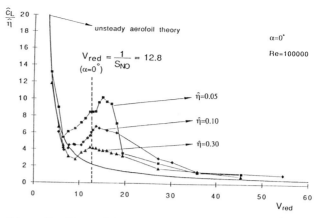

Fig. 6 Normalized lift coefficient $\hat{c}_L/\hat{\eta}$ as a function of reduced velocity; comparison of experiment with unsteady aerofoil theory.

for a reduced velocity $V_{red} = 35.8$ which is in a range where "pure" galloping occurs, well above the Kármán vortex induced effects. The graph shows the normalized lift coefficient $\hat{c}_{Ls}/\hat{\eta}$ as a function of the oscillation amplitude $\hat{\eta}$.

For amplitudes $\hat{\eta} < 0.4$ the agreement of theories and measurements is good. For larger amplitudes measured coefficients $\hat{c}_{Ls}$ rapidly decay and become negative.

Since measurements show that the normalized magnitude of the lift coefficient $\hat{c}_L/\hat{\eta}$ remains constant for increasing amplitude of oscillation this decay of $\hat{c}_{Ls}/\hat{\eta}$ and its change of sign is due to a gradual change in phase for increasing amplitude of oscillation.

Unsteady aerofoil theory assumes a linear increase of $\hat{c}_{Ls}$ with amplitude which results as a horizontal line in the display of $\hat{c}_{Ls}/\hat{\eta}$.

The coefficients determined with quasi-steady theory do not increase linearly with amplitude in accord with the lift coefficients of the stationary cylinder which only are linear for angles of incidence $\alpha < 6°$.

While the coefficient $\hat{c}_{Ls}$ includes phase information, the magnitude of the lift coefficient $\hat{c}_L$ at the frequency of excitation f_e does not depend on the phase.

Fig. 6 shows a comparison of measured values of $\hat{c}_L$ with unsteady aerofoil theory according Luo/Bearman. The comparison

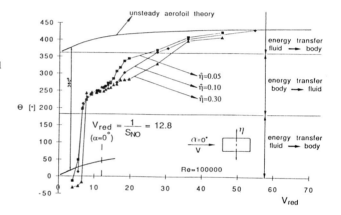

Fig. 7 Phase Θ between displacement and lift force as a function of reduced velocity without incidence; comparison of experiment with unsteady aerofoil theory.

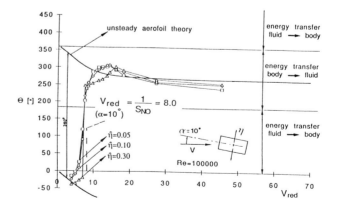

Fig. 8 Phase Θ between displacement and lift force as a function of reduced velocity for a mean incidence of $\alpha = 10°$; comparison of experiment with unsteady aerofoil theory.

shows reasonable agreement for high but also for very low reduced velocities. Generally the amplitudes are slightly underestimated.

The range in between is dominated by the Kármán vortex effects. It should be noted that in this range the coefficients do not increase linearly with amplitude of oscillation even for very small values of $\hat{\eta}$. In this range the coefficients $\hat{c}_L$ are rather independent of the oscillation amplitude.

The two cases of oscillation without incidence ($\alpha = 0°$) and with a mean incidence ($\alpha = 10°$) are compared in the Fig. 7 and 8. The phase angles Θ between lift and displacement are displayed as a function of reduced velocity for three different amplitudes of oscillation. The prediction of quasi-steady theory for this angle Θ generally is $\pi/2$ respectively $2\pi+\pi/2$ since this is the basic assumption of quasi-steady theory.

Measurements show for $\alpha = 0°$, in Fig. 7, increasing angles Θ for high reduced velocities. Unsteady aerofoil predicts the same trend but at too low reduced velocities. In the experiment a phase jump is observed in the range of Kármán vortex effects. Such jumps are inherent to vortex interactions for many different types of cylinders, but obviously cannot be predicted by aerofoil theory.

At reduced velocities below Kármán vortex effects (high oscillation frequencies) unsteady aerofoil theory gives inaccurate estimates of the phase angle Θ because the lift curve slope values employed in the unsteady aerofoil approximate at at low reduced velocities only roughly the real fluid forces.

For the case with a mean incidence of $\alpha = 10°$, unsteady aerofoil theory again predicts the trend of the curves of the phase angle Θ. The quantitative prediction for $V_{red} > 15$ is even better than for $\alpha = 0°$. Again, the phase jump is of course not predictable. Unfortunately the case of incidence of $\alpha = 10°$ is of less practical importance since no flow induced vibration of galloping type will occur ($\hat{c}_{Ls} < 0$),

however this comparison shows the potential power of unsteady aerofoil theory in prediction of lift and phase.

4 CONCLUSIONS

That quasi-steady theory by Parkinson predicts for high reduced velocities well lift forces and flow induced vibration was demonstrated by various authors through comparisons of predictions with experiments for cylinders of different shapes. The limit of quasi-steady theory, in case of incidence $\alpha = 0°$, is found approximatively at reduced velocities of $V_{red} \approx 30$ for a rectangular cylinder with $L/D = 2$. For an incidence of $\alpha = 10°$ this limit goes down to a reduced velocity of $V_{red} \approx 15$.

Equally, unsteady aerofoil theory employed by Luo/Bearman gives for high reduced velocities good results and additionally it predicts physically correct trends at low reduced velocities. However the quantitative agreement at lower reduced velocities is not very good except for the magnitude of the lift force at very low reduced velocities ($v_{red} < 6$). This agreement reflects that unsteady aerofoil theory well predicts inertia (added mass) effects at very low reduced velocities.

Besides inertia effects, the cylinder will shed motion-induced vortices at low reduced velocities. Such vortex formation depends largely on the shape of the oscillating cylinder, e.g. reattachement may occur. Agreement of theory and experiment will be better for aerofoil-type cylinders. For other types of cylinders, such as the rectangular cylinder investigated here, using the lift curve slope values in the unsteady aerofoil approach that have been obtained from stationary cylinders signifies a rough estimate of the forces induced by a complex flow.

Unsteady aerofoil theory includes - in contrast to quasi-steady theory - phase information of the resulting lift force. This phase together with the magnitude of the force are a measure for the energy transfer from the fluid to the cylinder. For cases with positive energy transfer – cases of major practical interest – phase prediction with unsteady aerofoil theory is good for $V_{red} > 35$. For the case with incidence of $\alpha = 10°$ – a case where no galloping oscillation occurs – the agreement of prediction and experiment is good for $V_{red} > 15$. It should be noted that natural vortex shedding occurs for $\alpha = 0°$ at forty percent lower frequencies than for $\alpha = 10°$ and therefore Kármán vortices affect coefficients at higher reduced velocities for the case without incidence. An improvement of unsteady aerofoil theory concerning the dependency on amplitude of oscillation (see Fig. 5) could be achieved introducing the lift curve or its derivative of the stationary cylinder as it is done for quasi-steady theory.

Predictions within the range influenced by Kármán vortex effects are physically incorrect with either theory, but it is important to know that such predictions of oscillations of elastically mounted bodies will generally give adequate and safe estimates.

REFERENCES

(1) Luo, S.C. and Bearman, P.W. Prediction of Fluctuating Lift on a Transversely Oscillating Square-Section Cylinder, *J. of Fluids and Structures*, 1990, 4, 219-228.

(2) Parkinson, G.V. and Brooks, N.P.H. On the aeroelastic stability of bluff cylinders, *J. of Applied Mechanics*, 1961, 28, 225-258.

(3) Parkinson, G.V. and Smith, J.D. The square prism as an aeroelastic non-linear oscillator, *Quarterly Journal of Mechanics and Applied Mathematics*, 1964, 17, 225-239.

(4) Staubli, T. Eine Untersuchung der instationären Kräfte beim querangeströmten, erzwungen schwingenden Kreiszylinder, PhD Thesis, Swiss Federal Institute of Technology, Zürich, No 73 22, 1983.

(5) Theodorsen, T. A General Theory of Aerodynamic Instability and Mechanism of Flutter, NACA Technical report No. 496, 1939, 413-433.

Correlation measurements along a vibrating cylinder near a wall in oscillatory flows

A KOZAKIEWICZ, PhD, B M SUMER, PhD and J FREDSØE, PhD,
Institute of Hydrodynamics and Hydraulic Engineering, Technical University of
Denmark, Lyngby, Denmark

SYNOPSIS   Spanwise correlation measurements have been made for a transversely vibrating cylinder placed near a wall and exposed to oscillatory flows. The investigated range of gap−to−diameter ratio is 0−2.3, that of Keulegan−Carpenter number is 6−65 and the range of double amplitude−to−diameter ratio is 0−0.25. It was found that the correlation coefficient increases significantly with increasing amplitudes of vibrations. It was also found that the effect of the close proximity of a wall on the correlation coefficient is not quite significant.

NOTATION

c_p	pressure coefficient
D	cylinder diameter
KC	Keulegan−Carpenter number
M	number of oscillatory−flow cycles sampled
N	number of transverse vibrations for one cycle of oscillatory flow
$\bar{p}$	pressure
P_o	hydrostatic pressure
P	mean pressure
p'	fluctuating pressure
$R(z,\omega t)$	correlation coefficient
$R(z)$ or R	period−averaged correlation coefficient
Re	Reynolds number
t	time
T	period of oscillatory flow
U	outer flow velocity
U_m	maximum value of the outer flow velocity
z	separation distance in spanwise direction
α	angular position of pressure transducers
ζ	spanwise coordinate
ν	kinematic viscosity
ρ	fluid density
ω	angular frequency of oscillatory flow

1   INTRODUCTION

Knowledge about the correlation along a cylinder becomes an impor−tant issue, when the total fluid load on cylinders is considered. It is known that the correlation varies with Reynolds number, surface roug−hness and turbulence, King (1). It is also known that the vibrations of the cylinder has a significant effect on correlations; it has been de−monstrated that the correlation for a transversely vibrations cylinder exposed to a steady current increases tremendously with increasing amplitudes of vibrations, Koopman (2), Toebes (3) and Ramberg and Griffin (4).

Correlation measurements have also been made for stationary cylinders exposed to oscillatory flows, Obasaju, Bearman and Graham (5). These measurements have clearly demonstrated that the correla−tion is strongly dependent on the Keulegan−Carpenter number. The highest correlation in the studied KC range $KC = 10−42$ was obtained for K$C = 10$. It decreased with increasing KC number, attained its minimum level at around $KC = 20$ and then increased to relatively higher values for further increase in KC number.

The purpose of the present study is to investigate 1) the effect of transverse vibrations and 2) that of close proximity of a wall on the correlation in oscillatory flows.

2   EXPERIMENTAL SET−UP

The measurements were made in a water flume 3 m wide, 1 m high and 35 m long. The circular cylinder used was an aluminum pipe, and it was 9 cm in diameter and 2 m in length. The surface of the pipe was hydraulically smooth. The pipe was fixed to a vertical frame with two holders, and was allowed to vibrate in the vertical direction only. The pipe could further be oscillated in vertical direction by a hydraulic system. The system comprising the cylinder and the frame was moun−ted to a carriage. The pipe could be placed at any distance from a wall. The wall was the bottom surface of a horizontal plate with sharp edges on both ends. The plate itself was fixed to a carriage. See Fig. 1 for a schematic description of the test set−up.

The oscillating flow was simulated by driving the carriage back and forth in otherwise still water. This was achieved by a hydraulic system where the movement of the carriage was controlled by a servo mechanism. With this arrangement, the carriage could be oscillated with a purely sinusoidal motion.

The tests were conducted in such a way that the cylinder vibrations and the carriage motion were synchronized.

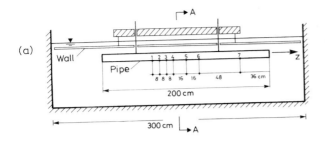

(a)

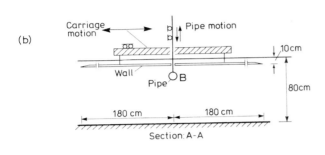

(b)

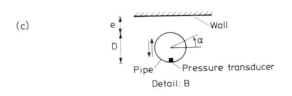

(c)

Fig 1   Test set−up. In (a), the numerical figures
1,2,..,7: Pressure transducers.

Seven pressure transducers (Endevco Model 8510B−2 with a range of 0−2 psi and with a sensitivity of 150 ± 50 mV/psi at 10 Vdc and 24° C) were mounted on the surface of the cylinder in such a way that they were aligned in the direction of the cylinder axis, as shown in Fig. 1a. The angular position of the line along which the pressure transducers are mounted on the cylinder surface could be changed by rotating the cylinder. Most of the experiments were conducted with the pressure trans−ducers positioned at $\alpha = +90°$ and $\alpha = -90°$ (Fig. 1c). The correlation measurements appeared to be not very sensitive to the particular position of the pressure trans−ducers.

Throughout the present paper, only the results obtained with the transducers positioned at $\alpha = -90°$ (i.e. the position shown in Fig. 1c) will be presented.

Test conditions are summarized in Table 1. In the table, the Keulegan−Carpenter number KC is defined by

$$KC = \frac{U_m T}{D} \tag{1}$$

in which D = the cylinder diameter, T = the period of the oscillatory flow and U_m = the maximum velocity defined by

$$U = U_m \sin(\omega t) \tag{2}$$

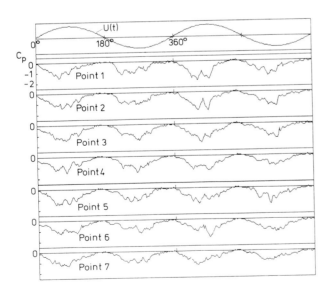

Fig 2   Stationary−cylinder pressure traces. $KC = 65$.
$e/D = 0.7$. For the particular locations of points where the pressures were measured, see Fig. 1a.

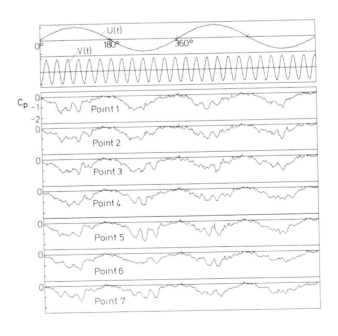

Fig 3   Vibrating−cylinder pressure traces. $KC = 65$.
$e/D = 1.5$. $2A/D = 0.15$. $N = 13$. For the particular locations of points where the pressures were measured, see Fig. 1a.

in which U = the flow velocity, t = the time, and ω = $2\pi/T$, the angular frequency of the flow. The Reynolds number is defined by

$$Re = \frac{U_m D}{\nu} \qquad (3)$$

Also, in the table, e = the gap between the cylinder and the wall, $2A$ = the double amplitude of the cylinder vibrations in vertical direction.

Keulegan Carpenter number KC	Range of gap ratio e/D	Cylinder Reynolds number Re	Range of double amplitude $2A/D$
6	0−2.3	3.4×10^4	0−0.20
20	0−2.3	6.8×10^4	0−0.25
65	0−2.3	6.8×10^4	0−0.25

Table 1. Test conditions

Pressures were measured simultaneously at the previously mentioned seven points along the length of the cylinder together with the displacement of the carriage plus the vertical displacement of the cylinder. Figs. 2 and 3 give sample pressure traces. Here, c_p = the pressure coefficient defined by

$$c_p = \frac{p - p_o}{(1/2)\rho U_m^2} \qquad (4)$$

p = the pressure measured at the point in consideration and p_o = the hydrostatic pressure measured at the same point.

2 RESULTS AND DISCUSSION

Stationary cylinder

Fig. 4 illustrates the time evolution of the correlation coefficient as the flow progresses. Here $KC = 65$, $e/D = 1.5$ and $z/D = 1.8$. The correlation coefficient itself is calculated through

$$R(z, \omega t) = \frac{\overline{p'(\zeta, \omega t)\ p'(\zeta + z, \omega t)}}{[\overline{p'^2(\zeta, \omega t)}]^{1/2}\ [\overline{p'^2(\zeta + z, \omega t)}]^{1/2}} \qquad (5)$$

in which ζ is the spanwise distance, z is the spanwise separation between two pressure transducers, p' is the fluctuation in pressure defined by

$$p' = p - \overline{p} \qquad (6)$$

The overbar in the preceding equations denotes ensemble averaging in the sense that for example the numerator in Eq. (5) is calculated as

$$\overline{p'(\zeta, \omega t)\ p'(\zeta + z, \omega t)} =$$

$$\frac{1}{M} \sum_{j=1}^{M} p'[\zeta,\ \omega(t + (j - 1)T)] \cdot \qquad (7)$$

$$p'[\zeta + z,\ \omega(t + (j - 1)T)]$$

in which M is the total number of cycles. In the tests the total number of cycles sampled was at least $M = 60$. However, no significant improvement in the consistency of the statistics was obtained with increase in M.

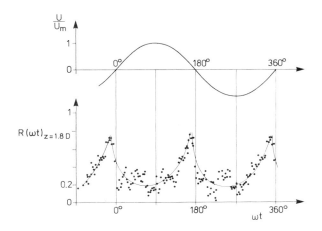

Fig 4   Stationary−cylinder correlation coefficient as function of phase ωt. $KC = 65$. $e/D = 1.5$, $z/D = 1.8$.

Fig. 4 shows that the correlation coefficient increases towards the end of the deceleration portion of every half period, and attains its maximum at the phase $\omega t \cong 165^o$, about 15^0 before the outer flow reverses. This phase value corresponds to the instant where the flow around the cylinder comes to a stand still, as is seen from the pressure traces in Fig. 2. Thus obviously the correlation at this instant should be close to unity. As the flow progresses from this point onwards, however, the correlation gradually decreases and assumes its minimum value for some period of time. Then it increases again towards the end of the next deceleration period.

Fig. 5 depicts the period−averaged correlation coefficients

$$R(z) = \frac{1}{2\pi} \int_0^{2\pi} R(z, \omega t)\ d(\omega t) \qquad (8)$$

The correlation coefficients presented hereafter in the paper are all the period−averaged ones. In the figure, Obasaju et al.'s (5) wall−free cylinder data for oscillatory

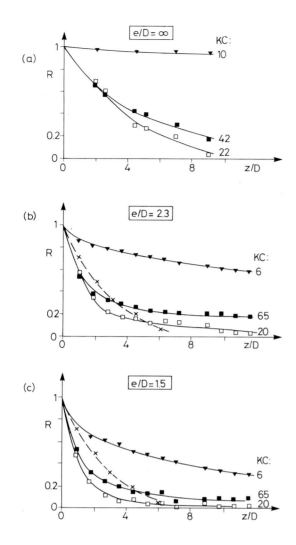

Fig 5 Stationary−cylinder period−averaged correla−
tion coefficient. (a): Obasaju, Bearman &
Graham (5). Wall−free cylinder $Re = 7 \times 10^3$
for $KC = 10$, $Re = 1.5 \times 10^4$ for $KC = 22$
and $Re = 3 \times 10^4$ for $KC = 42$. (b) and (c):
Present experiments. $e/D = 2.3$ and 1.5,
respectively. Dashed lines: Toebes' (3) stea−
dy−current results. $Re = 7 \times 10^4$.

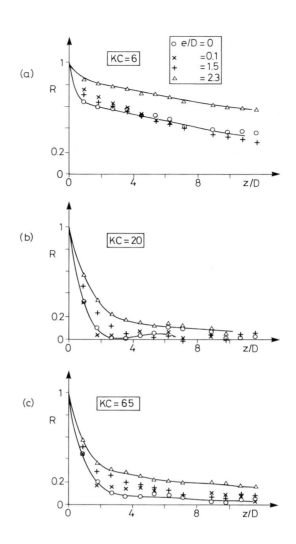

Fig 6 Stationary−cylinder period−averaged correla−
tion coefficient. Wall−proximity effect.

flows (Fig. 5a) and Toebes' (3) wall−free cylinder data for
a steady current (Figs. 5b and 5c) are also shown for
comparison. It appears that the present data reconcile
with the steady−current data when KC becomes large,
namely $KC = 65$, although the cylinder in the present
study is not completely wall free. Comparison of the
present data with those of Obasaju et al., on the other
hand, indicates that the two data show exactly the same
trend; namely the correlation coefficient takes very large
values when KC is small ($KC = 10$ in Obasaju et al. and
$KC = 6$ in the present case), while it takes the lowest
value when KC is around 20. Obasaju et al. gives a detail−
ed account of the behaviour of the correlation coefficient
as function of KC number. They point out that where the
correlation coefficient becomes lower, there is a drop in
the lift coefficient.

Fig. 6 gives the correlation diagrams for various
values of the gap ratio, again for a stationary cylinder. The
general trend is that the correlation coefficient increases
with an increase in the gap ratio.

Vibrating cylinder.

Fig. 7 presents the results obtained for a vibrating
cylinder in oscillatory flows together with Toebes' (3)
corresponding steady−current results. Note that both in
Toebes' study and the present study, the cylinder is
oscillated with a frequency equal to its vortex shedding
frequency. This, in the present study, corresponds to 13
transverse oscillations for one cycle of the oscillatory flow,
$N = 13$ for $KC = 65$, $N = 4$ for $KC = 20$ and $N = 2$ for
$KC = 6$.

Fig. 7 indicates that the present results are quite
consistent and that they are in accord with the steady−
current data. The correlation coefficient increases with
increasing amplitude of vibrations in much the same way

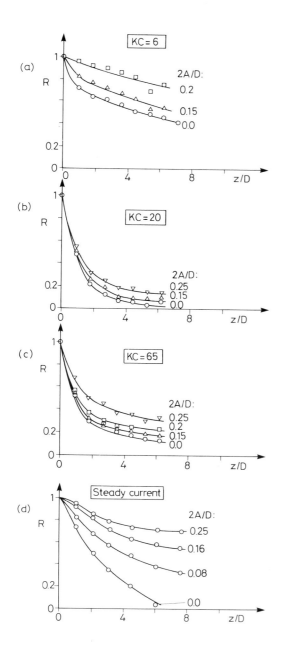

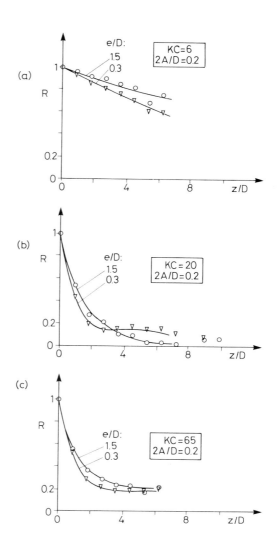

Fig 7   Vibrating—cylinder   period—averaged   correlation coefficient. (a), (b) and (c): Present
results. e/D = 1.5. Vibration frequencies: N
= 2 for KC = 6, N = 4 for KC = 20 and N
= 13 for KC = 65. (d): Toebes′ (3) steady—
current results for a wall—free cylinder, e/D
= ∞. Re = 7×10^4.

Fig 8   Vibrating—cylinder   period—averaged   correlation coefficient.   Wall—proximity   effect e/D =
1.5. Vibration   frequencies: N = 2 for KC =
6, N = 4 for KC = 20 and N = 13 for KC =
65.

as in steady currents. However, this increase is not as
large as in steady currents.

Fig. 8 illustrates the effect of close proximity of the
wall on the results. From the figure, the correlation
generally decreases (yet slightly) with decreasing the gap
ratio. For KC = 20 and large values of the separation
distance, however, the trend is in the opposite direction.
No clear explanation has been found for this behaviour.

4   CONCLUSIONS

a) The   correlation   coefficient   evolves   in   an   orderly
fashion, as the flow progresses throughout the cycle of the
oscillatory   motion.   It   attains   its   maximum   value   at   the
instant   when   the   flow   around   the   cylinder   comes   to   a
stand still at the times of flow reversal.

b) The effect of the close proximity of the wall on the
correlation   coefficient   is   not quite significant,   irrespective
of whether   the   cylinder   is   stationary   or   it   is   vibrating.

c) The   correlation   coefficient   increases   with   increasing
amplitude   of   transverse   vibrations,   in   much   the   same   way
as   in   steady   currents.   However,   the   increase   in   the
correlation   coefficient   is   not   as   large   as   in   steady   currents.

ACKNOWLEDGEMENT

The study is partially supported by the research programme "Marine Sciences" of The Danish Scientific Council (STVF).

REFERENCES

(1) KING, R. A Review of Vortex Shedding Research and Its Application. Ocean Engineering, 1977, 4, 141−171

(2) KOOPMANN, G.H. The Vortex Wakes of Vibrating Cylinders at Low Reynolds Numbers. J. Fluid Mech., 1967, 28, 501−512

(3) TOEBES, G.H. The Unsteady Flow and Wake Near an Oscillating Cylinder. Trans. ASME J. Basic Eng., Sept. 1969, 493−502.

(4) RAMBERG, S.E., and GRIFFIN, O.M. Velocity Correlation and Vortex Spacing in the Wake of a Vibrating Cable. Trans. ASME, J. Fluids Eng., 1976, 98, 10−18.

(5) OBASAJU, E.D., BEARMAN, P.W. and GRAHAM, J.M.R. A study of forces, circulation and vortex patterns around a circular cylinder in oscillating flow. J. Fluid Mech., 1988, 196, 467−494.

Non-linear vibration characteristics of a cylinder in an oscillating water flow

P W BEARMAN, MA, PhD, FRAeS and P R MACKWOOD, BSc(Eng)
Department of Aeronautics, Imperial College of Science, Technology and Medicine, London

SYNOPSIS Experiments have been carried out to investigate the response characteristics of a circular cylinder exposed to an oscillating water flow generated in a U-tube. The cylinder was mounted on a pendulum suspension system and was free to move in two-dimensional motion. However, most of the experiments were carried out with the cylinder fixed in the in-line direction. Displacements were measured for a range of Keulegan Carpenter numbers up to about 50 for a constant value of β of 750. At peak transverse response the dominant oscillation frequency is always some integer multiple of the flow frequency, irrespective of the cylinder natural frequency, and for a given frequency ratio the value of this integer depends on the Keulegan Carpenter number. Despite these findings, the largest peak responses do not occur for integer values of the ratio of cylinder natural frequency to flow frequency. Transverse response was investigated for a range of structural damping coefficients from 0.0007 to 0.06. When the frequency ratio takes an integer value it was found that increasing the damping increased the response. It is supposed that this is caused by a shift in the phase at which the fluid force due to vortex shedding attains its maximum value.

1. INTRODUCTION

It has long been known that vortex shedding from bluff bodies exposed to a steady flow causes a fluctuating force perpendicular to the incident flow direction. Over the past 40 years a great many studies have examined the vortex induced transverse forces and associated vibrations of flexibly mounted circular cylinders and the phenomenon is well documented. Both the magnitude and frequency of the forces play an important role in determining the response of the cylinder but the situation is complicated by fluid-structure interactions causing modification of the fluid forces. With the advent of offshore structures came the demand for the understanding of the forces on bodies in an oscillating flow. Although fewer studies have investigated these oscillatory flows, there is an ever increasing amount of data available particularly in respect to the in-line loading, and to a lesser degree the transverse forces, on fixed cylinders in both two-dimensional harmonic flows and in waves.

To date most offshore design has utilised force coefficients based on rigid cylinder data, but for instance, riser pipes which are long and thin should really be considered as flexible members. Furthermore, with the increasing use of compliant designs and the continued demand for more cost effective structures it is crucial that this flexibility be taken into account. Relatively little research has been conducted in the field of hydroelastic response of cylinders in oscillatory flows, but it is evident from earlier studies ((1), (2) and (3)) as for steady flow, that there is a fluid-structure interaction causing magnification of the lift forces, modification of in-line forces, and in some instances transverse motions exceeding those in-line. Additionally, it is clear that the frequency of transverse motions is significantly higher than that in-line, and this has an important bearing on analysis of fatigue life.

In harmonic oscillatory flow it is known (4) that the fluid forces are governed by both the Keulegan Carpenter number $KC = U_mT/D$, and Reynolds number $Re=U_mD/\upsilon$, where U_m is the maximum fluid velocity, T is the period of the flow, D is the diameter of the cylinder, and υ is the fluid kinematic viscosity. The Keulegan Carpenter number

may be interpreted as a ratio of the amplitude of water particle displacement during an oscillation period to the diameter of the cylinder. In the case of planar harmonic motion $KC = 2\pi A/D$, where A is the amplitude of the water motion. The pattern of vortex shedding from cylinders in oscillatory flow is governed by the value of KC. It has been shown (5) that one additional vortex is generated and shed per half cycle of the flow oscillation each time KC is increased by an increment of about 8. Hence it can be anticipated that transverse response characteristics will be strongly dependent on the value of KC. In the in-line direction the situation is somewhat simpler with the response expected to increase monotonically with KC, the dominant frequency of cylinder oscillation being equal to that of the incident flow.

It is common practice in oscillatory flow studies to combine KC and Re into the β parameter, where $\beta = Re/KC = D^2/\upsilon T$. This has the advantage that for a given cylinder diameter the viscous parameter is only dependent on the flow oscillation period. In a U-tube facility, where the natural period of water oscillation is fixed, β is a constant for a given cylinder for all KC values. Typically, a riser piper might experience a β of the order of 10^5. In a small scale laboratory experiment, using a cylinder with a diameter of 50 mm, β might be around 10^3. Such differences introduce scaling problems which are very familiar to researchers working with circular cylinders in unidirectional flows.

In addition to the fluid properties the response characteristics can also be expected to depend on the mass, damping and stiffness of a cylinder. We have estimated the effective mass in air, m_e, including a contribution from the support system but excluding any added mass effect from the water. The non-dimensional mass ratio is given by $m_e/\rho D^2L$, where ρ is water density and L the immersed length of the cylinder. The damping, ξ_s, is the structural damping measured in air, expressed as a damping coefficient. A difficulty arises over the derivation of a cylinder natural frequency, f_n, in particular as to whether this should be measured in air or in water. Since the added mass of a cylinder in still water may be different from that measured when both the cylinder and the water are in motion, there is an argument for taking the in air value (6).

However, we have chosen to use the value measured in water, since it can sometimes be detected in response spectra. The key parameter involving the frequency is the frequency ratio, f_n/f_w, where $f_w = 1/T$, the flow oscillation frequency. In steady current flow it is common to use the reduced velocity V_r, which in oscillatory flow becomes $U_m/f_n D$. The frequency ratio f_n/f_w can be equated to the ratio of KC to V_r, but whereas in steady flow maximum responses can be expected when $V_r = 5$ to 6, in oscillatory flow maximum transverse displacement does not seem to occur at a unique value of V_r.

The main aim of the present investigation was to examine the transverse response characteristics of a circular cylinder in planar oscillatory flow at KC values less than 50 and frequency ratios less than 4. A rig with low structural damping was constructed and the effects on response of increasing the damping were studied. Some surprising non-linear characteristics were observed.

2. EXPERIMENTAL ARRANGEMENT

A 'U-tube' water tank was used in the present study to generate the oscillatory flow. As its name implies , the tank is in the form of a large U of all aluminium and perspex construction. The tank has a square cross-section of about 0.6 m, vertical limbs of 2.5 m, and an horizontal working section of 1.5 m. The tank is normally filled with water to within 0.6 m of the top of the vertical arms. A small blower is attached to the top of one of the limbs, the other limb is open to atmosphere and contains a conductance wave probe to measure the water elevation. The water once set in motion performs oscillations at a constant frequency (determined by the dimensions of the tank) which slowly decay due to frictional losses. These losses are overcome by imparting a small amount of energy every cycle via the blower. A custom designed controller, triggered by the water level passing through MWL, activates the fan after a set interval and for a fixed time. The amplitude of the water oscillations is controlled by varying the speed of the fan and thus the amount of energy fed into the system. In this way a 2-D harmonic flow, with a period of about 3 seconds and with virtually all of its energy at the fundamental frequency can be generated in the working section. The experiments to be described were performed using a circular cylinder of 50 mm diameter giving a value of β of about 750. The maximum amplitude of the water displacement was about 0.4 m; this corresponds to KC equal to about 50.

The main design criteria for the test cylinder support mechanism were as follows: (i) the cylinder should have uniform displacement along its length; (ii) the natural frequency of the system should be easy to adjust; (iii) the structural damping should be low and independent of amplitude; (iv) the system should have 2 degrees of freedom with provision to restrain the cylinder in one direction without affecting the structural properties in the other direction. These criteria rule out a carriage type system such had been used earlier (3) on several counts; runners and bearings are required which introduce large and variable amounts of damping, two carriages are needed which results in different effective masses in the two directions, helical springs are used to control the natural frequency and tend to be difficult to obtain in small increments of spring constant. The final design of support mechanism used was in effect a type of pendulum and is shown in figure 1. The system consists of a square, flat, horizontal plate to which the cylinder is rigidly mounted. Four vertical arms are attached to the corners of the plate and to a rigid frame overhead, via thin spring steel strips or flexures, thus avoiding the use of any bearing or hinge. Two sets of flexures set at right angles to each other provide the two degrees of freedom, whilst one degree of freedom is achieved by simply removing one set of

flexures. The rigid arms have turn-buckle type adjusters enabling their length, and hence the natural frequency, to be infinitely varied without the need for completely dismantling the system. This set up meets all the design requirements and avoids all the problems encountered with other systems, but does inevitably suffer the minor drawback that the cylinder will perform small vertical motions. At worst, for the shortest length of suspension arms and a cylinder displacement of 1 diameter, the vertical displacement is of the order of 1-2 mm.

Since the main aim of the project was to examine the response of the cylinder an accurate method of measuring the displacement was required. The use of spring steel flexures had the advantage that the surface strain on them was directly proportional to the cylinder displacement, and therefore one flexure from each set was strain gauged to provide a simple non contact displacement measuring system. A difficulty when working with a U-tube is that the working section is pressurised by virtue of the columns of water in the upright limbs. To use the suspension system outlined above meant constructing an airtight, pressurised chamber attached to the top of the working section. The chamber, measuring 0.45 m square by 1.8 m high, was made from 1 inch thick perspex with an aluminium lid and aluminium angle as corner bracing, having one removable panel for access to the cylinder. The pressure in the chamber was maintained using a Druck DPI 500 pressure controller, with the source of compressed air being a small electrical compressor. This system enabled the water level to be kept at the top of the working section and since the controller was able to feed small leaks the U-tube could be left unattended even over-night. The complete system, with a cylinder attached, mounted inside the chamber is shown in figure 2. Clearance between the tank floor and the lower end of the cylinder was kept as small as possible. End plates were not used because of the unknown level of hydrodynamic damping they might introduce.

Due to the corrosion inhibitor used in the water, the resulting wave height calibration was non linear and a calibration was performed every day before starting any runs. The wave probe was calibrated over 17 values of water surface elevation, and a cubic calibration curve fitted by the method of least squares was found to be adequate. The maximum calibration error, defined as the the maximum difference between a measured and fitted point, was always less than about 0.4%. A PC-AT clone microcomputer was used to both control the U-tube and collect the data. The main U-tube controller mentioned above provides all the timing functions to maintain water oscillations, the only input required is a DC voltage proportional to the desired amplitude. The PC was fitted with a Scientific Solutions data acquisition expansion card comprising an 8 input A/D converter and 2 D/A converters, one of which was used to supply the drive voltage to the controller.

It was required in some tests to artificially increase the structural damping of the system. For small amounts of damping the simplest form of damper is the 'flat plate in oil' system. Due to the constraints of the experimental setup the damping system used was somewhat unusual in that the oil bath was attached to the moving suspension system and the damper plates rigidly fixed to 'earth'. Up to a total of three plates could be immersed in the oil, the level of which could also be varied to give a wide range of damping.

As mentioned earlier the strain in one of the suspension flexures was used as a measure of the displacement of the cylinder, and thus the displacement/strain calibration depended upon the length of suspension arm. The calibration was achieved by using

© IMechE 1991 C416/004

accurately machined spacers to displace the cylinder in 1 cm steps over a range of ±1 diameter. The calibration was linear for all lengths of arm. The natural frequency of the system was estimated from the displacement signal of naturally decaying oscillations. For this so called 'twang test' the system was released from rest and an initial displacement of approximately 1 diameter. The natural frequency was calculated from zero crossing or spectral analysis. Although of a non-stationary process, the spectral analysis technique served to provide an estimate of the fundamental frequency and also a measure of any harmonics present. The in-water natural frequency was estimated in all cases. The in-air frequency was also measured in certain instances and spectral analysis revealed no harmonic content. The in-air frequency was amplitude independent and even in water the differences were hard to measure.

The damping coefficient ξ_s was also estimated from the twang tests and defined as $(1/2\pi) \ln (A_r)$, where A_r is the ratio of the amplitude of successive displacement peaks. ξ_s was calculated on a cycle by cycle basis so as to provide amplitude dependency information. The damping coefficient of the basic system in air was found to be independent of amplitude, varied little with natural frequency, and averaged out at a value of about 0.0007. It was discovered that a 10% difference in damping could be measured with and without the cylinder attached to the suspension system (an equal mass replacing the weight of the cylinder) which was attributed to the aerodynamic damping of the cylinder. The oil bath damper described earlier was used to increase the structural damping in some tests. As a consequence of having a moving oil bath, the standing waves set up drastically increased the damping even with no damper plates. Interestingly, the damping at first increased with increasing depth of oil up to a maximum and then decreased as the effect of the additional mass became dominant. However, immersing 1 or more plates in the oil had by far the largest effect and in all cases the damping was constant with amplitude. With the oil bath the damping coefficient could be increased to 0.06.

The suspension setup is a compound mass-spring/pendulum system and thus it was not possible to measure the system mass directly. The effective mass was therefore estimated from the measured stiffness and natural frequency in air using the relation

$$\omega = \sqrt{\frac{k}{m_e}}$$

For such small amounts of damping the measured natural frequency, actually the damped frequency, is for all intents and purposes exactly the same as the true natural frequency. The effective mass, m_e, was calculated to be approximately 5.5 kg giving a mass ratio of $m_r =3.69$. The effective mass varies slightly with different length arms due to the additional mass of the longer arms.

3. EXPERIMENTAL PROCEDURE AND DATA ANALYSIS

Once a particular experimental setup had been decided upon, the arms of the suspension system were adjusted to obtain the desired in-water cylinder natural frequency. The displacement calibration was then measured, the system stiffness estimated, a twang test performed and the damping coefficient calculated. The cylinder was then sealed into the pressurised chamber, the water pumped into the U-tube, and the wave probe calibration coefficients obtained.

A Fortran program was written which controlled both the U-tube and data collection and performed some on line data analysis. The data collection criteria were decided during commissioning of the system. A sampling frequency of 10 Hz was used giving a Nyquist frequency well in excess of any frequency of interest. The total sampling time was determined from a running calculation of the R.M.S cylinder displacement and it was found that the R.M.S reached a steady value, to within a couple of percent, for 7000 samples or more. 8192 samples were finally chosen, representing a sampling time of over 13 minutes and almost 250 cycles of the flow.

In oscillatory flow the short term past history is very important, the wake flow of one half cycle becoming the incident flow for the next half cycle. For this reason an adequate settling time must be allowed following a change in the flow amplitude, so that any changes in flow pattern can become fully established. It was decided that the flow amplitude and hence KC would never be changed by more than about a KC of 1-2, and a settling time of 5 minutes was found to be adequate. As a final check on these criteria, a series of runs were performed for both increasing and decreasing KC and no hysteresis noted. Repeatability was excellent over a period of several weeks, and more than acceptable for repeat test cases performed several months apart. The facility was designed to operate automatically once flow oscillations had been initiated and required only the number of runs and desired range of KC to be specified. After every run the R.M.S displacement was calculated and displayed on a hard copy plotter, and during the settling times the cylinder displacement was continuously monitored and displayed on the computer V.D.U. This enabled any odd features or obvious problems with the suspension system to be noticed at a glance.

4. RESULTS AND DISCUSSION

The results presented are mainly measurements of the RMS of the transverse response of the cylinder, Y_{rms}/D, against the Keulegan Carpenter number KC, for various values of frequency ratio, f_n/f_w, and structural damping coefficient ξ_s. The majority of tests were performed with the cylinder restrained in the in-line direction. However, the very first tests conducted examined both the in-line and transverse responses for cylinders with either 1 or 2 degrees of freedom. These first cases utilised a set of fixed length suspension arms whilst the adjustable set were being manufactured. Thus the frequency ratios obtained were fixed by the system used. Some results for these tests are shown in Figure 3 as response curves against KC, with slightly different frequency ratios of 1.83 and 1.67. The two sets of data show similar features with the in-line response increasing monotonically with KC, and the transverse response showing a peak at a KC of about 10. The form of the in-line response leads one to suspect that it may not be too difficult to predict. Spectral analysis of the cylinder motion reveals for the in-line cases a fundamental frequency component equal to the flow frequency, f_w, for all KC, and for the transverse motion spectral peaks at even multiples of f_w at low KC, the maximum power occurring at $2f_w$. At very high KC the response is much more random and the peaks at multiples of f_w are barely discernible.

The sets of results shown in figure 3 for $f_n/f_w= 1.67$ are response curves when the cylinder is free to move in both directions. The form of the response curves is somewhat different from those of the above 1 d.o.f cases, the transverse motion exhibiting a small peak at KC = 4, a larger broad peak centred on KC=12, and the in-line motion appearing to show some distortion of the curve over a band of KC corresponding to the peak transverse response. These differences could be due to the different value of f_n/f_w and would have to be verified by performing 1 d.o.f tests at the same frequency ratio. However, tests reported by Bearman (7) on a large scale compliant cylinder in waves showed that for $f_n/f_w = 4$, there was an increase in drag coefficient, C_D, with increasing transverse response. The general conclusion to be drawn from figure 3 is that broadly similar responses are recorded in the transverse directions whether or not the cylinder is free to move in the in-line direction.

Probably the most important feature of the above set of results is that the transverse motion can under some conditions be considerably larger than that in-line. Furthermore, the transverse response frequency is a multiple of that in-line, an important fact when considering fatigue. For these reasons the subsequent tests concentrated on the transverse response.

4.1 Transverse response at low damping

Figure 4 shows transverse response curves for values of frequency ratio ranging from 1.79 to 3.5. All these tests were performed using the same suspension system, the natural frequencies being controlled by adjusting the length of the suspension arms. At first glance there appears to be no general trend running through all the data although certain groups of results do have some similarities.

For the three cases, $f_n/f_w = 1.79 - 2.13$, the cylinder begins to oscillate at a KC of about 3, the response rising quickly with KC and the peak response occurring in the range of KC = 8-13. The structural damping was the same in all these cases. Spectral analysis of the cylinder displacement corresponding to peak response reveals large narrow peaks at even integer multiples of f_w, the largest occurring at $2f_w$. The peak at twice the tank frequency is some 2 or more orders of magnitude larger than those at the higher multiples. Except in the case when $f_n/f_w = 2.01$, there is absolutely no evidence of the cylinder natural frequency, which leads one to the conclusion that the cylinder is simply being driven at a frequency determined by the flow. Figure 5 shows a typical spectrum and portion of the displacement time history for $f_n/f_w = 1.79$, KC = 12.71. The time history is very regular and confirms that the fundamental response frequency is at exactly $2f_w$.

Over the range of frequency ratio $f_n/f_w = 2.47 - 3.07$ the response curves have several general features in common. Oscillation is not initiated until the KC number is 5 or more, there is a small peak in the response when KC = 8-10, and a much larger and broader peak centred at a KC of between 20 and 24 depending upon the frequency ratio. The maximum Y_{rms}/D is about 0.5 and examination of time histories has revealed peak cylinder displacements in excess of 2 diameters peak to peak. There is in some cases a not so well defined third peak in the response. A further feature common to all these cases is the very sudden increase in cylinder motion for KC values between 12 and 15, this being most pronounced when $f_n/f_w=2.72$, the response increasing fourfold for a change in KC of only 1.

Spectral analysis again shows strong peaks at integer multiples of the flow frequency, but for these cases at peak response the odd multiples are in evidence, maximum power occurring at $3f_w$. For the smaller secondary response peak the dominant spectral components are at 2,4,6 f_w etc. and there is often evidence of a broader band of energy at or close to the cylinder natural frequency. Another common feature, when the cylinder is undergoing large changes in Y_{rms} with KC, is a series of pairs of peaks of almost equal amplitude centred about 3,5,7 f_w. Examination of time histories reveals that this spectral phenomenon represents a cylinder motion with

fundamental frequency $3f_w$, modulated by a much lower frequency. Figure 6 shows a peak response spectrum and associated time history for $f_n/f_w = 2.47$, KC = 26.14.

$f_n/f_w = 3.5$ was the highest frequency ratio tested and the response curve exhibits similar features to the above, but the largest response peak is much broader and flatter and the response falls off less rapidly with increasing KC. Spectral analysis for this case at maximum response again reveals peaks at integer multiples of f_w but this time it is again the even multiples with maximum power occurring at $4f_w$.

4.2 Behaviour at resonance

Interpretation of the spectra together with the time history information has confirmed that the cylinder oscillates predominantly at either $2f_w$, $3f_w$, or $4f_w$ dependent upon f_n/f_w and/or KC. It would therefore be expected that tuning the natural frequency to an exact multiple of f_w would result in oscillations with the largest peak amplitude. This does not appear to be the case, for when $f_n/f_w = 3.00$ the peak response is smaller than that for frequency ratios close to 3. More surprisingly, for $f_n/f_w = 2.01$, the peak response is the smallest recorded for any frequency ratio. These findings are in opposition to those of previous studies by Hayashi (8), Maull and Kaye (9) and Phillipou (10), all who found response peaks at integer values of frequency ratio. The above studies were all conducted in waves using bottom pivoted cylinders and as such exhibit three dimensional flow, depth dependent displacement, fluid damping, and input forcing with much of the energy input over a small part of the wave period during passage of the wave crest. It is quite conceivable that these gross differences in incident flow and structural parameters can account for the very different results in the present study, and it is questionable whether results from bottom pivoted cylinders can be used to predict riser vibrations, for example.

However, McConnell and Park (11) conducted similar experiments with planar oscillatory flow by oscillating a cylinder in still water and examined the frequency components of the response and fluid lift forces for KC > 37. They found that for a fixed cylinder the dominant lift force components were at 5,7,9 f_w, in line with similar work by Bearman and Hall (3). In addition, McConnell and Park (11) discovered that when the cylinder was free to oscillate, the frequency composition of the lift force was modified, the dominant components no longer at integer multiples of f_w. They also found that the frequency components of the response corresponded to those of the lift force, the dominant spectral peak of the response dependent upon f_n/f_w and not necessarily at the same frequency as the dominant component of the lift force. McConnell and Park (1) have also investigated the transverse motion of a cylinder for frequency ratios in excess of 3.0 and KC values of 25 and higher and found response peaks for integer values of f_n/f_w. Sumer and Fredsoe (12) also oscillated a flexible cylinder in still water for a limited number of values of KC but for a large range of frequency ratio, and found very little agreement with McConnell and Park's work except for KC values of about 100. Figure 7 reproduces some of Sumer and Fredsoe's results for three values of KC, but replotted against f_n/f_w, together with results from the present study. Although only a limited number of results from the present study can be directly compared, the overall agreement is surprisingly good and clearly shows minimum response at or near to integer values of f_n/f_w for a large range of KC and frequency ratio.

Some researchers have preferred to plot response data against reduced velocity V_r, rather than frequency ratio. A number of response curves with the same level of structural damping but different frequency ratios, are replotted against reduced velocity in figure 8. The data does not collapse completely but for $f_n/f_w \geq 2.47$ the collapse is reasonably good up to $V_r = 5$. For these frequency ratios the peak response is centred on about $V_r = 7.5$ and there appears to be two distinct sets of curves for $9 < V_r < 14$; thereafter all results seem to reach a level of Y_{rms}/D of about 0.15. The picture for frequency ratios less than 2.47 is more inconsistent. Peak response occurs again at $V_r = 7.5$ for $f_n/f_w = 1.79$ but at about 4 for $f_n/f_w = 2.01$ and 2.13.

4.3 Effect of increased structural damping

One of the original aims of this investigation was to study vortex induced vibrations of a system with very low structural damping so as to determine likely maximum responses. This was successfully achieved but since in other studies the structural damping, where quoted, was sometimes considerably higher it was decided to examine the effect of artificially increasing the damping. For these tests two frequency ratios were selected; a 'resonant' case: $f_n/f_w = 2.0$ because of the unexpected behaviour of reduced response at 'resonance', and $f_n/f_w = 2.72$ this being an untuned case. By the use of the oil bath and damping plates it was possible to increase the damping by approximately two orders of magnitude.

The measurements of response for $f_n/f_w = 2.72$ show nothing particularly unexpected with decreasing response with increasing damping, the most noticeable differences occurring at the peak response. As with the lowest damping case there is still a very sudden increase in response for small changes in KC when KC is in the range 14 to 16, this being less pronounced at higher damping levels. It should be noted that the effective mass for these tests was slightly higher than for the basic system due to the added weight of the damping oil bath. The peak response, occurring at a KC of about 20, is shown plotted in figure 9 against damping coefficient.

Response measurements for $f_n/f_w = 2.0$ are shown plotted in figure 10 against KC for 5 values of damping coefficient. Very surprisingly, for this frequency ratio the peak response initially actually increases with greater damping, an increase of almost 25% for a change in ξ_s from 0.0007 to 0.0383. Thereafter further increases in ξ_s result in a decreased response although for $\xi_s = 0.0598$ it is still larger than that for the smallest structural damping. Again the peak responses, this time occurring at a KC value of about 10, are plotted in figure 9 against damping coefficient. It is only at the highest damping level that the responses at the two frequency ratios have a similar magnitude.

To sum up, it is clear from the above that vortex induced vibration in harmonic flow is complex and dependent upon parameters such as KC, f_n/f_w, ξ_s, and that there are obviously very subtle interactions between the flow and the motion of the cylinder, involving its structural parameters. It is not understood why what is thought to be a resonant condition results in small responses, and enhanced response with increased damping is even more difficult to reconcile. For so called untuned cases, large changes in response for small changes in incident flow are similarly difficult to explain. However, it should be recalled that the transverse response can only result from the generation and shedding of vortices. The level of response will depend on the structural parameters and the magnitude of the vortex-induced transverse force and its phase angle to the cylinder displacement. It is thought that some of the non-linear characteristics observed in oscillatory flow are linked to the behaviour of this phase angle. In the case of the "tuned" frequency ratio, for example, perhaps it is possible that the addition

of structural damping modifies the fluid/structure interaction such that the vortex force is brought more closely 90° out of phase with the cylinder displacement. At this stage it is only possible to speculate on why these effects occur and clearly further investigation is required and it is suggested that simultaneous transverse force and displacement measurements ought to be made.

5. CONCLUSIONS

The results show a number of interesting features but, as expected, the in-line response increases monotonically with Keulegan Carpenter number, the dominant cylinder oscillation frequency equal to that of the incident flow. There is some evidence of modification of the in-line response when the cylinder is free to oscillate in the transverse direction. For Keulegan Carpenter numbers of less than about 16 and frequency ratios of less than about 2.5, the transverse response can be considerably greater than that in-line. When in-line motion is restricted, the transverse response versus Keulegan Carpenter number curves vary considerably with frequency ratio, but in all cases a peak response is noted, the magnitude and position of which depends upon the frequency ratio. At peak response the dominant oscillation frequency is always some integer multiple of the flow frequency irrespective of the cylinder natural frequency, whilst the value of this integer is determined by both the Keulegan Carpenter number and the frequency ratio. Despite these findings, the largest peak responses occur for non integer values of the frequency ratio ., whilst the smallest peak response was recorded for a frequency ratio of exactly 2. Large increases in cylinder displacement for very small changes in incident flow, and enhanced response with increased structural damping (for certain values of frequency ratio), indicate extremely complicated, subtle interactions between the flow, cylinder response, and structural parameters. The mechanisms involved are not at all well understood and further research is clearly indicated, particularly in the comparison between me .surements of local fluid forces and responses.

6. ACKNOWLEDGEMENTS

The research described in this paper forms part of the work of the 1987-89 Fluid Loading Programme. This is a managed programme of research sponsored by SERC, (via Marine Technology Directorate Ltd.), Department of Energy and the Offshore Industry. The authors gratefully acknowledge this support.

7. REFERENCES

(1) McCONNELL, K.G. and PARK, Y.S. "The response and the lift-force analysis of an elastically-mounted cylinder oscillating in still water". Proc. Int. Conf. Behaviour of Offshore Structures. Vol. 2, p. 671, 1982.

(2) SARPKAYA, T. "Hydroelastic response of cylinders in harmonic flow". The Royal Institution of Naval Architects, paper No. 4, Spring meetings 1979.

(3) BEARMAN, P.W. and HALL, P.F. "Dynamic response of cylinders in oscillatory flow and waves". Proc. Int. Conf. on Flow Induced Vibrations, Bowness-on-Windermere, England, pp. 183-190, BHRA, May 1987.

(4) SARPKAYA, T. and ISAACSON, M. "Mechanics of Wave Forces on Offshore Structures". Van Nostrand Reinhold, 1981.

(5) OBASAJU, E.D., BEARMAN, P.W. and GRAHAM, J.M.R. "A study of forces, circulation and vortex patterns around a circular cylinder in oscillating flow". J. Fluid Mech. Vol. 196, pp. 467-494, 1988.

(6) SARPKAYA, T. "Fluid forces on oscillating cylinders". Journal of the Waterways, Port, Coastal and Ocean Division, ASCE, Vol. 104, No. WW4, Proc paper 13941, pp. 275-290, 1978.

(7) BEARMAN, P.W. "Wave Loading Experiments on Circular Cylinders at Large Scale". Proc. Int. Conf. Behaviour of Offshore Structures, Trondheim, Vol. 2, pp. 471-487, Tapir, June 1988.

(8) HAYASHI, K. "The non-linear vortex-excited vibration of a vertical cylinder in waves". PhD thesis, Liverpool University, 1984.

(9) MAULL, D.J. and KAYE, D. "Oscillations of a flexible cylinder in waves". Proc. Int. Conf. Behaviour of Offshore Structures. Vol. 2, p. 535-547, Tapir, June 1988.

(10) PHILLIPOU, P.S. "The dynamic response of a vertical flexible cylinder in wave flows". 3rd year project, Department of Aeronautics, Imperial College, 1985.

(11) McCONNELL, K.G. and PARK, Y.S. "The frequency components of fluid-lift forces acting on a circular cylinder oscillating in still water". *Experimental Mechanics*, Vol. 22, No. 6, pp. 216-222, June 1982

(12) SUMER, B.M. and FREDSOE, J. "Transverse vibrations of an elastically mounted cylinder exposed to an oscillatory flow". Proceedings of the 6th International Offshore Mechanics and Arctic Engineering Symposium, Houston, Texas, March 1987.

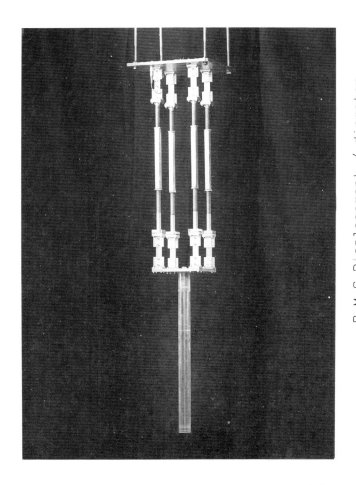

Figure 1   View of the cylinder and the pendulum suspension system.

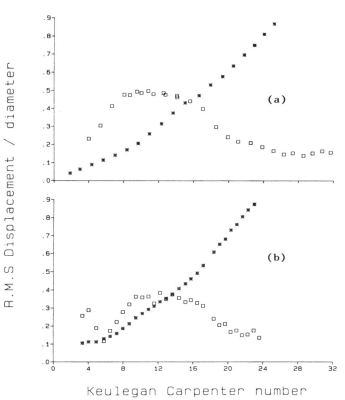

Figure 3   Cylinder response versus Keulegan Carpenter number
(a) one degree of freedom, $f_n/f_w = 1.83$;
(b) two degrees of freedom $f_n/f_w = 1.67$.
*, in-line motion; □, transverse motion.

Figure 2   The cylinder mounted in the U-tube.

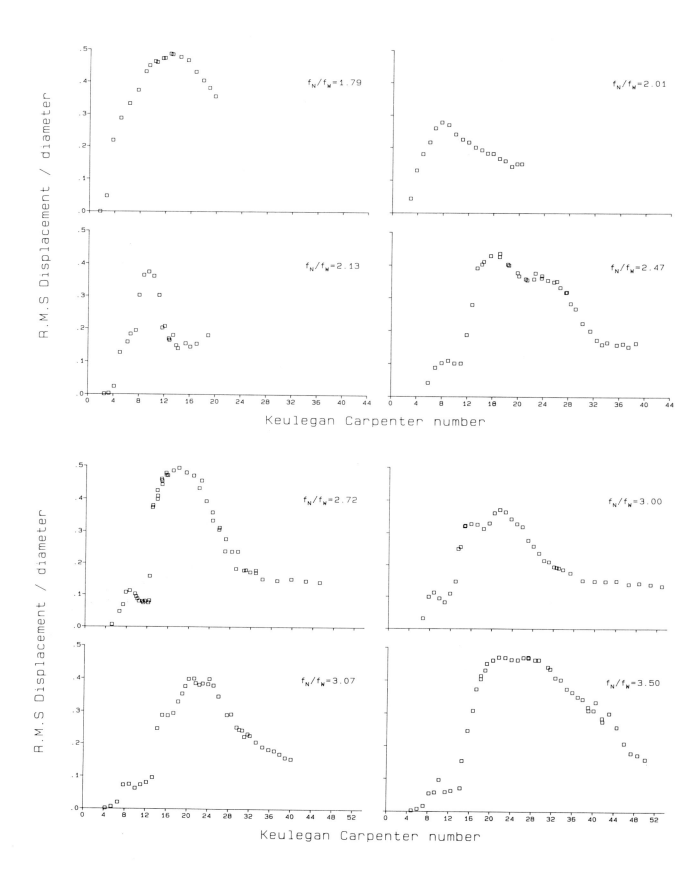

Figure 4   Transverse response versus Keulegan
Carpenter number for various frequency
ratios; in-line direction fixed.

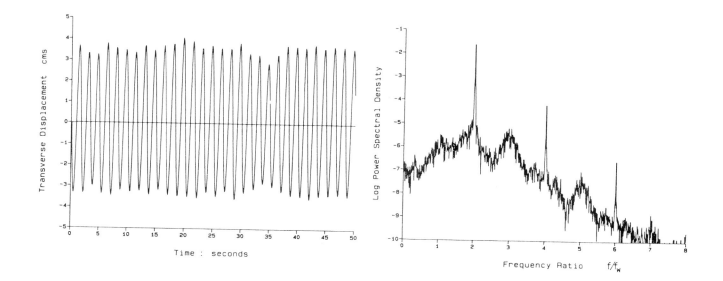

Figure 5   Time history and power spectrum of transverse response for KC = 12.71 and $f_n/f_w = 1.79$.

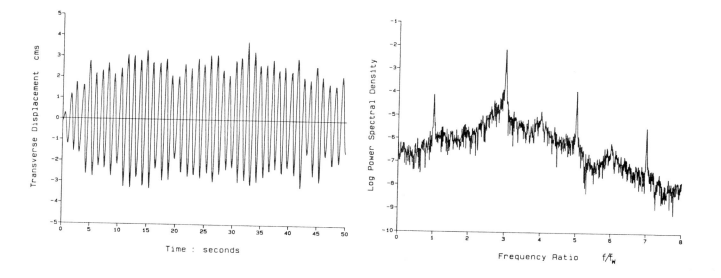

Figure 6   Time history and power spectrum of transverse response for KC = 26.14, $f_n/f_w = 2.47$.

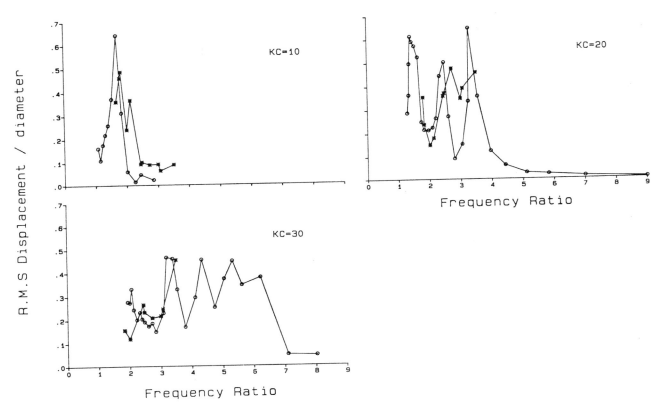

Figure 7   Transverse response at a fixed KC number versus Frequency ratio. *, Present results; 0, Sumer and Fredsoe (12).

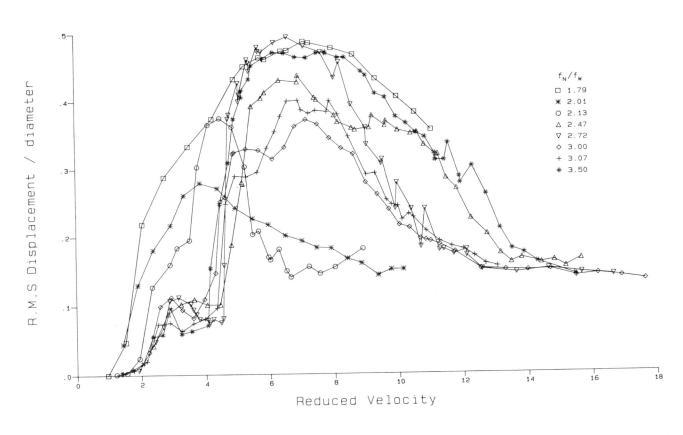

Figure 8   Traverse response versus reduced velocity for various frequency ratios.

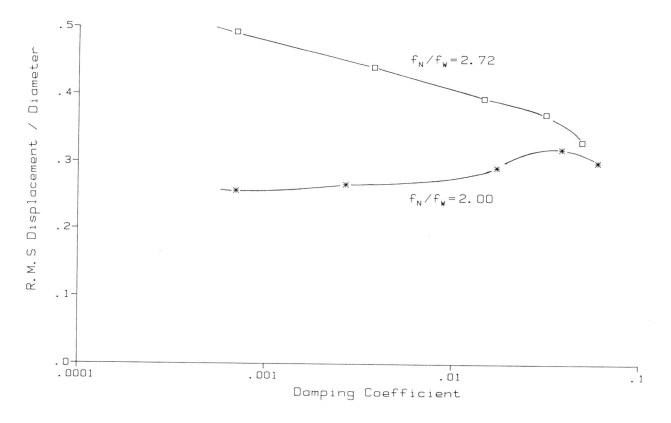

Figure 9   Effect of structural damping level on
maximum transverse response.
*, f_n/f_w = 2.0; □, f_n/f_w = 2.72.

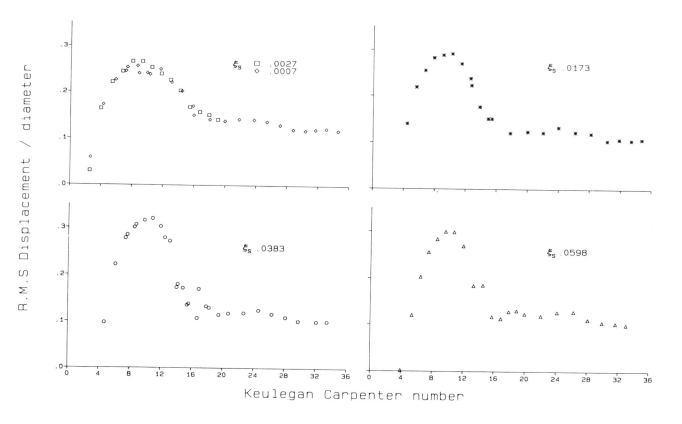

Figure 10   Transverse response versus KC number for
various damping levels and f_n/f_w = 2.0

C416/020

Simulation of flow induced vibration characteristics of a steam generator U-tube

E R FRANCE, BSc, ARCS
N N C Limted, Warrington, Cheshire
H J CONNORS, PhD, MASME
Westinghouse Science and Technology Center, Pittsburgh, Pennsylvania, United States of America

SYNOPSIS Fluidelastic excitation may cause tube vibration in the U-bend region of steam generators at some tube/AVB support locations where clearance exists between the tube and AVB (antivibration bar). The vibration induces nonlinear impact forces and sliding motions between the tube and AVB. In-air shaker tests are run on a full-size U-bend tube with model AVB supports instrumented to measure these wear-producing forces and motions, and the tube wear potential expressed as workrate, is determined. A special feedback control circuit, used to power the out-of-plane shaker, simulates the fluidelastic excitation as negative damping. Workrate trends as a function of tube/AVB clearance and the excitation level are presented.

NOTATION

D = Tube diameter, m

f_n = Natural frequency, Hz

f_s = Shaker frequency, Hz

FIR = Power spectral density of in-plane excitation N^2/Hz

F_i = Tube/AVB impact force, N

G = Gain of feedback circuit, dimensionless

L = Tube length, m

m_j = Mass of tube per unit length in the vicinity of the j'th lumped mass of the finite element model, including the added mass of fluid outside the tube, Kg/m

m_o = Reference mass of tube per unit length including the added mass of fluid outside the tube, Kg/m

N = Number of lumped masses used in the finite element model, dimensionless

U_{cn} = Critical reference flow velocity at which fluidelastic vibrations initiate, m/s

U_{en} = Effective reference flow velocity, as defined by Eq. (3), m/s

U_j = Reference flow velocity in the vicinity of the j'th lumped mass in the finite element model, m/s

WR = Workrate m-N/s

X_i = In-plane tube displacement associated with impact force F_i, m

y = Vibration amplitude

Δz_j = Incremental length used in finite element model, m

β = Threshold instability constant, dimensionless

δ = Damping expressed as logarithmic decrement, dimensionless

ζ = Damping ratio, dimensionless
  = $\delta/2\pi$

ζ_n = Positive damping ratio, dimensionless

ζ_d = Negative damping ratio, dimensionless

$\Delta\zeta$ = Excess negative damping, dimensionles
  = $\zeta d-\zeta n$

ρ_j = Fluid density in the vicinity of the j'th lumped mass of the finite element model, Kg/m³

ρ_o = Reference fluid density, Kg/m³

ϕ_{jn} = Normalized displacement of the j'th lumped mass in the finite element model, in the n'th mode, dimensionless

ω = Circular frequency, rad/s
  = $2\pi f$

ω_n = Circular natural frequency, rad/s

1 INTRODUCTION

Many steam generators used with pressurised water reactors contain inverted U-tubes through which the primary fluid flows, while the secondary steam-water mixture flows over the outside of the tubes. The straight leg sections of the tubes are support by tube support plates and the curved U-bend region of the tubes are supported by antivibration bars (AVBs).

The number and location of the AVBs are selected to prevent fluidelastic vibration when all of the AVBs are assumed to be active supports (ie, ideally pinned conditions are assumed). However, in practice, the effect of manufacturing tolerances required for assembly dictate that statistically some tubes may pass through the clearance in some AVB supports without making contact (1). This effectively increases the unsupported span length. Depending on the details of U-bend configuration, fluidelastic instability may occur for these longer spans, and the tubes may impact against the AVBs.

An experimental investigation was conducted, using an existing shaker facility (2) for testing full-size U-bends, to generate design information concerning the wear producing forces and motions that act between tubes and AVBs in the U-bend region. A feedback control system for the mechanical shaker was developed to simulate the fluidelastic excitation as negative damping. Random excitation simulates the in-plane turbulence-induced vibration. The U-tube is instrumented to measure the tube/AVB impact forces and sliding motions.

The tube wear potential is expressed in terms of workrate, defined as the integrated product of the tube/AVB impact force times the sliding distance during the impact, expressed on a per time basis. The tube wear volume for service applications can be predicted by the product of the workrate, the appropriate wear coefficient, and the operating time according to Archard's wear equation (3).

The shaker tests are believed to provide conservative quantitative information concerning tube wear potential. They are also useful in establishing trends and in making relative evaluations of wear potential.

Gap-limited fluidelastic vibration is the subject of ongoing investigation in the literature. Simulation of fluidelastic excitation has often been accomplished using sinusoidal forces. More recently, analytical (4) and experimental (5) simulation of fluidelastic vibration as negative damping has been reported.

2 SIMULATION OF FLUIDELASTIC EXCITATION

2.1 Fluidelastic Excitation

The critical cross flow velocity U_c above which self-excited fluidelastic tube vibration initiates is commonly given by (6)

$$\frac{U_{cn}}{f_n D} = \beta \ \frac{m_o \delta_n}{\rho_o D^2} \tag{1}$$

The rate at which the vibration amplitude increases as the flow velocity is increased above U_c depends on the rate of increase of positive damping with vibration amplitude. Limit cycles will be established if the positive damping increase is sufficient. Otherwise, the tube amplitude will increase until a physical stop is reach (impacting AVBs or neighbouring tubes, for example).

The critical damping ratio is related to the logarithmic decrement by

$$\zeta = \delta/2\pi \tag{2}$$

Substituting the critical damping ratio into Equation 1 and rearranging

$$\rho_o U^2{}_{cn} = 2\pi m_o \beta^2 f^2{}_n \delta_n \tag{3}$$

Equation (3) defines the flow velocity at which fluidelastic vibration initiates. At the critical velocity the system positive damping, ζ_n is exactly balanced by the fluidelastic negative damping. For any flow, the negative damping, ζ_d, is given by

$$\rho_o U^2{}_{en} = 2\pi m_o \beta^2 f^2{}_n \zeta_d \tag{4}$$

where U_e is the effective velocity commonly given by (7,8)

$$U^2{}_{en} = \frac{\sum\limits_{i=1}^{N} \frac{\rho_i}{\rho_o} U^2{}_j \phi^2{}_{jn} \Delta z_j}{\sum\limits_{j=1}^{N} \frac{m_i}{m_o} \phi^2{}_{jn} \Delta z_j} \tag{5}$$

When U_e/U_c is greater than one, fluidelastic vibration initiates.

Equation 4 demonstrates that fluidelastic instability may be treated as negative damping (ie, a positive feedback from the fluid to the tubes).

Consider a rigid tube on external springs constrained to vibrate in one plane with its longitudinal axis always parallel to its equilibrium position. The equation of motion for this simplified model is

$$m_o L \ddot{y} + 2 \ m_o L \ \omega \zeta_n \dot{y} + Ky = \rho_o U^2 L \ F \ (y, \omega) \tag{6}$$

where it is assumed that the fluidelastic force is proportional to $\rho_o U^2$ and to a function $F(y, \omega)$ of the tube displacement y and the circular frequency ω. At resonance (ie, the instability threshold).

$$U = U_{cn} \text{ and } m_o L \ddot{y} + Ky = 0 \tag{7}$$

Noting that $\omega_n = 2\pi f_n$ and $\delta_n = 2\pi \zeta_n$, and substituting Equations 3 and 7 into Equation 6

$$F(y, \omega) = \frac{4\pi \dot{y}}{\beta^2 \omega_n} \tag{8}$$

Applying complex notation $\dot{y} = j\omega_n y$

$$F(y, \omega) = \frac{4\pi j y}{\beta^2} \tag{9}$$

Equation 9 indicates that fluidelastic instability may be treated as a complex stiffness (with positive feedback) or alternatively as negative damping. In order to simulate the fluidelastic forces, the applied force must be proportional to displacement y, with a 90° phase lead. Equation 9 is only demonstrated to apply for $\omega = \omega_n$. However, fluidelastic vibration typically takes place at about the tube natural frequency. In any event, assuming that fluidelastic excitation is reasonably represented by quasi-steady models (5, 6) for the U-bend region, then $F(y, \omega)$ is independent of frequency and Equation 9 is generally applicable.

Dividing Equation 4 by Equation 3 gives

$$\varsigma_d = \varsigma_n \ \frac{U^2{}_{en}}{U^2{}_{cn}} \tag{10}$$

The excess negative damping, $\Delta\zeta$, is defined by

$$\Delta\varsigma = \varsigma_d - \varsigma_n \tag{11}$$

or

$$\Delta\varsigma = \varsigma_n \left\{ \frac{U^2{}_{en}}{U^2{}_{cn}} - 1 \right\} \tag{12}$$

The expression for the excess negative damping Equation 12 is the same as that used by Antunes et al (5). They also devised a feedback control system to simulate fluidelastic excitation as negative damping, and conducted tests on a cantilevered, flat-strip model.

Fricker (4) derived an expression for negative damping that he uses in analytical investigations. The excess negative damping can be inferred from his expression.

$$\Delta \varsigma = \varsigma_n \left\{ \frac{U_{en}^2}{U_{cn}^2} \cdot \frac{\omega_n}{\omega} - 1 \right\} \qquad (13)$$

Fricker's relationship for excess negative damping differs from the one used in the present investigation by the inclusion of the ratio of the natural frequency to the response frequency of the system. This tends to reduce the excitation level as the response frequency increases. If the vibration frequency ω does not deviate significantly from the natural frequency ω_n, the difference in excess negative damping provided by Equations 12 and 13 will not be large.

2.2 Feedback Control System

The feedback control system operates by sensing the tube displacement at the same location where the out-of-plane shaker force is applied, conditioning the displacement signal using a control system designed to Equation 9, and then feeding the conditioned signal via a power amplifier to the shaker attached to the tube. The circuit was developed to have the required properties over the desired frequency range. The transfer function of the system is shown in Figure 1. It can be seen that a reasonably constant quadrature component has been achieved over the frequency range of main interest, 10-100 Hz. The in-phase, or stiffness term, is negligible compared with the tube mechanical stiffness.

The feedback control system was qualified using a simple cantilever bar model prior to applying the method to the full-size U-bend model.

3 TEST APPARATUS

3.1 U-Bend Shaker Test Setup

The tests were conducted using an existing U-bend shaker test apparatus (2). Figure 2a is a schematic of the test setup. The Inconel tube has a 17.5 mm OD and a 15.4 mm ID. The top tube support plate is simulated by four steel knife-edge strips positioned 90 degrees apart around the tube circumference. The diametral clearance between the tube and the knife-edge is about 0.025 mm.

The curved U-bend tube is vibrated in the out-of-plane direction by a shaker located at the tube apex. This shaker provides the simulated fluidelastic excitation (and also out-of-plane random excitation if desired). Flow-induced vibration tests on U-bends conducted at Westinghouse, as well as results reported in the literature (9,10), indicate that the fluidelastic excitation for U-bends occurs only in the out-of-plane direction.

The tube is vibrated in the in-plane direction by a shaker positioned 54 degrees from the horizontal. Random excitation is provided by supplying this shaker with white noise input. The power spectral density (FIR) of the single driving force is selected to provide approximately the same excitation that the tube would receive from the distributed, turbulence-induced fluid forces for the main in-plane modes of interest.

The shakers are attached to small force gauges that are in turn attached to the tube. A 0.914 mm diameter rod about 146 mm long connects the shaker to the force gauge. The rod is relatively stiff in the drive direction and very flexible in the transverse direction. In this way the drive rod for a given direction does not interfere with the tube motions in the transverse direction.

The U-bend tube is filled with water and pressurised to 8.273×10^6 Pa in order to simulate the differential pressure that acts on a steam generator tube.

3.2 Instrumentation

The small piezoelectric force gauges attached to the U-bend tube permit the drive forces to be measured.

The simulated AVBs are instrumented to measure the impact forces generated when the tube strikes an AVB. The simulated AVBs are made of brass. The AVBs have a 6.96 mm square cross section and are 12.7 mm long. They were attached directly to a piezoelectric force gauge. Figure 2b shows the simulated AVB configuration, and the various features are identified. The AVB stiffness simulation device is used to support the AVB and force gauge, and can be tailored to provide the desired AVB stiffness.

Optical transducers are used to measure the very small in-plane wear producing motions that occur while the tube and AVB are in contact. See Figure 3d. These fibre-optic devices have a very high output, 19.7 V/mm and very low noise.

The out-of-plane tube motions are measured with transducers that operate on a variable impedance principle. Their sensitivity is 0.8 V/mm. They are adequate for measuring the tube vibration and are also used to set accurately the tube/AVB clearances. One of these non-contacting transducers is mounted directly opposite from the point at which the shaker is attached to the tube. The output of this transducer is used in the feedback control system.

3.3 System Linear Calibration and Test Procedure

Computer codes are used in design to predict the instability ratio U_e/U_c for U-bend configurations having various combinations of active and inactive AVB supports. Typically, the calculations are made assuming ideal-pinned conditions at the active supports, and no constraint at the inactive supports.

The first stage of the experiment is to simulate as closely as possible the boundary conditions used in the computer calculations, and then perform a linear calibration of the tube for the particular configuration of interest. Consider the configuration with active supports at C1, C2, C5 and C6, and inactive supports at C3 and C4. See Figure 2a. The rig was set up with four "D" section inserts (instead of the usual eight AVBs) at C1, C2, C5 and C6. The shape of the insert approximates an ideal pinned support. The inserts are positioned to give alternative front and back support in a manner that results in a tube-support preload of about 5N. At C3 and C4, the inactive supports, the clearance is made very large to avoid tube/AVB impacts during the calibration. The tube natural frequency is about 12.1 Hz before the shaker is attached, and the mechanical damping is very low 0.04%.

With the shaker connected both mechanically and electrically to the control circuit, but with zero amplifier gain, the tube is plucked by hand and the vibration decay is recorded. The system frequency increases to 16.4 Hz because of the added stiffness of the shaker. The damping is determined using the logarithmic decrement method.

$$\delta = \frac{1}{N} \ln \frac{Y_o}{Y_N} \qquad (14)$$

where

Y_o = initial amplitude
Y_n = amplitude after N cycles

The gain, G, of the control circuit is increased and the process of determining the tube damping is repeated. The control circuit introduces negative damping into the system. Hence as the gain is continually increased, the net positive damping decreases. At the critical gain, the negative damping from the control circuit and the positive damping from the rig are exactly balanced. The tube can be be plucked to maintain any desired constant vibration amplitude. As the gain is increased above the critical value, the tube vibration is self-starting (it is not necessary to pluck the tube) and there is an exponential increase in vibration amplitude. Examples of positive and negative damping are given in Figure 4 for the configuration. The logarithmic decrement relationship given in Equation 14 is used to calculate the negative damping from the exponential increase in amplitude in the same manner as for the exponential decrease in amplitude. The damping is measured at various values of gain. The damping versus gain plot is shown in Figure 5. A straight-line relationship is observed.

$$\zeta, \text{ per cent} = 4.6 - 3.23G \qquad (15)$$

The gain at which the damping equals zero is equivalent to the point of fluidelastic instability. The tube damping at zero gain is 4.6% (with most of the positive damping being the electromagnetic shaker damping). The fact that the positive damping of the shaker has to be overcome before zero damping is obtained does not invalidate the calibration.

Damping versus gain relationships obtained for each configuration of interest have different constants, but they all display straight-line relationships.

Once the damping versus gain relation-has been obtained, the D section supports are replaced by the simulated AVBs and the desired gaps are set at the active and inactive supports. At a given gain setting, the feedback loop will provide the negative damping associated with the linearised system with the shaker attached. Hence, the same fluidelastic excitation acting on the linearized system is assumed to be reasonably replicated in the shaker test when the desired clearances are established. This replication is most accurate when the tube response frequency in the test is approximately the same as the calibration frequency.

The experimental impact forces, sliding motions, and workrates obtained are associated with the combined system of the tube and the shaker. The combined system has a natural freuency of 16.4 Hz, rather than the 12.1 Hz natural frequency for the tube alone. This frequency change does not affect the workrate trends and observations presented. However, the workrates measured at a given excess negative damping in the test are corrected for the frequency difference in order to obtain the workrates appropriate for the tube alone. The correction procedure was checked by retesting a configuration with the shaker moved much nearer to an active support in order to reduce the effective stiffness of the shaker on the tube. It was found that application of the correction to the two sets of data gve very similar workrate results. Discussion of the correction method is beyond the scope of the present treatment.

The experimental workrates can be used to predict the workrate for a steam generator tube subjected to the prescribed flow conditions and tube damping used in the design calculations. As noted above, the design calculations are made (for the same configuration tested above) assuming ideal-pinned conditions at active supports, and no constraint at the inactive supports. The excess negative damping for the config-uration is calculated from Equation 12, using the U_e/U_c ratio obtained from the design calculation, and the value of the positive damping used in the analysis. The workrate for an actual tube with clearances corresponding to those in the shaker test is obtained from the corrected experimental workrate plots at the calculated value of excess negative damping.

4 DISCUSSION OF TESTS RESULTS

4.1 Typical Time Histories of Tube Motions and Tube/AVB Impact Forces

Figure 3 shows typical time histories of tube/AVB impact forces and tube motions for a configuration with active supports at C1, C2, C5 and C6, and inactive supports at C3 and C4. See Figure 2a. Simulated fluid-elastic vibration is occurring corresponding to U_e/U_c equal 2.2. The same reference value of FIR, the power spectral density of the in-plane random excitation, is used in all the tests discussed. Tube/AVB impacting is occurring at both inactive supports.

Figure 3a shows the tube vibration

amplitude and tube/AVB impact forces at C3. The gap-limited motion is steady. The impact forces are fairly steady with some modulation (random variation in amplitude) evident. It has been shown (2) that the impacting observed in flow-induced vibration tests on U-bends and straight tubes is more highly modulated than the impacting observed in this investigation. In addition, the impacting in flow-induced vibration tests is more intermittent with time periods when no impacts occur. This suggests that experimental or analytical damping (for which the excitation is always in phase with tube velocity) are more efficient than actual flow-induced vibration forces, particularly under tube/AVB impacting conditions, and therefore will provide conservative workrates.

Figure 3b shows the same information as Figure 3a on a shorter time scale. It can be seen that the tube motion resembles a truncated sine wave with flat regions that correspond to the duration of the tube/AVB contact.

Figure 3c shows expanded time histories of the tube/AVB impact forces that occur on the front and rear AVBs at locations C2 (an active support) and C3 (an inactive support). The impacts are typically comprised of multiple spikes. The duration of the impacts at the active support are considerably longer that the duration of impacts at the inactive support, as would be expected.

Figure 3d shows the tube/AVB impact forces at C3 and the associated radial and tangential in-plane motions at C3. The time histories of the impact forces and in-plane tube motions, such as shown in Figure 3d are digitized; and the data are processed as described in Section 4.2 to evaluate the workrate.

4.2 Determination of Workrates

The outputs of the various force and motion transducers are recorded on magnetic tape at 30 ips, which corresponds to a 0 to 20 kHz frequency range. The signals can be played back at lower tape speeds and displayed conveniently as time histories on a strip chart. Time histories of the impact forces and in-plane motions, such as shown in Figure 3d are digitized using a digital oscilloscope, and the data are processed using a computer to evaluate the workrate. The workrate is defined as the integrated product of the tube/AVB impact force, F_i, times the sliding distance during the impact, expressed on a per time basis. The work per impact is obtained using the formula

$$\frac{Work}{Impact} = \sum_{i=1}^{P} F_i \left[\frac{|X_i - X_{i-1}| + |X_i - X_{i+1}|}{2} \right] \quad (16)$$

A number of impacts are evaluated. The average work per impact is determined separately for the radial and tangential directions. The average work per impact for the two direction is then combined as the square root of the sum of the squares. The workrate is obtained by multiplying the average work per impact times the vibration

frequency (since the impacts are continuous). The progression of tube wear with time can be predicted from Archard's wear equation (3) using the workrate in combination with known impact/sliding wear coefficients.

It is necessary to filter the in-plane tube motions to remove, high frequency noise, particularly when evaluating the workrate for the smaller clearances, and the associated smaller fluidelastic excitation levels. Otherwise, the noise can result in an appreciable fictitious sliding distance. That is, the noise appears as motion reversals at high frequency in the calculation of workrate using Equation 16. Accordingly, the in-plane motion signals from the U-bend shaker tests are filtered at a low pass frequency of 1280 Hz. It is believed that the main wear producing frequencies, associated with the frequencies of the in-plane modes of tube, are lower than the 1280 Hz filter frequency.

4.3 Tests on a Configuration with Active Supports at C1, C2, C5 and C6 and Inactive Supports at C3 and C4

Figure 6, shows a typical frequency/stability plot for the configuration with inactive supports at C3 and C4 and active supports (with small clearances) elsewhere. It is seen that fluidelastic vibration initiates at less than the 16.4 Hz frequency of the tube/shaker system with ideal pinned conditions at the active supports.

The frequency steadily increases with increasing excessive negative damping, and eventually exceeds the 16.4 Hz frequency. This behaviour can be explained using the simple, idealized example for a four-span tube shown in Figure 7. The frequency determined for a given configuration approaches the calculated pinned natural frequency as the tube motion in the large (inactive) gap increases as a results of increasing excitation. It is evident that the clearances in the active supports result in lower-frequency vibratory shapes for lower excitation levels. Once impacting occurs in the inactive support (and it may occur at a frequency less than the 16.4 Hz value, depending on the clearance at the inactive support), the frequency will tend to increase with increasing excitation since the motion is gap limited. In a fluidelastically unstable configuration with gap-limited motion, the tube impacts the AVBs. The excess negative damping contributes to the magnitude of the impact forces, and also contributes to an increase in vibration frequency, which may in turn act to reduce the effective instability ratio U_e/U_c. Hence, there is a balance between the excess negative damping, the level of impacting, and the resulting frequency.

The rate of increase in frequency (above the 16.4 Hz value for ideal-pinned joints at the active supports) with increasing excess negative damping, appears to be greater than that observed in flow-induced vibration tests on U-bends (2). Again, it may be that the actual fluidelastic excitation is not as efficient as the feedback system used to simulate negative damping, particularly under tube/AVB impacting conditions. On this basis it is probable that the experimental workrates are conservative.

Figure 8a shows the workrate versus excess negative damping for two different values of clearance. The intercept on the excess negative damping axis is an indication of an increase in positive tube damping introduced by nonlinearities associated with the clearances at the supports.

Figure 8b shows the trends for workrate at the active and inactive supports versus excess negative damping. It is seen that while the workrate at the inactive support increases approximately linearly with excess negative damping, the workrate at an active support increases at a lesser rate. This is related to the fact that, once impacting is occurring at the inactive support, the reaction force at the active support is more influenced by the tube flexural stiffness and the size of the adjacent clearance, than by the excitation level (2).

4.4 Configuration With Inactive Support at C3 and Active Supports at All Other Locations

Figure 9 shows the frequency/stability plot for a configuration with an inactive support at C3, and active supports at all other locations. The active supports are provided by five "D" sections that replace the ten rectangular AVBs. The "D" sections are setup to give alternate front and back support in the manner described for the system linear calibration in Secion 3.3.1. Since the positive damping prior to impacting in the inactive support is the same as the positive damping in the calibration configuration, the instability occurs when the excess negative damping is slightly greater than zero.

Figure 10 shows that the workrate increases linearly with the clearance at the inactive support when the excess negative damping is held constant.

Figure 11 demonstrates the concept of workrate sharing. In Case A, the single-sided clearance at the front AVB is set at a prescribed value, while the clearance at the rear AVB is made large enough to prevent impacting. For Case B the front and rear AVBs are set at the prescribed value used in Case A. The data for Case B is the sum of the workrates at the front and rear AVBs, while for Case A the workrate at the front AVB is shown. Although there is some scatter, it is reasonably established that the total workrate at the inactive support is the same for both cases at a given value of excess negative damping. The concept of workrate sharing is important in the analysis of long term tube wear (11). For example, the tube wear depth with impact at both AVBs would be about one-half that with impact on only one AVB.

5. CONCLUSION

A feedback control system has been developed to drive an electromagnetic shaker. The control system simulates fluidelastic excitation as negative damping and is used in shaker tests conducted on a full-size U-bend tube instrumented to measure the tube/AVB impact forces and motions. The tube/AVB clearances can be accurately set, and various combinations of active and inactive support conditions can be tested. The simulated fluidelastic excitation is applied in the out-of-plane direction. In-plane turbulence-induced vibration is also simulated using a second shaker.

The instability threshold and the tube wear potential, expressed as workrate, are obtained for postulated tube/AVB fitups. Trends showing the variation of workrate with tube/AVB clearance and the level of the simulated fluidelastic excitation (excess negative damping level) are presented. The concept of workrate sharing (among AVBs) is demonstrated

ACKNOWLEDGEMENT

The NNC contribution to this work was under contract to CEGB (now Nuclear Electric). The authors thank the Westinghouse Nuclear Services Division, NNC, and Nuclear Electric for permission to publish this work, and thank Mr F A Kramer for valuable assitance in carrying out the shaker tests.

REFERENCES

(1) LANGFORD, P J, Design Assembly, and Inspection of Advanced U-Bend/Antivibration Bar Configurations for PWR Steam Generators, Journal of Pressure Vessel Technology, 1989, 111, 371-377.

(2) CONNORS, H J, and KRAMER F A, U-Bend Shaker Test Investigation of Tube/AVB Wear Potential, Presented at the I Mech E Fifth International Conference on Flow-Induced Vibrations, May 21-23, 1991 Brighton, UK.

(3) ARCHARD, J F and HIRST, W, The Wear of Metals Under Unlubricated Conditions, Proc. Royal Society of London, Series A, 236. 1956, 397.

(4) FRICKER, A J Numerical Analysis of the Fluidelastic Vibration of a Steam Generator Tube with Loose Supports, 1988 International Sumposium on Flow-Induced Vibration and Noise, Flow-Induced Vibration in Heat Transfer Equipment, 5, 105-120.

(5) ANTUNES, J, AXISA, F and VENTO, M A, Experiments on Vibro-Impact Dynamics Under Fluidelastic Instability, Flow-Induced Vibration - 1990, ASME, PVP-189, 127-138.

(6) CONNORS, H J, Fluidelastic Vibration of Tube Arrays Excited by Cross Flow, Flow-Induced Vibration of Heater Exchangers, ASME, December 1970, 42-56.

(7) PETTIGREW, M J, SYLVESTRE Y, and CAMPAGNE A O, Vibration Analysis of Heat Exchanger and Steam Generator Designs, Nuclear Engineering and Design, 48, 1978, 97-115.

(8) CONNORS, H J Fluidelastic Vibration of Heat Exchanger Tube Arrays, Trans. ASME J Mech Design, 1978, 100, 347-353.

(9) WEAVER, D S and SCHNEIDER, W, The Effect
     of Flat Bar Supports on the Cross Flow
     Induced Response of Heat Exchanger
     Tubes, ASME Journal of Engineering for
     Power, 105, 1983.

(10) YETISIR, M, and WEAVER, D S, The
     Dynamics of Heat Exchanger U-Bend Tubes
     With Flat Bar Supports, ASME Journal of
     Pressure Vessel Technology, 108, 1986.

(11) LANGFORD, P J and CONNORS H J
     Calculation of Tube/AVB Wear from
     U-Bend Shaker Tests, Presented at I
     Mech E Fifth International Conference
     on Flow-Induced Vibrations, May 21-23,
     1991, Brighton, UK.

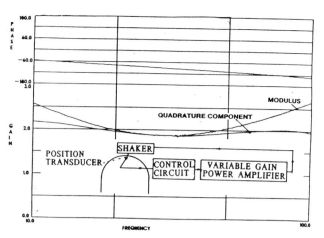

Fig 1 Transfer function for the the feedback control circuit showing the
modulus and quadrature components

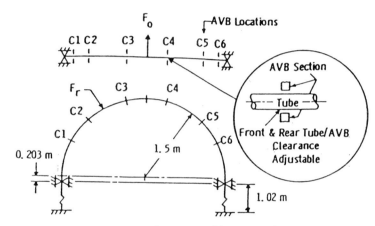

(a) U-tube configuration

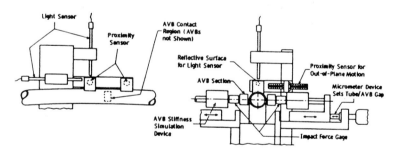

(b) Simulated AVB tube-support location.
The transducers used to measure tube/
AVB forces and motions, and micrometer
adjusting devices used to establish
accurately the tube/AVB clearances
are shown

Fig 2 U-bend shaker test apparatus

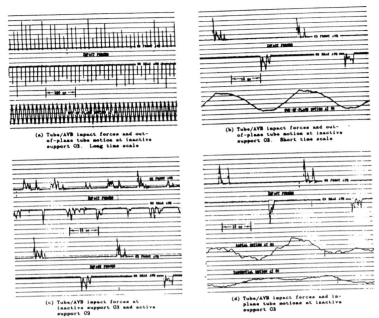

(a) Tube/AVB impact forces and out-of-plane tube motion at inactive support C3. Long time scale

(b) Tube/AVB impact forces and out-of-plane tube motion at inactive support C3. Short time scale

(c) Tube/AVB impact forces at inactive support C3 and active support C2

(d) Tube/AVB impact forces and in-plane tube motions at inactive support C3

Fig 3 Typical time history of out-of plane tube motion, tube/AVB impact forces, and in-plane tube motion at an AVB location. Configuration with active supports (with small clearance) at C1 C2, C5 and C6, and active supports at C3 and C4. Simulated fluidelastic vibration is occuring corresponding to Ue/Uc = 2.2. In-plane random excitation is applied.

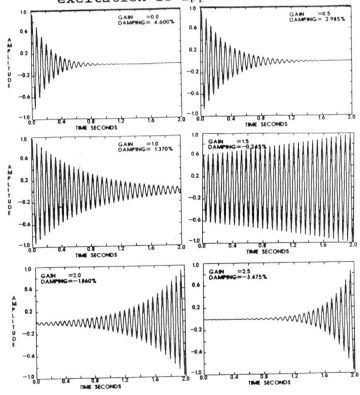

Fig 4 Time history plots showing the exponential decay/increase in tube displacement, following an initial displacement, for various values of amplifier gain G. Configuration with ideal active supports at C1, C2 C6, and active supports at C3 and C4

40

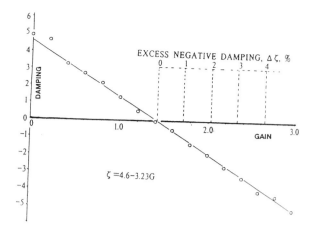

Fig 5 Variation of damping with gain for a
U-bend tube with ideal active supports
at C1, C2, C5 and C6, and inactive
supports at C3 and C4. Developed
from data shown in Fig 4

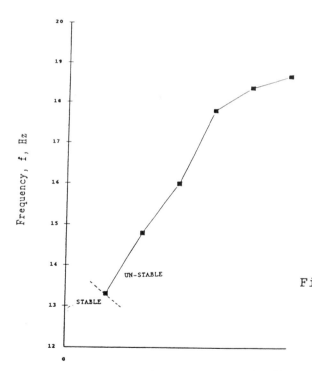

Fig 6 Frequency/Stability plot as function
of excess negative damping. Configuration with active supports (with
small clearance at C1, C2 and C6,
and inactive supports at C3 and C4

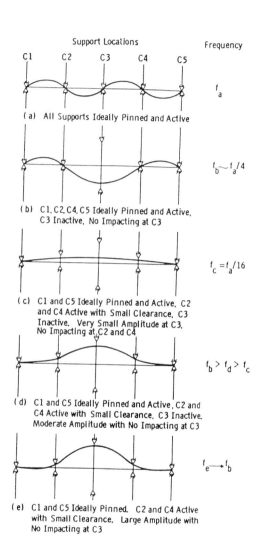

Fig 7 Idealised example of the effect of
active/inactive supports on the
possible mode shapes and vibrational
frequencies for a tube subject to
fluidelastic excitation

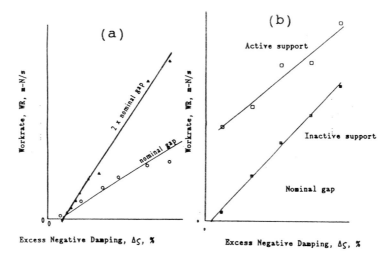

(a) Variation of the average of the workrates at inactive supports C3 and C4
with excess negative damping. Trends
shown for two valuse of tube/AVB
clearances at C3 and C4

(b) Comparison of the variation with excess
negative damping of the average workrates at the active supports C3 and C4
(nominal clearance) with the average
workrate at active support C2 (workrate
and damping scales are not the same as
in (a))

Fig 8 Typical workrate trends for a configuration with active supports (with
small clearance) at C1, C2, C5 and C6
and inactive supports at C3 and C4

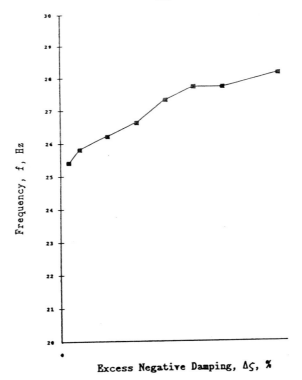

Fig 9 Frequency/Stability plot for a
configuration with an inactive
support at C3, and ideal active
supports at C1, C2, C4, C5 and C6

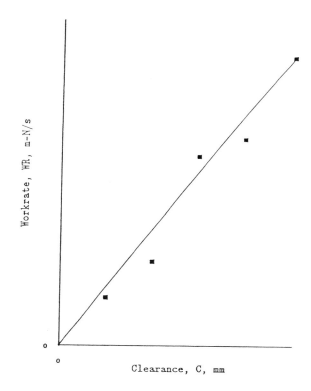

Fig 10 Workrate versus clearance at C3
at a fixed value of excess negative
damping for a configuration with an
inactive support at C3, and ideal
active supports at C1, C2, C4, C5
and C6

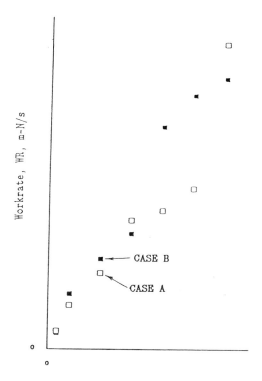

Fig 11 Workrate versus excess negative
damping for a configuration with an
inactive support at C3, and ideal
active supports at C1, C2, C4, C5
and C6. Case A involves tube/AVB
impacting at only the front AVB
(the clearance at the back AVB is
made very large). Case B involves
impacting at both the front and rear
AVBs (the rear AVB is moved in to
provide the same clearance as at the
front AVB), and the workrate sum for
the front and rear AVBs is plotted

C416/040

Calculation of tube-AVB wear from U-bend shaker test data

P J LANGFORD, MSc, PhD, MASME
Westinghouse Electric Corporation, Pensacola, Florida, United States of America
H J CONNORS, PhD, MASME
Westinghouse Science and Technology Center, Pittsburgh, Pennsylvania,
United States of America

SYNOPSIS A semi-empirical procedure is defined to calculate the tube/AVB wear potential which has been characterized by measured workrates from shaker tests of full-size steam generator U-bend tubes. Tube wear in the U-bend region of some operating steam generators results from vibration within clearances allowed by conventional fabrication practice as a consequence of fluidelastic excitation rather than flow turbulence. Sample calculations illustrate the relative effects of various design and assembly variables on potential tube wear.

NOTATION

AVB	antivibration bar
C_e	single-sided tube/AVB clearance
c_f	fluidelastic force coefficient
D	tube diameter
f_n	natural frequency
F_n	effective fluidelastic driving force
FOS	out-of-plane sinusoidal shaker force
K, K_a, K_t	wear coefficients: general, AVB, tube
L, L_e	length, effective length
m_j	mass of tube per unit length in the vicinity of the j'th lumped mass of the finite element model, including the added mass of fluid outside the tube
m_o	reference mass of tube per unit length including the added mass of fluid outside the tube
N	number of lumped masses used in the finite element model
t	time
U_{cn}	critical reference flow velocity at which fluidelastic vibrations initiate
U_{en}	effective reference flow velocity
U_j	reference flow velocity in the vicinity of the j'th lumped mass in the finite element model
WR	workrate for wear volume calculation
W_r	empirical coefficient from U-bend shaker tests
z_j	position of the j'th lumped mass in the finite element model
β	threshold instability constant
Γ	function used in workrate equation to adjust for untested tube diameters
γ	AVB cross-section local angle of twist
δ_o	reference damping log decrement
ρ_j	density of fluid outside the tube in the vicinity of the j'th lumped mass of the finite element model
ρ_o	reference density of fluid outside the tube
$\phi_c, \phi_F, \phi_{jn}, \phi_n$	modal displacements
ψ	function used in equation for FOS to adjust for shaker location

1 INTRODUCTION

Fluidelastic excitation can cause tube vibration in shell-and-tube heat exchangers. For vibration modes which are associated with pinned conditions at each AVB location, antivibration bars prevent fluidelastic vibration from initiating in the U-bend region of nuclear steam generators with the general arrangement shown on Fig 1. However, ideal pinned conditions do not exist at every tube/AVB intersection: tube/AVB gaps may exist due to manufacturing tolerances required for fabrication. Fluidelastic tube response may initiate within the gap(s) at which a tube is free to vibrate before contacting the adjacent AVBs, if excitation exceeds the reduced threshold for the longer span afforded by the gap(s)(1). Flow-induced vibration forces may then cause nonlinear, wear-producing impacting and sliding between the tube and the AVB.

Shaker tests have been performed on full-size U-tubes to characterize the potential wear-producing impact/sliding forces and motions in terms of workrates for various tube/AVB fitup conditions and simulated flow excitation levels. Results from these tests are used to calculate tube and AVB wear as a function of time to illustrate the relative effects of variables which can be controlled in design of advanced support configurations.

The effort described in this paper was undertaken to develop an engineering tool that can estimate the

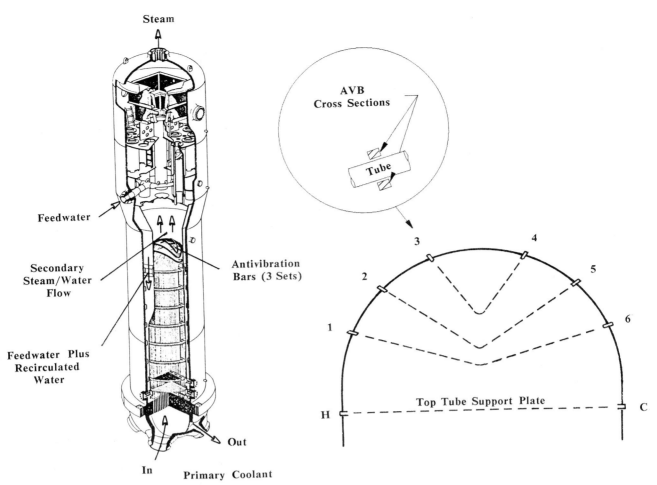

Fig 1 Typical steam generator arrangement with sample tube/AVB detail

sensitivity of U-bend tube wear to design and manufacturing variables. A semi-empirical calculation procedure is defined which simulates trends from the tests consistent with referenced thermal/hydraulic boundary conditions and calculated vibration response. This tool then permits development of manufacturing requirements necessary to achieve acceptable tube wear. Effects of several tube/AVB fitup parameters on potential wear depth are evaluated. These include the magnitude of the gap(s) between the tube and adjacent AVBs, the tube eccentricity within the gap, the number of adjacent tube/AVB intersections with gaps, and the local twist control of the AVB cross-section. Basic features of the tube and AVB design are also considered. These include the material couple which determines the wear coefficients and the size of each which determines the geometric depth-volume wear relationship.

2 U-BEND SHAKER TESTS

Fig 2 provides sample velocity and density distributions (arbitrary scale) as a framework for discussion. Such representations of the external flow across a tube in the U-bend region are obtained from qualified thermal/hydraulic analyses which allow calculation of consistent water/steam mixture density and velocity components normal to the tube. Both the presence of the AVBs in the U-bend and the differences in primary coolant temperatures (inside the tubes) in the hot and cold legs contribute to the observed variability in external flow distributions. Tube/AVB interaction resulting from tube vibration response to such external flows was investigated by simulating appropriate fluid forces in U-bend shaker tests (2,3).

2.1 Simulation of vibration mechanisms

Fluidelastic vibration is characterized by a threshold velocity, below which the vibration amplitude is primarily caused by turbulence and is relatively small, and above which the amplitude increases rapidly. The threshold or critical velocity, U_{cn}, is given (4) by

$$U_{cn} = \beta\, f_n\, D \left(\frac{m_o\, \delta_o}{\rho_o\, D^2} \right)^{0.5} \qquad (1)$$

with the corresponding effective velocity, U_{en}, for the multispan tube defined (5) by

$$U_{en} = \left[\frac{\sum\limits_{j=1}^{N} \dfrac{\rho_j}{\rho_o}\, U_j^2\, \phi_{jn}^2\, \Delta z_j}{\sum\limits_{j=1}^{N} \dfrac{m_j}{m_o}\, \phi_{jn}^2\, \Delta z_j} \right]^{0.5} . \qquad (2)$$

Fluidelastic forces in phase with the tube vibration velocity follow when the instability ratio, U_{en}/U_{cn}, exceeds unity. These forces are a function of geometric and fluid flow conditions which can be defined for conditions such as shown on Fig 2 using results of thermal/hydraulic and linear vibration analyses. The magnitude of the fluidelastic force, F_n, which results in vibration within a controlled clearance, C_e, was determined by auxiliary flow-induced vibration investigations (2). Resulting forces varied linearly with diametral clearance over the tested .05-.76 mm range. Fluidelastic forces generated by fluid conditions such as those of Fig 2 have the form (2)

$$F_n = c_f \rho_o D U_{en}^2 \left[\frac{C_e}{D}\right]\left[1 - \left[\frac{U_{cn}}{U_{en}}\right]^2\right]L \quad (3)$$

for the simplest case of a single force applied at one location for a tube modelled as a rigid tube of length, L, on external springs subjected to a uniform cross flow.

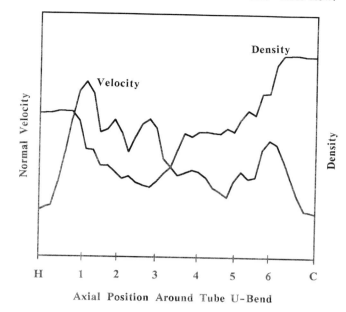

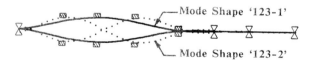

Fig 2 Sample velocity and density distributions with selected linear vibration mode shapes and tube/AVB fitup configurations

Such fluidelastic forces were simulated by equivalent sinusoidal shaker forces (*FOS*, Force, Out-of-Plane, Sinusoidal, rms) applied to the tube at a frequency close to the natural frequency of the tube during the reference U-bend shaker tests (2) using a more generalized equation

$$FOS = c_f \rho_o D U_{en}^2 \left[\frac{C_e}{D}\right]\left[1 - \left[\frac{U_{cn}}{U_{en}}\right]^2\right]\psi\left(\phi_C, \phi_F, L_e\right) \quad (4)$$

where ϕ_c is the modal deflection at the controlling clearance, C_e, ϕ_F is the modal displacement at the point of application of *FOS*, and L_e is the modal effective length. Alternatively, the fluid forces represented by Eq 3 can also be applied with an electromagnetic shaker powered by a feedback system that simulates negative damping. This approach was followed during a separate series of tests

using the same tube, shakers, and force/displacement measurement transducers (3). The vibrating tube establishes its own frequency during such testing. The modal effective length, L_e, is defined by

$$L_e = \sum_{j-1}^{N} \left[\frac{m_j}{m_o}\right]\left[\frac{\phi_{jn}}{\phi_n}\right]^2 \Delta z_j \quad (5)$$

when calculating appropriate fluidelastic forces for various tested/analyzed configurations.

Tube response to turbulent excitation is characterized by narrow band random vibration about the natural frequency of the tube for the existing support configuration. Concentrated random forces that give the same tube response as that predicted for the distributed flow forces are used to simulate both in-plane and out-of-plane turbulence in U-bend shaker tests (2,3).

2.2 Measurement of workrates

Tube/AVB contact forces and motions at selected tube/AVB intersections were recorded during U-bend shaker tests and assimilated in terms of workrate for use in calculating tube and AVB wear. The workrate, the product of the tube/AVB impact force, times the sliding distance during impact, expressed on a unit time basis, was obtained by numerical integration of the forces and motions.

2.3 Results

Numerous support configurations and loading conditions were tested and analyzed to obtain workrates at tube/AVB intersections (2,3). Measured workrates are generally conservative relative to those resulting from actual fluidelastic flow forces because impacting is more continuous, and the impact force peaks are less modulated, in the U-bend shaker tests with simulated fluidelastic vibration excitation than in flow-induced vibration tests (2,3). Other specific areas of conservatism exist as noted subsequently. Most tests had either one or two consecutive gaps with tube responses similar to those illustrated for mode shapes '1' and '12' on Fig 2. Responses to configurations with three or more consecutive gaps were evaluated to a lesser extent.

Fig 3 shows idealized workrate trends obtained during reference tests with configurations having one relatively large gap and simulating tube response to increasing fluidelastic excitation. The relatively large gap, such as at support 1 on mode shape '1' of Fig 2, is considered inactive in the sense that the tube can respond with a local maximum amplitude at the gap (i.e. as an antinode), and at a lower frequency (consistent with the longer span) than would otherwise be possible if the support constrained tube response to have a node at the support. The adjacent relatively small gap is considered active in the sense that it constrains the characteristic tube response to have an out-of-plane vibration node at the support even though it may still not act as a theoretical 'pinned' support.

Curve ABCDE on Fig 3 illustrates the workrate trend resulting at an inactive support as the *FOS*, simulating the fluidelastic excitation force, F_n, increases. The tube can vibrate within the clearance at the inactive support with no impacting, hence zero workrate, at the inactive support for values of *FOS* that are low relative to the size of the clearance. The vibration amplitude at the inactive support increases as *FOS* increases until tube/AVB impacting occurs (ABC on Fig 3). The workrate at the inactive support increases approximately linearly as *FOS* increases further (CDE on Fig 3). When excitation is simulated by negative damping, the tube can also vibrate without impacting within the inactive support if the increase in positive damping with vibration amplitude results in a limit cycle being established.

This trend illustrates the workrate response to increasing excitation for a fixed arbitrary support configuration. It is therefore analogous to the response to increasing velocity, decreasing damping, or changing other factors which increase fluidelastic excitation levels in a steam generator. If wear occurs at the inactive support during operation, the initial clearance will increase by the sum of the tube and AVB wear depths. Since the fluidelastic excitation forces can also increase with clearance (even at constant flow conditions), several test series were conducted at different clearances with *FOS* levels consistently increased (linearly). The workrate at the inactive support was found to also increase linearly with clearance under these conditions. This fundamental response is analogous to the consequence of wear with time subject to constant flow conditions which exceed the fluidelastic threshold for the existing support configuration. The workrate at inactive AVB locations with relatively large gaps and consequential tube wear potential, therefore is proportional to the magnitude of the tube/AVB gaps which are present during operation (before considering other effects discussed later, such as sharing the total workrate at multiple intersections, which tend to ameliorate this response in typical tube/AVB fitup configurations). The trend line illustrated by ACDE on Fig 3 is used in subsequent calculations even though it is conservative for small excitation levels relative to the clearance (AC response used rather than actual AB from Fig 3).

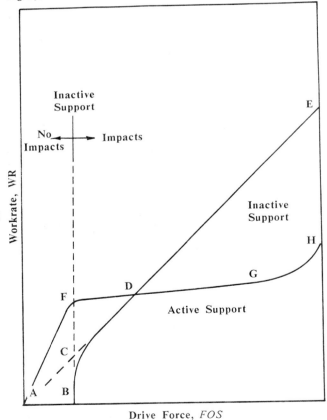

Fig 3 Conceptual curves showing idealized workrate trends for active and inactive supports

While the tube may vibrate within the clearance at the inactive support without impacting at the inactive support (AB on Fig 3), alternating tube/AVB impacting

may occur at adjacent active supports. Very small gaps were used to conservatively determine potential effects at supports which are active in the sense that out-of-plane tube motion has a node at the support, but in-plane motion is not restricted by preloads which would effectively 'pin' the tube at the support. The workrate at such active supports increases approximately linearly with *FOS* during the time that tube vibration amplitude within the inactive support increases linearly with *FOS* (AF on Fig 3). When impacting initiates at the inactive support, the workrate at the active support increases much more slowly with *FOS* (FDGH on Fig 3) than the workrate at the inactive support (CDE on Fig 3). This occurs because reaction forces generated at the active support depend to a large degree on the tube flexural stiffness and on the maximum tube displacement at the adjacent inactive support. The maximum tube displacement at the inactive support is limited by the gap when impacting occurs. Thus, wear potential at such active supports with small gaps is also dependent upon the magnitude of the tube/AVB gaps which may exist at adjacent inactive supports during steam generator operation.

The relative severity of workrate trends for inactive and active supports, as generally shown on Fig 3, in terms of potential tube wear depth after a prescribed operating period, is a function of many factors which cannot be treated within the scope of the present study. If an arbitrary gap at an inactive support consistent with the dashed vertical line on Fig 3 were increased, the relative severity of workrate at the active gap would increase. However, at some point in time, the active support could then become inactive as a consequence of wear. Analytical treatment of this transition, including the changing characteristic modes, is not included in the present study which emphasizes consequences of workrate trends at the inactive supports with relatively large gaps.

Two additional results including workrate sharing are significant to the analytical model for tube wear based on U-bend shaker tests. Fig 4 provides a basis for explaining their implications.

1) The workrate at one of two adjacent inactive supports, when impacting occurs only at that one inactive support (as at support 2 on mode shape '12' of Fig 2), is about twice as high as the workrate at the same support when impacting is equally shared at the two inactive supports (2). This is a direct observation of measurements made during shaker tests which include nonlinearities in tube response (see Fig 8 and related text in Ref 2 for example). Trends plotted on Fig 4 reflect workrates applicable to one side of a tube for various configurations. Curve ABCDE is the same trend for inactive gaps already discussed relative to Fig 3. As the fluidelastic excitation force increases with increasing wear beyond point C, a proportional increase in workrate results until impacting begins at the second support (point D on Fig 4). Subsequent workrates at the first support then decrease to half the original values, and the trend DFG is applicable (subject to relative mode shape constraints) as vibration and wear continues. Transition of the workrate trend illustrated by CD on Fig 4, to that illustrated by FG on Fig 4 as additional supports share the overall workrate (consistent with the tube characteristic mode shape), has basic significance in the analysis of long term wear.

2) The workrate on one side of an inactive support, when impacting occurs on one side of the tube having a radial gap equal to C_e (afforded by a larger gap on the other side), is about twice as high as the workrate at the same support when impacting is

© IMechE 1991 C416/040

equally shared as a result of having the same radial gap C_e on both sides of the tube (3). Again, this is a direct result of measurements made during shaker tests which include nonlinearities in tube response (see Fig 11 and related text in Ref 3 for example). Thus, a tube which is nearer an AVB on one side than the other will have a workrate trend characterized by AJ on Fig 4. This trend will continue until tube and AVB wear causes the gap on both sides to be equal, as at M on Fig 4, or until interaction at another support initiates, as at I on Fig 4. Possible transitions at M, I, or O on Fig 4 depend upon the fitup conditions.

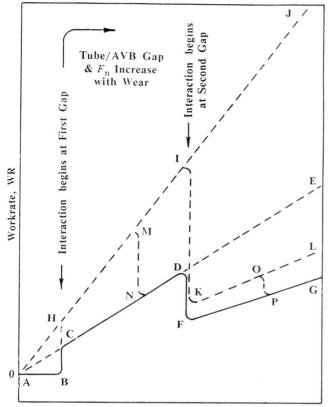

Fig 4 Workrate trend framework for inactive supports inferred from U-bend shaker test results

Overall results of the test program were provided in the form of workrate coefficients, W_r, for use in an equation of the form

$$WR = W_r f_n D F_n \Gamma(D) \qquad (6)$$

where F_n is the appropriate fluidelastic force consistent with Equations 3 and 4. The function $\Gamma(D)$ is analytically derived consistent with dimensional requirements to cover evaluation of tubes with a different diameter (stiffness) than that tested, and it does not affect sample calculations in this study. The workrate coefficients are specified as a function of frequency for each level of in-plane turbulent excitation evaluated. They are obtained from average trends determined from shaker test data. Variability of the data is covered by use of a 1.5 factor with Eq 6. The reference configuration is for double-sided interaction consistent with response illustrated by the CD portion of trends on Fig 4. Effects of single-sided interaction and of interaction at multiple supports are included in the analytical model by considering the number of supports involved and enforcing consistency of the mode shape during the wear process as explained in Section 3. The linear mode shape calculated with ideal pinned conditions at active supports, and no constraint of

inactive supports, is used as a first approximation in these calculations.

3 MATHEMATICAL MODEL

Separate tube and AVB wear calculations can be performed using conventional approaches based upon observations that wear volume is proportional to the normal load, proportional to the distance of sliding, and inversely proportional to hardness. This formulation was proposed for adhesive wear calculations by Holm (7) based on dimensional analysis considerations and applied by Archard (8), where the proportionality constant, K, was considered to be the probability of forming a wear particle. Rabinowicz (9) showed that abrasive wear could be treated using the same approach (with a different meaning for K). Similar statements apply for other potential wear mechanisms as summarized by Ko (10) for delamination, oxidation, and fatigue wear processes. Thus, reasonable wear calculations can be expected, even for combined mechanisms, provided that the wear coefficients are obtained from prototypic tests.

The particular form of the wear equation used in the current study,

$$V = K (WR) (t), \qquad (7)$$

is an extension of that described by Frick et al. (11) for tubes vibrating within a circular hole. The specific wear coefficient, K, incorporates the material hardness and therefore has units mm^2/N rather than being dimensionless as in classical treatment (7-9). The product of workrate and time provides a measure of accumulated normal load times sliding distance consistent with original derivations. Wear volume calculations therefore require knowledge of the wear coefficients for the tube and support materials and the applicable normal force/sliding motion workrates. Geometric depth/volume relationships are used to compute consistent wear depths from the accumulated wear volumes.

3.1 Wear Coefficients

Establishing the appropriate wear coefficient for a particular application, such as for tube/AVB interaction in the U-bend region of steam generators, is not a simple, straightforward process (10,12,13). The scope of this study does not permit discussion of the many potential variables and uncertainties. Yet, predicted wear volumes are proportional to the values used for both interacting components. Further, as is shown later, the relative values for each are important when treating tube response, constrained within small clearances, to the fluidelastic mechanism, because driving forces are a function of wear evolution which determines how operating gaps change after operation begins.

Wear coefficients for tube/AVB interaction are derived from tests that involve combined impact and sliding (but not pure impact) motions in as nearly a prototypic environment as possible. Variability in individual data points for such tests from several different laboratories is likely to exceed an order of magnitude for a specified material couple. Thus, individual data points can differ from the mean by factors exceeding three. This is consistent with typical expectations (13) that 68 percent of individual data would be within a factor of four of the mean in a typical log normal distribution of wear coefficients. Careful consideration of variables such as run-in effects and relative hardnesses of individual samples may allow reduction of the uncertainty to smaller values (perhaps to within a factor of 1.5 times the mean), but such variability must be considered when evaluating wear potential.

Comparison of relative wear potential for a tube when interacting with two different support materials is expected to be more accurate than calculating the absolute potential of either. This presumes that wear coefficients are similarly obtained for the right kind of motion in the right environment for each material by the same laboratory. For purposes of this study, nominal specific tubing wear coefficients for interaction with two different AVB materials are defined to illustrate the different wear potential for conventional and advanced design configurations. The ratio of nominal wear coefficients is assumed to be eight with attendant uncertainties in each as noted above. This assumption is consistent with EPRI conclusions (14) for relative values when typical Ni-Cr-Fe tubing interacts with Ni-Cr-Fe Alloy 600 or ferritic stainless steel AVBs.

3.2 Workrates

Evaluation of the wear potential for a given set of steam generator design and operating conditions requires appropriate workrates for use in Eq 7. Nonlinear models are available, or are being developed, (11,15-17) to calculate workrates analytically for various flow excitation mechanisms. However, analysis time and costs make it difficult to use these models in practical sensitivity studies of various design and assembly variables which include the iterative interaction of wear evolution and changing fluidelastic forcing functions. Empirical data obtained from U-bend shaker tests can be scaled to desired design and operating conditions using results from thermal/hydraulic and linear vibration analyses to establish overall trends, and to bound potential wear, in an iterative framework such as defined here.

Initial workrates for a given application are defined using Eq 6 following thermal/hydraulic analyses which define fluid flow conditions, and linear vibration analyses which provide the remaining parameters for the tube/AVB configuration of interest. The empirical workrate coefficients, W_r, are obtained directly from shaker test data trends based on the calculated frequency of the mode(s) of interest. Multiple cases are required to cover various potential initial fitup conditions.

Several factors contribute potential uncertainty to the selected workrates. These include both shaker tests and thermal/hydraulic plus vibration analyses contributions. Uncertainty analysis and propagation of the cumulative uncertainty considering the various potential effects have not been completed. Peak workrate coefficients are within a factor of 1.5 times the average trend, but the average trend is considered conservative. Individual analysis contributions are expected to have less uncertainty. The difference in the average trends defined by the equivalent sinusoidal (2) and negative damping (3) approaches for the same test configuration is considered a reasonable estimate of the overall uncertainty. This difference is about a factor of two for the range of simulated flow conditions which were tested.

3.3 Depth/volume relationship

Nominal AVB cross-sections are oriented relative to the tube as shown on the inset to Fig 1. The AVB surface is nominally parallel to the tube surface such that line contact exists across the AVB width. Potential tube wear resulting from tube vibration effectively involves only the length of the tube which defines this line contact since in-plane tube motion relative to the AVB is small. This is confirmed both by examination of selected tubes from operating conventional steam generators which experienced wear and by wear generated during prototypic wear tests. The cumulative wear volume of both the tube and AVB as wear progresses is then totally

defined by the volume of projected interference as the tube and AVB centerlines are assumed to be moved closer together.

Fig 5 illustrates sample total depth versus total volume relationships for both the nominal configuration with parallel tube/AVB surfaces, and for the potential misaligned interaction if local twist of the AVB leg is not carefully controlled. These curves are a function only of the tube and AVB geometry and the angle of twist, γ. They are calculated from appropriate geometry and mensuration formulae (e.g. volume of an ungula of a right circular cylinder) for each interacting configuration of interest. Geometrical relationships such as those of Fig 5 require additional consideration to properly apportion the total volume of wear between the tube and AVB during the calculation procedure as wear progresses. This is done iteratively by an interpolation procedure based on the ratio of tube and AVB wear coefficients.

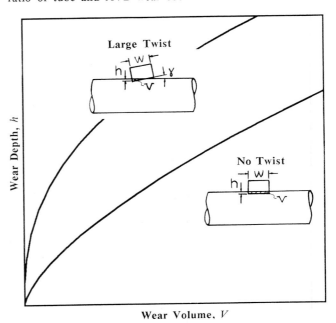

Fig 5   Sample tube/AVB depth/volume relationships

Alternative analytical approaches can be defined using individual depth/volume relationships for the tube and AVB separately. These individual relationships require assumption of the interfacing geometry as wear progresses. One such formulation (18) assumes the wear geometry will be cylindrical, with the tube and AVB having the same radius wear scar (which is greater than the tube radius), of common width. This radius is then determined based on the ratio of tube and AVB wear coefficients. One consequence of this approach is the conclusion that the depths of wear in the two components are in the ratio of their specific wear coefficients (18).

Comparisons have been made using both approaches, and calculated volumes differ by less than ten percent for depths of interest. The ratio of calculated depths for the components is also within ten percent of the ratio of specific wear coefficients for the reference approach. This observation is of practical use when interpreting matching wear surfaces taken from operating units or from wear tests.

3.4 Analysis flowchart

Components of the mathematical model are combined to iteratively calculate tube and AVB wear for any given support configuration as shown on Fig 6. This logic sequence is amenable to application using a spreadsheet on

© IMechE 1991 C416/040

a personal computer. Bounds on tube wear in the U-bend region of steam generators, which have been shown (1,19) to be limited by tube response to fluidelastic rattling within tube/AVB fitup constraints, can be obtained with reasonably sized models using this approach. Relative effects of various design and fabrication factors can also be treated effectively. Several examples are given in Section 4.

Definition of the various tube/AVB support configurations to be analyzed is the first step. Measurement of fitup during fabrication is an important factor in this process because resulting tube wear is sensitive to the initial support configuration for the controlling mechanism. Several potentially limiting configurations can be defined which cover possible fitup conditions, and the most limiting result selected after several analyses. The vibration modes shown on Fig 2 are examples of potential limiting mode shapes for the illustrated flow distribution. Potential gap(s) magnitudes at operating conditions must be established to calculate tube wear potential.

Thermal/hydraulic analyses provide boundary conditions including parameters such as velocity and density distributions similar to those on Fig 2. Linear vibration analyses, for any of several potential fitup configurations with characteristic mode shapes similar to those on Fig 2, provide the necessary parameters to relate calculated operating conditions to loads used in U-bend shaker tests using Equations 1-5.

The starting workrate for the support configuration of interest is then defined from Eq 6. Workrates from Eq 6 reflect empirical trends measured during U-bend shaker tests which are available for a range of frequencies and in-plane turbulence levels.

Subsequent steps are repeated on an incremental basis as necessary to cover a specified time. Parallel calculations are performed for each AVB intersection with a gap which interacts with the tube for the selected fitup configuration, and hence, characteristic mode shape of interest. Results of these parallel calculations, designated by the large dashed-line envelope, are compared with those from other locations to assure that the calculated

mode shape is not violated as a consequence of the wear process. Consistent adjustments are made to the workrates for the next time step (at box J) based on the number of sites involved using the logic explained relative to Fig 4.

The first of the incremental calculations (box E) provides best estimate tube and AVB wear depths at the end of the current time step. Eq 7 is separately applied to each using specified wear coefficients to obtain wear volumes. Multiple coefficients can be used for the AVB, with switching after a prescribed wear depth, to evaluate coated materials. Best estimate wear depths are calculated by interpolating between maximum and minimum possible tube depths based on the ratio of wear coefficients. There are actually eight substeps involved in these calculations using total depth/volume equations which define relationships such as those shown on Fig 5.

The next three steps are self explanatory with reference to Fig 6. The initial gap is incremented by the wear depths, calculated values are printed, and parameters for the next time step are selected. At this point (box I) a check is made to assure that the workrate for the next time step is consistent with the mode shape, i.e. that the adjusted gaps after wear do not change the number of possible interacting sites from that appropriate to the previous time step. This is done by comparing the ratio of possible tube displacements after the new gaps are calculated to the theoretical ratio for the linear mode shape. Workrates for each parallel site being considered are adjusted, maintaining a constant total workrate at all intersections, using the logic explaining the observed trends on Fig 4 if a change is indicated. Iterations defined by boxes C-J are repeated until the specified time is covered.

Sample calculations were made using this procedure to verify that the iterative process and the depth/volume relationships for a tube and AVB provide results consistent with prototypic wear tests. EPRI test FR-56 (14) involved impact/sliding interaction between a steam generator tube and an AVB removed from a conventional steam generator. Reported results of the test included applied workrates, derived wear coefficients, and the measured tube wear depth after testing. Profilometry

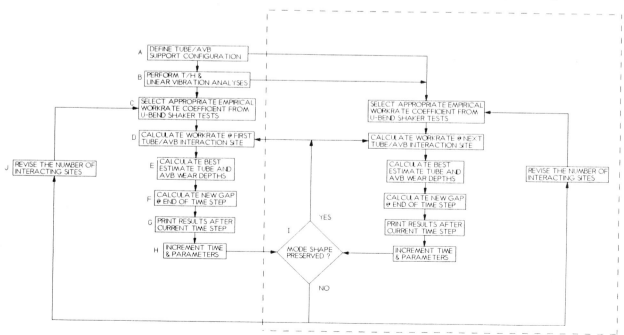

Fig 6 Analysis Flowchart: parallel calculations in dashed envelope are repeated for each gap

plots of the matching AVB allowed reasonable estimation of the AVB wear depth. Use of workrates and wear coefficients consistent with the test in the mathematical model yielded calculated results which differed from test results by two and ten percent for the tube and AVB, respectively.

This semi-empirical analytical model is considered a valid engineering tool for several reasons:

1) Workrates used in the analysis of tube wear depth follow experimentally derived trends obtained from simulated prototypic tests, using two different approaches (2,3), on full-size tubes. Both the starting workrates as a function of fitup, and the observed sharing response at multiple sites, are obtained from shaker tests which include nonlinearities in tube response. The nature of both the effective sinusoidal and negative damping simulations provides impact forces which are less modulated than those observed in flow-induced tests (2,3), such that the basic workrates are conservative.

2) The components of the model are assimilated in a wear model shown to have broad applicability to mechanisms of interest in steam generators (7-10).

3) Its application to simple examples, such as wear tests (14), for which all wear controlling parameters are known, yields results in close agreement with measured tube and AVB wear depths, thereby indicating the component parts of the wear model are assimilated properly.

4) Its application to configurations considered representative of various conventional operating steam generators matches available data on overall trends and relative effects. This is only briefly described elsewhere (1) and is beyond the current scope.

4 ANALYSES

Workrates obtained from U-bend shaker tests (2,3) can be used in the mathematical model to calculate relative potential tube wear effects as a consequence of fluidelastic vibration within tube/AVB fabrication clearances. Eddy current tests have revealed indications in some conventional operating steam generators which have been attributed to tube wear resulting from this mechanism (1). This engineering tool is useful in evaluating relative wear potential for various parameters which can be controlled in design and fabrication of advanced configurations with enhanced vibration and wear resistance. Sample analyses provide predicted tube wear responses with time of operation for several arbitrary postulated operating conditions. All results are shown in nondimensional form for the same arbitrary time and wear depth references so that comparisons from different figures are valid. These trends differ in character from those resulting from flow turbulence in the U-bend because fluidelastic forces can increase as controlling fitup clearances increase with wear.

4.1 Design parameters

The AVB material, size, and form tolerances are obvious parameters of interest to the design engineer. Fig 7 illustrates relative tube wear potential for two different AVB materials which result in specific tube wear coefficients having a ratio of eight as noted in Section 3.1. These trends were calculated for a postulated tube/AVB configuration such as that shown on Fig 2 with

predominant response assumed to be characterized by the linear mode '123-1'. The same AVB geometry with nominal tube/AVB fitup as shown on Fig 5 was used for all cases plotted on Fig 7. It was also assumed that gaps at AVB locations 1 and 3 are relatively much larger than that at location 2 such that interaction at multiple sites is not involved for the time evaluated. This assumption is associated with the degree of tube/AVB fitup control; effects of multiple interaction sites are addressed in Section 4.2.

The central trend in each of the two sets of three shown on Fig 7a represents the nominal effect for each of the levels considered (8K, K). The tube and AVB wear coefficients are equal for each nominal trend. The other two show potential effects of uncertainty in the tube wear coefficient using a factor of 1.5 above and below each nominal. Fig 7b shows potential effects of varying the AVB wear coefficient by a factor of 3 on both sides of the

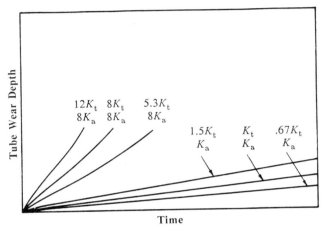

(a) Tube wear coefficient variations

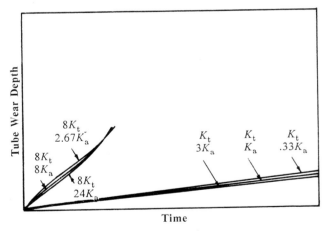

(b) AVB wear coefficient variations

Fig 7 Effects of magnitude and uncertainty in wear coefficients on tube wear depth

same nominal values. The larger factor was considered in this instance to reflect the possibility of having AVB material chemistry or structure variations leading to either 'softer' or 'harder' material than the tube. Notwithstanding the larger range evaluated for AVB wear coefficients, the resulting tube wear depth is clearly more sensitive to changes in the wear coefficient for the tube when the tube and AVB interact nominally with parallel surfaces. This phenomenon (relative insensitivity to change in K_a for nominal fitup) is a result of counteracting effects of increasing (decreasing) AVB wear leading to larger (smaller) surfaces contacting the tube, such that the tube wear depth decreases (increases) for the same wear volume.

This relative insensitivity is not preserved if local AVB twisting occurs at the tube interaction site. Fig 8a shows trends which result if the large angle of twist depth/volume relationship from Fig 5 is postulated to apply as a result of not controlling this tolerance during AVB fabrication and assembly. The same three curves shown on Fig 7b (for the material with eight times higher wear coefficient) are repeated on Fig 8a for comparison with three new trends calculated for locally twisted AVBs. For a given tube wear coefficient (same for all six curves), tube wear depth is less sensitive to AVB misalignment if K_a is greater than K_t, again due to the higher tube wear volume required per unit depth as the AVB wear increases. Thus, to the extent that higher AVB wear coefficients can be correlated with hardness (inversely) resulting from chemistry and structure, AVB material procurement specifications can be tailored to provide maximum insensitivity to off-nominal tube/AVB orientation. In any case, enhanced tube wear resistance can be obtained by controlling AVB twist as is illustrated by the sample analyses on Fig 8a. A similar statement applies to increasing the AVB width as is shown on Fig 8b where relative effects for doubling or tripling a reference width are plotted.

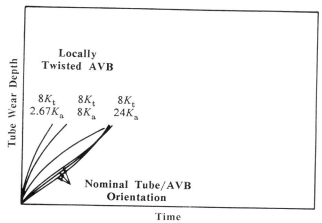

(a) AVB twist and AVB wear coefficient variations

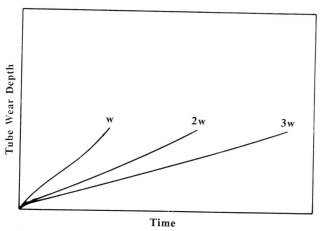

(b) AVB width variation

Fig 8 Effect of sample design parameters on tube wear depth

4.2 Assembly/fitup parameters

Given a design configuration with reference tube and AVB materials, a range of potential tube wear trends is possible for the same steam generator operating conditions depending upon the tube/AVB fitup achieved by the design and assembly process. Curves A through G on Fig 9 represent a selected sample of such trends. They summarize various individual contributions which are treated by the model. They were consistently calculated for the same configuration and assumed characteristic linear mode used in the previous Section 4.1. However, in this case, different gaps and relative tube positions are considered. Postulated conditions proceed from the most severe, without considering for the moment the possibility or probability of such fitup in practice, to the most benign.

Curve A represents an extreme case of a twisted AVB which is near one side (AVB) of a large gap at location 2 (see Fig 2, mode shape '123-1') when operation begins. Further, large gaps are assumed at adjacent locations 1 and 3 such that the workrate trend AJ of Fig 4 applies. Curve B is for the same conditions except that the AVB is not twisted. Curve C follows if the same gap for curve B is assumed for each side of the tube such that the workrate trend AE applies. These trends all result from interaction only at AVB location 2. They are therefore possible only for fitup conditions with large gaps at 1 and 3 (also at 2 to allow single-sided response for the duration shown). These gaps are larger than typically expected in either conventional or advanced designs, and a reduction in rate of wear depth progression would be expected in practice as discussed in Section 4.3.

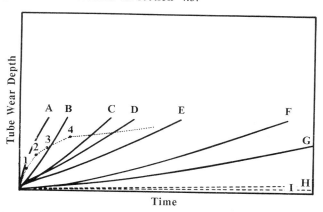

Fig 9 Effect of tube/AVB fitup on tube wear depth (see text for description of fitups)

Slower tube wear results if adjacent gaps are reduced. For example, if only the gap at location 1 is assumed equal to that at location 2 (still large at 3), then Curve B changes to D as a consequence of following workrate trend AIKL on Fig 4. Similarly, Curve C changes to E as a consequence of following workrate trend ADFG on Fig 4. This illustrates the potential benefit of a consistent fitup distribution.

Further enhancement results if the average gaps are reduced. Curve F results if the gaps at locations 1 and 2 are reduced from levels typical in conventional configurations to levels typical of advanced configurations (1). Fig 10 illustrates one of many possible intermediate progressions from a looser fitup condition to the trend for Curve F which is the same on both Fig 9 and Fig 10. Curves A through E on Fig 10 show the effect of progressively decreasing the gap at location 1 for a constant small gap at location 2 (not the same as for Curve E of Fig 9). Sharing of the available energy between the two locations occurs earlier and earlier with overall reduction in wear depth potential at location 2. Wear at location 1 initiates at different times (when sharing begins) long after startup depending on the fitup.

Curve G on Fig 9 represents calculated wear if all three of the postulated inactive gaps are made the same size as previously considered for locations 1 and 2. This illustrates the potential benefit of tightening the tube/AVB fitup within available design and fabrication constraints. Actual benefits are likely to be greater as a consequence of conservatism in the trends used for small gaps, and as a consequence of increased probability of the tube contacting the AVB such that the reduced frequency fluidelastic response is eliminated altogether. Curves H and I on Fig 9 are provided as a basis for comparison of relative magnitudes of wear calculated for fluidelastic vibration within available clearances (e.g. Curves A - G depending upon the noted fitup conditions) with those resulting from response to flow turbulence alone. Curve H represents continuous application of the workrate measured when the tube was subjected to random forces simulating expected out-of-plane, as well as in-plane, turbulence levels for a representative fitup condition. Curve I approximates the effect of measured changes in workrate as the gap was increased during the test series to simulate the effect of wear on workrates due to turbulence alone.

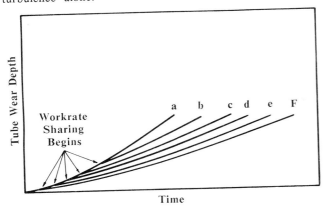

Fig 10 **Effect of sample progression from looser (a) to tighter (F) tube/AVB fitup on tube wear depth: sharing at one adjacent gap begins earlier as fitup is tightened.**

4.3 Discussion

Only a limited sample of analyses is possible within the scope of this study. Figures 7-9 illustrate effects of various individual parameters on tube wear depth at locations with gaps in the U-bend. Consideration of cumulative effects of AVB material (tube and AVB wear coefficients), AVB geometry (depth/volume relationship), and fitup conditions (initial workrate) is a straightforward process with a broad spectrum of overall responses. The approach to such analyses may differ depending upon the immediate objective.

For example, if bounding wear potential for a given design is the objective, then a range of potential limiting fitup configurations can be evaluated to determine the one with highest wear potential. Measured workrates from shaker tests for various gap conditions, which include nonlinearities in tube response, can thereby be combined with conservative assumptions on tube wear progression to obtain bounding estimates. Such assumptions may include (1) postulating the tube position within a potential gap to maximize tube wear, (2) neglecting redistribution of wear to multiple sites, i.e. neglecting likely changes to more favorable boundary conditions, as wear progresses, (3) use of bounds on AVB twist and fitup, and others associated with the analytical model components as already discussed. The sample fitup conditions on Fig 2 yield different potentials with maximum wear at different locations. Relative ranking

depends not only on the configuration, but also on the level of fluid excitation.

If the objective is to correlate field experience, then best estimate parameters and fitup conditions can be evaluated to obtain trends for comparison. One possible composite trend is schematically illustrated by the dotted line on Fig 9. Individual effects on Fig 9 represented by Curves A - G are extremes of various postulated conditions used to explain various factors. For a given realistic fitup configuration, each individual effect would probably last only a fraction of the time plotted. For example, an initial high growth rate in wear depth caused by one-sided wear on a moderately twisted AVB would change to the rate of Curve B after wearing the AVB corner, as at point 1 on Fig 9. The new, slower rate would continue only until wear on one side increased the gap enough for wear to begin on both sides of the tube. Then, the even slower rate of Curve C would apply after point 2, until reaching point 3, after which wear would then proceed at the Curve E rate until yet another AVB intersection began sharing the overall workrate as at point 4. Composite trends following this logic follow from application of the model to any consistent set of expected tube/AVB fitup conditions.

If the objective is to evaluate potential design and assembly alternatives, specific comparisons of relative individual effects such as those already discussed are appropriate. Cumulative combination of individual contributions can then be evaluated to define design and assembly combinations leading to fluidelastic vibration and wear resistance equal to or better than that for turbulence in the U-bend region of steam generators. This model is particularly valuable in evaluating the design and manufacturing requirements necessary to obtain acceptable tube wear in the U-bend region. Manufacturing experience applying these methods has shown that performance typified by Curves H or I is achievable in advanced design configurations.

5 CONCLUSION

A mathematical model is defined which can be used as an engineering tool to predict tube wear potential using workrates for tube/AVB impacting in the U-bend region of steam generators. This semi-empirical approach uses workrate trends obtained from laboratory shaker tests on full-size U-tubes and parameters obtained from linear vibration analyses to estimate wear potential. Evaluation of the potentially larger fluidelastic tube response is emphasized. Turbulence effects are included in measured workrates and predicted tube wear response.

6 REFERENCES

(1) LANGFORD, P. J. Design, Assembly, and Inspection of Advanced U-bend/Antivibration Bar Configurations for PWR Steam Generators, *Journal of Pressure Vessel Technology*, 1989, 111, 371-377.

(2) CONNORS, H. J., and KRAMER, F. A. U-bend Shaker Test Investigation of Tube/AVB Wear Potential, Presented at *I Mech E* Fifth International Conference on Flow-Induced Vibrations, May 21-23, 1991, Brighton, UK.

(3) FRANCE, E. R., and CONNORS, H. J. Simulation of Flow-Induced Vibration Characteristics of a Steam Generator U-Tube, Presented at *I Mech E* Fifth International Conference on Flow-Induced Vibrations, May 21-23, 1991, Brighton, UK.

(4) CONNORS, H. J. Fluidelastic Vibration of Tube Arrays Excited by Cross Flow, *Flow-Induced Vibration of Heat Exchangers*, 1970, 42-56 (ASME).

(5) CONNORS, H. J. Fluidelastic Vibration of Heat Exchanger Tube Arrays, *Journal of Mechanical Design*, 1978, 100, 347-353.

(6) CONNORS, H. J. Flow-Induced Vibration and Wear of Steam Generator Tubes, *Nuclear Technology*, 1981, 55, 311-331.

(7) HOLM, R. *Electric Contacts*, 1946, (Almqvist and Wiksells, Stockholm).

(8) ARCHARD, J. F. Contact and Rubbing of Flat Surfaces, *J. Appl. Phys.*, 1953, 24, 981-988.

(9) RABINOWICZ, E., DUNN, L. A., and RUSSELL, P. G. The Abrasive Wear Resistance of Some Bearing Steels, *Lubrication Engineering*, 1961, 17, 587-593.

(10) KO, P. L. Metallic Wear - A Review, with Special References to Vibration-Induced Wear in Power Plant Components, 1986, *PVP-1*, 1-15 (ASME).

(11) FRICK, T. M., SOBEK, T. E., and REAVIS, J. R. Overview on the Development and Implementation of Methodologies to Compute Vibration and Wear of Steam Generator Tubes, *Symposium on Flow-Induced Vibrations*, 1984, 3, 149-161.

(12) HOFMANN, P. J., SCHETTLER, T., and STEININGER, D. A., Pressurized Water Reactor Steam Generator Tube Fretting and Fatigue Wear Characteristics, 1986, *PVP-2*, 1-12 (ASME).

(13) RABINOWICZ, E. Wear Coefficients -Metals, *Wear Control Handbook*, 1980, 475-506 (ASME).

(14) HOFMANN, P. J., SCHETTLER, T., and STEININGER, D. A., *PWR Steam Generator Tube Fretting and Fatigue Wear*, 1989, (EPRI NP-6341).

(15) ANTUNES, J., AXISA, F., and VENTO, M. A., Experiments on Vibro-Impact Dynamics Under Fluidelastic Instability, *Flow-Induced Vibration - 1990*, 1990, 127-138 (ASME PVP-189).

(16) RAO, M., STEININGER, D., and EISINGER, F. Numerical Simulation of Fluidelastic Vibration and Wear of Multispan Tubes with Clearance at the Supports, 1988, *Flow-Induced Vibration in Heat Transfer Equipment*, 5, 235-249 (ASME).

(17) FRICKER, A. J. Numerical Analysis of the Fluidelastic Vibration and Wear of Multispan Tubes with Clearance at the Supports, *Flow-Induced Vibration in Heat Transfer Equipment*, 5, 105-120 (ASME).

(18) PARRY, A. A. The Wear Volume Losses of Tubes Fretted by Rectangular Bars, CEGB Report TPRD/B/1070/R88, obtainable from the Librarian, Berkeley Nuclear Laboratories, Berkeley, Glos., GL13 9PB, UK.

(19) FRICK, T. M., and WAISMAN, R. Methodologies for the Computation of Steam Generator Tube Wear with Applications for Turbulence in the U-Bend Region, 1989, *FE-15* (ASCE/ASME).

C416/014

U-bend shaker test investigation of tube-AVB wear potential

H J CONNORS, PhD, MASME and F A KRAMER
Westinghouse Science and Technology Center, Pittsburgh, Pennsylvania,
United States of America

SYNOPSIS Tube wear attributed to fluidelastic vibration is sometimes observed in the U-bend region of steam generators. In-air shaker tests were run on a full-size U-bend tube with model AVBs (antivibration bars) for various combinations of active and inactive AVBs, and for various levels of simulated fluidelastic vibration. The tube/AVB impact forces and motions were measured, and the wear potential, expressed as workrate, was determined. Workrate trends as a function of tube/AVB clearance and the excitation level are presented. The general dynamic behavior of the tube in the shaker test is compared with the behavior of tubes in flow-induced vibration tests.

NOTATION

C_e = Single-sided tube/AVB clearance, m
c_f = Fluidelastic force coefficient, dimensionless
D = Tube diameter, m
F_c = Positive damping force, N
F_f = Total fluidelastic driving force (in-phase with tube velocity), N
F_i = Tube/AVB impact force, N
F_n = Effective fluidelastic driving force, N
  = F_f-F_c
f_n = Natural frequency, Hz
f_s = Shaker frequency, Hz
FOS = Out-of-plane sinusoidal shaker force, N rms
FIR = PSD of in-plane excitation N^2/Hz
K = Wear coefficient
L = Tube length, m
m_j = Mass of tube per unit length in the vicinity of the j'th lumped mass of the finite element model, including the added mass of fluid outside the tube, Kg/m
m_o = Reference mass of tube per unit length including the added mass of fluid outside the tube, Kg/m
N = Number of lumped masses used in the finite element model, dimensionless
t = Time, s
U_{cn} = Critical reference flow velocity at which fluidelastic vibrations initiate, m/s
U_{en} = Effective reference flow velocity, as defined by Eq. (3), m/s
U_j = Reference flow velocity in the vicinity of the j'th lumped mass in the finite element model, m/s
V = Wear volume, m^3
WR = Workrate m-N/s
X_i = In-plane tube displacement associated with impact force F_i, m
y = Vibration amplitude, m
Δz_j = Incremental length used in finite element model, m
α = Stability exponent, (see Eq. (4)), dimensionless
β = Threshold instability constant, dimensionless
λ = Stability exponent (see Eq. (4)), dimensionless

δ_o = Damping expressed as logarithmic decrement, dimensionless
ρ_j = Fluid density in the vicinity of the j'th lumped mass of the finite element model, Kg/m³
ρ_o = Reference fluid density, Kg/m³
ϕ_{jn} = Normalized displacement of the j'th lumped mass in the finite element model, in the n'th mode, dimensionless

1. INTRODUCTION

Tube wear is sometimes observed in the U-bend region of operating nuclear steam generators. Each of the U-tubes is supported by a number of tube support plates in the straight leg section of the tube bundle. AVBs (antivibration bars) support the tubes in the U-bend region in order to minimize the potential for fluidelastic instability (for modes of vibration associated with ideal pinned conditions at each AVB location) and to control the magnitude of the turbulence-induced vibration. Because of manufacturing tolerances and assembly factors, a nominal clearance exists between the tube and AVB. At some locations the clearance may be less than nominal, while at other locations it may be greater than nominal.

Eddy current inspections of operating steam generator tubes have given indications of tube thinning. The thinning has been attributed to vibration-induced wear (1,2). It is believed that some tubes are free to vibrate within the tube/AVB clearance (ideal pinned conditions do not exist everywhere) and cause wear producing impacting between the tube and AVB. Prior evaluations (1,3) of tube wear in field units indicate that the tube vibration and the associated wear is caused primarily by fluidelastic instability, rather than by turbulence. Therefore, the vibration excitation force, and hence the wear potential, increases with tube/AVB clearance.

If pinned conditions are assumed at all the AVB locations, the calculated stability ratio, U_e/U_c (where U_e is the effective flow velocity, and U_c is the critical flow velocity above which fluidelastic vibration initiates), is considerably less than one in Westinghouse steam generators. Hence, it is predicted that fluidelastic vibration will not occur. If tube/AVB clearance is assumed to exist at some AVB locations, the calculated stability ratio for the resulting lower frequency modes with antinodes (locations of maximum tube amplitude in a mode) near certain AVB locations may be greater than one in some cases. This indicates that gap-limited fluidelastic vibration may occur.

All the AVBs are active in that they physically limit the tube motions. For present purposes, however, the AVBs will be said to be inactive supports at locations where the tube/AVB clearance is large relative to the clearances at other locations. The AVBs at the latter locations will be said to be active supports. Wear may take place at the inactive support locations when tube/AVB impacts occur. The impacting process limits the tube vibration amplitude. Wear may also occur at active AVB locations due to the vibration amplitudes that occur at neighboring inactive AVB locations. These amplitudes cause the tube to move within the clearance of the active support. Figure 1 is an idealized example of the effects of active and inactive supports on the tube vibratory shape and response frequency when fluidelastic vibration takes place.

An experimental investigation was conducted to provide design information concerning the wear-producing forces and motions that act between tubes and AVBs in the U-bend region of steam generators. Fluidelastic excitation for the U-bend is simulated in the out-of-plane direction. As discussed in Section 3, only out-of-plane fluidelastic vibration is observed in flow-induced vibration tests on U-bends. Turbulence-induced vibration is simulated in the in-plane direction. The tube is centered in the tube/AVB clearance at an inactive support for the treatments in this paper. It should be noted that tube/AVB eccentricity in the clearance space, static contact, or preload of the tube and AVB can significantly reduce or eliminate fluidelastic vibration and the associated potential for wear. The results of the investigation provide a basis for predicting and controlling tube wear in steam generators, as a function of mechanical parameters such as tube/AVB clearance.

The tube wear potential is expressed in terms of workrate that is defined (1,4) as the integrated product of the tube/AVB impact force times the sliding distance during the impact, expressed on a per time basis. The tube wear volume for a time t can be expressed as the product of the workrate times the appropriate wear coefficient according to Archard's wear equation (5).

$$V \sim K(WR)t \qquad (1)$$

The tests are believed to provide conservative, quantitative information. They are also useful in making relative comparisons, and in establishing trends. In the present paper, some of the significant trends are presented.

Numerous experimental and analytical investigations of tube/support dynamic interaction caused by fluidelastic excitation are reported in the literature (see (6-13) for

examples) Most of the investigations are concerned with, or involve straight tubes vibrating within circular holes. Relatively few investigations (see (2,14-17) for examples) have involved curved, U-bend tubes.

2. EXPERIMENTAL APPROACH

2.1 U-Bend Shaker Test Facility

Figure 2 is a schematic representation of the test facility that was built to allow full-size-radius U-bend tubes to be supported by simulated AVBs. The curved U-bend tubes have 1.02-m straight leg sections that are fixed at the lower end of the tube. The curved U-bend region of the tube is vibrated in the out-of-plane and in-plane directions by electro-magnetic shakers. The Inconel tubes have a 17.5 mm OD and a 15.4 mm ID. Figure 2a shows a U-bend tube with four AVB locations, while Figure 2b shows a U-bend tube with six AVB locations. The top tube support plate in a steam generator is simulated in the test by four steel knife-edge strips positioned 90° apart around the tube circumference. The diametral clearance between the tube and the knife-edge strips is about 0.025 mm. The radius of the U-bend tube is 1.5 m.

A shaker located at the apex of the U-bend provides sinusoidal excitation in the out-of-plane direction to simulate fluidelastic vibration. The same shaker can also be used to provide random excitation in the out-of-plane direction to simulate turbulence-induced vibration. A shaker oriented to drive in the radial in-plane direction is positioned 54 degrees from the horizontal. Random excitation provided by this shaker simulates in-plane turbulence-induced vibration.

The shakers are attached to small force gages that are in turn attached to the tube. A 0.914-mm diameter rod about 146 mm long connects the shaker to the force gage. The rod is relatively stiff in the drive direction, but very flexible in the transverse direction. The flexibility in the transverse direction prevents the drive rod from restraining the wear-producing in-plane motions in the case of the shaker that provides out-of-plane forces, and prevents the drive rod from restraining out-of-plane motions in the case of the shaker that provides in-plane forces.

The rms value of FOS, the out-of-plane sinusoidal drive force, is measured after the force gage signal is conditioned by a low-pass filter set at 250 Hz. The filter eliminates high frequencies associated with modes of the drive rod. The maximum out-of-plane drive force frequency was about 25 Hz in the present test program.

Random excitation is provided by supplying the shakers with a white noise input. Both the in-plane and the out-of-plane shakers can provide random excitation. Only in-plane random excitation (FIR) was used for the tests described in this paper. The power spectral density level of the single driving force is selected to provide approximately the same excitation for the main modes of interest that the tube would receive from the distributed, turbulence-induced, fluid forces.

The U-bend tube is filled with water and pressurized to 8.273×10^6 Pa in order to simu-

© IMechE 1991 C416/014

late the differential pressure that acts on a steam generator tube.

2.2 Instrumentation

The small, piezoelectric force gages attached to the U-bend tube permit the drive forces to be measured.

The simulated AVBs are instrumented to measure the impact forces generated when the tube strikes an AVB. The simulated AVBs are made of brass. They have a 6.96 mm square cross section and are 12.7 mm long. The AVBs are attached directly to a piezoelectric force gage. Figure 3 shows an AVB location, and the various features are identified. The AVB stiffness simulation device, shown in Figure 3, is used to support the AVB and the force gage, and can be tailored to provide the desired AVB stiffness. The stiffness, determined using an impact pendulum method, increases gradually with the level of the impact force, but it is reasonably constant for the range of impact forces F_i measured in the shaker tests.

Optical displacement tranducers are used to measure the in-plane, wear-producing tube motions that occur while the tube and AVB are in contact. See Figure 4d. These fibre-optic devices have a very high output, 19.7 volt/mm, and very low noise. They are well suited for this application since the wear-producing motions are very small, ranging from less than 0.025 mm to 0.075 mm or more, depending on the test configuration and the magnitudes of the shaker forces.

The out-of-plane tube displacements, are measured with transducers that operate on a variable impedance principle. These devices are less sensitive, 0.8 volt/mm, than the optical transducers. However, they are quite adequate for measuring the out-of-plane motions, and are also used to set accurately the desired tube/AVB clearances.

2.3 Test Procedure

Fluidelastic excitation is simulated by a sinusoidal forcing function, FOS, applied at a prescribed value of frequency, f_s. The simulation is an engineering approximation since the actual fluidelastic vibration will occur at a frequency (not necessarily exactly equal to f_s) that is determined by the characteristics of the nonlinear system and the magnitude of the forcing function.

The driving frequency is related to the level of the driving force FOS . The test frequency is determined by first conducting pretests with the clearance at the inactive support(s) opened up to prevent tube/AVB impacting, and the clearances at the active supports set at the desired test condition. The tube is driven at preselected values of FOS over a range of frequencies in the vicinity of the natural frequency, calculated assuming pinned conditions at the active supports. The frequency at which the ratio of the vibration amplitude to the driving force amplitude is a maximum is determined. This frequency is then used in the tests in which the clearance at the inactive support(s) is set to the desired clearance so that impacting can occur at the inactive support(s).

The frequency at which the ratio of the vibration amplitude to drive force amplitude is

a maximum varies from 9 Hz to 11.6 Hz as FOS is increased for the configuration with six AVB locations and inactive supports at C3 and C4 (see Figure 2b). The calculated pinned natural frequency is 11.6 Hz for this configuration. It is evident that the clearances at the active supports result in lower "modal" frequencies for lower values of FOS. This is illustrated in Figure 1 for a simple, idealized example involving a four-span tube. The test frequency determined for a given configuration approaches the calculated pinned natural frequency as the tube motion in the large gap increases, as a result of increasing FOS (the small clearances in the active supports become a smaller fraction of the amplitude at the inactive support).

Following the pretests, the clearance at the inactive support(s) is adjusted to the desired value, the test value for FOS is determined, and the driving force is applied at the frequency identified in the pretests.

The method given above for selecting the drive frequency is a first approximation since it is expected that the vibration frequency for self-excited vibration will increase somewhat as the impacting becomes heavier in the inactive support. However, as discussed in Section 5, our flow-induced vibration tests, as well as data from the literature, indicate that the expected frequency change is relatively small for the range of U_e/U_c anticipated for the main configurations of interest in the shaker tests. It is believed that when the fluidelastic forcing function causes relatively steady impacting at an inactive support, the expected frequency changes do not have a major effect on the resulting workrate. However, when the fluidelastic forcing function is such that impacting is either intermittent (or does not occur) at the inactive support, then close adjustment of the driving frequency can, of course, have a signficant effect on tube response.

3. SIMULATION OF FLUIDELASTIC EXCITATION BY A SINUSOIDAL FORCE

Fluidelastic vibration is characterized by a threshold velocity, below which the vibration amplitude is primarily caused by turbulence and is relatively small, and above which the amplitude increases rapidly. The threshold or critical velocity U_{cn} is commonly given by (18) :

$$ U_{cn} = f_n D \beta \left[\frac{m_o \delta_o}{\rho_o D^2} \right]^{0.5} \qquad (2) $$

Instability is predicted when the effective velocity, U_{en}, is greater than the critical velocity. The effective velocity is commonly given by (19,20)

$$ U_{en}^2 = \frac{\sum\limits_{j=1}^{N} \frac{\rho_j}{\rho_o} U_j^2 \phi_{jn}^2 \, \Delta Z_j}{\sum\limits_{j=1}^{N} \frac{m_j}{m_o} \phi_{jn}^2 \, \Delta Z_j} \qquad (3) $$

It has been suggested by Paidoussis (21), and others, that a more general form for Equation 2 can be written

$$U_e = f_n D\beta \left[\frac{m_o}{\rho_o D^2}\right]^\alpha [\delta_o]^\gamma \qquad (4)$$

Discussion of the form of the instability equation is beyond the scope of the present paper. However, information from several sources suggests that Equation 2 is reasonable for square tube patterns operating in the steam-water environment found in the U-bend region. The data base can be scaled if at a later date another form of the instability equation is found to be more appropriate.

The effective fluidelastic force can be derived in simplest form as a single force applied at one location for a tube modeled as a rigid bar on external springs subjected to uniform cross flow.

Let

U_{en} = cross flow velocity

U_{cn} = critical cross flow velocity for fluidelastic vibration

F_f = total fluidelastic driving force (in-phase with tube velocity)

F_c = positive damping force that must be exceeded in order for fluidelastic vibration to initiate

F_n = effective fluidelastic driving force
= $F_f - F_c$

Assume that the form of the driving force is similar to that obtained for a single row of straight tubes (18)

$$F_f = c_f \rho_o U_{en}^2 \left(\frac{y}{D}\right) DL\sin\omega t \qquad (5)$$

For the tube/AVB impact situation, assume

$$\frac{y}{D} = \frac{C_e}{D} .$$

Where C_e is the single-sided tube/AVB clearance.

$$F_f = c_f \rho_o U_{en}^2 \left[\frac{C_e}{D}\right] DL\sin\omega t \qquad (6)$$

$$F_n = \left[c_f\rho_o U_{en}^2\left[\frac{C_e}{D}\right]DL - c_f\rho_o U_{cn}^2\left[\frac{C_e}{D}\right]DL\right]\sin\omega t \qquad (7)$$

The magnitude of the effective fluidelastic force is

$$F_n = c_f \left[\frac{C_e}{D}\right] \rho_o D U_{en}^2 \left[1 - \left[\frac{U_{cn}}{U_{en}}\right]^2\right] L \qquad (8)$$

Equation 8 is applicable when $U_e/U_c \geq 1.0$.

For tubes on multiple supports a somewhat more complicated equation is obtained.

It can be readily shown by examining the expressions for the energy extracted from the fluid (19), and the energy dissipated by damping, that the dimensionless fluidelastic force coefficient c_f can be expressed by

$$c_f = 4\pi/\beta^2 \qquad (9)$$

The fluidelastic forcing function given in Equation 8 represents a force in-phase with the tube vibration velocity. For purposes of the present investigation, the fluidelastic force is simulated by an equivalent sinusoidal shaker force applied to the tube at a frequency close to the natural frequency of the tube. Tests on U-bend tube arrays conducted in our steam loop and in our wind tunnel, as well as tests reported in the literature (15,16), indicate that the fluidelastic excitation of U-bends occurs only in the out-of-plane direction. Accordingly, fluidelastic excitation is simulated in the shaker tests by only an out-of-plane force. The in-plane shaker is used in some test to simulate in-plane turbulence-induced vibration.

The simulated fluidelastic excitation can also be applied as negative damping. The vibrating tube establishes its own frequency when negative damping excitation is applied. Tests were conducted in the shaker apparatus in which the electromagnetic shaker was powered by a feedback system that simulates negative damping. These tests are described elsewhere (17).

4. DISCUSSION OF TEST RESULTS

4.1 Typical Time Histories of Tube Motions and Tube/AVB Impact Forces

The test configuration has four AVB locations, as shown in Fig. 2a. Active supports exist at locations C1, C2, and C4. An inactive support is at C3. The calculated natural frequency is 15.4 Hz, assuming pinned conditions at the active supports and no support at C3.

Fluidelastic excitation is simulated by an out-of-plane sinusoidal force, FOS, applied at about 15.4 Hz. The motion is essentially sinusoidal at the inactive AVB location when the clearance is large enough to avoid tube/AVB impacting. When tube/AVB impacting occurs at the inactive AVB location, the motion is steady and ostensively sinusoidal as shown in Figure 4a. However, when the same data are displayed on a expanded time scale, as shown in Figure 4b, the tube motion resembles a truncated sine wave with flat regions that correspond to the duration of the tube/AVB contact.

Figure 4c shows expanded time histories of the the impact forces that occur on the front and rear AVBs at locations C2 and C3. The impacts are typically comprised of multiple spikes, and the duration of the impact in the inactive support is considerably shorter than the duration of the impact in the active support, as expected. The characteristics of the individual tube/AVB impacts in the inactive support are similar to those observed in wind tunnel tests on a model U-bend when fluidelastic vibration is occurring. As discussed in Section 5, the impact force peaks are modulated (randomly varying in amplitude), however not nearly to the degree observed in wind tunnel tests on tube arrays. It is concluded that the sinusoidal forcing function results in less modulation of the impact forces in the shaker tests than is observed in flow-induced vibration tests. Therefore, the shaker tests tend to provide conservative workrates at a given excitation frequency.

The overall tube motion in the in-plane direction is measured using the optical transducers shown in Figure 3. Random excitation, provided by band-limited white noise from the output terminal of the FFT analyzer, is applied to the in-plane shaker located as shown in Figure 2a. The main response peak for the tangential direction is at about 5.6 Hz. The main response peaks in the radial direction are at 5.6 Hz and 22.0 Hz with a small response at about 11.8 Hz. These frequencies are in reasonable agreement with the calculated values of 5.1, 23.0, and 12.1 Hz for the first three in-plane modes of vibration. The level of the random white noise is selected to simulate the turbulence-induced excitation for the lowest in-plane natural frequency. Therefore, the excitation is believed to be conservative for the higher-frequency in-plane modes. The relative magnitudes of the random responses are affected by the point of application of the drive force with respect to the mode shape.

Figures 4d shows the tube/AVB impact forces and the corresponding radial and tangential in-plane motions at C3. The time histories of the impact forces and motions, such as shown in Figure 4d, are digitized; and the data are processed as described in Section 4.2 to evaluate the workrate.

4.2 Determination of Workrates

The outputs of the various force and motion transducers are recorded on magnetic tape at 30 ips, which corresponds to a 0 to 20 kHz frequency range. The signals can be played back at lower tape speeds and displayed conveniently as time histories on a strip chart. Time histories, of the impact forces and in-plane motions, such as shown in Figure 4d are digitized using a digital oscilloscope, and the data are processed using a computer to evaluate the workrate. The workrate is defined as the integrated product of the tube/AVB impact force, F_i, times the sliding distance during the impact, expressed on a per time basis. The work per impact is obtained using the formula

$$\frac{Work}{Impact} = \sum_{i=1}^{P} F_i \left[\frac{|X_i - X_{i-1}| + |X_i - X_{i+1}|}{2} \right] \quad (10)$$

A number of impacts are evaluated. The average work per impact is determined separately for the radial and tangential directions. The average work per impact for the two directions is then combined as the square root of the sum of the squares. The workrate is obtained by multiplying the average work per impact times the vibration frequency. The progression of tube wear with time can be predicted from Equation 1 using the workrate in combination with known impact/sliding wear coefficients.

The data reduction method described above is for sinusoidal excitation (FOS) that results

in an impact each cycle at a given AVB. Impacting does not occur every cycle when only out-of-plane random excitation is applied. When impacting does not occur each cycle, the workrate is evaluated by processing a number of time slices, rather than individual impacts.

It is necessary to filter the in-plane motions to remove high frequency noise, particularly when calculating the workrate for the smaller clearances and the associated smaller out-of-plane driving forces FOS. Otherwise, the noise can result in an appreciable fictitious sliding distance. That is, the noise appears as motion reversals at high frequency in the calculation of workrate using Equation 10. Accordingly, the in-plane motion signals from the U-bend shaker tests are filtered at a low pass frequency of 1280 Hz. It is believed that the main wear producing frequencies are associated with the much lower frequency in-plane modes of the tube.

4.3 Workrate Trends

A conceptual discussion of workrate trends, based on the tests, may be helpful prior to the presentation of the specific results. Figure 5 shows in an idealized manner the general workrate trends that apply at an inactive support, and at an adjacent active support, as the fluidelastic excitation force increases. The workrate trends for the inactive support and the active support are quite different. The tube vibrates within the clearance at the inactive support with no impacting, hence zero workrate for low values of FOS. The vibration amplitude of the tube at the inactive support increases as FOS increases. Finally, tube AVB impacting occurs at the inactive support. The workrate at the inactive support increases approximately linearly as FOS is further increased. While the tube vibrates without impacting within the clearance at the inactive support at low values of FOS, alternating tube/AVB impacting does occur in the adjacent active supports. The workrate in the active support increases approximately linearly with FOS during the time the vibration amplitude at the inactive support increases linearly with FOS. When impacting finally occurs at the inactive support, the workrate at the active support tends to increase much more slowly with increasing FOS. This occurs because the reaction forces generated at the active support are related to a large degree to the tube flexural stiffness and the tube displacement at the adjacent inactive suppport. The motion at the inactive support is clearance limited once impacting begins. As FOS is increased to still larger values, particularly for large clearances at the inactive support, there appears to be a trend toward increasing workrate at the active support, probably due to increased in-plane tube motions resulting from the impact forces generated at the inactive support. Figure 6 shows experimental results that support the idealized trends shown in Figure 5.

The workrate at an inactive support, and the workrate at an adjacent active support, increases linearly with the clearance at the inactive support when the driving force is also increased proportional to the clearance at the inactive support. See Figure 7.

In the case of two adjacent inactive supports, the workrate is about twice as large when impacting occurs at only one of the inactive supports than when the impacting is equally shared at the two inactive supports. See Figure 8. This observation is important in the analyses of long term tube wear. The modal displacements (based on linear model calculations with no restraint at C3 and C4, the inactive supports) at the two adjacent inactive supports are equal for the configuration shown in Figure 8. Hence the workrate is equally shared when the clearances at C3 and C4 are equal and impacting is occurring. For a configuration with unequal modal displacements at adjacent inactive supports, the workrate sharing will be unequal.

The workrate increases as FIR, the in-plane random excitation that simulates turbulence, increases. However, the amount of increase depends on the clearance and/or out-of-plane force level as shown in Figure 9. The ratio of the workrate at active AVB location C2 for FIR equal to a reference value, to the workrate for FIR equal zero is about 1.4 when the clearances are large at the inactive supports. However, when the clearances at the inactive supports are small, the ratio of the workrates is about 4.6. With larger clearances at the inactive supports, it is believed that the associated larger FOS values (and impact forces) combine with mechanical coupling effects and/or friction force effects to induce in-plane wear producing motions. These motions are independent of the wear producing motions caused by the in-plane random excitation. For smaller clearances at inactive supports, corresponding to smaller FOS values, the in-plane random excitation forces (that are the same for both the smaller and larger clearances) have much greater relative influence.

5. COMPARISON OF TUBE DYNAMIC BEHAVIOR IN THE SHAKER TEST WITH THE DYNAMIC BEHAVIOR OBSERVED IN FLOW-INDUCED VIBRATION TESTS

5.1 Impact Forces and Out-Of-Plane Tube Motions

The characteristics of the tube dynamics in the shaker test can be compared with the characteristics in flow-induced vibration tests in order to judge the degree of conservatism in the shaker tests.

The characteristics of the tube/AVB impact forces and the out-of-plane tube motions observed for gap-limited fluidelastic vibration are found to be similar for several different test configurations.

Figure 10 shows a 0.27 scale U-bend tube model that was tested in a wind tunnel. The apparatus permits tube vibration and the tube/AVB impact forces to be measured. Figure 11a shows typical time histories of tube motion and the impact force obtained while fluidelastic vibration is occurring. It is seen that the impact forces are highly modulated. After a number of impacts occurs, an interval with no impacting is evident. The tube motion is fairly sinusoidal, however some modulation is evident. The intervals of no impacting correspond to slight decreases in tube vibration amplitude, as would be expected. It is believed that both the turbulence-induced vibration, which is a relatively greater factor for small clearances than for large clearances, and the disruptions caused by the impacts tend to make the fluidelastic excitation mechanism less effective for small clearances,

corresponding to small fluidelastic forces, than for large gaps, corresponding to large fluidelastic forces.

Tests conducted by Chen et al. (7) display the same type of modulation of the impact forces and the tube motions that are observed in our tests.

It is concluded that the impacting is not as continuous in flow-induced vibration tests as the impacting observed in the shaker tests. The shaker tests are therefore conservative. It is postulated that the tube motion perturbations caused by tube/AVB impacts, perhaps in combination with out-of-plane turbulence-induced vibration, reduce the effectiveness of the self-excited flow forces. That is, self-excited flow forces may not stay in-phase with tube velocity over the entire cycle when tube/AVB impacting occurs. This suggests that experimental or analytical representation of fluidelastic excitation by negative damping (for which the driving force is always in-phase with tube velocity) may also result in conservative workrates. The degree of conservatism should be estimated by reviewing the character of the impact forces and tube motions.

5.2 Tube Vibration Frequency

Another factor to consider is the frequency of tube vibration for values of U_e/U_c greater than unity. Self-excited excitation has the potential for increasing the vibration frequency in gap-limited situations as the flow is progressively increased above the critical value, since the energy input increases while the motion is constrained.

Figure 11b shows the increase in frequency observed in our wind tunnel tests on a model U-bend. The measured frequency of 27.5 Hz for U_e/U_c equal to about 1.2 is very nearly the same as the 27.6 Hz calculated value, for all tube/AVB clearances tested. When the velocity ratio U_e/U_c is increased to 2.7, the vibration frequency increases by 1.5% to 5%, depending on the clearance, with the larger frequency increases associated with the larger clearances. The rapid change (increase) in frequency from about 30 Hz to about 37 Hz that occurs in the U_e/U_c range from 4 to 5.5 (most pronounced for the two larger clearances) may be due in part to the increased excitation. It may also be related to a nonlinear increase in the stiffness of model tube/AVB configuration.

In general, it is expected that the increase in frequency for gap-limited vibration as the fluidelastic excitation increases will be a function of the dynamic properties of the tube/support system.

6. CONCLUSION

Workrates for tube/AVB impacting in the U-bend region of steam generators are obtained from laboratory shaker tests on full-size U-tubes. The experimental workrate results can be used (22) in semi-empirical procedures to predict tube wear potential. Both fluidelastic and turbulence-induced excitation can be simulated in the shaker tests. Workrate trends are provided that make it possible to estimate on a relative basis the effects of design variables, such as tube/AVB clearance, and fluidelastic excitation levels on tube wear life.

ACKNOWLEDGMENT

A portion of the work described was carried out as part of a joint program sponsored by Westinghouse, Commissariat a l'Energie Atomique, Electricite de France, and Framatome.

REFERENCES

(1) LANGFORD, P. J., Design Assembly, and Inspection of Adavanced U-Bend/Antivibration Bar Configurations for PWR Steam Generators, Journal of Pressure Vessel Technology, 1989, 111, 371-377.

(2) LUBIN, B. T. , HASLINGER, K. H. , CEPKAUSKAS, M. M. , AND HEILKER, W. J., Flow-Related Excitation in the U-Bend Region of a PWR Steam Generator, 1988 International Symposium on Flow-Induced Vibration and Noise, Flow-Induced Vibration in Heat Transfer Equipment, 5, 31-48

(3) FRICK, T. M. and WAISMAN, R., Methodologies for the Computation of Steam Generator Tube Wear with Applications for Turbulence in the U-Bend Region, ASCE/ASME Mechanics, Fluids Engineering, and Biomechanical Conference, Paper 89-FE-15, San Diego, Ca, July 9-12, 1989

(4) FRICK, T. M., SOBEK, T. E., and REAVIS, J. R., Overview on the Development and Implementation of Methodologies to Compute Vibration and Wear of Steam Generator Tubes, ASME WAM, Decemmber, 1984, Symposium on Flow-Induced Vibrations, Vol. 3, 149-161

(5) ARCHARD, J. F., and HIRST, W., The Wear of Metals Under Unlubricated Conditions, Proc. Royal Society of London, Series A, 236, 1956, 397

(6) ROGERS, R. J. , and PICK, R. J., Factors Associated with Support Forces Due to Heat Exchanger Tube Vibration Contact, Nuclear Engineering and Design, 44, 1977, 247-253

(7) CHEN, S. S., JENDRZEJCZYK, J. A., and WAMBSGANSS M. W., Dynamics of Tubes in Fluid with Tube-Baffle Interaction, ASME WAM, Decemmber, 1984, Symposium on Flow-Induced Vibrations, Vol. 2, 285-304

(8) AXISA, F., DESSEAUX, A, AND GIBERT, R. J., Experimental Study of Tube/Support Impact Forces in Multi-Span PWR Steam Generator Tubes, ASME WAM, Decemmber, 1984, Symposium on Flow-Induced Vibrations, Vol. 3, 139-148

(9) FRICKER, A. J., Numerical Analysis of the Fluidelastic Vibration of a Steam Generator Tube with Loose Supports, 1988 International Symposium on Flow-Induced Vibration and Noise, Flow-Induced Vibration in Heat Transfer Equipment, 5, 105-120

(10) ANTUNES J., AXISA, F., and VENTO, M. A., Experiments on Vibro-Impact Dynamics Under Fluidelastic Instability, Flow-Induced Vibration - 1990, ASME, PVP-189, 127-138

(11) RAO,M., STEININGER, D., and EISINGER, F., Numerical Simulation of Fluidelastic Vibration and Wear of Multispan Tubes with Clearance at the Supports, 1988 International Symposium on Flow-Induced Vibration and Noise, Flow-Induced Vibration in Heat Transfer Equipment, 5, 235 -249

(12) PETTIGREW, M. J., and KO, P.L., A Comprehensive Approach to Avoid Vibration and Fretting in Shell and Tube Heat Exchangers, Flow-Induced Vibration of Power Plant Components, PVP-41, ASME, 1980, 1-18

(13) CONNORS, H. J., Flow-Induced Vibration and Wear of Steam Generator Tubes, Nuclear Technology, 1981, 55, 311-331

(14) HASLINGER,K. H. and Martin, M. L., Experimental Investigation into the Non-Linear Dynamic Behavior of a U-Tube Bundle with Dynamically Active Support Strips, 1988 International Symposium on Flow-Induced Vibration and Noise, Flow-Induced Vibration in Heat Transfer Equipment, 5, 219-234

(15) WEAVER, D. S., and SCHNEIDER, W., The Effect of Flat Bar Supports on the Cross Flow Induced Response of Heat Exchanger Tubes, ASME Journal of Engineering for Power, 105, 1983

(16) YETISIR, M., and WEAVER, D. S., The Dynamics of Heat Exchanger U-Bend Tubes With Flat Bar Supports, ASME Journal of Pressure Vessel Technolooy, 108, 1986

(17) FRANCE, E. R., and CONNORS, H. J., Simulation of Flow-Induced Vibration Characteristics of a Steam Generator U-Tube, Presented at I Mech E Fifth Internation Conference on Flow-Induced Vibrations, May 21-23, 1991, Brighton, UK

(18) CONNORS, H. J., Fluidelastic Vibration of Tube Arrays Excited by Cross Flow, Flow-Induced Vibration of Heat Exchangers, ASME, December 1970, 42-56

(19) CONNORS, H. J., Fluidelastic Vibration of Heat Exchanger Tube Arrays, Trans. ASME, J. Mech Design, 1978, 100, 347-353

(20) PETTIGREW, M. J., SYLVESTRE, Y., and CAMPAGNA, A. O., Vibration Analysis of Heat Exchanger and Steam Generator Designs, Nuclear Engineering and Design, 48 , 1978, 97-115

(21) PAIDOUSSIS, M. P., Fluidelastic Vibration of Cylinder Arrays in Axial and Cross Flow - State of the Art, Flow-Induced Vibration Design Cuidelines, PVP-52, ASME, 1981 11-46

(22) LANGFORD, P. J., and CONNORS, H. J., Calculation of Tube/AVB Wear from U-Bend Shaker Tests, Presented at I Mech E Fifth International Conference on Flow-Induced Vibrations, May 21-23, 1991, Brighton, UK

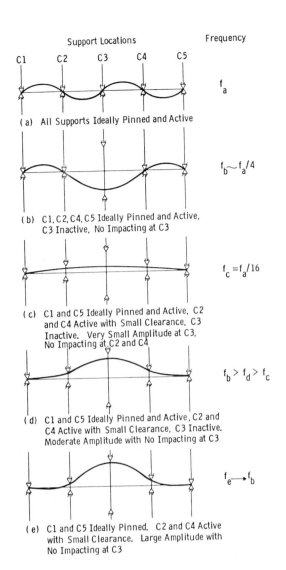

Support Locations   Frequency

C1 C2 C3 C4 C5

f_a

(a) All Supports Ideally Pinned and Active

$f_b \sim f_a/4$

(b) C1, C2, C4, C5 Ideally Pinned and Active, C3 Inactive, No Impacting at C3

$f_c = f_a/16$

(c) C1 and C5 Ideally Pinned and Active, C2 and C4 Active with Small Clearance, C3 Inactive. Very Small Amplitude at C3, No Impacting at C2 and C4

$f_b > f_d > f_c$

(d) C1 and C5 Ideally Pinned and Active, C2 and C4 Active with Small Clearance, C3 Inactive. Moderate Amplitude with No Impacting at C3

$f_e \rightarrow f_b$

(e) C1 and C5 Ideally Pinned. C2 and C4 Active with Small Clearance. Large Amplitude with No Impacting at C3

Fig 1 Idealized example of the effects of the active/inactive supports on the possible mode shapes and vibrational frequencies for a tube subjected to fluidelastic excitation

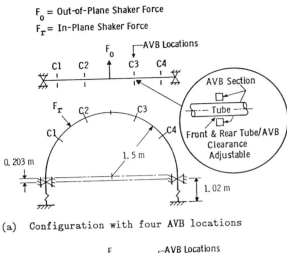

F_o = Out-of-Plane Shaker Force

F_r = In-Plane Shaker Force

(a) Configuration with four AVB locations

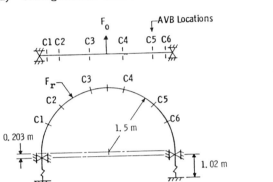

(b) Configuration with six AVB locations

Fig 2 U-bend configurations tested in the shaker test facility

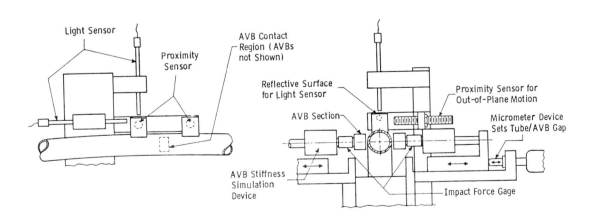

Fig 3 Simulated AVB tube-support location. The transducers used to measure tube/AVB forces and motions, and the micrometer adjusting devices used to establish accurately the tube/AVB clearances are shown

64

© IMechE 1991 C416/014

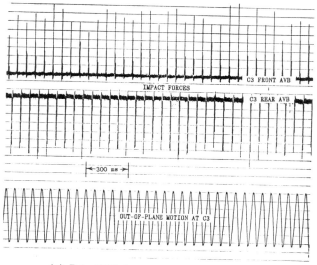

(a) Tube/AVB impact forces and out-of-plane tube motion at inactive support C3. Long time scale

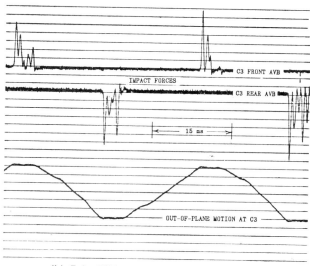

(b) Tube/AVB impact forces and out-of-plane tube motion at inactive support C3. Short time scale

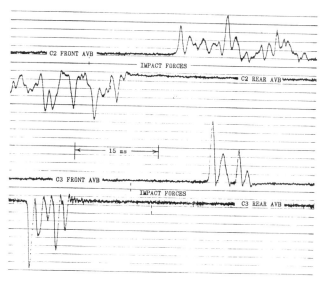

(c) Tube/AVB impact forces at inactive support C3 and active support C2

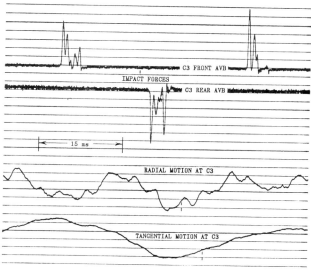

(d) Tube/AVB impact forces and in-plane tube motions at inactive support C3

Fig 4 Typical time histories of out-of-plane tube motion, tube/AVB impact forces, and in-plane tube motions at an AVB location. Configuration with four AVB locations (see Figure 2a) and an inactive support at C3. Active supports at C1, C2, and C4. Out-of-plane sinusoidal force FOS applied at 15.4 Hz. In-plane random force FIR applied

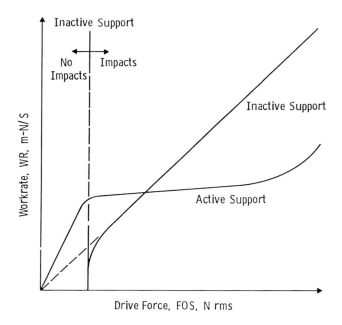

Fig 5 Conceptual curves showing idealized
workrate trends for active and inactive
supports

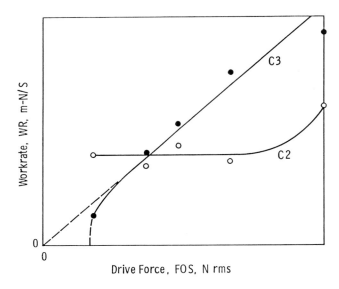

Fig 6 Measured workrate trends at active
support C2 and inactive support C3 for
configuration with six AVB locations
(see Figure 2b). Inactive supports at
C3 and C4 (clearance at C4 adjusted
to prevent tube/AVB impacting), and
active supports at C1, C2, C5, and C6.
Out-of-plane sinusoidal force applied.
In-plane random excitation FIR is also
applied

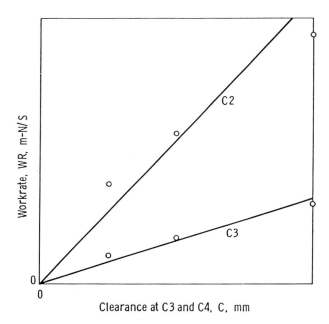

Fig 7 Variation of the workrate at inactive
support C3 and at active support C2,
when the out-of-plane sinusoidal drive
force FOS is increased linearly with the
clearance at C3. Configuration with six
AVB locations and inactive supports at
C3 and C4. The clearance C3 = C4

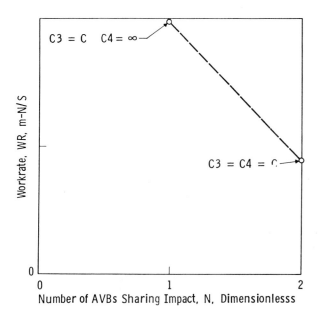

Fig 8 Reduction in the workrate (workrate
sharing) at inactive support C3 when
impacting occurs at both C3 and C4
(also an inactive support), rather than
at C3 alone. Configuration with six
AVB locations and inactive supports at
C3 and C4. Out-of-plane sinusoidal
force FOS is applied. In-plane random
excitation FIR is also applied

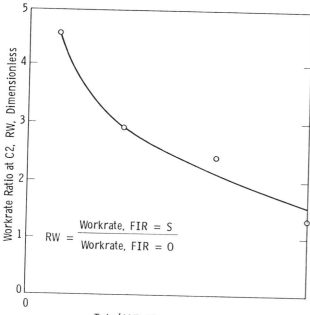

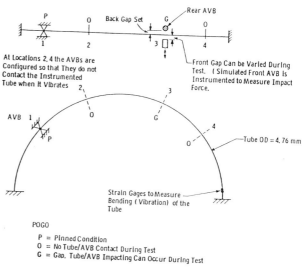

Fig 9 Variation of the ratio of the workrate with in-plane excitation FIR equal S applied to the workrate with FIR equal zero. Configuration with six AVB locations and inactive supports at C3 and C4. Tube/AVB impacting occurring at C3 but not at C4. The out-of-plane sinusoidal force varies linearly with the clearance at C3

Fig 10 U-bend configuration (0.272 - scale) tested in the wind tunnel. Active support at C1, and inactive supports at C2, C3, and C4. Tube/AVB impacting occurs at C3. The clearances at C2 and C4 are made large enough to avoid impacting

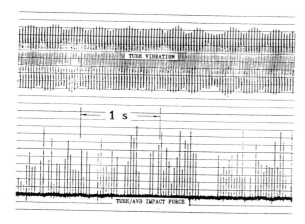

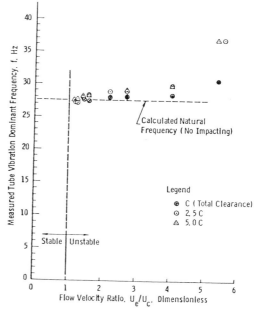

a. Tube vibration amplitude (strain gage signal) and the tube/AVB impact force measured at C3

b. Measured vibration frequency as a function of stability ratio U_e/U_c for operation in the unstable region

Fig 11 Wind tunnel test data obtained for the Configuration shown in Figure 10

C416/014 © IMechE 1991

C416/008

Prediction and measurement of vortex induced vibration in marine drilling operations

J R BROWNRIDGE, BSc, CEng, MIMechE
BP Exploration, Dyce, Aberdeen, Scotland

Marine drilling risers are known to suffer significant levels of vortex induced vibration particularly in deep water and high current velocities. This causes increased drag loading and cyclic stresses in subsea wellhead equipment which can ultimately lead to catastrophic failure.

This paper outlines the existing methods used to predict vortex induced vibration and details the specific problems encountered in marine drilling operations. The deep water riser monitoring exercise performed by BP in 1989 is described and the principal results and conclusions are discussed.

NOTATION

Vr	reduced velocity
V	current velocity
n	natural frequency
D	hydrodynamic diameter
Ks	stability parameter
m	equivalent mass/unit length
d	logarithmic decrement
r	density of water
Cd	drag coefficient

INTRODUCTION

As the search for oil moves into deeper water and harsher environments, the occurrence and effects of vortex induced vibrations are becoming increasingly important in the design of marine drilling systems. There are three potential areas of concern:

(a) Deep water drilling risers
(b) Casing deployment through open water
(c) Jack-up drilling conductors

Deep Water Drilling Risers

When drilling from a drillship or semi-submersible vessel rig, the marine drilling riser is a vital component, allowing direct access to the subsea well from the surface.

Typical drilling risers have a nominal outside diameter of 16 or 21 inches (406 to 533 mm) and have been used to drill in water as deep as 2300 metres (1). The riser is connected to the subsea blow-out preventer stack (BOP) via a flex-joint which allows up to 10 degrees angular deflection. Under normal drilling conditions, the mean angle is maintained within the allowable 2 degree limit (2) by applying axial tension using a riser tensioning system. In water depths greater than approximately 300 metres, additional buoyancy is fitted to the riser to reduce the load on the vessel.

Vibration of the riser due to vortex shedding causes potentially damaging fatigue stresses in the riser and the subsea equipment to which it is connected (3). The associated increase in drag forces causes higher mean stresses and necessitates a greater tensioning capability to maintain the flex-joint angle within allowable limits.

Surface Casing Deployment

The 20" surface casing in a subsea well is often deployed through open water. Although fatigue failure has occurred during operations in the very high currents from the Amazonian outflow (4), this is not normally a concern in most offshore exploration regions.

Jack-up Drilling Conductors

Jack-up rigs are used in water depths up to 100 metres. The well is accessed through a conductor pipe set between 60 and 120 metres into the seabed. The conductor has a nominal outside diameter between 24 and 36 inches and is not normally tensioned. The BOP is fitted above the conductor and is often supported on it.

Vortex induced vibrations can cause fatigue failure of the pipe in high currents even in relatively shallow water (5).

DESIGNING FOR VORTEX INDUCED VIBRATION

There are a number of solutions to the problems associated with vortex induced vibration in marine drilling systems. These include designing the riser or conductor to avoid the critical lock-on velocities, increasing the structural damping and fitting suppression devices (6).

Design for Fatigue

In most cases it is impractical or uneconomic to avoid critical lock-on velocities or provide additional structural damping. It is preferable to accept the vibration and to design subsea components to resist fatigue. This may be as simple as increasing the wall thickness of critical areas or improving the quality of welded connections. BP's Universal Wellhead Specification specifies a minimum preload of 500 000 lbs (2224 kN) in the lockdown mechanism between the wellhead body and the 30" housing to ensure the dissipation of fatigue energy from the wellhead body into the conductor.

Suppression Devices

If the fatigue stresses or drag forces cannot be accepted, there are many hydrodynamic devices which can be used to suppress the vibration (7).

Helical strakes have been successfully fitted to jack-up conductors by BP and British Gas (5), and to 20" casing deployed by Esso (4). Although the amplitudes of vibration are reduced considerably, the drag forces are amplified.

For this reason, they are not suitable for floating drilling where the flex-joint angle is critical. Aerofoil shaped fairings have been deployed by Esso (4) and Petrobras (8) with some success, although these devices are large and cumbersome. BP is currently researching a number of alternative vortex suppression devices.

ANALYTICAL METHODS

A combination of traditional methods and state-of-the-art research is used by BP to predict the occurrence of vortex induced vibration and to calculate its effects. Where theoretical calculations are considered to be insufficient, these are supported by model testing.

Fatigue failures can then be avoided by selecting a riser configuration which minimises the vibrations, designing subsea equipment to resist fatigue, optimising the top tension and fitting vortex suppression devices if required.

Prediction of Vortex Induced Vibrations

Eigen analysis is performed using a finite element riser analysis programme such as DWRSR (9) or Aqwa-Riser (10) to determine the natural frequencies. In most cases, it is sufficient to consider only the first five or six modes of oscillation although there is evidence to suggest that more than 20 modes can occur in very deep water.

The range of current speeds at which each of these frequencies is excited (i.e. the lock-on range) is determined from the reduced velocity:

$$V_r = V/nD$$

In practice the current is rarely uniform in magnitude or direction, particularly in deep water, and overlapping modes can be suppressed or extended. This can give rise to complex behaviour which is difficult to predict. In sheared currents the lock-on ranges will be wider but the peak amplitude of vibration will be lower. The lock-on ranges and the corresponding amplitudes of oscillation used by BP are based on unpublished data from joint industry research into the vibration of cylinders in sheared flows. In-line oscillations are normally ignored because, although they occur at lower current velocities, they are insignificant in comparison to cross-flow oscillations (6).

When drilling from a jack-up rig, a significant length of the conductor is above mean sea level. In this case, the amplitudes are modified in accordance with the stability parameter (6):

$$K_s = 2md/rD^2$$

For deep water drilling risers with added buoyancy modules the calculations are more complex. BP's simplified method assumes that the excitation due to the bare and buoyant diameters is independent and that the amplitudes can be scaled according to the proportion of bare and buoyant lengths. This approach ignores the damping effect of the non-excited region and is therefore over conservative. The "steady state" energy balance method may be more appropriate for these cases (11).

Reliable current exceedence and directionality data are required to determine accurately the number of cycles in a given period for each mode. For locations where these are unavailable, a typical distribution can be assumed although this will lead to significant uncertainty in the final results.

Calculation of Fatigue Life

As well as the riser itself, the critical components in a deep water drilling system include the wellhead connector, the wellhead and the wellhead extension joint.

Using further results from the eigen solution, the bending moment amplitudes at the critical location for each mode are calculated and a fatigue spectrum is derived. Where appropriate, this is added to the wave induced fatigue spectrum, although in most deep water locations wave effects at the bottom the riser are insignificant. The fatigue life is then estimated using an appropriate S-N curve from the DEn guidelines (12) and the Palmgren-Miner's rule method to sum the damage.

DEEP WATER RISER MONITORING

Several oil companies have carried out offshore monitoring of drilling risers (13,14). Most of this research has been concerned with the forces on the riser due to wave action, vessel motion, top tension and mud weight, although the major unknown in deep water drilling is the effect of vortex induced vibration.

© IMechE 1991 C416/008

Universal Stress Monitoring Equipment

BP has developed a subsea data collection system that allows readings from remote subsea sensors to be logged and transmitted to a surface station (15). The subsea data logging, processing and transmission parameters can be controlled from the surface. The equipment is designed to be retro-fitted by divers where water depths allow.

In order to reduce the volume of data being stored and transmitted, data reduction and manipulation can be carried out on the raw data. Data are retrieved to the surface via a high speed acoustic link in response to commands transmitted from the topsides equipment. The design also features a hot stab connector for hardwire data retrieval through an ROV umbilical. The complete system is battery powered and has been successfully operated at water depths of 1000 metres.

The system (fig.1) consists of four main elements:

(a) Subsea transducers
(b) Subsea data logger and battery pack
(c) Hydro-acoustic data link
(d) Surface data processing and storage

Deep Water Riser Monitoring Exercise

In 1989, BP deployed the Universal Stress Monitoring Equipment on the semi-submersible Santa Fe Rig 140 drilling in 635 metres of water on the UK continental slope, west of Shetland. Due to the high currents in this region there is a recognised risk of wellhead failure due to vortex induced vibration (3).

Subsea transponders and dataloggers were fitted at two locations on the 21" riser (fig.2). The "deep-sea" package was located on the first riser joint above the flex-joint approximately 50 feet above the seabed. This consisted of a pair of transponder bars, an LVDT tension unit, subsea datalogger, battery pack and an ROV interface. The "shallow-sea" package was positioned just below the wave zone at a depth of approximately 100 feet below mean sea level. This consisted of a pair of transponder bars, subsea datalogger and battery pack.

Data were also collected from the rig's positioning system, a gyroscope located on the main deck and from two instrumented pins fitted to the riser tensioner shackles. Environmental data were recorded separately using a microwave radar and an acoustic doppler current profiler.

The subsea packages were installed and tested on the riser during deployment in less than five hours. The deep-sea package was initialised in the moonpool and began logging immediately. The shallow-sea package however failed due to ingress of water and no data were collected.

Communication with the deep-sea datalogger was established soon after the BOP had landed. It was configured to log time histories of four transducer bar channels and three LVDT channels for 20 minutes every three hours at a logging frequency of 20 hertz. The surface channels were logged for corresponding periods. Data

retrieval was erratic and not as fast as had been expected. This was partly due to acoustic interference from the current profiler which operated at a different mid-band frequency but a much higher power level causing overlap of the two frequency ranges. A direct serial link was used successfully via the ROV umbilical to obtain data during periods of poor acoustic communication.

ANALYSIS OF RISER MEASUREMENTS

From the two months of data collected, 54 periods were selected for post-processing and detailed analysis. Time histories for selected channels were plotted to check the data quality and to correlate subsea, rig and environmental data.

Spectral analysis was performed using a fast fourier transform routine to find principal frequencies of oscillation. Comparisons were then made between the measured response of the riser and the theoretical analysis.

The current profile measurements revealed a strong north easterly residual flow and a tidal component of similar magnitude. Maximum total currents were in excess of 2 knots (1.0 m/s) with general uniformity of flow through depth. Substantial velocity shear was evident on occasions due to the passage of internal waves.

Flex-joint Angle and Drag Coefficient

The DWRSR program (9) was used to model the riser with actual environmental data for specific 20 minute periods. This included the correct directional current profile and measured top tension. Static analysis was used since the dynamic effect at the bottom riser joint was found to be minimal.

The mean flex-joint angles measured within the subsea datalogger were compared with DWRSR analysis results. Using a base drag coefficient Cd = 1.2, the flex-joint angle was generally underestimated by up to 30% except during periods with strong shear currents when the angle was overestimated by 90%. However, a riser subject to vortex induced vibration will have a higher drag coefficient. A better correlation was therefore obtained for certain periods by using Cd = 2.0 (fig.3).

Dynamic Behaviour of the Riser

Time histories of the transducer bar outputs showed clearly the cyclic bending response of the riser (fig.4) and comparison with the corresponding environmental data confirmed that this response was generally strongest when the current profile was uniform in magnitude and direction (fig.5).

Comparison of the spectral analysis of this bending response with the rig motions suggested that the oscillation was not due to wave action or rig motion because the response frequencies do not correspond. Results from the DWRSR model for the maximum wave conditions showed that the dynamic bending moment range at the bottom riser joint due to wave action and rig motion was considerably less than the measured response.

It was confirmed therefore that the cyclic response was entirely due to vortex induced vibration.

Frequencies of Vibration

The natural frequencies of the riser were calculated using the DWRSR eigen analysis (fig.6) and compared with the measured frequencies determined by spectral analysis. For the observed current range, the calculated lock-on velocities indicated that up to 5 modes could be excited.

Both single and multiple modes of vibration were observed. The frequencies of the single mode vibration corresponded accurately with the calculated 1st, 2nd and 3rd modes. The example (fig.7) shows the 2nd mode response with a peak period of 15.4 seconds. The depth mean current at this time was 0.56 knots (0.29 m/sec) corresponding to a reduced velocity of 5.7. The multiple mode vibrations (fig.8) occurred at unexpected frequencies in between the predicted modes. These did not correspond to the measured rig surge or sway responses and tended to occur only during periods of high current. They are thought to have been caused either by complex behaviour due to the combined effect of the bare and buoyant diameters or by a forced riser response giving frequencies outside the normal range. Further work is necessary to explain this response.

Amplitudes of Vibration

The amplitudes of individual modes could have been derived by further processing of the available data. This has not been carried out to date as it is felt that the indirect relationship between bending at the bottom of the riser and the maximum displacement at the anti-node is insufficiently defined.

CONCLUSIONS

The prediction of vortex induced vibrations in deep water drilling operations is complicated by the variable diameters of partially buoyed risers and complex current regimes. The basic theory can be adapted to account approximately for these effects but further work is required to update the current methodology in line with the latest research.

Within the limitations of existing vortex shedding theory and the data available from the drilling riser monitoring exercise, it has been possible to perform basic comparisons between the predicted and measured response of the riser.

The riser response for single mode vibrations was as predicted with reduced velocities typically in the range from 4.5 to 6. However multimodal responses were detected at unexpected frequencies. Drag amplification due to vortex induced vibration was found to increase the estimated drag coefficient by as much as 70%.

Further development of the monitoring equipment is recommended to enable direct measurement of the frequencies and amplitudes of vibration.

ACKNOWLEDGEMENTS

The author wishes to thank BP Exploration for permission to publish this paper and acknowledges the support of BP Engineering, BP Research, Santa Fe Drilling Company (UK), Miros Ltd, Wimpol Ltd and BHR Group.

REFERENCES

(1) OFFSHORE. Deepwater Drilling Report. October 1989, pages 50 to 56.

(2) API RP2Q. Design and Operation of Marine Drilling Risers Systems. American Petroleum Institute, 1984.

(3) C T HOPPER. Vortex Induced Oscillations of Long Marine Drilling Risers. Proceedings of Deep Offshore Technology Conference, Malta, 1983.

(4) T N GARDNER and M W COLE. Deepwater Drilling in High Current Environment. OTC 4316, 1982.

(5) M J EVERY and R KING. Suppression Flow Induced Vibrations - An Experimental Comparison of Clamp-on Devices. BHRA, November 1979.

(6) M G HALLAM, N J HEAF and L R WOOTON. Dynamics of Marine Structures: Methods of Calculating the Dynamic Response of Fixed Structures Subject to Wave and Current Action. CIRIA. October 1978.

(7) M J EVERY, R KING and R S WEAVER. Vortex-excited Vibrations of Cylinders and Cables and their Suppression. Ocean Engineering. 1982.

(8) J ALBERS and M L DASILVA. Innovative Risers Speed Drilling in the High Current Areas off Brazil. Oil and Gas Journal, 1977.

(9) R J OLSON, W F COFER, D R STEPHENS and D P MCCONNELL. Applications Manual for DWRSR - A Design Analysis Methodology for Deep Water Marine Risers.

(10) ATKINS RESEARCH AND DEVELOPMENT. Aqwa-Riser Manual.

(11) I H BROOKES. A Pragmatic Approach to Vortex Induced Vibrations of a Drilling Riser. OTC 5522, 1987.

(12) DEPARTMENT OF ENERGY. Offshore Installations: Guidance on Design and Construction. London, 1984.

(13) M F COOK and T N GARDNER. Riser and Vessel Motion Data from Deep Water Drilling Operation. OTC 5004, 1985.

(14) P H J VERBEEK. Analysis of Riser Measurements in the North Sea. OTC 4562, 1983.

(15) P J BENSTEAD and J R BROWNRIDGE. Equipment and Techniques for Remote Monitoring with High Speed Recovery of Data. Ocean Science and Engineering, November 1989.

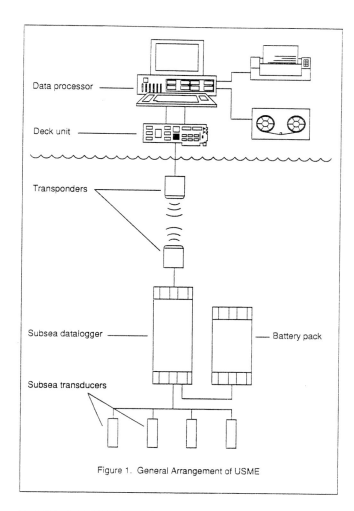

Figure 1. General Arrangement of USME

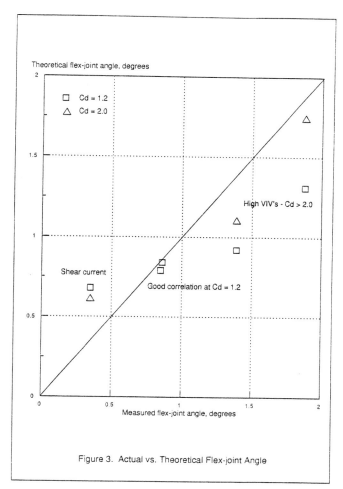

Figure 3. Actual vs. Theoretical Flex-joint Angle

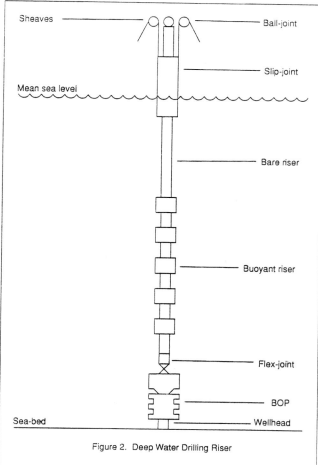

Figure 2. Deep Water Drilling Riser

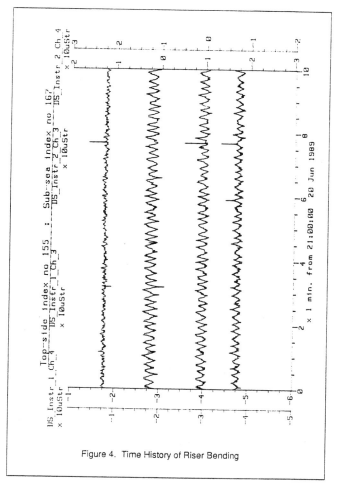

Figure 4. Time History of Riser Bending

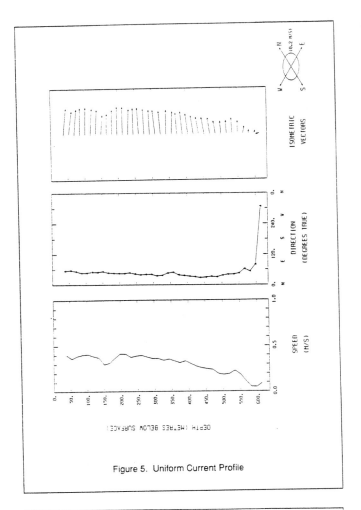

Figure 5. Uniform Current Profile

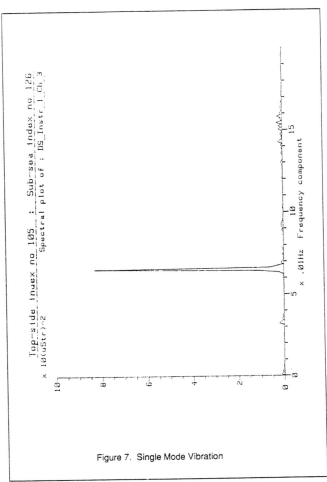

Figure 7. Single Mode Vibration

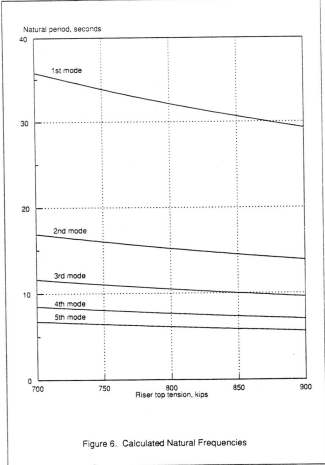

Figure 6. Calculated Natural Frequencies

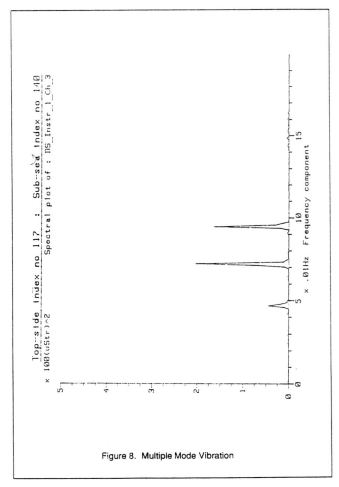

Figure 8. Multiple Mode Vibration

C416/042

Vortex induced vibrations of tensioned and catenary marine risers

G J LYONS, BSc(Eng), PhD, AMIMechE, MRINA and J I E FANG, BSc(Eng), PhD
Department of Mechanical Engineering, University College, London

SYNOPSIS Theoretical models for vortex induced vibrations in tensioned vertical and catenary risers are presented. These involve time domain simulations using a modal analysis approach. The parameters used in the formulations are obtained from two nonlinear governing equations for fluids and structures. The numerical calculation procedure allows for the variation of fluid properties along the length of the riser as well as in time through a cycle of flow oscillation. This approach permits an investigation of the influence of the separate and combined effects of wave, vessel motion and current.

NOTATION

C_D	drag coefficient
C_{DO}	drag coefficient (non-vibrating)
D	riser diameter
D_S	diameter at vortex shedding section
F	amplification factor
$f_i\vert_{p=0}$	frequency for zero axial load
f_n	natural frequency in water
f_V	vortex shedding frequency
I	modal shape factor
k_S	reduced damping
L	length of riser
m	mass per unit length
P	axial load
P_b	buckling load
S	Strouhal number
$s(x)$	lock-on parameter
V	approach velocity
V_r	reduced velocity
W_r	wake stability parameter
x	axial distance along riser
Y	amplitude of vibration
δ	log decrement
γ	geometric function of mode shape
ν	effective mass ratio
ρ	fluid density
ξ	mode shape
ζ	damping ratio
ζ_s	effective damping ratio

1. INTRODUCTION

Vortex induced vibrations are known to occur in many marine structures. The forms of marine risers lend themselves particularly well to this phenomenon. They constitute intrinsic parts of hydrocarbons exploration and production facilities. It is therefore important to understand how they are likely to respond in the rather varied environment in which they are sited so that failures and operational difficulties are avoided. The effects of vortex cell spacing, timing, modal interaction and the influence of damping are demonstrated as leading to complex and sometimes unexpected forms of response. The reasons for this are explained herein.

Considerable operational experience exists with tensioned risers. They are essentially used supported from a surface platform which may be floating, and act as conduits from the sea bed to the surface platform. This form of riser is essential for drilling operations acting as the conduit for drilling fluids and debris. By the nature of the operation this form of riser will continue to be used for this duty even in very deep waters. Vortex induced vibrations have been the cause of operational difficulties in the past, and vortex spoiling devices must sometimes be used to avoid excessive vibrations.

The duties for which flexible risers are being used are increasing as confidence and experience in their use improves. They can offer many benefits compared with tensioned risers, particularly in terms of deployment, and associated equipment required for their operation. As experience is gathered they will be subjected to more severe operating climates. It is most important to have as good an understanding of their possible behaviour as can be achieved. Their performance has the possibility of being by the very nature quite dynamic.

The forms of these risers, generally as modified catenaries, are relatively complex. The loading opportunities more so, given that they are subject to the combined influences of waves, currents and vessel motions. As if this was not enough to provide difficulties in determining their behaviour, there are possibilities for excitation owing to the transport of the internal fluids (which may not be homogeneous eg. include slugs) and also owing to the effects of vortex shedding. The importance of these vortex induced vibrations is that there is the potential for significant vibrations in many modes. As higher modes are excited the bending stresses in the riser may well increase. Hence there is concern for these vibrations in respect of wear and fatigue.

Work by Lyons and Patel (1) provides a prediction method for multi-moded vortex induced vibrations of tensioned risers. This work was supported by verification through model testing. This is further reported in Lyons and Patel (2,3). Based on this work the method has been extended to catenary flexible risers described herein. Additional physical information has been obtained to improve the model. This includes parametric studies of structural damping for cable and riser structures, Lyons and Fang (4).

2.   VORTEX INDUCED VIBRATIONS

2.1   Vortex Induced vibrations of tensioned vertical risers

Considerable work has been done to investigate the effects in steady flow of vortex induced forces that act along the in-line and transverse direction to the excitation flow, (5,6,7,8,9,10,11). However, the flow around a riser will generally vary with time and axial location owing to the oscillatory and depth decaying nature of waves, possibly complicated by surface vessel motions.

Comprehensive reviews in respect of vortex shedding and associated vibrations are given in refs (12,13,14,15,16,17). The CIRIA report (18) presents a background and some example solutions for simplified vortex induced vibration problems.

Many of the theories that have been developed to predict the vortex induced oscillations of bluff cylindrical members attempt to include physical phenomena underlying the fluid mechanics of vortex behaviour and the structural member response to the consequent loading. The first of these is lock-on of vortex shedding frequencies (determined by the Strouhal relationship) to a natural frequency of the cylinder. Thus

$$f_v = f_n \quad \text{at lock - on}$$

and   (2.1.1)

$$f_v = SV/D_s \quad \text{otherwise}$$

The following parameters are of major importance in determining the amplitude of vibrations and the range of lock-on or synchronisation for a given body:

$$\text{Reduced Damping,} \quad k_s = \frac{2m\delta}{\rho D_s^2} \quad (2.1.2)$$

$$\text{Reduced Velocity,} \quad V_r = V/(f_n D_s) \quad (2.1.3)$$

The reduced damping is the product of the logarithmic decrement of structural damping (it does not include fluid damping) and the mass density of the structure relative to the fluid.

The reduced velocity may be used to determine the existence and degree of vortex induced vibration. For transverse vibrations of a cylindrical bluff body, it has been shown from experiments in water by many researchers that excitation begins when the reduced velocity reaches a value of between 3.5 and 5.0. A peak occurs around 6.0 and decays to no vibration at around 8.0 to 12.0, (19,20). For in-line oscillations, the onset of vibration occurs at a reduced velocity of around 1.0 to 1.5 for the case where two vortices of opposing sign are shed symmetrically and continues to a reduced velocity of about 2.5, when a stream of alternating vortices is formed. Vibration ceases for the in-line case at a reduced velocity of 3.0 to 3.5, (21).

It has been shown for right circular cylinders in uniform flow, that there is a relationship between the maximum possible amplitude of transverse vibrations and the reduced damping which applies for flexible and flexibly mounted rigid cylinders. Various workers give this relationship as follows and as compared in Figure 1:

Griffin et al (7) give

$$\frac{Y_{max}}{D} = \frac{1.29 \, \gamma}{\left[1 + 0.43 \left(2\pi S^2 k_s \right) \right]^{3.35}} \quad (2.1.4)$$

Blevins (12) gives

$$\frac{Y_{max}}{D} = \frac{0.07 \, \gamma}{(1.9 + k_s) S^2} \left[0.3 + \frac{0.72}{(1.9 + k_s) S} \right]^{1/2} \quad (2.1.5)$$

Iwan (22) gives

$$\frac{Y_{max}}{D} = \frac{\gamma}{\left[1 + 9.6 \left(k_s / \pi \right)^{1.8} \right]} \quad (2.1.6)$$

where a geometric function of mode shape

$$\gamma = \xi_{max} \left[\frac{\int_0^L \xi^2 (x)\, dx}{\int_0^L \xi^4 (x)\, dx} \right]^{\frac{1}{2}} \qquad (2.1.7)$$

is used to collapse the data for the different modes of response for the systems shown in Figure 2. ξ_{max} is the maximum value of the modal shape ξ over the span extending from $x = 0$ to $x = L$.

2.2 Vortex induced vibrations of catenary flexible risers

The main types of catenary flexible risers: Simple catenary, Lazy-S, Steep-S, Lazy-Wave and Steep-Wave, are shown in Figure 3. The major advantage over tensioned vertical risers is that being more compliant they can accommodate larger surface vessel motions and have low stress levels under severe sea conditions compared with tensioned risers.

These authors are not aware of any observations having been reported on vortex shedding induced high frequency vibrations for flexible risers in service. Relatively little research has been done on the subject. Zare and Datta (23) proposed a method to calculate vortex induced vibration of a Lazy-S riser subjected to an in-plane or a normal-to-plane current. They assumed that vortex shedding is monoharmonic at lock-on and a lift force is used as loading. They predict a vibration with an maximum amplitude of five diameters. This is not thought to be realistic because vortex induced vibration is self-limiting, and when the response amplitude exceeds two diameters, the well-formed vortex street breaks down.

The vortex induced vibration problem of flexible risers is much more complicated than that of vertical tensioned risers. The latter being essentially two dimensional structures, for which irrespective of the flow direction the response is substantially the same. That is an in-line Morison loading response is excited in the general flow direction with vortex induced vibration in the transverse and in-line directions (the transverse being the more substantial).

For catenary flexible risers the problem is more evidently three dimensional. Flow may excite responses both in and out of the plane of the riser.

In the case for which this is only in-plane or normal-to-plane flow, the problem is somewhat simplified. The differences between this case and the tensioned riser are less significant apart from the requirement that in the case of in-plane flow the slope variation along the length of a flexible riser needs to be considered. According to King (13) and Hallam et al (18), the normal velocity determines the shedding frequency and the lift force may be calculated by using the normal velocity rather than the approach velocity. In the light of this the analysis model by Lyons and Patel (1) for tensioned risers has been extended to predict vortex induced vibration of flexible risers under the combined action of wave, current and surface vessel motion.

It is this simplified planar form of flow loading that is presented here to enable the main effects to be demonstrated for the effects of transverse vortex induced vibrations only. The in-line vortex induced vibrations are known to be significantly less.

3 VORTEX CELLS

Vortices are shed in cells behind cylinders in uniform and oscillatory flow. The length of cells depends on many parameters such as Reynolds number, length/diameter ratio, end conditions, surface roughness, turbulence, and amplitude of cylinder vibration.

In sheared flow, vortices are shed in cells with different frequencies. Little information on the cell length and boundaries of the cells is available.

The problem is even more complicated in the presence of waves or other oscillating flow. The flow velocity varies along the member as well as with time. Flow visualizations are the only direct way of revealing the process of vortex shedding. Some interesting work demonstrating cell formation along the length of non-vibrating circular cylinders in uniform and relative oscillatory flow at low Reynolds appears in Tatsuno and Bearman (24). However these results are not applicable to the problem in question since the cylinder is not subject to vortex induced vibrations. Further work in this area is required.

3.1 The influence of vortex cell size in vortex induced vibration

For a flexible cylinder or a flexibly mounted rigid cylinder, lock-on can occur when the vortex shedding frequency is close to one of the cylinder natural frequencies. Because the vortices are shed in cells the forces acting on a cylinder are not in phase with each other. This results in a reduction in the net oscillating force. The larger the cell length, the higher the vortex induced vibration amplitude.

When a cylinder vibrates with an amplitude larger than a certain value, the vortex correlation length is increased. This interaction between fluid and structure goes on until energy balance is reached. The stable state is determined by reduced velocity and reduced damping. For a non-uniform structure under the combined action of sheared flow, surface vessel motion and wave, many modes may be excited. The whole length of a cylinder can be considered as being divided into several sections, each corresponding to a vortex cell whose shedding frequency may be locked on to one of the natural frequencies of the cylinder.

However, the criteria for determining the boundaries of those cells are yet not clear.

3.2 Influence of damping

Damping is the limiting factor for this resonant phenomenon. The sources are the fluid damping and the structural (including material) damping of the cylinder. In the approach followed herein the fluid damping is related to the drag coefficient. In respect of structural damping, one must know the damping values for the structure in question. For steel risers values are available. These on their own may lead to conservatively large estimates of vibration amplitude if the effects of support friction (amongst other components), which may well occur in the system, are overlooked in defining the overall structural damping value.

For flexible risers the situation is more complicated owing to the complex composite structure of the multiple layers of the riser cross-section, and also because the damping levels are even more dependent on the mode of vibration of the riser, Lyons and Fang (4).

The value of drag coefficient has been fixed within the computation to permit a simplified implementation with good agreement with measurements. In reality, the drag coefficient is a function of Reynolds number and of vibration amplitude. Griffin and Ramberg (20) give this function from the results of full scale measurements in current flow as

$$c_D/c_{Do} = 1 + 1.16/(W_r - 1)^{0.65} \quad \text{for } W_r > 1$$

and

$$c_D/c_{Do} = 1 \quad \text{for } W_r < 1$$

(3.2.1)

where the wake stability parameter,

$$W_r = (1 + 2Y/D) / (V_r S).$$

The definition of drag coefficient to be used remains an unclear area but the above equations may be used within this method to incorporate a more refined variation of drag coefficient. Values of C_D/C_{DO} of up to 4.5 have been demonstrated. The situation is complicated for multi-riser bundles. Depending upon the configuration, the entrained fluid may often result in riser behaviour as if it were a single body. Patel and Sarohia (25) have demonstrated multi-tube vortex flow visually. Drag coefficients for bundled risers have been obtained by Demirbilik and Halvorsen (26).

4. MATHEMATICAL MODELLING

Models for vortex shedding and vortex induced vibrations of risers appear in refs (12,15,20,27 to 36). These are commented on in Lyons and Patel (2).

More recent models, in an attempt to reduce the level of empiricism by using operator splitting, random walk, and the vortex-in-cell method have been pursued, Skomedal et al (37), and Hansen et al (38), with encouraging results.

4.1 Theory

The method used here is based on that of Lyons and Patel (2) for application to the dynamics of marine risers. It invokes the following assumptions:

(a)   The vortex shedding phenomenon is dependent on instantaneous relative flow velocity.

(b)   Transverse vibration is approximated to begin at a reduced velocity of 4, reach a maximum at 6, and cease beyond 10.

(c)   The amplitude of vibration for each mode is calculated for each mode using a scheme devised by Iwan (39) described below where the regions of excitation are those defined in (b).

(d)   Regions exciting higher modes do not excite lower modes, ie modal priority of higher modes occurs.

(e)   The drag coefficient, which will vary with time and along the length, is fixed at 2.0 for tensioned risers, and 1.2 for catenary flexible risers, for computational simplicity. The higher value for the tensioned riser is chosen since this form of riser generally experiences greater vortex induced vibration amplitudes.

(f)   The added mass coefficient, which is also likely to vary with time and along the length, is fixed at 1.0.

(g)   For the vertical tensioned risers the mode shapes and frequencies are obtained using a tensioned beam formulation, Blevins (40). For the catenary risers the mode shapes and frequencies are obtained independently through a separate finite element formulation, Baradaran-Seyed (41).

(h)   For the cases presented here the wave, current and surface vessel motion are each in the same plane.

© IMechE 1991 C416/042

Iwan's scheme presents a simple analytical model for the vortex induced transverse oscillation of non-uniform structures in which the effects of limited spatial extent of lock-on and fluid damping of inactive elements are accounted for. The theory is based on a modal decomposition approach.

The appropriate equations used are given below.

The amplitude of locked-on oscillation of the structure is given by

$$Y_n(x) = D_s \, F_n \, I_n^{-1/2} \, \xi_n(x) \qquad (4.1.1)$$

where D_S is the cylinder diameter and the modal shape factor is

$$I_n = \frac{\int_0^L m(x) \, \xi_n^4(x) \, dx}{\int_0^L m(x) \, \xi_n^2(x) \, dx} \qquad (4.1.2)$$

The amplification factor is taken to be

$$F_n = \left(1 + 9.6 \left(\mu_r^n \, \zeta_n^s\right)^{1.8}\right)^{-1} \qquad (4.1.3)$$

where ζ_n^s is the effective damping, although expressions by other authors may be used as indicated in section 2.1. A particularly important parameter is the effective mass ratio,

$$\mu_r^n = \frac{\nu_n}{\frac{1}{4} \pi \rho D_s^2} \qquad (4.1.4)$$

in which the effective mass is given by

$$\nu_n = \frac{\int_0^L m(x) \, \xi_n^2(x) \, dx}{\int_0^L s(x) \, \xi_n^2(x) \, dx} \qquad (4.1.5)$$

where $s(x) = \begin{cases} 1 \text{ for those portions of the} \\ \text{structure where vortex shedding} \\ \text{is locked on to the structural} \\ \text{motion} \\ \\ 0 \text{ otherwise} \end{cases}$

The effect of the position of locked-on regions determined by this parameter on the amplitude of vibration is demonstrated in Figure 4. for the first mode of vibration for pinned-end modes. It is clearly seen that the amplitude of vibration is greater when the region of excitation is near the centre (antinode) and increases with the extent of the excited region. Similar effects occur for all other modes.

4.2 Implementation

The preceding is implemented in a time domain theoretical model. Relative velocities along the length are calculated and the extent of regions of vortex shedding excitation are identified for incremental time steps. Iwan's method is implemented for the length of the member in each mode which is excited to obtain the modal amplitude.

Since this amplitude is the peak resonant amplitude, it is necessary to modify it to determine the amplitude of vibration at the reduced velocities in the region of excitation. Use is made of assumption (b) in section 4.1. From this an amplitude is modified dependent on the range of reduced velocities in the excited region. The method utilises the maximum amplitude inducing reduced velocity detected in each region of excitation. The amplitude values for each mode are constructed into time histories which are then superimposed to obtain the overall member vibration time history. During vortex induced vibration of a particular mode, the member amplitude is set at the value given by the above procedure. When this mode is inactive, however, its vibration is taken to be due to its damped motion in still water from the vortex induced vibration during its last active condition. This time history procedure thus accounts for the following features:

(a) decay of vibration using the member structural and fluid damping in still water, ζ_n^s.

(b) phase of vibration changes randomly if a mode has a period of inactivity.

(c) vibration amplitude for any mode not being lower than that due to decay from a previous event.

The above model is applied here to a tensioned vertical riser and a flexible catenary riser for realistic scenarios.

4.2.1 Vertical tensioned risers

The case to which the model is applied represents a realistic top tensioned riser pin-jointed at its suspension point and built-in at the sea bed. It is supported from a fixed, rather than a floating platform. The riser details are given in Table 1.

Table 1 Tensioned riser details

water depth	51.7 m
effective diameter	0.244 m
mass per unit length	126.03 kgm^{-1}
EI	16.06 MNm^{-2}
fundamental freq (in air)	0.76 Hz
structural damping, log dec	0.08

mode	natural freq (in water)(Hz)
1	0.55
2	1.11
3	1.85
4	2.63
5	3.80
6	5.21
7	6.86
8	8.75

A regular long crested wave of 11.5m height , with a period of 11.1s is combined with the current profile given in Table 2.

Table 2 Sheared current for tensioned riser

	(m)	current (ms⁻¹)
surface	51.70	2.060
	49.96	1.609
	40.21	1.630
	34.47	1.500
	28.72	1.450
	22.98	1.430
	17.23	1.410
	11.49	1.390
	5.74	1.200
bottom	0.00	1.100

The structural damping value for a fluid filled pipe is believed to be realistic, Hallam et al (18). The log decrement value for steel tube of 0.08 in air is used.

The natural frequencies and mode shapes of the riser were calculated assuming a uniform beam with uniformly varying tension, Blevins (40):

$$\frac{f_i\big|_{p \neq 0}}{f_i\big|_{p=0}} = \left(1 + \frac{P\xi_1^2}{|P_b|\xi_i^2}\right)^{\frac{1}{2}} \qquad (4.2.1)$$

Bending moments are also presented. Here these are conservative in that they were calculated from the arithmetic sum of the maximum possible amplitudes of vibration for each mode and do not take account of the relative phases of the displacements which appear in the time series synthesis.

Table 3 gives the amplitudes of vibration for each of the modes shown in Figure 5. No modes higher than the eighth are predicted, and none lower than the second. This is because the maximum flow velocity is such that through the reduced velocity criterion the eighth mode is the highest which can possibly be excited, and the effects of the modal priority scheme are such that at all times there is sufficient flow to excite modes above the fundamental, which is as a consequence not itself excited.

Table 3 Modal amplitudes (Y/D)

mode	log dec 0.08	1.0	2.0
1	-	-	-
2	0.871	0.009	0.002
3	1.109	0.163	0.049
4	1.038	0.107	0.026
5	0.768	0.047	0.012
6	0.506	0.018	0.005
7	0.267	0.005	0.001
8	0.059	0.001	-
9	-	-	-
10	-	-	-

realistic *for comparison*

The maximum amplitude is shown to be in the third mode (1.109 diameters). Combining the modal contributions taking due account of the points discussed in 4.2, a combined maximum of around 2.5 diameters is generated in the simulation, compared with about 3.5 diameters using a simple arithmetic sum of the individual modal amplitudes shown in Figure 5.

Although not presented in detail here, the effect of structural damping has been shown to be significant and is shown in Table 3 for arbitrarily chosen higher values of log decrement of *1.0* and *2.0*. These result in a profound reduction in predicted amplitudes of vibration.

Table 4 shows that the third and fourth modes are continuously excited, whilst the others are excited for only part of the wave cycle.

Table 4 Modal activity

mode	% of time excited	Y/D
1	-	-
2	13.6	0.454
3	100.0	1.109
4	100.0	1.038
5	86.4	0.768
6	77.3	0.506
7	59.1	0.267
8	36.4	0.059

© IMechE 1991 C416/042

Figure 6 shows that for a significant proportion of the riser length the level of bending moment is substantially constant, whilst being a maximum at the sea bed (built in) and a minimum at the surface (pinned).

Evidently, if the response is to be correctly predicted, then the structural damping factors need to be accurately known.

4.2.2 Catenary flexible risers

Four cases are presented, two with the incident flow along the vertical plane, and two normal to the vertical plane of a Lazy-wave riser. Wave only, and current only excitation are used here to demonstrate the vortex-induced response.

Table 5 Lazy-wave riser details

external diameter	0.1524m
internal diameter	0.1016m
mass/length in air	26.7kgm^{-1}
mass/length inc. conts.	35.0kgm^{-1}
bending stiffness (EI)	3400Nm^2
torsional stiffness (GJ)	2600Nm^2
axial stiffness (EA)	115MN
water depth	110m
total riser length	173.79m
buoyancy module dia.	0.4064m
buoyancy module length	20.0m
buoyancy module density	400.00kgm^{-3}
length of riser from buoyancy module to sea level	110m

The natural frequencies and mode shapes were obtained using a finite element formulation (41) for a Lazy-wave riser in 110m water depth. The natural frequencies for in-plane and normal-to-plane modes are listed in Table 6. The log decrement for each mode has been fixed at 0.01.

Table 6 Natural frequencies of Lazy-wave riser (Hz)

mode	normal-to-plane	in-plane
1	0.027	0.031
2	0.054	0.057
3	0.074	0.085
4	0.108	0.102
5	0.139	0.116
6	0.156	0.148
7	0.189	0.187
8	0.222	0.215
9	0.244	0.275
10	0.307	0.306

In the wave only cases, the riser is subjected to regular long crested waves of 12m height and 10s period. Results of the prediction are shown in Figure 7 for the in-plane waves and Figure 8 for the normal-to-plane waves. These show that the lowest mode excited by the waves is the fourth mode. This is because the natural frequencies of the first three modes in both in-plane and normal-to-plane directions are lower than the wave frequency. Since at least one pair of vortices is shed during each wave cycle, the exciting force owing to vortex shedding has a frequency equal to or higher than the wave frequency. Therefore those modes with natural frequencies which are lower than the wave frequency are unable to be locked-on.

No significant level of vibration is predicted for either incident wave direction. The reason revealed by the prediction model is that the lock-on regions for each mode which is excited are only a small proportion of the whole riser length. This results in low excitation levels with high fluid damping over the regions which are not locked on. The response amplitude is not sensitive to structural damping in wave only cases where the fluid damping is usually one or two orders larger than the structural damping. This is demonstrated in Tables 7 and 8, in which the vortex induced vibration response levels are substantially the same irrespective of the level of structural damping assumed.

Table 7 Modal amplitudes (Y/D): in-plane wave

mode	log dec 0.01	0.1
1	-	-
2	-	-
3	-	-
4	0.0123	0.0101
5	0.0051	0.0040
6	0.0195	0.0143
7	0.0017	0.0013
8	0.0004	0.0003
9	0.0003	0.0002
10	0.0013	0.0009

as used   *for comparison*

Table 8 Modal amplitudes (Y/D): normal-to-plane wave

mode	log dec 0.01	0.1
1	-	-
2	-	-
3	-	-
4	0.0025	0.0021
5	0.0050	0.0040
6	0.0280	0.0233
7	0.0032	0.0027
8	0.0003	0.0003
9	0.0006	0.0005
10	0.0003	0.0002
	as used	*for comparison*

In the current only cases a uniform current with a low speed of 0.028 ms^{-1} is considered (this flow rate is chosen since it is shown to excite vortex induced vibrations for both in-plane and normal-to-plane current). Figures 9 and 10 show the response amplitudes for the in-plane and normal-to-plane current respectively. These figures show that the amplitudes of vibration for both cases are quite high. This is because the velocity of the current is such that a sufficient proportion of riser is locked on to one mode. This is however a somewhat contrived scenario to demonstrate how relatively large amplitudes of vortex induced vibration might be achieved for this form of flexible riser. More realistic environmental conditions provide for flows which are in general sheared, and lead, like the wave excitation cases shown here, to provide very low levels of vibration.

The equivalent fluid damping for the current only cases here is much lower than that in wave only cases. Consequently structural damping becomes important in contributing to the total damping.

5. CONCLUSIONS

The potential vortex induced vibration behaviour for risers in the ocean environment is more complex than simple models allow one to predict. The approach taken here allows one to examine these complexities more thoroughly. However, our understanding is by no means complete. The cellular shedding of vortices from bodies undergoing vortex induced vibrations, in particular, needs to be better understood. No attempt to include the effects of the in-line vortex induced response is made in the model presented here, although a similar approach can be taken as for the transverse sense. Nor is any account of the coupling effects of in-line and transverse response made.

A representative level of structural damping for flexible risers which has been measured by the authors has been incorporated in the theoretical model for catenary risers. Whilst it has been demonstrated that this parameter is particularly important in determining the amplitudes of vibration for vertical tensioned risers (for which in a wide range of environmental loadings significant levels of vortex induced vibration may be excited), there are other factors in realistic catenary flexible cases which are more significant than the attenuating effect of structural/material damping. Its effect is however more significant for the uniform flow cases where the majority of the length of the catenary riser is excited for a single mode of vibration. In more realistic situations low amplitudes of vibration result even for a single mode. Here the effect of structural damping coupled with the highly non-uniform flow on the riser (which is a function of both the wave, current shear, and vessel motion contributions, and importantly for a catenary riser, the shape, which reduces the amount of normal flow) results in very low amplitudes of vortex induced vibrations for the catenary riser configurations examined.

It is known that some model tests have demonstrated significant high frequency vibrations. It is believed that these may not have realistically modelled physical properties (particularly internal damping) and environmental conditions, but provided configurations and flow conditions which were optimum for vortex induced vibrations. For example, having a lower section which was essentially a tensioned riser subjected to flow providing well correlated vortex excitation. It is also quite likely that the sub-surface buoy is a source of flow induced vibrations rather than the riser itself. Investigations should be carried out to examine the influence of the buoy in this respect. Full scale data on riser performance are required to improve our understanding.

ACKNOWLEDGEMENTS

This work was carried out as part of a managed programme of research into Floating Production Systems (1987-1989) which was jointly funded by the Science and Engineering Council and a number of industrial sponsors.

REFERENCES

(1) LYONS G J and PATEL M H . Final Report for Compliant Systems cohesive program of research, 1985, SERC, UK.

(2) LYONS G J and PATEL M H . A prediction technique for vortex induced transverse response of marine risers and tethers. *Journal of Sound and Vibration*, 1986, 111 (3), 467-487.

(3) LYONS G J and PATEL M H. Application of a general technique for the prediction of riser vortex-induced vibration in waves and current. *Journal of Offshore Mechanics and Arctic Engineering*, 1989, 111, 82-91.

(4) LYONS G J and FANG J. Structural damping effects on flexible risers. Final report project - C1- Floating Production Systems, 1989, SERC, UK.

(5) CHRYSSOSTOMIDIS C and PATRIKALAKIS N. A comparison of theoretical and experimental prediction of the vortex induced response of marine risers. Proc. 3rd Int. Offshore Mechanics & Arctic Engineering Symposium, 1984, 1, 318-327, ASME.

(6) EVERY M J, KING R and GRIFFIN O M. Hydrodynamic loads on flexible marine structures due to vortex shedding. *Journal of Energy Resources Technology*, 1981, 104, 330-336.

(7) GRIFFIN O M, SKOP R A and KOOPMAN G H. The vortex excited resonant vibrations of circular cylinders. *Journal of Sound and Vibration*, 1973, 31(2), 235-249.

(8) GRIFFIN O M, PATTISON J H, SKOP R A, RAMBERG S E and MEGGITT D. Vortex excited vibrations of marine cables. *Journal of Waterways: Port Coastal and Ocean Division*, May 1980, 106, 183-205.

(9) GRIFFIN O M and VANDIVER J K. Vortex induced strumming vibrations of marine cables with attached masses, Proc 3rd Int Offshore Mechanics & Arctic Engineering Symposium, 1984, 1, 300-309, ASME.

(10) KING R, PROSSER M J and JOHNS D J. On vortex excitation of model piles in water. *Journal of Sound and Vibration*, 1973, 29(2), 169-188.

(11) PELZER R D and ROONEY D M. Near wake properties of a strumming marine cable: an experimental study. Proceedings of the 3rd Int. Offshore Mechanics & Arctic Engineering Symposium, 1984, 1, 310-317.

(12) BLEVINS R D. Flow-induced vibration. 1977, Van Nostrand Reinhold.

(13) KING R. review of vortex shedding research and its application. *Ocean Engineering*, 1977, 4, 141-171.

(14) SARPKAYA T. Vortex induced oscillations, A selective review. *Journal of Applied Mechanics*, 1979, 46, 241-258.

(15) SARPKAYA T and ISAACSON M. Mechanics of wave forces on offshore structures. 1981, Van Nostrand Reinhold.

(16) SHAW T L (Ed). Mechanics of wave induced forces on cylinders. 1979, Pitman.

(17) SIMPSON A S. Cables: dynamic stability aspects - a review. Dept. of Aeronautical Engineering, Univ. of Bristol, Symp. on Mechanics of Wave-Induced Forces On Cylinders, 3-6 Sept. 1978.

(18) HALLAM M G, HEAF N J, WOOTON R L. Dynamics of marine structures. Construction Industry Research and Information Association (CIRIA) Report UR8, London, England, 1978, 175- 206.

(19) PARKINSON G V, FENG C C and FERGUSON N. Mechanics of vortex excited oscillation of bluff cylinders. Paper 27, Symp. on Wind Effects On Building and Structures, Longhborough, England, 1968.

(20) GRIFFIN O M and RAMBERG S E. Some recent studies of vortex shedding with application to marine tubulars and risers. *Journal of Energy Resources Technology*, 1982, 104, 2-13.

(21) DEAN R B, MILLIGAN R W and WOOTON L R. An experimental study of flow induced vibration. EEC Report 4, 1977, Atkins Research & Development, Epsom, U.K.

(22) IWAN W D. The vortex induced oscillation of elastic structural elements. *Journal of Engineering for Industry*, 1975, 97, 1378-1382.

(23) ZARE K and DATTA T K. Vibration of Lazy-S Riser Due to Vortex Shedding under Lock-in, Proceedings of 20th Offshore Technology Conference, Houston 1988, OTC 5795, 451-458, ASME.

(24) TATSUNO M and BEARMAN P W. A visual study around an oscillating circular cylinder at low Keulegan-Carpenter numbers and low Stokes numbers. *Journal of Fluid Mechanics*, 1990, 211, 157-182.

(25) PATEL M H and SAROHIA S. On the dynamics of production risers. Proceedings of the Third International Conference on Behaviour of Offshore Structures (BOSS 82), 1982, 1, 599.

(26) DEMIRBILIK Z and HALVORSEN T. Hydrodynamic forces on multi-tube production risers exposed to currents and waves. Proceedings of the 4th Offshore Mechanics and Arctic Engineering Symposium, 1985, 363-370, ASME.

(27) BISHOP R E D and HASSAN A Y. The lift and drag forces on a circular cylinder in a flowing field. *Proc. Roy. Soc. (London)*, 1964, Ser A, 277, 51-75.

(28) HARTLEN R T and CURRIE I G. Lift oscillation model for vortex induced vibration. *Journal Eng. Mech. Div. ASCE*, 1970, 96, 577-591.

(29) NORDGREN R P. Dynamic analysis of marine risers with vortex excitation. *Journal of Energy Resources Technology*, 104, 1982, 14-19.

(30) IWAN W D and BLEVINS R. A model of vortex induced oscillation of structures. *Journal of Applied Mechanics*, 1974, 41, 581-586.

(31) BLEVINS R D and BURTON T E. Fluid forces induced by vortex shedding. *Journal of Fluid Engineering*, March 1976, 19-26.

(32) KENNEDY M and VANDIVER J K. A random vibration model for cable strumming predictions. *Civil Engineering in the Oceans*, IV, 1979, ASCE, 273-292.

(33) WHITNEY A K and NIKKEL N G. Effects of shear flow on vortex shedding induced vibration of marine risers, Proceedings of 15th Offshore Technology Conference, 1983, OTC 4595, 127-137, ASME.

(34) RAJABI F, ZEDAN M and MANGIAVACCHI A. Vortex shedding induced dynamic response of marine risers. *Journal of Energy Resources Technology*, 1984, 106, 214-221.

(35) BENAROYA H and LEPORE J A. Statistical flow-oscillator modelling of vortex shedding, *Journal. of Sound and Vibration*, 1983, 86(2), 159-179.

(36) LANDL R. A mathematical model for vortex excited vibrations of bluff bodies. *Journal of Sound and Vibration*, 1975, 42(2), 219-234.

(37) SKOMEDAL N E, TEIGEN P and VADA T. Computation of vortex induced vibration and the effect of correlation on circular cylinders in oscillatory flow. Proc. 8th Offshore Mechanics and Arctic Engineering Conf.,The Hague, 1989, 311-318, ASME.

(38) HANSEN H T, SKOMEDAL N G and VADA T. A method for computation of integrated vortex induced fluid loading and response interaction of marine risers in waves and current. Proc. Int. Conf. on Behaviour of Offshore Structures, BOSS 88, 1988, 841-857.

(39) IWAN W D. The vortex induced oscillation of non-uniform structural systems. *Journal of Sound and Vibration*, 1981, 79(2), 291-301.

(40) BLEVINS R D. Formulas for natural frequencies and mode shape. 1979,Van Nostrand Reinhold.

(41) BARADARAN-SEYED F. On the dynamics of flexible and suspended pipelines,1989, PhD thesis, Univ. of London.

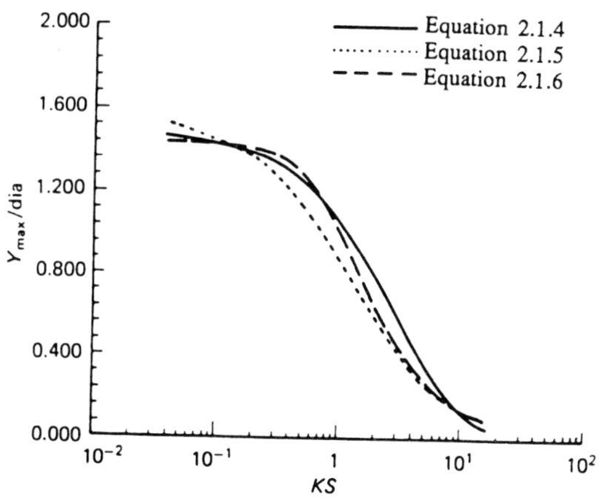

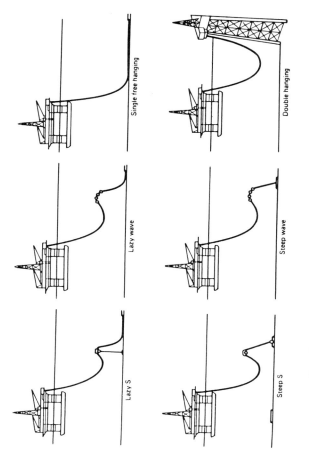

Figure 1 Calculated maximum transverse vortex induced vibration amplitude *versus* reduced damping for mounted cylinders by various authors

Structural element	γ
Rigid cylinder	1
Pivoted rod	1.291
String or cable	1.155
Simple support beam	1.155
Cantilever beam, 1st mode	1.305
Cantilever beam, 2nd mode	1.499
Cantilever beam, 3rd mode	1.531

Figure 2 Normalised maximum amplitude of response *versus* mass ratio damping parameter

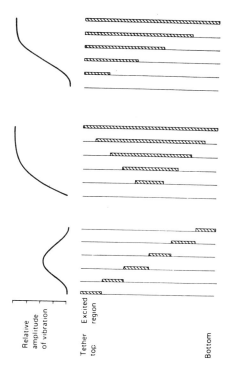

Figure 3 Flexible risers; an illustration of current configurations

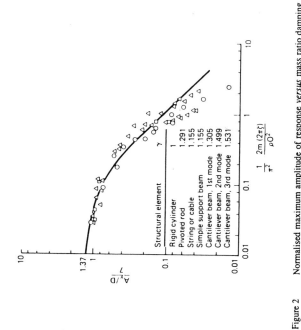

Figure 4 The effect of position of lock-on; variation of the amplitude of vibration with extent of excited region for the first mode of pinned-end sinusoidal vibrations

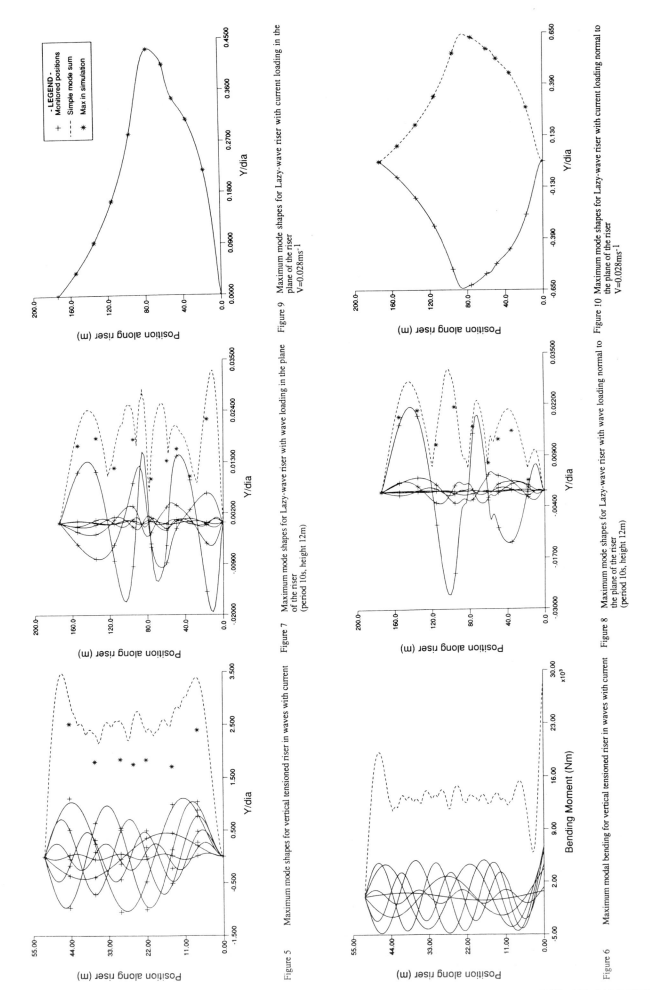

- LEGEND -
+ Monitored positions
--- Simple mode sum
* Max in simulation

Figure 5   Maximum mode shapes for vertical tensioned riser in waves with current

Figure 6   Maximum modal bending for vertical tensioned riser in waves with current

Figure 7   Maximum mode shapes for Lazy-wave riser with wave loading in the plane of the riser (period 10s, height 12m)

Figure 8   Maximum mode shapes for Lazy-wave riser with wave loading normal to the plane of the riser (period 10s, height 12m)

Figure 9   Maximum mode shapes for Lazy-wave riser with current loading in the plane of the riser V=0.028ms⁻¹

Figure 10   Maximum mode shapes for Lazy-wave riser with current loading normal to the plane of the riser V=0.028ms⁻¹

C416/013

A response prediction model for flow induced vibration of marine risers in sheared flow

T Y CHUNG, PhD, MASME and Y Y NAM, MSc
Korea Research Institute of Ships and Ocean Engineering, Daejeon, Korea

SYNOPSIS A response prediction method is proposed for the non-lockin vibration of a marine riser in sheared flow using the Green's function of a linearly varying tensioned-beam. The hydrodynamic damping and the excitation force spectrum models are proposed based on a linear random vibration theory. According to the predicted response of a marine riser in sheared flow, the dynamic bending stress in the high flow velocity region is much larger than that in the low flow velocity region and stress distribution along the length does not show the dominant contribution of any specific mode. It may come from the non-resonant modal contribution to the response due to large hydrodynamic damping.

1 INTRODUCTION

Many cylindrical offshore structures like marine risers are sometimes exposed to strong enough currents to introduce significant vortex-induced vibration. Fatigue life estimates are required in the design of these structures, and good response predictions to vortex-induced vibration are essential for making this determination.

The vortex-induced vibration of long-tensioned cylinders in a uniform flow can be predicted reasonably well on the basis of existing experimental data. However, real ocean currents are not spatially and directionally uniform. In contrast to the uniform flow case, a sheared flow can excite flexible cylinders at spatially varying frequencies, thus making prediction more difficult. Most previous attempts to predict vortex-induced vibration of flexible cylinders have been devoted to the uniform flow case. Some attempts have been made to predict responses in sheared flow[1]. However, due to the lack of publicly available response data for long flexible cylinders in sheared flow, these models remain unrefined and untested.

Vandiver and Chung [2] carried out the field experiments to investigate the dynamic response characteristics of long-tensioned flexible cylinders in sheared flow and they found that single mode lockin response is not possible under the condition that many modes are simultaneously excited by a sheared flow due to large hydrodynamic damping. Chung [3], and Vandiver and Chung [4] proposed a response prediction model for the non-lockin vortex-induced vibration of a taut cable in sheared flow based on a Green's function approach and random vibration theory. Their model gave excellent results compared with experimental observations. In this paper, their model is extended to the case of ma-

rine risers by using a linearly varying tensioned beam model.

2 PREDICTION MODEL

In a linear one-dimensional continuous system, the displacement response spectrum at a location can be specified by following integral equation

$$S_D(x,\omega) = \int_0^\ell \int_0^\ell G(x/\xi,\omega) \cdot G^*(x/\xi',\omega) \cdot S_{FF}(\xi,\xi',\omega)d\xi d\xi' \quad (1)$$

where,

$S_D(x,w)$	=the displacement response spectrum at location x
$S_{FF}(\xi,\xi',w)$	=lift force spectrum due to vortex-shedding
$G(x/\xi,w)$	=Green's function of continuous system
$G^*(x/\xi,w)$	=conjugate Green's function of continuous system
ℓ	=the length of continuous system

The velocity and acceleration spectra can be calculated from the displacement spectrum as shown below respectively.

$$S_V(x,\omega) = \omega^2 S_D(x,\omega) \quad (2)$$

$$S_A(x,\omega) = \omega^4 S_D(x,\omega) \quad (3)$$

By specifying the Green's function and lift force spectrum of Equation (1), we can calculate the response by straight forward discrete numerical integration of the equation.

2.1 Green's Function of a Marine Riser

A marine riser may be modelled as a tensioned beam. The tension is varying along the length due to the self-weight of a riser including its contents, and hydrodynamic damping force is also varying along the length in the case of sheared flow. Neglecting the effects of nonuniform tension and damping force may cause erroneous prediction of the response of a riser.

The normalized governing equation of a tensioned beam can be expressed as follows:

$$\frac{\partial^2}{\partial s^2}\left[P(s)\frac{\partial^2 Y}{\partial s^2}\right] - \frac{\partial}{\partial s}\left[Q(s)\frac{\partial Y}{\partial s}\right] + R(s)\frac{\partial Y}{\partial \tau}$$
$$+ M(s)\frac{\partial^2 Y}{\partial \tau^2} = F(s,\tau) \tag{4}$$

where,

$$s = \frac{x}{\ell}, Y = \frac{y}{D}, \tau = \omega_o t, \omega_o = \sqrt{\frac{EI_o}{m_o \ell^4}}$$

$$P(s) = \frac{I(x)}{I_o}, Q(s) = \frac{T(x)\ell^4}{EI_o}, R(s) = C(x)\sqrt{\frac{\ell^4}{EI_o m_o}}$$

$$M(s) = \frac{m(x)}{m_o}, F(s,\tau) = \frac{f(x,t)\ell^4}{EI_o D}$$

D = the outer diameter of a riser
E = Young's modulus of a riser material
$I(x)$ = the moment of inertia of a riser section
$T(x)$ = tension
$m(x)$ = the effective mass of a riser including added
         mass per unit length
$C(x)$ = the effective damping including hydrodynamic
         damping per unit length
$f(x,t)$ = exciting force per unit length

The subscript 'o' in the above discription means a property at a reference section.

Equation (4) forms an ordinary differential equation with non-constant parameters. It is difficult to get an analytical solution for such equation. Usually we rely on numerical methods to solve the equation. In this paper, we utilized the Green's function of Equation (4) obtained by perturbation method under the assumption of the slowly varying rates of the system parameters. Higher order derivatives than the first are ignored in the formulation of Green's function. The procedure to get the Green's function is introduced briefly in here. For detail derivation, Kim's thesis[5] may be refered.

The general solution of Equation (4) is given by

$$\phi = K_2\left[C_1\sin\left(\int_0^s J_2 d\psi\right) + C_2\cos\left(\int_0^s J_2 d\psi\right)\right]$$
$$+ K_1\left[C_3\sinh\left(\int_0^s J_1 d\psi\right) + C_4\cosh\left(\int_0^s J_1 d\psi\right)\right] \tag{5}$$

where,

$$K_1(s) = \frac{1}{\sqrt{P}}\{\frac{1}{2}(\frac{Q}{P})^3 + 2(\frac{QU}{P})^2 + \frac{1}{2}[(\frac{Q}{P})^2 + 4\frac{U}{P}]^{3/2}\}^{-1/4}$$

$$K_2(s) = \frac{1}{\sqrt{P}}\{-\frac{1}{2}(\frac{Q}{P})^3 - 2(\frac{QU}{P})^2 + \frac{1}{2}[(\frac{Q}{P})^2 + 4\frac{U}{P}]^{3/2}\}^{-1/4}$$

$$J_1(s) = \sqrt{\frac{1}{2}\frac{Q}{P} + \frac{1}{2}\sqrt{(\frac{Q}{P})^2 + 4\frac{U}{P}}}$$

$$J_2(s) = \sqrt{-\frac{1}{2}\frac{Q}{P} + \frac{1}{2}\sqrt{(\frac{Q}{P})^2 + 4\frac{U}{P}}}$$

$$U(s) = -\Lambda R(s)i + \Lambda^2 M(s), \Lambda = \frac{\omega}{\omega_o}$$

$C_1 - C_4$ in the above equtation are coefficients which will be determined from the given boundary conditions. Simply supported conditions at both ends are given by

$$\phi(0) = \phi(1) = \phi''(0) = \phi''(1) = 0 \tag{6}$$

Frequency equation and mode function can be obtained by applying the boundary conditions of Equation (6) to Equation (5) without damping terms.

$$\int_0^1 \sqrt{-\frac{1}{2}\frac{Q}{P} + \frac{1}{2}\sqrt{(\frac{Q}{P})^2 + 4\frac{M\Lambda^2}{P}}}\, d\psi = n\pi \tag{7}$$

$$\Phi_n(s) = K_2\sin\left[\int_0^s \sqrt{-\frac{1}{2}\frac{Q}{P} + \frac{1}{2}\sqrt{(\frac{Q}{P})^2 + 4\frac{M\Lambda^2}{P}}}\, d\psi\right] \tag{8}$$

The normalized Green's function is obtained by applying an excitation force $\delta(s-\eta)e^{i\Lambda\tau}$ on the beam in Equation (5) and using new boundary conditions at the excitation point $s = \eta$ with the boundary conditions at the ends given in Equation (6). The new boundary conditions at the excitation point are given by

$$\phi_1(\eta) = \phi_2(\eta), \phi_1'(\eta) = \phi_2'(\eta), \phi_1''(\eta) = \phi_2''(\eta)$$
$$\phi_2'''(\eta) - \phi_1'''(\eta) = \frac{1}{P(\eta)} \tag{9}$$

where,

$\phi_1(\eta)$ = general solution given by Equation (5)
       for $0 \le s \le \eta$
$\phi_2(\eta)$ = general solution given by Equation (5)
       for $\eta \le s \le 1$

The obtained normalized Green's function is as follows

$$g(s/\eta, \Lambda) = \frac{K_2(s)K_2(\eta)}{B_2}\sin\left(\int_0^s J_2 d\psi\right)\sin\left(\int_\eta^1 J_2 d\psi\right)$$
$$- \frac{K_1(s)K_1(\eta)}{B_1}\sinh\left(\int_0^s J_1 d\psi\right)\sinh\left(\int_\eta^1 J_1 d\psi\right)$$
$$for, 0 \le s \le \eta$$
$$= \frac{K_2(s)K_2(\eta)}{B_2}\sin\left(\int_0^\eta J_2 d\psi\right)\sin\left(\int_s^1 J_2 d\psi\right)$$
$$- \frac{K_1(s)K_1(\eta)}{B_1}\sinh\left(\int_0^\eta J_1 d\psi\right)\sinh\left(\int_s^1 J_1 d\psi\right)$$
$$for, \eta \le s \le 1 \tag{10}$$

where,

$$B_1 = \sinh(\int_0^1 J_1 d\psi)$$

$$B_2 = \sin(\int_0^1 J_2 d\psi)$$

The Green's function of a real system is obtained from the normalized Green's function as follows

$$G(x/\xi,\omega) = \frac{\ell^3}{EI_o} g(s/\eta,\Lambda) \qquad (11)$$

And the stress for unit force $\delta(s-\eta)e^{i\Lambda\tau}$ can be obtained by double differentiation of Equation (10) about s.

2.2 Hydrodynamic Damping and Lift Force Spectrum

Drag force per unit length at any specific location may be defined as the force in the direction of the instantaneous velocity of fluid particle relative to the riser. The fluid velocity relative to the cylinder is vector sum of the free stream velocity and the negative of the velocity of local motion of cylinder in cross flow direction(Fig.1). If one assume the drag force to be proportional to the relative velocity squared, then the drag force takes the form given below

$$\mid f_d(x,t) \mid = \frac{1}{2}\rho_w C_d D(V_F^2 + \dot{y}^2)^2 \qquad (12)$$

where,

$f_d(x,t)$ =hydrodynamic drag force at x
ρ_w =fluid density
C_d =drag force coefficient
V_F =flow velcoity
$\dot{y}(x,t)$ =vibration amplitude of response at location x

The component of damping in the y direction can be written as

$$f_{d,y} = -\frac{1}{2}\rho_w C_d D\sqrt{V_F^2 + \dot{y}^2}\,\dot{y} \qquad (13)$$

Therefore hydrodynamic damping is given by

$$C(x) = \frac{1}{2}\rho_w C_d D\sqrt{V_F^2 + \dot{y}^2} \qquad (14)$$

For the case of $V_F^2 >> \dot{y}^2, C(x)$ can be reduced to

$$C(x) \cong \frac{1}{2}\rho_w C_d D \mid V_F \mid \qquad (15)$$

Such a model of damping or dissipative force ignors the effect of the vortex-shedding process itself. When wake synchronization occurs for some region, there is high correlation between cylinder motion and vortex shedding phenomena. Under such conditions the force may be in phase with the velocity and hence may pump the power into the system. Vibration at frequencies which are uncorrelated with the local lift forces will lead to damping and vibration at frequencies which are correlated to lift forces is responsible for the power flow into the riser. The model of damping must be able to distinguish between regions of power in and out as a function of frequency and location. For example, if a wave length which is excited on a cylinder at 5Hz travels into a region of the cylinder which is shedding vortices at 2Hz, the 5Hz waves will be damped out in the region that 2Hz waves are being excited. In very long riser in sheared flows correlation length, wake sychronization length, will be relatively short compared to the total riser length and so for the purpose of computing, it may be adequate that damping is in effect everywhere.

The lift force per unit length in a sheared flow can be modelled as a spatially distributed excitation [6].

$$f_L(x,t) = \frac{1}{2}\rho_w DV_F^2(x)C_L(x,t) \qquad (16)$$

where, $C_L(x,t)$ is local and time varying lift coefficient.

If we assume that the local lift coefficient $C_L(x,t)$ is random varible having the characteristics of being zero mean, Gaussian and time stationary-ergodic, then we can completely characterize the local lift coefficient by the space-time correlation function on its power spectrum. The spectrum of local lift coefficient may be given by following Equation [3,4]

$$\begin{aligned}
S_{LL}(\xi,\xi',\omega) =\ & \frac{C_{L,rms}^2}{\sqrt{2b b'\pi}}[e^{-\frac{(\omega-\omega_s)^2}{4b^2}} + C_{L,2}e^{-\frac{(\omega-2\omega_s)^2}{4(2b)^2}} \\
& + C_{L,3}e^{-\frac{(\omega-3\omega_s)^2}{4(3b)^2}} + C_{L,4}e^{-\frac{(\omega-4\omega_s)^2}{4(4b)^2}} + \cdots] \cdot \\
& [e^{-\frac{(\omega-\omega_s')^2}{4(b')^2}} + C_{L,2}e^{-\frac{(\omega-2\omega_s')^2}{4(2b')^2}} \\
& + C_{L,3}e^{-\frac{(\omega-3\omega_s')^2}{4(3b')^2}} + C_{L,4}e^{-\frac{(\omega-4\omega_s')^2}{4(4b')^2}} + \cdots] \cdot \\
& e^{-(\xi-\xi')^2/2\ell_c^2}
\end{aligned} \qquad (17)$$

where,

$C_{L,rms}$ =root mean square lift coefficient
ω_s =local mean vortex shedding frequency at $x = \xi$
ω_s' =local mean vortex shedding frequency at $x = \xi'$
b, b' =deviation of local mean vortex shedding frequency at $x = \xi, \xi'$
$C_{L,1}, C_{L,2}, \cdots$ =lift coefficients of higher order harmonics
ℓ_c =correlation length

The center frequency ω_s and deviation b are specified by next equations.

$$\omega_s = 2\pi S_t \cdot \frac{V_F(x)}{D} \qquad (18)$$

$$b = 2\pi S_t \frac{\triangle V_{rms}(x)}{D} \qquad (19)$$

where,

S_t =Strouhal number
$\triangle V_{rms}(x)$ =standard deviation of local flow velocity

Given the lift coefficient spectrum as defined in Equation (17), the lift force spectrum can be written as

$$S_{FF}(\xi, \xi', \omega) = [\frac{1}{2}\rho_w DV_F(\xi)^2][\frac{1}{2}\rho_w DV_F(\xi')^2]S_{LL}(\xi, \xi', \omega) \qquad (20)$$

3 APPLICATION AND DISCUSSION

A computer program is developed to implement the response prediction method described in section 2. In order to confirm the validity of the present response prediction model for the non-lockin case, sample runs are made for the constant tensioned cable for which the experimental results have already been available[3]. Specification of the cable is given in Table 1(a) and sheared flow velocity profile for sample runs is the flow profile FP.1 in Fig. 2. Strictly speaking, the present response prediction model cannot be applied to cables having no bending rigidity. This limitation can be overcome numerically by giving a very small artificial bending rigidity to the cable which is expected not to cause significant errors on the response prediction. Table 2 shows the calculated natural frequencies of the cable with and without the artificial bending rigidity. Fig. 3 shows the root-mean-square values of the cable displacements obtained by the present model with the experimental results. It appears that they are in good agreements. The values of hydrodynamic coefficients used in the prediction are summarised in Table 3.

Whitney et al. [1] carried out the vortex-induced vibration analysis of a production riser, which has the specification shown in Table 1(b), in the sheared flow profile FP.2 given in Fig. 2 using their prediction model. The present response prediction model is applied to calculate the vortex- induced vibration response of the same riser in the same flow condition for the comparison of the results. The same hydrodynamic coefficients used in the calculation of the cable response in Table 3 are used.

Fig. 4 shows the predicted displacement spectra of the riser at two locations, 0.2L and 0.8L from the top, and Fig. 5 shows the integrated displacement spectra at 0.2L and 0.8L. These integrated displacement spectra give cumulative estimates of the rms displacements as a function of frequency. Integration of the displacement spectra were carried out numerically from high to low frequencies just for convenience.

The spatial distribution of the fluctuating stress level along the length is shown in Fig. 6. The solid line is for the actual varying tension case and the dotted line is for the constant mean tension case. Fig. 6 shows the stress level of the top side of the riser is much larger than that of the bottom side and the response of the constant mean tension model gives the overestimated result about 20% for this specific case. In addition to this, it should be noticed that the dynamic stress distribution along the length is much different from the result obtained by Whitney et al.[1] as shown in Fig. 7. Authors may think that this big difference comes from their ignorance of non-resonant modal contributions to the response. It was found by Vandiver and Chung [2] that the hydrodynamic damping was much larger than structural damping in sheared flow with the exception of pure single mode lockin and for the large value of the product of mode number n and damping ς, non-resonant modal contributions are substantial and the mode superposition method should include many other modes' contributions to the response.

4 SUMMARY

A response prediction method is proposed for the non-lockin vortex-induced vibration of a riser in sheared flow using the Green's function of a linearly varying tensioned beam. The hydrodynamic damping and the excitation spectrum models are proposed based on linear random vibration theory, and neccessary parameters for these models are estimated by tuning up the calculated response to the measured one of a cable in sheared flow.

The present response prediction model is applied to get vortex-induced vibration response of a production riser. The important results are

- The dynamic bending stress in the high flow velocity region is much larger than that in the low flow velocity region.

- The constant mean tension model gives overestimated result compared to the varying tension model.

- Non-resonant model contributions are substantial for the vortex-induced vibration of a marine riser in sheared flow due to large hydrodynamic damping.

REFERENCES

1. Whitney, A.K.and Nikkel,K.G., Effects of Shear Flow on Vortex-Shedding-Induced Vibration of Marine Risers, Offshore Technology Conference,Paper OTC4595, 1983.

2. Vandiver,J.K. and Chung,T.Y.,Hydrodynamic damping on flexible cylinders in sheared flow ,Journal of Waterway,Port,Coastal, and Ocean Engeering, Vol. 115, No.2, March, 1989.

3. Chung,T.Y.,Vortex-Induced Vibration of Flexible Cylinders in Sheared Flow ,Ph.D.Thesis, Massachusetts Instituate of Technology, 1987.

4. Vandiver,J.K. and Chung,T.Y.,Prediction and measured response of flexible cylinder in sheared flow, Symp. on Vortex-Induced Vibration, ASME Winter Meeting , Nov., 1988.

5. Kim,Y.C.,Nonlinear Vibrations of Long Slender Beams, Ph.D.Thesis, Massachusetts Institute of Technology, 1983.

6. Kennedy,M.B.,A linear Random Vibration Model for Cable Strumming, Ph.D. Thesis, Massachusetts Institute of Technology, 1979.

Table 3 Hydrodynamic coefficients

added mass coeff.C_a	1.000
drag force coeff.C_d	1.300
rms lift coeff. $C_{L,rms}$	1.270
higher harmonic of lift $C_{L,2}$	0.040
higher harmonic of lift $C_{L,3}$	0.060
higher harmonic of lift $C_{L,4}$	0.001
higher harmonic of lift $C_{L,5}$	0.010
Strouhal number S_t	0.170

Table 1 Specifications of the cable and riser

a) Cable(from Chung[3])

length(m)	17.45
outer diameter(cm)	2.86
mass(kg/m)	0.857
tension(N)	644.6

b) Riser(from Whitney[1])

length(m)	457.2
outer diameter(cm)	24.4
pipe wall(cm)	1.59
mud mass(kg/m)	12.8
wet mass(kg/m)	89.3
top tension (kN)	889.1

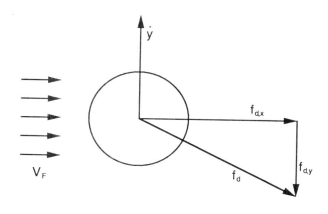

Fig. 1 Drag force vector decomposition

Table 2 Natural frequency of the cable(Hz)

order	pure cable	with artificial bending rigidity
1 st	0.59	0.59
2 nd	1.18	1.19
3 rd	1.77	1.79
4 th	2.36	2.39
5 th	2.95	3.00
6 th	3.54	3.62
7 th	4.13	4.24
8 th	4.72	4.88
9 th	5.32	5.53
10th	5.91	6.20

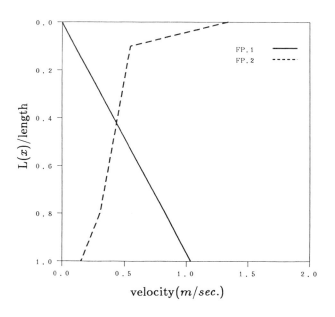

Fig. 2 Flow profiles

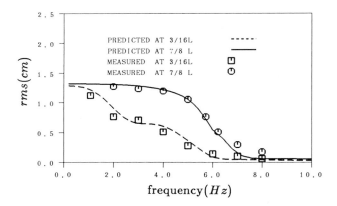

Fig. 3 Integrated displacement spectra
of the cable in the flow profile FP.1

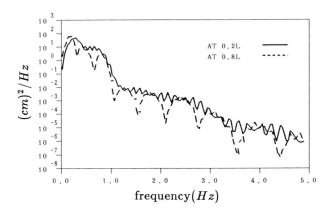

Fig. 4 Predicted displacement spectra
of the riser in the flow profile FP.2

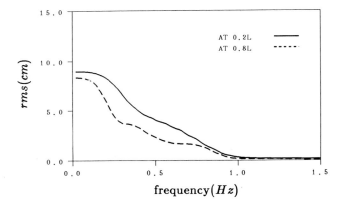

Fig. 5 Integrated displacement spectra
of the riser in the flow profile FP.2

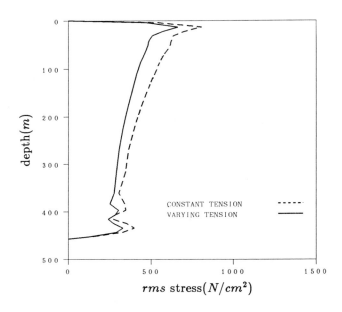

Fig. 6 Dynamic bending stress distribution
of the riser in the flow profile FP.2

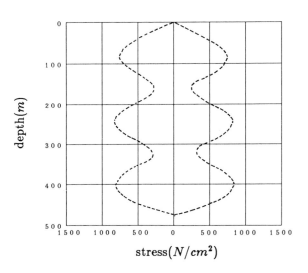

Fig. 7 Dynamic bending stress distribution
of the riser in the flow profile FP.2
calculated by Whitney and Nikkel[1]

C416/044

Dynamic actions due to wave motion on horizontal submerged cylinders oscillating in vertical direction

M FALCO, G MIMMI and E TANZI
Department of Mechanics, Milan Polytechnic, Italy

SYNOPSIS In the present paper the effects of wave motion on a horizontal submerged cylinder, freely oscillating in the vertical direction, are investigated. In order to detect dynamic response produced by wave motion, a large number of experiments has been performed on a specifically designed dynamometric cylinder in a water tank. The dependence of the phenomenon on a range of parameters has been explored by testing cylinders characterized by different diameters at various amplitudes and wave frequencies. The experimental results obtained are compared with values computed by analytical models reported in literature.

NOTATION

C_a = added mass coefficient;

C_d = drag coefficient;

C_m = $(C_a + 1)$ equivalent water mass coefficient;

d = depth of the cylinder downward from the water surface;

d_w = water depth;

D = cylinder diameter;

f_{na} = cylinder natural frequency in air;

f_n = cylinder natural frequency in water;

f_S = Strouhal frequency = $N_{Sr} \dfrac{u_{max}}{D}$;

The Strouhal frequency is a characteristic parameter of the steady current. The use of this parameter in wave motion conditions is particular and concerns the maximum value of upstream flow velocity horizontal component at the cylinder depth.

f_w = wave frequency;

H = peak to peak wave height;

k = stiffness of the cylinder suspension system;

L = cylinder length;

u, w = horizontal and vertical components of fluid velocity;

u_{max} = maximum value of horizontal component of the fluid velocity at cylinder depth;

$\underline{u}$ = vector of fluid velocity;

$\underline{v}$ = vector of cylinder velocity;

$x, \dot{x}, \ddot{x}$ = displacement, velocity and acceleration of the cylinder in the horizontal direction;

$z, \dot{z}, \ddot{z}$ = displacement, velocity and acceleration of the cylinder in the vertical direction;

ρ = water density.

Adimensional parameters:

$\dfrac{f_S}{f_n}$ = reduced Strouhal frequency: Strouhal frequency over cylinder natural frequency;

$\dfrac{f_w}{f_n}$ = reduced frequency: wave frequency over cylinder natural frequency;

$h_a = \dfrac{r}{r_c}$ = structural equivalent damping coefficient of the cylinder in air;

$h_w = \dfrac{r}{r_c}$ = structural equivalent damping coefficient of the cylinder in water;

$K_C = \dfrac{u_{max}}{f_w D}$ = horizontal Keulegan-Carpenter number;

The maximum value of the horizontal component of the fluid velocity at the cylinder depth was taken into account.

The choice of the horizontal component instead of the vertical one is completely arbitrary.

$\dfrac{z}{D}$ = vertical oscillation amplitude over cylinder diameter.

1 INTRODUCTION

The experimental investigation of the kinematic field, through the fluid visualization in proximity of the horizontal submerged cylinders subjected to wave motion, showed the presence of vortices at each wave cycle [1-7]. The formation of these vortices depends on wave frequency and amplitude as well as on the cylinder dimensions and depth.

In order to measure the forces in the horizontal and vertical directions induced by the wave motion on a fixed dynamometric cylinder [11], a first series of experimental tests were carried out in a water tank.

A second series of tests were performed on elastically suspended cylinders, with one degree of freedom in a vertical direction. In order to explore a wide range of values of characteristic parameters systematic tests were carried out using cylinders of different diameters (characterized by different natural frequencies of oscillation) and different wave amplitudes.

In the present paper a synthesis of the experimental results obtained on both a fixed and an oscillating cylinder is reported. One of the aims of the present research is to study how the Morison equation can reproduce the response of an oscillating cylinder using the coefficients C_d and C_m measured on a fixed cylinder.

2 LOADING

In design of submerged structures the unitary loading produced by wave motion is usually computed by means of the Morison equation which in the vectorial form is

$$\underline{F} = \frac{1}{2} C_d \rho \, D \, |\underline{u}-\underline{v}| \, (\underline{u}-\underline{v}) + (C_m-1)\rho \frac{\pi D^2}{4} (\underline{\dot{u}}-\underline{\dot{v}}) + \\ + \rho \frac{\pi D^2}{4} \underline{\dot{u}} \tag{1}$$

This corresponds to the two scalar components

$$F_x = \frac{1}{2} C_d \rho \, D \, V_r \, (u-\dot{x}) + (C_m-1)\rho \frac{\pi D^2}{4} (\dot{u} - \ddot{x}) + \\ + \rho \frac{\pi D^2}{4} \dot{u} \tag{2}$$

$$F_z = \frac{1}{2} C_d \rho \, D \, V_r \, (w-\dot{z}) + (C_m-1)\rho \frac{\pi D^2}{4} (\dot{w} - \ddot{z}) + \\ + \rho \frac{\pi D^2}{4} \dot{w} \tag{3}$$

where V_r, the relative velocity, is

$$V_r = \sqrt{(u - \dot{x})^2 + (w - \dot{z})^2} \tag{4}$$

In the present case of a cylinder free of oscillation in the vertical direction $\dot{x} = \ddot{x} = 0$ and F_x becomes

$$F_x = \frac{1}{2} C_d \rho \, D \, V_r \, u + C_m \rho \frac{\pi D^2}{4} \dot{u} \tag{5}$$

The coefficients C_d and C_m are obtained from experimental tests. They are reported in literature [1] with a great amount of data in the case of cylinders immersed in a sinusoidally oscillating flow in a U tube. In the case of wave motion C_d and C_m are functions of K_C related to the relative velocity at the cylinder depth, to Re, and to the u/w ratio between horizontal and vertical fluid velocity components at the cylinder depth. In the case of u/w = 1 and k > 20 the coefficients are reduced to 1/2 of those measured in the U tube with w = 0 (see [1]).

3 TEST SETUP

The tests were carried out in a 30 m long channel having a 1.0 m wide × 0.7 m high section closed at its ends and used as a tank.

To produce the waves a special apparatus has been designed, previously described in [10, 11]. A wave generator has been equipped with an oscillating blade whose instantaneous center of oscillation can· be regulated from the bottom of the channel - closed at its ends and used as a tank - to infinity [12] (see Fig.1). The blade is mounted on ball-bushing couplings hydraulically operated through a servo-control valve. A synthesizer provides suitable harmonic signals with an accuracy up to 1·10⁻⁴ Hz, while the feedback signal is supplied by an LVDT type position transducer.

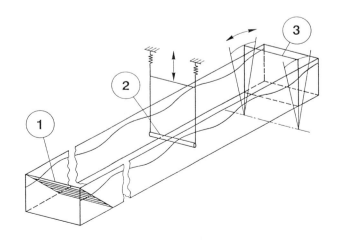

Fig. 1) Tank scheme with: 1) wave reflection absorber; 2) cylinder free of oscillating in vertical direction; 3) wave generator.

© IMechE 1991 C416/044

Wave monitoring was obtained by two probes measuring the electrical conductivity, between two wires, that is proportional to their depth. The probes were located in two points of the channel one of which was close to the cylinder.

In order to minimize wave reflections, wave absorbers were fixed at the end of the tank [12].

Perfectly harmonic waves can be produced only in the frequency range $f_w = 0.6$ to 1 Hz and amplitude range $H = 1$ to 7 cm.

4 TESTS ON FIXED CYLINDERS

In the case of fixed cylinders, dynamometric cylinders were used with the characteristics shown in fig. 2

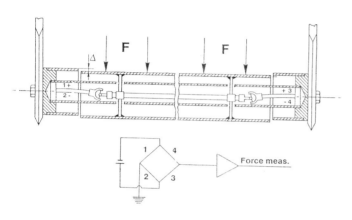

Fig. 2) Scheme of the dynamometric cylinder used for the experiments.

which allow measurement of the horizontal and vertical components of the force acting on the cylinder due to the wave action.

The experimental force in line and perpendicular to the direction of the wave propagation (vertical), has been found for different diameter values. The ratio between the experimental data and the values computed by the Morison theory is plotted in fig. 3.

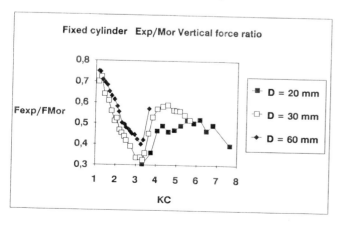

Fig. 3) Experimental vertical force versus K_C, (D = 20,30,60 mm, $f_w = 0.8$ Hz, Re = 800 to 9000).

The C_m and C_d coefficients used in the computation are those reported in [1] in the case of monodirectional periodic motion of the fluid in a U tube.

A minimum for $K_C = 3$ to 3.5 is observable, that is for a diameter of the fluid orbit almost equal to the cylinder diameter.

From the experimental measurements of the forces we can obtain our coefficient values. The fig. 4 shows the mean value of Cm coefficient.

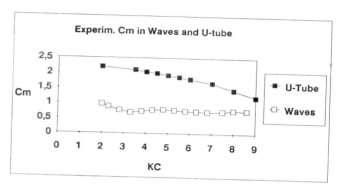

Fig. 4) Experimental coefficients.

Yet aim of the present research was not to find coefficient values better than those that can be found in literature, but rather to investigate on the presence and importance of the second harmonic component due to the fluid action.

In fact the experimental results show also the presence of higher harmonics. A significant representation is reported in fig 5 and shows the experimental force during a complete wave cycle in a polar plane.

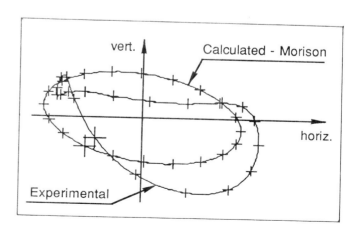

Fig. 5) Experimental and 'Morison' polar force shape on a fixed dynamometric cylinder, (D = 20 mm, $f_w = 0.6$ Hz, $K_C = 4.6$, H = 27 mm, Re = 1100).

The shape obtained experimentally shows the presence of a second harmonic probably due to the shedding of one vortex, as it has been observed through direct visualization. On the contrary, the shape obtained by applying the Morison theory remains elliptic for any C_d and C_m value.

In order to find a better fitting between the experimental and Morison second harmonics of the force, the second order Stokes theory was also used to calculate the kinematic values of the fluid. Nevertheless, even when this procedure is used, the calculated values of the second harmonics of the forces appear negligible with respect to the experimental values (Fig. 6).

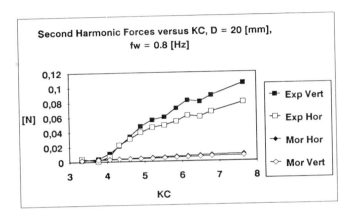

Fig. 6) Experimental and Morison second harmonic components, fixed cylinder, D = 20 mm, f_w = 0.800 Hz.

In fig. 7 the ratio between the second and the first harmonic of experimental vertical forces obtained through a spectral analysis is plotted.

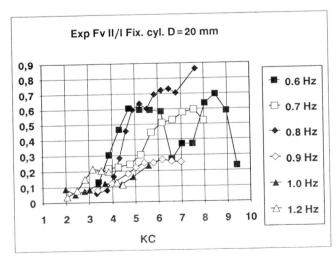

Fig. 7) Ratio between the second and the first harmonic of experimental vertical force versus KC, (Re = 800 to 2000).

As can be seen, for KC > 4 the components of the second harmonic become important.

5 OSCILLATING CYLINDER TEST DESCRIPTION

The tests described in the following part have been obtained on rigid non dynamometric oscillating cylinders.

The dynamic response of two cylinders having D = 10 mm and D = 20 mm respectively, freely oscillating in vertical direction, was measured.

The apparatus was set up according to previous results, obtained using fixed dynamometric cylinders [11]. The cylinders were kept at a depth ratio of about d/D = 10 under the water level. Different values of wave amplitude and frequency as well as of diameter, in order to cover the range of Keulegan-Carpenter number (KC) from 0 to 30, were used.

First the cylinder natural frequency (f_{na}) was determined and the structural damping in air ($h_a = r/r_c$) was deduced from the recorded data of the decay in air. The same cylinder characterization was then carried out in still water; the natural frequency of the cylinder in water (f_n) was found to be lower than in air, due to the water added mass and the higher equivalent damping ($h_w = r/r_c$).

Some tests were performed using oscillating cylinders with a natural frequency equal to wave frequency; then, in order to observe the effect of the second harmonic, many other tests with double frequency and also with other various frequencies were carried out.

5.1 Experimental tests with synchronous excitation: $f_w \simeq f_n$

These tests are performed using a wave frequency exactly equal to f_n.

The results are shown in diagrams, in which the values of the experimental ratio between oscillation amplitude and diameter (z/D) are plotted versus K_C. The K_C is computed through the horizontal velocity component (u_{max}). In the same diagrams the curves obtained through the Morison equations are also reported.

The cylinder oscillations are calculated by integrating the differential equation

$$m\ddot{z} + r\dot{z} + kz = F_z \qquad (6)$$

where m represents the mass of the oscillating system, r the damping factor in air, k the stiffness of the suspension system while F_z is reported in (3).

Some tests were carried out using rough cylinders obtained through the use of a shroud consisting of a thin net (meshes of 2 mm; thickness 0.2 mm) helicoidally rolled around the cylinder (pitch $\approx$3 cm).

The results concerning the D = 10 mm cylinder set in turn at f_n = 0.800 and f_n = 0.982 Hz in steady water-are shown in Fig. 8 with the results obtained using wave frequencies exactly equal to the cylinder natural frequency.

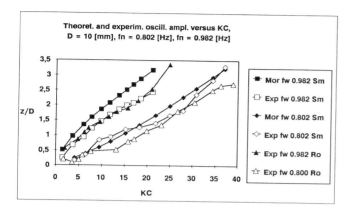

Fig. 8) Displ./diameter plots, as a function of K_C for smooth and rough cylinders, D = 10 mm, d/D = 10 with synchronous excitation: f_w = f_n. Experimental and calculated curves; (Re = 400 to 3000, h_w = 0.014 to 0.016).

The first four curves are related to smooth cylinders; the last two curves are related to rough cylinders.

The experimental tests showed that the cylinder roughness does not sensibly affect the oscillation amplitude of the cylinder.

In the case of smooth cylinders, the experimental results may be compared to those computed according to the Morison theory.

In Figure 9 an example of experimental and calculated results of a build-up from steady state conditions due to wave action is shown. The comparison between the time histories of the experimental and calculated build-up shows that the model reproduces the experimental results well.

Moreover the experimental results show more evident beatings due to the non linearity of the system.

5.2 Subharmonic excitation: f_w/f_n = 1/2 - Considerations on the second harmonic

A series of tests have been performed by exciting the cylinder with a wave frequency that is half the cylinder natural frequency (f_w = 1/2 f_n). The peculiar aspect of the dynamic response observed in this case is that the FFT analysis shows that the maximum peak appears in

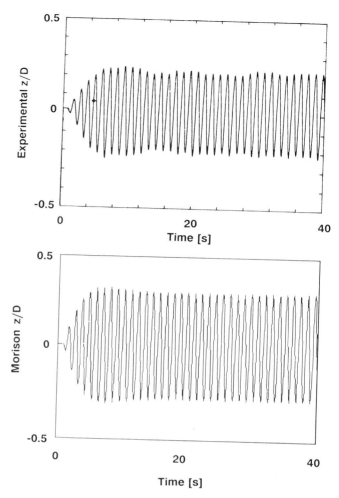

Fig. 9) Experimental an computed build-up of a cylinder, (D = 10 mm, H = 50 mm, k = 101 N/m, h_w = 0.0125, m = 2.56 kg, f_n = 0.987 Hz, f_w = 0.950 Hz).

correspondence to the cylinder natural frequency while the exciting frequency harmonic is negligible.

The excitation of the natural frequency is mostly produced by vortex shedding. In fact this appears relevant at the frequencies at which, using dynamometric fixed cylinders, the second harmonic of the forces was particularly strong. In this case the vortex shedding determines a transient oscillation which occurs at the natural cylinder frequency.

Figures 10 and 11 show some examples of the ratio between the oscillation amplitude and the diameter (z/D), in the case of a cylinder having D = 10 mm as a function of f_S/f_n.

A maximum in the oscillation amplitude, although characterized by a lower magnitude order with respect to previous results (§ 5.1), is observed at $f_S/f_n \simeq 1$. The Strouhal frequency f_S was computed using the maximum value of the fluid velocity at cylinder depth.

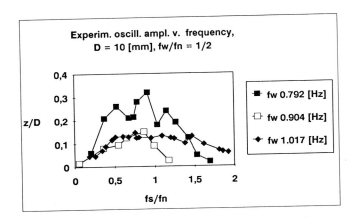

Fig. 10) Displacement over diameter ratio for cylinders (D = 10 mm, D = 20 mm, f_w/f_n = 1/2, versus f_S/f_n, Re = 100 to 2000).

In Fig. 11 a D = 20 mm cylinder is considered.

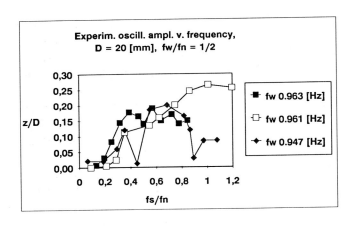

Fig. 11) Displacement over diameter ratio for cylinders (D = 20 mm, f_w/f_n = 1/2, versus f_S/f_n, Re = 250 to 4000, h_w = 0.010 to 0.012).

5.3 Subharmonic excitation: f_w/f_n = 2/5, 3/5, 3/7

We have observed that, though the wave frequency was neither equal to the cylinder natural frequency nor to a submultiple of this (1/2), the cylinder vibrates at its own natural frequency also when f_w/f_n assumes the values: 2/5, 3/5, 3/7 etc.

Figure 12 shows the displacement/diameter ratio versus f_S/f_n at different wave frequencies.

In this case too the amplitudes of vibration show a maximum at $f_S/f_n \simeq 1$.

The time histories of the cylinder displacement and wave height confirm what was observed in this case of f_w/f_n = 1/2, i. e. the shedding of one vortex synchronized every n cycles determines a transient

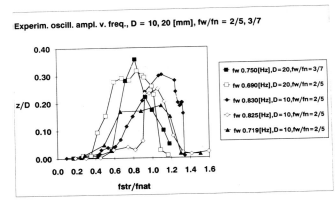

Fig. 12) Displacement over diameter ratio for cylinders (D = 10 and 20 mm, f_w/f_n = 2/5, 3/7, versus f_S/f_n, Re = 200 to 2500).

oscillation which occurs at the cylinder natural frequency. Fig. 13 shows the time histories in the case of f_w/f_n = 3/7 with seven cylinder cycles every 3 wave cycles.

D = 20 mm Smooth; fc = 1.700 Hz; fw = 0.760 Hz; fw/fc = 3/7

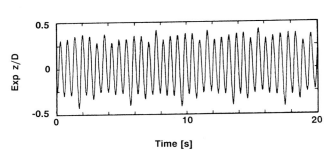

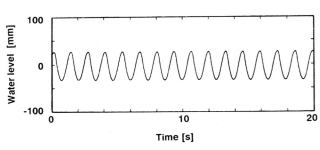

Fig. 13) Adimensional displacement for a (D = 10 mm cylinder, f_w = 0.76 Hz, f_n = 1.7 Hz, f_w/f_n = 3/7, h_w = 0.0087).

The synchronization in proximity of Strouhal range, i. e. when f_S/f_n ratio is close to one, is similar to the lock-in vortex shedding on cylindrical bodies in uniform flow [8].

6 CONCLUSIONS

The results of the experimental analysis of the dynamic behaviour of oscillating cylinders whose motion is produced by the presence of monochromatic waves allow us to conclude that:

a) the Morison theory, with coefficients obtained in the case of waves, fits the experimental fluidodynamic actions of the first harmonic well;

b) on the other hand the effects of the second harmonic are remarkably underestimated with respect to the experimental findings.

7 ACKNOWLEDGEMENTS

The authors gratefully acknowledge the support of *Cavi Pirelli S.p.a.* through a contract of research as well as of *Ministero dell'Università e della Ricerca Scientifica e Tecnologica* and *Consiglio Nazionale delle Ricerche* grant n. 90.00990.CT07.

8 REFERENCES

[1] Sarpkaya T. - Isaacson M., "Mechanics of Wave Forces on Offshore Structures", Van Nostrand Reinhold Company, New York, 1981.

[2] Williamson C. H. K., Roshko A., Vortex Formation in the Wake of an Oscillating Cylinder, Journ. of Fluids and Struct., 1988, 2, 355-381.

[3] Vandiver J. K., Jong J.-Y., The Relationship Between in-line and Cross-Flow Vortex Induced Oscillations of Cylinders, Journal of Fluids and Structures, 1987, 1,381-399.

[4] Grass A.J., Kemp P.H., Stuart R.J., Vortex Induced Velocity Magnification and Loading Effects for Cylinders in Oscillatory Flow. London Centre for Marine Technology, Dept. Civ. Engng., Univ. Coll. LONDON. Report No. FL28.

[5] Grass A. J., Simons R. R., Cavanagh N. J., Fluid Loading on Cylinders Undergoing Large Orbital Oscillations in a Steady Current. ASME Paper No. OMAE-1267. Proc. 5th OMAE Symp., Tokyo, pp.631-638.

[6] Grass A.J., Simons R.R. and Cavanagh N.J., Fluid Loading on Horizontal Cylinders in Wave Type Orbital Oscillatory Flow. ASME Paper No. OMAE-262. Proc. 4th OMAE Symp. Dallas Febr. 1985, pp. 576-583.

[7] Grass A.J., Simons R.R. and Cavanagh N.J., Fluid Loading on Cylinders Undergoing Large Orbital Oscillations in a Steady Current, 1986.

[8] Donazzi F. - Diana G. -Falco M. - Guoxum P., Induced Oscillation on a Cylinder at High Reynold's Number due to the Vortex Shedding, International Symposium on Hydrodynamics in Ocean Engineering Trondheim, 24 - 28 August 1981.

[9] Diana G. - Donazzi F. - Mimmi G. - Peng G.X., Dynamic Response of an Undersea Cable to a Turbulent Flow, L'Energia Elettrica N.6, Vol. LIX, June 1982.

[10] Falco M., Mimmi G., Tanzi E., Comportamento dinamico di un cilindro investito da vena fluida I - Effetto della corrente, II - Effetto del moto ondoso, Internal report, Dipartimento di Meccanica, Politecnico di Milano, February 1988.

[11] Falco M., Mimmi G., Tanzi E., Azioni Dinamiche Dovute al Moto Ondoso su Cilindri Orizzontali Sommersi, X Congresso Nazionale AIMETA, Pisa, 2/5 October 1990.

[12] Tsahalis D. T., Vortex-Induced Vibrations of a Flexible Cylinder Near a Plane Boundary Exposed to Steady and Wave-Induced Currents, Journal of Energy Resources Technology, Vol. 106/206-213, June 1984.

[13] Angrilli F.- Cossalter V.- Transverse Oscillations of a Vertical Pile in Water Waves, Journal of Fluids Engineering, Trans. of the ASME, March 1982, Vol. 104, pp. 46-53.

[14] Grass A.J., Kemp P.H., Stuart R.J., Vortex Induced Velocity Magnification and Loading Effects for Cylinders in Oscillatory Flow. London Centre for Marine Technology, Dept. Civ. Engng., Univ. Coll. LONDON. Report No. FL28.

[15] Grass A. J., Simons R. R., Cavanagh N. J., Fluid Loading on Horizontal Cylinders in Wave Type Orbital Oscillatory Flow. ASME Paper No. OMAE-262. Proc. 4th OMAE Symp., Dallas pp.576-583.

[16] Sulla generazione del moto ondoso in laboratorio - Acts of the IX Conv. di Idraulica e Costruz. Idrauliche, Trieste [Italy], 1965.

[17] van der Vegt J.J.W., van Walree F., Progress in the Prediction of Forces on Cylinders, Floating Structures and Offshore Operations, Elsevier - Amsterdam, 1987.

[18] Borthwick A. G. L., Loading and Response of a Small Diameter Flexibly Mounted Cylinder in Waves, Journal of Fluids and Structures, 1988, 2 479-501.

[19] Douglas J.F. "Solving Problems in Fluid Mechanics", Longman Scientific & Technical, 1986.

[20] Wootton L. R., Oscillations of piles in marine structures, Ciria Underwater engineering group, Report N. 40.

Dynamic response of an undersea cable under current and waves

S BROGLIO, F CHELI and F SCARAMELLI
Department of Mechanics, Milan Polytechnic, Italy
L MONTELATICI, PhD
Societa Cavi Pirelli Research and Development, Milan, Italy

SYNOPSIS This paper deal with an analytical approach to define the static and dynamic behaviour of a single span submarine cable or flexible pipe under the action of marine current and wave loads, keeping account of the effects of vortex shedding . The submarine cable is considered as a circular beam laid under the sea level, supported at both ends. The structure is schematized by F.E.M.: the generalized forces due to the water flow actions are applied to each node of the structure. The static behaviour of the cable under the action of constant current has been computed. The time history of the velocity field has been reproduce in correspondence to each nodal point of the cable. To compute the fluid forces Morison's equations have been used, keeping account of the vortex shedding effects by means of an equivalent non-linear oscillator.

NOTATION

i — node number;

j — beam number;

l_j — length of the generic beam;

Y,Z — lateral and vertical displacements inside the beam (local coordinates, ξ distance from left node);

Y_{iL}, Z_{iL} — lateral and vertical displacements of the i-th node (local coordinates);

ξ_i — displacement of the i-th node in local coordinates (component orthogonal to $\overrightarrow{V_s}$ direction);

$\underline{X}_{jL}$ — 12 d.o.f vector of the beam in local coordinates;

$\underline{X}_j$ — 12 d.o.f vector of the beam in global coordinates;

$\underline{X}$ — vector of the global cable schematization d.o.f.;

$\underline{X}_o$ — vector defining the static equilibrium position;

$\underline{X}_d$ — vector of the dynamic displacements;

$[\Lambda_j]$ — transformation matrix;

$[K_{jL}]$ — stiffness matrix in local coordinates;

$[M_{jL}]$ — mass matrix in local coordinates;

$\underline{P}$ — weight generalized forces;

$\underline{F}_e$ — elastic generalized forces;

$\underline{F}_d$ — damping generalized forces;

$\underline{F}_i$ — inertial generalized forces;

$[M_o]$ — global mass matrix;

$[R_o]$ — global damping matrix;

$[K_o]$ — global stiffness matrix;

$\underline{\eta}$ — vector containing the d.o.f. η_i of the oscillators;

$[m_{aer}]$ — mass matrix of the equivalent oscillators (m_{aeri});

$\underline{F}_2$ — generalized forces on the equivalent oscillators (components F_{2i});

$\underline{F}_1$ — generalized forces on the cable due to the equivalent oscillators (components F_{1i});

$\underline{F}_c$ — generalized forces on the cable due to Morison forces (global components $\underline{F}_{mj}$, local components $\underline{F}_{mjL}$);

t — time;

ρ — fluid density;

D — diameter of the cable;

C_D — cable drag coefficient;

C_m — cable mass coefficient;

$\overrightarrow{V}$ — stream velocity in absolute reference system (components V_x, V_y, V_z);

$\overrightarrow{V_s}$ — stream velocity orthogonal to the cable section in local reference system (components U, W);

$\overrightarrow{V_c}$ — cable section velocity (components $\dot{Y}$, $\dot{Z}$);

$\dot{}$ — first total time derivative;

$\ddot{}$ — second total time derivative;

$\overline{}$ — mean value;

$\Rightarrow$ — geometrical vector;

$\delta*$ — virtual (displacement, work).

1 INTRODUCTION

Many analytical and experimental studies have been carried out to define the dynamic behaviour of an undersea cable subjected to the effects of submarine currents and waves ([1], [2], [3], [4], [5]).

As well known, the excitation in current is mainly due to the vortex shedding phenomenon, while the excitation in waves mainly depends on the drag and inertial effects due to the velocity field of the wave motion.

From this point of view, as regards the vortex shedding phenomenon in a current, there are many experimental works and analytical works based on an integration of Navier-Stokes equations or using an equivalent oscillator ([6], [7], [8], [9], [10], [11]).

To reproduce analytically the dynamic behaviour of the cylindrical body under the excitation due to the wave motion, Morison's equations are generally used. In a wide range of Carpenter number ([1], [13], [14]) these equations reproduce the phenomenon, but the same equations cannot reproduce the real behaviour of the cable when vortex shedding occurs.

In a paper [3], to be published and resulting from studies carried out at the Dipartimento di Meccanica of Politecnico di Milano, a new simplified approach has been proposed to outline the complexity of the fluid-elastic phenomenon, keeping account of both vortex shedding phenomenon and Morison's equations, which, in some Carpenter number range ([1], [12], [13], [14]) interact with each other: in the paper an analytical approach is proposed using an equivalent oscillator in order to introduce the complexity of the phenomenon.

Many researches were carried out to define ([16], [17]) the dynamic behaviour of undersea cables or pipes under wave effects. These approaches schematize the cable and apply the loads due to the wave motion coming from Morison's equations.

From this point of view, they don't keep account of any excitations due to higher frequencies, generally multiple of wave frequencies, that seem to be due to a vortex shedding mechanism ([3], [15]).

The aim of this paper is to develop an analytical model based on:
(a) the finite element schematization of the cable and the supporting structure;
(b) for what concerns the fluid actions, both Morison's equations and vortex shedding mechanism are reproduced by an equivalent oscillator.

The procedure:
(a) needs the definition of the static equilibrium position of the cable under its own weight and due to the medium value of the velocity: this is a non linear problem due to the structural geometric non linearity;
(b) allows to simulate the dynamic behaviour of the cable, that is the motion of the cable, due to submarine current and wave motion or the combined effects, integrating numerically the equation of motion .

The analysis of the dynamic motion of the cable is studied in time domain, integrating the equation of motion of the cable:
(a) linearized as regards the structural terms in the neighbourhood of the static equilibrium position;
(b) keeping account of the non linear effects introduced in Morison's equations and in the equivalent oscillator.

Some numerical results are reported.

2 MATHEMATICAL MODEL OF THE SYSTEM CABLE-FLUID ACTIONS

2.1 Mathematical model of the cable

The cable is schematized by means of finite element approach ([18], [19]) using tensioned beam elements with 6 degrees of freedom for each node (fig.1): the 12 independent variables (node's displacements) used to describe the static and dynamic behaviour of the beam in local coordinates are reported in $\underline{X}_{jL}$ vector. In each beam we keep account of both flexural stiffness EJ_{yj}, EJ_{zj} and geometrical stiffness due to the inner tension T_j.

$[K_{jL}]$ stiffness and $[M_{jL}]$ mass matrices of the j-th beam in local coordinates are reported in Tab.I.

The equations of motion are written with respect to a global cartesian reference ($\overline{X}$-$\overline{Y}$-$\overline{Z}$) system defined in fig.1.

$\underline{X}_j$ vector includes the 12 displacements describing the behaviour of the generic j-th beam in global coordinates: local displacements $\underline{X}_{jL}$ are related to global displacements $\underline{X}_j$ by means the $[\Lambda_j]$ transformation matrix in the relation:

$$\underline{X}_{jL} = [\Lambda_j] \underline{X}_j \qquad (1)$$

This relation allows us to define the $[K_j]$ stiffness and $[M_j]$ mass contributions in global coordinates by means of the well-known relationships:

$$[K_j] = [\Lambda_j]^T [K_{jL}] [\Lambda_j] \qquad (2)$$
$$[M_j] = [\Lambda_j]^T [M_{jL}] [\Lambda_j]$$

2.2 Mathematical model of fluid forces

2.2.1 Morison's forces

The fluid forces, as already said, are reproduced by Morison's equations: Morison's forces per unit length ([1], [2]) on a cylindrical section are:

$$F_y = \frac{1}{2}\rho D C_D |\overset{\Rightarrow}{V}_s \text{-} \overset{\Rightarrow}{V}_c| (U\text{-}\dot{Y}) + (C_m\text{-}1)\frac{\pi D^2}{4}\rho(\dot{U}\text{-}\ddot{Y}) + \frac{\rho\pi D^2}{4}\dot{U}$$
$$(3)$$

$$F_z = \frac{1}{2}\rho D C_D |\overset{\Rightarrow}{V}_s \text{-} \overset{\Rightarrow}{V}_c| (W\text{-}\dot{Z}) + (C_m\text{-}1)\frac{\pi D^2}{4}\rho(\dot{W}\text{-}\ddot{Z}) + \frac{\rho\pi D^2}{4}\dot{W}$$

in which (see fig.2):
- D is the diameter of the cable;
- $\overset{\Rightarrow}{V}_s$ is the absolute velocity vector of the stream orthogonal to the beam, with horizontal component U and vertical component W;
- $\overset{\Rightarrow}{V}_c$ is the velocity of the section (components $\dot{Y}$ and $\dot{Z}$);
- ρ is the fluid density;
- C_D is the drag coefficient;
- C_m is the mass coefficient.

As we consider the component $\overset{\Rightarrow}{V}_s$ of the $\overset{\Rightarrow}{V}$ absolute velocity in a local reference system related with each beam, force coefficients are not dependent on the angle between the cable and the direction of the current or the wave motion.

As regards in eq.(3) the acceleration factors (terms function of $\ddot{Z}$ and $\ddot{Y}$), their contribution can be included in the inertial matrix $[M_{jL}]$ linearized in the neighbourhood of the static equilibrium position, keeping account of the added mass of the water as an additional mass per unit length in each beam, so Morison's forces can be reduced to the form:

$$F_{my} = \frac{1}{2}\rho D C_D |\overset{\Rightarrow}{V}_s \text{-} \overset{\Rightarrow}{V}_c| (U\text{-}\dot{Y}) + C_m \frac{\rho\pi D^2}{4}\dot{U} \qquad (4)$$

$$F_{mz} = \frac{1}{2}\rho D C_D |\overset{\Rightarrow}{V}_s \text{-} \overset{\Rightarrow}{V}_c| (W\text{-}\dot{Z}) + C_m \frac{\rho\pi D^2}{4}\dot{W}$$

In order to calculate the generalized forces per unit length F_{my} and F_{mz} (eq.(4)), acting on a generic section of the generic j-th beam (see figs.1 and 2), we must evaluate the two components U and W of the fluid velocity in local coordinates and the velocities $\dot{Z}$ and $\dot{Y}$ of the generic section distant ξ from the left extremity of the beam (see fig.1).

The fluid absolute velocity $\overset{\Rightarrow}{V}$ (due to current and waves, see fig.1) is defined in global coordinates as a function of time and space (fig.3).

Let us consider vector $\underline{V}$ containing the components of the fluid velocity $\overset{\Rightarrow}{V}$ in global coordinates (fig.1):

$$\underline{V} = \begin{Bmatrix} V_x \\ V_y \\ V_z \end{Bmatrix} \qquad (5)$$

In this way, the analytical model can keep account of any module and direction of the current or wave motion velocity $\vec{V}$.

Vector $\underline{V}_L$ containing the components of the fluid velocity $\vec{V}$ in local coordinates (fig.4) can be evaluated by means of :

$$\underline{V}_L = [\Lambda_j] \underline{V} \qquad (6)$$

being $\underline{V}_L$:

$$\underline{V}_L = \begin{Bmatrix} V_l \\ U \\ W \end{Bmatrix} \qquad (7)$$

In the model the effect of the V_l longitudinal component is neglected.

$\dot{Y}$ and $\dot{Z}$ transverse velocity components of the generic section of the generic beam (figs.1 and 2) can be obtained from the velocities of the extremities of the beam in local coordinates $\underline{\dot{X}}_{jL}$ (related to the velocity $\underline{\dot{X}}_j$ of the nodes from the relationship (1)), keeping account of the shape function $[f(\xi)]$ of the beam itself:

$$\begin{Bmatrix} \dot{Y} \\ \dot{Z} \end{Bmatrix} = [f(\xi)]^T \underline{\dot{X}}_{jL} \qquad (8)$$

$\underline{F}_{mjL}$ generalized forces, in local coordinates, can be computed from the virtual work $\delta^* L_{mjL}$ of Morison's forces eq.(4):

$$\delta^* L_{mjL} = \int_0^{l_J} (F_{my}\, \delta^* Y + F_{mz}\, \delta^* Z)\, d\xi \qquad (9)$$

and F_{my} and F_{mz} are Morison's forces per unit length (see eq.(4)) and $\delta^* Y$ and $\delta^* Z$ the virtual displacements of the generic section inside the beam dependent on virtual displacements $\delta^* \underline{X}_{jL}$ of the extremity nodes, in local coordinates, through the relationship:

$$\begin{Bmatrix} \delta^* Y \\ \delta^* Z \end{Bmatrix} = [f(\xi)]^T\, \delta^* \underline{X}_{jL} \qquad (10)$$

Once $\underline{F}_{mjL}$ forces in local coordinates are calculated, we can compute the $\underline{F}_{mj}$ generalized forces in global coordinates by means of the following expression:

$$\underline{F}_{mj} = [\Lambda_j]^T\, \underline{F}_{mjL} \qquad (11)$$

$\underline{F}_{mj}$ are assembled in a vector $\underline{F}_c$ containing the generalized Morison's forces on the global model of the cable.

In order to calculate the generalized forces due to Morison's equations (eqs. (9), (4), (7), (6), (5)), fluid velocity $\vec{V}$ must be defined along the span and inside each finite element beam. We compute the time-space history on the cable using the linear theory for the wave motion from the definition of Pierson-Moskowitz spectra.

2.2.2 Effect of vortex shedding

The effects introduced from vortex shedding mechanisms are simulated by means of an equivalent oscillator (see [10], [11], [12], [3]) that is a non linear one d.o.f. system.

This approach considers that vortex shedding induces a set of forces on the cable which are non linear function of:

(a) the displacement Y, Z and the velocity $\dot{Y}$ and $\dot{Z}$ of the cable;
(b) the displacement, velocity and acceleration of an equivalent fluid-dynamic mass ([9], [10], [11]).

At each generic i-th node of the mesh there is an equivalent oscillator (see fig.5): let us consider with η_i the displacement of the m_{aeri} fluid-dynamic equivalent mass of the generic i-th oscillator and ξ_i the displacement of the cable in local coordinates in the direction orthogonal to the local fluid speed of the fluid $\vec{V}_s$ (fig.5) which changes in space and time both in module and direction.

The equations of motion of the single equivalent oscillator are:

$$m_{aeri}\, \ddot{\eta}_i = F_{2i}(\xi_i, \dot{\xi}_i, \eta_i, \dot{\eta}_i, |V_s|^2, \rho) =$$

$$= \qquad +g_{kacc}\,(\xi_i{-}\eta_i) +g_{racc}\,(\dot{\xi}_i{-}\dot{\eta}_i) +$$

$$- g_{kaer}\,(\eta_i) - g_{raer}\,(\dot{\eta}_i) \qquad (12)$$

in which:
- m_{aer} is the fluid equivalent mass;
- $|V_s|$ is the module of the velocity $\vec{V}_s$ (orthogonal component in respect to the generic section in local coordinates);
- ρ is the fluid density;
- g_{kacc}, g_{raer}, g_{kacc} and g_{raer} are non linear functions of $|V_s|$ and of $\xi_i, \eta_i, \dot{\xi}_i, \dot{\eta}_i$ ([10], [11], [3]).

The F_{1i} forces transmitted from the oscillator to the cable are :

$$F_{1i} = F_{1i}(\xi_i, \dot{\xi}_i, \eta_i, \dot{\eta}_i, |V_s|^2, \rho) =$$

$$= +g_{kacc}\,(\xi_i{-}\eta_i) +g_{racc}\,(\dot{\xi}_i{-}\dot{\eta}_i) \qquad (13)$$

The equivalent non linear oscillator model for a circular cylinder under steady current was yet proposed in ([9], [10], [11]) and the related $g_{ki}(\tau_i)$ (being i="acc" and $\tau_i=(\xi_i-\eta_i)$ or i="aer" and $\tau_i=\eta_i$) and $g_{ri}(\dot{\tau})$ (with $\dot{\tau}_i=(\dot{\xi}_i-\dot{\eta}_i)$ or $\dot{\tau}_i=\dot{\eta}_i$) functions of eq.(12) were assumed cubic.

$$g_{ki}(\tau_i) = K_i'\, \tau_i - K_i''\,\tau_i^3 \qquad (14)$$

$$g_{ri}(\dot{\tau}_i) = R_i'\, \dot{\tau}_i - R_i''\, \dot{\tau}_i^3$$

To avoid some numerical instability in wave motion expressions (12) and (13) were modified ([3]): the generic $g(\tau)$ function of eq. (14) was replaced by the following one:

$$g(\tau) = \left(A\,\tau - B\,\frac{|\tau|}{\tau} \right) e^{(-\lambda|\tau|)} + B\,\frac{|\tau|}{\tau} \qquad (15)$$

where coefficients A, λ e B are related to the K_i', R_i', K_i'' and R_i'' coefficients in equation (14) and are described in Appendix A and widely explained in [3]: these coefficients are determinated with a minimization procedure with a best fitting between experimental and analytical data on a rigid oscillating cylinder in current and wave motion.

The generalized forces introduced by the equivalent oscillators can be calculated by means of the virtual work done in local coordinates:

$$\delta*L_{oL} = \sum_{i=1}^{nodes} F_{1i} \sin(\Theta_i)\, \delta*Y_{iL} - F_{1i}\cos(\Theta_i)\, \delta*Z_{iL} \qquad (16)$$

$\delta*Y_{iL}$ and $\delta*Z_{iL}$ being the virtual displacements of the i-th node in local coordinates, Θ_i the angle of attach of $\overrightarrow{V}_s$ velocity (see fig.5) in respect to the generic section of the generic beam (fig.1).

F_{1i} and Θ_i can be calculated in each node of the schematization and then, with an analogous procedure shown for the Morison's generalized forces, the generalized forces transmitted by the generic i-th oscillator $\underline{F}_{1i}$ can be calculated: $\underline{F}_{1i}$ forces are assembled in the $\underline{F}_1$ vector containing the generalized forces due to the oscillators on the global cable.

2.3 The static equilibrium position

The equations which define the static equilibrium position (due to its own weight and the medium value of the current $\overline{V}$) can be expressed as:

$$\underline{F}_e(\underline{X}_o) = \underline{P} + \underline{F}_c(\overline{V}) \qquad (17)$$

where:
- $\underline{X}$ represents a vector containing the displacements of the nodes of the cable schematized by means of finite element method;
- $\underline{X}_o$ the value (unknown) of these displacements in the static equilibrium position;
- $\underline{F}_e$ the non linear elastic generalized forces;
- $\underline{P}$ the vector of the forces due to the weight;
- $\underline{F}_c$ the external generalized forces due to Morison terms due

to the current, with mean velocity $\overline{V}$.

$\underline{F}_c$ forces change the spatial position of the cable and therefore the position of the generic beam, in respect to the global reference system, changes.

The problem, as already said, is geometrically non linear and the equation (17) is solved by means of the Newton-Raphson iterative method ([18], [19]): with this iterative procedure, $\underline{F}_e(\underline{X})$ forces are linearized in the neighbourhood of a generic guessed solution $\underline{X}_g$:

$$\underline{F}_e(\underline{X})=\underline{F}(\underline{X}_g)+\left(\frac{\partial \underline{F}_e}{\partial \underline{X}}\right)_{\underline{X}=\underline{X}_g} (\underline{X}-\underline{X}_g) =$$
$$=\underline{F}(\underline{X}_g)+[K_g]\ (\underline{X}-\underline{X}_g) \qquad (18)$$

where $[K_g]$ is the tangential global stiffness matrix evaluated, in the $\underline{X}_g$ position, assembling the single $[K_j]$ matrices, in local coordinates (eq.(2)), of the single beam elements.

2.4 The dynamic equation of motion

Generally, the non linear equation of motion of the cable can be written as follow:

$$\underline{F}_i\ (\underline{X},\underline{\dot{X}},\underline{\ddot{X}}) + \underline{F}_s(\underline{X},\underline{\dot{X}}) + \underline{F}_e(\underline{X}) = \underline{P} + \underline{F}_c(\underline{\dot{X}},\overrightarrow{V}(s,t)) +$$
$$+ \underline{F}_1(\underline{X},\underline{\dot{X}},\underline{n},\underline{\dot{n}}) \qquad (19)$$

where $\underline{F}_i$ are the inertial forces (for large displacements these forces are generally non linear functions of the displacements $\underline{X}$ and their derivatives), $\underline{F}_s$ the damping forces, $\underline{F}_e$ the elastic generalized forces.

Morison's generalized forces $\underline{F}_c$ become (see eqs.

(9), (11), (4)) function of both velocities of the cable $\underline{\dot{X}}$ and

of velocity $\dot{W}$ and $\dot{U}$ and accelerations $\ddot{W}$ $\ddot{U}$ of the stream (due both to current and waves motion).

In eq.(19) $\underline{F}_1$ represents the generalized forces transmitted from (see eqs. (16) and (13)) the equivalent oscillators at the nodes of the schematization and $\underline{n}$ is the vector containing the displacements η_i of the equivalent oscillators placed along the span.

Eq.(19) is a non linear differential equation and cannot be solved without considering another matricial equation (see eq.(12)):

$$[m_{aer}]\ \underline{\ddot{n}} = \underline{F}_2(\underline{X},\underline{\dot{X}},\underline{n},\underline{\dot{n}}, |V_s(s,t)|^2) \qquad (20)$$

where matrix $[m_{aer}]$ contains the m_{aeri} fluid-dynamic masses of the equivalent oscillators. In (20) $\underline{F}_2$ contains the non linear F_{2i} non linear forces acting on the oscillator (see eq.(12)).

The global system cable+fluid actions is then described by means of the two matricial equation systems (19) and (20): the two systems are coupled and then they must be solved simultaneously.

In the presence of current and wave motion, the cable oscillates in the neighbourhood of the static equilibrium position. If the oscillations are small in respect to this position we can linearize the structural characteristics in the neighbourhood of the equilibrium position defined by eq.(17). Expanding generic force $\underline{F}$ in (19) in Taylor series around the equilibrium position defined by (17) we obtain:

$$\underline{F} = \underline{F}(\underline{X}_o) + \left(\frac{\partial \underline{F}}{\partial \underline{X}}\right)_{\underline{X}=\underline{X}_o} (\underline{X}-\underline{X}o) =$$
$$= \underline{F}(\underline{X}_o) + [A_o]\ (\underline{X}-\underline{X}o) \qquad (21)$$

where $[A_o]$ is the generic Jacobian matrix evaluated in the neighbourhood of the static equilibrium position $\underline{X}_o$.

Keeping account of eqs.(21) and (17) and with a change of coordinates:

$$\underline{X} = \underline{X}_o + \underline{X}_d \qquad (22)$$

in which $\underline{X}_d$ represents the dynamic displacements of the cable from the equilibrium position, the equations of motion (19) and (20) become:

$$[M_o]\ \underline{\ddot{X}}_d + [R_o]\ \underline{\dot{X}}_d + [K_o]\ \underline{X}_d = \underline{F}_c(\underline{\dot{X}}_d,\overrightarrow{V}(s,t)) - \underline{F}_c(\overline{V}) +$$
$$+ \underline{F}_1(\underline{X}_d,\underline{\dot{X}}_d,\underline{n},\underline{\dot{n}}) \qquad (23)$$

$$[m_{aer}]\ \underline{\ddot{n}} = \underline{F}_2(\underline{X}_d,\underline{\dot{X}}_d,\underline{n},\underline{\dot{n}}, |V_s(s,t)|^2) \qquad (24)$$

In (23) matrices $[M_o]$, $[R_o]$ and $[K_o]$ are obtained suitably assembling the $[K_j]$, $[R_j]$ and $[M_j]$ matrices of the single beam in global coordinates (eq.(2)), evaluated (using the matrices $[\Lambda_j]$ of the single beams) in the static equilibrium position. $[M_o]$, $[R_o]$ and $[K_o]$ matrices are therefore constant in time.

Equations (23) and (24) are solved by means of a modified Newmark step by step numerical integration method (widely described in [20], [21]).

An iterative procedure at "frozen time", to converge to the solution a $t+\Delta t$ time, must be activated because:
- the mutual interdependence of equation (23) and equation (24);
- the necessity, with the Newmark method, to solve the same equations a $t+\Delta t$ time;
- the forces $\underline{F}_c$, $\underline{F}_1$ and $\underline{F}_2$ are non linear function of the independent variables, that is of the unknowns.

© IMechE 1991 C416/016

2.5 Natural frequencies and related deformation shapes

Natural frequencies and related deformation shapes are evaluated solving the homogeneous equation:

$$[M_o]\, \ddot{\underline{X}}_d + [K_o]\, \underline{X}_d = \underline{0} \tag{26}$$

with an eigenvalue-eigenvector procedure ([22]).

3 SOME ANALYTICAL RESULTS

Many analytical simulations were carried out to investigate the dynamic behaviour of an under-sea cable under current and wave motion.

To better outline the problem connected with vortex shedding induced oscillation in wave motion, as an example, we report the results obtained with a cable (principal data are reported in Tab.II) subjected to a harmonic wave.

Static equilibrium position without current was calculated by means eq.(17): in fig.6 $\underline{X}_o$ static equilibrium deformation shape is shown and the numerical outputs of the program related to the $\underline{X}_o$ position of the nodes and the tensions T_j [kg] in each beam are reported.

Natural frequencies and related deformation shape was evaluated solving eq.(25): in fig.7 the first eigenvectors are shown.

The first mode is an horizontal symmetric mode with frequency $f_1=0.042$ Hz. The second mode is a vertical antisymmetric mode ($f_2=0.054$ Hz) with a central vibration node: this deformation is due to the geometrical stiffness of the static catenary shape assumed by the cable.

The third mode is an horizontal mode ($f_3=0.079$ Hz), while the fourth mode in a I-III mode ($f_4=0.097$ Hz).

It's possible to note also two horizontal modes ($f_5=0.11$ Hz, $f_7=0.154$Hz) and another vertical one ($f_6=0.139$ Hz).

As already said, we simulate the dynamic behaviour of the cable under a sinusoidal wave in the $\overline{X}$ direction (see fig.1), with peak to peak height H (see fig.3) of 2 meters and a period T of 20 seconds (corresponding to a wave frequency $f_w=0.05$ s.)

In correspondence of nodes 50, 45 and 19 of the schematization (see fig.6) there are three different values for the maximum fluid velocity due to the wave motion:

$V_{node 50} = 0.23$ m/s

$V_{node 45} = 0.10$ m/s

$V_{node 19} = 0.03$ m/s

Fig.8a shows longitudinal displacement [m] X_{50} at node 50 of the f.e. mesh, while fig.8b shows transverse displacements Y_{50} at the same node (see fig.6).

Fig.9a shows longitudinal displacement X_{19} at node 19 of the f.e. mesh, while fig.9b shows transverse displacements Y_{19} at the same node (see fig.6).

As You can see, first harmonic frequency f_w, due to wave motion and introduced by means of Morison's forces, is mainly excited in longitudinal $\overline{X}$ direction in both the nodes.

At node 50 in transverse direction $\overline{Y}$ an higher harmonic frequency appears (with a frequency triple in respect to the wave frequency f_w) introduced by equivalent oscillators, while the same oscillator introduce at node 19 an oscillation with frequency equal to the f_w wave frequency.

In Fig.10 the spatial transverse deformation shapes, at different instants, are reported: the coupling of the two different modes (related to f_1 and f_7 natural frequencies, see fig.7) is shown.

The different behaviour of the cable at different depth is due to the different value of the velocity and therefore the different value of the ratio $\dfrac{V}{V_s}$.

In fact:
- the f_s Strouhal frequency associated with the maximum value of the velocity at the top of the cable (node 50, see fig.6) is 0.219 Hz, that is in the synchronization range in respect with the $f_7=0.157$ Hz frequency of the 7-th vibration mode (see fig.7);
- f_7 frequency has a value of three time the f_w wave frequency.

Therefore, it is confirmed that the excitation due to the vortex shedding in wave motion is important when the ratio between natural vibration frequency f_i and wave frequency f_w is an integer value and the frequency f_i is close to Strouhal frequency f_s.

4 CONCLUSIONS

The paper deals with an analytical approach to define the static and dynamic behaviour of a single span submarine cable or flexible pipe under the action of marine current and wave loads.

The dynamic behaviour of the cable structure is analyzed by reproducing the time history of the water around the cable at each point of the structure by computing the fluid forces by Morison's equations, keeping account of the effects of vortex shedding by an equivalent oscillator.

The results obtained seem to reproduce the principal characteristics of the vortex shedding phenomenon in wave motion.

5 REFERENCES

[1]   CIRIA UNDERWATER ENG. GROUP, "Dynamics of marine structures: methods of calculating dynamic response of fixed structures subject to wave and current action", Atkins Research and Development, Report UR8 (Second Edition).

[2]   SARPKAYA, T., ISAACSON, M.,"Mechanics of waves forces on offshore structures", Van Nostrand Reinhold Company Incorp., 1981, New York.

[3]   FALCO, M., DONAZZI, F., MONTELATICI, L. Mathematical model of a rigid oscillating cylinder under wave action, keeping account of the effects of vortex shedding, to be published.

[4]   TSAHALIS, D.T. Vortex-induced vibrations of a flexible cylinder near a plane boundary exposed to steady and wave-induced currents, *Journal of Energy Resources Technology*, 1984, 106, 206-213.

[5]   VAN der VEGT, J.J.W., VAN WALREE, F. Progress in the prediction of forces on cylinders, floating structures and offshore operations, Elsevier, 1987, Amsterdam.

[6]   WILLIAMSON, C.H.K. Vortex formation in the wake of an oscillating cylinder, *Jour. of Fluids and Structures*, 1988, 2, 355-381.

[7]   CURRIE, J.G., TURNBULL, D.H. Streamwise oscillations of cylinders near the critical Reynolds Number, oscillations of cylinders, *Jour. of Fluids and Structures*, 1987, 1, 185-196.

[8] BEARMAN, P.W., OBASAJU, E.D. Transverse forces on a circular cylinder oscillating in-line with a steady current, 8-th OMAE, 19-23 March, 1989, The Ague.

[9] DONAZZI, F., DIANA, G., FALCO, M., PENG, G.X. Induced oscillation on a cylinder at high Reynolds number due to the vortex shedding, Int. Symp. on Hydrodynamics in Ocean Eng., 24-28 August, 1981, Trondheim.

[10] DIANA, G., FALCO, M. On the forces transmitted to a vibrating cylinder by a blowing fluid, *Meccanica*, N.1, VI, 1971.

[11] DIANA, G., GASPARETTO. , M. The equivalent oscillator: simulation of vortex shedding on cylindrical bodies bye means of an equivalent oscillator, *L'Energia Elettrica*, 1980, N.8.

[12] RIVA, R., SCARAMELLI, F. Studio con modello ad oscillatore equivalente delle vibrazioni eoliche di una coppia di cilindri uno in scia dell'altro, 4° Congresso Nazionale AIMETA, 25-28 Ottobre 1978, Firenze.

[13] SARPKAYA, T. A critical assessment of Morison's equation, Int. Symp. on Hydrodynamics in Ocean Engineering, 24-28 August 1981, Trondheim.

[14] KAPLAN, P., JIANG, C.W. Determination of offshore structure Morison equation force coefficients via system identification techniques, Int. Symp. on Hydrodynamics in Ocean Engineering, 24-28 August 1981, Trondheim.

[15] FALCO, M., MIMMI, G., TANZI, E. Dynamic actions due to wave motion on horizontal submerged cylinders oscillating in vertical direction, I MECH E, 5-th International Conference on Flow Induced Vibrations, 21-23 May 1991, Brighton.

[16] OTTESEN HANSEN, N.E., JACOBSEN, V. Hydro-elastic instability of pipes arrays in waves, Int. Symp. on Hydrodynamics in Ocean Engineering, 24-28 August 1981, Trondheim.

[17] ISAACSON, M. Dynamic response of vertical piles in waves, Int. Symp. on Hydrodynamics in Ocean Engineering, 24-28 August 1981, Trondheim.

[18] BATHE, K.J. "Finite element procedures in engineering analysis", Prentice Hall Inc., 1982, New Jersey.

[19] PRZEMIENIECKI, J.S. "Theory of structural analysis", Mc-Graw Hill Company, 1968, New York.

[20] DIANA, G. , CHELI, F. A numerical method to define the dynamic behaviour of a train running on a deformable structure, Meccanica, 1988, 23, 27-42, Milano.

[21] DIANA, G. , CHELI, F. , MANENTI, A. et al. Oscillations of bundle conductors in overhead lines due to turbulent wind, 90 WM 112-3 PWRD, IEEE/PES 1990 Winter Meeting, 4-8 Feb. 1990, Atlanta.

[22] MEIROVITCH, L. "Elements of vibration analysis", Mc-Graw Hill Company, 1986, New York.

[23] DIANA, G., DONAZZI, F., MIMMI, G., PENG, G.X. Dynamic response of an undersea cable to a turbulent flow, *L'Energias Elettrica* , 1982, LIX.

[24] ANGRILLI, F., COSSALTER, V. Transverse oscillations of a vertical pile i.. water waves, *Journal of Fluids Enginnering*, Trans. of ASME, 1982, 104, 46-53.

6 APPENDIX A

The equivalent non linear oscillator model functions $g_{ki}(\tau_i)$ and $g_{ri}(\tau_i)$ for a circular cylinder under steady current were expressed ([9], [10], [11]) with a cubic curve (see eq.(14)). For large vibration amplitudes of the cylinder, the cubic function gave negative values for the functions g_{ki} and g_{ri}, as if the springs and the dampers were introducing energy in the system at the same time, producing instability (not noticed in the steady stream model as the oscillation amplitudes were locked around the equilibrium position). In order to avoid this, the cubic functions g_{ki} or g_{ri} was changed into the generic exponential curve $g_{ji}(\tau_i)$ of the type reported in eq.(15) (with j="k" or j="r").

The coefficients A_{ji}, B_{ji}, λ_{ji} are choosen so the generic $g_{ji}(\tau_i)$ function follows the further cubic function for small values of τ_i, and does not tend to infinity for large values of τ_i.

The determination of A_{ji}, B_{ji}, λ_{ji} follows the conditions:
- the positive maximum $g_{ji}(\tau_i)$ is equal to the maximum positive value of the cubic curve;
- these two positive maxima fall at the same value of τ_i;
- parameter B_{ji} defines the asymptotic value of the generic g_{ji} function for very high cylinder vibration amplitudes.

From these conditions it follows:

$$A_{ki} = \frac{\lambda_{ki} B_{ki}}{(\lambda_{ki} \sqrt{\frac{K_i'}{3K_i''}}) - 1} \; ; \; \lambda_{ki} = \frac{\varepsilon_{ki}}{\sqrt{\frac{K_i'}{3K_i''}}} \qquad (a.1)$$

if the function represents springs elements ("j"="k") and

$$A_{ri} = \frac{\lambda_{ri} B_{ri}}{(\lambda_{ri} \sqrt{\frac{R_i'}{3R_i''}}) - 1} \; ; \; \lambda_{ri} = \frac{\varepsilon_{ri}}{\sqrt{\frac{R_i'}{3R_i''}}} \qquad (a.2)$$

if the function represent damper elements ("j"="r").

The generic ε_{ji} term is carried out from the implicit function:

$$(\xi_{ji}-B_{ji}) (\varepsilon_{ji}-1) - B_{ji} \exp(-\varepsilon_{ji}) = 0 \qquad (a.3)$$

where

$$\xi_{ki} = \frac{2}{3} K_i' \sqrt{\frac{K_i'}{3K_i''}} \quad or \quad \xi_{ri} = \frac{2}{3} R_i' \sqrt{\frac{R_i'}{3R_i''}} \qquad (a.4)$$

respectively in the case of springs ("j"="k") or dampers ("j"="r").

The parameter B_{ji} can be seen as a suitable positive value that prevents springs and dampers to assume negative values that is to introduce in the oscillator negative energy generating instability. In the model it has been assumed $B_{ji}=1$.

The parameters are choosen with a best fitting procedure between experimental and analytical results in the case of a rigid oscillating cylinder ([3]).

In the case of wave motion Morison's model and the equivalent oscillator have been added.

The aerodynamic and coupling parameters adequate to reproduce the cylinder behaviour under both current and wave motion are reported in Tab.I.A.

Tab.Ia: [K$_{jL}$] stiffness matrix in local coordinates

Tab.Ib: [M$_{jL}$] mass matrix in local coordinates

Parameter	Value
K'$_{aer}$	3.3
K''$_{aer}$	2.24
K'$_{acc}$	0.75
K''$_{acc}$	0.66
r'$_{aer}$	4.00
r''$_{aer}$	0.00
r'$_{acc}$	4.00
r''$_{acc}$	4.50

Tab.I.A: aerodynamic and coupling coefficients

Span length	200 m
External diameter	0.21 m
Weight per unit length (in water)	109.4 kg/m
Horizontal component of the tension T	5000 kg
Axial stiffness EA (see Tab.I)	8.7 10^7 kg
Flexural stiffness EJ	2.784 10^3 kgm^2
Torsional stiffness GJ	9.28 10^2 kgm^2
Difference between the height at the ends	200 m
Drag coefficient C$_D$	1.5
Mass coefficient C$_m$	1.1
Non-dimensional damping of the cable $\frac{r}{r_c}$	2%

Tab.II: principal data of the analyzed cable

node	X(m)	Y(m)	Z(m)	tension(Kg)
1	0.00	0.00	0.00	9499.85
2	3.50	0.00	-5.66	8908.54
3	7.00	0.00	-10.82	8369.49
4	10.50	0.00	-15.52	7879.56
5	14.00	0.00	-19.78	7435.85
6	17.50	0.00	-23.63	7035.78
7	21.00	0.00	-27.10	6676.99
8	24.50	0.00	-30.20	6357.38
9	28.00	0.00	-32.95	6075.07
10	31.50	0.00	-35.36	5828.41
11	35.00	0.00	-37.46	5615.95
12	38.50	0.00	-39.25	5436.44
13	42.00	0.00	-40.74	5288.82
14	45.50	0.00	-41.95	5172.24
15	49.00	0.00	-42.87	5086.01
16	52.50	0.00	-43.53	5029.62
17	56.00	0.00	-43.91	5002.74
18	59.50	0.00	-44.02	5005.22
19	63.00	0.00	-43.86	5037.06
20	66.50	0.00	-43.43	5098.46
21	70.00	0.00	-42.74	5189.78
22	73.50	0.00	-41.78	5311.55
23	77.00	0.00	-40.51	5464.43
24	80.50	0.00	-38.97	5649.48
25	84.00	0.00	-37.13	5867.62
26	87.50	0.00	-34.98	6120.20
27	91.00	0.00	-32.50	6408.68
28	94.50	0.00	-29.70	6734.77
29	98.00	0.00	-26.54	7100.38
30	101.50	0.00	-23.01	7507.64
31	105.00	0.00	-19.09	7958.96
32	108.50	0.00	-14.75	8456.98
33	112.00	0.00	-9.98	9004.62
34	115.50	0.00	-4.74	9605.10
35	119.00	0.00	1.01	10261.93
36	122.50	0.00	7.28	10978.98
37	126.00	0.00	14.12	11760.45
38	129.50	0.00	21.58	12610.92
39	133.00	0.00	29.68	13535.38
40	136.50	0.00	38.49	14539.26
41	140.00	0.00	48.05	15628.46
42	143.50	0.00	58.41	16809.35
43	147.00	0.00	69.65	18088.87
44	150.50	0.00	81.82	19474.52
45	154.00	0.00	95.00	20974.44
46	157.50	0.00	109.26	22597.43
47	161.00	0.00	124.69	24353.00
48	164.50	0.00	141.37	26251.46
49	168.00	0.00	159.42	28303.96
50	171.50	0.00	178.92	30522.52

Tab.III: $\underline{X}_O$ static deformation shape Z$_{(m)}$ ant tension T$_j$ in each j-th beam.

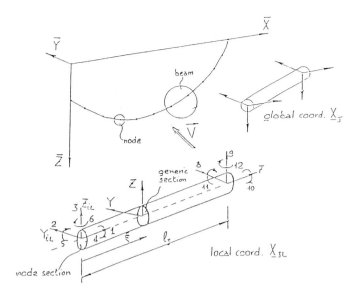

fig.1: global reference system and tensioned beam element in local coordinates

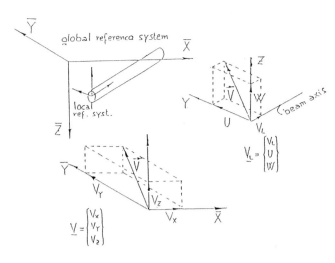

fig.4: fluid velocities and beam velocities in global and local coordinates

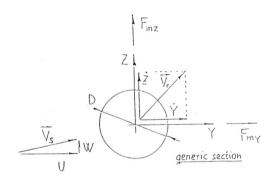

fig.2: Morison's forces

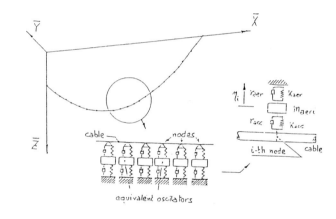

equivalent oscillators

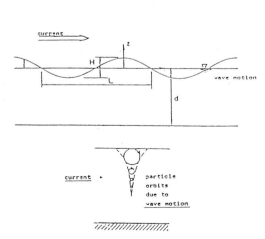

fig.3: time-space distribution of the velocity on the cable

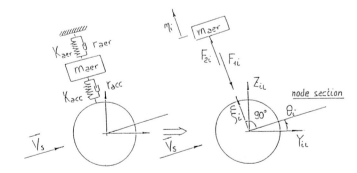

fig.5: the cable and the equivalent oscillators reproducing vortex shedding

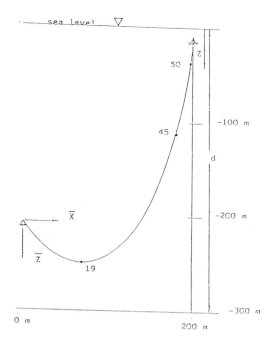

fig.6: $\underline{X}_0$ static deformation of the cable

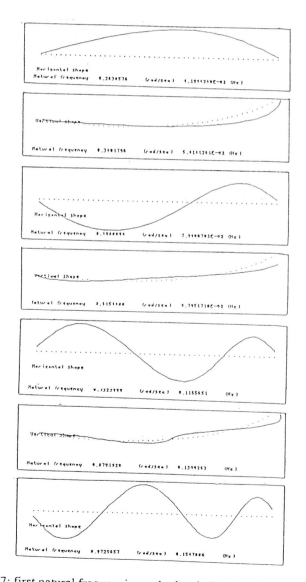

fig.7: first natural frequencies and related vibrational modes

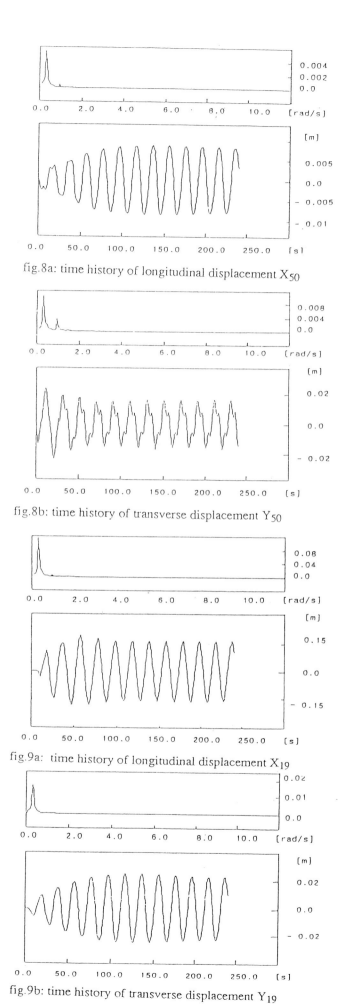

fig.8a: time history of longitudinal displacement X_{50}

fig.8b: time history of transverse displacement Y_{50}

fig.9a: time history of longitudinal displacement X_{19}

fig.9b: time history of transverse displacement Y_{19}

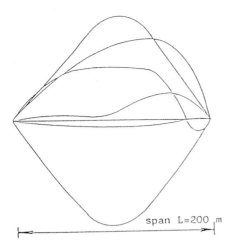

fig.10: spatial transverse deformation shapes Y of the cable
at different moments

A review of dynamic tube-support interaction in heat exchanger tubes

S S CHEN, PhD, MASME
Argonne National Laboratory, Argonne, Illinois, United States of America

SYNOPSIS The supports for heat exchanger tubes are usually plates with drilled holes; however, other types of supports have also been used. To facilitate manufacture and allow for thermal expansion of the tubes, small clearances are used between tubes and tube supports. The dynamics of tube/support interaction in heat exchangers is fairly complicated. Understanding tube dynamics and their effects on heat exchangers is important. This paper summarizes the current state of the art on this subject and identifies future research needs. Specifically, the following topics are discussed: dynamics of loosely supported tubes, tube/support gap dynamics, tube response in flow, tube damage and wear, design considerations, and future research needs.

1 INTRODUCTION

The supports for heat exchanger tubes (baffle plates) are usually plates with drilled holes. Other types of supports have also been used, including three-lobed broach holes, egg crates, and lattice bars. For the U-bend region in curved tubes, various types of 'anti-vibration bars' are inserted between tubes. In this paper, baffle plates, anti-vibration bars, and other types of tube supports are referred to as tube supports. To facilitate manufacture and to allow for thermal expansion of the tubes, small clearances are used between tubes and tube supports. When tubes oscillate due to flow-induced vibration, tube failure can occur through fretting wear or fatigue associated with dynamic tube/support interaction. Such failures have resulted in numerous plant shutdowns, which are often very costly. In the past decade, extensive studies to improve the understanding of dynamic tube/support interaction and to prevent tube failures have been published.

Tube failures caused by flow-induced vibration may be categorized as follows: impact and rubbing between tubes, impact and wear between tube and tube supports, tube fatigue, and tube-to-tubesheet joint failure (Horn et al. 1988). Tube failures associated with tube/support interaction have been reported by Frick et al. (1984), Yu (1986), and Yeh and Chen (1990).

The dynamics of tube/support interaction in heat exchangers is fairly complicated. From a practical point of view, what is needed is a design guide to predict the useful life of tubes under specific design flow conditions. To achieve this goal, it is necessary to understand tube dynamics, tube/support interaction characteristics, impact and wear due to flow excitations, wear rate, and effects of various system parameters. This paper reviews various aspects of this problem.

2 DYNAMICS OF LOOSELY SUPPORTED TUBES

Current design practices often consider heat exchanger tubes to be simply supported at the supports without clearances. For small clearances, this assumption is applicable. The tube responds as a continuous beam supported by all supports; this type of mode is called 'support-active.' When the clearance is relatively large, the tube may rattle inside some of the support clearances with small-amplitude oscillations. This type of mode, in which some supports do not provide effective support, is called 'support-inactive' (see Fig. 1). For intermediate clearances, tube response depends strongly on the excitation amplitude; for small excitations, the tube vibrates within the clearance (support-inactive mode) and for large excitations, the tube contacts all supports for most of the time (support-active mode). In reality, the tube response is composed of both support-active and support-inactive modes; the system is highly nonlinear.

One of the key steps in understanding the tube/support interaction phenomena is knowing the dynamics of loosely supported tubes. Extensive experiments and analyses have been performed to learn these dynamics, and results have been published in the literature. Particular attention has been given to multiple supports, clearance, alignment, support thickness, and support spacing. The objectives of these studies have been to find the general dynamic characteristics of tubes, including natural frequencies, mode shapes, damping values, and their responses to flow excitations. Most studies have focused on tube support-active modes.

Linear vibration codes are usually inadequate for analyzing the general dynamic response of loosely supported tubes. Two methods have been used extensively: a modal superposition method that uses explicit solutions of a piecewise linear system and a method that uses direct integration of a nonlinear system (Axisa et al. 1988; Frick et al. 1984; Fricker 1988; Nakamura and Fujita 1987; Rao et al. 1987; Rogers and Pick 1977; Shin et al. 1978). In the piecewise linear model, the forced vibration response can be described in terms of either a set of constrained or unconstrained modes (Davies and Rogers 1979). In terms of unconstrained modes, the constraint is treated as an applied load, whereas in terms of constrained modes, the constraint is treated as an essential part of the structure. In a piecewise linear system, the modal superposition method provides a significant reduction in the number of equations to be solved. In direct-time-integration schemes, a small time step is needed to maintain operator stability and obtain required accuracy. However, long time histories are needed for statistical and spectral analyses. The advantages of the direct integration approach are that the detailed interaction characteristics may be modeled, and parameters related to tube wear calculation may be extracted. Normally, for direct numerical simulations, a finite-element technique is used. The models used for the tubes include Bernoulli beam and Timoshenko beam (Ko and Rogers 1981).

Experimental studies of loosely supported tubes have been performed by either exciting a tube mechanically (Axisa et al. 1984; Blevins 1975; Goyder 1982; Haslinger et al. 1987, 1988; Moretti and Lowery 1973; Shin et al. 1977) or by placing the tubes in flow (Chen et al. 1984; Nakamura and Fujita 1987; Weaver and Schneider 1983). Several investigators have considered various aspects of the problem.

Some of the general characteristics of loosely supported tubes and the effects of system parameters that have been studied theoretically and experimentally are clearance, baffle alignment and thickness, orientation, fluid medium, and coefficient of friction.

2.1 Clearance

The natural frequencies of support-inactive modes can be significantly lower than those of support-active modes. In general, natural frequencies of support-inactive modes increase with excitation amplitude, whereas those of support-active modes decrease with excitation amplitude. As clearance increases, tube natural frequencies of support-active modes decrease slightly (Moretti and Lowery 1973). For small-amplitude oscillations, the effect of clearance on natural frequencies of support-active modes can be ignored. In general, for loosely supported tubes, damping and frequency bandwidths become much larger and rattling occurs when excitation frequency is close to natural frequency (Moretti and Lowery 1973).

A support-inactive mode can be excited in resonance. The dominant support-inactive mode depends on the amplitude and frequency of the excitation as well as other parameters. Midspan displacement of a continuous tube is almost proportional to the excitation level and clearance (Axisa et al. 1984; Ko and Rogers 1981). A significant variation in displacement amplitude was observed for clearances of more than 20 mils, and smaller clearances have a tendency to lower displacement amplitudes (Shin et al. 1977).

Clearance slightly affects the shear force but greatly affects normal force and contact duration (Fisher et al. 1988). For a given excitation, the contact force level first increases with clearance and then decreases as tube/baffle contacts occur less often (Rogers and Pick 1977). Impact forces averaged over a cycle of vibration are almost proportional to excitation. Wear rate increases as the tube/support clearance is increased, until a limit is reached where contacts are no longer maintained and the wear rate drops off rapidly (Ko 1985b).

2.2 Baffle Alignment

Baffle alignment of the intermediate supports is called propping (Moretti and Lowery 1973). Propping may exist permanently or be caused by steady fluid forces, such as drag force, and it may play an important role in tube response. It has very little effect on natural frequencies. The natural frequencies (support-active modes) of misaligned cases are a little higher than the corresponding frequencies of aligned cases. Propping also has very little effect on tube response and damping values (Shin et al. 1977). For small excitation levels, misalignment reduces tube response amplitudes. However, for large excitation levels, propping may be important and affect system characteristics significantly.

2.3 Baffle Thickness

Changing baffle thickness has no major effect on tube natural frequencies. However, damping increases with thickness (Blevins 1975); the damping for a 5/8-in. plate is about twice that of a 1/8-in. plate (Moretti and Lowery 1973). Furthermore, thicker support plates have a definite tendency to lower displacement amplitude for a given excitation (Shin et al. 1977).

Maximum reaction force at supports increases with stiffness and maximum displacements are not significantly affected. Fisher et al. (1988) have shown that tube support stiffness has little effect on shear force and moderate effect on normal force and contact duration. On the other hand, Rogers and Pick (1976) reported only a few percent change in rms impact forces when stiffness was increased four times.

Fluid and squeeze film effects are proportional to baffle thickness (Haslinger et al. 1989). The wear parameter for egg crate supports decreases with increase in stiffness, but does not change significantly for the baffle plates (Rao et al. 1987). The local penetration rate increases with reduced tube support area (Ko 1985a).

2.4 Orientation

Tube natural frequencies and damping values are not much different for tubes oriented vertically or horizontally. The displacements of a tube subjected to a sinusoidal force in a horizontal orientation are, in general, higher than those of a tube in a vertical orientation (Shin et al. 1977). This may be associated with more impacting in the vertical orientation.

2.5 Fluid Medium

Tubes submerged in a liquid had additional inertia and damping due to the surrounding fluid. Measured displacements in water were, in general, higher than those in air for the span nearest the excitation span. The opposite behavior was observed for the span away from the excitation span (Shin et al. 1977). Experimental support-impact forces are smaller in water than in air (Ko and Rogers 1981), due to the squeeze film effect in tube/support clearance spaces. The damping associated with the fluid in the clearance between the tubes and the supports is much more significant for support-inactive modes. Detailed studies were performed by Jendrzejczyk (1985) and Esmonde et al. (1990), who found that fluid damping increased with baffle thickness and excitation force level.

2.6 Coefficient of Friction

The friction phenomenon in heat exchanger tubes is still a delicate subject, because the nature of surface interaction processes is extremely complex and the frictional forces are highly nonlinear at near-zero sliding velocities (Antunes et al. 1988). For forced excitation with drilled hole supports, the smaller coefficient of friction results in slightly lower force levels, whereas with the larger coefficient, the force levels are slightly higher (Rogers and Pick 1977). For egg crate supports, the maximum reaction decreases slightly with an increase in friction coefficient. Fisher et al. (1988) showed that the friction coefficient also greatly affects contact duration and consistently tends to reduce wear work rate. However, Eisinger et al. (1989) found that tube displacements and work rate are approximately the same for various friction coefficients and consequently the friction can be ignored. In general, the Coulomb friction model does not satisfactorily model the effect of boundary lubricant (Rogers and Pick 1976).

3 TUBE/SUPPORT GAP DYNAMICS

Two types of motion can occur at baffle plates: a rocking motion (odd motion) or a bending motion (even motion), as shown in Fig. 1 (Goyder 1982, 1985, 1987). The rocking motion is associated with a support-active mode and the bending motion is associated with support-active or -inactive modes. Various models have been used to simulate the support characteristics.

• A nonlinear elastic contact spring and dashpot model has been used to represent a tube/support interaction (Shin et al. 1978). The contact force/displacement relationship is based on the classical Hertz contact theory for an elastic pin in a circular hole and the contact damping is based on a hysteresis loop.

• The components of the interaction force at the support are the normal and frictional forces. Rogers and Pick (1976) used the product of the tube-annulus stiffness and the radial deformation to calculate the normal force. The frictional force is proportional to the normal force and is either independent of velocity or increases slightly as the velocity diminishes.

• Axisa et al. (1988) used an equivalent spring to model the contact force. The spring is determined by using the stiffness associated with the local ovalization.

• Yetisir and Weaver (1986) used a spring damper system to model the flat bars of U-tube supports.

Tube/support interactions contribute to damping. Various experiments have been performed to measure tube damping (Haslinger and Steininger 1984). Haslinger et al. (1989) used four methods to calculate damping values. Damping data were widely scattered. This may be caused by the dependence of damping energy on sliding/impacting at the supports. Damping was found to increase with an increase in baffle thickness and its values varied from 1.33 to 2.38 percent from the tests by Haslinger et al. (1987).

The effect of the fluid in the clearance between tubes and supports can be accounted for by using fluid added mass and fluid damping. Extensive studies have been published to understand these effects. Using the linearized Navier-Stokes equation, Mulcahy (1980) derived approximate expressions for the fluid forces acting on a centrally located, rigid rod that was translating periodically in a finite-length annular region of a confined fluid. Experimental data and analytical results were in reasonable agreement; fluid added mass and damping were applicable to small motions. Additional experiments to verify these expressions and to understand the effect of other parameters, such as forcing magnitude, baffle width, and clearance, were performed by Jendrzejczyk (1985) and Rogers et al. (1984).

Rogers and Ahn (1986) conducted theoretical and experimental studies on added mass and damping for support-inactive modes with amplitude-to-clearance ratios up to 0.6 and oscillation Reynolds numbers ranging from 3 to 300. Simplified expressions that incorporated the effect of oscillation amplitude were obtained for added mass and damping.

Using experimental data to develop semi-empirical formulas, Haslinger et al. (1989) characterized the fluid effect. Two cases were considered: non-impacting and impacting. For cases of non-impacting tube motion, fluid forces were adequately represented by the added-mass and damping terms. For impacting cases, fluid forces were functions of the instantaneous tube velocity and tube-to-support clearance. The mass proportionality term appeared to play a secondary role. These authors also showed that anti-vibration bars do not exhibit significant squeeze film effects; the fluid effects can be represented by the added-mass and damping proportionality terms across the entire range of tube motion.

Added mass due to the gap fluid between tube and support appeared to have a negligible effect on system response (Shin et al. 1977). A nonlinear jump phenomenon of response amplitude was measured from the spectral density curves by sweeping the forcing frequency in upward/downward directions (Shin et al. 1978). The impact forces were smaller in water than in air. This is due to the squeeze film effect in the tube/support clearance spaces (Ko and Rogers 1981).

4 TUBE RESPONSE IN FLOW

A loosely supported tube responding to flow excitation can result in very complex phenomena. As the tube begins to vibrate, one of two possibilities will occur. If the tube strikes the support, it will stay in contact until dynamic forces overcome the static force and the tube will either rebound from the support or slide against the support. If the tube is not in contact with the support, the amplitude of motion will be able to increase until the tube strikes the support. The tube amplitude at a loosely supported location is limited by the magnitude of the clearance (Goyder 1987). Therefore, the response is nonlinear, depending on various system parameters.

4.1 Fluidelastic Instability

Because the natural frequency of a support-inactive mode is much lower than that of a support-active mode at a given flow velocity, the reduced flow velocity is much larger for a support-inactive mode. Consequently, the support-inactive mode may become unstable when the support-active mode is still in the stable region. An extensive experimental study to demonstrate the significance and response characteristics of support-inactive modes has been reported by Chen et al. (1984). A typical case is shown in Fig. 2. Tube response characteristics associated with the instability of a support-inactive mode are different from the response to other types of excitation and the response of support-active modes. When a tube becomes unstable in a support-inactive mode because of constraints at supports, large tube oscillations will not occur. With increased flow velocity, tube displacement remains almost constant until the instability of other modes occurs. However, the peak impact force at supports and the number of impacts per cycle of oscillation and, consequently, the work-rate parameter, do increase with flow velocity. In addition, tube displacement, impact force, and number of impacts at a given flow velocity increase with the diametral clearance in practical cases.

© IMechE 1991 C416/012

The fluid in the clearance between the tube and supports affects tube response characteristics: it increases system damping and reduces tube response. For the instability of a support-inactive mode, the fluid in the gap reduces tube displacement and impact force so wear rate is reduced. Detailed fluid dynamics associated with the tube/support interaction are important to quantify the wear of heat exchanger tubes. More detailed analysis and experiments are needed to understand these effects.

The alignment of the tube is important for support-inactive modes. Misalignment of the tube is beneficial; it reduces tube displacement and the work-rate parameter. Therefore, tubes located centrally in the support clearances represent the worst case.

4.2 Forced Vibration and Chaotic Motion

Severe rattling was observed at frequencies near the natural frequency, although virtually no rattling was observed at resonance (Moretti and Lowery 1973; Shin et al. 1978). The motion of a cantilevered tube with a loose support at the free end appears to have a small chaotic component superimposed on a larger periodic component (Fricker 1988). Axisa et al. (1988) calculated the response of multiple loosely supported tubes. When the flow velocity is larger than the critical flow velocity of a support-inactive mode, chaos is noted in certain flow velocity ranges, based on the computed power spectral densities of tube response and phase space plots. Using a negative damping model, Langre et al. (1990) considered fluidelastic instability of a single flexible tube in a rigid tube array. They demonstrated the existence of a unique limit cycle and found no chaotic motion. For forced excitation, some regular motions were predicted and the motion became chaotic as the force magnitude was increased. The transition from a periodic to chaotic regime showed evidence of sudden jumps in impact force levels during time histories. A velocity feedback loop was used to simulate fluidelastic forces for loosely supported tubes (Antunes et al. 1990). Results show that several steady-motion regimes may arise, depending on the system parameters and initial conditions of the motion.

Very limited information on the chaotic motion of loosely supported tubes is available. In particular, tube wear during chaotic motion is not known. It is expected that fluidelastic instability of loosely supported tubes in a support-inactive mode, which represents a typical autonomous fluid/structure system component, will receive more attention.

5 TUBE DAMAGE AND TUBE WEAR

Two types of tube/support interactions are important for tube wear: sliding and impacting against the supports, with motion consisting of support-active and -inactive modes, and sliding with reciprocating sliding motion primarily associated with support-active modes. Most in-service heat exchanger designs are based on the linear model in which the tubes are simply supported at each support plate. Wear calculations have been made for these systems by considering sliding motions at tube/support plate interfaces that result from the response of support-active modes (Connors 1981). If gaps exist between the tube and its supports, the tube motion can be one of intermittent contact or sliding at one or more plates, resulting from a combination of support-active and -inactive modes. Recent operating experiences with steam generators and heat exchangers confirm that this mechanism can indeed occur in practice (Frick et al. 1984; Yeh and Chen 1990).

Testing equipment has been developed to study wear between tube and supports by several investigators (Blevins 1979; Cha et al. 1987; Ko 1979). Plastic deformation, fatigue, delamination, and metal transfer due to adhesion are considered the main wear mechanisms in tube/support interaction wear (Ko and Magel 1989). Although the parameters affecting tube wear can be measured during wear tests, in practical heat exchangers, analytical techniques are necessary to estimate these effects from flow and vibration information.

When a tube strikes a support, the impact causes tube wear and dilation of the hole in the baffle plate. The impact is generally associated with brief sliding, which causes the wear. Indeed, sliding or sliding with bumping causes more wear than bumping alone. The impact forces, either normal or oblique, at the tube supports are a parameter related to wear. The wear rate is dependent upon material combination, contact configuration, environmental conditions, and tube/support interaction. Wear rate for short duration tests increases linearly with increasing force level (Fisher and Ingham 1988). However, the total reaction force alone is not sufficient to correlate wear damage when other parameters are allowed to vary. Ko (1979) demonstrated that wear rate correlates with tube/support contact force for similar tube motion. For different types of tube motion, Ko et al. (1982), Ko and Basista (1984), and Ko (1985) showed that wear rate correlates well with a force function that represents the integrated area of the force histogram of the shear force component. To correlate wear data, others (Haslinger et al. 1987; Rao et al. 1987; Blevins 1985;

Axisa et al. 1984; Frick et al. 1984) used the work rate parameter, which is the normal component of the contact force integrated over the real sliding distance.

To predict wear during service, a systematic analysis is needed to model tube response, tube/support interaction, wear characteristics, and the effects of other system parameters. Various numerical procedures have been proposed to achieve this goal (Frick et al. 1984; Ko et al. 1982).

The wear model adopted by most investigators is based on the Archard wear relationship: the wear volume, V, is related to the normal force between the wear surfaces, F, the sliding distance, S, and the empirical wear coefficient, K, as follows:

$$V = K F S . \tag{1}$$

A few variations of this model have been developed for applications to heat exchanger tubes. Connors (1981) combined this equation with flow-induced vibration to predict tube life. Frick et al. (1984) modified the wear equation by replacing the normal force and sliding distance by a work rate term, W, to relate the nonlinear model to wear volume according to the equation

$$V = K W T , \tag{2}$$

where T is total time. Goyder and Teh (1988) described wear in terms of the wear coefficient, the number of impacts per second, impulse, and the tangential tube velocity.

An empirical model for tube wear was developed by Blevins (1979) to predict fretting wear. The model accounts for the variation in fretting wear due to transverse vibration with frequency of oscillations, amplitude, clearance, tube wall thickness, and mean load. The main mechanism of wear in Blevins' model is impact. This is contrary to the experimental data of Ko (1985b) and the criterion used by Connors (1981).

Cha et al. (1986) used the data of a series of tests performed in air, water, and oil to develop an empirical formula to predict impact/fretting wear rate. In their formula, wear rate is a function of the resultant interaction force at the support, oscillation frequency, and time.

Ko (1985a) considered that fretting-wear rate is proportional to the tube-to-support contact force and to a force function representing the integrated area of the force histogram of the shear force component. Ko (1985b) also correlated tube wear

with the tangential component of the support impact force. In addition, a simple wear volume was developed for specific material (Ko 1980; Ko and Rogers 1981):

$$W = a\,t^b , \tag{3}$$

where, for Cu-Ni alloy tubes with 11 N impact force, $a = 0.078$ and $b = 0.93$.

All the above models are empirical and do not consider the detailed mechanisms of wear. Recently, Ko and Magel (1989) have tried to look into detailed wear mechanisms under various circumstances and to modify wear models.

6 DESIGN CONSIDERATIONS

Fretting damage of tubes associated with tube/support interaction in heat exchangers can cause the need for costly repair and should be avoided. For example, a design objective for a nuclear power plant steam generator is a 40-year design life. Even relatively small tube wear rate can be unacceptable, because of very stringent safety requirements. For example, according to USNRC commercial safety requirements, only 40 percent of the tube wall thickness can be allowed to degrade before tube plugging becomes mandatory.

Current design practices consider the heat exchanger tubes to be simply supported at the baffles, without clearance. This assumption is not acceptable if the clearance is relatively large so that support-inactive modes may be important. In addition, the design parameters that are considered should be based on frequencies rather than tube length. Integrated procedures to predict tube wear with nonlinear finite-element modeling, measured forcing functions, and wear data have been utilized in research and practical applications (Blevins 1988; Frick et al. 1984; Rao et al. 1987, 1988; Fricker 1988). The procedures appear to be useful in the assessment of practical cases.

After long periods of operation, magnetite and other deposits may be formed at the holes in the support plate. The clearance may increase due to cleaning. Au-Yang (1988) has estimated that, with an increase of 67 percent in clearance in steam generator tubes, the wear rate will increase by a factor of 2-3. Consideration should be given to tube wear if any cleaning of the heat exchanger is planned.

From a fretting point of view, the support clearance should be kept as small as practically possible (Weaver and Schneider 1983; Ko 1985;

Godon and Lebert 1988), preferably less than 0.4 mm diametrically in baffle plates. The support landing areas should be maximized since local penetration rate increases with reduced tube support area.

Scale-model testing may not provide satisfactory answers because of nonlinear response behavior, which results in scaling laws and similitude requirements not being directly applicable. In general, the geometrically scaled clearance simulates the prototype better. However, the responses of the prototype and the scale model cannot be correlated directly for some excitation amplitudes, because of nonlinear behavior. Therefore, for tubes supported by multiple supports with relatively large clearances, tests should be conducted on the prototype tube and supports. Great care should be exercised in applying data obtained from a scale model to a prototype.

It is very difficult to predict long-term wear from short-term results, as wear rate is low and hardly measurable. However, once a significant wear depth has been reached, the rate may start to increase with a time exponent >1. This happens because of the increase in tube/tube support clearance and the change in tube motion; both can increase the impact forces at the support and wear rate (Ko 1985a).

7 CLOSING REMARKS

Dynamic tube/support interaction and fretting wear are very complicated. Although existing techniques to predict tube wear appear to be practically applicable, some fundamental questions remain unanswered. For example, how much detail about the tube/support interaction process do we have to understand to accurately predict tube wear? In addition, the detailed flow field associated with tube/support interaction, tube motion at supports, correlations of tube motion and wear rate, and effects of various system parameters are not clearly understood.

Fluid added mass and damping at the supports have been studied extensively. The effects for support-inactive modes can be calculated reasonably well for small motion. However, for large amplitude oscillations in support-inactive modes, the effects are difficult to predict. In addition, the effects for support-active modes have not been studied in detail. Furthermore, fluid added mass and damping for two dimensional oscillations, such as whirling of tubes, have not been considered in the literature.

Wear prediction methods for forced excitations are available. However, wear due to fluidelastic instability of support-inactive modes are not known. More detailed studies are needed to quantify the effects of instability.

Forcing functions, wear mechanisms, and tube/support interaction in heat exchangers are extremely complicated. The current state of the art appears to be adequate to predict the wear in heat exchangers if sufficient data on wear, support geometries, and forcing functions are available. An in-depth study of the detailed interaction process is needed. Specifically, the following topics are of particular importance.

• Fluid effects for relative large-oscillation amplitudes (i.e., the tube vibration amplitude at the support is comparable with the clearance), linear flow theories are no longer applicable. Nonlinear effects of the fluid in the tube/support clearance are not well understood. An integrated analytical/experimental study of the nonlinear effects is recommended.

• Wear rates for different oscillations induced by different mechanisms including subcritical vibration and fluidelastic instability are not well quantified. In order to predict tube life, wear rate is a key parameter. Extensive studies are needed to quantify the wear rate as a function of different system parameters and excitation mechanisms.

• Tubes with loose supports are intrinsically nonlinear. Their response includes periodic oscillations, chaotic vibration, and random vibration. Very limited studies have been performed to understand the nonlinear behavior. A systematic study including analysis and experiment is needed.

It is expected that dynamic tube/support interaction will be a subject of continuing research for some years to come.

ACKNOWLEDGMENT

This work was performed for Taiwan Power Company under an agreement with the U.S. Department of Energy under Contract 31-109-Eng-38-85847.

REFERENCES

ANTUNES, J., AXISA, F., BEAUFILS, B., and GUILBAUD, D. 1988 Coulomb friction modelling in numerical simulations of vibration and wear work rate of multispan tube bundles. *1988 Int. Symp. on Flow-Induced Vibration and Noise*, Vol. 5, pp. 157-176 (ASME).

ANTUNES, J., AXISA, F., and VENTO, M. A. 1990 Experiments on vibro-impact dynamics under fluidelastic instability. Presented at the Pressure Vessels and Piping Conference, Nashville, TN, June 17-21, 1990.

AU-YANG. M. K. 1988 Effect of chemical cleaning on steam generator tube wear. Presented at the ANS/ASME Nuclear Power Conference, Myrtle Beach, SC, 1988.

AXISA, F., ANTUNES, J., and VILLARD, B. 1988 Overview of numerical methods for predicting flow-induced vibration. *Journal of Pressure Vessel Technology*, 110, 6-14.

AXISA, F., DESSEAUX, A., and GIBERT, R. J. 1984 Experimental study of tube/support impact forces in multi-span PWR steam generator tubes. *Symp. on Flow-Induced Vibrations*, Vol. 3, pp. 139-148, (ASME).

BLEVINS, R. D. 1975 Vibration of a loosely held tube. *Journal of Engineering for Industry*, 97, 1301-1304.

BLEVINS, R. D. 1979 Fretting wear of heat exchanger tubes: Part 1, experiments; Part 2, models. *Journal of Engineering for Power*, 101, 625-633.

BLEVINS, R. D. 1985 Vibration induced wear of heat exchanger tubes. *Journal of Engineering Material and Technology*, 107, 61-67.

BLEVINS, R. D. 1988 A rational algorithm for predicting vibration-induced damage to tube and shell heat exchangers. *Symp. on Flow-Induced Vibrations*, Vol. 3, pp. 87-110 (ASME).

CHA, J. H., WAMBSGANSS, M. W., and JENDRZEJCZYK, J. A. 1987 Experimental study on impact/fretting wear in heat exchanger tubes. *Journal of Pressure Vessel Technology*, 109, 265-274.

CHEN, S. S., JENDRZEJCZYK, J. A., and WAMBSGANSS, M. W. 1984 Dynamics of tubes in fluid with tube-baffle interaction. *Symp. on Flow-Induced Vibrations*, Vol. 2, pp. 285-304 (ASME).

CONNORS, H. J. 1981 Flow-induced vibration and wear of steam generator tubes. *Nuclear Technology*, 55, 311-321.

DAVIES, H. G., and ROGERS, R. J. 1979 The vibration of structures elastically constrained at discrete points. *Journal of Sound and Vibration*, 63, 437-447.

EISINGER, F. L., RAO, M. S. M., and STEININGER, D. A. 1989 Numerical simulation of fluidelastic instability of multispan tubes partially exposed to crossflow. *Trans. of the 10th International Conference on Structural Mechanics in Reactor Technology*, T, 45-56.

ESMONDE, H. et al. 1990 Analysis of non-linear squeeze films: part 1–Physical theory and modelling; Part 2–identification and simulation. Presented at the Pressure Vessels and Piping Conference, Nashville, TN, June 17-21, 1990.

FISHER, N. J., and INGHAM, B. 1988 Measurement of tube-to-support dynamic forces in fretting-wear rigs. *1988 Int. Symp. on Flow-Induced Vibration and Noise*, Vol. 5, pp. 137-156 (ASME).

FISHER, N. J., OLESEN, M. J., ROGERS, R. J., and KO, P. L. 1988 Simulation of tube-to-support dynamic interaction in heat exchange equipment. *1988 Int. Symp. on Flow-Induced Vibration and Noise*, Vol. 5, pp. 121-136 (ASME).

FRICK, T. M., SOBEK, T. E., and REAVIS, R. J. 1984 Overview on the development and implementation of methodologies to compute vibration and wear of steam generator tubes. *Symp. on Flow-Induced Vibrations*, Vol. 3, pp. 149-161 (ASME).

FRICKER, A. J. 1988 Numerical analysis of the fluidelastic vibration of a steam generator tube with loose supports, *1988 Int. Symp. on Flow-Induced Vibration and Noise*, Vol. 5, pp. 105-120 (ASME).

GODON, J. L., and LEBERT, J. 1988 Influence of the tube-support plate clearance on flow-induced vibration in large condensers. *1988 Int. Symp. on Flow-Induced Vibration and Noise*, Vol. 5, pp. 177-186 (ASME).

GOYDER, H. G. D. 1982 Measurements of the natural frequencies and damping of loosely supported tubes in heat exchangers. Vibration in Nuclear Plants, 3rd Keswick Conference, England, May 1982.

GOYDER, H. G. D. 1985 Vibration of loosely supported steam generator tubes. ASME Winter Annual Meeting, Miami Beach, Florida, November 1985, pp. 35-42 (ASME).

GOYDER, H. G. D. 1987 The structural dynamics of the tube bundle vibration problem. Int. Conf. on Flow Induced Vibrations, Bowness-on-Windermere, England, 12-14 May, Paper K4, pp. 467-475.

© IMechE 1991 C416/012

GOYDER, H. G. D., and TEH, C. E. 1988 A study of the impact dynamics of loosely supported heat exchanger tubes. *1988 Int. Symp. on Flow-Induced Vibration and Noise,* Vol. 5, pp. 87-104 (ASME).

HASLINGER, K. H., AND MARTIN, M. L. 1988 Experimental investigation into the non-linear dynamic behavior of a U-tube bundle with dynamically active support strips. *1988 Int. Symp. on Flow-Induced Vibration and Noise,* Vol. 5, pp. 219-234 (ASME).

HASLINGER, K. H., MARTIN, M. L., and STEININGER, D. A. 1987 Pressurized water reactor steam generator tube wear prediction utilizing experimental techniques. Int. Conf. on Flow Induced Vibrations, Bowness-on-Windermere, England, 12-14 May, Paper K2, pp. 437-448.

HASLINGER, K. H., MARTIN, M. L., and VOELKER, R. F. 1987 Dynamic response testing of a single tube and tube array with various tube support geometries. In *Flow-Induced Vibrations-1987,* ASME Publication, PVP-Vol. 122, pp. 117-126.

HASLINGER, K. H., MARTIN, M. L., and STEININGER, D. A. 1989 Experimental characterization of fluid and squeeze film effects in heat exchanger tube supports. In *Flow-Induced Vibration-1989,* ASME Publication, PVP-Vol. 154, pp. 31-41.

HASLINGER, K. H., and STEININGER, D. A. 1984 Steam generator tube/tube support plate interaction characteristics. *Symp. on Flow-Induced Vibrations,* Vol. 3, pp. 45-61 (ASME).

HORN, M. J., HEWITT, E. W., and BIZARD, A. 1988 Staking solutions to tube vibration problems. *1988 Int. Symp. on Flow-Induced Vibration and Noise,* Vol. 5, pp. 187-199 (ASME).

JENDRZEJCZYK, J. A. 1985 Dynamic characteristics of heat exchanger tubes vibrating in a tube support plate inactive mode. In *Fluid-Structure Dynamics,* ASME Publication, PVP-Vol. 98-7. pp. 251-262.

KO, P. L. 1979 Experimental studies of tube fretting in steam generators and heat exchangers. *Journal of Pressure Vessel Technology,* 101, 125-133.

KO, P. L. 1980 Fretting-wear studies of heat exchanger tubes. In *Flow-Induced Heat Exchanger Tube Vibration -1980,* ASME Publication, HTD-Vol. 9, pp. 11-18.

KO, P. L. 1985a Heat exchanger tube fretting wear: review and application to design. *Journal of Tribology,* 107, 149-156.

KO, P. L. 1985b The significance of shear and normal force components on tube wear due to fretting and periodic impacting. *Wear,* 106, 261-281.

KO, P. L., and BASISTA, H. 1984 Correlation of support/impact force and fretting-wear for a heat exchanger tube. *Journal of Pressure Vessel Technology,* 106, 69-77.

KO, P. L., and MAGEL, E. 1989 Impact and sliding wear in steam generators and heat exchangers: new experimental test rig and wear model. In *Flow-Induced Vibration-1989,* ASME Publication, PVP Vol. 154, pp. 63-69.

KO, P. L., and ROGERS, R. J. 1981 Analytical and experimental studies of tube/support interaction in multi-span heat exchanger tubes. *Nuclear Engineering and Design,* 65, 399-409.

KO, P. L., TROMP, J. H., and WECKWERTH, M. K. 1982 Heat exchanger tube fretting wear: correlation of tube motion and wear. *ASTM Special Publication STP-780 Materials Evaluation Under Fretting Conditions,* Symp. on Erosion and Wear, Warminster, Pennsylvania.

LANGRE, E. DE, DOVEIL, F., PORCHER, G., and AXISA, F. 1990 Chaotic and periodic motion of a non-linear oscillator in relation with flow-induced vibrations of loosely supported tubes. Presented at the Pressure Vessels and Piping Conference, June 17-21, 1990, Nashville, TN.

MORETTI, P. M., AND LOWERY, R. L. 1973 Heat exchanger tube vibration characteristics in a no flow condition. Oklahoma State University, Final Report for Tubular Exchanger Manufacturers Association Experimental Program.

MULCAHY, T, M. 1980 Fluid forces on rods vibrating in finite length annular regions. *Journal of Applied Mechanics,* 47, 234-240.

NAKAMURA, T. and FUJITA, K. 1987 A study on impact vibration of loosely held tube by cross flow. Int. Conf. on Flow Induced Vibrations, Bowness-on-Windermere, England, 12-14 May, Paper K1, pp. 427-436.

RAO, M. S. M., GUPTA, G. D., EISINGER, F. L., HIBBITT, H. D., and STEININGER, D. A. 1987 Computer modeling of vibration and wear multi-span tubes with clearances at tube supports. Int. Conf. on Flow Induced Vibrations, Bowness-on-Windermere, England, 12-14 May, Paper K3, pp. 449-466.

RAO, M. S. M., STEININGER, D. A., and EISINGER, F. L. 1988 Numerical simulation of fluidelastic vibration and wear of multispan tubes with clearances at supports. *1988 Int. Symp. on Flow-Induced Vibration and Noise*, Vol. 5, pp. 235-250 (ASME).

ROGERS, R. J., and AHN, K. J. 1986 Fluid damping and hydrodynamic mass in finite length cylindrical squeeze films with rectilinear motion. *Flow-Induced Vibration-1986*, ASME Publication, PVP-Vol. 104, pp. 99-105.

ROGERS, R. J., and PICK, R. J. 1976 On the dynamic spatial response of a heat exchanger tube with intermittent baffle contacts. *Nuclear Engineering and Design*, 36, 81-90.

ROGERS, R. J., and PICK, R. J. 1977 Factors associated with support plate forces due to heat-exchanger tube vibratory contact. *Nuclear Engineering and Design*, 44, 247-253.

ROGERS, R. J., TAYLOR, C., and PETTIGREW, M. J. 1984 Fluid effects on multi-span heat-exchanger tube vibration. *Topics in Fluid Structure Interaction*, pp. 17-26 (ASME).

SHIN, Y. S., JENDRZEJCZYK, J. A., and WAMBSGANSS, M. W. 1977 Effect of tube/support interaction on the vibration of a tube on multiple supports. Argonne National Laboratory, Technical Memorandum, ANL-CT-77-5.

SHIN, Y. S., SASS, D. E., and JENDRZEJCZYK, J. A. 1978 Vibro-impact responses of a tube with tube-baffle interaction. Presented at the Joint ASME/CSME Pressure Vessels & Piping Conference, Montreal, Canada, June 25-30, ASME Paper 78-PVP-20.

WEAVER, D. S., and SCHNEIDER, W. 1983 The effect of flat bar supports on the crossflow induced response of heat exchanger U-tubes. *Journal of Engineering for Power*, 105, 755-781.

YEH, Y. S., and CHEN, S. S. 1990 Flow-induced vibration of component cooling water heat exchangers. Presented at the Pressure Vessels and Piping Conference, June 17-21, 1990, Nashville, TN.

YETISIR, M., and WEAVER, D. S. 1986 The dynamics of heat exchanger U-bend tubes with flat bar supports. *Journal of Pressure Vessel Technology*, 108, 406-412.

YU, X. 1986 An analysis of tube failure in a U-shape tube bundle. *Flow-Induced Vibration-1986*, ASME Publication PVP-Vol. 104, pp.187-192.

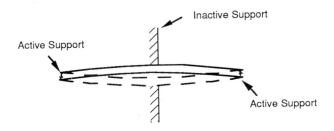

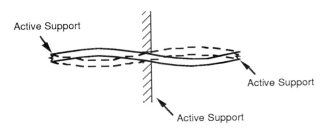

Fig. 1. Support-inactive and support-active modes

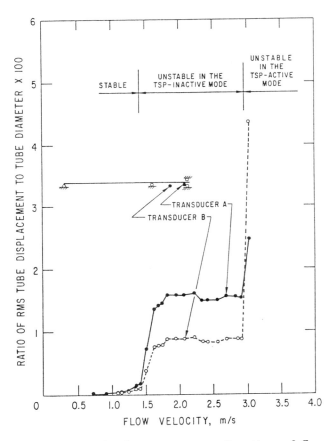

Fig. 2. Tube displacement as a function of flow velocity for a two-span tube among a rigid tube row with a loose support (Chen, Jendrzejczyk, and Wambsganss 1984)

C416/090

Non-linear dynamics of a single flexible cylinder within a rotated triangle array

M M PAIDOUSSIS, PhD, CEng, FIMechE, FRSC, FASME, FCSME, MIAHR
S J PRICE, BSc, PhD, MASME, MAIAA and W N MUREITHI, MEng
Department of Mechanical Engineering, McGill University, Montreal, Canada

SYNOPSIS The response of a heat exchanger tube, under the excitation of an experimentally determined non–linear fluid force field has been simulated for a rotated triangle array ($P/D = 1.375$) using an explicit time integration algorithm. After the onset of self–excited oscillation, limit cycle amplitudes were found to increase approximately linearly with flow velocity for large values of the reduced mass damping parameter. The existence of multi–instability regions has been confirmed for low values of the mass damping parameter. Complex tube dynamics are predicted due to the non–linearities introduced by impact/sliding at a loose support. Periodic motion has been found over a significant portion of the parameter range studied. Chaotic response where the tube is continuously in sliding contact with the support occurs eventually, after successive states of stable periodic motion.

NOTATION

a	ratio of gap velocity to free-stream velocity, U/U_∞
c	equivalent modal mechanical damping
$\bar{c}$	non–dimensional modal mechanical damping, $c/m\,\omega_o$
C_D, C_L	drag and lift coefficients based on U_∞
D	cylinder diameter
e	coefficient of restitution
e_r	radial tube/support clearance
$\bar{e}_r$	non–dimensional tube/support clearance, e_r/D
F_{xf}, F_{yf}	in–flow and cross–flow fluid forces
$\bar{F}_{xf}$, $\bar{F}_{yf}$	non–dimensinal fluid forces
F_{xi}, F_{yi}	impact forces in the x and y directions
$\bar{F}_{xi}$, $\bar{F}_{yi}$	non–dimensional impact forces
k	equivalent modal mechanical stiffness
m	cylinder mass per unit length
$\bar{m}$	non–dimensional cylinder mass $m/\rho D^2$
N_r, N_t	radial and transverse impulses at impact
r	tube radial position, $(x^2 + y^2)^{1/2}$
t	time
T	spacing between cylinders in the y direction
U	reference gap velocity
U_r	flow velocity relative to the cylinder
U_∞	free–stream velocity
V	non–dimensional velocity, $U/\omega_o D$
x, y	in–flow and cross–flow cylinder displacements
$\bar{x}$, $\bar{y}$	non–dimensional cylinder displacements
α	induced incidence of the cylinder
δ	cylinder mechanical logarithmic decrement
μ	flow retardation parameter
ρ	fluid density
τ	dimensionless time, $\omega_o t$
$\Delta\tau$	dimensionless time delay
ω_o	radian frequency of the cylinder

1 INTRODUCTION

The dynamics of tube arrays subject to fluid cross–flow are extremely complicated due to the turbulent separated flow in the array, coupled with geometric irregularities. This complexity is compounded by tube intermediate support conditions which vary from fixed or preloaded (with permanent tube/support contact) to completely free.

The flow field (and its effects) can, at present, only be realistically studied experimentally. One experimental approach, involves direct measurement of the fluid forces acting on a representative cylinder within the array. Hot-wire anemometry is also used to probe the flow field itself; such measurements yield turbulence intensities in the interstitial gaps as well as frequencies of any dominant periodicities (e.g., vortex shedding) within the array.

Of practical importance is the resulting tube excitation by the flow. Fluidelastic instability is the most potent and damaging mechanism in tube arrays. Instability may be of the negative damping type, involving only one degree of freedom, which predominates at low values of the mass damping parameter $\bar{m}\delta$ (1,2), or of the coupled–mode fluid stiffness type, which predominates in the high range of $\bar{m}\delta$.

Fluidelastic instability is characterized by a critical flow velocity past which tube limit–cycle motion is initiated, the limit cycle amplitudes increasing with flow velocity. The limiting amplitudes are caused by non–linearities either in the fluid force field, or in the structure, i.e, impacting at support locations.

The critical flow velocity for fluidelastic instability (U_c) is probably of most practical importance to the heat exchanger designer. Several theoretical models for predicting U_c have been developed. The approach taken ranges form the purely analytical (3), through the quasi-steady semi–analytical models (4), to the semi–empirical unsteady models (2,5); the latter, as might be expected, showing the best agreement with experiment — they, however, require the largest amount of experimental data as input.

Considerably less work has been done on the post-instability behaviour of tube arrays. Due to the linearization of the fluid forces (about the tube equilibrium position), limit cycle amplitudes could not be predicted by the above mentioned models. The analysis of (6) was the first to include fluid force non-linearities, enabling limit cycle amplitudes to be predicted. A single degree of freedom model was considered by (6), with tube motion occurring only in the cross-flow direction. The rate of increase of the limit cycle amplitude was found to be greater at low values of $\overline{m}\delta$, than for higher values.

Post instability tube behaviour is important because of the damage that results when tube/support or tube/tube contact occurs. An understanding of the tube dynamics in the presence of tube/support interaction is essential for predicting tube wear rates.

This study is one such endeavour and will be presented in two parts. Firstly, the non-linear fluid force field is measured in a rotated triangular array of pitch-to-diameter $P/D = 1.375$. This experimentally measured force field is employed with a quasi-steady model (4). Fluidelastic instability, and the resulting limit-cycle motion are investigated for a tube located in row 3 of the array.

In the second part of this study, structural non-linearities are included in the dynamic analysis (via a circular tube support). Numerical simulations are performed to uncover the resulting tube behaviour in the post-instability regime. The existence of chaotic motion is also investigated; phase flows, response spectra, bifurcation diagrams, and Poincaré sections are used to confirm the existence of, and to probe the nature of, chaotic vibrations.

2 THEORY

Consider a single flexibly mounted cylinder within an array of rigid cylinders, Fig.1(a). The gap flow velocity approaching the cylinder (U), is related to the upstream flow velocity (U_∞) by,

$$\frac{U}{U_\infty} = \frac{T}{T - \frac{1}{2}D} = a\,.$$

Motion of the cylinder is limited by impact forces at the support plate; the tube/support clearance is e_r.

The equations of motion for the orthogonal directions are,

$$\begin{aligned} m\ddot{x} &+ c\dot{x} + kx = F_{xf} + F_{xi}, \\ m\ddot{y} &+ c\dot{y} + ky = F_{yf} + F_{yi}, \end{aligned} \quad (1)$$

where m is the modal mass per unit length, including added mass, and c and k represent the modal structural damping and stiffness, respectively. Subscripts 'f' and 'i' represent fluid and impact forces, respectively. Equations (1) can be non-dimensionalized to give

$$\begin{aligned} \overline{x}'' &+ \overline{c}\,\overline{x}' + \overline{x} = \overline{F}_{xf} + \overline{F}_{xi}, \\ \overline{y}'' &+ \overline{c}\,\overline{y}' + \overline{y} = \overline{F}_{yf} + \overline{F}_{yi}, \end{aligned} \quad (2)$$

where $\overline{x} = x/D$, $\overline{y} = y/D$, D being the cylinder diameter; $\overline{c} = c/m\,\omega_o$, where $\omega_o^2 = k/m$; ( )' indicates differentiation with respect to non-dimensional time $\omega_o t$.

2.1 The fluid forces

The fluid related forces are derived following a quasi-steady analysis (4). Considering the x-motion for instance, the fluid force per unit tube length is

$$F_{xf} = \frac{\rho\,U_r^2\,D}{2\,a^2}\left[C_L\,\sin\alpha + C_D\,\cos\alpha\right], \quad (3)$$

where ρ is the fluid density, U_r is the flow velocity relative to the tube, $U_r^2 = (U - \dot{x})^2 + \dot{y}^2$, and α is the flow approach angle given by $\alpha = \sin^{-1}(\dot{y}/U_r)$. The factor $a = (U/U_\infty)$ accounts for the fact that C_L and C_D are based (as measured) on the upstream flow velocity, U_∞.

Introducing the non-dimensional parameters $\overline{m} = m/\rho D^2$ and $V = U/\omega_o D$, the fluid forces become,

$$\begin{aligned} \overline{F}_{xf} &= \left(\frac{1}{2\overline{m}a^2}\right)\left\{(V - \overline{x}')^2 + \overline{y}'^2\right\}^{1/2} \\ &\quad \times \left[\overline{y}'\,C_L + (V - \overline{x})\,C_D\right], \\ \overline{F}_{yf} &= \left(\frac{1}{2\overline{m}c^2}\right)\left\{(V - \overline{x}')^2 + \overline{y}'^2\right\}^{1/2} \\ &\quad \times \left[(V - \overline{x}')\,C_L - \overline{y}'\,C_D\right]. \end{aligned} \quad (4)$$

An important quantity in the quasi-steady analysis, is the time delay $\Delta\tau$ between tube displacement and readjustment of the fluid force field to reflect the new tube position. Supposing C_L and C_D to be known as functions of $\overline{x}$ and $\overline{y}$, then at a given time τ, the effective $\overline{x}$ and $\overline{y}$ are those corresponding to a previous time $\tau - \Delta\tau$; hence,

$$\begin{aligned} C_L(\tau) &= C_L\left(\overline{x}(\tau - \Delta\tau), \overline{y}(\tau - \Delta\tau)\right), \\ \text{and} \quad C_D(\tau) &= C_D\left(\overline{x}(\tau - \Delta\tau), \overline{y}(\tau - \Delta\tau)\right). \end{aligned} \quad (5)$$

The time delay $\Delta\tau$ is estimated (4) to be,

$$\Delta\tau = \mu\,\omega_o\,D/U, \quad \text{where } \mu = O(1).$$

2.2 The tube/support forces

The support forces $\overline{F}_{xi}$ and $\overline{F}_{yi}$ in equation (2) are not explicitly calculated. Instead, the support effect is introduced using an impact model for the radial motion, and a Coulomb friction model for the transverse motion of the tube relative to the support. Planar motion of the tube centre of mass may be represented as shown in Fig.1(b). At the contact location c, the tube approach velocity is u, while the velocity after impact is v. Considering the momentum change in the radial direction, we have

$$m\,u_r + N_r = m\,v_r, \quad (6)$$

where N_r is the impulse of the radial impact force. The corresponding equation for the momentum change in the transverse direction is,

$$m\,u_t + N_t = m\,v_t. \quad (7)$$

To account for the energy loss at impact (radial direction only), a coefficient of restitution, e, is used; hence,

$$\tfrac{1}{2}\,m\,v_r^2 = e^2\left(\tfrac{1}{2}\,m\,u_r^2\right). \quad (8)$$

The normal and transverse impulses are related by the coefficient of friction,

$$\mu = N_t/N_r. \qquad (9)$$

By using equations (6) and (8) we obtain

$$N_r = m|u_r|(1 + e). \qquad (10)$$

From equations (7), (9) and (10), the transverse velocities before and after impact are related by

$$v_t = u_t - \mu\, u_r (1 + e), \qquad (v_t > 0), \qquad (11)$$

where the velocity directions are as defined in Fig.1(b). Clearly equation (11) is only valid if $v_t > 0$; otherwise we have the adherence condition, for which $v_t = 0$. The velocity vector diagram in Fig.1(c) relates the polar coordinate velocities derived above to their Cartesian counterparts. The transformation equations before impact, for instance, are

$$\begin{aligned}
\overline{x}' &= (u_r \cos\theta - u_t \sin\theta)/\omega_o D, \\
\overline{y}' &= (u_r \sin\theta + u_t \cos\theta)/\omega_o D,
\end{aligned} \qquad (12)$$

where $\theta = \tan^{-1}(\overline{y}/\overline{x})$; $\overline{x}, \overline{y}$ are coordinates of the impact location c. When $u_r = 0$, pure sliding motion occurs. The radial tube/support contact force is then mu_t^2/e_r. This results in a transverse frictional force given by $\mu m u_t^2/e_r$.

2.3 Solution of the equations of motion

The final form of the equations of motion is

$$\begin{aligned}
\overline{x}'' + \overline{c}\overline{x}' + \overline{x} &= \left(\frac{1}{2\overline{m}a^2}\right)\left\{(V - \overline{x}')^2 + \overline{y}'^2\right\}^{1/2} \\
&\quad \times \left[\overline{y}'\, C_L(\tau) + (V - \overline{x}')C_D(\tau)\right], \\
\overline{y}'' + \overline{c}\overline{y}' + \overline{y} &= \left(\frac{1}{2\overline{m}a^2}\right)\left\{(V - \overline{x}')^2 + \overline{y}'^2\right\}^{1/2} \\
&\quad \times \left[(V - \overline{x}')\, C_L(\tau) - \overline{y}'\, C_D(\tau)\right], \quad (13)
\end{aligned}$$

where $C_L(\tau)$ and $C_D(\tau)$ are as in equation (5) to account for the time delay. Equations (13) are valid as long as the tube radial displacement $\overline{r} = (\overline{x}^2 + \overline{y}^2)^{1/2}$ is less than $\overline{e}_r$, the radial clearance. When $\overline{r} = \overline{e}_r$, impacting occurs.

Equations (13) are numerically integrated using a fourth order Runge-Kutta algorithm from the starting set of initial conditions $\overline{y} = 0.04$, $\overline{x} = \overline{x}' = \overline{y}' = 0$. When the impact condition ($\overline{r} = \overline{e}_r$) is satisfied, equations (8) and (11) are used to determine the new velocities after impact, which are converted to Cartesian coordinate velocities through a transformation similar to equation (12).

Before presenting the results of the numerical simulations, the steady lift and drag coefficients which were measured experimentally, will be presented.

3 EXPERIMENTAL MEASUREMENT OF THE FLUID FORCES

Fluid force coefficient measurements were conducted in a blow-down wind tunnel; a detailed description of the tunnel may be found in ref.(7). The test array of rotated triangle geometry ($P/D = 1.375$) consisted of 7 tube rows, with alternate rows containing 14 and 15 tubes. All the tubes in the array were rigidly fixed. The tube under test, located in the third row of the array, was mounted on a biaxial force balance.

Preliminary tests on the effect of Reynolds number, Re, on C_L and C_D showed that, while a significant change in the force coefficients occurred at low values of Re, ($< 9.9 \times 10^3$), a steady state was reached for Re $> 9.9 \times 10^3$. The force coefficients to be presented were measured at Re $= 1.04 \times 10^4$. A bi-directional traversing mechanism on which the force balance was mounted allowed the test tube to be displaced in increments of $0.019D$, where $D = 1$ in. (25.4 mm). This enabled a complete map of of C_L and C_D as functions of $\overline{x}$ and $\overline{y}$ to be obtained in the range $|\overline{x}|$ and $|\overline{y}| \leq 0.23$.

Fig.2(a, b) shows the steady lift and drag coefficients as functions of in-flow and cross-flow tube displacements. The lift coefficient is extremely sensitive to cross-flow displacements ($\overline{y}$) in the vicinity of the equilibrium position $\overline{y} = 0$. For upstream displacement ($-\overline{x}$), $\partial C_L/\partial\overline{y} = -180$ in the band $|\overline{y}| < 0.02$. Outside this band, C_L is more dependent on the in-flow position. The dependence of C_D on $\overline{y}$ is the same for most values of $\overline{x} < 0$ (Fig.2(b)). However, downstream ($\overline{x} > 0$), an increasing trend is observed at the extreme values of $\overline{y}$, as the tube increasingly blocks the gap between its two downstream neighbours.

4 DYNAMICS OF A SINGLE FLEXIBLE CYLINDER

For the purpose of determing the non-dimensional critical flow velocity (V_c) for fluidelastic instability, as well as the uninhibited rate of growth of the limit cycle amplitude, the tube support was initially ignored. Hence, the support reaction, represented by the terms F_{xi} and F_{yi} in equation (1) is zero.

Previous studies have shown that, at large values of the mass damping parameter ($\overline{m}\delta$), V_c varies approximately linearly with $\overline{m}\delta$. For $\overline{m}\delta = 1000$, the non-linear analysis gives a critical flow velocity of $V_c = 10.8$, in agreement with the linearized quasi-steady analysis of ref.(4). Fig.3 shows the post-instability limit cycle amplitude for cross-flow motion as a function of non-dimensional flow velocity, V. The instability was found to be of the supercritical Hopf type; hence, for $V < V_c$, tube oscillations decayed to zero for all initial conditions. The lowest limit cycle amplitude is $\overline{y} = 0.02$. This value of $\overline{y}$ corresponds to the limit of the band (centered around $\overline{y} = 0$) in which C_L varies linearly with $\overline{y}$, as described earlier. Due to this linear behaviour of C_L near $\overline{y} = 0$ (for the most part of the $\overline{x}$ range), the minimum limit cycle amplitude is 0.02, for any velocity at which the system is unstable. For $V > V_c$ the limit cycle amplitude increases almost linearly with V. The instability was of the negative damping type, and occurred only in the cross-flow direction. In-flow vibration resulting from fluid coupling exhibits a trend similar to Fig.3. However, in-flow amplitudes are two orders of magnitude lower than the cross-flow amplitudes. The drag coefficient, C_D, is relatively independent of $\overline{y}$ near the equilibrium position ($\overline{x} = \overline{y} = 0$); hence, despite large cross-flow vibration, there is little in-flow excitation.

Low $\overline{m}\delta$ linear stability behaviour has previously been charaterized by regions of instability, interspersed with stable regions over a certain range of V — until a final velocity is reached, past which, stability is no longer regained.

Fig.4(a, b) shows in-flow and cross-flow limit cycle amplitude variations with V for $\overline{m} = 100$, $\delta = 0.01$. An unstable region is observed prior to the final instability.

Notice that in the unstable velocity range, the lowest cross–flow amplitude is 0.02.

In–flow motion (Fig.4(a)) is three orders of magnitude smaller than its cross–flow counterpart. Once again, the in–flow direction is stable and motion is only induced through the weak fluid coupling between the orthogonal directions.

When δ is decreased by a factor of 10 to 0.001, vibration amplitudes increase to approximately double their values at $\delta = 0.01$, Fig.4(c). For this lower damping level, a second instability region exists in the lower velocity range $0.065 < V < 0.077$. A third instability region is observed when δ is reduced to 0.0001, Fig.4(d). [1] The velocity ranges corresponding to these instability regions are identical to those predicted by the linearized analysis. This indicates that non–linearities in the fluid forces (at least position–dependent non–linearities) do not eliminate these multiple instability regions. The increase in amplitude with the second reduction in δ is much lower than that associated with the first, being only approximately 15% at $V = 0.13$ and less than 5% at $V = 0.45$. This variation in limit cycle amplitude with δ is summarized in Fig.5, where the amplitude at a constant non–dimensional flow velocity $V = 0.13$ is plotted versus δ.

5 THE EFFECT OF A LOOSE SUPPORT ON TUBE RESPONSE

In this section, the presence of the tube motion–limiting support is taken into account. The most important effect of the support is to introduce strong coupling between the two orthogonal directions once vibration amplitudes surpass the tube/support clearance. The results presented and discussed in this section are for tube and fluid parameters in the low mass–damping parameter range ($\overline{m} = 10$, $\delta = 0.05$). For the tube support, the coefficient of restitution used is 0.7, while the Coulomb friction coefficient $\mu = 0.1$. The tube/support clearance $e_r = 0.08D$. The tube natural frequency is 10 Hz. For these tube parameters, final instability occurs at $V_c = 0.32$.

Over a small range of V above V_c, the vibration amplitude remains below the tube-to-support gap size. Although coupling with the in–flow direction is limited, a distinct orbital motion is observed, with in–flow vibration being at double the cross–flow frequency. Fig.6(a) shows this orbital motion at $V = 0.34$. A time trace of the induced in–flow vibration and the corresponding frequency spectrum are shown in Fig.6(b, c).

The limit cycle amplitude quickly grows to reach e_r. At $V = 0.36$ impacting occurs at essentially two locations. As shown in Fig.6(d), the orbital motion is complex and appears chaotic. This chaotic character is well depicted in the in–flow time trace and the corresponding frequency spectrum, see Fig.6(e, f). Cross–flow motion is predominantly periodic. At this velocity, the effect of fluid coupling is still significant, as supported by the peak near 20 Hz (in Fig.6(f)) corresponding to the figure–of–eight motion observed at lower velocities (with no impacting).

The velocity range over which this chaotic motion occurs is fairly limited. Such that when V is increased to 0.38, even the in–flow motion is primarily periodic, with intermittent periods of chaotic motion. At $V = 0.40$, the response is entirely periodic. A period doubling (flip) bifurcation in the orbital motion occurs near $V = 0.42$. As the flow velocity is increased further, a more complex sequence of changes occurs, eventually leading again to chaotic motion.

The sequence of changes or 'bifurcations' leading to chaos is best represented in the form of a bifurcation diagram. Any quantity deemed a representative system excitation parameter may be used to generate the diagram. Global changes in the variational trend of a selected quantity representing the system response (e.g. amplitude or peak velocity) as the excitation parameter is varied indicate bifurcations in the global system response. Certain bifurcation trends (e.g. a period doubling sequence), have been identified as precursors to chaos. The flow velocity V is the excitation parameter that is varied. In the pair of bifurcation diagrams shown in Fig.7, the magnitudes of vibration amplitudes are plotted in the $\overline{x}$ and $\overline{y}$ directions.

The sequence of changes (after the Hopf bifurcation) described above was: periodic motion (no impacting) $\rightarrow$ chaotic $\rightarrow$ period 1 $\rightarrow$ period 2 motion. Representative values of V corresponding to this sequence are: 0.34, 0.36, 0.40, and 0.45 in Fig.7. The period 2 motion is not symmetrical about $\overline{y} = 0$. However, this motion approaches symmetry as V is increased, which is achieved near $V = 0.47$. This situation seems to be unstable, resulting in the sudden change in tube response past this flow velocity.

The next important bifurcation occurs at $V \simeq 0.60$. The resulting motion is almost purely cross–flow at a frequency close to $3\omega_o$. From Fig.7(a), the diminution in in–flow motion is seen to be large. The onset of this new motion coincides with a decrease of the transverse impact velocity to zero; i.e., sliding motion is replaced by sticking. The same high frequency motion is sustained at higher V. However, the initial symmetry (about $\overline{y} = 0$) breaks down near $V = 0.68$. The two branches in the bifurcation diagram in the range $0.68 < V < 0.91$ therefore represent asymmetric motion (with alternately one of two possible amplitudes), as opposed to period–2 motion as is the case near $V = 0.44$. Symmetric motion returns in the velocity range $0.91 < V < 1.06$. The next bifurcation, at $V \simeq 1.06$, results in chaotic motion as reflected in Fig.7.

Typical response in the chaotic regime is shown in Fig.8 for $V = 1.09$. A significant proportion of the response now involves continuous rubbing contact. The in–flow frequency spectrum (Fig.8(c)) is broad–banded with significant low frequency content, typical of chaotic motions.

The Poincaré section method is usually applied to chaotic systems to uncover any underlying organization in the apparently random response. This would be particularly useful in experimental studies when trying to distinguish truly chaotic vibration from that due to random excitation. The Poincaré section presented here is a plot of $\overline{x}'$ versus $\overline{x}$ whenever the system crosses the plane $\overline{y} = 0$ with velocity $\overline{y}' > 0$. The Poincaré section at $V = 1.09$ is shown in Fig.9. Distinct structure and organization is seen to exist in this cross section of the phase space.

---

[1]It should be remarked that it is not pretended that such low values of δ are achievable in practice; the intention here was to see what the effect of increasing or decreasing δ is on the number of unstable regions.

Chaotic motion is sustained at higher values of V, except for a periodic window near $V = 1.38$.

6 CONCLUSION

The position dependent non–linear steady fluid force field in row 3 of a rotated triangle array has been determined experimentally. The steady fluid forces were found to be relatively independent of Reynolds number (Re) for Re $> 9.9 \times 10^3$.

In the vicinity of the cylinder equilibrium position, C_L was found to be extremely sensitive to cross–flow cylinder displacement, which is responsible for the highly unstable nature of this array.

Application of the measured forces to a quasi–steady stability analysis model confirmed the existence of multiple instability regions for low values of the mass–damping parameter, previously predicted by linear models. Coupling between the unstable cross–flow direction and the stable in–flow direction was found to be weak; in the neighbourhood of the cylinder equilibrium position. At high values of $\overline{m}\,\delta$, limit cycle amplitudes increased almost linearly with flow velocity.

Some preliminary work on the effect of a loose support on the tube response has also been reported. Strong in–flow/cross–flow coupling was introduced by the loose support. A complex sequence of bifurcations was observed as flow velocity was increased above the Hopf bifurcation value. Over most of the velocity range, tube response is periodic, eventually becoming chaotic at the higher velocities.

Chaotic motion involved significant tube/support sliding contact with high response frequencies due to impacting. This has important implications on the amount tube wear that would result in the chaotic regime.

ACKNOWLEDGEMENT

The authors are grateful to Le programme "Formation de chercheurs et Aide à la Recherche" (FCAR) of Quebec and the Natural Sciences and Engineering Research Council of Canada for supporting this research programme.

REFERENCES

(1) PRICE, S.J. and PAÏDOUSSIS, M.P. A constrained mode analysis of the fluidelastic instability of a double row of flexible circular cylinders subject to cross flow: a theoretical investigation of system parameters. *Journal of Sound and Vibration*, 1986, 105, 121–142.

(2) CHEN, S.-S. Instability mechanisms and stability criteria of a group of circular cylinders subject to cross–flow. *ASME Journal of Vibration, Acoustics, Stress and Reliability in Design*, 1983, 105, 51–58.

(3) LEVER, J.H. and WEAVER, D.S. A theoretical model for the fluid–elastic instability in heat exchanger tube bundles. *ASME Journal of Pressure Vessel Technology*, 1982, 104, 147–158.

(4) PRICE, S.J. and PAÏDOUSSIS, M.P., An improved mathematical model for the stability of cylinder rows subject to cross–flow. *Journal of Sound and Vibration*, 1984, 97, 615–640.

(5) TANAKA, H. and TAKAHARA, S. Fluid elastic vibration of tube array in cross flow. *Journal of Sound and Vibration*, 1981, 77, 19–37.

(6) PRICE, S.J. and VALERIO, N.R. A non–linear investigation of single–degree–of–freedom instability in cylinder arrays subject to cross–flow. *Journal of Sound and Vibration*, 1990, 137, 419–432.

(7) PRICE, S.J., MARK, B. and PAÏDOUSSIS, M.P. An experimental stability analysis of a single flexible cylinder in an array of rigid cylinders and subject to cross flow. *ASME Journal of Pressure Vessel Technology*, 1986, 108, 62–72.

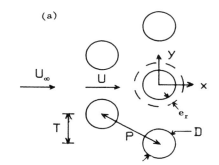

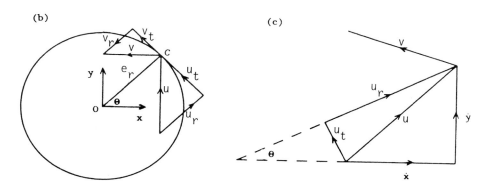

Fig. 1. (a) Tube array in cross–flow; (b) impact circle geometry; (c) velocity vector diagram for coordinate transformation.

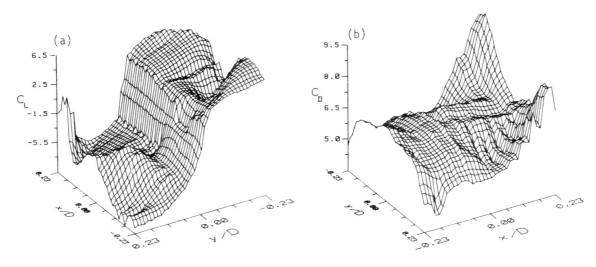

Fig. 2. The measured force coefficients: (a) lift; (b) drag.

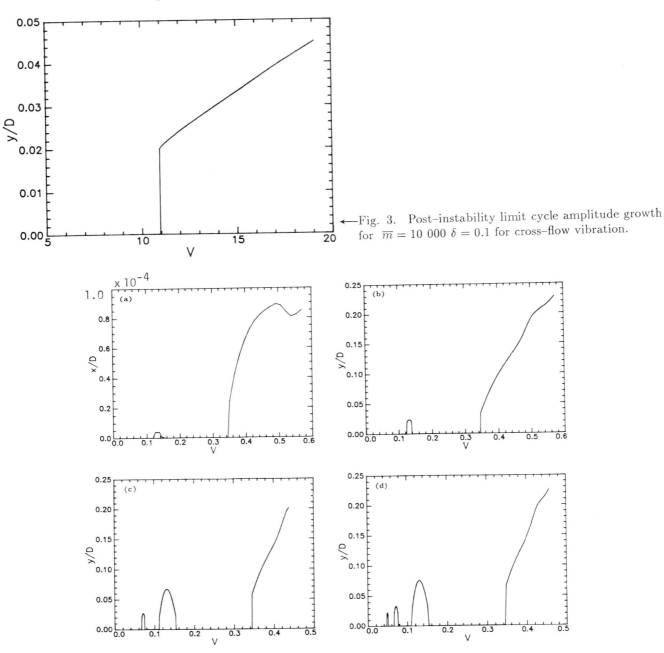

←Fig. 3. Post–instability limit cycle amplitude growth for $\overline{m} = 10\,000$ $\delta = 0.1$ for cross–flow vibration.

Fig. 4. Limit cycle amplitude growth for (a) $\overline{m}\delta = 1.0$ in–flow, (b) $\overline{m}\delta = 1.0$ cross–flow, (c) $\overline{m}\delta = 0.1$ cross–flow, (d) $\overline{m}\delta = 0.01$ cross–flow.

© IMechE 1991 C416/090

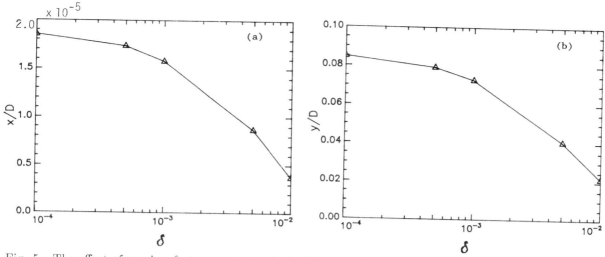

Fig. 5. The effect of varying δ at a constant velocity $V = 0.13$ ($\overline{m} = 100$): (a) in-flow ; (b) cross-flow.

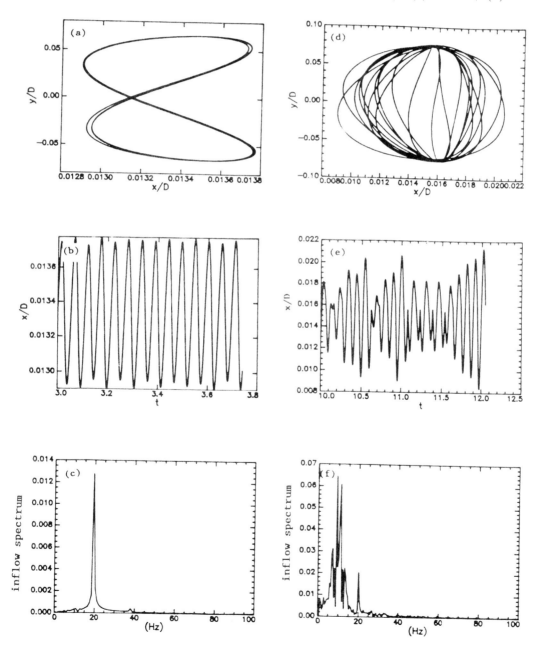

Fig. 6. Tube response at $(a - c)$ $V = 0.34$, $(d - f)$ $V = 0.36$; (a) and (d) show motion in the $(\overline{x}, \overline{y})$ plane; (b) and (e) are in-flow time traces; (c) and (f) power spectra for in-flow motion.

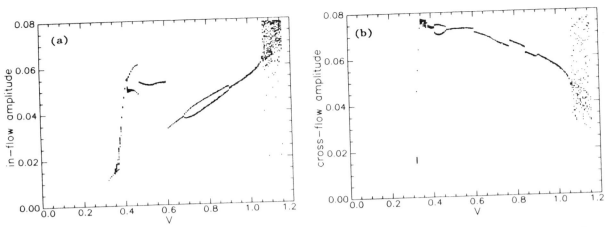

Fig. 7. Bifurcation diagrams based on V: (a) in-flow peak amplitude; (b) cross-flow peak amplitude.

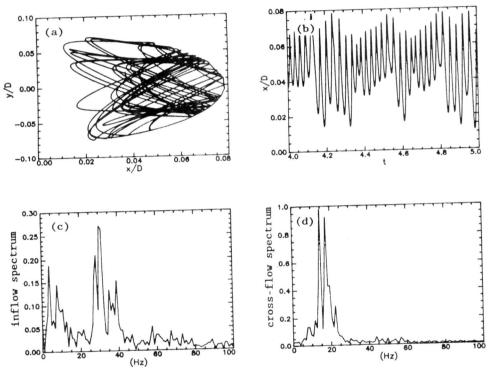

Fig. 8. Tube response in the chaotic regime ($V = 1.09$).

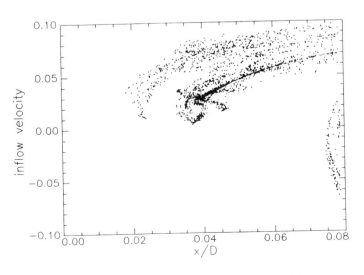

Fig. 9. Poincaré section at $V = 1.09$.

C416/021

Vibro-impacting behaviour of fluid-elastically unstable heat exchanger tubes with support clearances

A J FRICKER, BSc, CEng, MIMechE
Technology and Environmental Centre, National Power, Leatherhead, Surrey

SYNOPSIS Flow-induced vibration of PWR steam generator tube bundles can lead to wear, especially in the U-bend region where the tubes are supported by anti-vibration bars (AVBs). The presence of clearances between the tubes and AVBs can allow impacting and fretting to occur, leading to high wear rates in some cases. Computer simulations of the nonlinear vibration of loosely supported tubes have been carried out to predict impact forces. Results are given for the analysis of an outermost U-bend with a gap at one AVB location. One-sided and symmetrical two-sided impacting have been analysed and the results compared with a simplified one degree-of-freedom (dof) model in order to derive design equations for general use.

NOTATION

C	clearance on one side of tube
m	modal mass
$\bar{P}$	mean impact force
U_c	critical flow velocity for fluid-elastic instability
U_e	effective flow velocity
λ	empirical constant
ω	effective vibration frequency when impacting occurs
ω_n	tube natural frequency
ζ_o	damping ratio at zero flow velocity

1 INTRODUCTION

The U-tubes in PWR steam generators are supported in the U-bend region by anti-vibration bars (AVBs). These AVBs pass between the tube rows in order to prevent the two-phase flow from causing high vibration levels. However, clearances exist between the tubes and AVBs, therefore it is possible for some tubes vibrate within these clearances and cause wear.

A programme of work is being carried out to provide methods of analysing non-linear tube vibration and wear in PWR steam generators. Part of this programme is the development of a computer program (IMPACT) for analysing the nonlinear vibration of a tube when gaps are present at the AVBs.

The present Paper describes an analysis of the fluid-elastic instability of an outermost U-bend when gaps are present at one AVB location. The results are compared with a simplified one degree-of-freedom (dof) model in order to derive design equations.

2 NONLINEAR BEHAVIOUR OF AN IMPACTING TUBE

2.1 Numerical Model

The system to be analysed is shown in Fig. 1. It consists an outermost U-bend which is supported at six locations by AVBs which pass down between the rows of tubes. The AVBs prevent excessive out-of-plane motion of the tubes and also provide frictional forces to reduce the in-plane motion. In this model it is assumed that AVB support number 3 contains a gap on each side of the tube but all the other support points are 'active' (i.e. provide perfect pinned supports for out-of-plane motion). The U-bend was modelled by the finite element method using a total of 70 beam elements to model the U-bend (10 elements between each AVB support). Only out-of-plane motion was allowed in the finite element model.

In the nonlinear analysis, the loose AVB support was modelled by a rigid stop on each side of the tube with a gap between the tube and the stop. The impact stiffness between the tube and the stop (which represents the effects of local tube and AVB flexibility) was modelled by a linear spring with a nominal stiffness of 2×10^6 N/m. No impact damping was included in the model since this has previously been found to have only a small effect on the impact dynamics. The damping ratio of the fundamental mode at zero flow was assumed to be 2% and the damping ratio of the higher modes was assumed to be proportional to

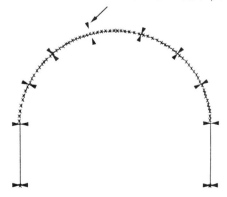

Fig. 1 Finite element model of U-bend with one inactive AVB support

$1/\sqrt{frequency}$, with a lower limit of 0.5%. The analysis used the lowest 40 modes of vibration, which included frequencies up to 1667 Hz. The time history output was generated at 100 μs intervals and the timestep length used during the impacts was 10 μs. Convergence tests had demonstrated that these values provided adequate accuracy.

A modal method is used for the transient solution of the nonlinear system using a 'pseudo-force' method [1,2]. Similar nonlinear analyses have been described in references [3] and [4]. The critical velocity ratio (i.e. the actual flow velocity divided by the critical flow velocity at the point of instability) for the fundamental mode was specified as input to the program and the positive or negative damping of the tube was calculated from the equation:

$$\zeta_{tot} = \zeta_o \left[1 - \frac{\omega_n}{\omega} \frac{U_e^2}{U_c^2} \right] \qquad (1)$$

where ζ_o is the damping ratio at zero flow, ω_n is the natural frequency of the mode without impacting, ω is the effective vibrational frequency with impacting, U_e is the effective flow velocity and U_c is the critical flow velocity. Equation (1) was derived from a simple fluid-elastic model which fits the well known Connors equation [5] and agrees reasonably well with some of the two-phase measurements made at NPTEC.

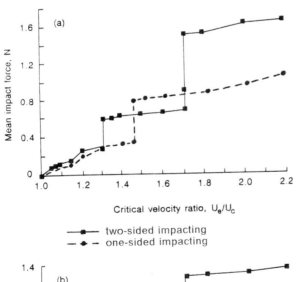

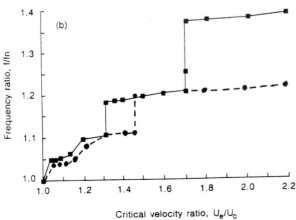

Fig. 2   Variation of mean impact force and frequency ratio with critical velocity ratio

If $U_e > U_c$, the total damping will be negative and, given non-zero initial conditions, the tube vibrational amplitude will increase with time until impacting occurs. Some sort of steady-state is generally reached when the energy input per cycle is equal to the energy dissipated due to impacting. The energy dissipation is caused by the impacts transferring energy from the fundamental (unstable) mode to the higher frequency (damped) modes. When impacting occurs the effective frequency of the fundamental mode increases somewhat and therefore, according to equation (1), the instability is reduced. The effective frequencies of all the modes of vibration are regularly re-calculated during the simulation and the damping in each mode is updated according to equation (1).

2.2 Symmetrical Two-sided Impacting

The tube was initially analysed with a gap of 0.2 mm on each side. Each analysis was started by applying an impulsive force to the tube to cause impacting to occur. In most cases the simulation was carried out for a four second period, with the time histories for the last second recorded on disk for subsequent analysis.

It was found that changing the gap size had no effect on the frequency of vibration and the amplitude of motion and impact forces scaled linearly with gap size. Therefore, there was no need to conduct simulations using more than one gap size provided fluid-elastic instability was the only excitation mechanism. (This is only strictly true if the impact stiffness and fluid-elastic forces are both linear, as assumed in the present analyses). It was found that, over certain ranges of instability, the tube motion was entirely periodic, whereas in other ranges it was non-periodic. It was also found that the mean impact forces and periodic frequencies did not increase smoothly with increasing levels of instability but, instead, increased in a series of jumps.

The variation of mean impact force and frequency ratio (periodic frequency with impacting divided by fundamental natural frequency) with the critical velocity ratio for the fundamental mode is given in Fig. 2. (In this Paper mean impact force is defined as the modulus of the impact force averaged over all time, including the time between impacts and, for two-sided impacting, it includes impacts on both sides of the tube.) It can be seen that at $U_e/U_c = 1.3$ two distinct steady-state solutions exist with different periodic frequencies (and mean impact forces). Similarly, at $U_e/U_c = 1.7$ three different steady-state solutions could be found, according to the initial conditions used. In both cases finite ranges of U_e/U_c existed where multiple solutions existed, but these were not investigated in detail.

The change in the character of the vibrations with increasing levels of instability is shown in Fig. 3. This shows plots of the 'phase-plane' (i.e. velocity versus displacement), the acceleration spectrum and the impact force time history at the impact site for $U_e/U_c = 1.2$ and 1.8. It can be seen from the phase-plane plot that at $U_e/U_c = 1.2$ the results for the one second period all overlay exactly onto one orbit, demonstrating that the motion is exactly periodic. The spectrum contains sharp peaks at exactly integer odd harmonics of the fundamental frequency, again show-

© IMechE 1991 C416/021

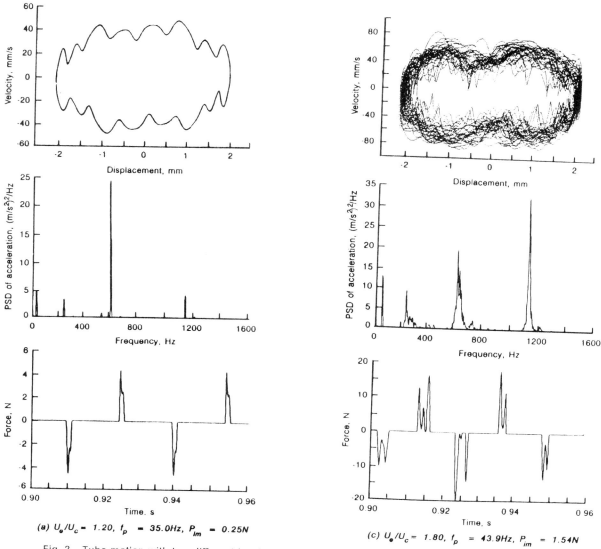

(a) $U_e/U_c = 1.20$, $f_p = 35.0$Hz, $P_{im} = 0.25$N

(c) $U_e/U_c = 1.80$, $f_p = 43.9$Hz, $P_{im} = 1.54$N

Fig. 3   Tube motion with two different levels of instability showing periodic and non-periodic motion

ing that the motion is periodic and symmetrical about the equilibrium position. At higher levels of instability ($U_e/U_c = 1.4$ and above), the phase-plane plots become 'fuzzy', indicating that the motion is no longer exactly periodic.

2.3 Single-sided Impacting

The previous analyses were repeated but with one of the stops removed so that single-sided impacting took place with a gap of 0.2 mm. Fig. 2 shows the variation of mean impact force and frequency ratio with increasing critical velocity ratios. As before, jumps in the impacting frequency and force were present.

It can be seen from Fig. 2 that a jump occurs at $U_e/U_c = 1.45$. The phase-plane plots in this region are shown in Fig. 4. At $U_e/U_c = 1.30$ the motion is exactly periodic. At $U_e/U_c = 1.40$ the motion is still exactly periodic but a second 'strand' has appeared in the orbit, indicating a period doubling has occurred. At $U_e/U_c = 1.45$ the overall motion and the impact forces are still similar to before but the motion has lost its exact periodicity, as shown in Fig. 4(d). However, under these same conditions a second solution exists, as shown in Fig. 4(e). This solution is exactly periodic and has a mean impact force which is more than twice as high. When the level

of instability is further increased, the exact periodicity is again lost, as shown by Fig. 4(f).

3   APPROXIMATE ANALYSIS OF A SINGLE DOF SYSTEM WITH IMPACTING

A simple single dof impact oscillator was analysed so that its behaviour could be compared with the numerical results predicted for a multi-dof steam generator tube. It was hoped that such a comparison would provide an insight into the complicated behaviour observed for an impacting tube and, perhaps, help to produce simplified design equations for predicting tube wear. The derivation of this simplified single dof model is given in Appendix 1.

The relevant dynamic properties of the tube when vibrating in its fundamental mode with one AVB inactive are: m = 0.402 Kg, $f_1 = 32.1$ Hz, $f_2 = 182.0$ Hz and $\zeta_o = 0.02$. The second natural frequency should correspond to the tube frequency when it is in contact with the stop. The frequency of 182 Hz corresponds to the mode with tube pinned at the inactive AVB and with approximately symmetric motion of the tube on either side of this position. (There was a lower frequency mode with anti-symmetric motion about the AVB position, but this mode would not be excited

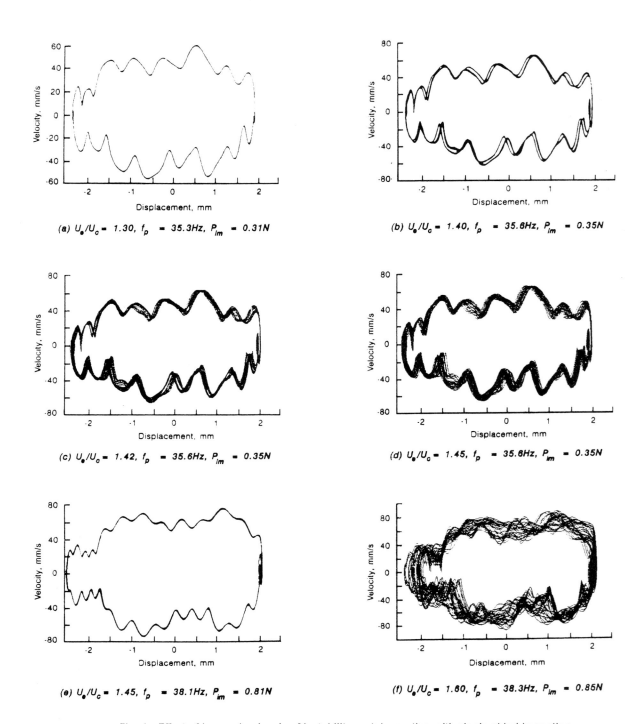

(a) $U_s/U_c = 1.30$, $f_p = 35.3Hz$, $P_{im} = 0.31N$

(b) $U_s/U_c = 1.40$, $f_p = 35.6Hz$, $P_{im} = 0.35N$

(c) $U_s/U_c = 1.42$, $f_p = 35.6Hz$, $P_{im} = 0.35N$

(d) $U_s/U_c = 1.45$, $f_p = 35.6Hz$, $P_{im} = 0.35N$

(e) $U_s/U_c = 1.45$, $f_p = 38.1Hz$, $P_{im} = 0.81N$

(f) $U_s/U_c = 1.60$, $f_p = 38.3Hz$, $P_{im} = 0.85N$

Fig. 4   Effect of increasing levels of instability on tube motion with single-sided impacting

by the impacting of the tube).

A simple computer program was written to solve equations (A11) to (A14) in an iterative manner for symmetrical two-sided impacting using a range of different values of α, the coefficient of restitution. The resulting mean impact forces and frequency ratios are shown in Fig. 5 for two values of α (0 and 0.8) and compared with the results from the full numerical simulations. (The mean impact forces include the impacts on both sides and so are twice the values given by equation (A16)).

It can be seen that the one dof model predicts a smooth increase in mean impact force and fre-

quency ratio as the negative damping increases whereas the full nonlinear analysis predicts jumps between 'plateau' regions. These plateaux can be interpreted by the one dof model as regions where the coefficient of restitution reduces as the instability increases. It can be seen from Fig. 5 that the jumps occur when the motion approaches the line for the single dof system with $\alpha=0$.

This observation gives some physical insight into the reason for the jump phenomena. The coupling between modes caused by the impacts tends to cause mode-locking between the fundamental periodic frequency and a higher natural frequency

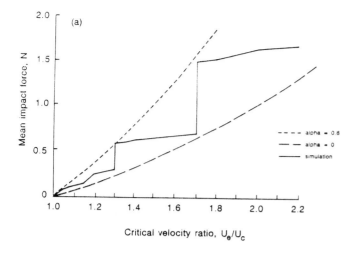

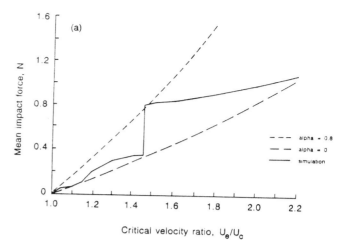

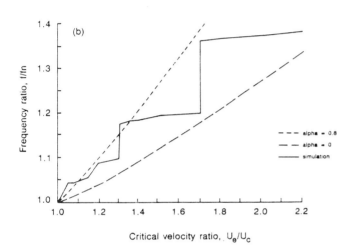

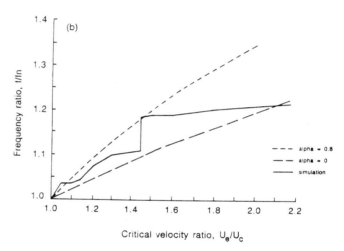

Fig. 5   Comparison between full nonlinear simulations and one DOF model for two-sided impacting

Fig. 6   Comparison between full nonlinear simulations and one DOF model for single-sided impacting

which happens to coincide approximately with a harmonic of the fundamental frequency. This lock-in tends to keep the periodic frequency constant and, because of the inter-dependence between periodic frequency and impact force, the impact force also tends to remain constant with increasing levels of instability. This can only occur if more energy is transferred to the higher modes during an impact. This appears to be achieved by adjustments to the phase relationships between the fundamental and higher frequency modes which enable energy to be transferred more efficiently into the higher modes and subsequently dissipated. However, there comes a point when most of the energy in the fundamental mode is transferred at each impact (i.e. α approaches zero in the one dof model) and this places a limit on the range over which the mode locking can occur. If the instability is further increased mode-locking with a different mode (or, possibly, the same mode locking with a different harmonic of the fundamental) must occur which causes a sudden increase in periodic frequency and impact force.

It can be seen that the one dof results with α set to 0 and 0.8 provide reasonable upper and lower bounds to both the impact forces and frequency ratios for this particular case. The fact that, with a suitable choice of α, the impact force and frequency ratio are both predicted reasonably accurately gives some confidence in the applicability of the simple one dof model.

Fig. 6 shows an equivalent set of results for one-sided impacting. Again, the one dof results with $\alpha = 0$ and $\alpha = 0.8$ give reasonable upper and lower bounds to the range of values predicted by the full numerical simulations.

4   SIMPLIFIED ASSESSMENT METHOD FOR FLUID-ELASTIC IMPACTING

Simplified methods are required for assessing wear in heat exchanger tube bundles. It has been shown that for the specific case of a fluid-elastically unstable tube impacting at one support site, the simple one degree-of-freedom model gives a reasonable upper bound using a coefficient of restitution of 0.8. However, even this requires an iterative solution for each critical velocity ratio and so simplified equations based on curve fits would seem to offer a better solution.

In order to have more general applicability, it is necessary to express the results in non-dimensional form. Thus a non-dimensional mean impact force is defined by $\bar{P}/m\omega_n^2 C$, where m is the modal mass (calculated with the mode normalized to 1 at the impact location) and C is the clearance on one side (i.e. x_1 in the one dof analysis). This non-dimensional force is the ratio between the impact force and the elastic restoring force caused by a displacement C. Fig. 7 shows the variation of the non-dimensional impact force with the negative damping parameter ($\zeta_o(U_e^2/U_c^2 - 1)$) for single and double-sided impacting.

It can be seen that the one dof model predicts an almost perfectly linear relationship between impact force and negative damping in both cases. This result is not obvious; indeed a simplified analysis would conclude that the mean impact force squared would be proportional to the negative damping (energy gained $\propto -\zeta$; energy lost $\propto$ $impulse^2 \propto$ mean impact $force^2$). However, this does not take into account the effect of changes in the periodic frequency and amplitude of motion away from the impact site.

The one dof results shown in Fig. 8 produce a relationship of the form

$$\frac{\bar{P}}{m\omega_n^2 C} = \lambda \zeta_o (\frac{U_e^2}{U_c^2} - 1) \qquad (2)$$

where λ is an empirical constant. For two-sided impacting, the upper bound results (α =0.8) are given by $\lambda = 13.1$ and the mean value is given by $\lambda = 9.1$. (It should be remembered that, for symmetrical two-sided impacting, C is the clearance on one side only and $\bar{P}$ is the impact force averaged over all time and includes impacts on both sides). For one-sided impacting the upper bound impact forces are given by $\lambda = 10.5$ and the mean values by $\lambda = 7.4$.

5 DISCUSSION

It has been shown that the dynamics of an unstable U-tube with one loose AVB support are complicated, showing many of the typical characteristics of nonlinear dynamical systems (e.g. periodic solutions, bifurcations, subharmonics and chaotic behaviour). However, the most significant effect, as far as tube wear is concerned, is the existence of multiple solutions over certain ranges and the sudden jumps that can occur in the severity of impacting. Thus, over certain ranges, the impact forces are relatively insensitive to changes in the level of instability; however, there are thresholds above which a small increase in instability can lead to large increases in the impact force.

The U-tube model that has been studied is highly idealized since it is assumed that, apart from the one loose AVB, all the other AVBs provide perfect supports. In practice, other AVBs will

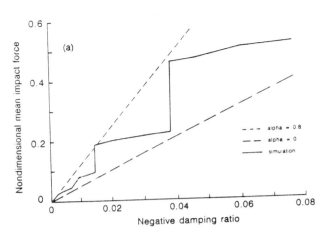

(a) Symmetrical two-sided impacting

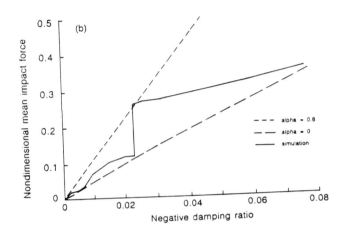

(b) One-sided impacting

Fig. 7 Variation of nondimensional mean impact force ($\bar{P}/m\omega_n^2 C$) with negative damping for (a) symmetrical two-sided impacting and (b) one-sided impacting

introduce some nonlinearities due to impacting and sliding. The limited experimental data currently available indicates that the predicted jump behaviour is less clearly defined in experimental tests, probably due to the presence of nonlinearities at the other AVB locations.

The simplified one dof analysis has proved to be very useful for understanding the more complicated behaviour predicted for the multi-dof system and for providing data suitable for design assessments. The main problem with this simplified approach is that it cannot be used for analysing a tube with more than one loose AVB.

ACKNOWLEDGEMENT

This work was carried out at National Power Technology and Environmental Centre and is published with the permission of Nuclear Electric plc.

REFERENCES

(1) Fricker, A J, The analysis of impacts in vibrating structures containing clearances between components, Int. Conf. Numerical Methods for Transient and Coupled problems , Venice, 1984

(2) Fricker, A J, Numerical analysis of the fluidelastic vibration of a steam generator tube with loose supports, Journal of Fluids and Structures , to be published

(3) Axisa, F, Antunes, J and Villard, B, Overview of numerical methods for predicting flow-induced vibration, Journal of Pressure Vessel Technology , 1988, 110, 6-14

(4) Rao, M S M, Steininger, D A, and Eisinger, F L, Numerical simulation of fluidelastic vibration and wear of miltispan tubes with clearances at supports, Int Symp Flow-Induced Vibration and Noise , ASME WAM, 1988, Chicago, USA

(5) Connors, H J, Fluidelastic vibration of heat exchanger tube arrays, Trans. ASME, J. Mech. Design , 1978, 100, 347-353

(6) Timoshenko, S, Young, D H, and Weaver, W, Vibration Problems in Engineering , 1974, 190-193 (Wiley)

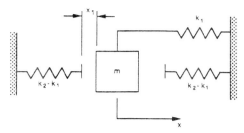

(a)   1 DOF model

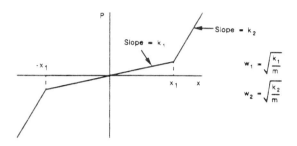

(b) Force / displacement relationship

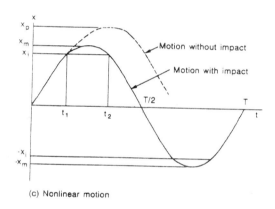

(c) Nonlinear motion

Fig. 8 One degree-of-freedom model of impacting tube

APPENDIX 1 - Theory for One Degree-of-Freedom Model

The one dof model with a piece-wise linear spring is shown in Fig. 8 . The mass m and stiffness k_1 represent the modal mass and stiffness of the fundamental (unstable) mode of the tube when the support is inactive. The definition of the second spring stiffness, k_2 is not so clear. If the stop were very flexible then k_2 would represent the combined stiffness of the fundamental mode and the stop acting together. However, if the stop were very stiff, the tube motion during contact would be controlled by the tube dynamics and not the stop stiffness. The tube motion during an impact is complicated and multiple impacts can occur; however, overall it might be expected that the modes of vibration that occur with the support point pinned would control the motion during the impact. Therefore, it was assumed that k_2 was equal to $m\omega_2^2$ where ω_2 was equal to a suitable tube frequency with a pinned support.

The exact equations governing the motion of the impacting model shown in Fig. 8 with an impact damper are transendental, which means that numerical solution methods must be used. Furthermore, the model that has been used for modelling fluid-elastic instability of tubes produces a negative damping which is frequency dependent. Therefore, rather than attempt to solve the exact equations, an approximate method was used.

If it is assumed that there is no damping (positive or negative) in the system and the impacting is symmetrical, the solution is reasonably straightforward [6]. If it is assumed that the displacement, x, is zero at time t=0, the equation of motion in the first stiffness range $-x_1 < x < x_1$ is given by

$$x = x_p \sin \omega_1 t \qquad (A1)$$

where x_p is the maximum displacement that would have occurred if the stop were not present (see Fig. 11). The time until the first impact occurs, t_1, is given by

$$t_1 = \frac{1}{\omega_1} \sin^{-1}\left(\frac{x_1}{x_p}\right) \qquad (A2)$$

The corresponding impact velocity, $\dot{x}_1$, is given by

$$\dot{x}_1 = \omega_1 x_p \cos \omega_1 t_1$$
$$= \omega_1 x_p \left(1 - \frac{x_1^2}{x_p^2}\right)^{1/2} \qquad (A3)$$

It can be shown [6] that the impact duration is given by

$$t_2 - t_1 = \frac{2}{\omega_2} \tan^{-1}\left(\frac{k_2 \dot{x}_1}{k_1 \omega_2 x_1} \right)$$

$$= \frac{2}{\omega_2} \tan^{-1}\left[\frac{\omega_2}{\omega_1} \left(\frac{x_p^2}{x_1^2} - 1 \right)^{1/2} \right] \qquad (A4)$$

where t_2, ω_1 and ω_2 are defined in Fig. 11.

Therefore, the time for a complete cycle is given by

$$T = \frac{4}{\omega_1} \sin^{-1}\left(\frac{x_1}{x_p} \right) + \frac{4}{\omega_2} \tan^{-1}\left[\frac{\omega_2}{\omega_1} \left(\frac{x_p^2}{x_1^2} - 1 \right)^{1/2} \right]$$

$$(A5)$$

The maximum displacement, x_m, is given by

$$x_m = \left(1 - \frac{k_1}{k_2} \right) x_1 + \left[\left(\frac{k_1}{k_2} x_1 \right)^2 + \left(\frac{\dot{x}_1}{\omega_2} \right)^2 \right]^{1/2}$$

$$= \left(1 - \frac{\omega_1^2}{\omega_2^2} \right) x_1 + \frac{\omega_1}{\omega_2} x_1 \left(\frac{\omega_1^2}{\omega_2^2} + \frac{x_p^2}{x_1^2} - 1 \right)^{1/2} \qquad (A6)$$

It will now be assumed that, providing the negative damping is reasonably small, the above equations describe the motion reasonably accurately when a steady-state is reached. The steady-state occurs when the energy gained by the unstable mode over one cycle equals the energy dissipated due to impacting over one cycle. In the present analysis the energy lost due to an impact will be represented by a coefficient of restitution. If the tube motion is assumed to be approximately sinusoidal with a maximum amplitude x_m and a periodic frequency ω, the energy gained per cycle by the unstable mode is given by

$$E_{gained} = -2\pi m \zeta \omega_1 \omega x_m^2 \qquad (A7)$$

The energy lost per impact is given by

$$E_{lost} = \frac{m}{2} \dot{x}_1^2 (1 - \alpha^2) \qquad (A8)$$

where α is the coefficient of restitution.

If there are two impacts per cycle, the energy balance gives

$$-2\pi m \zeta \omega_1 \omega x_m^2 = m \dot{x}_1^2 (1 - \alpha^2) \qquad (A9)$$

Substituting for $\dot{x}_1$ from equation (A3) gives, after some manipulation,

$$\frac{x_p^2}{x_1^2} = \frac{-2\pi \zeta}{1 - \alpha^2} \frac{\omega}{\omega_1} \frac{x_m^2}{x_1^2} + 1 \qquad (A10)$$

Equations (A5), (A6) and (A8) provide three equations in the three unknowns x_p, x_m and ω (= $2\pi/T$) and so a unique solution can be found.

The fluid-elastic instability model described previously has the form

$$\zeta = \zeta_O \left(1 - \frac{\omega_1}{\omega} \frac{U_e^2}{U_c^2} \right)$$

where ζ_O is the damping at zero flow velocity and U_e/U_c is the critical velocity ratio for the instability. It can be seen that, in this model, the negative damping is dependent on the periodic frequency ω as well as the critical velocity ratio.

Using this equation for the damping together with equations (A5), (A6) and (A10) leads to the following set of equations which can be used in an iterative solution

$$\frac{x_p}{x_1} = \left[\frac{-2\pi}{1 - \alpha^2} \zeta_O \left(\frac{\omega_1}{\omega} \frac{U_e^2}{U_c^2} - 1 \right) \frac{\omega}{\omega_1} \frac{x_m^2}{x_1^2} + 1 \right]^{1/2} \qquad (A11)$$

$$\frac{x_m}{x_1} = \left(1 - \frac{\omega_1^2}{\omega_2^2} \right) + \frac{\omega_1}{\omega_2} \left(\frac{\omega_1^2}{\omega_2^2} + \frac{x_p^2}{x_1^2} - 1 \right)^{1/2} \qquad (A12)$$

$$T = \frac{4}{\omega_1} \sin^{-1}\left(\frac{x_1}{x_p} \right) + \frac{4}{\omega_2} \tan^{-1}\left[\frac{\omega_2}{\omega_1} \left(\frac{x_p^2}{x_1^2} - 1 \right)^{1/2} \right]$$

$$(A13)$$

$$\omega = \frac{2\pi}{T} \qquad (A14)$$

Equation (A11) is first solved by setting the unknown parameters ω/ω_1 and x_m/x_1 equal to unity. The resulting value for x_p/x_1 is then substituted in equations (A12) and (A13) to give improved values for ω/ω_1 and x_m/x_1. The iteration is continued until convergence is reached (about five iterations are usually sufficient). After convergence the peak impact force can be calculated from

$$\hat{P} = (k_2 - k_1)(x_m - x_1)$$

$$= m(\omega_2^2 - \omega_1^2)(x_m - x_1) \qquad (A15)$$

The mean impact force on one side (i.e. the average over all time, including the time between impacts), assuming the impact forces are half sine waves is given by

$$\bar{P} = 0.64 m(\omega_2^2 - \omega_1^2)(x_m - x_1) \frac{(t_2 - t_1)}{T} \qquad (A16)$$

One-sided impacting can be analysed in a similar manner but in this case the maximum amplitude is x_m on the impacting side and x_p on the non-impacting side. In order to calculate the energy input per cycle, the motion in each of the two half cycles has to be considered separately. If the periodic time for the half-cycle containing the impact is $\bar{T}$ and the frequency for this half of the cycle is $\bar{\omega}$, then the energy gained per cycle is given approximately by

$$E_{gained} = -\pi m \zeta \omega_1 (\bar{\omega} x_m^2 + \omega_1 x_p^2) \qquad (A17)$$

With one impact per cycle, equating energy gained and energy lost gives

$$-\pi m \zeta \omega_1 (\bar{\omega} x_m^2 + \omega_1 x_p^2) = \frac{m}{2} \dot{x}_1^2 (1 - \alpha^2) \qquad (A18)$$

Substituting for $\dot{x}_1$ from equation (A3) gives, after some manipulation,

$$\frac{x_p^2}{x_1^2} = \left(\frac{-2\pi\zeta}{1-\alpha^2} \frac{\omega}{\omega_1} \frac{x_m^2}{x_1^2} + 1 \right) \Big/ \left(1 + \frac{2\pi\zeta}{1-\alpha^2} \right) \qquad (A19)$$

with ζ given by equation (1).

Equation (A12) is still valid for one-sided impacting, but equation (A13) must be replaced since the time taken for the two half cycles (with and without impacting) are different. The periodic time for the half cycle containing the impact is give by

$$\bar{T} = \frac{2}{\omega_1} \sin^{-1}\left(\frac{x_1}{x_p} \right) + \frac{2}{\omega_2} \tan^{-1}\left[\frac{\omega_2}{\omega_1} \left(\frac{x_p^2}{x_1^2} - 1 \right)^{1/2} \right]$$

$$(A20)$$

The frequency for this part of the cycle is given by $\bar{\omega} = \pi/\bar{T}$. The total periodic time is given by

$$T = \bar{T} + \frac{\pi}{\omega_1} \qquad (A21)$$

and the total periodic frequency is given by $\omega = 2\pi/T$

The iterative solution is now similar to that for two-sided impacting except that equation (A11) is substituted by equation (A19) and equation (A13) by equation (A21).

It should be noted that various approximations have been made when deriving the above equations. The errors should be small provided the negative damping is small ($-\zeta < 0.05$) but for higher levels of instability the approximations will no longer be valid.

C416/063

Impact analysis of loosely supported heat exchanger tubes

C E TEH, BSc, PhD and H G D GOYDER, BSc, MA, PhD
AEA Industrial Technology, Harwell Laboratory, Oxfordshire

SYNOPSIS The tube dynamics associated with the vibration of loosely supported heat exchanger tubes are very nonlinear and cannot be accurately modelled theoretically. An experimental study of the dynamics of tube-to-support impacts within a tube bundle is presented. The bundle comprises an in-line tube array with anti-vibration bar supports. Important parameters relating to wear assessment such as impact force, impact rate, contact time and tube-to-support clearance are examined under single-sided impacting conditions for a range of excitation force levels and support flexibility.

1 INTRODUCTION

In shell and tube heat exchangers and steam generators, tube vibrations are generated by the external cross flow over the tubes. The vibrations generated can be large and extremely damaging in the short term if vortex shedding or fluidelastic instability occurs. In the long term, tube impacting/fretting wear will result from the low amplitude vibrations generated by the random turbulent buffeting in the flow. To minimise such vibrations, the tubes are supported at strategic locations along its length.

Unfortunately, manufacturing tolerances as well as lack of tube straightness will result in some support locations having little or no contact between the tube and its support. The presence of loose supports has been found to promote vibration which may cause tube damage due to impacting and fretting. It is important therefore to study the dynamics of the tube/support interactions in order that the dynamic response characteristics of the suport can be accurately modelled theoretically for use in wear assessment codes.

To date, there is a large volume of published literature on impact/fretting wear in heat exchanger tubes. One end of the spectrum is concerned with experimental studies to obtain wear data for single and multi-span tube configurations subjected to either mechanical excitation or fluid crossflow (eg. Ko and Rogers(1), Ko(2), Cha et al(3), Haslinger and Martin(4), Fisher and Ingram(5) and Ko and Magel(6)). These studies have highlighted the important parameters which influence the wear rate such as tube-to-support clearance, tube-to-support preload or contact force, amplitude and frequency of tube vibration and different combinations of tube and support materials.

At the other end of the spectrum, numerical simulation of the tube motion for both single and multi-span tube configurations ranging from simple (undergoing free vibration) to detailed modelling of the excitation have been attempted. Using this approach, parameter studies can be carried out easily (Teh and Goyder(7), Axisa et al(8), Fricker(9) and Rogers and Pick(10)). More recently, Goyder and Teh(11) derived relationships for wear based on a theoretical approach using dimensional analysis and physical modelling.

For the majority of straight heat exchanger tubes, the tube supports used are generally in the form of baffle plates (perforated plates with clearance holes). In a steam generator (consisting of a bank of U-tubes), the tubes are supported by baffle plates along the straight portion and by anti-vibration bars (AVBs) along the U-bend regions. The flow direction along the straight lengths of the tube is axial and does not induce significant vibration. Cross flow conditions prevail over the U-bend and this region will therefore be most vulnerable to damaging vibrations. The anti-vibration bars are used to limit the low frequency vibrations of the U-bend in the out-of plane direction. In-plane vibrations of the U-bend can be generated by buffeting and this is resisted by friction between the tube and the AVB. Clearly, the AVBs will restraint the in-plane motion of the tubes only if there is tube/AVB contact with preload. Experimental work in this area was carried out by Weaver and Schneider(12) to study the effectiveness of AVBs against fluidelastic instability for a triangular array of U-tubes. In this instance, the tube-to-AVB impact dynamics was not studied but this problem was tackled by Yetisir and Weaver(13) using numerical simulation.

The present investigation is aimed at studying the dynamics of the tube/AVB impacts in order that important parameters such as mean tube/AVB impact force, average impact force time signature, contact time etc. can be established.

Single-sided impacting tests were conducted on the tube/AVB cluster for two extremes of tube/AVB support flexibility. The tube bundle comprises an in-line array of 25 tubes with multiple AVB supports. For these tests, both discrete frequency excitation and random excitation were employed to excite a tube to impact against an AVB for a range of tube/AVB support clearance and excitation force level. Discrete frequency excitation was used to investigate the relationship between impact signatures and specific resonance frequencies. Random excitation was used to simulate the characteristics of the flow turbulence under service conditions. Parameters such as mean impact force, contact time, average impact force time signature are measured for a range of tube-to-support clearances and excitation force levels.

2 EXPERIMENTAL APPARATUS

2.1 Test Rig

The experimental test rig is shown in Figure 1. A cluster of tubes are supported at five positions along its length. The tube cluster consists of an array of five tube columns. There are five tubes per column with the exception of the first column where the middle tube has been removed to accommodate the instrumented AVB and the 'impacting' tube. This 'impacting' tube is coupled to an electrodynamic shaker which drives the tube to impact against an instrumented AVB at one location only. At each of the five tube support locations, vertical AVBs are sandwiched between the tube columns. At the two end support locations, horizontal bars are inserted between the tube rows to maintain the bundle geometry as well as to minimise the amount of sagging of the tubes. Each tube within the cluster was 3m in length with AVB supports placed at 0.7m intervals. The tube material was stainless steel type 321. The inner and outer diameter of the tube are 15.5mm and 17.5mm respectively. Each AVB has a 7mm square cross-section and a length of 180mm and is constructed of the same material as the tubes. The tube/AVB static preload is achieved by looping rubber bands over each tube row thus pulling the tubes against the C-shaped support as illustrated in Figure 2.

The impacting tube is significantly longer than the tubes in the bundle and is only supported near each end by a baffle plate. This tube was 7.7m long and the supports were positioned at 1.7m from each end of the tube. Each end of the driven tube is embedded in a large sand-filled box which helps absorb the tube vibration hence simulating the damping effect of the straight leg portion of the U-tube. The position of the baffle plate support at each end can be fine-tuned in the orthogonal directions for accurate tube-to-support alignment. The tube-to-support radial clearance at the baffle plate was 1.25mm.

2.2 Instrumentation

Tube/AVB impacting was achieved by using an electrodynamic shaker to drive the tube against the instrumented AVB within the tube cluster. This set-up is illustrated in Figure 2. The excitation force was monitored using a piezo-electric force transducer attached to the driven tube. The tube/AVB impact force was monitored using a second force transducer attached to the AVB. The acceleration response of the driven tube was monitored using a piezo-electric accelerometer. The impact site was located at the middle tube support.

3 EXPERIMENTAL PROCEDURE

For this investigation, measurements of the tube/AVB impact forces were obtained for two cases of AVB support flexibility. One configuration was rigid and the other flexible. For each case, measurements were carried out for a range of tube/AVB support clearances using both discrete frequency and random excitation.

3.1 Rigid Tube/AVB Setting

The layout for this configuration is shown in Figure 2. It comprises the full cluster of tubes, except for the location taken up by the driven tube, with static preloads of approximately 10N (achieved by looping a pair of rubber bands over each tube row). In this case, each AVB is in hard contact with all its neighbouring tubes.

3.2 Flexible Tube/AVB Setting

For this configuration (shown in Figure 2), the instrumented AVB is only in contact with its neighbouring tubes at its ends. The intermediate tube neighbours have been removed from the cluster. The resultant tube rows have static preloads applied in a similar fashion using rubber bands.

3.3 Tube/AVB Support Clearance Setting

For each configuration, tests were carried out for tube/AVB clearance settings of 0mm, 0.3mm, 0.5mm and 1.0mm. This clearance is the gap between the tube and AVB in the equilibrium position.

It was not possible to set up the required clearance by

means of feeler gauges due to physical restrictions of the rig. The clearance was firstly approximated by moving the position of the driven tube using the end baffle support adjustors. Secondly, the clearance setting of 0.3mm, 0.5mm and 1.0mm was obtained by carefully monitoring the displacement of the driven tube (using sinewave excitation) at conditions just before impacting occurred. The clearance setting of 0mm corresponds to the tube just touching the AVB in its equilibrium position. This condition was obtained by monitoring the tube/AVB impact forces with the smallest possible excitation level and carefully adjusting the position of the driven tube until impacting stopped.

3.4 Impacting Tube Stiffness Setting

Similar tests were carried out using different impacting tube stiffness. This was achieved by using tube lengths of 7.5m, 3.0m and 1.5m. The set-up for the 7.5m length tube has been described in section 2.1. For 3.0m tube length, its ends were supported at the outermost pair of C-shaped supports. These supports were modified to allow the impacting tube to be clamped using an adaptor which provides both horizontal and vertical adjustment. This allows for accurate setting of the tube-to-AVB clearance. For the 1.5m length tube, the innermost pair of supports were used.

3.5 Data Analysis

In each test, both the excitation force and the resultant tube/AVB impact force time histories were digitised and analysed in the following manner:-

Data acquisition of the time histories of the excitation force, tube/AVB impact force and tube acceleration was carried out at a rate of 15000 samples per second for a duration of 10 seconds.

For each impact force time history, statistical properties such as rms impact force and probability density distribution were estimated. The probability analysis was carried out on the normalised force time history (ie. divided by the mean impact force). In calculating these estimates, only 'in-contact' forces are used ie. above the threshold level. Subsequently, a measure of the contact time was obtained and was expressed as a percentage of the total time-in-contact divided by the total record length.

For each test, the average tube/AVB impact force time signature was estimated using a computer algorithm which detects and captures all impacts based upon user defined threshold settings. Individual impacts are 'captured' in the following manner:- The magnitude of the force signal is scanned until it exceeds a user-specified threshold level deemed as the start of an impact. This event initiates the storage of a successive number of data points defined as a captured impact segment. The duration of each captured impact segment (also user-defined) was fixed for each time history analysed. However, the duration per capture may vary for different tests and is very much dependant upon the observed characteristics of the impact time history. In the majority of cases, each captured impact segment will contain only a single impact. An average of all the captured impact time segments is calculated along with a measure of the variance of the estimate. This estimate is defined as the average impact force time signature. The calculated impact rate is defined as the total number of captured segments divided by the record length.

3.6 Excitation and Filter Bandwidth Setting

Measurements of the tube/AVB impact force were taken for the rigid tube cluster subjected to random excitation. The objective of these measurements was to ascertain the minimum excitation bandwidth needed for this investigation. Five excitation frequency ranges were used namely,

© IMechE 1991 C416/063

0-10Hz, 0-100Hz, 0-500Hz, 0-1kHz and 0-5kHz. For each excitation range tested, the maximum achievable forcing level was used and the average tube/AVB impact force time signature was estimated in the following manner:-

Figure 3a illustrates a typical example of the measured tube/AVB impact time history. It can be seen that there will be considerable difficulty in defining an average impact time signature due to the diverse range of impacts observed. However, an attempt was made to rationalise these impacts into different categories of force amplitudes. The computer algorithm was adapted to selectively detect and capture impacts with its peak force amplitude occurring within a specified range and its corresponding mean impact time signature calculated. Three peak force amplitude ranges were used for each excitation bandwidth tested namely 1-30N, 30-50N and greater than 50N. It was found that the mean impact signature was similar for 0 to 1kHz and 0 to 5kHz bandwidths. Also the characteristic shape of the mean signature was shown to be very similar for each amplitude range. Hence, subsequent mean impact signatures are calculated by accounting for all captured impacts.

In order to obtain an accurate measure of the tube/AVB impact force, tests carried out to determine the optimum analogue filter setting required for this study clearly indicated that the mean impact signatures can be adequately represented by using filter settings of 5kHz and above.

The dynamic response characteristics of the impacting tube was determined by measuring the transfer function relating the impacting tube velocity with the applied excitation force. Transfer functions were measured at each excitation level tested. The results clearly indicated the quasi-linear behaviour of the tube characteristics as the shift in resonance frequency with increasing excitation level was negligible over the excitation bandwidth tested. This trend was evident in the measured transfer functions for the 7.5m, 3.0m and 1.5m impacting tubes as typified by Figure 3b for the 7.5m impacting tube.

4 RESULTS

4.1 Tube/AVB Impacts using Sinewave Excitation

For both rigid and flexible tube clusters, tests were carried out for a range of excitation force levels. The measured tube-to support impact force time histories were obtained using discrete frequency excitation tuned to the tube resonances. Three frequencies were used namely, 10Hz, 25Hz and 120Hz. The tube-to-support clearance for this study was set to 0mm . Figure 4 shows a comparison of the averaged impact force signature measured for both the rigid and flexible tube cluster with an excitation force level of 5N. The average force signatures were obtained using the computer algorithm as described in section 3.5. The variance in each computed average was very small because of the periodic nature of the response in every case.

At the lowest resonance frequency, the characteristic impact shape for the rigid cluster comprises a dominant initial impulse followed by a long succession of significantly smaller impulses indicating tube chattering. At the next resonance frequency, there is less chattering in the signature. The chattering decreases with subsequent resonances and finally evolves to just a single impulse at the higher resonance frequencies.

For the flexible tube cluster, the magnitude of the measured impact force signatures in all cases were smaller than that observed from the rigid tube cluster. It was found that the strong initial impulse (a characteristic shown from the rigid cluster tests) was absent in all cases. Apart from that, the impact shapes were correspondingly similar to those from the rigid cluster tests. However, the time-in-contact of the impact was longer for this case. This trend is due to the increased flexibility of the support.

The above trends were obtained from similar tests with increased excitation force level.

4.2 Tube/AVB Impacts using Random Excitation

Using random excitation, tube-to-AVB impacts were analysed at four excitation levels. To investigate the effect of the stiffness of the impacting tube on the impact dynamics, three different lengths of impacting tube were used namely, 7.5m, 3.0m and 1.5m. The effect of the stiffness of the AVB on the impact characteristics was studied using a rigid and a flexible tube cluster. The above tests were carried out for tube-to-AVB clearance settings of 0mm, 0.3mm, 0.5mm and 1.0mm.

Impact statistics

The effect of the stiffness of the impacting tube on the important tube-to-support impact parameters (such as rms impact force, impact rate and contact time) are plotted in Figures 5 and 6 for the rigid and flexible clusters with 0mm, 0.3mm and 0.5mm tube-to-support clearance.

Wear parameters such as contact time and impact rate are estimated. The contact time is defined as a percentage of the total time-in-contact divided by the record length. The impact rate is defined as the number of captured impact segments per second.

From Figures 5a to 5c, the percentage time-in-contact for the rigid cluster was relatively independant of excitation level with values averaging at approximately 10.5%, 8% and 10% for increasing impacting tube stiffness. The impact rate was also independant of excitation level but tended to increase from 37 to 57 with impacting tube stiffness. The measured impact force was found to be directly proportional to the excitation level. This is shown by the computed ratio of rms impact force divided by the excitation force being constant at approximately 2.9 for the 7.5m impacting tube. Corresponding values of 3.2 and 3.0 were obtained for the 3.0m and 1.5m impacting tubes.

Although similar trends were evident from the statistics measured for the flexible cluster (see Figures 6a to 6c), the percentage time-in-contact was generally higher with average values of 13.5%, 13.8% and 14.5% for increasing tube stiffness. The impact rate was also independant of excitation level and only slightly larger than the values obtained for the rigid cluster.

With tube-to-support clearances of 0.3mm and 0.5mm, a larger threshold value of excitation force was needed to cause impacting. Results corresponding to 1.0mm support clearance are not presented here because trends could not be established due to insufficient force range imposed by the limiting current of the shaker coil.

The impact rates and contact times were found to be smaller and dependant on excitation level for clusters with a support clearance present. For corresponding excitation levels, the impact rate did not alter very much for both 7.5m and 3.0m impacting tubes with 0.3mm clearance. With the 1.5m tube however, corresponding impact rates were considerably lower. For both clusters with 0.3mm and 0.5mm clearances, quasi-linear behaviour between the impact force and excitation force was clearly shown in the 7.5m tube results only. With 0.5mm clearance, the impact rate decreased with increasing impacting tube stiffness.

The computed probability distribution functions of the normalised impact force were found to be quite unaffected by the level of excitation as typified by Figure 7 for 0mm and 0.3mm clearances.

Impact force time signatures

To study the effect of excitation level, each averaged impact signature is expressed in terms of a non-dimensional ratio of the impact force to the rms excitation force. Normalised impact time signatures are shown in Figure 8 for both rigid and flexible tube clusters with a tube-to-AVB clearance of 0mm and using different impacting tube stiffness.

For the rigid tube cluster, the normalised time signatures correlated extremely well over the range of excitation levels tested. This reflects quasi-linear behaviour between the impact force and the excitation force level. This trend is also evident in tests using different lengths of impacting tube. The characteristic shape consists of an initial impulse with an exponentially decaying train of impulses. The tail-end of this signature has a larger variance because of the occasional occurrence of a second impact within the captured segments. It is more likely that the typical impact comprises a predominant impulse only. The peak value of the normalised time signature tended to increase with stiffness of the impacting tube from approximately 5 to 6.

For the flexible tube cluster, the normalised signatures were also shown to be independent of the excitation force level. In comparison with the rigid cluster, the impact signature had a broader peak and there was no evidence of a dominant initial impulse. The broadness of the peak reflects the increased flexibility of the support resulting in the tube being in contact with the AVB for a longer duration before bouncing off again. The high frequency modulations superimposed on the peak can be attributed to the AVB response. The normalised peak value of the force signature is significantly smaller with values of approximately 3.2 to 4.0 for increasing impacting tube stiffness.

With clearance settings of 0.3mm and 0.5mm, the characteristic shape of the normalised impact force signature for the rigid cluster was quite similar in most cases but showed some dependence on excitation level. Similar trends were observed in the signatures for the flexible cluster.

For both rigid and flexible clusters in general, the time duration of the average impact signature decreased with an increasing stiffness of the impacting tube.

5 DISCUSSION

It is clear that even though the observed trends relate to single-sided impacting conditions for tubes with one loose support, this experimental study provides important information on the dynamic characteristics of tube impacts and indicates the important parameters necessary for accurate modelling of the tube-to-support interactions in wear assessment codes.

The results clearly show that in single-sided impacting conditions, the impact force is directly proportional to the excitation force for the case where there is no tube-to-support clearance and even for small clearances of 0.3mm. Such behaviour under these special conditions have been predicted by Goyder and Teh [11] using dimensional analysis and numerical simulations. This quasi-linear behaviour is also independent of tube support flexibility and the stiffness of the impacting tube.

For the special condition where the tube-to-support clearance is zero, parameters such as the impact rate and contact time were relatively constant with increasing excitation level. Although an increase in the stiffness of the impacting tube did increase the impact rate, its effect on the contact time was less clear. This is because the percentage contact time is governed by a combination of the impact rate and the duration of each impact. Referring to the rigid tube cluster results in Figure 5b, it can be seen that although the average impact rate had increased from 37 (using the 7.5m tube) to 56 (using the 1.5m tube), the corresponding percentage contact times were quite similar at approximately 10.5%. The percentage contact time had not increased accordingly because of the shorter time duration of the average impact generated using a stiffer impacting

tube (see Figure 8). Although similar impact rates were measured for the flexible tube cluster, the percentage contact time was slightly higher at approximately 13.5%.

The results also suggest that a characteristic normalised impact force time signature can be defined for different tube support flexibilities which is independent of excitation level. It is possible to relate these impact signatures to a work rate for wear prediction. $\int P ds$ is commonly referred to as the 'work rate' but more correctly as 'integral-P-ds' where P is the normal force and s is the sliding distance. Taking the integral of the impact force time signature ie. $\int P dt$, the 'work rate' can be obtained by multiplying $\int P dt$ with a mean tangential or sliding velocity of the tube. If a constant sliding velocity is assumed, the results imply that a more flexible tube support will generate more wear.

For clearances of 0.3mm up to 0.5mm, both the total contact time and impact rate were much lower in comparison to a zero clearance condition as expected. However, with an increase in clearance, the magnitude of the impact will also increase and coupled with a larger sliding velocity, a greater work rate will result.

6 CONCLUDING REMARKS

An experimental investigation was carried out to study tube-to-support impacting within loosely supported heat exchanger tubes. A tube cluster with anti-vibration bar supports was used and parameters such as impact rate, contact time and impact force time signatures were obtained for two extremes of support flexibility. Single-sided impacting was used and the effects of tube-to-support clearance and stiffness of the impacting tube on the impact characteristics were examined.

1. This study has shown that for single-sided impacting at least, it is possible to define an average impact force time signature from an impact time history. The signature of the impact associated with a rigid support was distinctly different to that associated with a flexible support. With the former, the signature primarily consisted of a dominant initial impulse whilst the latter signature had a smaller but much broader peak. These characteristics remained consistent when normalised with the excitation level. In general, only the time duration of the average signature decreased with the impacting tube stiffness. With knowledge of the tangential velocity, it is possible to infer an estimate of the work rate from the time signature.

2. For the case where the impacting tube is just in contact with the support at static equilibrium, the impact force increased linearly with the excitation level. For small clearance settings (0.3mm), this quasi-linear characteristic between impact force and excitation was also detected at large tube displacements.

3. Although the impact rate and contact time were independent of excitation level for zero clearance, a longer percentage contact time was measured on a flexible support. The impact rate also increased with tube stiffness. With support clearance, both impact rate and contact time were significantly reduced and dependant on excitation level but generated larger impact forces.

ACKNOWLEDGEMENTS

The work presented here was undertaken as part of the Underlying Research Programme of the United Kingdom Atomic Energy Authority. The authors gratefully acknowledge the assistance provided by Mr. M. Brockman in the experimental testing.

REFERENCES

(1) KO, P.L. and ROGERS, R.J., "Analytical and experimental studies of tube/support interaction in multispan heat exchanger tubes", Nuclear Engineering and Design 65, 1981, pp 399-409.

(2) KO, P.L., " Experimental studies of tube fretting in steam generators and heat exchangers", Journal of Pressure Vessel Technology, Vol. 101, 1979, pp 125-133.

(3) CHA, J., WAMBSGANSS M. and JENDR-ZEJCZYK, J., "Experimental study on impacting/fretting wear in heat exchanger tubes", ASME Pressure Vessels and Piping Conference, Chicago, 1986, Paper 86-PVP-3.

(4) HASLINGER, K.H. and MARTIN, M.L., "Pressurised water reactor steam generator tube wear prediction utilising experimental techniques", Int. Conference on Flow Induced Vibration, Bowness, England, 1987, edited by Roger King, pp 437-448.

(5) FISHER, N.J. and INGHAM, B., "Measurement of tube-to-support dynamic forces in fretting-wear rigs" Int. Symposium on Flow Induced Vibration and Noise, Chicago, 1988, Vol.5, pp 137-156.

(6) KO, P.L. and MAGEL, E., "Impact and sliding wear in steam generators and heat exchangers: New experimental test rig and wear model", ASME Pressure Vessels and Piping Conference, 1989, PVP Vol.154, pp 63-69.

(7) TEH, C.E. and GOYDER, H.G.D., "Non-linear Vibrations of a loosely supported beam", 3rd. Int. Conference on Recent Advances in Structural Vibration, Southampton, England, 1988, Vol. 2, pp 693-703.

(8) AXISSA, F., ANTUNES, J. and VILLARD, B, "Overview of numerical methods for predicting flow induced vibration", Journal of Pressure Vessel Technology, Vol. 110, 1988, pp 6-14.

(9) FRICKER, A.J., "Numerical analysis of the fluidelastic vibration of a steam generator tube with loose supports", Int. Symposium on Flow Induced Vibration and Noise, Chicago, 1988, Vol.5, pp 105-120.

(10) ROGERS, R.J. and PICK, R.J., "On the dynamic spatial response of a heat exchanger tube with intermittent baffle contacts", Nuclear Engineering and Design 36, 1976, pp 81-90.

(11) GOYDER, H.G.D. and TEH, C.E., "A study of the impact dynamics of loosely supported heat exchanger tubes", Journal of Pressure Vessel Technology, 1989, Vol.111, pp 394-401.

(12) WEAVER, D.S. and SCHNEIDER, W., "The effect of flat bar supports on the crossflow induced response of heat exchanger U-tubes", Journal of Engineering for Power, 1983, Vol.105, pp 775-781.

(13) YETISIR, M. and WEAVER, D.S., "The dynamics of heat exchanger U-bend tubes with flat bar supports", Journal of Pressure Vessel Technology, 1986, Vol. 108, pp 406-412.

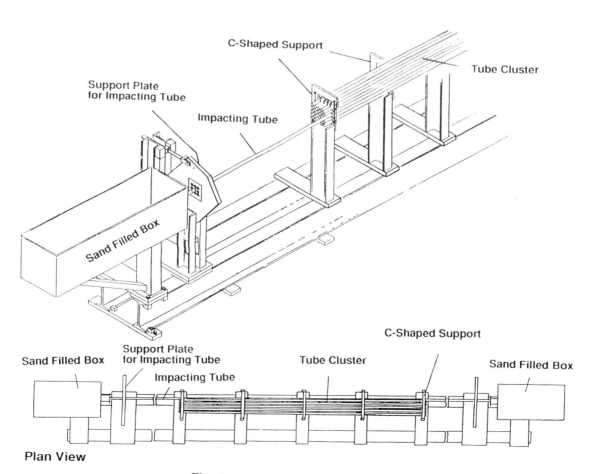

Fig. 1   Layout of Test Rig

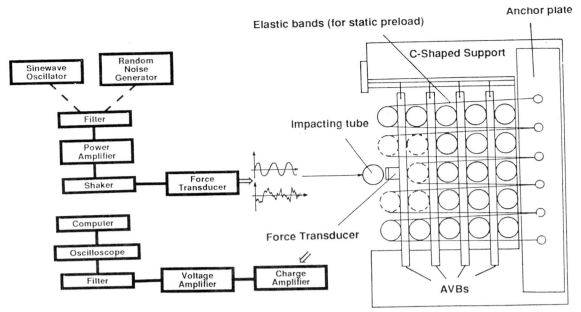

Fig. 2 Details of the tube/AVB cluster located at the C-shaped supports for
(a) rigid bundle configuration (all tubes present)
(b) flexible bundle configuration (dotted-lined tubes absent).

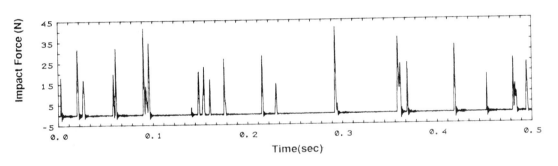

Fig. 3a An example of a typical time history segment of the measured
tube-to-support impact force (Tube-to-AVB clearance : 0mm).

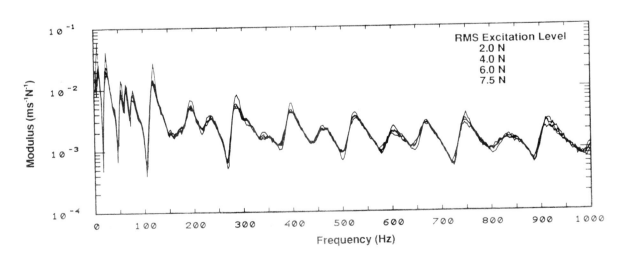

Fig. 3b Effect of excitation force level on the modulus of the measured
transfer function of the 7.5m impacting tube, rigid tube/AVB
setting (Tube-to-AVB clearance : 0mm).

144

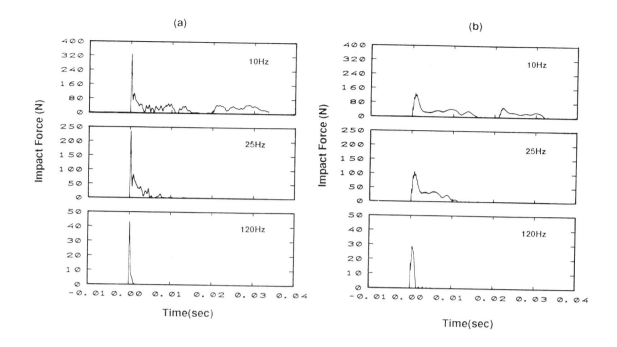

Fig. 4   Measured impact force time signatures for (a) rigid and (b) flexible
          tube clusters using discrete frequency excitation of 10 Hz, 25 Hz and
          120 Hz. Tube-to-AVB clearance : 0mm, RMS excitation force : 5 N

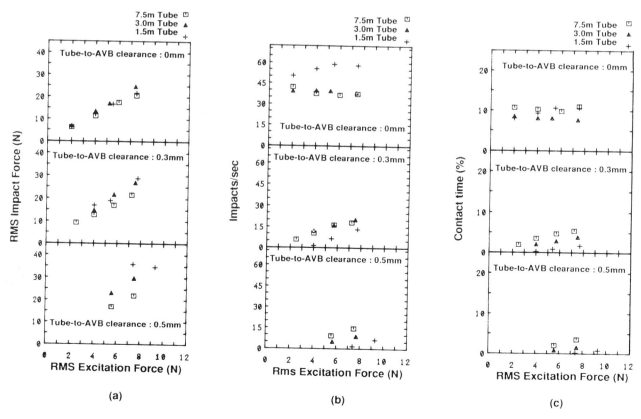

Fig. 5   Influence of impacting tube stiffness on (a) tube-to-AVB impact
          force (b) impact rate (c) contact time for a rigid tube cluster.

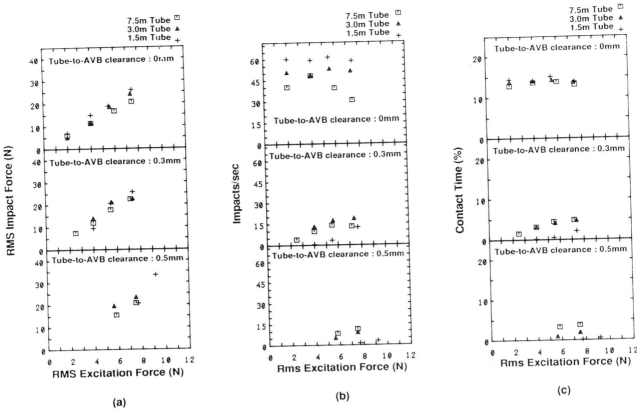

Fig. 6 Influence of impacting tube stiffness on (a) tube-to-AVB impact force (b) impact rate (c) contact time for a flexible tube cluster.

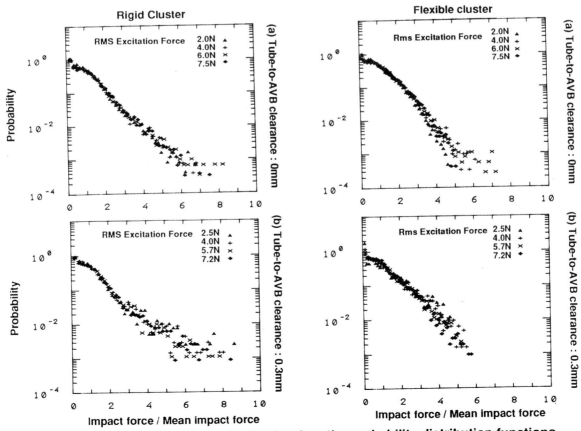

Fig. 7 Effect of excitation level on the probability distribution functions of the normalised impact force. Tube-to-AVB clearance : 0mm and 0.3mm. Length of impacting tube : 7.5m.

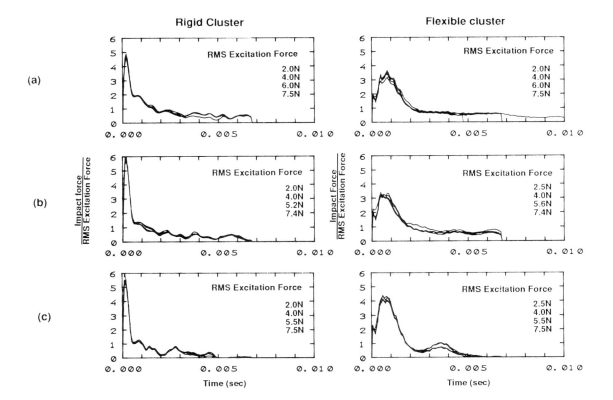

Fig. 8   Effect of excitation level on the non-dimensional impact force time
signatures obtained for both rigid and flexible tube clusters using
random excitation. Tube-to-AVB clearance : 0mm. Length of
impacting tube for case (a) 7.5m, (b) 3.0m and (c) 1.5m.

C416/053

Fretting wear damage prediction in the inlet region of nuclear steam generators

N J FISHER, MSc, MASME, J G ING, BSc and M J PETTIGREW
Atomic Energy of Canada Limited Research Company, Chalk River, Ontario, Canada
R J ROGERS, PhD
Department of Mechanical Engineering, University of New Brunswick, Canada

ABSTRACT Flow-induced vibration of steam generator tubes results in fretting-wear damage due to impacting and rubbing of the tubes against their supports, or against adjacent tubes. Fretting-wear damage can be predicted by computing tube response to flow-induced excitation forces using analytical techniques, and then relating the tube response to resultant wear damage using experimentally derived wear coefficients.

Fretting-wear damage prediction is illustrated in this paper through the example problem of the inlet region of a nuclear steam generator. Computer simulations using the VIBIC (VIbration of Beams with Intermittent Contact) code are used to show the effect of support type (tri-lobe broached hole versus drilled hole), and of increased tube-to-support clearances due to chemical cleaning. Wear coefficients derived from fretting-wear tests of 500 h duration at typical steam generator conditions are used to predict tube wear damage in the example problem.

NOMENCLATURE

c_r	tube-to-support radial clearance (m)
d_o, d_i	tube outside and inside diameters (m)
e_y, e_z	tube-to-support eccentricity (m)
E	tube elastic modulus (Pa)
$F(t)$	external known forcing function (N)
$F_s(t)$	tube-to-support contact forces (N)
f	modal frequency (Hz)
F_f	friction force (tangential component of contact force) (N)
F_n	impact force (normal component of contact force) (N)
g	acceleration due to gravity (m/s^2)
K	wear coefficient (Pa^{-1})
k	equivalent tube/support stiffness (N/m)
L	tube length (m)
r	tube or support hole radius (m)
t	tube support thickness (m)
u	displacement (m)
$\dot{V}$	tube wear rate (μm^3/s)
$\dot{W}_N$	tube-to-support work-rate (mW)
x, y, z	cartesian coordinates
f	friction coefficient
ε	void fraction (%)
γ	support material damping coefficient (s/m)
θ	angular position (radians)
ζ	tube modal damping ratio (%)
μ	dynamic viscosity (Ns/m^2)
ν	Poissons ratio
ρ	density (kg/m^3)
τ	contact duration (%)
ω	modal frequencies (rad/s)
ϕ	eigenvectors

1. INTRODUCTION

Tubes within shell-and-tube heat exchange components are supported at intermediate points by support plates. Current practice is to allow clearances between the tubes and plates for design and manufacturing considerations. Flow-induced vibration of a tube can cause it to impact or rub against a support plate or against adjacent tubes and can result in tube fretting-wear. To increase the reliability and design life of heat exchange components, design criteria that establish acceptable limits of vibration and minimize fretting-wear are necessary.

To understand tube fretting-wear mechanisms, fretting-wear studies have been conducted in single-span test rigs that simulate the conditions and tube motions in steam generators and heat exchangers. The fretting-wear rate is dependent upon material combination, contact configuration, environmental conditions and tube-to-support dynamic interaction. Ko [5] demonstrated that the fretting-wear rate correlates well with tube-to-support contact force for similar tube motion. For different tube motion types, Ko [6-8] showed that the wear rate correlates well with a force function representing the integrated area of the force histogram of the shear force component. Other researchers [19, 20] have defined a similar parameter, called the work-rate, for correlating wear data. It is the normal component of the contact force (impact force) integrated over the real sliding distance.

The tube-to-support work-rate is used to relate experimental wear data from single-span test rigs to real multi-span heat exchanger configurations. Work-rate can be measured during experimental wear tests. However, it is difficult to measure in real heat exchangers. Therefore, analytical techniques are required to predict tube-to-support work-rates in real heat exchangers.

The VIBIC (VIbration of Beams with Intermittent Contact) computer code is a finite element model of a multi-span heat exchanger tube. It includes non-linearities due to clearances between the tube and its supports. The code simulates the tube response to external sinusoidal or random force excitation and predicts tube motion and tube-to-support dynamic interaction. The dynamic interaction at the supports is quantified in terms of force levels, contact durations and work-rates.

The code structure and organization have been described in detail in previous publications [1-3]. In brief, the tube is discretized using beam finite elements, each having 12 degrees of freedom. In accordance with standard finite element techniques, complete mass and stiffness matrices for the modelled tube are obtained by combining the stiffness and inertia characteristics of the elements, and including the effects of rotational inertia and shear deformation. The rigidly constrained degrees of freedom are removed, and the resulting equations of motion, written in matrix form, are:

$$[M]\{\ddot{u}\} + [C]\{\dot{u}\} + [K]\{u\} = \{F(t)\} + \{F_s(t)\} \qquad (1)$$

where the number of equations, n, corresponds to the number of unconstrained degrees of freedom. The column matrix $\{u\}$ represents all of the possible displacements and rotations of the tube, and $\{F(t)\}$ represents the known forcing functions. The matrices $[M]$, $[C]$ and $[K]$ represent the system mass, damping and stiffness, respectively.

In addition to the known forcing functions, forces $\{F_s(t)\}$ are applied to the tube at the support locations when the tube is in contact with the support. These contact forces are dependent on the tube motion. Therefore, equation (1) cannot be solved in closed-form, but must be numerically integrated.

Some computer codes, such as H3DMAP [15,16] and ABAQUS-EPGEN [21,22], use direct numerical integration to solve equation (1). However, to reduce the computational effort and cost, modal superposition (also called the normal mode method) can be used to decrease the number of equations to be integrated. Numerical and experimental studies by several authors [10-12] demonstrate that this is an appropriate computational technique for tube impact-sliding problems. It is particularly effective for localized nonlinear problems, such as impact-sliding tube motion, because solutions need only be computed at a few critical locations, i.e., supports and midspans.

Modal superposition is used in the VIBIC code and in the GERBOISE code developed by Commissariat à l'Energie Atomique (CEA) [23-25]. The modal equations of motion for the first m modes are given by,

$$\{\ddot{q}\} + 2[\zeta\omega]\{\dot{q}\} + [\omega^2]\{q\} = [\phi]^T\{F(t) + F_s(t)\} \qquad (2)$$

where ζ and ω are the damping ratio and natural frequency, respectively, for each mode and $[\phi]$ is the matrix of modal eigenvectors normalized with respect to the mass matrix. The m modal degrees of freedom are defined by the transformation

$$\{u\}_n = [\phi]_{n \times m}\{q\}_m \qquad (3)$$

The motion of the tube is described in terms of the linear combination of the unconstrained modes of vibration (modes are assumed to be free at the loose supports), as shown analytically by Davies and Rogers [9]. The number of modes, m, required in the solution is physically limited by the equivalent stiffness of the tube and support, as it is useless to consider modes with greater modal stiffness. In the case of steam generator tubes, approximately 25 modes in each plane are sufficient to achieve correct representation of the constrained tube motion and local contact forces. To achieve satisfactory solutions, short time steps, scaled by the contact force time history, must be employed. In VIBIC, step-by-step time integration is performed using the de Vogelaere explicit method of integration as formulated by Fu [13,14].

The VIBIC code embodies state-of-the-art flow-induced vibration and fretting-wear technology and has been extensively tested against experimental measurements, benchmark solutions and direct integration simulation results [1-3, 27, 28].

The purpose of this paper is to illustrate fretting-wear damage prediction through the example problem of the inlet region of a nuclear steam generator. Computer simulations using the VIBIC code are used to show the effect of support type (tri-lobe broached hole versus drilled hole), and of increased tube-to-support clearances due to chemical cleaning. Wear coefficients derived from fretting-wear tests of 500 h duration at typical steam generator conditions are used to predict tube wear damage in the example problem.

2. FINITE ELEMENT MODEL

The example problem is the inlet region of a nuclear steam generator.

2.1. Four-Span Tube Model

The VIBIC model of a tube in the inlet region of the steam generator is shown in Fig. 1. Flow-induced vibration excitation occurs all along the steam generator tube. However, cross-flow excitation in the lower span where water enters the steam generator through the inlet port is responsible for most of the tube vibration. Because the excitation is mainly restricted to the lower span, the dynamic interaction at the two lower supports is of primary interest. Only a four-span section of the tube was modelled since the motion of the tube at greater distances from the lower supports has little effect on the resultant motion at the lower supports. Therefore, the tube was assumed to be clamped into the tubesheet at the lower end and pinned at the fourth clearance support.

The overall tube length is 3.4 m, with the lowest (first) span at 638 mm length and the three upper spans at 933 mm length per span. The tube material is Incoloy 800 with 15.9 mm outside diameter and 1.3 mm nominal wall thickness. The support plates are 410 stainless steel at 22.2 mm thickness and 0.38 mm nominal diametral clearance.

The holes in the support plates are broached. The geometry of the broached hole is shown in Fig. 2. Three support lands, spaced at 120° intervals and subtending 30° each, provide support for the tube.

2.2. Contact Model : Broached Hole versus Drilled Hole

The forces acting on the tube when it contacts a support are dependent on the tube motion and the geometry of the support. The general contact between a circular tube and support is shown in Fig. 3. Note that the tube in Fig. 3 is shown much smaller than the support hole for illustration. Tube-to-support contact occurs when the tube centre displacement exceeds the clearance between the tube and support. When contact occurs, impact and friction forces are generated at the contact point.

The impact force, F_n, is modelled as a linear spring force due to deflection of the tube and support. This force is normal to the support surface and is given by the product of the specified tube/support stiffness and the radial deformation. Tube/support stiffness is controlled by local ovalization of the tube and is estimated using expressions by Lukasewicz [29] or Morley [30].

The friction force, F_f, is proportional to the impact force, and acts tangentially to the support surface and opposite to the direction of the tube tangential velocity. To avoid sharp discontinuities in the friction force when the tangential velocity changes direction, a combination of Coulomb and viscous friction models is used. At velocities greater than a specified cut-off velocity, the friction force is proportional to the impact force, but at velocities less than the cut-off, the force is proportional to the velocity. The Antunes friction model [25], which includes the effect of tube/support adherence, is currently being implemented in VIBIC.

The contact point is easily computed for drilled hole supports as the point at which a line drawn through the hole and tube centres intersects the hole surface. However, contact between the tube and a broached hole support is more complicated because contact can occur on or between support lands.

To compute contact between the tube and a broached hole support, a two-step process is used in VIBIC. First, the general intersection points of two intersecting circles, P_1 and P_2 (see Fig. 3), are calculated, and then the coordinates of these points are evaluated to determine if one or both of them lie on a support land, or in the space between the lands. Note that the existence of two intersection points is a result of the geometrical modelling of two intersecting circles, not the actual contact of tube and support. These intersection points are used to define the type of contact and the contact point.

There are four possible types of contact:

1) Simple Contact -- If both intersection points lie on the same land, the contact has occurred similarly as for drilled hole supports, and the contact point is the point at which a line drawn through the hole and tube centres intersects the land surface.

2) Single Contact -- If one intersection point lies on a land and the other lies in an adjoining space, then a single contact has occurred. If a line drawn through the hole and tube centres also intersects the land surface, then simple contact has occurred as discussed above. However, if the line does not intersect a land, then contact has occurred on the corner of the land. In this case, the direction of the impact and friction forces must be adjusted as discussed below.

3) Double Corner Contact -- If the intersection points lie on different lands, then double corner contact has occurred and two sets of contact forces are generated.

4) No Contact -- If both intersection points lie in the same space between lands, then no contact has occurred and no forces are generated. Note that the tube will eventually contact one or two land corners.

The directions of the impact and friction forces are easily calculated for simple contact, where the normal and tangential unit vectors of the support surface are defined relative to the hole centre. However, for corner contact, the directions of the impact and friction forces are defined relative to the tube centre since most of the contact flexibility is in the tube wall. A typical corner contact is shown in Fig. 4 to illustrate the effect of defining the directions relative to the tube centre.

2.3. Excitation Forces

Random excitation forces were applied in the y and z coordinate directions over the bottom 479 mm of tube length to simulate random turbulence excitation caused by recirculating water entering the steam generator through the inlet port.

Equal random forces were applied in each of the y and z directions. In each direction, the force was distributed uniformly over six nodes, with the six individual nodal forces fully correlated in the time-sense. The forces in the two directions were uncorrelated. Three force levels were used: low (1.5 N rms total force in each direction), medium (fives times greater than low), and high (ten times greater than low).

The random forces were generated as white noise and then low-pass filtered with a first-order Butterworth filter at a cut-off frequency of 40 Hz. This value of cut-off frequency was suggested by Taylor et. al.'s experimental data for random turbulence excitation [36].

2.4. Other Parameters

The effects of structural damping, hydrodynamic mass and damping of the external fluid, added mass of the internal fluid, and squeeze film damping at the supports were also included. Shell-side void fraction and density profiles (see Figs. 5 and 6) for the tube were generated from thermal-hydraulic data and values were assigned to each element. The added mass of the internal and external fluids was lumped at the tube nodes.

The structural, external fluid and squeeze film damping were calculated using design guidelines of Pettigrew et. al. [31-33]. The total damping, as shown in Table 1, was applied as viscous damping on a modal basis. An instantaneous squeeze film damping model is currently under development and will be implemented in VIBIC.

Pettigrew's damping guidelines are based on world-published data derived from experimental measurements on multi-span tube configurations with predominately drilled hole supports and diametral clearances of either 0.38 or 0.76 mm. For this study, damping was maintained constant as tube-to-support diametral clearance was varied. Experimental evidence is required to justify this assumption for diametral clearances outside the range of 0.38 to 0.76 mm.

The effect of tube-to-support clearance on support damping of multi-span tubes is not well understood, and little experimental data has been published for broached hole and flat bar type supports with larger clearances. Since support damping accounts for a significant portion of overall tube damping, experimental studies should be undertaken to provide additional data.

3. SIMULATION RESULTS

All simulations were conducted using 25 modes in each direction and a 30 μs timestep.

3.1. Parameter Study

Several simulations were conducted to assess the effects of tube/support stiffness, friction coefficient and tube-to-support eccentricity. The low force level was used for these simulations. The results of the parameter study are shown in Table 2, where the results are compared to a "baseline" case with the following support parameter values: $k = 16$ N/μm, $f = 0.25$, $c_r = 0.19$ mm and tube-to-support eccentricity of Type A. Note that as shown in Fig. 1, for Type A eccentricity, the support rests against lands at Supports 1 and 3 and between lands at Support 2, while for Type B eccentricity, the tube is between lands at Supports 1 and 3 and on a land at Support 2. Results are not tabulated for Support 3 because, as discussed previously, the vibration excitation is retricted to the lower span and the resulting dynamic interaction at the two lower spans is of primary interest.

Reducing the support stiffness by a factor of two, from 16 to 8 N/μm, reduced the work-rate at Support 1 by 15 per cent, but had no effect on the work-rate at Support 2. Increasing the friction coefficient from 0.25 to 0.5, or changing from Type A to Type B eccentricity decreased the work-rates at both supports. In both cases, the work-rate at Support 1 decreased by 50 per cent. The work-rate at Support 2 decreased by 5 per cent with the increased friction coefficient and by 15 per cent with the changed eccentricity. The "baseline" values for these support parameters were used for all further simulations, since use of these values resulted in conservative work-rates.

3.2. Effect of Support Type

Broached hole and drilled hole supports were compared at three levels of force excitation : low, medium and high. The total magnitude of the low force excitation in each direction was 1.5 N rms, as discussed previously. The medium and high levels were five and ten times greater, respectively. The results of this study are given in Table 3. For this comparison the "baseline" case was the broached hole simulation at each force level. All other support parameters were maintained at the "baseline" case values.

The results are not exhaustive, nor completely consistent. However, it appears that the work-rate for broached hole supports is less than for drilled hole supports at the same level of force excitation. This result is not surprising since the geometry of a broached support should promote more impact motion and, therefore, less sliding. A greater difference was observed at greater levels of force excitation, where the tube was moving across the full support clearance gap. Orbital plots for Support 2 under high force excitation and with both broached and drilled support geometry are shown in Fig. 7.

3.3. Effect of Tube-to-Support Clearance

Simulations were conducted for a range of tube-to-support clearances using the medium level of force excitation for two different tube-to-support eccentricities : concentric (eccentricity = 0) and Type A eccentric (eccentricity = 0.19 mm). The results of this study are shown in Table 4. The trends for both values of eccentricity were similar. Therefore, the analysis of results for this study is focussed on the eccentric case, because this case is more likely to be found in real steam generators.

Increasing the diametral clearance caused the work-rate at Support 1 to decrease. For small increases in clearance, the work-rate at Support 2 increased. However, for larger clearances, the work-rate decreased at both Supports 1 and 2. At these larger clearances, the work-rate increased at Support 3 as it decreased at Supports 1 or 2.

The peak work-rate at Support 2 was 50 per cent greater than the work-rate corresponding to the nominal clearance and occurred at a diametral clearance of 0.635 mm, which is 70 per cent greater than nominal. At this clearance, the work-rate at Support 1 was 70 per cent of the value corresponding to the nominal clearance.

4. PREDICTED WEAR DAMAGE

4.1. Fretting-Wear Test Results

A series of fretting-wear tests was conducted in the Chalk River Laboratories (CRL) impact fretting-wear test facility to determine the wear coefficient for the Incoloy 800/410 stainless steel material combination. The environment for all tests was pressurized water at 265°C with typical secondary side chemistry: pH 8-9, 50 ppb Hydrazine, 5 ppm Morpholine, and <5 ppb oxygen.

Tests were conducted for both drilled and broached hole supports, and under both random and sinusoidal force excitation to verify that work-rate is an effective normalizing parameter. A typical pair of wear specimens is shown in Fig. 8. Work-rates ranging from 0.5 to 55 mW were used in the test program. Test durations ranged from 200 to 800 h. The support surface finish, thickness, eccentricity and diametral clearance were also varied.

The test results showed that the tube wear rate varies linearly with work-rate. The wear coefficient derived from the test data was 40×10^{-15} Pa^{-1}.

4.2. Effect of Tube-to-Support Clearance on Tube Wear Damage

To estimate the effect of tube-to-support clearance on tube wear damage, tube wear rates at Supports 1 and 2 were calculated from the predicted work-rates and the experimental wear coefficient. The tube wear rate is plotted versus diametral clearance in Fig. 9. In computing tube wear rates, wear was assumed to occur equally on all three lands and station operating capacity was assumed to be 85 per cent.

The predictions of tube wear damage presented in Fig. 9 are restricted to the 0.38 to 0.76 mm diametral clearance range because, as discussed earlier, damping was assumed to remain constant as diametral clearance increased. This assumption is based on damping guidelines derived from experimental data for the 0.38 to 0.76 mm range. Therefore, damage predictions for clearances outside of this range would not be supported by experimental damping data. Also, predicted work-rates for larger clearances (see Table 4) indicate that Support 1 may become inactive, which suggests that the potential for fluid-elastic instability at larger clearances should be considered.

From the predicted wear damage shown in Fig. 9, it is apparent that an increase in diametral clearance as a result of chemical cleaning would result in decreased wear at Support 1 and increased wear at Support 2. However, to be conservative only the increase in wear damage at Support 2 should be considered. A decrease in wear damage at Support 1 would be beneficial, but cannot be ensured.

The result of this analysis, therefore, is that overall tube wear damage in this example problem is expected to increase proportionally with increased diametral clearance, as observed for Support 2. If chemical cleaning increases the diametral clearance by 30 to 50 per cent, then the tube wear rate is expected to also increase by 30 to 50 per cent.

5. CONCLUSIONS

The conclusions of this analysis are:

1) Simulations for an example problem of an inlet region of a nuclear steam generator indicate that tube wear damage would increase proportionally with increased clearance due to chemical cleaning over the 0.38 to 0.76 mm diametral clearance range.

2) Simulations also indicate that at larger clearances some tube supports may become inactive, which suggests that the potential for fluid-elastic instability at larger clearances should be considered.

3) The tube motion within broached hole supports is different than the motion within drilled hole supports. It appears that the work-rate for broached hole supports is less than for drilled hole supports at the same level of force excitation. It is important, therefore, that the support geometry be appropriately modelled.

4) The VIBIC code combined with specific material wear coefficients can be used to predict fretting-wear damage in nuclear steam generators and other heat exchange equipment, and to assess the effect of changed parameters, such as increased support clearances, on tube wear rates.

6. ACKNOWLEDGEMENTS

The authors are grateful to C.E. Taylor for her assistance with the analytical portion of the program, and to M.K.Weckwerth, B.M. Cotnam and B.E.N. Pettit for their assistance with the experimental portion.

This work was partly funded by CANDU Owners Group R&D work package WPIR 1915. Support for R.J. Rogers was funded through a Joint Industry/University R & D Grant from the Natural Sciences and Engineering Research Council of Canada.

7. REFERENCES

[1] Rogers, R.J. and Pick, R.J., "On the Dynamic Spatial Response of a Heat Exchanger Tube with Intermittent Baffle Contacts", Nuclear Engineering and Design, Vol 36, No 1, 1976 January, pp. 81-90.

[2] Rogers, R.J. and Pick, R.J., "Factors Associated with Support Plate Forces due to Heat Exchanger Tube Vibratory Contact", Nuclear Engineering and Design, Vol 44, No 2, 1977 November, pp. 247-253.

[3] Ko, P.L. and Rogers, R.J., "Analytical and Experimental Studies of Tube/Support Interaction in Multi-Span Heat Exchanger Tubes", Nuclear Engineering and Design, Vol 65, 1981, pp. 399-409.

[4] Rogers, R.J., Taylor, C. and Pettigrew, M.J., "Fluid Effects on Multi-Span Heat-Exchange Tube Vibration", ASME Special Publication Topics in Fluid Structure Interaction, edited by H. Chung and M.D. Bernstein, Pressure Vessels and Piping Conference, San Antonio, Texas, 1984 June 17-21.

[5] Ko, P.L., "Experimental Studies of Tube Fretting in Steam Generators and Heat Exchangers", J. of Pressure Vessel Technology, Vol 101, 1979 May, pp. 125-133.

[6] Ko, P.L., Tromp, J.H. and Weckwerth, M.K., "Heat Exchanger Tube Fretting Wear: Correlation of Tube Motion and Wear", ASTM Special Publication STP-780 Materials Evaluation Under Fretting Conditions, Symposium on Erosion and Wear, Warminster, Pennsylvania, 1981 June 3.

[7] Ko, P.L. and Basista, H., "Correlation of Support/Impact Force and Fretting-Wear for a Heat Exchanger Tube", J. of Pressure Vessel Technology, Vol 106, 1984 January.

[8] Ko, P.L., "The Significance of Shear and Normal Force Components on Tube Wear due to Fretting and Periodic Impacting", Wear, No 1-3, Vol 106, 1985, pp. 261-281.

[9] Davies, H.G. and Rogers, R.J., "The Vibration of Structures Elastically Constrained at Discrete Points", J of Sound and Vibration, Vol 63, No 3, 1979 April, pp. 437-447.

[10] Shah, V., Bohm, G. and Nahavandi, A., "Modal Superposition Method for Computationally Economical Nonlinear Structural Analysis", J of Pressure Vessel Technology, Vol 101, 1979, pp. 134-141.

[11] Ting, E., Chen, S. and Wambsganss, M., "Dynamics of Component-Support Impact : An Elastic Analysis", Nuclear Engineering and Design, Vol 52, 1979, pp. 235-244.

[12] Salmon, M.A., Verma, V.K. and Youtsos, T.G., "Elastic Analysis of Beam-Support Impact", J of Pressure Vessel Technology, Vol 107, 1985 February, pp. 64-67.

[13] Fu, C.C., "A Method for the Numerical Integration of the Equations of Motion Arising from a Finite Element Analysis", J of Applied Mechanics, 1970, pp. 599-340.

[14] Wu, R.W.H. and Witmer, E.A., "Stability of the De Vogelaere Method for Timewise Numerical Integration", AIAA Journal, Vol 11, 1973, pp. 1432-1436.

[15] Sauve, R.G. and Teper, W.W., "Non-Linear Dynamic-Impact Simulation of Process Equipment Tubes with Tube/Support Plate Interaction", Thermal Hydraulics of Nuclear Reactors Vol II, Santa Barbara, California, 1983 Jan, pp. 740-751.

[16] Sauve, R.G. and Teper, W.W., "Impact Simulation of Process Equipment Tubes and Support Plates - A Numerical Algorithm", J of Pressure Vessel Technology, Vol 109, 1987 February, pp. 70-79.

[17] Haslinger, K.H. and Steininger, D.A., "Steam Generator Tube/Tube Support Plate Interaction Characteristics", ASME Special Publication Symposium on Flow-Induced Vibrations: Volume 3 Vibration in Heat Exchangers, edited by M.P. Paidoussis, J.M. Chenoweth and M.D. Bernstein, New Orleans, Louisiana, 1984 December 9-14.

[18] Haslinger, K.H., Martin, M.L. and Steininger, D.A., "Pressured Water Reactor Steam Generator Tube Wear Prediction Utilizing Experimental Techniques", International Conference on Flow-Induced Vibrations, Bowness-on-Windermere, England, 1987 May 12-14.

[19] Frick, T.M., Sobek, T.E. and Reavis, J.R., "Overview on the Development and Implementation of Methodologies to Compute Vibration and Wear of Steam Generator Tubes", ASME Special Publication Symposium on Flow-Induced Vibrations: Volume 3 Vibration in Heat Exchangers, edited by M.P. Paidoussis, J.M. Chenoweth and M.D. Bernstein, New Orleans, Louisiana, 1984 December 9-14.

[20] Blevins, R.D., "A Rational Algorithm for Predicting Vibration-Induced Damage to Tube and Shell Heat Exchangers", ASME Special Publication Symposium on Flow-Induced Vibrations: Volume 3 Vibration in Heat Exchangers, edited by M.P. Paidoussis, J.M. Chenoweth and M.D. Bernstein, New Orleans, Louisiana, 1984 December 9-14.

[21] Rao, M.S.M., Gupta, G.D., Eisinger, F.L., Hibbitt, H.D. and Steininger, D.A., "Computer Modelling of Vibration and Wear Multispan Tubes with Clearances at Tube Supports", International Conference on Flow-Induced Vibrations, Bowness-on-Windermere, England, 1987 May 12-14.

[22] Rao, M.S.M., Steininger, D.A. and Eisinger, F.L., "Numerical Simulation of Fluidelastic Vibration and Wear of Multispan Tubes with Clearances at Supports", ASME Special Publication Flow-Induced Vibration and Noise - 1988 : Volume 5 Flow-Induced Vibration in Heat-Transfer Equipment, edited by M.P. Paidoussis, J.M. Chenoweth, S.S. Chen, J.R. Stenner and W.J. Bryan, Chicago, Illinois, 1988 November 27-December 2.

[23] Axisa, F., Desseaux, A. and Gibert, R.J., "Experimental Study of Tube/Support Impact Forces in Multi-Span PWR Steam Generator Tubes", ASME Special Publication Symposium on Flow-Induced Vibrations: Volume 3 Vibration in Heat Exchangers, edited by M.P. Paidoussis, J.M. Chenoweth and M.D. Bernstein, New Orleans, Louisiana, 1984 December 9-14.

[24] Axisa, F., Antunes, J. and Villard, B., "Overview of Numerical Methods for Prediction Flow-Induced Vibration", J of Pressure Vessel Technology, Vol 110, 1988 February, pp. 6-14.

[25] Antunes, J., Axisa, F., Beaufils, B. and Guilbaud, D., "Coulomb Friction Modelling in Numerical Simulations of Vibration and Wear Work Rate of Multispan Tube Bundles", J of Fluids and Structures, Vol 4, 1990 May, pp. 287-304.

[26] Antunes, J., Axisa, F. and Vento, M.A., "Experiments on Vibro-Impact Dynamics Under Fluidelastic Instability", 1990 Pressure Vessels and Piping Conference, Nashville, Tennessee, 1990 June 17-21.

[27] Ko, P.L., "Computer-Aided tube Fretting-Wear Predictions", AECL-8350, 1984 April.

[28] Fisher, N.J., Olesen, M.J., Rogers, R.J. and Ko, P.L., "Simulation of Tube-to-Support Dynamic Interaction in Heat Exchange Equipment", J of Pressure Vessel Technology, Vol 111, 1989 November, pp. 378-384.

[29] Lukasewicz, S., Local Loads in Plates and Shells, Noordhoff International Publishers, 1979.

[30] Morley, L.S.D., "The Thin-Walled Circular Cylinder Subjected to Concentrated Radial Loads, Q J of Mechanics and Applied Mathematics, XIII, (Part 1), 1960, pp. 24-39.

[31] Pettigrew, M.J., Goyder, H.G.D., Qiao, Z.L. and Axisa, F., "Damping of Multispan Heat Exchanger Tubes, Part 1 : In Gases", Flow-Induced Vibration - 1986, edited by S.S. Chen, J.C. Simonis and Y.S. Shin, ASME Publication PVP - Vol 104, 1986, pp. 81-87.

[32] Pettigrew, M.J., Rogers, R.J. and Axisa, F., "Damping of Multispan Heat Exchanger Tubes, Part 2 : In Liquids", Flow-Induced Vibration - 1986, edited by S.S. Chen, J.C. Simonis and Y.S. Shin, ASME Publication PVP - Vol 104, 1986, pp. 89-98.

[33] Kim, B.S., Pettigrew, M.J. and Tromp, J.H., "Vibration Damping of Heat Exchanger Tubes in Liquids : Effects of Support Parameters", J of Fluids and Structures, Vol 2, 1988, pp. 593-614.

[34] Pettigrew, M.J., Taylor, C.E. and Kim, B.S., "Vibration of Tube Bundles in Two-Phase Cross-Flow : Part 1--Hydrodynamic Mass and Damping" , J of Pressure Vessel Technology, Vol 111, 1989 November, pp. 466-477.

[35] Pettigrew, M.J., Tromp, J.H., Taylor, C.E. and Kim, B.S., "Vibration of Tube Bundles in Two-Phase Cross-Flow: Part 2--Fluid-Elastic Instability", J of Pressure Vessel Technology, Vol 111, 1989 November, pp. 478-487.

[36] Taylor, C.E., Currie, I.G., Pettigrew, M.J. and Kim, B.S., "Vibration of Tube Bundles in Two-Phase Cross-Flow : Part 3--Turbulence-Induced Excitation" , J of Pressure Vessel Technology, Vol 111, 1989 November, pp. 488-500.

[37] Au-Yang, M.K., "Effect of Chemical Cleaning on Steam Generator Tube Wear", Proceedings of the 1988 Joint ASME-ANS Nuclear Power Conference, Myrtle Beach, South Carolina, 1988 April 17-20.

Table 1: Total Modal Damping

Mode	Frequency (Hz)	Modal Damping Ratio (%)
1	4.4	16
2	14	6.0
3	29.2	3.5
4	49.8	2.5
5	76.1	2.0
6	108	1.8
7	147	1.6
8	187	1.5
9	235	1.4
10	288	1.4
11	352	1.3
12	413	1.3
13	481	1.3
14	552	1.2
15	637	1.2
16	721	1.2
17	812	1.2
18	910	1.2
19	1003	1.2
20	1106	1.2
21	1214	1.2
22	1350	1.2
23	1454	1.1
24	1572	1.1

© IMechE 1991 C416/053

Table 2: Parameter Study

Support Parameter	Contact Force (N_{rms}) Support 1	Support 2	Work-Rate (mW) Support 1	Support 2
Tube/Support Stiffness $k(N/\mu m)$				
16	baseline	baseline	baseline	baseline
8	no change	30% less	15% less	no change
Friction Coefficient f				
0.25	baseline	baseline	baseline	baseline
0.5	5% greater	5% less	50% less	5% less
Eccentricity				
Type A	(l) baseline	(sp) baseline	(l) baseline	(sp) baseline
Type B	(sp) 30% less	(l) 50% less	(sp) 50% less	(l) 15% less

l   = land
sp = space between lands

Table 3: Effect of Support Type

Force Level	Support Type	Contact Force (N_{rms}) Support 1	Support 2	Work-Rate (mW) Support 1	Support 2
low	broached	baseline	baseline	baseline	baseline
	drilled	15% greater	5% less	no change	15% greate
medium (5 X low)	broached	baseline	baseline	baseline	baseline
	drilled	no change	15% less	50% greater	15% greate
high (10 X low)	broached	baseline	baseline	baseline	baseline
	drilled	2% less	25% less	80% greater	25% less

Table 4: Effect of Support Clearance

Force Level	Diametral Clearance (mm)	Eccentricity (mm)	Contact Force (N_{rms}) Support 1	Support 2	Work-Rate (mW) Support 1	Support
medium	0.127	0	17	8.5	83	28
(5 X low)	0.254	0	15	10	82	33
	0.381	0	12	12	66	41
	0.508	0	10	10	40	36
	0.635	0	6.0	7.2	9	13
	0.762	0	3.5	6.4	5	27
	0.889	0	1.9	8.9	1	37
	0.38	0.19	13	11	71	36
	0.508	0.19	11	11	50	44
	0.635	0.19	9.7	8.9	50	53
	0.762	0.19	8.8	7.3	20	29
	0.889	0.19	5.8	7.1	14	16

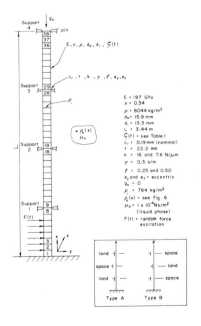

Figure 1:   VIBIC Model of Inlet Region

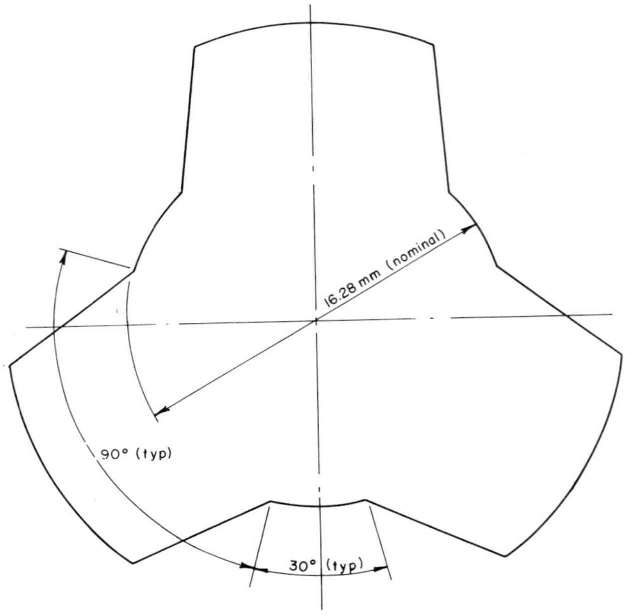

Figure 2:   Broached Hole Geometry

© IMechE 1991 C416/053

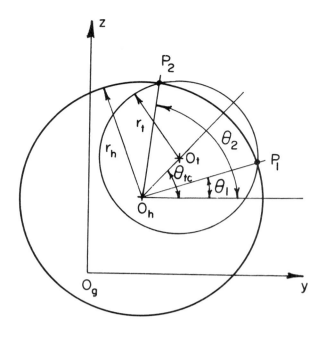

Figure 3:   General Intersection of Two Circles

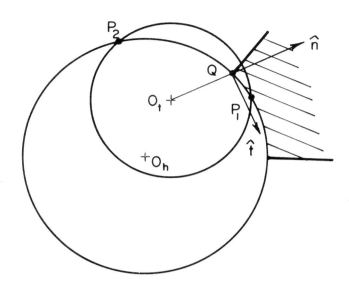

Figure 4:   Corner Contact

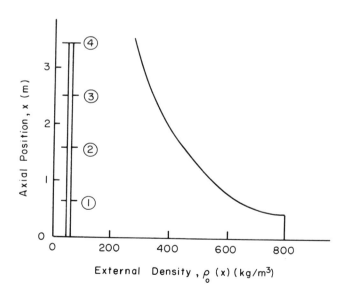

Figure 5:   Shell-Side Density Profile

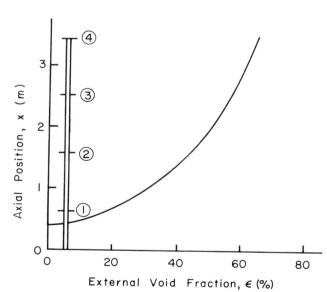

Figure 6:   Shell-Side Void Fraction Profile

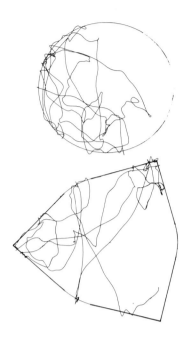

Figure 7:   Typical Orbital Plots

Figure 8:   Typical Wear Specimens

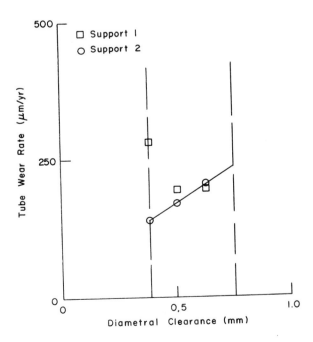

Figure 9:   Tube Wear Damage

C416/088

Dynamic flow characteristics of reactor internal components – a scale model experiment

T FUJII, BSc, MJSME, MAESJ, T YAMAMOTO, MSc, MAESJ, H MIYANO, BMechEng, MISME, MAESJ and O OZAKI, PhD, MJSME, MAESJ
Toshiba Corporation, Kawasaki, Japan
T SAITO, PhD, MJSME, ANS, MAESJ
Toshiba Corporation, Yokohama, Japan

SYNOPSIS   In order to investigate the dynamic behavior of reactor internal components, a water flow experiment was conducted using a model reactor pressure vessel. The characteristics of the complex flow are revealed by the experiments in flow visualization, and in flow velocity and pressure fluctuation measurements. A simple practical method for evaluating flow-induced vibration characteristics of a tube array subject to turbulent excitation is described.

1   INTRODUCTION

In internal pump-type boiling water reactors, the impellers for reactor internal pumps are inside the pressure vessel bottom, and water is circulated by these impellers. The characteristics of pump discharge flow and the shapes of the flow passage are very complicated and differ from those of external recirculation pump-type BWRs. The pump discharges a flow into the lower part of reactor internals (tube array) as a cross flow; that is to say, the arrays experience a fluid excitation force around the whole circumference. In this complicated flow field, it is hardly possible to adopt an existing technique (1,2) directly. One of the authors has already carried out some studies regarding dynamic fluid forces acting on reactor internals (3).

In this paper, in order to estimate the fluid force acting on reactor internals, the flow velocity at representative points and the dynamic fluid forces acting on the model reactor internals were measured. The test vessel dimensions are 1/5th of an actual reactor. The vessel was equipped with simulated lower reactor internals (tube array), and with reactor internal pumps both of which are also scaled down to a 1/5th of actual size, as shown in Fig 1. Two representative tube locations were chosen for measuring the flow. One is located in front of the pump, and the other between the two adjacent pumps, as shown in Fig 2. At first, to enable qualitative examinations of the flow field, flow visualization was carried out using a laser light sheet, and flow velocities were measured with a laser anemometer. Next, in order to quantitatively estimate the fluid forces acting on tubes, pressure fluctuations at the tube surface were measured.

However, for its application in the actual field, further considerations are to be taken into account, regarding the scale-up and high temperature effects. For example, only two representative tubes were treated here, spatial correlation between pressure fluctuations at different locations should be important and interesting problem. The authors are carrying out this study both from analytical and experimental standpoints (4). And also, the model test results should be verified by the results of flow analysis and full-size experiment.

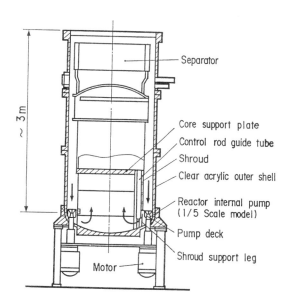

Fig 1   Experimental facility

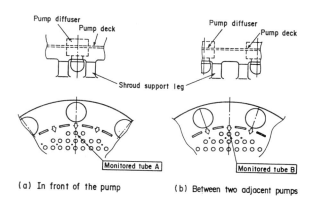

(a) In front of the pump   (b) Between two adjacent pumps

Fig 2   Monitored tube location

2 EXPERIMENTAL FACILITY AND PROCEDURE

The experiments were conducted in a circulating vessel with 10 pumps. To simulate flow passages, the inside of the vessel was designed down to a 1/5th scale model. The vessel was filled with water. Circulating water was driven by the impellers of the 10 pumps on the bottom of the vessel. Water flowed through shroud support leg openings into the lower part of the array as a crossflow, and finally turned its direction to the upper portion of the array as an axial flow.

In order to measure the dynamic pressure at the tube surface, pressure transducers in the form of strain gauge sensors were attached directly to the tubes. These sensors had a 3.2mm diaphragm diameter, and their combined nonlinearity and hysteresis was less than ±1%FS. Pressure transducers were installed at three longitudinal locations in the control rod drive housing (CRDH, 30mm dia.) and one location for control rod guide tube (CRGT, 55mm dia.). To estimate the differential pressure at the tube surface, pressure transducers were also installed on opposite sides of the tubes, as shown in Fig 3.

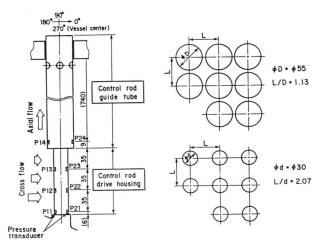

Fig 3 Monitored tube assembly

In order to measure the flow velocity, the fiber-optic probe of a laser Doppler velocimeter was inserted into the water and moved in the vertical plane. Polystyrene latex particles were used as seeding. Pump speed and water temperature measurements were carried out using an optical sensor and a thermocouple, respectively. Since it is necessary to determine the flow rate of circulating water, the differential pressure at suitable positions in the vessel was measured, using pressure transducers.

The monitored tube was inserted into the vessel, and output signals from all the sensors were recorded. The monitored tube was then rotated by an angle of 10°. In this way, measurements of the pressure distribution around the tubes were completed.

Output signals were recorded on floppy-disks, using a data logger with a 2ms sampling interval and a total recording length of 2 seconds. Response data were processed statistically to obtain average values, root mean square values, and frequency spectra.

3 EXPERIMENTAL RESULTS

3.1 Flow visualization and flow velocity measurement

Flow visualization results of pump discharge region using the laser light sheet are shown in Fig 4. From these results, two types of flow pattern were observed. One is (a)the region just in front of the pump where the discharge flows from individual pumps passed straight along the inner surface of the vessel. The other is (b)the region between two adjacent pumps where the discharges joined and were mixed up in the middle of two adjacent pumps. Then, fluid flowed through shroud support leg openings.

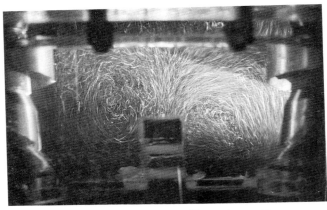

(b) Between two adjacent pumps

Fig 4 Flow visualization result

Flow velocity measurement results are shown in Fig 5. In this figure, V_{ave} represents the average component and V_{rms} represents the fluctuating component at each measuring point. Both components are normalized by the mean flow velocity at the leg opening, and plotted. From these results, above mentioned two types of flow pattern were confirmed quantitatively. At the leg opening just in front of the pump, the main flow is only near the bottom portion. At the leg opening between two adjacent pumps, the velocity profile (both V_{ave} and V_{rms}) is almost flat throughout the full length of the leg opening. It should be noted that the results shown here indicate only horizontal velocity components at each point. For example, the maximum velocity near the bottom surface of the vessel would actually be almost 1.2 times the measured value.

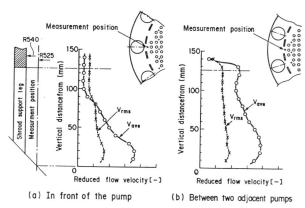

(a) In front of the pump   (b) Between two adjacent pumps

Fig 5 Flow velocity distribution

3.2 Pressure fluctuation measurements

Measured pressure fluctuations are shown in Fig 6. In this figure, rms values of tube surface pressure are plotted in non-dimensional form as

$$\delta P_{i,j\theta} \;=\; \frac{(P_{rms})_{i,j\theta}}{(1/2)\,\rho\,V_0^2} \qquad (1)$$

where i indicates the pressure transducer column number (i=1,2), j indicates the pressure transducer row number (j=1,2,3,4), P_{rms} is the rms value obtained from measured pressure data for every 10° interval, ρ is fluid density, and V_0 is the mean flow velocity at the leg opening. The angle 0° is the direction corresponding to the vessel center, and the fluid mainly flows in the 180° direction.

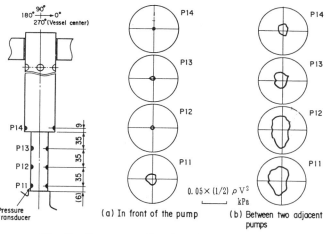

(a) In front of the pump   (b) Between two adjacent pumps

Fig 6 Pressure fluctuation distribution

It can be seen from Fig 6, that on tube A, which is located just in front of the pump, the longitudinal distribution of pressure fluctuation indicates a peak at P11 (CRDH bottom), as compared to P12 (CRDH middle), P13 (CRDH top), and P14 (CRGT bottom). The distributions on each plane (P11, P12, P13 and P14) are almost symmetrical along the flow direction.

On tube B, which is located between two adjacent pumps, the longitudinal distributions of pressure fluctuation are rather flat, while at the same time the tube undergoes strong oscillations. That is to say, tube B is subject to a large excitation force along the full length of CRDH and even at the lower end of CRGT too. The distributions on each plane (P11, P12, P13, and P14) are asymmetrical along the flow direction and have unique profiles.

There was no predominant frequency (corresponding to the vortex shedding frequency) in the pressure fluctuation spectra. Furthermore, there was no correlation between neighboring sensor output signals (e.g. P11 and P12, P11 and P21). This leads to the conclusion that the tubes experience a random excitation.

4 TURBULENT EXCITATION FORCE AND MAXIMUM STRESS ESTIMATION

The procedure for estimating the excitation force, based on the measured values of pressure fluctuation, is shown in Fig 7. The pressure fluctuations acting on the tubes are regarded as random fluctuations in the circumferential and longitudinal directions. The excitation force can be obtained from the bending moment caused by the fluid pressure fluctuations.

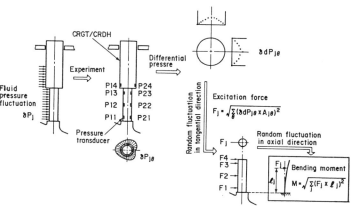

Fig 7 Turbulent excitation force estimation procedure

According to the procedure described in Fig 7, the differential pressure distribution was calculated from the outputs of the pressure transducers on both sides of the tubes, as

$$\delta dP_{j\theta} \;=\; \delta P_{1,j\theta} \;-\; \delta P_{2,j\theta} \qquad (2)$$

where j indicates the longitudinal position, θ indicates the circumferential angle and δ indicates rms value. Calculated differential pressure fluctuations are shown in Fig 8.

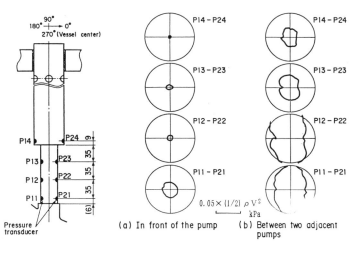

(a) In front of the pump   (b) Between two adjacent pumps

Fig 8 Differential pressure fluctuation distribution

On tube A, which is located just in front of a pump, the differential pressure fluctuations have nearly the same distributions as the pressure fluctuations shown in Fig 6. On tube B, which is located between two adjacent pumps, the differential pressure distribution becomes quite large.

Individual excitation forces for every 10° interval are obtained from the differential pressures multiplied by effective area. Based on the assumption that random fluctuations occur in the circumferential direction, the excitation forces at each sensor height (F1, F2, F3, and F4) can be obtained as

$$F_j = \sqrt{\sum_\theta (\delta dP_{j\theta} \times A_{j\theta})^2} \qquad (3)$$

where $A_{j\theta}$ is the tube effective surface area projected on a flat vertical plane, for an angle of 10°, corresponding to each sensor location.

The bending moment for each sensor height is obtained from the excitation force multiplied by the corresponding sensor height. Again, based on the assumption of random correlation in the longitudinal direction, the total bending moment is obtained as

$$M = \sqrt{\sum_j (F_j \times \ell_j)^2} \qquad (4)$$

where ℓ_j is the distance from the bottom fixed (welded) point to the point at where F_j acts.

Finally, the maximum stress caused by the total bending moment is obtained as

$$\sigma = M / Z \qquad (5)$$

where Z is the section modulus of the tube. In Table 1 are listed the estimated maximum stresses, where the values are normalized to the maximum stress of tube A. Tube B is subject to almost six times as much stress as tube A.

Table 1   Estimated maximum stress

Location	Estimated value
Tube A	1.0
Tube B	5.2 - 6.0

5   CONCLUSION

In order to investigate the dynamic flow characteristics of reactor internal components, a water flow experiment was conducted using a model reactor pressure vessel. Complex flow characteristics were clarified, and a simple practical method for estimating the maximum stress has been described.

The following results were obtained:
(1) The flow profile is quite different in the two regions under consideration. The discharges from individual pumps (a) passed straight along the inner surface of the vessel in the region just in front of the pump, (b) joined and mixed up between two adjacent pumps.
(2) Between two adjacent pumps, the flow generates quite strong pressure fluctuations. These fluctuations cause a large random excitation force on the tubes throughout their length in the crossflow region.
(3) Based on reasonable assumption that random fluctuations occur in tangential and axial directions, turbulent excitation force and maximum stress could be evaluated using measured differential pressure fluctuations . The estimated result is that a tube located between two adjacent pumps is subject to excitations almost six times as large as a tube located just in front of the pump.

REFERENCES

(1)   CHEN, S. S., Flow-induced vibration of circular cylindrical structures, Hemisphere Publishing Corp., Washington, 1987.

(2)   BLEVINS, R. D., Flow-induced vibration, Van Nostrand Reinhold Company, New York, 1977.

(3)   FUJII, T. and OHTOMI, K., Dynamic fluid forces acting on reactor internals. International symposium on flow-induced vibration and noise, ASME WAM, Volume 2, 1988, pp187-196.

(4)   YAMAMOTO, T., MIYANO, H. and FUJII, T., Study of the FIV exciting force on lower plenum structures of internal-pump-type BWRs, American nuclear society winter meeting, Volume 62, 1990, pp640-642.

© IMechE 1991 C416/088

C416/056

Flow induced vibrations in a normal triangular array subject to cross-flow: conventional and unexpected results

S J PRICE, BSc, PhD, ASME, AIAA and M L ZAHN, BEng, MEng
Department of Mechanical Engineering, McGill University, Montreal, Canada

SYNOPSIS The flow–induced vibratory response of a flexible cylinder in normal triangular array, with pitch–to–diameter ratio of 1.375 has been investigated experimentally in air–flow. Characteristics of the interstitial flow are presented showing the existence of periodicities within the flow. The nature of cylinder vibrational resonances and acoustic resonances with these flow periodicities are considered. Also, unconventional flow and vibrational behaviour were observed, namely a nonuniformity of the flow downstream of the array, and a fluidelastic instability in the first row triggered by an acoustic resonance.

NOTATION

d	Cylinder diameter (25.4 mm)
f_n	Natural frequency of oscillation for the flexible cylinder in still air (Hz)
f_p	Frequency of a periodicity in the interstitial flow (Hz)
m	Mass per unit length of the flexible cylinder
P	Pitch between cylinders
Re	Reynolds number, $U\,d/\nu$
S_t	Strouhal number, $f_p\,d/U$
U	Free stream velocity
U_c	Critical value of U for fluidelastic instability
δ	Cylinder logarithmic decrement in still air; subscripts I and X indicate different values of δ in the in–flow and cross–flow directions, respectively
ρ	Fluid density
ν	Kinematic viscosity of air

1 INTRODUCTION

It is only recently that flow–induced vibrations have joined heat transfer and pressure drop as one of the principal design criteria for tube–in–shell heat exchangers. This surge to a primary design parameter has been relatively fast, considering that prior to the mid–1960's the effects of unsteady fluid loads were often not considered in heat exchanger design. However, the financial implications of numerous failures over the past 30 years particularly those associated with nuclear reactors, have made todays designers very aware of its significance. Cross–flow–induced vibrations are responsible for the vast majority of these failures (1). Therefore, this has been the subject of the bulk of recent research in this field, including the present work.

Although there is now a general awareness of the problem, flow–induced vibration failures continue to occur. Possibly the reason for this is that uncertainties still remain in the fundamental nature of the vibration phenomena. Thus, to ensure the success of future designs, there is a need for fundamental research to give new insight into the nature of these mechanisms; this was the primary motivation behind the present study.

The vibrational response of a cylinder within an array subjected to cross–flow can be attributed to one or more of the following three excitation mechanisms; turbulent buffeting, resonance with a flow periodicity, and fluidelastic instability. The state of knowledge on these phenomena was reviewed by Paidoussis (2), and more recently by Weaver & Fitzpatrick (3), who emphasized developments between 1983 and 1987, and also by Chen (4).

The work presented in this paper, which is a continuation of an ongoing experimental research programme at McGill University, concentrates exclusively on the latter two phenomena for a single flexible cylinder in a normal triangular array with pitch–to–diameter ratio, P/d, of 1.375. However, some measurements of the turbulence–induced force spectra in this array are presented by Zahn (5).

While a single flexible cylinder in a rigid array is unquestionably a significant simplification of a heat exchanger, important insights into the nature of flow-induced vibrations can nonetheless be gained by its study. Furthermore, the principal objective of this study was to investigate the nature of the underlying excitation mechanisms, this can best be done by removing additional complications, such as multiple flexible cylinders, from the experiment.

2 APPARATUS

Experiments were performed on a seven–row normal triangular array with $P/d = 1.375$ (see Figure 1). The array completely spanned the wind tunnel, there being either 25 or 26 cylinders in each row of the array depending on which row the flexible cylinder was positioned in (this was because the flexible cylinder was located in a fixed position, and to change its row location, the rest of the array was moved with respect to it). In the vibration experiments, all but one of the cylinders were rigid and fixed to the top and bottom surfaces of the wind tunnel. The one remaining cylinder was flexibly mounted; the apparatus has been described in detail previously (5, 6), and thus, very few details will be given here. Suffice it to say that the natural frequency, f_n, and logarithmic decrement, δ, of the flexible cylinder may be varied, as can the cylinder mass (which enabled different values of nondimensional mass, $m/\rho d^2$, to be obtained). The flexible cylinder's mounting system permitted correction of the "blow–back", caused by the static drag force on the cylinder producing a mean deflection in the in–flow direction. If this is not done, then the array geometry is distorted and the results obtained are not representative of this particular array.

The cylinder vibration was monitored using two accelerometers, orthogonally mounted in the in–flow (parallel to the upstream flow) and cross-flow (normal to the upstream flow) directions. In addition to the vibration measurements, flow measurements were made in the interstitial gaps between cylinders using a hot–wire anemometer, some flow measurements were also made downstream of the array. The cylinder acceleration and anemometer signals were analyzed on a HP3562A dual channel Signal Analyzer coupled to a HP microcomputer.

3 RESULTS

Over 80 different vibration experiments were conducted in this array. The flexible cylinder was positioned in each of the seven rows and its response measured as a function of flow velocity for at least two $m/\rho d^2$, between 279 and 2480, and a range of δ between 0.007 and 0.95; f_n was varied between 5 and 40 Hz, although most of the experiments were done with f_n in the range 7 to 15 Hz. It was estimated that the errors in the damping and frequency measurements were less than 5.0% and 0.1%, respectively. In general, the flexible cylinder had the same damping and natural frequency in the in–flow and cross-flow directions. However, for $\delta < 0.01$ there was sometimes a difference between the in–flow and cross-flow δ's; this is always indicated in the relevant figures. This difference between the in–flow and cross-flow δ's is thought to be due to the accelerometer leads producing "extra" damping in one direction because of the way they were located on the "piano wires" supporting the flexible cylinder.

3.1 Fluidelastic instability

Fluidelastic instability occurred with the flexible cylinder located in all seven rows of the array. A typical instability, with the flexible cylinder positioned in row 3 of the array, is presented in Figure 2. At a nondimensional velocity (based on free–stream velocity), $U/f_n d$, of approximately 20 there is an abrupt increase in the cylinder cross-flow displacement, indicating a fluidelastic instability. Accompanied with the fluidelastic instability is a small gradual increase in the cross–flow fluidelastic frequency with increasing velocity. The instability in row 3 is purely cross-flow, with no in–flow motion; this was the case for all experiments with the flexible cylinder in rows 1, 2 and 3; however, in the other rows an in–flow instability was also obtained. The results of Figure 2 show the cylinder vibrational response for both increasing and decreasing flow velocity, it is apparent that there is very little difference between these two sets of results, indicating that there are no nonlinear effects for this instability. This is consistent with the results of Lever & Rzentkowski (7) who also found no hysteretic effects for a single flexible cylinder in a rotated

triangular array with $P/d = 1.375$; it should be noted that Lever & Rzentkowski did obtain substantial hysteretic effects in the same array with multiple flexible cylinders. Andjelic & Popp (8), on the other hand, did observe a hysteresis for a single flexible cylinder in a triangular array with $P/d = 1.25$, and obtained different values of $U_c/f_n d$ depending on whether the damping was being increased or decreased; however, their results were for $11.2 < m\delta/\rho d^2 < 13.3$, which is lower than the majority of results presented here. Somewhat surprisingly, in their experiments with multiple flexible cylinders, Andjelic & Popp did not obtain any hysteretic effects.

In addition to cross–flow instabilities, in–flow instabilities were also obtained with the flexible cylinder in rows 4, 5 and 6; the direction of the instability (in–flow or cross–flow) depending on the particular values of $m/\rho d^2$ and δ. In row 7 only in–flow instabilities were obtained. An example of a purely in–flow instability is shown in Figure 3(a) for a flexible cylinder ($m/\rho d^2 = 2370$, $\delta_I = 0.002$ and $\delta_X = 0.008$) in row 4[1] Increasing the damping to $\delta = 0.014$ (both directions now having the same damping) a combined in–flow and cross–flow instability is obtained at a slightly higher critical flow velocity, as shown in Figure 3(b). A further increase in δ to 0.045 produces a sensibly pure cross–flow instability. Teh & Goyder (9) also obtained an in–flow instability for this array, although in their experiments this was obtained with the flexible cylinder free to move in the in–flow direction only.

For each row of the array it is possible to collapse the fluidelastic instability results onto a single curve of nondimensional critical flow velocity, $U_c/f_n d$, versus mass-damping parameter, $m\delta/\rho d^2$. A typical example of this for the results of row 3 is shown in Figure 4; and a stability boundary, of the conventional form, may be written as

$$U_c/f_n d = A(m\delta/\rho d^2)^\alpha, \qquad (1)$$

where, for this row, A = 1.6 and α = 0.55. This was done for the other six rows of the array and the results obtained are summarised in Table 1. As previously mentioned, in rows 4, 5 and 6 an in–flow instability was obtained in addition to the cross–flow instability; however, for the in–flow instability there are insufficient data points to obtain a correlation of the form presented in Table 1.

Table 1 Summary of stability boundaries in the form $U_c/f_n d = A(m\delta/\rho d^2)^\alpha$ for the seven rows of the array; X and I indicate cross–flow or in–flow instabilities, respectively.

| | Direction | | | |
Row	I or X	A	α	range of $m\delta/\rho d^2$
1	X	20	0.11	4–100
2	X	1.34	0.49	20–700
3	X	1.6	0.55	20–400
4	X	0.87	0.80	4–100
5	X	0.87	0.78	4–400
6	X	0.66	0.87	4–100
7	I	24	0.12	6–50

---

[1]This figure shows an example of where two separate experiments were done with the same parameters, the repeatability is representative of that obtained in the complete set of experiments reported in this paper.

For a fixed value of $m\delta/\rho d^2$ the least stable row of the array is the second; $U_c/f_n d$ for the next least stable row, the third row, being approximately 50% greater. The stability boundaries for the fourth, fifth and sixth rows of the array are virtually the same, indicating that as far as fluidelastic instability is concerned, the interstitial flow seems to have reached some sort of equilibrium by the fourth row. By far the most stable rows are the first and last rows of the array. It is interesting that the exponent on $m\delta/\rho d^2$ is greater for the fourth, fifth and sixth rows vis-a-vis the second and third rows, which in turn have an exponent which is considerably greater than that obtained in the first or last rows.

3.2 Flow periodicities

With the flexible cylinder replaced by a rigid one, hot-wire measurements were made at positions A - S in the array (see Figure 1) for Reynolds numbers, Re, (based on free-stream velocity) in the range 2.2×10^3 to 1.74×10^4. Periodicities in the interstitial flow, with frequencies which varied approximately linearly with flow velocity, were detected in and behind the first two rows of the array, as well as a short distance upstream of the array. The most dominant of these periodicities had a Strouhal number, based on free-stream velocity, of 2.40; this compares very well with a Strouhal number of 2.51 suggested by the correlation given by Zukaukas, Ulinskas & Katinas (10) but is somewhat higher than the value of 1.54 suggested by Weaver & Fitzpatrick's correlation (3). A second flow periodicity, less dominant than the one described above, was observed in and behind the first row of cylinders; the average Strouhal number for this flow periodicity was 0.32 although it appeared to vary somewhat with Reynolds number, S_t ranging from 0.41 at Re $= 2.2 \times 10^3$ to 0.30 at Re $= 4.4 \times 10^4$. No such lower Strouhal number is reported in the correlations given by Weaver & Fitzpatrick (3) or Zukaukas et al. (10).

Neither of these Strouhal peaks produced a resonant vibration with the flexible cylinder for the simple reason that any such resonance would have occurred at a velocity lower than the minimum velocity of the wind tunnel. However, special vibration experiments were done with the frequency range of the FFT Analyzer extended above its usual maximum and off-resonant peaks were detected in the vibration spectra which corresponded to $S_t = 2.40$.

There were other significant resonance-type peaks in the vibrational response of the flexible cylinder (for some values of $m/\rho d^2$ and δ) when it was positioned in the latter rows of the array; these were characterized by vibration amplitudes considerably greater than those caused by turbulent buffeting. See, for example, Figure 5, where the vibration response of a flexible cylinder in row 5 is presented. A broad resonant peak is obtained in the nondimensional velocity range 12 - 22, with maximum response at $U/f_n d = 18$ corresponding approximately to $S_t = 0.056$. A broad resonant peak at a similar Strouhal number was obtained with the flexible cylinder ($m/\rho d^2 = 2370$, $\delta_I = 0.006$ and $\delta_X = 0.012$) positioned in row 6 of the array, while a Strouhal number of approximately 0.12 (twice 0.056) was obtained with the flexible cylinder in rows 4 and 5 ($m/\rho d^2 = 300$; $\delta = 0.081$ and $\delta = 0.086$, respectively). As mentioned previously in this section, no flow periodicities corresponding to these Strouhal numbers were detected deep in the array, and thus, the origin of these

broad resonant peaks is somewhat perturbing, at present the authors have no physical explanation for them.

3.3 Acoustic resonance

During the course of these experiments very loud acoustic resonances (these resulted in the authors being "banned" from doing day-time experiments) were obtained with this array for certain flow velocities. Further investigation of these resonances identified them as occurring at $U \approx 8.0$ and 10.2 m/s at frequencies of 733 Hz and 900 Hz, respectively; thus, it is immediately apparent that they were triggered by the $S_t = 2.40$ flow periodicity. At these acoustic resonances, hot-wire traverses were done across the half-width of the wind tunnel test section upstream of the array; the results obtained are presented in Figure 6. Bearing in mind that a single hot-wire anemometer measures the magnitude of the flow only, and not its direction, it is apparent that the two acoustic resonances correspond to standing waves with mode numbers (the number of half-waves across the tunnel section) of 4 and 5.

The acoustic resonances exhibited maxima in the measured acoustic velocity at the tunnel walls. However, the velocity recorded by the hot wire is not purely the acoustic velocity, but is the resultant of the streamwise velocity and acoustic velocity (directed across the tunnel cross-section). This resultant will be dominated by the streamwise component. Thus, a peak in the resultant velocity corresponds to a minima in the pressure fluctuations, and hence, the acoustic pressure achieves either a minima or maxima at the tunnel walls — as is usually obtained (11, 12).

Recently Ziada et al. (13) proposed a method of predicting the occurrence of acoustic resonances in staggered cylinder arrays. They defined a resonance parameter, G_s, which is based on the array geometry and properties of the flow (the complete expression is given by Ziada et al.), and predicted that acoustic resonances will occur only if G_s is greater than a critical value; for this array the critical value of G_s being approximately 2.1×10^{-4}. For the fourth- and fifth-mode acoustic resonances which occurred in this array, G_s was approximately 2.7×10^{-4} and 3.0×10^{-4}, respectively, which are above the critical value of 2.1×10^{-4}. A resonance of the third acoustic mode with the $S_t = 2.40$ flow periodicity would have occurred at a frequency and velocity of approximately 540 Hz and 5.7 m/s, respectively; the corresponding value of G_s is approximately 2.3×10^{-4}, which is very close to the critical value. In fact, in some experiments a very soft acoustic tone was noted near $U = 5.7$ m/s, although it was not as intense as the other two acoustic resonances. However, this suggests that the array may have been close to an acoustic resonance at this velocity. All of these results suggest that the prediction method of Ziada et al. is very accurate.

The acoustic resonances also produced some interesting interactions with both the array interstitial flow and flexible cylinder vibration behaviour; these interactions are discussed below.

The first effect of the acoustic resonance was to organize the flow throughout the array. Normally, no periodicities were detected beyond the second row of the array; however, coincident with the acoustic resonance, flow periodicities, at the same frequency as the acoustic tone, were evident throughout the complete array.

A second, and more puzzling, aspect of the acoustic resonances is that the 733 Hz tone produced a significant peak in the interstitial flow PSD, at a frequency of approximately 7.8 Hz, at locations N, L, J, H, F and D (see Figure 1). These locations correspond to the transverse gaps between cylinders in different rows of the array, it is interesting to note that the periodicity was not detected in the gaps between cylinders of the same row. There does not seem to be any obvious relationship between the frequency of this flow periodicity (7.8 Hz) and the acoustic resonance (733 Hz), and the authors have no explanation for the origin of this new interstitial flow periodicity.

The third, and most puzzling, consequence of the acoustic resonance at 733 Hz concerns the cylinder vibrational behaviour. With the flexible cylinder positioned in rows 2 to 7 of the array the acoustic resonances sometimes had a relatively minor effect on the cylinder vibrational response. Typically, there was a reduction or increase in the vibrational amplitude coincident with the acoustic resonance; examples of this are shown in Figures 3(a) and (b) where the 733 Hz resonance is marked as AR1 on the figure. However, when the flexible cylinder was positioned in the leading row of the array, the 733 Hz acoustic resonance sometimes had a much more pronounced effect, and appeared to be able to initiate a fluidelastic instability. An example of this acoustic resonance–induced instability is presented in Figure 7; large amplitude vibrations occurred at exactly the same instant as the acoustic resonance developed. However, if the velocity is increased, causing the acoustic resonance to cease, the large amplitude vibrations continue; indeed, even if the cylinder is manually brought to rest, upon releasing the cylinder the large vibrations reappear. Even more surprising, is that if δ is increased from 0.019 to 0.1, the instability still occurs at the same flow velocity (still coincident with the acoustic resonance). A further increase of δ to 0.22 still produced large amplitude vibrations at the same velocity, although in this case if the velocity is further increased beyond the acoustic resonance and the vibrations are physically stopped they will not reappear. If the large amplitude vibrations were not physically stopped at velocities beyond the acoustic resonance they would continue indefinitely.

Table 2   Effect of natural frequency on the critical flow velocity for fluidelastic instability, when triggered by an acoustic resonance, with the flexible cylinder in row 1.

f_n (Hz)	10.9	16.8	24.2	40.1
δ		0.019	0.022	0.016	0.010
$m/\rho d^2$	300	300	338	338
U_c (m/s)	7.5	7.7	8.0	8.0

To further investigate the effect of the acoustic resonance, experiments were done with four different cylinder natural frequencies; the results obtained are summarised in Table 2 (in all cases, the occurrence of fluidelastic instability was coincident with the acoustic resonance). As is immediately apparent from the results of Table 2, a four–fold increase in frequency has virtually no effect on the critical flow velocity. One subtle difference was noticed between the results obtained with $f_n = 10.9$ and 16.8 Hz and those with $f_n = 24.2$ and 40.1 Hz. For the lower f_n's, the fluidelastic instability persisted when the velocity was increased past the acoustic resonance,

even if the cylinder was manually brought to rest the fluidelastic instability would restart as soon as the cylinder was released. For the higher frequencies, the fluidelastic instability would continue if the velocity was increased beyond the acoustic resonance (even for a time duration of greater than 5 minutes), but if the cylinder was manually brought to rest the fluidelastic instability would not redevelop. Considering the large frequency difference between the acoustic resonance and the natural frequency of the cylinder, it is not clear how the acoustic resonance can have such a dramatic effect on the cylinder vibrational behaviour, and, at present, the authors have no explanation for this interaction.

3.4   Interstitial and downstream flow

Velocity measurements in the interstitial gaps were made at the locations labelled A - S in Figure 1. Typical distributions of time average flow velocity and turbulence intensity throughout the array, at Re = 1.0×10^4, are presented in Figure 8. The time average flow velocity in the gap between cylinders in a row is relatively constant throughout the array at approximately 3.9 U, while the time average flow velocity in the gap between cylinders of different rows decreases in the first three rows of the array before reaching a relatively steady state value. For the latter rows of the array, the time average velocity between cylinders of different rows is much less than the corresponding time average flow velocity between cylinders in the same row, see Figure 8(a). Also, as seen in Figure 8(b), the turbulence intensity between cylinders in the same row is much less than that obtained in the gap between cylinders of different rows. These observations suggest that the position midway between cylinders of different rows is in the wake of the upstream cylinder; they also suggest that between this position and the surface of the downstream cylinder, the time average flow velocity must be considerably greater than the time average flow velocity in the gap between cylinders of a row. Thus, it appears that in the latter rows of the array the flow accelerates from the front stagnation point of the cylinder to the 30° point and then decelerates till, or possibly just past, the 90° position. These conclusions are qualitatively in agreement with the pressure measurements of Zdravkovich & Namork (14).

Hot–wire traverses across the test section were done at various distances downstream of the array; these revealed the existence of an asymmetric and nonuniform downstream flow. Measurements were initially made at Re = 1.26×10^4 with the flexible cylinder located in the fourth row; in this configuration, the downstream row of the array consisted of 26 cylinders. The velocity distribution 0.660 m (26 d) downstream of the array (0.152 m (6 d) upstream of the test section exit plane) was significantly skewed, as shown in Figure 9(a). Also shown in this figure is the velocity profile at this location measured when the flexible cylinder was replaced with a rigid one; the two velocity profiles are essentially the same, indicating that this behaviour is not a consequence of the flexible cylinder. This skewed velocity profile was found to exist along the entire height of the test section exit plane.

Further measurements were made closer to the array at 6 d downstream of the array, and the mean velocity profile, shown in Figure 9(b), exhibited significant humps at a distance of approximately 0.152 m (6 d) from the test section walls. Furthermore, a wool–tuft probe indicated frequent back–flow (flow in the upstream direction) in the wall regions, suggesting that the mean flow near the walls is less than that indicated in Figure 9(b). Vertical hot–wire traverses made over the test section height revealed even more surprising flow behaviour, as shown in Figure 9(c). While the vertical velocity profile along the horizontal centreline was very uniform, the vertical velocity profile at one of the humps in the horizontal profile was skewed, displaying a significant velocity defect near the test section ceiling. This suggests that the flow directly downstream of the array is very three–dimensional. Similar velocity distributions were also obtained at a Reynolds number of 8.4×10^3.

If the cylinder array was relocated such that the flexible cylinder was in the fifth row, the downstream row of the array had 25 cylinders, as opposed to 26 cylinders which was the case for the results of Figure 9. This seemingly insignificant change appeared to greatly influence the downstream flow pattern. The velocity profile 6 d behind the array was now relatively uniform, see Figure 10. Near the test section exit, 0.686 m (27 d) downstream of the array, the flow was no longer skewed, but relatively symmetrical. However, it was significantly nonuniform, with the maximum flow velocity surprisingly occurring near the walls. Vertical velocity profiles near the test section exit were relatively flat, suggesting that the mean flow pattern at the exit was fairly two–dimensional.

When the flexible cylinder was located in the sixth row, the overall array configuration was identical to when this cylinder had been in the fourth row. The double–humped velocity profile was again evident 6d downstream of the array, and at the test section exit the flow was again skewed, but this time towards the other side of the wind tunnel. Attempts to reverse the bias of the flow at the exit by twisting the array in alternate directions as much as the clearance between the end plates and the test section walls would allow were unsuccessful. However, to facilitate further vibration tests at a later date, the array was reassembled to relocate the flexible cylinder in row 6. Measurements indicated that this time the flow at the test section exit was consistently biased to the opposite side of that shown in Figure 9(b). Thus the nature of the mechanism which determines towards which side the flow will be biased is not clear.

As expected, locating the flexible cylinder in row 7 gave a downstream flow pattern similar to that observed when the cylinder was in row 5. The two possible overall configurations of the 7–row array therefore gave two significantly different downstream flow patterns. When the sequence of the number of cylinders in each row was 26–25–26–25–26–25–26, the flow directly behind the array was characterized by a double–humped velocity profile, and far downstream by a skewed velocity profile. When the sequence was 25–26–25–26–25–26–25, the velocity profile far downstream was symmetric, but nonuniform, with the flow biased towards the walls of the test section.

Zdravkovich & Stonebanks (15) recently reviewed other researchers' observations of nonuniform flow in and behind uniformly spaced cylinders subjected to cross–flow, and also presented results of their own surface–pressure–measurement experiments on a single– and double–row of cylinders. They attributed nonuniformity of the flow behind single– and double–row arrays to the irregular

coalescence of gap flows behind the final row, and postulated that such nonuniformity might exist behind the last row of a closely spaced array containing any number of rows. The observed nonuniform flow behind the present array supports this theory. One would expect the pattern of coalescence of gap flows to be affected by the number of cylinders (or gaps) in the last row of the array. The results of the present study also support this supposition in that the pattern of downstream flow was dependent on whether there were 25 or 26 cylinders in the final row of the seven–row array.

4 CONCLUSIONS

Based on the results presented in this paper and other results given by Zahn (5) the following conclusions can be made regarding the fluid–structure interaction of a single flexible cylinder in an otherwise rigid seven–row normal triangular array with $P/d = 1.375$.

(i) Fluidelastic instability occurs with the flexible cylinder in all rows of the array. In rows 1 through 6, the initial, or principal, instability occurs in the cross–flow direction. In rows 4, 5 and 6, there also exists an in–flow fluidelastic instability at a much higher critical flow velocity. In row 7, the principal instability occurs in the in–flow direction.

(ii) In the mass–damping parameter range $10 \leq m\delta/(\rho d^2) \leq 500$, the flexible cylinder is least stable in the second row.

(iii) The cross–flow stability boundary for row 1 and the in–flow stability boundary for row 7 exhibit only a weak dependence on the mass–damping parameter.

(iv) With respect to fluidelastic instability, the flow appears to achieve a regular repeating pattern by the fourth row, since the stability boundaries for rows 4, 5 and 6 are essentially the same.

(v) Periodicities occurring at a Strouhal number of 2.4 exist within the interstitial flow in and behind the first two rows of the array. Periodicities at a Strouhal number of approximately 0.32 occur behind the first row of cylinders only. In and beyond the third row, no periodicities could be detected above the random turbulence of the flow.

(vi) The periodicities associated with the Strouhal number of 2.4 are capable of causing acoustic resonances at 733 Hz and 900 Hz. Furthermore, the 733 Hz acoustic resonance is capable of causing a flexible cylinder in the first row of the array to go unstable, even though the acoustic frequency is more than 10 times greater than the cylinder natural frequency; the nature of this instability triggering mechanism is not understood. Both acoustic resonances can organize the flow throughout the array, causing peaks at the acoustic frequency to be visible in the flow spectra throughout the array. The 733 Hz acoustic resonance also produces a very significant peak at approximately 7.8 Hz in the spectra of flow velocity in the open transverse channels between the rows of cylinders.

(vii) The flow downstream of the array is very much dependent on the number of cylinders in the final row of the array and can be very nonuniform and asymmetric.

ACKNOWLEDGEMENTS

The authors gratefully acknowledge the financial support of the Natural Sciences and Engineering Research Council of Canada and Le Fonds FCAR of Québec.

REFERENCES

(1) PAIDOUSSIS, M.P. Flow–induced vibrations in nuclear reactors and heat exchangers: practical experiences and state of knowledge. *Proceedings IAHR/IUTAM Symposium on Practical Experiences with Flow–Induced Vibrations* (eds. E. Naudascher and D. Rockwell), Berlin: Springer-Verlag, 1980, 1–81.

(2) PAIDOUSSIS, M.P. A review of flow–induced vibrations in reactors and reactor components. *Nuclear Engineering and Design*, 1983, <u>74</u>, 31–60.

(3) WEAVER, D.S. and FITZPATRICK, J.A. A review of flow induced vibrations in heat exchangers. *Journal of Fluids and Structures*, 1988, <u>2</u>, 73-93.

(4) CHEN, S.S. Flow–Induced Vibration of Circular Cylindrical Structures. Hemisphere Publishing, 1987, Washington.

(5) ZAHN, M.L. Flow–induced vibration of a single flexible cylinder in a normal triangular array., 1989, M. Eng. Thesis. McGill University.

(6) PRICE, S.J., PAIDOUSSIS, M.P., MACDONALD, R. and MARK, B. The flow–induced vibration of a single flexible cylinder in a rotated square array of rigid cylinders with pitch–to–diameter ratio of 2.12. *Journal of Fluids and Structures*, 1987, 1, 359–378.

(7) LEVER, J.H. and RZENTKOWSKI, G. An investigation into the post–stable behaviour of a tube array in cross–flow. *Proceedings ASME Symposium on Flow–Induced Vibration and Noise*, Volume 3: Flow Induced Vibration and Noise in Cylinder Arrays (eds. M.P. Paidoussis, S.S. Chen, and M.D. Bernstein), ASME, New York, 1988, 95–110.

(8) ANDJELIC, A. and POPP, K. Stability effects in a normal triangular cylinder array. *Journal of Fluids and Structures*, 1989, <u>3</u>, 165–186.

(9) TEH, C.E. and GOYDER, H.G.D. Data for the fluidelastic instability of heat exchanger tube bundles. *Proceedings ASME Symposium on Flow–Induced Vibration and Noise*, Volume 3: Flow Induced Vibration and Noise in Cylinder Arrays (eds. M.P. Paidoussis, S.S. Chen, and M.D. Bernstein), ASME, New York, 1988, 77–94.

(10) ZUKAUSKAS, A., ULINSKAS, R. and KATINAS, V. Fluid Dynamics and Flow–Induced Vibrations of Tube Banks. 1988, Hemisphere Publishing, New York.

(11) TEMKIN, S. Elements of Acoustics. 1981 J. Wiley & Sons, New York.

(12) ZIADA, S., OENGOREN, A. and BUHLMANN, E.T. On acoustical resonance in tube arrays — Part I: Experiments. *Journal of Fluids and Structures*, 1989, <u>3</u>, 293–314.

(13) ZIADA, S., OENGOREN, A. and BUHLMANN, E.T. On acoustical resonance in tube arrays — Part II: Damping criteria. *Journal of Fluids and Structures*, 1989, <u>3</u>, 315–324.

(14) ZDRAVKOVICH, M.M. and NAMORK, J.E. Structure of interstitial flow between closely spaced tubes in staggered array. *Flow–Induced Vibrations* (eds. S. S. Chen and M. D. Bernstein), ASME, New York, 1979, 41–46.

(15) ZDRAVKOVICH, M.M. and STONEBANKS, K.L. Intrinsically non–uniform and metastable flow in and behind tube arrays. *International Symposium on Flow Induced Vibrations and Noise*, Volume 1: Flow-Induced Vibration in Cylindrical Structures: Solitary Cylinders and Arrays in Cross–Flow (eds. M. P. Paidoussis, O. M. Griffin and C. Dalton), ASME, New York, 1988, 61–73.

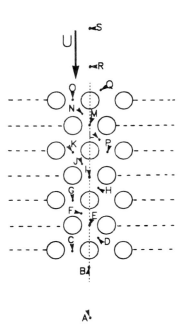

Figure 1. Schematic drawing of the middle portion of the cylinder array, A – S indicate positions at which hot-wire measurements were taken; in the interstitial gaps these positions are midway between cylinder centres.

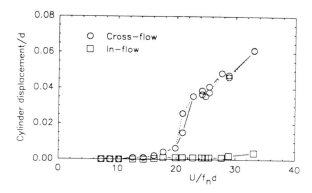

Figure 2. Vibrational response for the flexible cylinder in row 3 of the array as a function of nondimensional velocity; $f_n = 7.16$ Hz, $m/\rho d^2 = 2370$, $\delta = 0.041$, _____ increasing velocity, - - - - decreasing velocity.

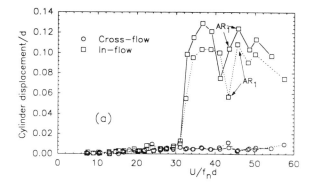

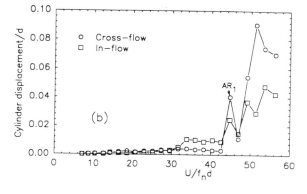

Figure 3. Vibrational response for the flexible cylinder in row 4 of the array as a function of nondimensional velocity; $m/\rho d^2 = 2370$, AR_1 indicates an acoustic resonance. (a) $f_n = 6.97$ Hz, in-flow $\delta = 0.002$, cross-flow $\delta = 0.008$ (_____ and - - - - indicate two separate experiments), (b) $f_n = 7.21$ Hz, $\delta = 0.014$.

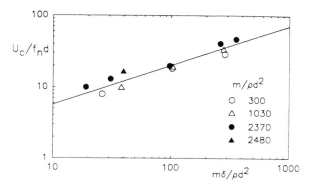

Figure 4. Correlation of the fluidelastic instability thresholds for the flexible cylinder in row 3 of the array.

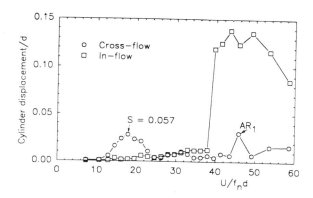

Figure 5. Vibrational response for the flexible cylinder in row 5 of the array as a function of nondimensional velocity; $m/\rho d^2 = 2370$, $f_n = 7.05$ Hz, $\delta_I = 0.002$, $\delta_X = 0.008$.

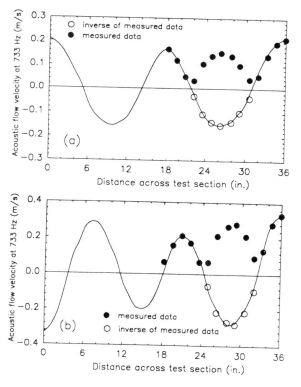

Figure 6. Acoustic velocity profile across the wind tunnel test section upstream of the array during the acoustic resonances. (a) $U = 8.0$ m/s, acoustic frequency = 733Hz: (b) $U = 10.2$ m/s, acoustic frequency = 900 Hz.

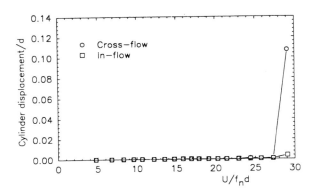

Figure 7. Vibrational response for the flexible cylinder in row 1 of the array as a function of nondimensional velocity; $m/\rho d^2 = 300$, $f_n = 10.9$ Hz, $\delta = 0.019$.

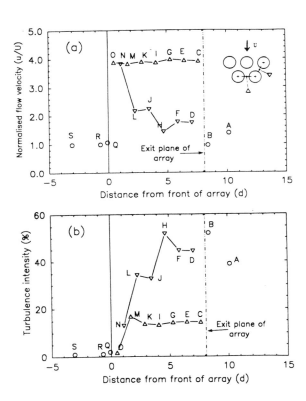

Figure 8. (a) Normalized time average flow velocity, and (b) turbulence intensity at various locations (see Figure 1) in the interstitial gaps of the array, Re $= 1.5 \times 10^4$.

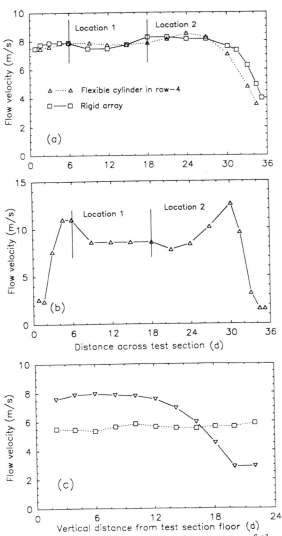

Figure 9. Mean velocity profiles downstream of the array with 26 cylinders in the downstream row, Re $= 1.5 \times 10^4$. (a) horizontal profile 26 d downstream of the array, at the mid-height of the test section; (b) horizontal profile 6 d downstream of the rigid array, at the mid-height of the test section; (c) vertical profiles 6 d downstream of the rigid array, ∇ at location 1 of figures (a) and (b), $\square$ at location 2 of figures (a) and (b).

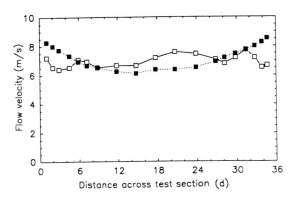

Figure 10. Mean velocity profiles downstream of the array with 25 cylinders in the downstream row. Re $= 1.5 \times 10^4$; $\square$ horizontal profile 6 d downstream of the array, at the mid-height of the test section; $\blacksquare$ horizontal profile 27 d downstream of the array, at the mid-height of the test section.

C416/024

An experimental analysis of the mechanisms underlying fluid-elastic coupling in a square-in-line tube bundle subject to water cross-flow

S GRANGER, R CAMPISTRON and J LEBRET
Electricité De France, Chatou, France

SYNOPSIS A series of experiments has been conducted on a square-in-line tube array subjected to water cross-flow. Three configurations have been tested. In the first one, a single flexible tube was positioned in the middle of an array of rigid cylinders; in the second one, a single flexible tube was positioned in the first row of an array of rigid cylinders; in the third one, the first three rows of the array were flexible, the other cylinders being rigid. Tube response measurements were analysed by the IMENE and MEIDEE methods. The results of these analyses are compared to previously published results.

1 INTRODUCTION

In the early 1960's, it was generally believed that the only mechanism exciting large-amplitude vibration cylinders in arrays subjected to crossflow was a phenomenon of vortex shedding similar to that observed in the case of a single cylinder in crossflow [i.e. the Karman Vortex Street].

Since the 1970's, another phenomenon, called fluidelastic instability, has been recognised as being the most potent, and sometimes the only mechanism responsible for exciting large amplitude vibration of cylinders in arrays. At present, there has been a great deal of progress on understanding flow-induced vibration problems in tube bundles [1], [2]. However, most efforts have been concentrated on the obtention of design guidelines to determine critical flow velocity. The physics associated with fluid-structure interaction and the resulting instability is not well understood : '...As a matter of fact, fluidelastic instability is probably one of the most debated and confusing topics in the area of fluid-structure interactions. For example, erroneous descriptions of the instability mechanism have been published in journals, these erroneous descriptions have been quoted by others working in this subject area, and the same physical phenomena have been given different interpretations.' (Chen 1988 [3]).

Recently, new methods for analysing response measurements taken on flow-excited structural components have been developed at the Research and Development Division of Electricité de France (EDF).

These are the IMENE and MEIDEE methods.

In comparison with the usual experimental methodology, these methods enable the investigator to extract more information from flow-induced vibration response measurements :

- IMENE is a time-domain-multi-degree-of-freedom-parametric method for modal identification with unmeasured random excitation. In particular, it provides precise modal damping ratio estimates and is able to identify even highly-coupled modes ;
- MEIDEE uses IMENE results and achieves an indirect estimation of the fluid dynamic forces acting on the structural component (i.e. both motion-dependent fluidelastic forces and turbulent buffeting excitation).

The theoretical background together with some practical applications have already been presented [4], [5]. Based on the estimation of fluid dynamic forces by the IMENE and MEIDEE methods, a semi-empirical model for flow-induced vibration of tube bundles in cross flow has been derived in Reference [6]. In the present paper, a square-in-line tube bundle subjected to water cross-flow is analysed by the IMENE and MEIDEE methods, but this time, attention is focused on the physical mechanisms underlying fluidelastic coupling. The results and conclusions of this study are compared to previously published results concerning similar tube arrays. The following points are especially addressed :

(i) may an array of flexible tubes be adequately represented, from a fluidelastic viewpoint, by a single flexible tube positionned in the middle of rigid cylinders ?

(ii) what are the physical features of the motion-dependent fluid forces ?

2 EXPERIMENTAL SET UP

The test facility is shown in Figure 1. The tube bundle consists of 49 tubes in 7 rows arranged in a square-in-line pattern. Three configurations have been tested :

(i) a single flexible tube is positioned in the middle of the array, the other cylinders being rigid;

(ii) a single flexible tube is positioned in the first row of the array, the other cylinders being rigid;

(iii) the first three rows of the array are fully flexible, the other cylinders being rigid.

These three configurations are shown schematically in Figure 2. Hereafter, they will be abbreviated as follows : (i) the Middle Tube (MT) Configuration, (ii) the First Row Tube (FRT) Configuration, and (iii) the Flexible Tube Array (FTA) Configuration.

In these experiments, a flexible tube was actually a rigid cylinder, which was flexibly mounted via a piano wire at each end onto a heavy rigid frame. It was instrumented for measuring response due to flow by using strain gauges at the base of its support rod. Strain gauge output was calibrated in terms of tube displacement. The response was found to be linear up to displacements large enough to cause tube-to-tube touching. Thus, displacement responses in the streamwise and transverse directions could be measured. In each direction and in the analysed frequency band, a flexible tube had one vibration mode with a natural frequency, f_n, of 40 Hz in still air and a constant spanwise mode shape in the test section. In the FTA configuration, 6 flexible tubes were instrumented : 3 in the first row and 3 in the second.

The value of a tube diameter D is 0.022 m. The tube bundle has a pitch-to-diameter ratio, P/D, of 1.44. The value of the mass ratio, $m/\rho D^2$, is about 4 [m denotes tube mass per unit length and ρ is fluid density]. The logarithmic decrement in still water, δ, was found to be 0.095 .

3 EXPERIMENTAL PROCEDURE

The flow was started at a low velocity and allowed to stabilise for several minutes. The flexible tube responses were then recorded for both the streamwise and transverse directions to the flow. When measurements were complete, flow velocity was incremented and the measurement process repeated. The experiment was terminated when tube amplitudes were large enough to

cause tube touching. For each investigated mean upstream flow velocity, recorded response measurements were used as input data in a modal identification procedure with unmeasured forces. The IMENE method [4], [5] was used to perform this modal analysis.

4 IMENE RESULTS

For each flow velocity and for each vibration mode, the IMENE method was used to provide estimates of the resonance frequency, the damping ratio and the rms response amplitude.

4.1 MT Configuration

For this configuration, the pitch flow velocity, U_p, was varied from 1.54 m/s to 4.38 m/s. In this range of U_p, tube motion was analysed in the transverse and streamwise directions. The variation of rms amplitude of tube displacement with U_p is shown in Figure 3. IMENE estimates of tube resonance frequency and damping ratio have been plotted against U_p in Figures 4 and 5 respectively. In the range $1.54 \leq U_p \leq 2.94$ m/s, tube response amplitudes in the streamwise and transverse directions are of the same order of magnitude and are increasing functions of U_p. For $U_p > 2.94$ m/s, while the tube response amplitude in the transverse direction goes on increasing, but with a lower slope, the tube response amplitude in the streamwise direction remains more or less constant. This is well correlated with the variation of damping. In the transverse direction, the damping ratio first increases in the range $1.54 \leq U_p \leq 2.94$ m/s, then decreases for $U_p > 2.94$ m/s. In the streamwise direction, except for a slight deviation in the vicinity of $U_p = 2.5$ m/s, the damping ratio does not stop increasing. In the entire investigated flow-velocity range, the resonance frequency in the transverse direction decreases with U_p, while the resonance frequency in the streamwise direction increases. These evolutions of the tube modal parameters seem to be quite typical of the fluidelastic excitation of a single flexible tube in the middle of a rigid tube array. In our laboratories, we have also tested triangular tube array patterns with a single flexible tube inside a rigid tube bundle. These tube arrays were subjected to water cross-flow. At each time, the behaviour of tube modal parameters was very similar to that described above (see, for instance, [5]). Furthermore, the divergence of the in-flow and cross-flow resonance frequencies with increasing flow velocity has also been noted by Price and Païdoussis for a single flexible cylinder placed in an in-line array of rigid cylinders and subjected to water cross-flow [7]. On the other hand, the 'increasing-decreasing' behaviour of the cross-flow damping ratio has already been observed by Weaver and El-Kashlan [8].

Though the above results show that fluidelastic coupling does exist for the MT Configuration, it is also clear, from the graphs in Figures 3 and 5, that the tube remained fluidelastically stable up to the maximum flow velocity obtainable in these experiments. This is a very disappointing result, especially as the variation of the cross-flow damping ratio suggests that with a further increase in flow velocity, fluidelastic instability could have been obtained in the transverse direction. In subsequent experiments performed on triangular tube array patterns, a further increase in the maximum flow velocity was made possible and indeed, fluidelastic instability was observed in the transverse direction for a single flexible tube in the middle of a rigid tube bundle [5]. These experiments showed that fluidelastic instability should be the ultimate consequence of the decrease of cross-flow damping, and that the decreasing part of the cross-flow damping ratio curve is more or less a linear function of U_p [5]. Based on these observations, we have tried extrapolating the present data to obtain an estimation of the presumed critical flow velocity for the MT Configuration. Assuming linear behaviour, a least squares regression technique has been used to fit a straight line to the decreasing part of the cross-flow damping ratio curve. As can be seen in Figure 5, this fit is reasonably good. The critical flow velocity is the velocity at which the damping ratio becomes zero. Consequently, our extrapolation process predicts a stability threshold at $U_p = U_{pc} \approx 5.5$ m/s.

4.2 FRT Configuration

For this configuration, U_p was varied from 0.49 m/s to 2.94 m/s. Tube motion was analysed in the transverse and streamwise directions in this flow velocity range. The variation of rms amplitude of tube displacement with U_p is shown in Figure 3. At $U_p = 2.46$ m/s, the tube response amplitude in the transverse direction increases abruptly and tube touching was observed during the experiments. As it can be seen in Figure 3, for $U_p > 2.46$ m/s no alleviation in the vibration was obtained and the experiment was terminated at $U_p = 2.94$ m/s to avoid damaging the flexible tube and its instrumentation. Tube modal parameters have been estimated by IMENE in the stable region. The variations of natural frequency and damping ratio with U_p are

shown in Figures 4 and 6 respectively. The curves in Figures 3, 4 and 6 show four distinct ranges of U_p for the FRT Configuration.

(i)   In the $0.49 \leq U_p < 1.07$ m/s range, the response amplitudes in the transverse and streamwise directions are very low, the cross-flow and in-flow frequencies are distinct but of the same order of magnitude, and the cross-flow and in-flow damping ratios increase with U_p. It is interesting to note that, in this range of relatively low flow velocities and low response amplitudes, the values of both the cross-flow and in-flow damping ratios remain lower, and generally much lower, than the value of the damping ratio in still water, which is about 1.5 %. For instance, at $U_p = 0.49$ m/s, the cross-flow and in-flow frequencies coincide and the values of the damping ratios in the transverse and streamwise directions, which are more or less identical, are both about equal to   0.2 %. It thus seems that, already in this low flow velocity range, the surrounding flow tends to supply energy to the mechanical system via fluid-structure coupling.

(ii) In the $1.07 \leq U_p < 1.45$ m/s range, there is an abrupt increase in amplitude, the predominant response being in the streamwise direction. The cross-flow and in-flow frequencies coincide and are increasing functions of U_p. The damping ratios in the streamwise and transverse directions fall off sharply and have very small values (typically about 0.03 % for the cross-flow damping ratio and $0.5 \ 10^{-3}$ %, i.e. more or less zero, for the in-flow damping ratio).

The behaviour described above looks very much like a phenomenon of resonance between the streamwise motion and a flow periodicity which should here be due to a symmetric vortex shedding rather than to the classical Karman vortex street. This lock-in phenomenon would also induce synchronisation of the streamwise and transverse motions via non linear effects. The flow periodicity should be characterised by a constant Strouhal number which, outside the flow velocity range where the lock-in phenomenon exists, should result in a peak in the response spectra, whose frequency should increase linearly with U_p. However, in these experiments, no such peak was observed at off-resonance conditions. Consequently, it seems that the observed response in this flow velocity range is not due to coupling of two independent physical mechanisms : tube streamwise motion on the one hand, and pre-existent flow periodicity on the other. On the contrary, it seems that the flow pattern responsible for the tube response in this range of U_p is triggered by tube motion at the very reduced frequency, or Strouhal number, corresponding to $U_p = 1.07$ m/s, i.e. $S = 0.64$. It is also interesting to note the value of the Strouhal number corresponding to the end of this phenomenon, i.e. $S = 0.48$. These points will be further addressed below and, to simplify, this range of U_p will be called the 'synchronisation range'.

(iii) For $1.45 \leq U_p \leq 2.46$ m/s, the cross-flow frequency decreases while the in-flow frequency increases. The cross-flow damping ratio increases sharply, reaches a maximum at $U_p = 1.99$ m/s, then decreases rapidly to attain a nearly zero value at $U_p = 2.46$ m/s. In this flow velocity range, the in-flow damping ratio increases. For $1.45 < U_p \leq 2.43$ m/s, the predominant response is still in the in-flow direction. At $U_p = 2.46$ m/s the cross-flow response amplitude increases abruptly while the in-flow response amplitude falls off sharply. As noted above, the tube became unstable in the transverse direction at $U_p = U_{pc} = 2.46$ m/s. It should be noticed that, in this range of U_p, the evolutions of tube modal parameters are quite similar to those described above for the MT Configuration. Hence, this strongly suggests that such modal parameter evolutions are typical, not only of the fluidelastic excitation of a single tube in the middle of a rigid bundle, as noted in section 4.1, but, more generally, of the physical mechanisms inducing the so-called damping-controlled fluidelastic instability in the transverse direction [9].

This range of U_p will hereafter be called the 'damping-controlled mechanism region'.

(iv) The $2.46 < U_p \leq 2.99$ m/s range corresponds to the post-stable region. In this flow velocity range, strong non-linear effects must influence the vibration due to the observed large amplitude motion in the transverse direction. However, it was found that successful modal identifications could still be performed with the IMENE method in this range of U_p. In this case, the estimated modal parameters should represent the behaviour of some equivalent linear system which approximates the actual non-linear system; the physical interpretation is therefore not straightforward. The following results were found.

In the transverse direction, we observed a single vibration mode whose frequency and damping ratio increased. In the streamwise direction, several modes were identified, the predominant mode being virtually identical to the cross-flow mode. The variations of resonance frequency comply with the results quoted by Price and Païdoussis in Reference [7]. The observed resonance frequency and damping ratio behaviours may be primarily due to tube impacting.

4.3 FTA Configuration

For this configuration, matters are more complicated because the system under study is now, in both directions to the flow, a multi-degree-of-freedom system with highly coupled modes. Though IMENE could correctly identify the predominant modes present in the clusters of peaks exhibited by response spectra, it is a very difficult task to follow the evolutions of the individual modes with U_p and extract a clear physical interpretation from this information. Consequently, to investigate the FTA Configuration, we will use the Global Model Approach (GMA). The GMA has been introduced in Reference [6], where the present FTA Configuration has also been addressed in detail. In the GMA, the natural frequencies and damping ratios of the individual modes present in a cluster are used to compute two averaged modal parameters, i.e. the global natural frequency and the global damping ratio, which represent, for a given flow velocity and from a statistical energy balance viewpoint, the global stiffness and global damping of the system under consideration. Having determined tube modal parameters in still water, it is then possible to calculate those parts of the global stiffness and damping which are due to the fluid flow, i.e. the global fluid stiffness and the global fluid damping [6].

In section 6, the global fluid stiffness and damping coefficients obtained for the FTA Configuration, will be compared to the fluid stiffness and damping coefficients obtained for the MT and FRT Configurations.

In this section, the following points can be noted :

- The FTA Configuration became unstable at $U_p = U_{pc} \approx 2.3$ m/s in both the transverse and streamwise directions. However, the instability seems to be monitored by the transverse motion with the in-flow response becoming unstable due to modal coupling with the cross-flow response.

- For the FTA Configuration, there is a flow-velocity range very similar to the synchronisation range that has been observed for the FRT Configuration. In this range of U_p, streamwise tube response is predominant, and all the response spectra, in any direction to the flow, exhibit the same dominant resonance frequency. The Strouhal numbers associated respectively with the beginning and the end of this flow-velocity range are similar to those obtained for the FRT Configuration.

5 INSTABILITY THRESHOLDS

In Figure 7 a stability map has been plotted in order to compare different experimental results. In this Figure, U_{rc} and A_r are respectively the reduced critical flow velocity, U_{pc}/f_nD, and the dimensionless mass-damping parameter, $m\delta/\rho D^2$. Apart from the present results, we have plotted : (i) results obtained by Price and Païdoussis for a single flexible cylinder placed in a square-in-line array of rigid cylinders, with $P/D = 1.5$ [7] ; (ii) results obtained by Teh and Goyder for a single flexible cylinder in the middle of a square-in-line array of rigid cylinders, with $P/D = 1.35$ [10] ; (iii) results obtained by Tanaka et al. for a single flexible tube inside a rigid square-in-line tube bundle, and for a flexible square-in-line tube bundle, both with $P/D = 1.33$ [11]. Though all the results, plotted in Figure 7 and concerning a single flexible tube in the middle of a square-in-line array of rigid tubes, have been obtained for very similar tube array geometries, the data are very scattered, especially for $A_r \geq 4$. This clearly indicates that this kind of stability map is not sufficient to adequately represent the fluidelastic instability phenomenon in all its complexity. However, some useful conclusions can be drawn by studying Figure 7.

Firstly, it is interesting to note that the critical flow velocity value obtained by extrapolation for the MT Configuration concords very closely with the results obtained by Tanaka et al., and Teh and Goyder, for similar configurations. This result also agrees reasonably well with the upper bound of the data obtained by Price and Païdoussis in this range of A_r. This fact has greatly reinforced our confidence in the soundness of our extrapolation procedure.

Moreover, the critical flow velocity obtained for the FTA Configuration is also very close to the results obtained by Tanaka et al. for a similar configuration.

The critical flow velocity obtained for the FRT Configuration is very close to the value obtained for the FTA Configuration. It is also in good agreement with the lower bound of the data obtained by Price and Païdoussis.

The present data demonstrate that, in general, it is not possible to represent the fluidelastic behaviour of a flexible tube bundle by a single flexible tube positioned in the middle of rigid cylinders. However, comparison of the critical flow velocities for the FRT and FTA Configurations suggests that a single flexible tube in the first row of a rigid tube bundle may have about the same fluidelastic behaviour as a full flexible tube array. This point will be further addressed in the next sections.

In the experiments undertaken by Price and Païdoussis, the flexible tube was positioned in the second, the third or the fourth row of the array of rigid cylinders, but these authors have plotted their critical flow velocity data irrespective of the flexible tube location [7]. This seems to be the major reason for the scattering of their data, and accounts for the fact that the FRT and the MT Configuration critical flow velocities are respectively close to the lower and upper bounds of the results obtained by Price and Païdoussis for A_r values of the same order of magnitude as the dimensionless mass-damping parameter associated with our experiments.

Furthermore, some of the scattering observed in Figure 7 may also be due to Reynolds number, Re, influence. Although Reynolds number effect on the fluidelastic phenomenon was long assumed to be negligible, the results obtained by Teh and Goyder in Reference [10] clearly indicate that Re can influence fluidelastic forces.

6 FLUIDELASTIC FORCE COEFFICIENTS

For the present experiments, the equation of motion for a tube vibrating in a tube bundle subjected to cross-flow can be written, in the stable region and with a good approximation, in the following form [5], [6]:

$$(M_s + M_f)\left(\ddot{x} + 2\xi_0\omega_0\dot{x} + \omega_0^2 x\right) + C_f\dot{x} + K_f x = f_t \tag{1}$$

where:

x denotes tube displacement;

M_s is the mass of the tube ;

M_f is the added mass estimated in still fluid ;

ξ_0 and ω_0 are respectively the tube damping ratio and natural circular frequency in still fluid ;

C_f and K_f are respectively the fluid damping and fluid stiffness. They represent those parts of the system damping and stiffness which are due to the fluid flow; f_t is the turbulent buffeting excitation, or more generally the resultant of the fluid forces which are independent of tube motion.

Non-dimensionalised fluid damping and stiffness coefficients can be defined as follows :

$$C_d = - 2C_f / \rho D L U_p$$

$$C_k = - 2K_f / \rho L U_p^2$$

where L is the length of the tube, because here the spanwise mode shape is constant in the test section. Using the IMENE results, the MEIDEE method enables us to derive C_d and C_k. For the FTA Configuration, Equation (1) represents the equation of motion of the global system and, in this case, C_d and C_k represent respectively the dimensionless global fluid damping and stiffness coefficients [6]. In order to be brief, we will limit the study of fluidelastic force coefficients to the transverse direction, which seems to be the very direction associated with the fluidelastic instability phenomenon. For the three investigated configurations, C_k and C_d have been plotted respectively in Figures 8 and 9 as functions of $U_{pr} = U_p/f_v D$ (where f_v is the cross-flow resonance frequency).

Fluid dynamic forces, obtained by Tanaka and Takahara [12] for a square-in-line tube bundle with P/D = 1.33, have also been used to calculate the corresponding values of C_d and C_k for a single flexible tube in the middle of an array of rigid cylinders. These data have also been plotted in Figures 8 and 9. Figures 8 and 9 allow the following conclusions to be drawn.

(i)   The fluid stiffness coefficient obtained from Tanaka and Takahara's data is in good agreement with the MT Configuration fluid stiffness coefficient, and in fair agreement with the FRT configuration fluid stiffness coefficient.

(ii) The behaviour of the global fluid stiffness coefficient associated with the FTA Configuration is completely different from the behaviour of the fluid stiffness coefficients associated with single flexible tube experiments. This shows that interaction of neighbouring flexible tubes induces stiffness-controlled coupling mechanisms which do not exist when a single flexible cylinder is positioned in an array of rigid cylinders.

(iii) The fluid damping coefficient obtained from Tanaka and Takahara's data shows good qualitative agreement with the fluid damping coefficient obtained for the MT Configuration :

these two functions first decrease with U_{pr}, then reach a minimum, increase and seem to approach a constant value for large U_{pr}. However, quantitative agreement is good for $U_{pr} \geq 4$ only. The discrepancy between the two data sets for $U_{pr} < 4$ may be due to Reynolds number effect, difference in pitch ratio, or even to experimental bias (this possibility can never be completely ruled out; estimation of fluidelastic forces is no easy business!). Further investigations are needed to clarify this point.

(iv) The C_d's associated with the FRT and FTA Configurations do not resemble that related to the MT Configuration. Taking into account the results in sections 4 and 5, this conclusion is not surprising.

(v)   The FTA Configuration fluid damping coefficient is an envelope of the FRT Configuration fluid damping coefficient. Our interpretation of this behaviour, which completes the remark made in section 5, is as follows : the fundamental fluid damping mechanisms for the FRT and the FTA Configurations are very similar but interaction of neighbouring flexible tubes tends to better organize and amplify the basic phenomena.

7   ON THE PHYSICAL MECHANISMS UNDERLYING MOTION-DEPENDENT FLUID FORCES

In this section, based on the above results and other previously published results, we will try to obtain an insight into the physics of the fluidelastic excitation mechanisms.

7.1 The damping-controlled fluidelastic phenomenon

From the foregoing analysis, the damping-controlled fluidelastic phenomenon seems to be the basic phenomenon responsible for cross-flow tube bundle instabilities, in the range of reduced flow velocities investigated in the present study. In single flexible tube experiments, this phenomenon can be characterised by the following typical modal parameter evolutions with increasing flow velocity : the in-flow frequency increases ; the cross-flow frequency decreases ; the in-flow damping ratio increases ; the cross-flow damping ratio first increases, reaches a maximum, then decreases becoming nearly zero in the vicinity of the fluidelastic instability threshold. These are the modal parameter variations obtained for the MT Configuration, and for the FRT Configuration in the damping-controlled

© IMechE 1991 C416/024

mechanism region.

The cross-flow and in-flow vibration modes are clearly distinct, and only the cross-flow vibration mode contributes to fluidelastic instability, via the decrease of its damping ratio. Hence, in this case, we may speak of a single mode flutter phenomenon.

Lever and Weaver [13] on the one hand, and Price and Païdoussis [14] on the other, have tried to give a mathematical formulation of this single mode flutter or damping-controlled phenomenon. In both cases, a flow retardation effect, i.e. a phase lag between tube motion and the associated flow perturbation, was introduced in the proposed models. However, it seems that the different authors do not use the same physical arguments to justify this mathematical procedure. Lever and Weaver assume that a mass flow redistribution occurs which lags behind tube motion due to fluid inertia [13]. Price and Païdoussis formulate a mechanism based on flow retardation around the stagnation region of the tube [14]. Obviously, these different justifications merely consist of different *a priori* interpretations of the same physical phenomenon, which is still not well understood. However, these two works clearly indicate that the introduction of a flow retardation effect is necessary to build up a mathematical model for simulating the single mode flutter phenomenon. In order to further investigate the validity of this kind of simplified model, we introduced, in slightly amended form, the latest version of the original Lever-Weaver model [15] into a numerical simulation procedure. We then computed different numerical solutions for the MT Configuration and the triangular configuration presented in Reference [5], by varying the unknown parameters of the model. For the most part, these unknown parameters concern the mathematical formulation of the flow retardation effect. This numerical procedure provides the variations of the cross-flow modal parameters with U_p (and not only the critical flow velocity). The numerical solutions were compared to the experimental results. Further details on this procedure are beyond the scope of the present paper; we shall simply present the main conclusions.

The cross-flow frequency was found to be a decreasing function of U_p, and the cross-flow damping ratio exhibited the 'increasing-decreasing' behaviour. These results were obtained consistently, irrespective of the values of the unknown parameters associated with the flow retardation effect.

However, if the qualitative behaviour of the computed modal parameters was in very good agreement with the experimental results, there was a marked contrast in terms of quantitative behaviour. For instance, frequency decreased much too abruptly : in some cases, static divergence was obtained before dynamic instability could develop. It was always possible to adjust the values of the unknown model parameters in order to obtain the right critical flow velocity, but in this case, the values of the modal parameters in the stable region differed substantially from the experimental data. This shows that the calculation of critical flow velocity is not sufficient to demonstrate the soundness of a mathematical model for fluidelastic coupling. Lastly, a most awkward point is the fact that the model solutions were very sensitive to variations of the unknown parameters associated with the flow retardation effect. Consequently, we can conclude that, though the analytical models seem to be on the right track, they must be regarded at present as being highly rudimentary. The key to the problem seems to be the derivation of a correct physical model for the flow retardation effect. The leading author of this paper recently proposed that the flow retardation effect may be due to diffusion, in the vicinity of the stagnation point, of the vorticity created by the tangential component of the velocity at the flexible cylinder surface, i.e. a phenomenon similar to the development of the boundary layer with time [16]. Contrary to the available models, this physical argument implies the introduction of the viscosity, and hence the Reynolds number, into the representation of the flow retardation effect. Further investigation of this point is currently proceeding in our laboratories.

7.2 Symmetric vortex shedding resonance

For the MT Configuration, only the damping-controlled fluidelastic phenomenon has been observed. However, for the FRT Configuration, another phenomenon appeared in the synchronisation range, just before the damping-controlled mechanism region. Moreover, this phenomenon seems to have a definite influence on the damping-controlled fluidelastic mechanism. Indeed, compared with the MT Configuration, the FRT Configuration becomes unstable at a lower flow velocity and the whole of the damping-controlled mechanism seems to be accelerated. Taking into account the results presented in sections 4, 5 and 6, it seems that these two phenomena must also exist and interact with each other, in the case of the FTA Configuration.

At this point, it is particulary interesting to recall the results obtained by Weaver and Abd-Rabbo in

Reference [17]. These two authors studied the flow-induced vibration of a flexible square-in-line tube bundle, with P/D = 1.5, subjected to water cross-flow. Before the onset of fluidelastic instability in the transverse direction, they also observed a flow velocity range where the cross-flow and in-flow frequencies coincided and where the predominant response was in the streamwise direction. 'Flow visualization photographs showed that coherent vortices were being shed in symmetric pairs from the first row tubes with all vortex pairs being in phase with one another... the pair of vortices shed from the first row tubes remain coherent past the second row... The developing turbulence seems to diminish the effect as the flow visualization showed no coherent vortices behind the third row tubes in this velocity range and the response of the fourth row tubes was quite small' (Weaver and Abd-Rabbo [17]). The Strouhal numbers, corresponding respectively to the beginning and the end of this synchronisation range observed by Weaver and Abd-Rabbo in their experiments, were about equal to 0.69 and 0.4. These two values are very close to the Strouhal numbers calculated in section 4.2 for the FRT Configuration. In a very interesting paper [18], Ziada et al. suggested that the symmetric vortex shedding phenomenon inducing the streamwise tube response observed by Weaver and Abd-Rabbo might be caused, or at least triggered, by a symmetric mode jet instability mechanism. Indeed, they observed one such jet instability mechanism in a rigid tube bundle subjected to water cross-flow, but the associated Strouhal number was S = 0.92. Although this value is not in accordance with the Strouhal numbers associated with the symmetric vortex shedding phenomenon observed by Weaver and Abd-Rabbo, the array geometries were also slightly different in these two cases. In section 4.2, we indicated that the symmetric vortex shedding phenomenon seems to be triggered by tube motion. Consequently, contrary to the vortex shedding excitation of a solitary cylinder in cross-flow, this mechanism is essentially of a motion-dependent excitation kind. The symmetric vortex shedding phenomenon may, in fact, be closely related to the physics of flow separation from the surface of a cylinder in cross-flow. Indeed, it is well-known that, at a separation point, the pressure gradient must be positive. An immediate consequence is that flow separation occurs only if the flow outside the boundary layer is retarded [16]. On the other hand, in the vicinity of the separation points associated with steady-state flow conditions when the tube is motionless, streamwise tube motion will induce successive symmetric accelerations and decelerations of the frictionless flow outside the boundary layer. This will tend to cause symmetric oscillations of the separation points which can result in symmetric vortex shedding. Furthermore, the movement of the separation points can in turn induce perturbations of the unsteady flow field around the moving cylinder. Under favourable circumstances, this phenomenon may have the following consequences :

(i) It may couple with the streamwise tube motion in some well-defined reduced frequency range, thereby sustaining streamwise resonance.

(ii) It may interact with the flow perturbations due to development of the motion-dependent fluid forces in the transverse direction. Hence, the damping-controlled excitation mechanism may be influenced, or even triggered, by the oscillations of the separation points.

Strictly speaking, the above arguments are valid only for laminar boundary layers, and they no longer hold for turbulent flows. This may explain why this phenomenon essentially concerns the first and the second row tubes and seems to disappear with the development of turbulence deeper in the tube array. With similar arguments, it can also be shown that transverse tube motion may induce anti-symmetric oscillations of the separation points. This behaviour has been observed experimentally by Hara for a single row of cylinders subjected to water cross-flow [19]. In these experiments, the movement of separation points was found to be in phase-lead to the cylinder motion, and it caused a change in the configuration of the jet passing through the gap between two neighbouring cylinders. Hence, Hara suggested that this phenomenon might be the source of development of the fluidelastic mechanism for a single row of cylinders subjected to water cross-flow. As instability seems to be driven by relative motion of neighbouring tubes [19], one cannot speak of single mode flutter in this case. However, in square-in-line tube bundles, as far as the authors know, this phenomenon has not been observed and it may be suppressed by the presence of downstream tubes. Obviously, the existence and the development of such phenomena as vortex shedding, oscillation of separation points or jet instability will largely depend on the particular tube array geometry and turbulence level in the flow.

8 CONCLUSIONS

Three configurations have been tested. In the first one, a

single flexible tube was positioned in the middle of an array of rigid cylinders [MT Configuration]; in the second one, a single flexible tube was positioned in the first row of an array of rigid cylinders [FRT Configuration]; in the third one, the first three rows of the array were flexible, the other cylinders being rigid [FTA Configuration]. In each case, the tube array was arranged in a square-in-line pattern with P/D = 1.44. Tube response measurements were analysed by the IMENE and MEIDEE methods. The results of these analyses have been compared to previously published data and to numerical solutions obtained from the latest version of the model originally developed by Lever and Weaver. The principal conclusions are as follows :

(i) A single flexible tube in the middle of an array of rigid cylinders can become unstable in the transverse direction under the action of a damping-controlled fluidelastic mechanism. From an experimental viewpoint, this phenomenon can be characterised by the following typical evolutions of tube modal parameters with increasing flow velocity : the in-flow frequency increases; the cross-flow frequency decreases; the in-flow damping ratio increases; the cross-flow damping ratio increases, reaches a maximum then decreases and becomes nearly zero in the vicinity of the fluidelastic instability threshold. The physics of the damping-controlled fluidelastic mechanism is still not well understood. It seems reasonable to assume that it is closely related to a flow retardation effect, i.e. a phase-lag between tube motion and the associated flow perturbation. The mathematical models currently available are based on this assumption. However, although the agreement between experimental data and numerical solutions is qualitatively good, it is very poor from the quantitative viewpoint. The key to the problem seems to be the derivation of a correct physical model for the flow-retardation effect. In this paper, it is suggested that this phenomenon may be due to diffusion, in the vicinity of the stagnation point where the local Re is small, of the vorticity created by the tangential component of velocity at the flexible cylinder surface. On the other hand, if an anti-symmetric oscillation of separation points, associated with cross-flow tube motion, can develop, it may have a decisive influence on the fluidelastic mechanism.

(ii) A single flexible tube positioned in the first row of an array of rigid cylinders also becomes unstable in the transverse direction, but at a much lower flow velocity. This instability seems to be induced by a damping-controlled mechanism similar to that described above for the MT Configuration. However, in this case, the damping-controlled mechanism seems to be influenced by another immediately preceding fluidelastic phenomenon, which thus occurs in a slightly lower flow velocity range, i.e. synchronisation range. This phenomenon has been identified as symmetric vortex shedding resonance triggered by streamwise tube motion. It may be due, basically, to symmetric oscillation of separation points. From an experimental viewpoint it is characterised by the following typical modal parameter evolutions with U_p : the cross-flow and the in-flow frequencies coincide and they both increase; the cross-flow and in-flow damping ratios fall off sharply at the beginning of the synchronisation range then remain more or less constant, the cross-flow damping ratio being only slightly larger than the in-flow damping ratio which is virtually zero.

(iii) The critical flow velocity for a flexible tube array is more or less the same as that obtained for the FRT Configuration. Hence, it is much lower than the critical flow velocity associated with the MT Configuration. The basic mechanisms of fluidelastic coupling in the FTA Configuration seem to be very similar to those described above for the FRT Configuration. However, the presence of neighbouring flexible tubes seems to better organise and amplify the involved phenomena. Moreover, the interaction of neighbouring flexible tubes induces stiffness controlled fluidelastic coupling which does not exist when a single flexible tube is placed in an array of rigid cylinders. Even if, in the present case, the interaction of neighbouring flexible tubes seems to have only a subsidiary influence on the onset of fluidelastic instability, this interaction may become important in other configurations (see Hara's experiments [19]).

(iv) The fluidelastic coupling phenomenon may be even more complex than it is usually thought. It may be caused by various physical mechanisms which may moreover interact. In every case, damping is a function of flow velocity and may be quite limited, even in the stable region. In general, from a fluidelastic viewpoint, it is not possible to adequately represent an array of flexible tubes by a single flexible tube positioned in an array of rigid cylinders, even if single flexible tube experiments are very useful to improve understanding of the basic physical phenomena. Sophisticated experimental methods seem necessary to investigate such complex phenomena.

REFERENCES

[1]   Païdoussis, M.P. 1987 Flow-induced instabilities of cylindrical structure. *Applied Mechanics Review*, 40 (2), 163-175

[2]   Weaver, D.S. and Fitzpatrick, J.A. 1988 A review of cross-flow induced vibrations in heat exchanger tube arrays *Journal of Fluids and Structures*, 2 (1), 73-93

[3]   Chen, S.S. 1988 Some issues concerning fluidelastic instability of a group of circular cylinders in cross-flow. In *Proceedings International Symposium on Flow-Induced. Vibration and Noise* (Eds. Païdoussis, M.P. Chen, S.S. Bernstein, M.D.), 3, 1-24

[4]   Granger, S. 1988 Time domain method for estimation of damping in flow-induced vibration problems. In *Proceedings Pressure Vessels and Piping Conference-Damping*, ASME, New-York (Eds. Hara, F. Chen, P.Y. Chen, S.S. Ware, A.G.), 133, 27-35

[5]   Granger, S. 1990 A new signal processing method for investigating fluidelastic phenomena. *Journal of Fluids and Structures*, 4 (1), 73-97

[6]   Granger, S. 1990 A global model for flow-induced vibration of tube bundles in cross-flow. In *Proceedings Flow-Induced Vibration - Pressure Vessels and Piping. Conference* (Eds. Chen, S.S. Fujita, K. Au Yang, M.K.), 189, 139-151

[7]   Price, S.J. and Païdoussis, M.P. 1987 The flow-induced response of a single flexible cylinder in an in-line array of rigid cylinders. *Journal of Fluids and Structures*, 3, 61-82

[8]   Weaver, D.S. and El-Kashlan, M. 1981 The effect of damping and mass ratio on the stability of a tube bank. *Journal of Sound and Vibration*, 76, 283-294.

[9]   Païdoussis, M.P. and Price, S.J. 1988 The mechanisms underlying flow-induced instabilities of cylinder arrays in cross-flow. *Journal of Fluid Mechanics*, 187, 45-59

[10]   Teh, C.E. and Goyder, H.G.D. 1988 Data for the fluidelastic instability of heat exchanger tube bundles. In *Proceedings International Symposium on Flow-Induced Vibration and Noise* (Eds. Païdoussis, M.P. Chen, S.S. Bernstein, M.D.), 3, 77-94

[11]   Tanaka, H. Takahara, S. and Ohta, K. 1982 Flow-induced vibration of tube arrays with various pitch-to-diameter ratios. *Journal of Pressure Vessel Technology*, 104, 168-176

[12]   Tanaka, H. and Takahara, S. 1981 Fluidelastic vibration of tube arrays in cross-flow. *Journal of Sound and Vibration*, 77, 19-37

[13]   Lever, J.H. and Weaver, D.S. 1982 A theoretical model for fluidelastic instability in heat exchanger tube bundles. *Journal of Pressure Vessel Technology*, 14, 147-158

[14]   Price, S.J. and Païdoussis, M.P. 1984 A theoretical investigation of the fluidelastic instability of a single flexible cylinder surrounded by rigid cylinders. In *Proceedings Symposium on Flow-Induced Vibrations*, ASME, (Eds. Païdoussis, M.P. Au-Yang, M.K. Chen, S.S.), 2, 117-133

[15]   Yetsin, M. and Weaver, D.S. 1988 On an unsteady theory for fluidelastic instability of heat exchanger tube arrays. In *Proceedings International Symposium on Flow-Induced Vibration and Noise* (Eds. Païdoussis M.P., Chen S.S., Bernstein M.D.), 3, 181-195

[16]   Prandtl, L. 1976 *Aerodynamic theory : a general review of progress* Vol. 3, Division G : Mechanics of Viscous Fluids, Ed. Peter Smith

[17]   Weaver, D.S. and Abd-Rabbo, A. 1984 A flow visualization study of a square array of tubes in water cross-flow. In *Proceedings Symposium on Flow-Induced Vibrations*, ASME (Eds. Païdoussis, M.P. Au-Yang, M.K. Chen, S.S.), 2, 165-177

[18]   Ziada, S. Oengoren, A. and Buhlmann, E.T. 1988 On acoustical resonance in tube arrays - Part 1 : experiments. In *Proceedings International Symposium on Flow-Induced Vibration and Noise* (Eds. Païdoussis,M.P. Chen, S.S. Bernstein, M.D.), 3, 219-244

[19]   Hara, F. 1987 Unsteady fluid dynamic forces acting on a single row of cylinders vibrating in a cross-flow. In *Proceedings Flow-Induced Vibrations - Pressure Vessel and Piping Conference* (Eds. Au-Yang, M.K. Chen, S.S.), 122, 55-58

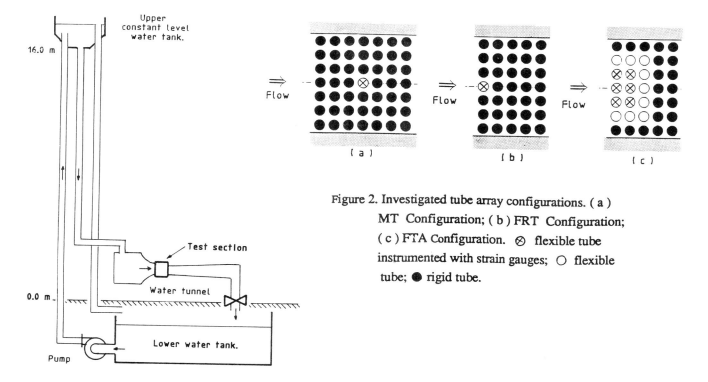

Figure 1. Flow - induced vibration test facility.

Figure 2. Investigated tube array configurations. (a)
MT Configuration; (b) FRT Configuration;
(c) FTA Configuration. $\otimes$ flexible tube
instrumented with strain gauges; $\bigcirc$ flexible
tube; $\bullet$ rigid tube.

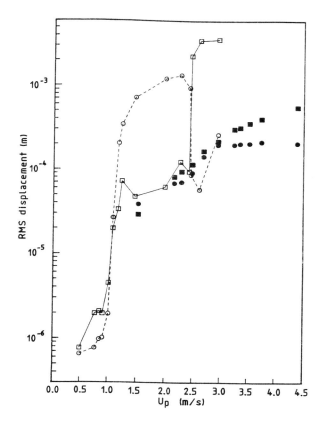

Figure 3. Variation of tube rms displacement with U_p.
$\blacksquare$ MT - transverse direction; $\bullet$ MT -streamwise
direction; $\square$—$\square$ FRT - transverse direction;
$\circ$---$\circ$ FRT - streamwise direction.

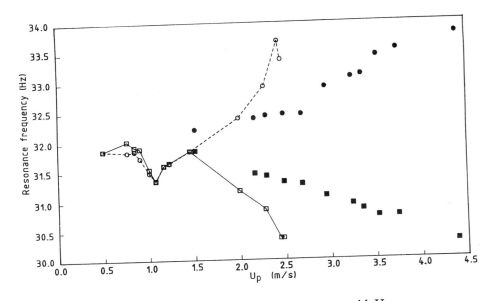

Figure 4. Variation of tube resonance frequency with U_p

■ MT - transverse direction; ● MT - streamwise
direction; □—□ FRT - transverse direction;
○--○ FRT - streamwise direction

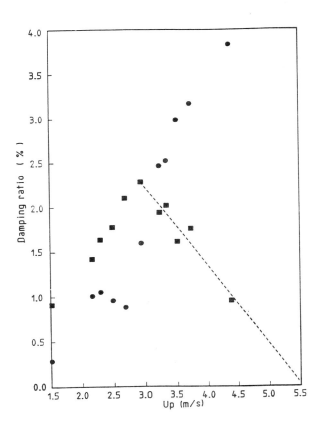

Figure 5. Variation of tube damping ratio with U_p.

■ MT - transverse direction; ● MT - streamwise
direction;   – – – – –   linear extrapolation.

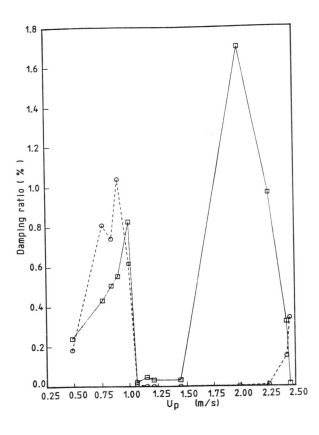

Figure 6. Variation of tube damping ratio with U_p.

□—□ FRT - transverse direction;
○--○ FRT - streamwise direction.

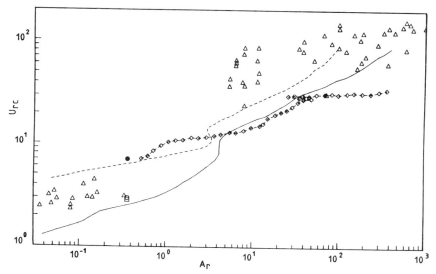

Figure 7. Stability map for square-in-line tube array:
comparison of different results; ● present
results - MT Configuration; o present results
- FRT Configuration; □ present results
FTA Configuration; △ Price and Paidoussis
1987 [7]; ◇--◇ Teh and Goyder 1988[10];
--- Tanaka et al.1982 - single flexibletube[11];
── Tanaka et al. 1982 flexible tube array[11].

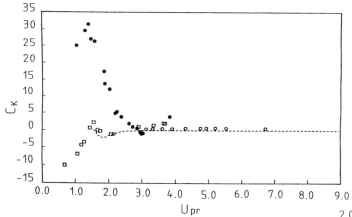

Figure 8. Fluid stiffness coefficient as a function of U_{pr}
o MT Configuration; □ FRT Configuration;
● FTA Configuration; ---- Tanaka and
Takahara 1981 [12]

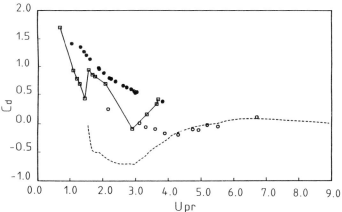

Figure 9. Fluid damping coefficient as a function of U_{pr}
o MT Configuration; □—□ FRT Configuration;
● FTA Configuration; ---- Tanaka and
Takahara 1981 [12].

On suppressing metastable interstitial flow behind a tube array

M ZDRAVKOVICH, MSc, PhD, Dipl-Eng, MASME,
Department of Aeronautical and Mechanical Engineering, University of Salford

SYNOPSIS   It has been shown in a previous paper (11) that the flow in and behind tube arrays is nonuniform and metastable. In this paper, an attempt is made to stabilise the interstitial flow. Guide vanes in various combinations are placed behind a single row of tubes. The effect of guide vanes on pressure distributions behind and around the tubes is examined experimentally. It is found that once the interstitial flow is stabilised it becomes uniform as well.

NOTATION

$\bar{C}_D$	mean drag coefficient
ΔC_D	variation from the mean drag coefficient
$\bar{C}_L$	mean lift coefficient
C_p, C_{pg}	pressure coefficient based on V_o and V_g, respectively
C_{pb}, C_{pbg}	base pressure coefficient based in V_o and V_g respectively
C_{ps}	mean side pressure coefficient based on V_o
D	tube diameter
R_{eg}	Reynolds number based on gap velocity
T	transverse pitch
V_g	gap velocity
V_o	free stream velocity

1. INTRODUCTION

Several hundred papers and reports have been devoted solely to flow induced vibration in heat exchangers and related equipment. This enormous research effort was reviewed from time to time and the latest reviews are by Paidoussis(1), Weaver and Fitzpatrick(2) and in a recent book by Chen(3). Despite three decades of intensive and extensive research our understanding of phenomena involved in flow induced vibration is still far from complete.

2. FLOW INDUCED VIBRATION IN TUBE ARRAYS

The first cause for flow induced vibration in tube arrays was thought to be some kind of vortex shedding. The analogy between the vortex shedding behind a single tube and in the tube array was assumed a priori to hold. The research culminated by establishing the Strouhal number charts covering all possible tube arrangements; see Chen(4), Fitzhugh(5), Ishigai et al(6), to mention only three. The designers could avoid synchronisation of tube and shedding frequency by using these charts. However, the occurrence of flow induced vibration continued unabated.

The second cause for flow induced vibration was thought to be some kind of interaction between closely packed tubes in an array.

Roberts(7) identified a jet switch mechanism in a single row leading to streamwise vibration. Connors(8) specified an energy transfer mechanism from the fluid to the tubes. The displacement of any tube in an array alters the flow field and upsets neighbouring tubes causing them to change their position. A recent review(9) attempted to classify the arrangements and flow regimes in closely packed arrays. The fluid-elastic mechanism could not explain why only some tubes became excited suddenly and violently.

The third cause for flow induced vibration was thought to be some kind of transfer of turbulent energy contained in the interstitial flow to the tubes. Owen(10) argued that the turbulence generated within the array excited buffeting of the tubes by some selective synchronization to the tube frequency. This mechanism explains buffeting, that is random small amplitude vibration but leaves out the large amplitude vibration observed.

There is another possible but not yet proven mechanism of flow induced vibration. This is a metastable and nonuniform interstitial flow in regular arrays(11). The aim of this paper is to describe an attempt to stabilise the interstitial flow.

3. EXPERIMENTAL ARRANGEMENT

The wind tunnel layout is shown in Fig. 1. The test section is 0.3m wide, 0.6m high and 0.9m long. It is driven by a ten-blade centrifugal fan followed by a silencer. The free stream velocity can be varied between 6 and 36 m/s and the intensity of free stream turbulence can be raised or lowered by inserting grids or gauzes, respectively. For the tests described in this paper the intensity of turbulence is 2%

Eleven aluminium tubes, 25.4mm o.d., 1.2mm wall thickness and 298mm long, spanned the test section horizontally and formed one vertical row as seen in Fig. 2. The central tube is designated as C all on top of it as T1...T5 and the tubes below C from B1 to B5. The pitch ratio is kept constant, T/D = 1.2. Three tubes are provided with 16 pressure tappings for pressure distribution measurements and the rest have four pressure taps for base, side and stagnation pressures. In all tests 80 pressures are measured simultaneously and metastable states are 'frozen' by clamping paraffin manometers.

Guide vanes are cut from aluminium sheet and spanned horizontally the test section, Fig. 2. They are 10D long and placed parallel to the axis of each tube and 1D behind the array. The thickness of the vanes is 1 mm.

4. NONUNIFORM INTERSTITIAL FLOW

The prominent but neglected feature of flow induced vibration in tube arrays is the randomness of the initial excitation and erratic vibration of tubes thereafter (12,13). The tubes are all of equal diameter, have the same dynamic characteristics, are equidistantly arranged in regular rows and are subjected to a uniform and steady flow. The paradox is that in spite of all that regularity and uniformity, the initial response and further development of vibration is random and nonuniform to such an extent that the large amplitude vibration of tubes resembles the Brownian motion of molecules.

To resolve this paradox it might be helpful to inverse the logic by assuming that the observed nonuniformity is caused, not in spite of, but because of the imposed uniformity. The uniformity cannot be maintained behind the array where the turbulent nearwakes and gap flows freely interact. The gap flows form two dimensional jets further downstream. The free jets tend to pair and coalesce further downstream in an irregular fashion. This in turn causes biased gap flows, narrow and wide nearwakes, and grossly nonuniform flow behind the array.

Fig. 3 shows a typical nonuniform base and side pressure measured simultaneously behind eleven tubes arranged in a single row. The base pressure nonuniformity reflects the unequal nearwakes in shape and size behind the tubes. The side pressures are unequal on the sides of each tube and also across the gap between the tubes. The latter are depicted with straight lines in Fig. 3 as the actual pressure gradient across the gap. The magnitude and slope of the pressure gradient are all different and reflect the extent and direction of the biased flow.

Table I Mean drag and lift coefficient measured on three tubes.

T/D	1.2	1.2R	1.3	1.4	1.5
$\bar{c}_D$	1.09	0.99	0.72	0.72	0.82
Δc_D	±0.11	±0.10	±0.15	±0.14	±0.17
$\bar{c}_L$	±0.41	±0.24	±0.09	±0.08	±0.08

Such a nonuniform and asymmetric flow around tubes is bound to produce drag and lift forces which vary from tube to tube. Table 1 is compiled as a summary form (11) and shows significant variation of mean drag and lift from tube to tube expressed through Δc_D.

5. METASTABLE INTERSTITIAL FLOW

It has been found in (11) that the nonuniform interstitial flow could change suddenly into another nonuniform state. One example of three metastable states observed in a single row of eleven tubes is shown in Fig. 4 and 5. It was noted that states 1 and 3 lasted longer than state 2.

Fig. 4 shows the simultaneous variations of base pressure behind all tubes while Fig. 5 shows simultaneous pressure distributions around tubes C, B1, B2 measured during the three metastable states. The metastable state 2 was characterised by more symmetric pressure distribution at least behind the monitored three tubes despite the considerable variation of the base pressure behind these tubes seen in Fig. 4.

Metastable states 1 and 3 produced a markedly asymmetric pressure distribution in Fig. 5. The difference in side pressures might exceed 20% indicating a vigorous biased flow.

6. GUIDE VANE AND JET PAIRING

It has been postulated in (11) that the cause of the observed nonuniform and metastable interstitial flow might be in an irregular and for some time stable pairing of jets emanating behind the array followed by an occasional re-pairing. The simplest way to control jet pairing is to introduce a guide vane which will separate two adjacent jets.

Fig. 6 shows the effect of a single guide-vane on the base pressure distribution behind eleven tubes. It may be seen that the presence of a single guide vane at any position downstream of the array fails to suppress the switch between two metastable regimes. There was no similarity between any two of the twenty two metastable states in Fig. 6.

Fig. 7 shows pressure distributions around tubes T1, T2, T3 when the guide vane was subsequently behind each one of them. Again there are two different pressure distributions for each tube and the guide vane has little effect even when it is behind the tube.

7. SUPPRESSION OF METASTABLE STATES

It is expected that when all tubes are followed by guide vanes the jet pairing will be inhibited. Fig. 8a confirms that and shows an almost uniform distribution of the base pressure when all guide vanes are fitted. The variation of the base pressure coefficient is less than 5%.

The residual nonuniformity may be due to a possible small misalignment of the guide vanes behind some tubes. Only one flow state is found to persist all the time. This proved that the irregular jet pairing and re-pairing are the cause of the nonuniform and metastable flow, respectively.

The pressure distribution around tubes T1, T2, T3 is shown in Fig. 9 for the fully guided jets. The symmetry of all pressure distributions is the main feature now which is in contrast with asymmetry found for the unguided flow. The guide vanes fully stabilise the jets behind the array.

If one guide vane is removed, see Fig. 8b, T4, the nonuniform base pressure re-appears. The tube is affected by two jets which can merge or bias upwards or downwards.

Another example is the effect of the displacement of the guide vane from the array. Fig 8c shows the base pressure distribution when the guide vane behind tube T2 is withdrawn for an additional 0.5D in the downstream direction. This affects not only B2 but also tubes C and T5. Hence it may be concluded that all tubes have to be fitted with guide vanes arranged at the same distance downstream in order to suppress metastable states.

It has been shown in (14) that four wires arranged circumferentially near each tube in an array also suppress flow induced vibration. The reason was not clear then but now it seems that the wires obstruct the interstitial flow and damp the metastable states. However the wires have an adverse effect on heat transfer which makes them impractical for heat exchangers. The guide vanes, on the other hand, do not interfere with the heat transfer within the array.

8. CONCLUSION

The hypothesis that the irregular jet pairing and re-pairing causes the nonuniform and metastable flow, respectively, has been proven experimentally. The guide vanes placed downstream behind all tubes stabilise the jets and produce a uniform and stable flow.

The effect of a single vane on the nonuniform flow behind the row is also examined as well as the effect of partial or full withdrawal of one guide vane from the fully guided row. It is found that only completely guided jets produce stable and uniform interstitial flow.

ACKNOWLEDGEMENT

The author would like to give credit to his former students I R Kendle, R J Purcell and K L Stonebanks for assistance. SERC awarded grant to K L Stonebanks

REFERENCES

(1) PAIDOUSSIS, M.P. Flow induced instabilities of cylindrical structures. Applied Mechanics Review, 1987, 40, 649-662.

(2) WEAVER, D.S. and FITZPATRICK, J.A. A review of flow induced vibrations in heat exchangers, Journal of Fluids and Solids, 1988, 2, 73-93.

(3) CHEN, S.S. Flow induced vibration of circular cylindrical structures, 1987, 464p. Hemisphere Publ. Co Washington D.C.

(4) CHEN, Y.N. Frequency of the Karman vortex streets in tube banks. Journal Roy. Aero. Soc. 1967, 71, 211-214.

(5) FITZHUGH, J.S. Flow induced vibration in heat exchangers. Proc. Int. Symp. Vibration Problems in Industry, Keswik, U.K. 1973 paper No. 427, UKAEA.

(6) ISHIGAI, S., NISHIKAWA, E. and YAGI, E. Structure of gas flow and vibration in tube banks with axes normal to flow. JSME Journal Int. Marine Eng. 1973, 1-5-23-1-5-53.

(7) ROBERTS, B.W. Low frequency aeroelastic vibration cascade of circular cylinders. Inst. Mech. Eng. 1966, Mechanical Engineering Science Monograph No.4.

(8) CONNORS, H.J. Fluid-elastic vibration of tube arrays by cross flow. in ASME Flow Induced Vibration in Heat Exchanger, 1970, 42-56. Winter Annual Meeting, New York.

(9) ZDRAVKOVICH, M.M. The effects of interference between circular cylinders in cross flow. Journal of Fluids and Structures, 1987,1, 239-261.

(10) OWEN, P.R. Buffeting excitation of boiler tube vibration. Journal Mechanical Engineering Science. 1965, 7, 431-439.

(11) ZDRAVKOVICH, M.M. and STONEBANKS, K.L. Intrinsically nonuniform and metastable flow in and behind tube arrays. Journal Fluids and Structures, 1990, 4 305-319.

(12) SOUTHWORTH, P.J. and ZDRAVKOVICH, M.M. Cross flow induced vibrations of finite tube banks in in-line arrangements. Journal Mechanical Engineering Science, 1975, 17, 190-198.

(13) ZDRAVKOVICH, M.M., SINGH, S., NUTTALL, J.A. and CAUSON, D.M. Flow induced vibrations in staggered tube banks. Proc. I.Mech.E. 6th Thermo and Fluid Mechanics Convention, 1976, 237-243.

(14)ZDRAVKOVICH, M.M. and NAMORK, J.E.
Excitation amplification and
suppression of flow induced
vibrations in heat exchangers. Nn
Practical Experiences in Flow
Induced Vibrations. 1978, 107-109,
Springer, Berlin, edt. Naudascher,
E.

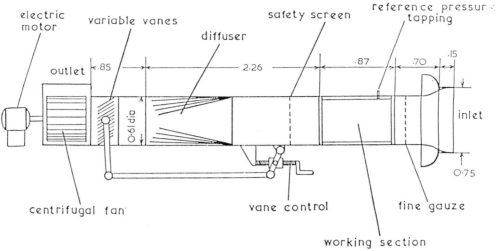

Fig. 1   Diagram of wind tunnel

Fig. 2   View of test section with tubes and guide vanes.

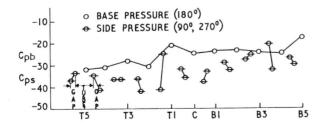

Fig. 3   Base o and side θ pressure measured simultaneously across tube row; Re_g = 78k.

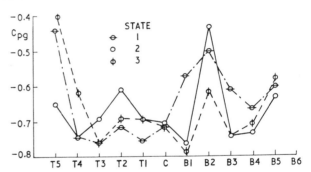

Fig. 4   Base pressure distribution of three metastable flow regimes; $Re_g = 2.1 \times 10^5$.

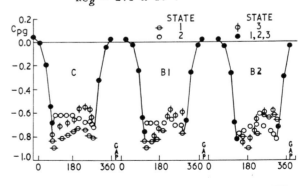

State	1		2		3	
Cylinder	$\bar{c}_D$	$\bar{c}_L$	$\bar{c}_D$	$\bar{c}_L$	$\bar{c}_D$	$\bar{c}_L$
B2	1.32	-.18	1.02	.16	1.32	.05
B1	1.45	-.43	1.14	.04	1.35	-.17
C	1.49	-.06	1.11	.01	.36	-.17

Fig. 5   Pressure around tubes T1, T2, T3 for three metastable states in Fig. 4.

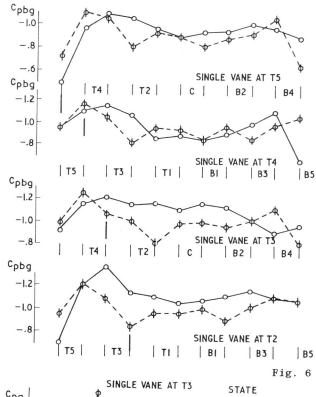

Fig. 6   Base pressure as affected by a single vane.

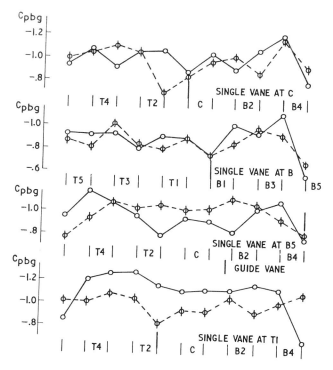

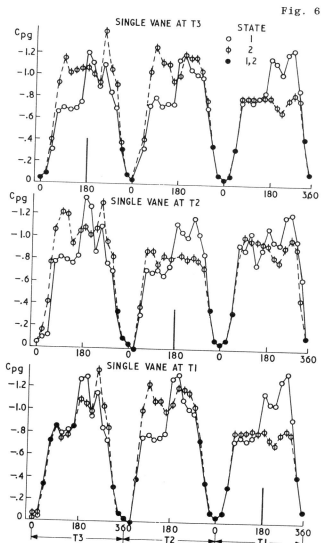

Fig. 7   Pressure around tubes T1, T2, T3 with single vane behind T1, T2, T3.

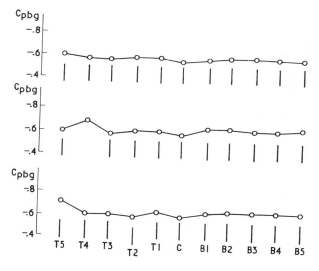

Fig. 8   Base pressure with guide vanes: a) all b) T4 without c) T2 displaced 0.5D downstream.

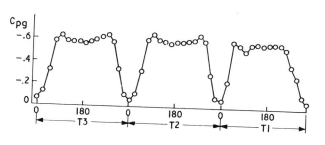

Fig. 9   Pressure distribution around T1, T2, T3 with all guide vanes fitted.

C416/098

Cleaning fabric filters – a useful application of flow induced vibration

H G D GOYDER, BA, BSc, PhD
Harwell Laboratory, Oxfordshire

SYNOPSIS Fabric filters are used to remove dust from a gas flow. During operation a cake of dust builds up on the filter fabric which reduces the filter efficiency. The cake is removed by applying an impulsive flow of gas which shakes the fabric. The mechanisms involved in this fabric cleaning process are investigated. It is found that the cake is removed by a wave induced in the fabric. The equations for the wave and the forces on the cake are constructed. Some approximate solutions to the equations are given.

NOMENCLATURE

a	Deceleration of fabric
c	Wave speed
c_0	Sound speed
F	Adhesive force per unit area of fabric
J	Stiffness of hoop stress
k	Wavenumber
m	Mass per unit area of fabric plus cake
M	Mass per unit area of cake
p	Pressure
p_0	Pressure outside filter
p_1	Pressure inside filter delivered by cleaning pulse
r	Radius of filter
R_0	Radius of filter when collapsed
R_1	Radius of filter when hoop stress begins to act
t	Time
T	Time for pressure to rise in wave front
T_1	Time for filter to expand to point where hoop stress acts
x	Distance along filter
ρ	Gas density
ρ_0	Gas density outside filter
γ	Ratio of specific heats
ξ	Displacement of plane in filter cross-section due to wave motion
ω	Frequency of wave (radians per second)
ω_1	Natural frequency of oscillations of fabric (radians per second)

1 INTRODUCTION

A fabric filter consists of an array of long slim cylinders of porous fabric. The axis of the cylinders is vertical and they hang from a horizontal plate. The bottoms of the cylinders are sealed with fabric. When performing their cleaning duty a dust laden gas passes from outside each cylinder through the fabric and out of the top. A low pressure plenum is located above the cylinders in order to draw the gas through the fabric. The fabric is prevented from collapsing by means of an open wire cage. With continued operation the dust from the gas builds up a cake on the outside of the filter which eventually limits its operation. In order to remove the cake a high pressure impulsive flow is periodically introduced into the top of the cylinder. The duration of this pulse is about

$300ms$. During the pulse the usual flow direction is reversed. This impulsive flow may remove the cake by two methods. First, the reverse flow propagates down the filter as a wave and accelerates the fabric outwards shaking off the cake. Secondly, the reverse flow creates a stress within the cake which pulls the cake away from the fabric. The first form of cleaning, known as acceleration cleaning, forms the subject of this paper.

The objective of this paper is to examine the dynamics of the fabric cleaning mechanism and to give equations for the processes involved. These equations may be used to assist in the design of these filters.

The role of the outward acceleration in cleaning the fabric was identified by Bakke (1) but no analysis was attempted. Some equations were first proposed by Ciliberti and Lippert (2) although the transient nature of the motion was not modelled. Finally Goyder et al (3) developed some simple equations for the fabric motion.

This paper examines the wave motion of the gas within the filter and its interaction with the filter fabric. The influence of the slackness of the fabric is found to be crucial. The role of the slackness in throwing off the cake is analysed.

2 OVERVIEW OF DYNAMICS

The dynamics of the reverse flow and the fabric motion are described in this section. The reverse flow is generated by suddenly opening a valve on a pressure vessel and allowing a jet of gas to be blown into the top of the filter cylinder. This arrangement allows individual filters, or rows of filters, to be cleaned without stopping the main flow of gas through other cylinders or altering the pressure in the suction plenum above the filters.

During normal cleaning, prior to the introduction of the reverse flow, the fabric is pressed against the wire cage by the external pressure. This is illustrated in Figure 1 (i). The cross section in this Figure is assumed to be located at some distance below the top of the filter. The cake builds up on the outside of the fabric often forming panels bounded by the location of the wires that prevent the filters from collapsing.

When the reverse flow is introduced into the filter an acoustic wave, travelling at the speed of sound, passes down the filter and equalises the pressure between the outside and the inside. This is shown in Figure 1 (ii).

As the reverse flow develops the pressure inside the filter begins to increase. The increase in pressure causes the fabric of the filter to expand outwards. The fabric is not rigid but is flexible and for small expansions the only outward resistance is from the fabric and cake inertia. This motion does not remove the cake since the inertia force will press the cake against the fabric. This part of the process is shown in Figure 1 (iii).

Eventually the fabric can no longer be expanded outwards and hoop stresses develop which oppose the outward motion. The fabric is now rapidly decelerated. Figure 1 (iv). If the deceleration is sufficiently rapid the inertia of the cake will cause it to keep moving and to break free from the fabric surface. It is this final motion which cleans the filter. The effect of the hoop stress is to bring the fabric to rest although some oscillations occur during this process.

From these considerations it is clear that the important parameters are the magnitude and rate of pressure rise, the inertia of the fabric and cake, the slackness in the fabric and the hoop stresses generated by the stretched fabric.

3 ANALYSIS OF THE WAVE MOTION

The reverse flow creates a wave which travels in the gas and in the fabric. The motion of the fabric is responsible for removing the cake. The motion of the wave and the pressure in the filter must therefore be considered in some detail.

A model for the motion of the fabric is required. Since the motion of the fabric and the pressure wave in the cylinder are closely coupled a wave equation for the fabric and the internal flow are needed. The dynamics of the fabric are non-linear because the hoop stresses act discontinuously as the fabric moves. Separate wave equations are therefore required for the motion before the hoop stress acts and after it acts.

The wave equation may be set up in the same manner as the acoustic wave equation in a rigid duct except an allowance must be made for the change in radius of the filter. Let the filter radius at any instant be r and let the average radius in the collapsed condition (ie during normal cleaning) be R_0. Due to its slackness the filter can expand a small distance with no hoop stress acting. Let the radius to which the filter can expand before the hoop stress acts be R_1. With this notation four equations may be set up to describe the dynamics of the motion. Figure 2 illustrates the change in conditions over a short length dx.

The expansion of the gas is adiabatic and thus can be modelled as

$$\frac{p}{\rho^\gamma} = \frac{p_0}{\rho_0^\gamma} \qquad (1.)$$

where the subscript 0 indicates conditions just prior to the arrival of the wave front when the internal and external pressures have been equalised.

The acceleration of the gas in the axial direction is proportional to the gradient of the pressure. Thus

$$\rho \frac{\partial^2 \xi}{\partial t^2} = -\frac{\partial p}{\partial x} \qquad (2.)$$

Where $\xi(x, t)$ is the displacement of a plane of gas.

The conservation of mass dictates that the mass of gas prior to the arrival of the wave is the same as the mass of gas after the arrival of the wave. No allowance will be made for any leakage of gas through the filter wall. This would complicate the analysis and is probably irrelevant since the wave passes relatively quickly compared with the velocity of the flow through the wall. The equation of mass continuity gives

$$\pi R_0^2 \rho_0 dx = \pi r^2 \rho \left(dx - \xi + \xi + dx \frac{\partial \xi}{\partial x} \right) \qquad (3.)$$

which may be simplified to

$$1 = \left(1 + \frac{(r - R_0)(r + R_0)}{R_0^2} \right) \left(1 + \frac{p - p_0}{p_0} \right)^{\frac{1}{\gamma}} \left(1 + \frac{\partial \xi}{\partial x} \right) \qquad (4.)$$

Here the pressure has been substituted for the density using the adiabatic relationship. Each factor on the right hand side consists of 1 plus a small quantity and as such may be expanded according to the binomial theorem to give to first order

$$0 = 2\frac{(r - R_0)}{R_0} + \frac{p - p_0}{\gamma p_0} + \frac{\partial \xi}{\partial x} \qquad (5.)$$

An equation in terms of the pressure may now be obtained by eliminating the acoustic displacement ξ using Equation 2. This is achieved by taking two time derivatives of the above equation and one derivative of Equation 2 with respect to x. The resulting equation for the pressure is

$$0 = \frac{2}{R_0} \frac{\partial^2 r}{\partial t^2} + \frac{1}{\gamma p_0} \frac{\partial^2 p}{\partial t^2} - \frac{1}{\rho} \frac{\partial^2 p}{\partial x^2} \qquad (6.)$$

The final equation gives the relationship between the radius and the pressure. This equation has two alternative versions depending on whether the hoop stress is acting. For the case where the hoop stress is not acting the pressure simply causes an outward acceleration according to

$$m \frac{\partial^2 r}{\partial t^2} = p - p_0 \qquad (7.)$$

where m is the combined mass per unit area of the fabric and cake. When the hoop stress is acting a stiffness term must be introduced so that the equation becomes

$$m \frac{\partial^2 r}{\partial t^2} + J(r - R_1) = p - p_0 \qquad (8.)$$

where J is the hoop stiffness. This equation is an oscillator equation for radial motion of the cylinder. Radial oscillations have a natural frequency given by

$$\omega_1 = \sqrt{\frac{J}{m}} \qquad (9.)$$

Oscillations will only occur when the hoop stress is acting and the fabric is tight. The above differential equations describe the dynamics of the wave motion. Their solution gives the motion of the fabric and the gas within the filter. Unfortunately these equations are difficult to solve because of the non-linear characteristics of the hoop stress. These equations will now be investigated to determine the type of waves that can propagate along the cylinder.

© IMechE 1991 C416/098

A free wave analysis will now be undertaken. Let waves harmonic in space and time propagating in the positive x direction be given by

$$r - R_1 = \hat{r}e^{i(kx - \omega t)} \qquad (10.)$$

and

$$p - p_0 = \hat{p}e^{i(kx - \omega t)} \qquad (11.)$$

where k is the wave number and ω is the frequency. The wave number is equal to the frequency divided by the wave speed. These equations when substituted into Equations 6, 7 and 8 will give the relationship between the wave speed and the frequency. It is simplest to use just Equations 6 and 8 and set the value of J to zero to deduce the relationship for Equation 7.

When the substitution into Equation 6 is made the result is

$$0 = -2\frac{\omega^2}{R_0}\hat{r} - \frac{\omega^2}{\gamma p_0}\hat{p} + \frac{k^2}{\rho}\hat{p} \qquad (12.)$$

and for Equation 8 the result is

$$-\omega^2 m\hat{r} + J\hat{r} = \hat{p} \qquad (13.)$$

Eliminating $\hat{p}$ and $\hat{r}$ gives

$$k^2 = \frac{\omega^2\rho}{\gamma p_0} + \frac{2\rho\omega^2}{R_0(J - \omega^2 m)} \qquad (14.)$$

This equation gives the relationship between the wave-number and the frequency. By writing $k = \omega/c$ where c is the wave speed and noting that the acoustic velocity is given by $c_o^2 = \gamma p_0/\rho$ this last equation may be written

$$\frac{1}{c^2} = \frac{1}{c_0^2} + \frac{2\rho}{R_0(J - \omega^2 m)} \qquad (15.)$$

It can be seen that the speed of the wave motion is dependent on the frequency of the wave. The wave motion is thus dispersive with waves of different frequencies travelling at different speeds. For $J \gg \omega^2 m$ ie for frequencies less than the radial oscillation frequency the waves travel at a speed slower than the acoustic velocity. High frequency waves, in contrast, travel at a speed that is faster than the acoustic velocity.

For the case where there is no hoop stress J must be set to zero in the above equation. This gives the interesting result that for small frequencies or for small mass per unit area the wave number squared is negative and thus the wave number is imaginary. An imaginary wavenumber corresponds to a nonpropergating wave. Physically this means that the pressure is released by the expansion of the cylinder and there is no wave motion. For large frequencies the wave number is positive. In this case the inertia of the cylinder is sufficient to contain the pressure and a wave is propagated.

The general behaviour of the wave can now be deduced. When the impulsive reverse flow is introduced a wave is set up in the cylinder. At the wave front the cylinder is expanding and here the wave does not propagate. Behind the wave front where the hoop stress provides stiffness the wave speed is finite although dispersive. This configuration is illustrated in Figure 3. The wave is divided into two parts.

The wave front where the cylinder is expanding and a region behind the wave front where the hoop stress is preventing any further expansion.

The wave motion is analogous to traffic congestion in which fast motor vehicles (the wave behind the wave front) are trapped behind an unpowered vehicle (the wave front). The fast waves push the non propagating wave front forwards.

In order to determine an expression for the cleaning of the filter it is necessary to construct a model for the motion in the wave front. An approximate model may be deduced from the following considerations. The time taken for the wavefront to move through its own length is the time taken for the cylinder to expand from the collapsed radius R_0 to the radius where the hoop stress begins to act R_1. This time is determined by the pressure in the cylinder and the motion as described by Equation 7. The pressure in the cylinder rises from the outside pressure at the leading edge of the wave front and reaches the pressure in the propagating part of the wave at the trailing edge of the wave front. The pressure at the trailing edge of the wave front is determined by the wave motion in the filter behind the wave front. Since this wave is being restricted and cannot propagate at its natural speed this pressure will rise to the pressure delivered at the top of the cylinder. Let the pressure delivered at the top of the cylinder be p_1. Thus within the wave front the pressure rises from p_0 to the pressure p_1. The time taken for the pressure to rise depends on the time taken for the cylinder to expand.

The above analysis has shown that the wave motion is controlled by the wave front where the cylinder expands from its collapsed radius to the radius where the hoop stress acts. The motion in the wave front is given by Equations 7 and 8. Further analysis thus requires that these equations be solved.

4 ANALYSIS OF FABRIC MOTION

In order to solve for the motion of the fabric in the wave front it is necessary to express the pressure rise as a function of time. This pressure rise will be assumed to be a liner rise with time. Thus the pressure rise at one location in the filter while the cylinder is expanding will be modelled as

$$p(t) = (p_1 - p_0)\frac{t}{T} + p_0 \qquad (16.)$$

Here p_0 is the pressure outside the filter and the pressure at the leading edge of the wave front and p_1 is the pressure inside the filter at the trailing edge of the wave front. The pressure p_1 is assumed to be equal to the pressure at the top of the cylinder. The time taken for the pressure to rise is T. At this point in the formulation the value of T is unknown. This value will equal the time taken for the cylinder to expand and thus it may be deduced from the subsequent analysis.

One final point must be considered. When the cylinder expands it first expands according to Equation 7 as illustrated in Figure 1 (ii). The expansion continues after the hoop stress acts, with some oscillation, until the motion is brought to rest. The problem is to decide when the pressure rise is completed and $t = T$. Should this event occur when the hoop stress begins to act or when the outward motion of the fabric is stopped? If the time taken for the hoop stress to stop the motion is small compared to the time taken for the fabric to reach the radius where the hoop stress acts then there is little difference between these two times. As will be shown a value for T may be calculated using either alternatives.

Substituting the model for the pressure into Equation 7 and integrating once gives the fabric velocity. Thus

$$m\dot{r} = \frac{1}{2}(p_1 - p_0)\frac{t^2}{T} \qquad (17.)$$

There is no constant of integration because the initial velocity is zero. Integrating a second time gives an equation for the displacement

$$mr = \frac{1}{6}(p_1 - p_0)\frac{t^3}{T} + mR_0 \qquad (18.)$$

Let the time taken for the fabric to reach the radius where the hoop stress acts be T_1. At time T_1 the radius has increased from R_0 to R_1. Thus

$$m(R_1 - R_0) = \frac{1}{6}(p_1 - p_0)\frac{T_1^3}{T} \qquad (19.)$$

The solution may now be continued with the hoop stress acting. The general solution of Equation 8 with the linear pressure model is

$$r = R_1 + A\cos\omega_1 t + B\sin\omega_1 t + \frac{(p_1 - p_0)t}{JT} \qquad (20.)$$

A and B are two constants which depend on the initial conditions at the instant the hoop stress begins to act. A and B may be determined from

$$0 = A\cos\omega_1 T_1 + B\sin\omega_1 T_1 + \frac{(p_1 - p_0)T_1}{JT} \qquad (21.)$$

and

$$\dot{r}(T_1) = \omega_1\sin\omega_1 T_1 + \omega_1 B\cos\omega_1 T_1 + \frac{p_1 - p_0}{JT} \qquad (22.)$$

where the former equation gives the initial displacement and the latter equation gives the initial velocity. The complete motion of the fabric expansion has now been determined.

The final missing item is the value of T. If it is assumed that this time is similar to the time taken for the fabric to expand to the point where the hoop stress acts then $T = T_1$ and from Equation 19

$$T = \sqrt{\frac{6m(R_1 - R_0)}{p_1 - p_0}} \qquad (23.)$$

A more accurate value of T could be deduced by choosing a value for r for which the wave is fully expanded and then substituting T for t in Equation 20 and solving for T.

The displacement, velocity and acceleration given by these equations has been plotted in Figure 4 (i), (ii) and (iii). For comparison some experimental data is shown in Figure 5 (i) and (ii). Figure 5 (ii) shows the pressure difference between the inside and outside of the filter ie $p(t) - p_0$. In order to simplify the figures based on the theory and to provide a direct basis for comparison with experiment they have been plotted in dimensionless form. The relationship between the nondimensional parameters (indicated by a *)

and their physical values is

$$t^* = \frac{t}{T} \qquad (24.)$$

$$R_0^* = \frac{R_0 m}{(p_1 - p_0)T^2} \qquad (25.)$$

$$r^* = \frac{rm}{(p_1 - p_0)T^2} \qquad (26.)$$

$$\dot{r}^* = \frac{\dot{r}m}{(p_2 - p_0)T} \qquad (27.)$$

$$\ddot{r}^* = \frac{\ddot{r}m}{p_1 - p_2} \qquad (28.)$$

With this nondimensional presentation the only variable that needed to be chosen was ω_1. This has been given the value $2\pi/T_1$. This value was chosen because it represented the conditions in the experiment. The time histories were stopped at the point shown in the figures because the removal of the cake changes the inertia of the fabric and a further modification of the equations would be necessary. The theory and experiment show good agreement.

5 THE CLEANING STRESS

The stress which acts on the cake during the deceleration may be found by calculating inertia forces induced by the cake mass. The deceleration is given by the second derivative, with respect to time, of the displacement as given by Equation 20. Thus

$$\ddot{r} = -\omega_1^2(A\cos\omega_1 t + B\sin\omega_1 t) \qquad (29.)$$

The maximum deceleration, a, is given by

$$a = \omega_1^2\sqrt{A^2 + B^2} \qquad (30.)$$

By substituting for A and B the maximum deceleration is calculated as

$$a = \frac{\omega_1}{T}\left(\frac{p_1 - p_0}{m}\right)\left(\frac{T_1^4}{4} + \frac{1}{\omega_1^4}\right)^{\frac{1}{2}} \qquad (31.)$$

The cake will be removed if the stress induced by the deceleration is greater than its adhesive stress. Thus if

$$aM > F \qquad (32.)$$

where M is the mass per unit area of the cake and F is the adhesive force per unit area of the cake, the cake will be thrown off.

6 DISCUSSION

The analysis presented in the previous sections is believed to represent the principle features of the cleaning mechanism. The most important item is the model of the wave motion. The differential equations for the fabric and pressure are reasonable. One notable omission is damping which is probably significant given the fibrous nature of the filter fabric. Also no account has been taken of any inhomogeneity in the circumferential direction. This effect would add three dimensional aspects to the analysis. A further refinement would be to extend the analysis to include the effects of axial tension in the fabric. However this tension may be small due to the fabric being slack.

The greatest difficulty comes when trying to solve the differential equations and to cope with the nonlinear operation of the hoop stress. The approach adopted seems reasonable given that the wave front does not propagate and is merely driven by the internal pressure. A numerical simulation of the wave motion could give further incites.

The effects of flow through the fabric in the expanded portion of the filter behind the wave front could be included. This flow will tend to decrease the pressure and reduce the acceleration at the wave front.

7 CONCLUSION

The dynamics of the fabric motion during a reverse flow cleaning pulse have been investigated. Differential equations for the fabric and pressure have been derived. The role of a hoop stress in stopping the outward motion of the fabric has been modelled. The wave equation for the propagation of the pulse along the filter has been determined. The wave is dispersive and has a non propagating regime when there is no hoop stress.

An approximate solution to the wave equation and fabric motion has been obtained. This has involved assuming a linear pressure rise within the filter for the front of the wave. The time for this pressure rise is assumed to be equal to the time taken for the fabric to expand outwards. The approximate solution gives results which are similar to experimental measurements.

The analysis gives equations for the tensile stress in the cake due to the deceleration of the fabric. This stress may be used to predict if the cake will be thrown off the fabric. The equations thus give a mathematical foundation for the design of the cleaning pulse in a fabric filter.

Finally it is interesting to note that this is a rare example of useful flow-induced vibration. In this application the larger the vibration the better.

8 ACKNOWLEDGEMENTS

The author wish to acknowledge the support of the Separation Processes Service, Harwell Laboratory. He also wishes to thank Prof. RWK Allen who suggested the study and Dr K Morris who undertook the experimental investigations. The study has been assessed by many useful discussions with Prof. Allen and Dr Morris.

9 REFERENCES

1) Bakke E. 1974."Optimising Filtration Parameters" Journal of the Air Pollution Control Association 1974 Vol.24 No.12

2) Ciliberti DF and Lippert TE 1985."Gas-Cleaning Technology for High-Temperature High-Pressure Gas Streams ". Electric Power Research Institute. Project 1336.1

3) Goyder HGD, Morris K and Allen RWK 1989 " Modelling Media Movement During Pulse Cleaning of Fabric Filters" European Symposium on Separation of Particles from Gasses. Nuremburg. West Germany.

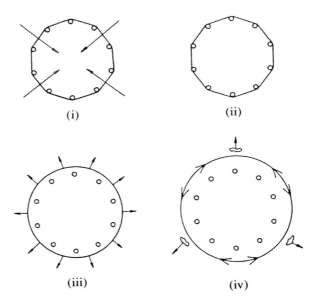

Figure 1. Cross sections through filter during pulse cleaning. (i) Quiescent state. (ii) Arrival of wave. (iii) Expansion of fabric. (iv) Removal of cake.

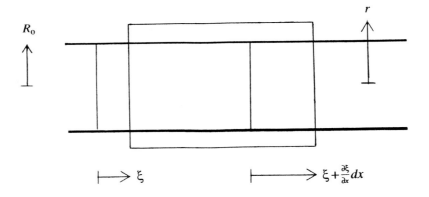

Figure 2. Displacements of gas and fabric during wave motion.

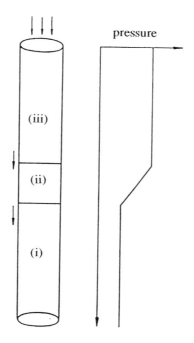

Figure 3. Wave motion in cylinder. (i) Quiescent region. (ii) Wave front. (iii) Expanded fabric.

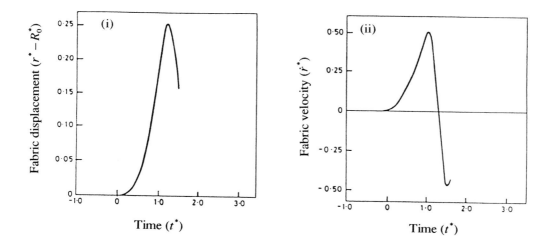

Figure 4. Calculated values of fabric motion. (i) Displacement. (ii) Velocity

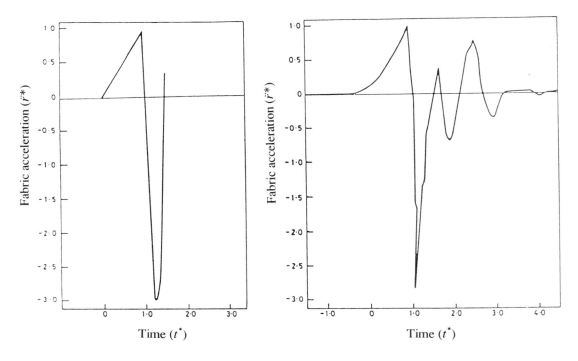

Figure 4.(iii) Calculated values of fabric acceleration

Figure 5. (i) Measured values of fabric acceleration

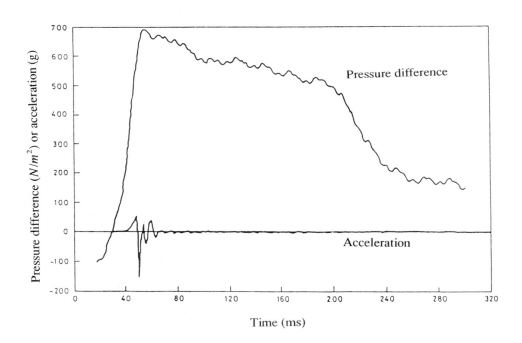

Figure 5. (ii) Measured values of pressure difference across fabric and fabric acceleration

A theory of vibrational instability of a rotating cylinder filled with two liquids of different density

F HARA, PhD
Department of Mechanical Engineering, Science University of Tokyo, Japan
K HAYAKAWA, MSc,
Honda Motor Company Limited, Japan

SYNOPSIS Based on two-dimensional Euler equations and a continuity equation for the motion of two liquids of different density contained in a high-speed rotating cylinder, the governing equations for fluctuating velocity and pressure, and boundary conditions are formulated. Applying the Galerkin method and a harmonic balance method, and obtaining the fluid force acting on the cylinder mounted on an elastic shaft, the dynamic instability condition for this vibration system is formulated. The theoretical instability criterion is compared with Kaneko's experiment, showing a good agreement.

NOTATION

H length of cylinder
K spring constant
M mass of rotating cylinder
p pressure
r_1 radial depth of liquid 1
r_2 radius of cylinder
r r_1/r_2
u radial velocity of liquid
v circumferential velocity of liquid
X displacement
α_{ij} phase angle
η radial coordinate of liquid-interface
ω rotation speed
Ω frequency
Ω_n natural frequency
ρ_i density of liquid i (i = 1 and 2)
ρ ρ_1/ρ_2
σ_1 $\omega + \Omega$
σ_2 $\omega - \Omega$

1. INTRODUCTION

The dynamic instability of a high-speed rotor, mounted on an elastic shaft and containing a coaxial cylindrical cavity partially filled with liquid, has been intensively studied by many researchers (1) – (7), and it is found that the mechanism governing the instability is the generation of a fluid force with a phase-lead to the vibrational displacement of the rotor-shaft system due to liquid waves traveling along the free surface in one direction.

Similar phenomenon can be suspected to occur in the case where the cavity is filled with two liquids of different density having an interface between them. In relation to the dynamic instability of a centrifuge rotating at a high speed, Kaneko (8) recently carried out the experiment to investigate the dynamic instability condition of a rotating cylinder mounted on an elastic shaft and filled with two liquids of different density ; and he found that 1) the rotating cylinder system underwent a whirling, unstable vibration when the rotation speed fell in a certain range around the natural frequency of the cylinder-shaft system, and 2) this instability range with respect to rotation speed depended on the density ratio and depth ratio of the two liquids contained in the cylinder. Based on the added mass analysis for the rotating cylinder-shaft system, Kaneko predicted theoretically the instability range and found that his prediction was not sufficient to explain the experimental results.

Although it is easily suspected that the rotating liquid-cylinder system may undergo an unstable whirling vibration, we still need to study the dynamic instability problem in order to develop the theoretical method for obtaining a more accurate instability condition of the rotating cylinder system.

In the present work, the dynamic instability of the foregoing type of rotating cylinder system is theoretically investigated by adopting the analytical approach similar to that taken by Jinnouchi et al (9). The system considered is an elastically supported high-speed rotor containing a coaxial cylinder filled with two liquids of different density. Assuming a small linear vibration of the cylinder-shaft system, the liquid motion is analyzed as a two-dimensional inviscid flow. An analysis of linearized, perturbed motion of the liquid-cylinder system using the Galerkin method and a harmonic balance method leads to a frequency equation of the third degree, which gives the information about the instability range of the cylinder-shaft system with respect to rotation speed. The theoretical range of rotation speed for the unstable vibration is compared with the experimental one obtained by Kaneko for various cases of the density ratio and depth ratio of two liquids.

2. ASSUMPTIONS

The system to be analyzed is shown schematically in Fig. 1. The rotor, having a coaxial cylinder of radius r_2 and length of H, rotates at a constant angular velocity ω. The cylinder is filled with two liquids of different densities ρ_1 and ρ_2. The O-XYZ coordinate system is fixed in space, while the o-xyz system is fixed to the rotating cylinder. A cylindrical coordinate system o-rθz is used as an alternative to o-xyz where the origin o is set at

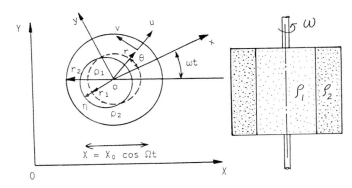

Fig. 1 Coordinate system for analysing the motion of liquids

the center of the cylinder and the z-axis coincides wih the cylinder's axis.

The following assumptions are used in the analysis:

(1) The cylinder is rigid and the shaft is modelled as a spring having a spring constant K,
(2) the liquids are inviscid and incompressible,
(3) the motion of liquids is two-dimensional and their deviant motions with respect to the equilibrium state are small,
(4) the Coriolis force and gravity are negligible,
(5) the cylinder-shaft system oscillates harmonically in only X-direction, written as $X = X_0 \cos \Omega t$, and
(6) the cylinder-shaft system has no external damping.

3. ANALYSIS

3.1 Basic equations for the motion of liquids

For a high speed rotation of the circular cylinder around the Z-axis, the centrifugal acceleration becomes much larger than the gravitational and Coriolis' ones and thus the two liquids of different density form circular annular layers as shown in Fig. 1, where the heavier liquid $i = 2$ occupies the outer annulus region, and the lighter $i = 1$ the inner cylindrical region. The fluctuation of the two-liquid interface is two-dimensional, i.e. is expressed by the deviation $\eta(\theta, t)$ from the equilibrium radius r_1 only in r-direction. The basic equations governing the motion of liquids are described, in the rotating coordinate system o-rθz, as follows:

$$\frac{u_i}{r} + \frac{\partial u_i}{\partial r} + \frac{1}{r}\frac{\partial v_i}{\partial \theta} = 0 , \tag{1}$$

$$\frac{\partial u_i}{\partial t} + u_i \frac{\partial u_i}{\partial r} + \frac{v_i}{r}\frac{\partial u_i}{\partial \theta} - \frac{v_i^2}{r}$$
$$= r\omega^2 - \frac{1}{\rho_i}\frac{\partial p_i}{\partial r} - \frac{d^2 X}{d t^2}\cos(\omega t + \theta), \tag{2}$$

$$\frac{\partial v_i}{\partial t} + u_i \frac{\partial v_i}{\partial r} + \frac{v_i}{r}\frac{\partial v_i}{\partial \theta} - \frac{u_i v_i}{r}$$
$$= -\frac{1}{\rho_i}\frac{1}{r}\frac{\partial p_i}{\partial \theta} + \frac{d^2 X}{d t^2}\sin(\omega t + \theta), \tag{3}$$

where the subscript $i = 1$ corresponds to the lighter liquid and $i = 2$ to the heavier one. Eq. (1) expresses the equation of continuity, and eqs

(2) and (3) are Euler equations for the motion of two liquids. The boundary conditions are as follows:

at $r = r_2$ (inner surface of cylinder)

$$u_2 = 0 , \tag{4}$$

while at $r = r_1 + \eta$ (two-liquid interface)

$$p_1 = p_2, \tag{5}$$

$$\frac{\partial \eta}{\partial t} = u_i - \frac{v_i}{r}\frac{\partial \eta}{\partial \theta} . \tag{6}$$

3.2 Linearization of basic equations

When we divide the solutions of the basic equations shown in eqs. (1), (2), and (3) into steady state, i.e., equilibrium parts and fluctuating ones, the former solutions are easily obtained after a simple calculation as

$$u_{10} = u_{20} = 0 , \qquad \eta_0 = 0 ,$$
$$v_{10} = v_{20} = 0 ,$$
$$p_{10} = \frac{1}{2}\rho_1 r^2 \omega^2 ,$$
$$p_{20} = \frac{1}{2}\rho_2 r^2 \omega^2 + \frac{1}{2}(\rho_1 - \rho_2)r_1^2 \omega^2 , \tag{7}$$

where the second subscript o attached to the variables u, v, η, and p indicates the equilibrium state. From this the fluctuating components in u, v, and p, denoted by the second subscript 1, are found to be governed by the following equations when we reject all but the small, linear terms in the manipulation of these equations;

$$\frac{\partial u_{i1}}{\partial r} + \frac{\partial u_{i1}}{\partial r} + \frac{1}{r}\frac{\partial v_{i1}}{\partial \theta} = 0 , \tag{8}$$

$$\frac{\partial u_{i1}}{\partial t} = -\frac{1}{\rho_i}\frac{\partial p_{i1}}{\partial r} + \frac{1}{2}X_0 \Omega^2 \sum_{j=1}^{2}\cos(\sigma_j t + \theta), \tag{9}$$

$$\frac{\partial v_{i1}}{\partial t} = -\frac{1}{\rho_i}\frac{1}{r}\frac{\partial p_{i1}}{\partial \theta}$$
$$- \frac{1}{2}X_0 \Omega^2 \sum_{j=1}^{2}\sin(\sigma_j t + \theta), \tag{10}$$

where $\sigma_1 = \omega - \Omega$ and $\sigma_2 = \omega + \Omega$.

Applying the perturbation method to eqs. (5) and (6) and taking into account the first-order small terms in each quantity u, v, p, and η, we find that the boundary conditions (5) and (6) can be expressed as follows:

at $r = r_2$

$$u_{21} = 0 , \tag{11}$$

at $r = r_1$

$$p_{11} - p_{21} = -(\rho_1 - \rho_2)r_1 \omega^2 \eta_1 , \tag{12}$$

$$\frac{\partial \eta_1}{\partial t} = u_{i1} . \tag{13}$$

© IMechE 1991 C416/097

Differentiating eqs. (9) and (10) with respect to θ and r, respectively, and eliminating the terms p_{i1} (i = 1, 2) from both the equations (9) and (10), the following relationship is found to be satisfied for u_{i1} and v_{i1}:

$$\frac{\partial^2 u_{i1}}{\partial \theta \partial t} - \frac{\partial v_{i1}}{\partial t} - r \frac{\partial^2 v_{i1}}{\partial r \partial t} = 0 \ . \quad (14)$$

3.3 Solutions

We introduce the stream function Ψ_i (i = 1, 2) for describing the fluctuating motion of each liquid, and since the function Ψ_i is known to satisfy the continuity equation eq. (8), eq. (14) may be rewritten in the form

$$\frac{\partial^3 \Psi_i}{\partial r^2 \partial t} + \frac{1}{r} \frac{\partial^2 \Psi_i}{\partial r \partial t} + \frac{1}{r^2} \frac{\partial^3 \Psi_i}{\partial \theta^2 \partial t} = 0 \ . \quad (15)$$

When the stream functions Ψ_i (i = 1, 2) are expressed in the form

$$\Psi_i = \sum_{j=1}^{2} R_{ij}(r) \Theta_{ij}(\theta) \cos(\sigma_j t + \alpha_{ij}) \ , \quad (16)$$

eq. (15) is easily rewritten as follows

$$-\sum_{j=1}^{2} \sigma_j \left(R_{ij}{}'' \Theta_{ij} + \frac{1}{r} R_{ij}{}' \Theta_{ij} + \frac{1}{r^2} R_{ij} \Theta_{ij}{}'' \right) \sin(\sigma_j t + \theta) = 0 \ . \quad (17)$$

Eq. (17) is divided into two differential equations by introducing a constant k as shown in eqs. (18) and (19), i.e.,

$$R_{ij}{}'' + \frac{1}{r} R_{ij}{}' - \frac{k}{r^2} R_{ij} = 0 \ , \quad (18)$$

$$\Theta_{ij}{}'' + k \Theta_{ij} = 0 \ . \quad (19)$$

In eq. (19), $k \geq 0$ since the stream functions Ψ_i (i = 1, 2) are circumferentially periodic, and thus we set $k = \lambda^2_{ij}$. As λ_{ij} represents the vibration mode of liquid motion in θ-direction, λ_{ij} may be set as

$$\lambda_{ij} = n \quad (n = 1, 2, \cdots) \ . \quad (20)$$

Furthermore the stream function Ψ_1 must be finite at r = 0, and thus we can assume the functions Ψ_1, and Ψ_2 to be of the form

$$\Psi_1 = \sum_{j=1}^{2} C_{1j1} r^n \{ C_{1j3} \sin(n\theta)$$
$$\quad (21)$$
$$+ C_{1j4} \cos(n\theta) \} \cos(\sigma_j t + \alpha_{1j}) \ ,$$

$$\Psi_2 = \sum_{j=1}^{2} (C_{2j1} r^n + C_{2j2} r^{-n}) \{ C_{2j3} \sin(n\theta)$$
$$+ C_{2j4} \cos(n\theta) \} \cos(\sigma_j t + \alpha_{2j}) \ . \quad (22)$$

In eqs. (21) and (22), C_{1j1}, C_{1j3}, C_{1j4}, C_{2j1}, C_{2j2}, C_{2j3}, and C_{2j4} are unknown coefficients. Using eqs. (21) and (22), we can easily describe the fluctuating velocity components u_{11}, v_{11}, u_{21}

and v_{21} as follows after introducing new unknown coefficients a_j and b_j instead of using the original coefficients C_{1jk} (k = 1, 3, 4) and C_{2jl} (l = 1, 2, 3, 4):

$$u_{11} = \sum_{j=1}^{2} n \left(1 - \frac{r_2^{2n}}{r_1^{2n}} \right) r^{n-1}$$
$$\times \{ a_j \sin(n\theta) + b_j \cos(n\theta) \}$$
$$\times \cos(\sigma_j t + \alpha_{1j}) \ , \quad (23)$$

$$v_{11} = \sum_{j=1}^{2} n \left(1 - \frac{r_2^{2n}}{r_1^{2n}} \right) r^{n-1}$$
$$\times \{ a_j \cos(n\theta) - b_j \sin(n\theta) \}$$
$$\times \cos(\sigma_j t + \alpha_{1j}) \ , \quad (24)$$

$$u_{21} = \sum_{j=1}^{2} n \left(1 - \frac{r_2^{2n}}{r^{2n}} \right) r^{n-1}$$
$$\times \{ a_j \sin(n\theta) + b_j \cos(n\theta) \}$$
$$\times \cos(\sigma_j t + \alpha_{2j}) \ , \quad (25)$$

$$v_{21} = \sum_{j=1}^{2} n \left(1 + \frac{r_2^{2n}}{r^{2n}} \right) r^{n-1}$$
$$\times \{ a_j \cos(n\theta) - b_j \sin(n\theta) \}$$
$$\times \cos(\sigma_j t + \alpha_{2j}) \ . \quad (26)$$

We should have said initially that the coefficients a_j and b_j (j = 1, 2) will be calculated by the Galerkin method.

Substituting eqs. (23) and (25) into eq. (13) and considering the continuity of fluctuating radial velocity $u_{11} = u_{21}$ at $r = r_1$, we obtain the relation $\alpha_{1j} = \alpha_{2j}$ (j = 1, 2), and the radial coordinate of the fluctuating interface η_1, is

$$\eta_1 = \sum_{j=1}^{2} n \frac{1}{\sigma_j} \left(1 - \frac{r_2^{2n}}{r_1^{2n}} \right) r_1^{n-1}$$
$$\times \{ a_j \sin(n\theta) + b_j \cos(n\theta) \}$$
$$\times \sin(\sigma_j t + \alpha_{1j}) \ . \quad (27)$$

Substituting eqs. (24) and (26) into eq. (10) and intergrating $\partial p_{i1}/\partial\theta$ (i = 1, 2) with respect to θ, we obtain the fluctuating pressure p_{11} and p_{21} in the form

$$p_{11} = \rho_1 \sum_{j=1}^{2} \left[\sigma_j \left(1 - \frac{r_2^{2n}}{r_1^{2n}} \right) r^n \right.$$
$$\times \{ a_j \sin(n\theta) + b_j \cos(n\theta) \}$$
$$\times \sin(\sigma_j t + \alpha_{1j})$$
$$\left. + \frac{1}{2} X_0 \Omega^2 r \cos(\sigma_j t + \theta) \right] \ , \quad (28)$$

$$p_{21} = \rho_2 \sum_{j=1}^{2} \left[\sigma_j \left(1 + \frac{r_2^{2n}}{r^{2n}} \right) r^n \right.$$
$$\times \{ a_j \sin(n\theta) + b_j \cos(n\theta) \}$$
$$\times \sin(\sigma_j t + \alpha_{1j})$$
$$\left. + \frac{1}{2} X_0 \Omega^2 r \cos(\sigma_j t + \theta) \right] \ . \quad (29)$$

The boundary condition eq. (12) imposed upon the pressures p_{11} and p_{21} at the interface $r = r_1$ is easily rewritten as

$$L = (\text{left hand side of eq.}(12)) - (\text{right hand side of eq.}(12)), \quad (30)$$

and the unkown coefficients a_j, b_j, and α_{1j} must be determined to satisfy eq. (30) at arbitrary time t and space coordinate θ. However eq.(30) is not rigorously satisfied for any t and θ, then we apply the Galerkin method to eq. (30)

$$I = \int_0^{2\pi} L \cos(n\theta) \, d\theta . \quad (31)$$

For each n, the unknown coefficients are determined by the vanishing of I. Then we can obtain the pressure fluctuation p_{11} and p_{21}, and the interface fluctuation η_1, as follows:

(1) for $n = 1$

$$p_{11} = \rho_1 \sum_{j=1}^{2} \{ \sigma_j (1 - \frac{r_2^2}{r_1^2}) \, r \, b_j \cos\theta$$
$$\times \sin(\sigma_j t + \alpha_{1j})$$
$$+ \frac{1}{2} X_\theta \Omega^2 r \cos(\sigma_j t + \theta) \}, \quad (32)$$

$$p_{21} = \rho_2 \sum_{j=1}^{2} \{ \sigma_j (1 + \frac{r_2^2}{r^2}) \, r \, b_j \cos\theta$$
$$\times \sin(\sigma_j t + \alpha_{1j})$$
$$+ \frac{1}{2} X_\theta \Omega^2 r \cos(\sigma_j t + \theta) \}, \quad (33)$$

$$\eta_1 = \sum_{j=1}^{2} \frac{1}{\sigma_j} (1 - \frac{r_2^2}{r^2}) \, b_j \cos\theta$$
$$\times \sin(\sigma_j t + \alpha_{1j}) , \quad (34)$$

where

$$b_j = -\frac{1}{2} \frac{\rho_1 - \rho_2}{\sigma_j b_j'} \frac{X_\theta \Omega^2}{\sin\alpha_{1j}} ,$$

$$b_j' = \rho_1 (1 - \frac{r_2^2}{r_1^2}) - \rho_2 (1 + \frac{r_2^2}{r_1^2})$$
$$+ \frac{\omega^2}{\sigma_j^2} (\rho_1 - \rho_2) (1 - \frac{r_2^2}{r_1^2}) ,$$

$$\cos\alpha_{1j} = 0 ,$$

(2) for $n \geqq 2$

$$p_{11} = \frac{1}{2} \rho_1 X_\theta \Omega^2 r \sum_{j=1}^{2} \cos(\sigma_j t + \theta) \} , \quad (35)$$

$$p_{21} = \frac{1}{2} \rho_2 X_\theta \Omega^2 r \sum_{j=1}^{2} \cos(\sigma_j t + \theta) \} , \quad (36)$$

$$\eta_1 = 0 . \quad (37)$$

3.4 Instability criteria

Since the fluid force acting upon the rotating cylinder is generated by the fluctuating pressure p_{21} at $r = r_2$, the x- and y- components of the fluid force are expressed as follows:

$$f_x = \int_0^{2\pi} p_{21} |_{r=r_2} r_2 \cos\theta \, d\theta , \quad (38)$$

$$f_y = \int_0^{2\pi} p_{21} |_{r=r_2} r_2 \sin\theta \, d\theta . \quad (39)$$

Then the fluid force is rewritten in the fixed coordinate system by using fx and fy as in the form

$$F_x = f_x \cos(\omega t) - f_y \sin(\omega t). \quad (40)$$

Substituting the expressions (33) and (36) for p_{21} into eqs. (38) and (39), and substituting the result, again, into eq. (40), the fluid force Fx is obtained in a explicit form:

(1) for $n = 1$

$$F_x = \pi \rho_2 r_2^2 \{ 2 \sum_{j=1}^{2} \sigma_j b_j \sin\alpha_{1j} \cos(\sigma_j t)$$
$$\times \cos(\omega t)$$
$$+ X_\theta \Omega^2 \cos(\Omega t) , \} , \quad (41)$$

(2) for $n \geqq 2$

$$F_x = \pi \rho_2 r_2^2 X_\theta \Omega^2 \cos(\Omega t). \quad (42)$$

Note that the fluid force shown here in eqs. (41) and (42) is that acting per unit length of the rotating cylinder.

Denoting the spring constant of the elastic shaft supporting the rotating cylinder as K, and the length of the cylinder as H, we have the following equation of vibration for the rotating cylinder mounted on the elastic shaft

$$M\ddot{X} + K X = H F_x . \quad (43)$$

Let us consider the case for $n \geqq 2$ in the first place, since the fluid force Fx has a simple mathematical expression as seen in eq. (42). Substituting eq. (42) into eq. (43), eq. (43) then yields

$$M\ddot{X} + K X = m_1 X_\theta \Omega^2 \cos(\Omega t) , \quad (44)$$

where $m_1 = \rho_2 \pi r_2^2 H$. The right hand side of eq. (44) expresses only the force generated by the added mass term m_1, and thus we can conclude that, for higer modes of liquid motion in the circumferential direction $n \geqq 2$, no unstable vibration is caused by the liquids contained in the cylinder.

For the fundamental mode of liquid motion $n = 1$, the equation of vibration for the cylinder-shaft system, eq. (43), is written after some tedious calculation in the form

$$M\ddot{X} + K X$$
$$= m_1 [2 \{ \sigma_1 b_1 \sin\alpha_{11} \cos(\omega + \Omega) t$$
$$\times \cos(\omega t)$$
$$+ \sigma_2 b_2 \sin\alpha_{12} \cos(\omega - \Omega) t$$
$$\times \cos(\omega t) \}$$
$$+ X_\theta \Omega^2 \cos(\Omega t)] . \quad (45)$$

As we assumed that the cylinder oscillates harmonically in X-direction, we substitute

$$X = X_0 \cos(\Omega t) \qquad (46)$$

into eq. (45) and apply the harmonic balance method to eq. (45). In the calculation, we introduce new parameters

$$\widetilde{\rho} \equiv \frac{\rho_1}{\rho_2}, \qquad \widetilde{r} \equiv \frac{r_1}{r_2} \qquad (47)$$

and new variables s_j $(j = 1,2)$ corresponding to $\sigma_1 = \omega + \Omega$ and $\sigma_2 = \omega - \Omega$, where

$$s_j \Omega^2 = \sigma_j b_j \sin\alpha_{1j} \frac{1}{X_0}. \qquad (48)$$

Eq. (45) is then rewritten into an equivalent form to the original expression as

$$-\Omega^2 + \Omega_n^2 = \frac{m_1}{M} \Omega^2 (1 + s_1 + s_2), \qquad (49)$$

$$s_1 = -\frac{1}{2} \frac{(\zeta+1)^2 (1-\widetilde{\rho})\widetilde{r}^2}{(\zeta+1)^2 \{\widetilde{\rho}(1-\widetilde{r}^2)+1+\widetilde{r}^2\}-(1-\widetilde{\rho})(1-\widetilde{r}^2)},$$

$$s_2 = -\frac{1}{2} \frac{(\zeta-1)^2 (1-\widetilde{\rho})\widetilde{r}^2}{(\zeta-1)^2 \{\widetilde{\rho}(1-\widetilde{r}^2)+1+\widetilde{r}^2\}-(1-\widetilde{\rho})(1-\widetilde{r}^2)},$$

where $\Omega_n = \sqrt{K/M}$ and $\zeta = \Omega/\omega$. Upon introduction of the following new parameters

$$\zeta_n = \frac{\Omega_n}{\omega} \qquad \widetilde{m}_1 = \frac{m_1}{M} \qquad (50)$$

eq. (49) is written in a simpler form

$$-\zeta^2 + \zeta_n^2 = \widetilde{m}_1 \zeta^2 (1 + s_1 + s_2). \qquad (51)$$

In eq. (51), we set $Y = F_1(\zeta)$ for the left hand side term and $Y = F_2(\zeta)$ for the right hand side term, i.e.

$$Y = F_1(\zeta) = -\zeta^2 + \zeta_n^2,$$
$$Y = F_2(\zeta) = \widetilde{m}_1 \zeta^2 (1 + s_1 + s_2). \qquad (52)$$

When a real value ζ satisfying

$$F_1(\zeta) = F_2(\zeta) \qquad (53)$$

does not exist or complex conjugate roots exist, the dynamic system in question exhibits instability, meaning that the vibration of the rotating cylinder, filled with two liquids of different density and supported by an elastic shaft, becomes unstable. We explain it more fully in the following:

Introducing a new parameter ζ_a defined as

$$\zeta_a = \sqrt{\frac{(1-\widetilde{\rho})(1-\widetilde{r}^2)}{\widetilde{\rho}(1-\widetilde{r}^2)+1+\widetilde{r}^2}}, \qquad (54)$$

we can rewrite s_1 and s_2 in the form

$$s_1 = -\frac{1}{2} \lambda \left\{ \frac{(1+\zeta)^2}{\zeta_a^2 - (1+\zeta)^2} \right\},$$

$$(55)$$

$$s_2 = -\frac{1}{2} \lambda \left\{ \frac{(1-\zeta)^2}{\zeta_a^2 - (1-\zeta)^2} \right\},$$

$$\lambda = \frac{(1-\widetilde{\rho})\widetilde{r}^2}{\widetilde{\rho}(1-\widetilde{r}^2)+1+\widetilde{r}^2}.$$

The expression of F_2 in eq. (52) is rewritten as follows:

$$Y = F_2(\zeta) = \widetilde{m}_1 \zeta^2 \left[1 + \frac{1}{2}\lambda \left\{ \frac{(1+\zeta)^2}{\zeta_a^2 - (1+\zeta)^2} \right.\right. \qquad (56)$$
$$\left.\left. + \frac{(1-\zeta)^2}{\zeta_a^2 - (1-\zeta)^2} \right\} \right].$$

In eq. (56), it is easily found that the vertical lines

$$\zeta = -1 \pm \zeta_a, \text{ and } \zeta = 1 \mp \zeta_a \qquad (57)$$

become the asymptotic lines of the graph $Y = F_2$ since the denominators of the first and second terms in the parenthesis $\{\ \}$ of the right hand side in eq. (56) become zero at $\zeta = -1 \pm \zeta_a$ and $\zeta = 1 \mp \zeta_a$, respectively. When we draw the graphs of $Y = F_1(\zeta)$ and $Y = F_2(\zeta)$ as shown in Fig. 2, we find that eq. (51) does not hold for the real value of ζ within the two ranges in the neighborhood of $\zeta = 1 - \zeta_a$ and $\zeta = -1 + \zeta_a$. This means that the solution of eq. (51) contains a complex conjugate $\Omega = \Omega_r \pm \sqrt{-1}\Gamma$ $(\Gamma > 0)$ for the given ω and then the motion of the cylinder-shaft system has a component of $\exp(\Gamma t) \cos \Omega_r t$ which will give rise to an unstable vibration.

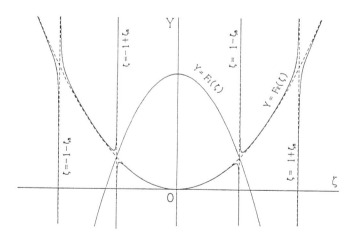

Fig. 2 $Y - \zeta$ diagram

Substituting the definition of s_1 and s_2 into eq. (49) and manipulating the expression, we obtain the following equation for eq. (49):

$$-\zeta^2 + \zeta_n^2 = \widetilde{m}_1 \zeta^2 \frac{C_5 \zeta^4 + C_6 \zeta^2 + C_7}{C_8 \zeta^4 + C_9 \zeta^2 + C_{10}}, \qquad (58)$$

where C_5 to C_{10} are defined as

$$C_5 = (1 - \tilde{\rho}^2) \tilde{r}^2 + (1 + \tilde{\rho})^2$$

$$C_6 = (1 - \tilde{\rho}^2) \tilde{r}^4 - (1 - \tilde{\rho})^2 \tilde{r}^2 - 4(1 + \tilde{\rho})$$

$$C_7 = 2 \{ (1 - \tilde{\rho}) \tilde{r}^2 + \tilde{\rho} \} \times \{ (1 - \tilde{\rho}) \tilde{r}^2 + 2 \tilde{\rho} \}$$

$$C_8 = (1 - \tilde{\rho})^2 \tilde{r}^4 + 2(1 - \tilde{\rho}^2) \tilde{r}^2 + (1 + \tilde{\rho})^2$$

$$C_9 = -4 \{ (1 - \tilde{\rho}) r^2 + 1 + \tilde{\rho} \}$$

$$C_{10} = 4 \{ (1 - \tilde{\rho}) \tilde{r}^2 + \tilde{\rho} \}^2$$

Since eq. (58) is a cubic equation of ζ^2, the condition that the equation does not have real roots or does have complex conjugate solutions is easily obtained from its discriminant being negative. From this criterion, we can obtain the rotation speed for the cylinder system to undergo unstable vibrations.

4. COMPARISON WITH KANEKO'S EXPERIMENT

To investigate the validity of instability criterion eq. (53) or eq. (58), we compared the analytical

Table 1 Parameters used in Kaneko's experiment

	$\tilde{\rho}$
water + turbine oil	0.824
water + spindle oil	0.818
water + kerosene	0.749
glycerine + spindle oil	0.683
fleon + water	0.674

results obtained from eq. (58) and the experimental ones described in Ref. (8) with respect to the relationship between the rotation speed causing the instability and the liquid-depth ratio $\tilde{r} = r_1/r_2$. Kaneko carried out the experiment to show the instability diagram in terms of $\tilde{\omega}$ and $\tilde{r}$ for five cases of $\tilde{\rho}$ as shown in Table 1 through adopting various combination of two different densities of liquid.

Figs. 3 (a) and (b) show the comparison between our analytical results and those of Kaneko's experiment. The region confined by two solid lines indicates that the cylinder system theoretically undergoes an unstable vibration at the corresponding rotation speed $\tilde{\omega}$ and liquid-depth ratio $\tilde{r}$. The broken lines were obtained, by Kaneko, from the condition that the added mass for this cylinder system be negative.

The vibration frequency Ω_m and rotation speed ω_m corresponding to the intersection at $\zeta = 1 - \zeta_a$ shown in Fig. 2 are easily obtained as

$$\frac{\Omega_m}{\Omega_n} = \frac{1}{\sqrt{\tilde{m}_1 \dfrac{1 + \tilde{\rho}}{(1 - \tilde{\rho}) \tilde{r}^2 + 1 + \tilde{\rho}} + 1}}, \quad (59)$$

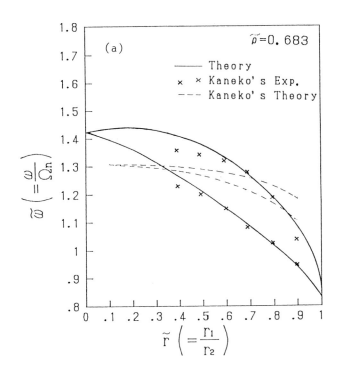

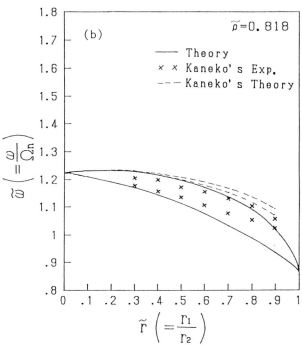

Fig. 3 $\tilde{\omega} - \tilde{r}$ diagram, (a) $\tilde{\rho} = 0.683$, (b) $\tilde{\rho} = 0.818$

$$\frac{\omega_m}{\Omega_n} = \frac{1}{1 - \zeta_a} \frac{\Omega_m}{\Omega_n}. \quad (60)$$

The dependency of Ω_m on r and ρ is shown in Fig. 4 and the relationship between ω_m and $\tilde{r}$ is also indicated by the broken line in Fig. 5, where the region confined by two solid lines is the instability region mentioned previously. Fig. 4 shows a weak dependency of Ω_m on r and ρ, then, as the dominant frequency of the unstable vibration of the cylinder system is seen to be nearly equal to Ω_m, the dominant frequency Ω_d is

© IMechE 1991 C416/097

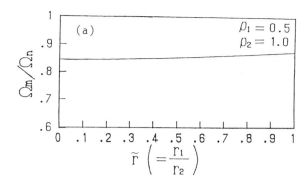

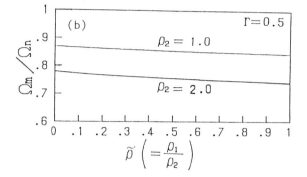

Fig. 4 $\Omega_m - \tilde{r}$ diagram (a), and $\Omega_m - \tilde{\rho}$ diagram (b)

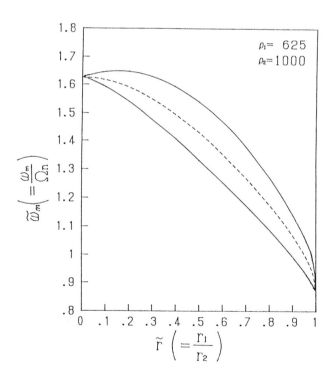

Fig. 5 $\tilde{\omega}_m - \tilde{r}$ diagram

$$\Omega_d \sim \Omega_m = \frac{\Omega_n}{\sqrt{\tilde{m}_1 + 1}} \quad \cdot \qquad (61)$$

Fig. 6 is the magnitude of $|s_1|$ and $|s_2|$ plotted against the rotation speed $\tilde{\omega}$, indicating that $|s_1|$ is almost constant and $|s_2|$ gives a sharp peak at $\tilde{\omega} = 1.28$. This means that large $|s_2|$ around $\tilde{\omega} = 1.28$ contributes to the non-existence condition

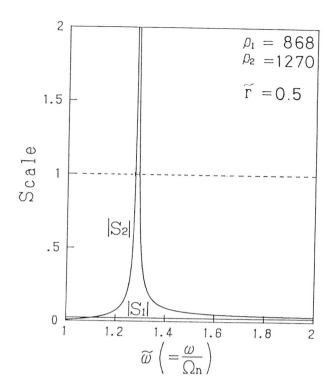

Fig. 6 $|s_1|$ and $|s_2| - \tilde{\omega}$ diagram

of a real root in eq. (51), that is, s_2 or $\sigma_2 = \omega - \Omega$ is the major contributor to the unstable vibration of the cylinder system.

5. CONCLUSION

In this paper the theoretical linear instability condition of a rotating circular cylinder mounted on an elastic shaft and filled with two liquids of different density was investigated, and the theory was verified by comparing the results with those experimentally obtained by Kaneko.

The results obtained are summarized as follows:

(1) The instability can occur when the cylinder undertakes the high-speed rotation where gravitational and Coriolis' accelerations are negligible compared to the centrifugal one,
(2) the first mode of circumferential waves generated in the interface between two liquids is the major cause to this instability,
(3) the fluid force term corresponding to the difference between rotation speed ω and vibration frequency Ω is the major contributor to the vibrational instability,
(4) The frequency of the unstable vibration is almost equal to the natural frequency of the system included the added mass effect of liquids contained in the cylinder.

REFERENCES

(1) KOLLMANN, F. G., Experimentalle und Theoretishe Untersuchungen ueber die Kritischen Drehzahlen Fluessigkeitsgefueller Hohlkoerper, Forschung auf dem Gebiete des Ingenieurwesens, Vol.28, No. 4, 5 (1962), 115-123 and 147-153
(2) WOLF, J. A. JR., Whirl Dynamics of a Rotor Partially Filled with Liquid, ASME J. of Applied Mechanics, Vol. 35 (1968), 676-682
(3) HENDRICKS, S. L., and MORTON, J. B., Stability of Rotor Partially Filled a Viscous Incompressible

Fluids, ASME J. of Applied Mechanics, Vol. 46 (1979), 913-918

(4) SAITO, S. and SOMEYA, T., Investigation of the Vibration of a Rotating Hollow Shaft Partially Filled with Liquid - Part III, Trans,. JSME, Vol 45, No. 400 C (1979), 1325-1331

(5) KANEKO, N. and HAYAMA, S., Self-Excited Oscillation of a Hollow Rotating Shaft Partially Filled with a Liquid (1st Report), Bulletin of JSME, Vol. 28, No. 246 (1985), 2994-3001

(6) BERMAN, A. S., LUNDGREN, T.S., and CHENG, A., Asynchronous Whirl in a Rotating Cylinder Partially Filled with Liquid, J. Fluid Mechanics, Vol. 150 (1985), 311-327

(7) INOUE, J., JINNOUCHI, Y., and ARAKI, Y., Forced Wave Motion of Liquid Partially Filling a High-Speed Rotor, ASME J. Vib., Acoustics, Stress and Reliability in Design, Vol. 107 (1985), 446-452

(8) KANEKO, N., Report of Scientific Research Grant, Japanese Ministry of Culture and Education, Investigation of Self-excited Vibration of Rotating Cylinder Filled with Two Liquids, (1988)

(9) JINNOUCHI, J., ARAKI, Y., INOUE, J., and KUBO, S., Dynamic Instability of a High-Speed Rotor Contaning a Partitioned Cavity Filled with Two Kinds of Liquids, ASME J. Pressure Vessel Technology, Vol. 111 (1989), 450-456

A stochastic model of parametric excitation of a straight pipe due to slug flow of a two-phase fluid

M F DIMENTBERG
Institute for Problems in Mechanics, USSR Academy of Sciences, Moscow, USSR

SYNOPSIS A stochastic model is presented for a parametric excitation of a straight pipe due to a slug flow of a two-phase fluid with alternating slugs of, say, water and steam, accounting for random inhomogenuities of the flow. Using stochastic averaging for the case of a resonant single-mode response explicit expressions are derived for stability thresholds both with respect to probability and in the mean square sense. The mean square analysis of a subcritical response to external random excitation is also presented.

NOTATION

Ω natural frequency of the pipe
ν expected value of the excitation frequency
G rms value of the excitation frequency variations
α damping factor
γ amplitude of parametric excitation
D intensity of the white-noise external excitation
A, φ response amplitude and phase respectively
x_c, x_s response inphase and quadrature components respectively
Δ detuning, $\Delta = 2\Omega - \gamma$.

1 INTRODUCTION

A "slug" flow of a two-phase fluid in a straight pipe, with periodically alternating slugs of, say, water and steam, may be a source of a parametric excitation of the pipe, this spatial periodicity leading in a time domain to periodic variations of the pipe's apparent mass between any pair of neighbouring supports. This may lead to dynamic instability of the pipe, with an unlimited growth of the amplitude of the pipe's lateral bending vibrations due to any disturbance; moreover, the pipe's subcritical response to any external excitation may be greatly amplified (1, 2).

For the basic case of a single-mode instability these phenomena may be analyzed by applying a single-term Galerkin-type approximation to the governing partial differential equation of bending vibrations. The latter is reduced then to the ordinary second-order differential equation with periodic coefficients for the modal response. Moreover, in a near-resonant case, with all excitation and damping forces being small compared with the inertia and stiffness ones, only one term may be retained in a Fourier series expansion for the periodic excitation, namely, the term with a near-resonant frequency (in most cases it corresponds to the main harmonic of the excitation (1)). Then the Mathieu equation is obtained, so that the stability may be studied with the well-known Ince-Strutt chart.

This approach, however, does not account for spatial random inhomogenuities of a slug flow, which lead in time domain to random timewise variations of the parametric excitation frequency (the corresponding random variations of the excitation amplitude may be regarded as being of secondary importance). The influence of the above excitation frequency variations is studied in this report. The results show that even a small random scatter of the excitation frequency, due to scatter of length of the slugs of steam and water, may greatly stabilize the pipe; and its subcritical response to an external excitation may also be strongly influenced.

It should be stressed, that the problem is that of a stochastic stability of the system with random parametric excitation. Whilst a variety of definitions for stochastic stability is known, two of these definitions will be used here, namely, stability with respect to probability and in the mean square sense (3). The first of these definitions implies, in fact, the decay of every sample of the random transient response due to any initial disturbance in the case of stability, whereas in the case of instability with respect to probability any disturbance will lead to the unbounded response with unity probability. The stability threshold in the mean square sense, which is based on the "usual" definition for stability as applied to the response variance, provides a useful conservative bound for the above threshold for "catastrophic" instability with respect to probability. If the system is unstable in the mean square but not with respect to probability, all transients will decay, however with the infinite variance, which physically means rather high random excursions of the response. Moreover, in this case the results of a correlational and/or spectral analysis of the measured response may become meaningless unless the appropriate nonlinear model is used for their interpretation. More details on the practical applications of various definitions for stochastic stability can be found in (3).

2 STABILITY WITH RESPECT TO PROBABILITY

Thus, consider the following equation of a single-mode response

$$\ddot{x} + 2\alpha\dot{x} + \Omega^2 x(1 + \lambda \sin v(t)) = 0$$
$$\dot{v} = \gamma + \xi'(t) \qquad (1)$$

where α/Ω and λ are small compared with unity, as well as a relative detuning Δ/Ω, $\Delta = 2\Omega - \gamma$, whereas $\xi'(t)$ is a zero-mean delta-correlated random sequence with the rms value σ and discrete-time step $2\pi/\gamma$. Using in (1) transformation

$$x = A\cos(v/2 + \varphi), \quad \dot{x} = -\Omega A\sin(v/2 + \varphi) \qquad (2)$$

and applying asymptotic method of stochastic averaging (3) yields the following pair of stochastic differential equations (SDEs)

$$\dot{A} = [-\alpha + (\lambda\Omega/4) \cos 2\varphi]A \qquad (3a)$$
$$\dot{\varphi} = \Delta/2 - (\lambda\Omega/4) \sin 2\varphi - \xi(t) \qquad (3b)$$

where $\xi(t)$ is now a continuous-time white noise with intensity $D = \pi\sigma^2/2\gamma$.

From (3a) the stability threshold with respect to probability (denoted by star subscript for the excitation amplitude λ) is seen to be

$$4\alpha/\Omega = \lambda_*\langle\cos 2\varphi\rangle \qquad (4)$$

Here the angular brackets denote mathematical expectation, which in this case may be obtained as

$$\langle\cos 2\varphi\rangle = \int_0^{2\pi} \cos 2\varphi \, w(\varphi)d\varphi \qquad (5)$$

where $w(\varphi)$ is a stationary probability density of the response phase $\varphi(t)$; it satisfies the following Fokker-Planck-Kolmogorov equation, which corresponds to the SDE (3b)

$$(d/d\varphi)\big[(\Delta/2 - (\lambda\Omega/4)\sin 2\varphi)w\big] =$$
$$= (D/2)(d^2w/d\varphi^2) \qquad (6)$$

The normalized 2π-periodic solution to (6) as obtained originally in (4) (see also (3)) is substituted into (5), reducing the stability condition (4) to the form

$$\frac{8\alpha}{\lambda_*\Omega} = \frac{I_{iq+1}(z)}{I_{iq}(z)} + \frac{I_{-iq+1}(z)}{I_{-iq}(z)} \qquad (7)$$

where $q = \Delta/2D$, $z = \lambda_*\Omega/4D$ and I's are the modified Bessel functions. For the "worst" case of the exact tuning ($q = 0$), which should also be the design one whenever the expected excitation frequency is uncertain, this condition reduces to

$$\lambda_*/\lambda_{*0} = I_0(z)/I_1(z), \quad \lambda_{*0} = 4\alpha/\Omega \qquad (8)$$

where λ_{*0} is the critical excitation amplitude for the case of perfect periodicity of the excitation. Curve 1 in Fig. 1 illustrates the dependence of λ_*/λ_{*0} on the coefficient of variation of the excitation frequency σ/γ as calculated from (8) for the case of damping ratio $\alpha/\Omega = 0.01$. It can be seen, that even a small scatter of the excitation frequency, with coefficient of variation σ/γ about 5 per cent, may greatly stabilize the system, leading to a 50 per cent increase of the critical excitation amplitude.

3 MEAN SQUARE RESPONSE ANALYSIS

The mean square stability of the system (1) may also be studied, by introducing in (3) new variables $x_c(t)$, $x_s(t)$ as

$$x_c = A \cos\varphi, \quad x_s = A \sin\varphi \qquad (9)$$

Then the following Stratonovich SDEs are obtained

$$\dot{x}_c = -(\alpha - \lambda\Omega/4)x_c - \Delta x_s/2 + x_s\xi(t)$$
$$\dot{x}_s = \Delta x_c/2 - (\alpha + \lambda\Omega/4)x_s - x_c\xi(t) \qquad (10)$$

Using the method of moments (3) three first-order deterministic equations may be derived from (10) for the second-order response moments $K_{cc,ss} = \langle x_{c,s}^2\rangle$, $K_{cs} = \langle x_c x_s\rangle$, namely

$$\dot{K}_{cc} = -(2\alpha - \lambda\Omega/2 + D)K_{cc} - \Delta K_{cs} + DK_{ss}$$
$$\dot{K}_{cs} = (\Delta/2)(K_{cc} - K_{ss}) - 2(\alpha + D)K_{cs} \qquad (11)$$
$$\dot{K}_{ss} = DK_{cc} + \Delta K_{cs} - (2\alpha + \lambda\Omega/2 + D)K_{ss}$$

From (11) the critical excitation amplitude λ_* for the neutral stability in the mean square is found as that corresponding to zero value of the determinant of the coefficients:

$$\lambda_* = \lambda_{*0}\left[1 + \frac{D(\alpha^2 + \alpha D - \Delta^2/4)}{\alpha(\alpha^2 + \Delta^2/4 + \alpha D + \Delta^2 D/4)}\right]^{1/2}$$

$$\lambda_{*0} = 4(\alpha/\Omega)(1 + \Delta^2/4\alpha^2)^{1/2} \qquad (12)$$

Thus, excitation frequency variations are seen to be destabilizing in case of a sufficiently high mean detuning (this means that in such a case the above variations may effectively drive the system closer to the resonance). For the case of the exact tuning ($\Delta = 0$) their effect is, of course, stabilizing and is illustrated in Fig. 1 by curve 2 (for $\alpha/\Omega = 0.01$). Of course, this curve lies below curve 1.

This analysis may be extended easily to the case where the mode in question is also excited externally by a broadband random force with spectral density $S(\omega)$. Then the SDEs (10) will contain two additional uncorrelated white-noise terms on their RHSs with the same intensity $D' = \pi S(\Omega)/\Omega^2$, leading to additional constant terms D' on the RHSs of the first and third equations for moments (11). Thus, the averaged-over-the-period steady-state mean square subcritical response $K_+/2 = (K_{cc} + K_{ss})/2$ may be obtained as

$$K_+/2 = (D'/2\alpha)\left[1 - \mu^2(1 + D/\alpha)\right]^{-1} \quad (13)$$

$$\mu^2 = (K_-^2 + 4K_{cs}^2)/K_+^2 = \quad (14)$$

$$= (\alpha^2\Omega^2/16)\left[(\alpha + D)^2 + \Delta^2/4\right]^{-1} \quad (15)$$

where $K_- = K_{cc} - K_{ss}$. Zero value of the expression in brackets in (13) corresponds to the stability threshold in the mean square (12), whereas its reciprocal (the second cofactor in (13)) is in fact the parametric amplification factor of the system's response to the external excitation.

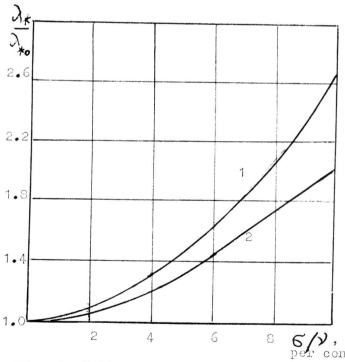

Fig. 1. Critical parametric excitation amplitude, corresponding to stability boundary with respect to probability (curve 1) and in the mean square (curve 2) as a function of the coefficient of variation of the excitation frequency for the case of the exact tuning and $\alpha/\Omega = 0.01$.

4 CONCLUSIONS

The implications of the results for the designers seem clear. Whenever parametric instability of the pipe is of concern, formulae (7), (8) and (12) may be used to obtain the improved estimates of the stability thresholds. As for the proper selection of the stochastic stability criterion, this topic is considered in some detail in (3); in general the choice should depend on the mechanism of the pipe failure in case of the excessive vibrations.

Furthermore, formula (14) may be used to estimate μ from the response measurements in a subcritical case with some external excitation being present. In the case of a perfectly periodic parametric excitation this yields an on-line estimate of the parametric response amplification factor as

$$(1 - \mu^2)^{-1} = (K_{cc} + K_{ss})^2/(4K_{cc}K_{ss} - 4K_{cs}^2) \quad (16)$$

However in presence of the excitation frequency variations the amplification factor according to (13) may be much higher. Therefore, if the measured quantity in the RHS of (16) is found to be sufficiently higher than unity, then some design modifications for the parametric amplification control (such as detuning) are certainly desirable.

REFERENCES

(1) FEDOROVICH, E.D., FOKIN, B.B., AKSEL'ROD, A.F., GOLDBERG, E.H. Vibrations of the elements of the nuclear power plants (in Russian). Energoatomizdat, Moscow, 1989.

(2) HARA, F. Two-phase flow induced parametric vibrations in structural systems. Pipes and nuclear fuel pins. Rept. Inst. Industrial Science. Tokio, 1980, vol. 28, N° 4, p. 161 - 223.

(3) DIMENTBERG, M.F. Statistical dynamics of nonlinear and time-varying systems. Research Studies Press, Taunton, England, 1988.

(4) STRATONOVICH, R.L. Topics in the theory of random noise. New York, Gordon&Breach, 1963 (v.1), 1967 (v.2).

C416/072

Flow induced oscillations of a set of coupled pendulums with impacts

A I MENYAILOV, PhD
Institute for Problems in Mechanics, USSR Academy of Sciences, Moscow, USSR
V D SYZAREV, PhD
Research and Development Institute of Power Engineering, Moscow, USSR

SYNOPSIS Oscillation of a set of coupled hinged spherical pendulums, a model of many internal elements of power plants, are situated within a channel of circular or almost circular cross-section with small gaps and excited by an upward of viscous fluid, are studied both analytically and numerically. Various regimes of motion are identified: plane or polarised oscillations with alternating impacts against the channel wall; and polarised oscillations within slowly rotating plane. The domains of these regimes are obtained in terms of height, gap, structural damping, factors of impacts, fluid viscosity, structural damping and channel eccentricity. Expected impact impulse and frequency of self-excited oscillations are obtained in term of fluid velocity. The domains of chaotic motion in the absence of any external random excitation are studied, where the system may behave like a strange attractor.

NOTATION

D, g	diameter and density of cylinder
ℓ_i	length of cylinder
m_i	mass of cylinder
M_i	virtual mass of cylinder
ρ_F	fluid density
v	mean flow velocity
Δ	gap
R_N	normal part of impact factor
R_τ	tangential part of impact factor
C_N	fractional coefficient of fluid
C_D	drag coefficient in still fluid
C_M	coefficient of added mass
C_K	coefficient of friction in the joints
t	time
A	cross-section of cylinder
$\vec{\tau}(\xi,t)$	radius-vector of any point of cylinder

Other quantities are defined in the text.

1 INTRODUCTION

Axial flows of viscous incompressible fluid around elastic cylinders in channels with narrow gaps may lead to flutter-type or divergence-type instabilities. Numerous studies of these phenomena (ref 1) were concerned with small oscillations, without impacts. However, in many structures with small gaps between cylindrical elements and channel walls the impacts become possible even for small lateral dynamic displacements (ref 3). Impacts may lead to an intensive wear and fretting of the contact surfaces. The plane impact motions of a simple pendulum with rigid barriers excited by a parallel flow were considered in (ref 2). Later studies for a single and double spherical pendulums revealed certain new, qualitatively different types of motion, which are presented in this report.

2 EQUATIONS OF MOTION

Consider a two-mass spherical physical pendulum, which is consisted of two cylinders, installed with small gaps = Δ within narrow tubes or channel with axial fluid flow, which has velocity = $\vec{v}$. We shall use spherical system of coordinates ($\varphi_1, \theta_1, \varphi_2, \theta_2$). The pendulums impact the wall of channel when the conditions $\varphi_i = r_i = \Delta/\ell_i$, where r_i – dimensionless gap is satisfied. We assume that the velocities $\varphi_1', \theta_1', \varphi_2', \theta_2'$ will change during the impact according to relations:

$$\varphi_{1+}' = -R_N \varphi_{1-}', \quad \varphi_{2+}' = -R_N \varphi_{2-}'$$
$$\theta_{1+}' = (1-R_\tau)\theta_{1-}', \quad \theta_{2+}' = (1-R_\tau)\theta_{2-}'$$

where φ_{i-}', θ_{i-}', φ_{i+}', θ_{i+}' are preimpact and afterimpact pendulum velocities. The equations of motion of system were derived with account forces:

a. inviscid hydrodynamic forces

$$\rho_1 = 2\rho_F C_M A |\vec{v}| \frac{\partial \vec{\tau}(\xi,t)}{\partial t \, \partial \xi}$$

b. frictional forces

$$\rho_2 = 0.5 |\vec{v}| [\dot{\vec{\tau}}(\xi,t) - \vec{v}] \rho_F C_N D$$

c. quadratic forces at zero flow velocity

$$\rho_3 = C_D |\dot{\vec{\tau}}(\xi,t)| \dot{\vec{\tau}}(\xi,t)$$

d. frictional forces in joints

$$\rho_4 = C_K |\dot{\vec{\tau}}(\xi,t)|^2 \dot{\vec{\tau}}(\xi,t)$$

The model will be developed on the basis of the method of Lagrange. The forces associated with the structure itself will be taken into account in the kinetic and potential energies of the system. The fluid forces will be incorporated partly in the kinetic energy partly left as generalized forces. The fluid forces on each cylinder must be calculated by integrating the hydrodynamic forces acting on each element of cylindrical structure per unit length. As a result of these calculations we obtain the following equations of motion of the system (Fig.1):

$$M\ddot{q} + B\dot{q} + S\upsilon\dot{q} + (K + K_1\upsilon^2)\sin q - K_2\upsilon^2\cos q + (C_D D_1 + C_K D_2)\dot{q} = 0, \quad q = (\varphi_1, \theta_1, \varphi_2, \theta_2)^T, \quad (1)$$
$$\sin q = (\sin\varphi_1, \sin\theta_1, \sin\varphi_2, \sin\theta_2)^T$$
$$\cos q = (\cos\varphi_1, \cos\theta_1, \cos\varphi_2, \cos\theta_2)^T$$

All matrices in eqs.(1) have dimention 4x4 and are too complicated to be presented here. Derivation of eqs.(1) was verified by computer program REDUCE.

2.1 Partial cases of common model

Consider a plane two-body pendulum. In the plane case $\theta_1 = \theta_2 = $ const we have $\theta_1' = \theta_2' = \theta_1'' = \theta_2'' = 0$, and system (1) in dimensionless parameters:

$$\tau = \omega t, \quad \omega_i^2 = m_i g/(M_i + m_i)\ell, \quad U = \upsilon/\omega_1\ell_1, \quad A_i = a_i\omega_i^{-1},$$
$B_i^* = b_i\omega_i^{-1}$, $C_i^* = c_i\omega_i^{-2}$, $D_i^* = d_i\omega_i^{-2}$, $\alpha_1 = (2\rho_F D_1^* C_N \ell_1^3/3 - M_1\ell_1^2)\upsilon/\ell_1^3(M_1+m_1)$, $b_1 = (2M_1\ell_1^2 - 0.25\rho_F D_1^* C_N\ell^3(M_1+m_1)$, $c_1 = (\rho_F D_1^* C_N\ell_1^2 + M_1\ell_1)\cdot\upsilon^2/(M_1+m_1)\ell_1^3$, $d_1 = (1.5 m_1 g\ell_1^2 - M_1\upsilon^2\ell_1 - 0.25\rho_F C_N\ell_1^2\upsilon^2 - 0.25\pi D_1^*\rho\ell_1^2)/\ell_1^3(M_1+m_1)$, $a_2 = 0.25\rho D_2^* C_N\ell_2^3\upsilon/\ell_2^3(M_2+m_2)$, $b_2 = (\rho_F D_2^* C_N\ell_2^3/6 + M\ell_2^2)\upsilon/\ell_2^3(M_2+m_2)$, $c_2 = [0.5\ell_2^2(m_2 - 0.25\pi D_2^{*2}\rho)/g]/\ell_2^2(M_2+m_2)$, $\alpha_1 = 18(8A_2/3 - A_1)/7$, $\beta_1 = 18(8B_2^*/3 - B_1^*)/7$, $\gamma_1 = 18 D_1^*/7$, $\delta_1 = 18(C_1^* - 8C_2^*/3)/7$, $(\cdot) = \frac{d}{d\tau}$ $\alpha_2 = 12 A_1^*/7$, $\beta_2 = 12(B_1^* - 3B_2^*)/7$, $\gamma_2 = 12 D_1^*/7$, $\delta_2 = 12(1.5 C_2^* - C_1^*)/7$, $\psi_i = \pi\varphi_i^*/\Delta$, $\varphi_1^* = \varphi_1$, $\varphi_2^* = \varphi_1 + \varphi_2$, $i = 1,2$.

reduced to:
for $|\psi_1| < \pi/2$, $|\psi_2| < \pi/2$
$$\ddot{\psi}_1 = \alpha_1\dot{\psi}_1 + \beta_1\dot{\psi}_2 + \gamma_1\psi_1 + \delta_1\psi_2$$
$$\ddot{\psi}_2 = \alpha_2\dot{\psi}_1 + \beta_2\dot{\psi}_2 + \gamma_2\psi_1 + \delta_2\psi_2 \quad (2)$$

and for $|\psi_1| = \pi/2$, $|\psi_2| = \pi/2$
$$\dot{\psi}_{1+} = -R_N\dot{\psi}_{1-}, \quad \dot{\psi}_{2+} = -R_N\cdot\dot{\psi}_{2-} \quad (3)$$

with $\alpha_i, \beta_i, \gamma_i, \delta_i$ ($i=1,2$) being much smaller than unity; coefficients $\alpha_i, \beta_i, \gamma_i, \delta_i$ are proportional:
$$\alpha_i \sim U, \quad \beta_i \sim U, \quad \gamma_i \sim U^2, \quad \delta_i \sim U^2.$$
where U is a dimensionless velocity. This system may be studied analytically by using piecewise-linear transformation (ref 5)and average method. Following the piecewise-linear transformation involve the functions:

$$\psi_1 = \Pi(x) + \lambda S(x), \quad \psi_2 = \Pi(y) + \lambda S(y), \quad \lambda = 2(1-R_N)/\pi(1+R_N), \quad \Pi'(x) = M(x), \quad S(x) = \int\Pi(x)dx, \quad (') \equiv d/dx,$$
$$\Pi(x) = \{\; x: -\pi/2 < x < \pi/2; \; -x: \pi/2 < x < 3/2\pi;$$
$$-x: -3/2\pi < x < -\pi/2\;\}, \quad \Pi(x) = \Pi(x+2\pi)$$

which reduce eqs. (2),(3) to the "non-impact" form:

$$\dot{x} = W_1, \quad \dot{y} = W_2, \quad \dot{W}_1 = -\lambda W_1^2 + \alpha_1 W_1 + \beta_1 M(y)\cdot M(x) W_2 + \gamma_1 M(x)\Pi(x) + \delta_1\Pi(y)M(x), \quad \dot{W}_2 = -\lambda W_2^2 + \alpha_2 M(x) M(y) + \beta_2 W_2 + \gamma_2\Pi(x)M(y) + \delta_2 M(y)\Pi(y)$$

Following the average method we shall considere resonant motions with $W_1-W_2\sim\varepsilon$, $\varepsilon \ll 1$, corresponding to pendulums with close natural frequencies. Applying averaging over the period (ref 6) yields the following system of equations:

$$\dot{\overline{\theta}} = W_1 - W_2, \quad \dot{\overline{W}}_1 = -\lambda\overline{W}_1^2 + \alpha_1\overline{W}_1 + 2\beta_1\Pi(\theta+\pi/2)\cdot\overline{W}_2/\pi + 2\delta_1 S(\theta-\pi/2)/\pi, \quad \dot{\overline{W}}_2 = -\lambda\overline{W}_2^2 + \alpha_2\overline{W}_1\Pi(\theta+\pi/2)/\pi + \beta_2\overline{W}_2 + 2\gamma_2 S(\theta-\pi/2)$$

with its steady-state solution providing impact velocity V^* and frequency W^* of self-oscillations as the functions of flow velocity; these functions V^*, W^* are illustrated in Figs.2 and 3 respectively.

Consider one-body spherical pendulum.

Equations (1) of motion between impacts can be written in dimensionless parameters:

$$\tau = \Omega t, \quad \Omega^2 = 3(1-\rho_F/\rho)g(\ell^2-\ell_0^2)/[2(1-C_M\rho_F/\rho)\cdot(\ell^3-\ell_0^3)], \quad U = V/\ell\Omega, \quad \beta = 3(\ell^5-\ell_0^5)/C_K/[5A\rho(\ell^3-\ell_0^3)], \quad \alpha = 3(\ell^4-\ell_0^4)C_D/[4A\rho(\ell^3-\ell_0^3)],$$
$$\gamma = \rho_F D\ell/2A\rho, \quad \delta = 3\rho_F D\ell^2(\ell^2-\ell_0^2)/[4A\rho\cdot(\ell^3-\ell_0^3)], \quad \varepsilon = 3\ell\rho_F(\ell^2-\ell_0^2)/[\rho(\ell^3-\ell_0^3)], \quad d/d\tau \equiv '$$
as

$$\varphi'' - \varphi\theta'^2 + [\alpha\sqrt{\varphi'^2 + \varphi^2\theta'^2} + \beta - (\gamma C_N + \varepsilon C_M)U]\varphi'(1+C_M\rho_F/\rho) + [1+\delta C_N U^2/(1+C_M\rho_F/\rho)]\varphi = 0$$
$$\theta'' + 2\theta'\varphi'/\varphi + [\alpha\sqrt{\varphi'^2 + \varphi^2\theta'^2} + \beta - (\gamma C_N + \quad (4)$$
$$\varepsilon C_M)U]\theta'/(1+C_M\rho_F/\rho) = 0, \quad \varphi < r;$$
$$\varphi'_+ = -R_N\varphi'_-, \quad \theta'_+ = (1-R_\tau)\theta'_-, \quad \varphi = r$$

where φ'_-, φ'_+ and θ'_-, θ'_+ - are pre-impact and after-impact pendulum velocity, and R_N - restitution coefficient of normal part of impact velocity and R_τ - coefficient of breaking of tangential part of impact velocity.

2.2 Numerical analysis of the equations of motion

There are two singularities of the motion solution which appear at the pendulum transition through the static position $\varphi = 0$, singularity type $1/0$ and at the moment of impact, $\varphi = r$, singularity type of $\delta(x)$-function. So it needs special algorithm (ref 4). For numerical treatment we used values of parameters:

$C_M = 6$, $\rho_F = 1000 \kappa\gamma/\mu^3$, $\rho = 11800 \kappa\gamma/\mu^3$, $\ell = 1.54 M$, $\ell_0 = 0.4 \mu$, $A = 364\cdot10^{-6}\mu^2$, $D = 21.53\cdot10^{-3}M$, $C_D = 0.127 \kappa\gamma/\mu^2$, $C_K = 0.2 \kappa\gamma/\mu^3 cek$, $\Delta = 4.5\cdot10^{-3}\mu$

The trajectories of the pendulum in the circular channel are shown in Fig.4. The self-oscillation characteristics will change in dependence on breaking coefficient P according to diagrams in Fig.5. For small P the self-oscillations approach the circling along the wall. For high values of breaking P = 1 the polarized self-oscillation arises and the pendulum impacts the wall in the opposite points of the channel. The polarized impact self-oscillation is most danger case of self-oscillation from point of view of the intensity of impact loading - impact velocity has maximum Fig.6.

2.3 Asymmetric barriers

In case of a slightly eccentric channel the following trends are found.
i) The motion of a double pendulum is almost always polarized along a small axis of the elliptic channel.
ii) Increasing the tangential restitution factor leads to bifurcations of the impact motion: first the regime with 4 impacts per one rotation around the channel appears, then with 6 impacts, etc. Hysteretic phenomena are observed in these transitions, i.e. critical values of the restitution factor are found to be different when it is decreasing. Furthermore, chaotic motion are observed within small ranges of this factor. These results are summarized in Fig.7.

3 CONCLUSION

The main results of this study of a double spherical pendulum may be summarized as follows
i) Numerical simulation procedure is developed for a double spherical pendulum, installed within a channel with narrow gaps and excited by a parallel flow, which effectively overcomes difficalties due to singularities at the channel wall (of the delta-function type due to impacts) and at the equilibriam position (of the type 1/0).
ii) The boundaries domains with various type of motions within axisymmetric channel are found, namely, plane or polarized oscillations, "almost" plane oscillation with slow rotation of the plane; rotation around channel wall without impacts.
iii) Impact velocity and frequency of impacts are found as the functions of flow velocity and system's parameters, these characteristics being important for structural reliability.
iv) For the case of plane (polarized) motions the impact characteristics were obtained analytically, this case corresponding to the heaviest dynamic loading.
v) For slightly eccentric channels the bifurcation phenomena of impact regimes is found, with hysteresis of transitions between regimes with various multiplicities. Chaotic motion are found in certain ranges of impact restitution factors, these factors being dependent on the materials and surface roughness of the channel walls.

REFERENCES

(1) PAIDOUSSIS,M.P. A review of flow-induced vibrations in reactors and reactor components. Nuclear Engineering and Design, 1983, v.74, 1.

(2) MENYAILOV,A.I., PETERKA,F.,CHIPERA, S. Vibroimpact self-oscillations of spherical pendulum in axial fluid flow. Transaction of 1-st conference of socialistcountries, Prague, 1987.

(3) MENYAILOV,A.I., SYZAREV,V.D. and etc. Vibration problem of fuel assemblies in channel-type nuclear reactors (in Russian). Voprosy atomnoi nauki i techniki (Topics of nuclear science and engineering), Series Physics and technology of nuclear reactors (Physika i technika yadernych reaktorov), 1(38), 1984.

(4) MENYAILOV,A.I., PETERKA,F. Simulation oscillations internal elements of reactors. Transaction of symposium on modelling, Ostrava, 1987.

(5) ZHURAVLEV,V.PH. Method of special function for vibroimpact systems analysis. Izvestia Akad. Nauk SSSR. Mechanika tverdogo tela (Mech.Solids), 1976, 2, 13-17.

(6) BOGOLIUBOV,N.N.,MITROPOLSKY,JU.A. Asymptotic methods in theory of nonlinear oscillations (in Russian). Moscow, Nauka, 1974.

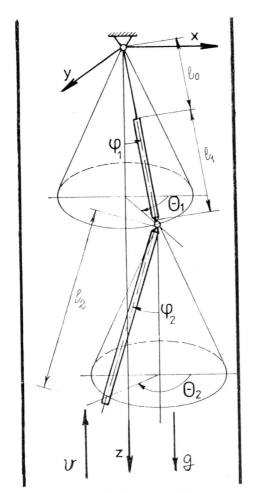

Fig.1 Double pendulum in flow channel.
Arrangement, dimensions and coordinates

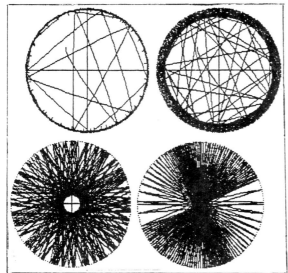

Fig.4 Typical trajectory of the system
of the pendulums movement within
channel

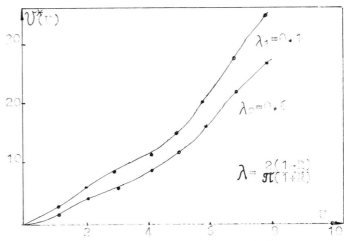

Fig.2 Impact velocity of pendulum as
function of flow-rate

$$\lambda = \frac{2(1-B)}{\pi(1+B)}$$

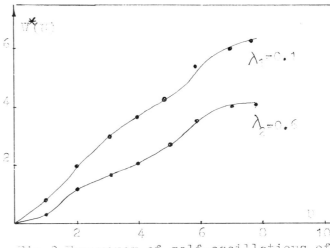

Fig.3 Frequency of self-oscillations of
the pendulums as a function of
flow-rate

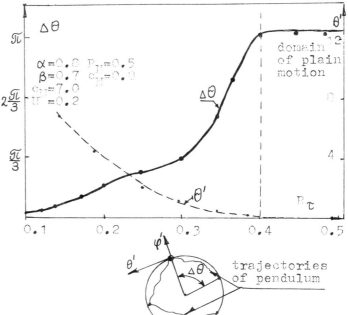

Fig.5 Tangential velocity of the pendulum and angle-difference between
consequent impacts of the pendulum as function of impact factor

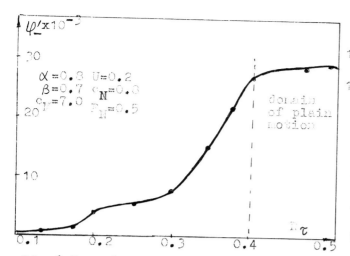

Fig.6 Normal part of the impact velocity as a function of the tangential part of the impact factor

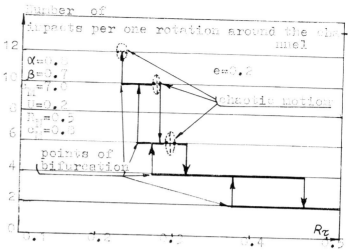

Fig.7 Number of impacts per one rotation around the channel as a function of the tangential part of the impact factor

C416/083

Cross-flow Strouhal numbers in square and triangular pitch tube arrays at Reynolds numbers from 0.8 – 3.5 x 10^5

A E COLLINSON, BSc, MSc and R G J ROBINSON, MA, MSc
AEA Technology, Risely, Warrington, Cheshire

SYNOPSIS Cross-flow Strouhal numbers have been measured for large tube arrays in water with Reynolds numbers between 0.8 x 10^5 and 3.5 x 10^5. Normal and parallel triangle geometries tested had pitch-to-diameter ratios of 1.3, 1.6 and 2.0, while for square geometries the P/D was 1.87 (normal) and 2.0 (rotated).

Strouhal numbers were dependent on tube pattern, position within the array, and Reynolds number, wide variations being recorded for a given geometry. Lift and drag responses were generally fairly similar.

The most varied behaviour was found for closely-packed triangular-pitch arrays, particularly for the upstream tube rows where notably high Strouhal numbers were observed. In addition, there was a very distinct transition at Re = 1.5 x 10^5 at which the Strouhal number fell sharply by a factor of four. In several cases, multiple Strouhals were observed, more usually for upstream tube rows.

It was concluded that, for certain geometries, the wide range of Strouhal numbers reported in the literature has been due to the inclusion of a broad spread of Reynolds numbers, turbulence levels, and tube positions within the arrays.

NOTATION

D   tube outside diameter
f   frequency peak on force PSD
L   tube length
P   tube pitch
PSD   power spectral density
Re   Reynolds Number (see Section 3.2)
Str   Strouhal Number (see Section 3.2)
V_g velocity in minimum gap (see Section 3.2)
ν kinematic viscosity of water

1. INTRODUCTION

The design of components containing tube arrays against flow-induced vibration requires knowledge of vortex-shedding Strouhal numbers. Whilst a considerable quantity of data exists for Reynolds numbers Re < 10^5, such as that summarised by Chen (Ref 1), it is sparse for higher values which encompass the critical region of 1 - 2 x 10^5 at which the boundary layer around single tubes becomes turbulent.

A water test rig (Figure 1) at the Northern Research Laboratory of AEA Technology, Risley, has been used to obtain such data using test sections containing rigidly supported tubes. Three triangular-pitched arrays, with pitch-to-diameter ratios P/D of 1.3, 1.65 and 2.0, and two square pitch arrays with P/D = 1.87 (normal) and P/D = 2.0 (rotated) have been tested at Re between 0.8 x 10^5 and 3.5 x 10^5 using water.

2. DESCRIPTION OF RIG

The tube arrays (Figure 1b) consisted of rows of tubes with a diameter of 32mm and a 2.0mm wall, arranged in a cubic test section. Each tube was 576mm long, and the length-to-diameter (L/D) ratio of approximately 18 represented that of typical heat exchanger inlet spans.

Selected tubes in inlet, mid-array and outlet rows were supported on triaxial force transducers, as shown in Figure 1c. These tubes extended through holes in the side walls of the test section, sealed using "O" rings with a stiffness much lower than that of the mounting. The side walls were fitted with half tubes for correct flow profiling. The natural frequency of the instrumented tubes, mounted on the transducers in water, was approximately 130 - 160Hz, compared with maximum measured Strouhal frequencies of 100Hz.

Water was pumped upwards into the test section through a square duct, fitted with a flow straightener, as shown in Figure 1. The flow was measured using a Dall tube to an accuracy of between ±2% at full flow and ±4% at low flows.

3. EXPERIMENTAL METHOD

3.1 Fluctuating Forces

Fluctuating lift and drag forces were measured using two triaxial piezo-electric force transducers (Kistler type 9251A), one at each end of the tube, clamped between the tube and the mounting plates (Figure 1c).

In each test, measurements were made of lift and drag components of the force at each end of the tube, which were then added to produce the total lift and drag force acting on the tube. The mean levels were filtered out using a 0.06Hz high pass filter prior to recording on magnetic tape. The residual fluctuating signals were replayed through a 2.0Hz high pass filter to remove a low-frequency oscillation associated with periodicity in the pumped supply. Power spectral densities (PSD's) of lift and fluctuating drag forces were obtained using a programmable Hewlett Packard 5451C Fourier Analyser. A typical set of PSD's is shown in Figure 2.

3.2 Definitions

Reynolds and Strouhal numbers are based on the mean flow velocity V_g in the minimum gap between tubes, ie. the gap which results in the highest velocity.

In all cases except the rotated square, the minimum gap equals (P-D). In the rotated square (P/D = 2.0) the minimum gap is (P$\sqrt{2}$-D).

$$\text{Thus Re} = \frac{V_g D}{\nu}$$

$$\text{and Str} = \frac{fD}{V_g}$$

where D = tube diameter
ν = kinematic viscosity of water at the operating temperature
and f = is a frequency peak identified from the force PSD

4. RESULTS AND DISCUSSION

4.1 Triangular Arrays

Figures 3-5 show response frequencies and appropriate Strouhal numbers for the three test arrays, in the normal and parallel orientations. Three symbols are used for points on these graphs to show whether the relative strengths of peaks on the PSD are qualitatively strong, medium or weak. Figure 6 then gives a summary of the most prominent Strouhal numbers, row by row, for each test array, in the lift and drag directions.

It was found that:

i.   Strouhal numbers varied considerably with P/D, orientation, tube position within the array and, in some cases, Reynolds number.

ii. In most configurations, Str for the first two tube rows differed significantly from that within the array. In addition, Str was sensitive to Re for these early rows: there was a transition at roughly Re = 1.5 x 10^5. The transition was particularly evident for P/D = 1.3, normal and parallel triangle, where Str fell dramatically from 0.6 to 0.15 as the transition was crossed. A similar but less marked effect occurred for P/D = 1.65 (normal triangle) and P/D = 2.0 (normal and parallel triangle).

iii. Two principal Strouhal peaks were apparent for some cases, viz P/D = 2.0 (normal triangle) and P/D = 1.3 (parallel triangle) for the lower Re range. These were not obvious multiples of each other, nor did the effect vary consistently with P/D. In addition, minor peaks often appeared as well. In many cases there was also a significant response at tube natural frequencies.

iv. Rows from 5 onwards seemed to represent typical mid-array conditions. Here Strouhal number was insensitive to Re, indicating consistent turbulence levels induced by the wakes of upstream tubes. In addition, Str did not vary much with P/D or geometry, ranging from about 0.16 to 0.26 for virtually all cases.

v.   Strouhal numbers recorded in lift and drag directions were in general very similar. In a few cases, response peaks were specific to direction, and in others, prominent spectral peaks were absent for part of the Re range.

vi. Str for the last rows conformed much more closely to the mid-array average than did the value for the first two rows.

vii. At higher flows the fundamental mode of vibration of the tubes was usually excited (at 150-180Hz). Amplitudes were notably strong when a prominent Strouhal frequency was 1/3 or 1/2 of the natural frequency. A particularly strong response occurred for the normal triangle P/D = 1.3, which is now described.

4.2 Resonant Response for P/D = 1.3

Very distinctive behaviour was seen in rows 1 and 2 for the P/D = 1.3 array, normal triangle (Figure 3). As the flow was raised, a pronounced resonance occurred at 433 1/s, corresponding to Re = 1.5 x 10^5, when the whole tube bank emitted a loud coherent humming noise at approximately 256Hz, corresponding to the natural frequency of the non-instrumented, built-in tubes. At this flow, the drag force frequency was about 256Hz with a lift frequency one third of this value, in each case the frequency peaks in the power spectra being very sharp.

At a lower Re of 1.1 x 10^5, the predominant lift and drag frequencies were similar, with corresponding Str = 0.59. At Re = 1.6 x 10^5 the resonance had disappeared, and Str had dropped to 0.14, although a 260Hz peak still persisted in the drag force spectrum.

This kind of general tube resonance was only found for this one case. It did not occur with the P/D = 1.3 parallel triangle geometry, which also had notably high Str. However, in this latter geometry the Str transition occurred before the lift predominant frequency reached 1/3 of the lowest natural frequency of the main bundle. This was also true for all the other test cases.

218

© IMechE 1991 C416/083

4.3 Square Arrays

Again, Str and Re have been calculated from minimum gap velocities as defined in Section 3.2. Figure 7a shows Strouhal numbers obtained for a normal square array with P/D = 1.87 at various Re and positions within the bundle. In all cases there were very clear frequency peaks.

There was little variation of Str with Re in the test range $0.8 < Re < 3.5 \times 10^5$. In the lift direction all Str were in the range 0.14 to 0.16. There was a tendency for response at the tube natural frequency (~130Hz) when this was three times the Strouhal frequency. For the drag direction, a low Str = 0.05 was noted at the inlet row 1, other rows also having somewhat lower Str than for the lift direction.

Data for a rotated square array with P/D = 2.0 are displayed on Figure 7b. For row 1, a double peak occurred in the lift response spectrum with Str = 0.29 and 0.40 at Re up to about 0.7×10^5, for which the drag Str was 0.31. At high Re response peaks in row 1 were not very distinct.

For the second row, lift Str was 0.27 to 0.35, with very clear peaks for $Re < 1.5 \times 10^5$. At higher Re, and also in the drag direction, peaks were rather less clear.

Interior rows showed clear lift response with Str = 0.33 throughout the whole test range ($0.5 < Re < 2.2 \times 10^5$). Drag response was weaker but at a consistent Str.

5. DISCUSSION

The tests conducted show that Strouhal numbers are dependent on several factors, viz P/D, tube array orientation, Re, position within the array and, by inference, turbulence level. Although not investigated here, tube length-to-diameter ratio is also probably important.

Comparison with data from other sources is therefore not straightforward, unless all of these parameters are similar; in many cases, some (eg. turbulence level) are not defined or were not measured. One of the principal objectives of the AEA tests reported here was to use Re, turbulence level and tube geometry (including length-to-diameter ratio) that would be generally appropriate to a large array, where flows were strongly turbulent and Re ~10^5. While it was not feasible to measure the turbulent levels in the array, the model geometry ensured that they would be reasonably representative of a large industrial heat exchanger.

5.1 Triangular Arrays

Chen (Ref 1) has published Strouhal numbers, originally collated by Weaver and Fitzpatrick (Ref 2), from a wide variety of sources for various P/D. Note that Chen's data are defined in terms of free-stream velocity, viz that without tubes present, and there is no differentiation according to Re or row number.

The AEA data, plotted using Chen's definitions, are given on Figures 8a and 8b for normal and parallel triangles respectively. Comparisons are made separately for Re above or below 1.5×10^5. In general, the data in the upper NRL Str band correspond to early tube rows and the lower band to mid-array.

For normal triangle and $Re < 1.5 \times 10^5$ there is fair agreement with Chen's data. Row 1 and 2 Str fall on Chen's upper bound whereas interior rows give Str close to his lower limit. On the other hand, Str for $Re > 1.5 \times 10^5$ all fall on Chen's lower bound, agreeing with the data from Konig and Gregorig.

With the parallel triangle, virtually all Str values are lower than Chen's collected data. The exception is the notable case with P/D = 1.3 with $Re < 1.5 \times 10^5$, for which the AEA Str value falls in the middle of the Chen data. Since Chen gives no experimental points for P/D ~2.0, comparison here cannot be made.

5.2 Square Arrays

Comparisons are made with data quoted by Chen (Ref 1) (again based on Weaver and Fitzpatrick (Ref 2)) on Figures 9a and 9b for normal and rotated square pitches respectively. Again the AEA results have been altered to have Str based on approach velocities.

In both cases the data agree well with the published results, both for lift and drag directions. The principal difference was for row 1, drag, for normal square, where the AEA Str = 0.05, which converts to Str = 0.11 using Chen's definition, is less than half of the lowest value in his collected data.

5.3 General

The results repeated here show that cross-flow induced Strouhal numbers for large tube bundles with strongly turbulent flow at Re ~10^5 depend not only on tube P/D but also on position within the bundle and (for upstream rows) Re. It was not possible to visualise flow patterns around tubes in these experiments to demonstrate how the variations recorded were related to changes in wake formation.

The transitional behaviour observed in triangular arrays at Re ~1.5×10^5 is probably associated with modification of the wake shedding already induced well inside the bundle by the high tube-generated turbulence.

The excitation of natural frequencies at three times basic Strouhal frequencies is also of importance for heat exchanger designers.

It is clear that Str is not a unique function of P/D, depending also on Re and row number. This fact needs to be more widely appreciated by investigators, who in some cases do not cite Re or geometric tube position on their data charts. Perhaps a better comparison with existing data might be made following an in-depth study of all of the data sources given by Chen.

The tests described were conducted on fixed tubes not free to rattle at their supports. A further test series is planned in which single tubes will be much less constrained and be able to have significant amplitude if excitation forces are high enough. This will show whether coherent excitation occurs at the Strouhal frequencies predicted by the initial tests.

6.   CONCLUSIONS

Cross-flow induced Strouhal numbers for large tube bundles have been found to be dependent on Reynolds number and position within the tube array.

This was particularly evident for triangular arrays, particularly close-pitched ones, where a transition often occurred at Re ~1.5×10^5.

Results compare reasonably with other data from the literature, bearing in mind that these are not usually categorised according to Re or tube position within a bundle.

Excitation of tubes at frequencies three times the basic Strouhal frequency was observed.

REFERENCES

1.   S S Chen - Flow-induced vibration of circular cylindrical structures - Hemisphere 1990.

2.   D S Weaver and J A Fitzpatrick - A review of flow-induced vibration in heat exchangers. Paper A1, Fourth International Conference on Flow-Induced Vibrations, Bowness, UK, 1987. British Hydromechanical Research Association 1987.

ACKNOWLEDGEMENTS

The authors wish to acknowledge the contributions of Mr W R Winn and Mr A I McIvor to the experimental work, and to thank AEA Technology for permission to publish the paper.

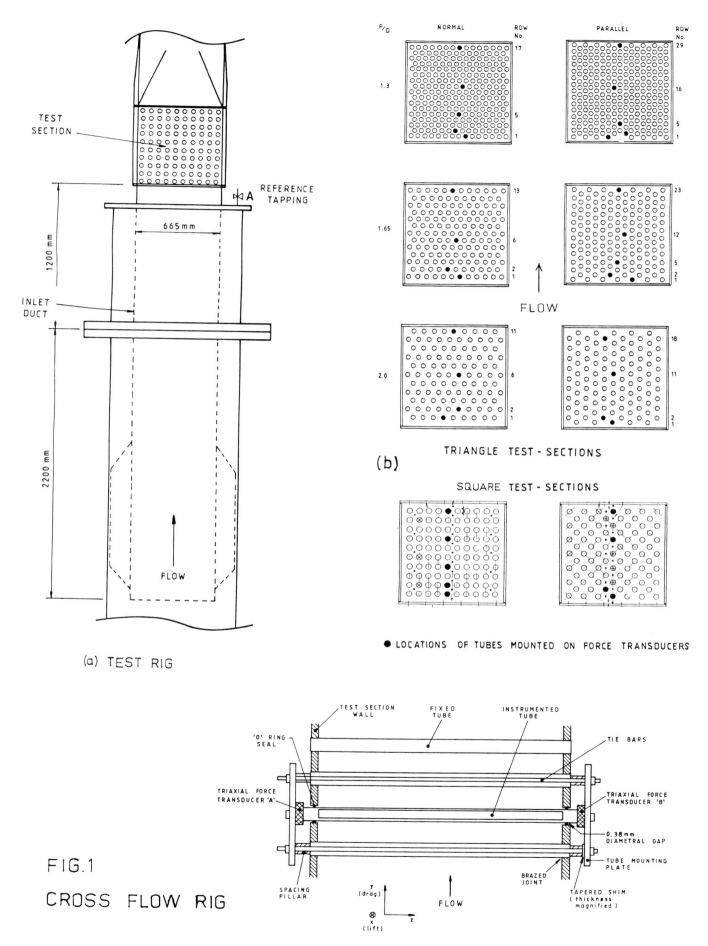

TEST SECTION

REFERENCE TAPPING

665mm

1200 mm

INLET DUCT

2200 mm

FLOW

(a) TEST RIG

FIG.1

CROSS FLOW RIG

P/D — NORMAL — ROW No. — PARALLEL — ROW No.

1.3 — 17, 5, 1 — 29, 16, 5, 1

1.65 — 13, 6, 2, 1 — 23, 12, 5, 2, 1

2.0 — 11, 6, 2, 1 — 18, 11, 2, 1

FLOW

(b)

TRIANGLE TEST - SECTIONS

SQUARE TEST - SECTIONS

● LOCATIONS OF TUBES MOUNTED ON FORCE TRANSDUCERS

TEST SECTION WALL — FIXED TUBE — INSTRUMENTED TUBE

'O' RING SEAL — TIE BARS

TRIAXIAL FORCE TRANSDUCER 'A' — TRIAXIAL FORCE TRANSDUCER 'B'

0.38mm DIAMETRAL GAP

TUBE MOUNTING PLATE

SPACING PILLAR — BRAZED JOINT — TAPERED SHIM (thickness magnified)

y (drag)
⊗ x (lift) z

FLOW

(c) INSTRUMENTED TUBE, MOUNTED RIGIDLY ON TRIAXIAL FORCE TRANSDUCERS

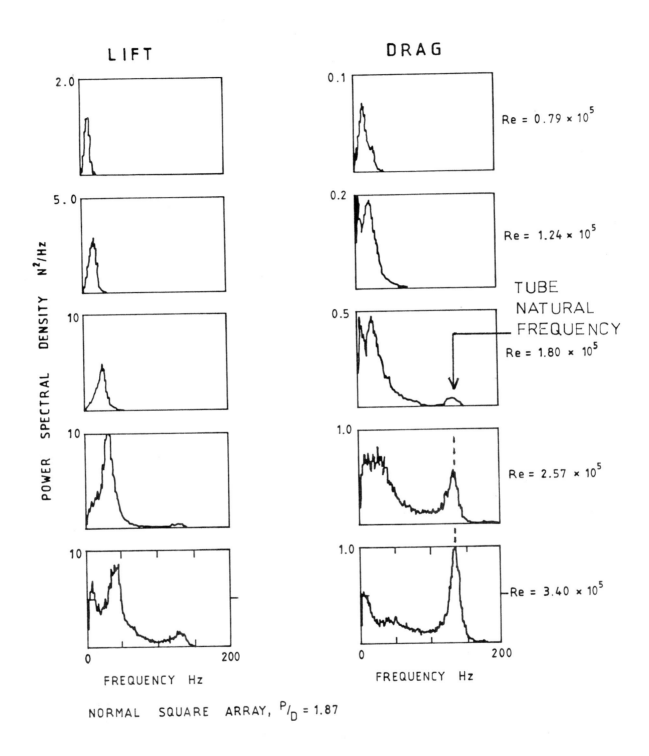

FIG. 2 EXAMPLE OF PSD'S OF FLUCTUATING FORCES

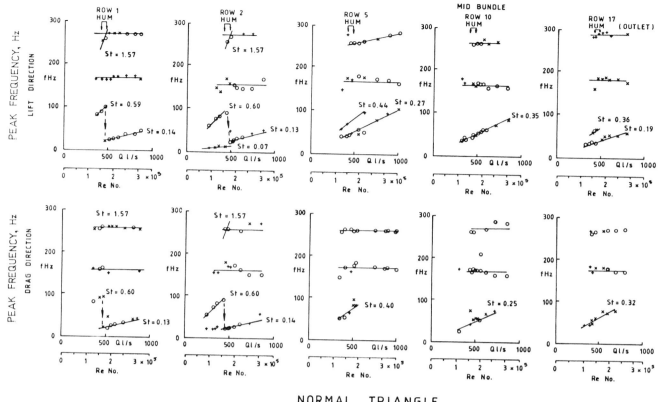

NORMAL TRIANGLE

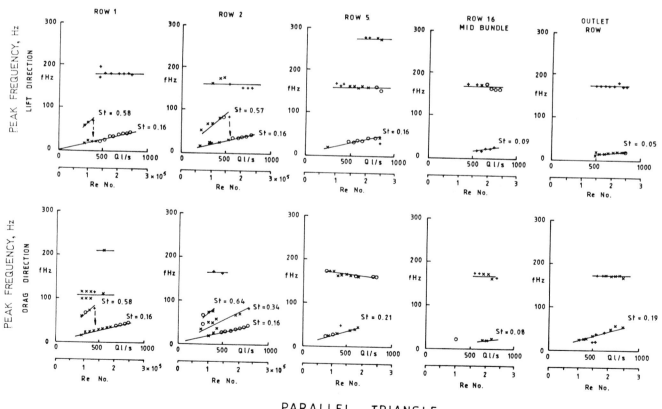

PARALLEL TRIANGLE

FIG.3 PROMINENT FREQUENCIES AND STROUHAL NUMBERS

TRIANGLE, P / d = 1.3

RESPONSE
o STRONG
x MEDIUM
+ WEAK

C416/083 © IMechE 1991

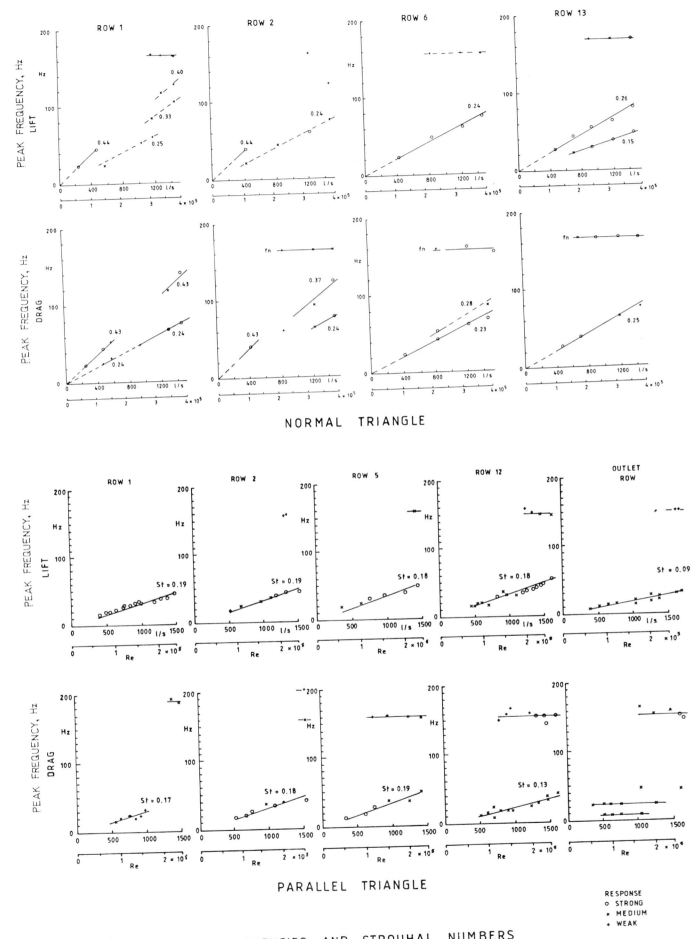

FIG.4 PROMINENT FREQUENCIES AND STROUHAL NUMBERS
TRIANGLE, P/d 1.65

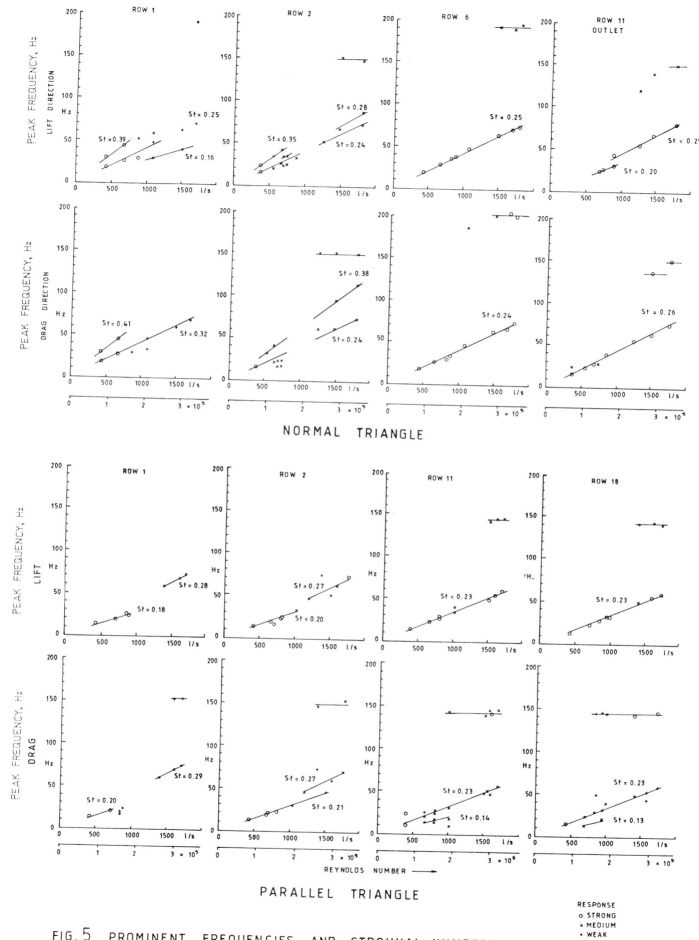

FIG. 5 PROMINENT FREQUENCIES AND STROUHAL NUMBERS

TRIANGLE, P / d = 2.0

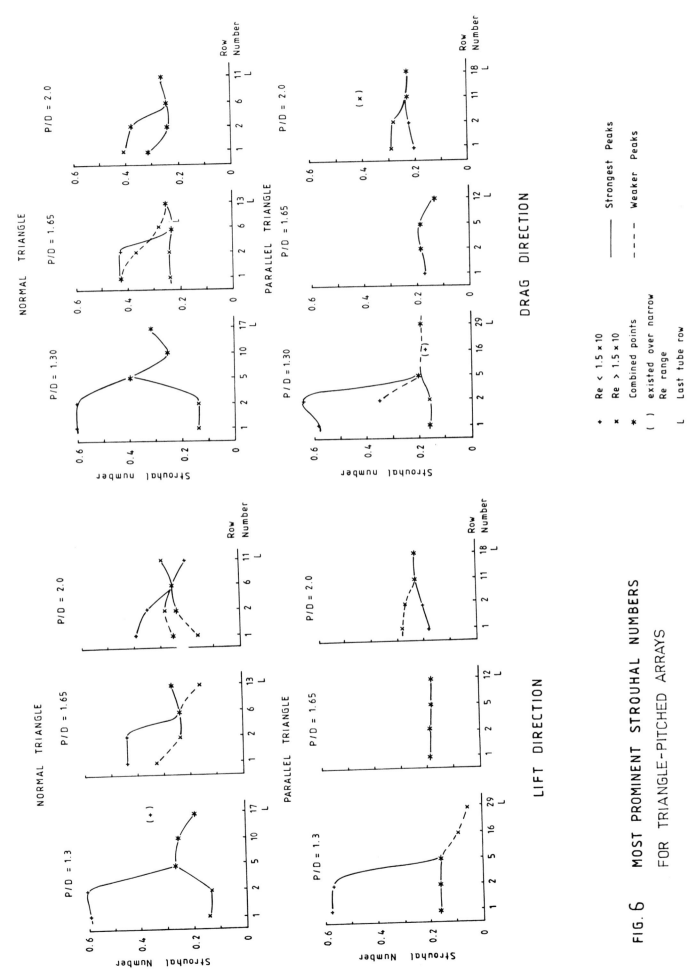

FIG. 6   MOST PROMINENT STROUHAL NUMBERS
          FOR TRIANGLE-PITCHED ARRAYS

226

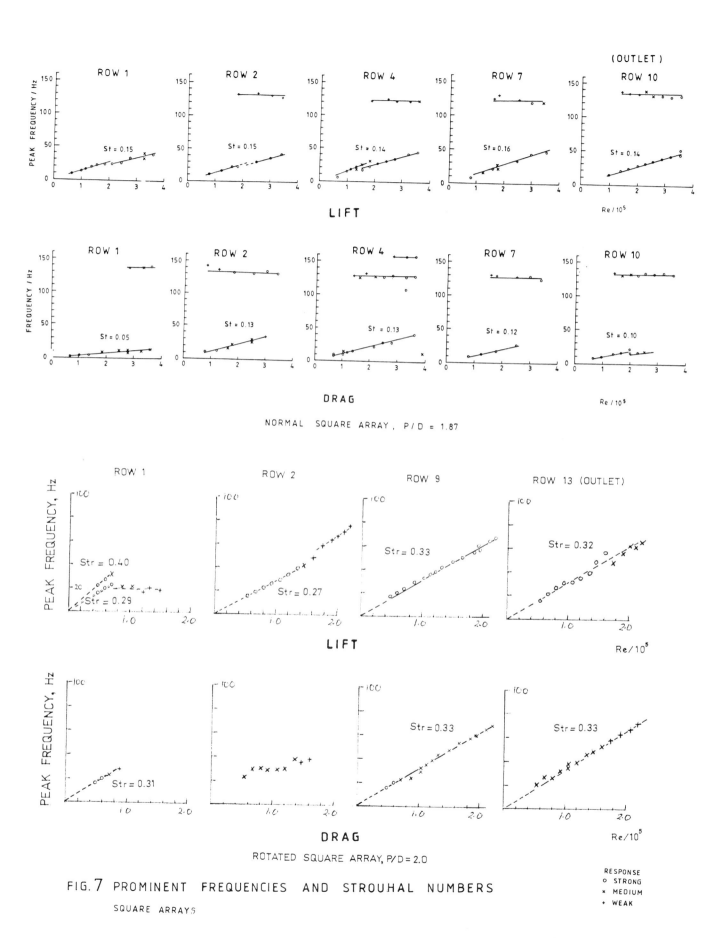

FIG. 7 PROMINENT FREQUENCIES AND STROUHAL NUMBERS

SQUARE ARRAYS

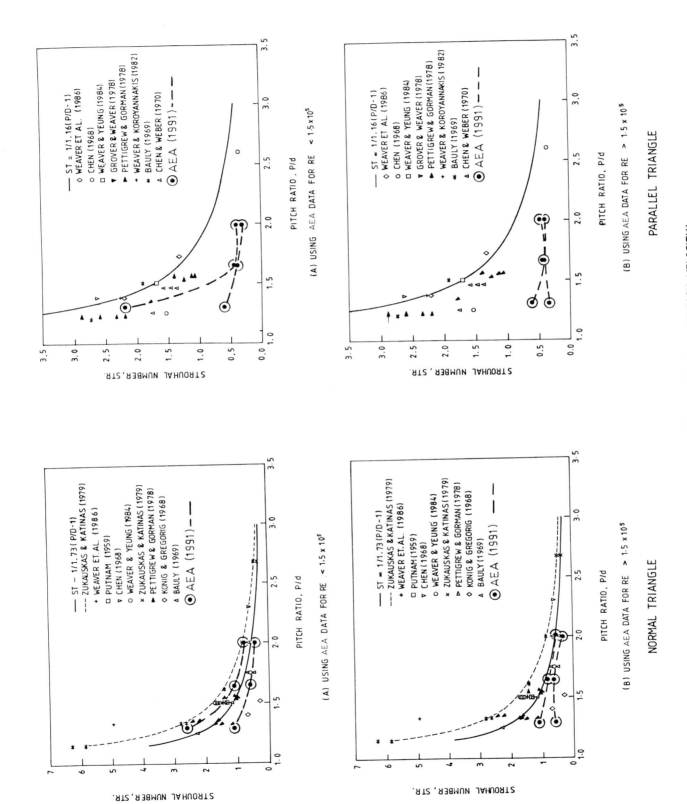

FIG.8 COMPARISON WITH OTHER DATA : TRIANGLE GEOMETRY (STR. BASED ON APPROACH VELOCITY)

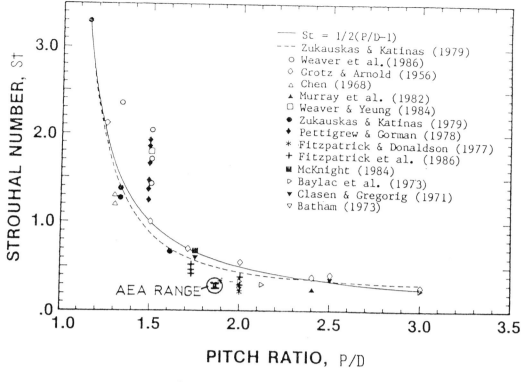

(a) NORMAL SQUARE

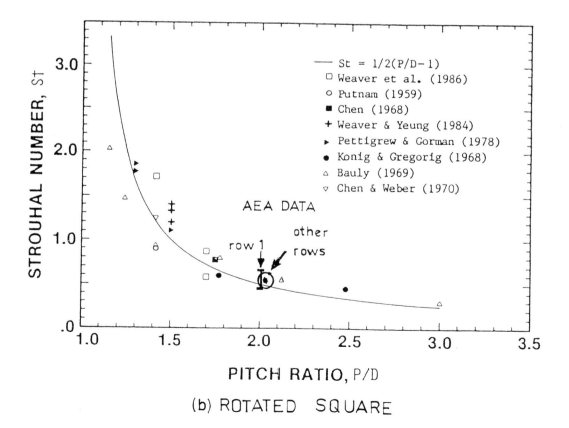

(b) ROTATED SQUARE

FIG. 9: COMPARISON WITH OTHER DATA

SQUARE ARRAYS (Str based on approach velocity)

Fluid viscosity effects on flow induced vibrations of tube bundles in cross-flow

D MEWES, Dr-Ing
and D STOCKMEIER, Dipl-Ing,
Institute of Process Engineering, University of Hannover, Hannover, Germany

SYNOPSIS In the region below the critical flow velocity, relative maxima of the vibration amplitudes of the tubes in the first row in staggered tube bundles can be observed in the situation when the kinematic viscosity of the working liquid is increased only slightly above the value for water. The relative maxima of the amplitude can be evaluated using simple relations based on the spring–mass–damped system model with viscosity dependent damping. The dependence of the influencing parameters on the kinematic viscosity is taken into account by using empirical correlations. The critical velocity is not unanimously dependent on the viscosity of the liquid. For the investigated tube bundle it can be determined by using an empirically evaluated stability criterion.

NOTATION

A	m	amplitude of tube vibration
B		nondimensional ascending gradient of the linear frequency function
c_A		effective value of force coefficient
$\hat{c}_A$		peak value of force coefficient
c_m		added mass coefficient
D_L		damping ratio (Lehr)
D_0		structural damping ratio (Lehr)
D_0'		structural damping ratio (Lehr)
D_v		viscous damping ratio (Lehr)
D_w		velocity dependent damping ratio (Lehr)
d	m	diameter
d_a	m	diameter of the dummy stiff tube
d_D	$N\ s/m$	damping coefficient
E	N/mm^2	modulus of elasticity
f	$1/s$	frequency
f^*	$1/s$	dimensionless frequency
f_0	$1/s$	natural frequency of the tube in air
f_y	$1/s$	frequency of the component of motion perpendicular to the approachflow direction
f_y^*		dimensionless frequency of the component of motion perpendicular to the approachflow direction
f_{min}	$1/s$	lowest natural frequency of the fluiddynamically coupled vibrating tube bundle
f_s	$1/s$	frequency of vibration at the stability boundary
F		function
F	N	exciting force
F_0	N	r.m.s. value of the exciting force
$\hat{F}_0$	N	peak value of the exciting force
I	m^4	area momentum of inertia
K		empirical constant

k	N/m	stiffness constant
l	m	tube length
M_{eff}	kg	vibrating point mass, the sum of tube mass and coupled hydrodynamic mass
m_L	kg/m	mass per unit length
r	m	tube radius
S_F^*		nondimensional power spectrum of random exciting forces
t	s	time
t_p	m	distance between tube centres
V		amplification ratio, Equation 10
V_{max}		maximum amplification ratio, Equation 11
$\bar{w}$	m/s	flow velocity in free cross section before the tube bundle
w_{sp}	m/s	flow velocity in the gap between the tubes, Equation 2
w_{sp}^*		dimensionless flow velocity in the gap between the tubes

Greek symbols

α		empirical coefficient
η_F	$mPas$	dynamic viscosity
ν_F	m^2/s	kinematic viscosity
ν^*		ratio of the kinematic viscosity of the working liquid and the kinematic viscosity of water at 20 °C
ϱ_F	kg/m^3	density of the liquid
ω_0	$1/s$	natural angular frequency of the tube in air
ω_r	$1/s$	natural angular frequency of the tube in the bundle, calculated at the resonance point
Ω	$1/s$	angular frequency of excitation
Ω^*		frequency ratio
Ω_{max}		frequency ratio in the maximum of the amplification function,

Equation 12

τ nondimensional time, Equation 5

Characteristic numbers

St Stokes number, Equation 15

Re_r resonance - Reynolds number, Equation 17

Sk vibration number, Equation 21

m^* mass-damping number, Equation 28

1. INTRODUCTION

In tube bundle heat exchangers the flow direction is predominantly perpendicular to the longitudinal axis of the tubes in order to achieve good heat transfer. The flow can induce vibrations of tubes and thus damage them. With the aid of calculations, operating conditions for which the tubes can be destroyed by vibrations in short or long operating periods should be recognized.

Depending on the flow velocity of the working fluid, vibrations in tube bundles can be caused by different mechanisms. The effects of these different mechanisms can be explained by analysing the amplitudes of tube vibrations as function of the flow velocity. In Fig 1 measured vibration amplitudes of a tube bundle in liquid flow are presented qualitatively.

By means of external excitation low amplitude vibrations are induced. The **random external excitation** is present in the total operating range of the heat exchanger, and it is caused by the turbulent flow. In the turbulent flow field velocity and pressure fluctuations are distributed over a broad frequency range. The tubes filter those frequencies close to their natural frequency from the whole spectrum. They respond to the applied excitation by small amplitude, irregular vibrations corresponding to their amplification function. The amplitudes increase proportionally to the second power of the flow velocity.

The **periodical external excitation** is superimposed to the random external excitation in a particular region of flow velocities. The periodical forces from the flow field are manifested with one dominant frequency, which changes proportionally to the flow velocity. When the excitation frequency is close to the natural frequency of the tubes, the amplitudes of tube vibrations increase with increasing flow velocities according to the amplification function of the tubes. This is manifested in a relative maximum of the amplitude function. The vibration direction of the tubes is predominantly perpendicular to the flow direction.

In the first two rows of a tube bundle periodical forces can be caused by vortex separation from the upper or lower portion of each tube in turn. This phenomenon is well known as the Karman vortex street. Deep inside the tube bundle, according to Owen (1), periodical flow forces can develop from large, high energy turbulent vortices. These vortices are repeatedly formed in the individual tube rows, and they cause a periodical excitation of the following rows.

Only by **self-excitation** is it possible to reach very high vibration amplitudes which can destroy the tube bundle heat exchanger within a short period of time, for tube bundles commonly used in technical applications. Self-excitation begins when the vibrations of a minimum amplitude are induced by external excitation and when a certain amount of energy is available. This is the case when the critical flow velocity is reached. After exceeding the critical flow velocity, amplitudes increase very strongly with the increasing flow velocity. This is possible because tubes vibrating due to self-excitation can absorb more energy with increasing vibration amplitudes. The general term of fluidelastic instabilities covers different mechanisms, discussed by Gog and Gelbe (2) and by Weaver and Fitzpatrick (3), which can cause self-excitation of tube vibrations.

By using known calculation techniques, generally only the critical flow velocity of the tube bundles can be calculated. But, as presented in Fig 1, the onset of vibration amplitudes causing fatigue of tube material or material loss due to friction between tubes and segmental baffles can also be observed at velocities below the critical flow velocity.

For this reason, an calculation technique for tube bundles in crossflow has been developed, to enable the determination of the vibration amplitudes versus gap velocity in the endangered tube rows in the total operating range of a tube bundle heat exchanger. This was preceeded by investigations on tube bundles in liquid crossflow for different values of liquid viscosity and density. In this way, the influence of material properties on the vibration behaviour of the tubes has been recognized and taken into account in the calculation.

2. EXPERIMENTAL SETUP AND EXPERIMENTS

The tube bundle used in this investigation consists of seven rows of tubes with eight tubes in each row, as presented in Fig. 2. The in-line and in staggered tube bundles are part of the test section standing mode 1 for the physical situation between two segmental baffles of a heat exchanger. The arrangement and the dimensions comply with current DIN norms. The diameter of the tubes is $d = 25 \ mm$, and the pitch between the centres of the tubes is $t_p = 32 \ mm$. Two tubes located in the centre of each row are equipped with strain gauges for measurement purposes. Both ends of the tubes are joint by plain bearings. The distance between the bearings is $l = 1.03 \ m$. The tubes are manufactured of aluminium alloy. The mass of the tubes per unit length is $m_l = 0.299 \ kg/m$. The natural frequency and the damping in air have values $f_0 = 63.25 \ 1/s$ and $D_L = 0.03$. The liquids used in the experiments were water and solutions of organic substances in water. The dynamic viscosity was varied in the region $\eta_F = 0.7 \ldots 88.1 \ mPas$ and the density in the region $\varrho_F = 992.2 \ldots 1284.1 \ kg/m^3$. Scaled by values for water at 20 °C, this corresponds to a variation of the reduced kinematic viscosity in the region $0.7 < \nu^* < 87.3$. In the experiments the flow velocity was increased stepwise and the time dependent displacement of the tubes was measured. The experiment was stopped when the vibration amplitudes were so high that tubes were beating against each other.

3. RESULTS OF THE EXPERIMENTS

In the bundle with **in–line tube rows** is the influence of the kinematic viscosity on the amplitude of tube vibrations for velocities below the critical flow velocity low. The tubes vibrate randomly due to external excitation with small vibration amplitudes.

Conversely, in the bundle with **staggered tube rows** a significant influence of the viscosity on tube vibrations for velocities below the critical flow velocity has been found. In flows of liquids with reduced viscosities in the region $0.7 < \nu^* < 12.7$, the onset of highest vibration amplitudes versus gap velocity was observed in the first row of tubes.

In Fig 3, the measured resulting vibration amplitudes of tubes in the first row are presented as a function of the dimensionless gap velocity for two liquids with different viscosities. The resulting amplitudes were calculated by geometrical composition of the amplitude components in flow direction and perpendicular to the flow direction — A_x and A_y — and presented as a percentage of the tube diameter d. These two components correspond to the r.m.s. value of the amplitude of a harmonic oscillation. It is related to the peak value of the amplitude by the following relation

$$\hat{A}_{x,y} = \sqrt{2} A_{x,y} \qquad . \qquad (1)$$

The gap velocity ω_{sp} is the velocity of the narrowest gap between the tubes. It is calculated from the mean flow velocity $\bar{\omega}$ in front of the tube bundle, from the pitch between the tubes t_p and the diameter d

$$w_{sp} = \frac{t_p}{t_p - d} \, \bar{w} \qquad . \qquad (2)$$

The gap velocity is related to the diameter of the tubes and the natural frequency in air f_0. In the case of water, the amplitudes increase continuously with increasing flow velocity. Above a certain value of the reduced viscosity $\nu^* = 0.92$, the tubes in the first row vibrate prevalently perpendicular to the flow direction. Also, the amplitude function versus the reduced gap velocity shows a distinctive maximum. This is presented in Fig 3, based on results of an investigation with a liquid of $\nu^* = 2.52$ viscosity. When viewing from the entry point of the flow in the tube bundle in flow direction, the amplitudes of the relative maxima decrease with increasing row number. In the fourth row, a constant final value $A_r^*/d \approx 0.01$, holding also for the following tube rows, is reached. The decrease of the amplitudes is connected with an increase of turbulence in the bundle. Sandifer and Bailey (4) have measured increasing turbulenceintensities in tube bundles until the second row. The periodical external excitation is afterwards perturbed by the increasing turbulence in the bundle.

To the relative maximum of the amplitude function, a typical behaviour of the vibration frequencies versus the

reduced gap velocity is related. In Fig. 4, the amplitudes versus gap velocity and the frequencies are presented. The frequencies of the component perpendicular to the flow direction f_y are reduced by the lowest natural frequency f_{min} of the tubes in the Ωfluiddynamically coupled bundle and designated as f^*. The natural Ωfrequencies of the fluiddynamically coupled vib rating tubes can be calculated by means of the potential theory relation by Chen (5). For a tube bundle with N tubes having two degrees of freedom, 2N natural frequencies can be calculated. To each of these natural frequencies a specific type of motion of the tubes relative to one another is corresponding. Starting with low values of the reduced gap velocity, the tubes first vibrate randomly and with different frequencies. As soon as the tubes start vibrating with lager amplitudes , the lowest natural fraquency of the bundle $f^* \approx 1$ is excited first. In the total range of gap velocities in which the amplitudes versus gap velocity increase and decrease around a relative maximum, the frequencies of tube vibrations increase nearly linearly with increasing gap velocity. In the then following region of stochastic external excitation, low frequency vibrations are excited.

The **critical flow velocity** at which the onset of self-excited vibrations can be observed, is only slightly dependent on the viscosity of the liquid streaming through the bundle. The critical velocities are determined from the measured amplitude and frequencies versus the gap velocity. The critical velocity has been reached when the gradient of the amplitudes versus gap velocity changes discontinuously and simultaneously significant frequencies are excited. In **staggered tube bundles** self-excitation starts in the last tube row. The tubes vibrate at the lowest natural frequency of the fluiddynamically coupled vibrating tube bundle. This lowest natural frequency can be calculated by using the potential-flow theory method of Chen (5) and it is only dependent on the density of the liquid. This statement is in contradiction with the results of Hesse (6), who has found a dependence of the natural frequency of the tube bundle on the viscosity. His results are based on an investigation with two to three vibrating tubes in stationary liquid in a large basin. There, the coupled fluid mass can increase, as there is enough space available. In densely packed tube bundles this space is not available, and the increasing viscosity has no influence on the natural frequency of the tubes. With increasing viscosity the critical velocity decreases compared to the values measured in water flows for an amount of maximum 27%.

Conversely, in the case of the **in-line tube bundle** the critical velocity increases to maximum 10%, compared to values measured in water. The onset of self-excitation can be observed for individual tubes in different tube rows and the tubes vibrate independently of their neighbours. As a consequence, they are not vibrating at the lowest natural frequency of the fluiddynamically coupled bundle. The vibration frequency corresponds to that of a single tube, surrounded by stiff tubes. This has been shown in comparison with frequencies measured by Moretti and Lowery (7). Their measurements were performed on a flexible tube surrounded by stiff tubes in a bundle.

4. CALCULATION OF VIBRATION AMPLITUDES

The behaviour of the tubes in the first row for velocities in the region below the critical flow velocity analysed above can be described by a simple physical model: the tubes can be represented as individual spring–mass–damping systems. The system consists of an effectively vibrating mass M_{eff}, a spring with a stiffness constant k, and the damping element has a damping coefficient d_D. The mass is externally forced by a time varying force

$$F(t) = F_0 \cos \Omega t \qquad (3)$$

and it vibrates with an amplitude $a(t)$. The excitation angular frequency is denoted with Ω, the time with t and the amplitude of the excitation force with $\hat{F}_0$. The amplitude $a(t)$ corresponds to the displacement in the centre between the two tube joints at both ends of the tube, which is performing bending vibrations in the first mode.

The described differential equation of the system has been formulated by Magnus (8). In dimensonless form it can be written as

$$a''(\tau) + 2D_L \, a'(\tau) + a(\tau) = \frac{\hat{F}_0}{k} \cos \Omega^* \tau \qquad (4)$$

The $'$ denotes the temporal derivative (natural time) of the amplitude of the tube centre

$$\tau = \omega_0 t \qquad (5)$$

of the system vibrating with the natural angular frequency calculated as

$$\omega_0 = \sqrt{\frac{k}{M_{eff}}} \qquad (6)$$

The damping is included as Lehr's nondimensional damping ratio

$$D_L = \frac{d_D}{2 M_{eff} \, \omega_0} \qquad (7)$$

The ratio of the excitation frequency and the natural frequency can be expressed as

$$\Omega^* \equiv \frac{\Omega}{\omega_0} \qquad (8)$$

The goal is the calculation of the effective amplitudes of tube vibrations. The equation for evaluating the amplitude has been discussed in detail by Stockmeier (9). In the analysis, stationary vibrations of the tubes are assumed. The mass, the stiffness and the excitation force should be constant along the tubes. Then, by using Equation 1, the effective value of the amplitude can be expressed as a percentage of the tube diameter

$$\frac{A}{d} = \frac{100}{\sqrt{2} \, d} \frac{F_0}{k} V = 2 \frac{100}{\sqrt{2}} \frac{\varrho_F \, w_{sp}^2 \, l^4}{\pi^5 \, E \, I} \hat{c}_A V \qquad (9)$$

In this equation ϱ_F is the density of the liquid and $\hat{c}_A$ is the peak value of the force coefficient. The force coefficient is the ratio of the force transferred from the flow to the tubes. Further, element V in Equation 9 is the amplification function of the system. It is a function of damping and of the frequency ratio

$$V = \frac{1}{\sqrt{\left(1 - \Omega^{*2} \right)^2 + \left(2 \, D_L \, \Omega^* \right)^2}} \qquad (10)$$

If the frequency ratio $\Omega \approx 1$, resonance is present. The maximum of the amplification function can be expressed as

$$V_{max} = \frac{1}{\sqrt{1 - \Omega_{max}^{*\,4}}} \qquad (11)$$

The frequency ratio in the maximum is dependent on the damping

$$\Omega_{max}^* = \sqrt{1 - 2D_L^2} \qquad (12)$$

By using Equations 9-12 and the measured frequency and amplitudes versus the gap velocity, the natural frequency of the tubes and the effective force coefficient can be calculated. The vibration frequency of the tubes is in these calculations set equal to their natural frequency. It is assumed that the force coefficient is independent of the amplitude. Then Equation 9 is rewritten, to enable the calculation of the resonant frequency and the gap velocity for the onset of resonance. It should be noted that resonance is present in the maximum of the function

$$F = \hat{c}_A V \left(\Omega^*, D_L \right) \qquad (13)$$

and not in the relative maximum of the amplitudes versus gap velocity.

The damping of the tubes D_L has three components:

The **structural damping** D_0 is a consequence of the internal friction in the tube material and the bearings. It can be determined from vibration experiments performed in air. It holds, as given in Equation 7, for a specific vibrating mass and a natural frequency, and it has to be modified according to the conditions dictated by the investigated tube bundle.

The **velocity dependent damping** D_w is dependent on the tube vibrations and on the velocity of the liquid. According to Chen and Jendrzejczyk (10), this component may be negative if self excitation is superimposed on the periodical external excitation. This is not observed in the experiments. So this kind of damping is neglected.

The **viscous damping** D_v is dependent on the kinematic viscosity and the density of the liquid, on the vibration frequency of the tubes Ω and on the distance between the tubes. The viscous damping is calculated using an equation of Pettigrew, Rogers and Axisa (11). This equation is based on the model of a single flexible tube surrounded by stiff tubes. They build a stiff external tube with a diameter d_a, the value depending on the tube arrangement. The flexible tube is vibrating inside the stiff one, which is filled with the liquid. The equation of the total damping is then given as follows

$$D_L = D_0' + D_v = \frac{D_0}{\sqrt{1 + \frac{c_m \, \varrho_F \, \pi \, r^2}{m_l}}} + \frac{\pi}{\sqrt{8}}$$
$$\frac{\varrho_F d^2}{m_l + c_m \, \varrho_F \, \pi \, r^2} \, \frac{1}{\sqrt{St}} \, \frac{1 + d^{*3}}{\left(1 - d^{*2}\right)^2} \quad (14)$$

with

$$d^* \equiv \frac{d}{d_a}$$

In Equation 14 is St the Stokes number defined as

$$St \equiv \frac{\Omega \, r^2}{\nu_F} \quad (15)$$

The added mass coefficient c_m is calculated from the ratio of the natural frequency in air ω_0 and the natural frequency in the liquid at resonance ω_r.

$$c_m = \frac{m_l}{\varrho_F \, \pi \, r^2} \left[\left(\frac{\omega_0}{\omega_r}\right)^2 - 1 \right] \quad (16)$$

The force coefficients obtained from the amplitudes versus gap velocity through Equation 9 by using Equation 14, are presented in Fig 5, as function of the resonance Reynolds number

$$Re_r = \frac{w_{sp} \, d}{\nu_F} \quad (17)$$

The resonance Reynolds number is calculated by using the gap velocity at the resonance point. The dependence of the measured values on the Reynolds number can be approximated by the empirical correlation

$$c_A = 0,205 \left(1 - 2e^{-8,5 \, 10^{-4} \, Re_r}\right)$$
$$- 2,95 \, 10^{-6} \, Re_r \quad (18)$$

in the region $10^3 < Re_r < 5.5 \, 10^4$. The maximal deviation between measured and calculated values is +26.6% and -46.4%. The striking dependence of the force coefficient on the Reynolds number cannot be explained so far. A qualitatively similar behaviour of the force coefficient was measured by Richter (12) in the study of a single cylinder in crossflow in a narrow channel.

Blevins (10) has found a dependence of the force coefficient on the amplitude of the tube vibration for a single tube in crossflow, with vibrations induced by vortex separation. The force coefficient increases with increasing amplitude. In order to check the possible dependence of the force coefficient on the vibration amplitude, the amplitude versus gap velocity are calculated using the force coefficient measured at resonance and the measured frequencies. The measured and the eva luated amplitude diagrams are presented in Fig 6. The calculated values are both below and above the measured values. A dependence of the force coefficient on the amplitudes cannot be confirmed. In order to be able to predict the relative maxima in the amplitudes versus gap velocity, knowledge of the vibration frequency as function of the gap velocity and of the added mass coefficient c_m is essential. The added mass coefficient c_m can be calculated iteratively as function of the Stokes number by means of equation

$$c_m = 1,93 \; - 8,98 \, \frac{1}{\sqrt{st}} \quad (19)$$

It holds in the range $10^3 < St < 4.2 \, 10^4$ with maximal deviations of the calculated values and the measured values of +11.8% and -6.5%.

The frequencies can be calculated in nondimensional form by using the following equation

$$\Omega^* = \Omega^*_{max} \, + \, B \, \left(\frac{2 \, \pi \, w_{sp}}{\omega_r \, d} - \frac{\Omega^*_{max}}{Sk}\right) \quad (20)$$

In this equation B is the nondimensional ascending gradient of the linear frequency function and Sk is the vibration number. It is defined as

$$Sk \equiv \frac{\Omega \, d}{w_{sp}} \quad (21)$$

and it represents the nondimensional excitation frequency in the case of resonance. Both the gradient and the vibration number are dependent on the resonance Reynolds number. The relation

$$Sk \, (Re_r) = 1,082 \, Re_r^{-0,0768} \quad (22)$$

holds with maximal deviations of +3.0% and -3.9%, and equation

$$B = 0,22 \; - 1,6 \, 10^{-6} \, Re_r$$
$$+ \, 0,67 \, e^{-7.1 \, 10^{-4} \, Re_r} \quad (23)$$

with maximal deviations of +10.7% and -16.7%.

By using equations 9-23, the vibration amplitudes versus gap velocity of the periodically externally forced tubes in the first tube row in the staggered arrangement bundle can be calculated. Apart from this, a random external excitation is present in the total operating range. The amplitudes versus gap velocity of the **random externally excited vibrations** can be calculated by using a half-empirical procedure described by Axisa, Villard, Antunes and Wullschleger (14). The procedure is based on the theory of random vibrations . Axisa and his coworkers (14) have assumed that the tubes vibrate with low damping at their natural frequency, that the turbulence is isentropic and stationary along the tube and that the average gap velocity is constant along the tube.

The authors evaluate the time average root mean square value of the amplitudes as a function of the nondimensional power spectrum of the excitation force $S_F^*(f^*)$. The dimensionless amplitudes in the middle of the tube performing bending vibrations in the first mode , can be described by the following equation

$$\frac{A}{d} = 100 \ (\varrho_F \ w_{sp}^2 \ l \ \pi)$$

$$\left[\frac{1,1 \ d}{16 \ \pi^2 \ l \ (m_l \ + c_m \ \varrho_F \ \pi \ r^2) \ \omega_r^3 \ D_L \ w_{sp}} \right. \qquad (24)$$

$$\left. S_F^*(f^*) \right]^{0,5}$$

with

$$f^* \equiv \frac{\omega_r \ d}{2 \ \pi \ w_{sp}} \qquad (25)$$

as the nondimensional natural frequency of the tubes. Axisa and his coworkers (14) have obtained boundary curves based on numerous experimental investigations with different fluids and different tube bundles for the investigated power spectra of the excitation forces.

$$S_F^* \ (f^*) = 4 \ 10^{-4} \ f^{*^{-0,5}} \quad \text{for} \quad 0,01 < f^* \leq 0,2 \quad (26.a)$$

$$S_F^* \ (f^*) = 3 \ 10^{-6} \ f^{*^{-3,5}} \quad \text{for} \quad 0,2 < f^* \leq 3 \quad (26.b)$$

The diagram of the spectra as function of the dimensionless frequency is presented in Fig 7. The influence of the fluid properties is taken into account through the natural frequency ω_F, through the added mass coefficient c_m, and through the damping D_L, according to Equation 14.

When the **critical velocity** is reached, the onset of self--induced oscillations can be observed. In such situations high amplitudes are possible, and the tube bundle heat exchanger is acutely endangered. The critical velocity, also termed stability boundary, is calculated using empirical correlations. They were given by Chen (15) for different tube arrangements. The correlations originate from a procedure by Connors (16), based on an energy balance for the tubes at the stability boundary. The following equations for the stability boundary are given by Chen (15)

$$\frac{w_{sp}}{f_0 \ d} = K \ \left(\frac{m_l \ 2 \ \pi \ D_0}{\varrho_F \ d^2} \right)^\alpha \qquad (27)$$

The constants K and α are dependent on the tube arrangement and on the expression in paretheses in Equation 27, termed mass-damping number

$$m^* = \frac{m_l \ 2 \ \pi \ D_0}{\varrho_F \ d^2} \qquad (28)$$

As the influence of the material properties on the critical velocity is to be investigated, the vibration frequencies of the tubes on the stability boundary, the damping ac-

cording to Equation 14 and the effective vibrating mass are taken into account. This means that the natural frequency, the damping and the oscillating mass in vacuum or air are not used, as it has been suggested by Chen (15). So now Equation 27 can be written as

$$\frac{w_{sp}}{f_s \ d} = K \ \frac{1}{\varrho_F \ d^2} \left[(m_l \ + c_m \ \varrho_F \ \pi \ r^2) \right. \qquad (29)$$

$$\left. 2 \ \pi \ \left(D_0^{'} \ + \ D_v \right) \right]^\alpha$$

In the case of the **staggered tube bundle** the onset of self induced vibrations can first be observed in the last row of tubes. The added mass coefficient c_m and the natural frequency f_s are calculated using the potential theory procedure for fluiddynamically coupled tubes by Chen (5). The maximum deviation between calculated and measured frequencies is 3%. For constants K and α the conservative lower boundary

$$K = 3,0 \qquad \text{and} \qquad \alpha = 0 \qquad \text{for} \qquad m^* < 2,0 \quad (30)$$

is set. The stability boundary function and the measured critical velocities are presented in the stability diagram in Fig 8.

In the **in-line tube bundle** self-excitation can be observed for single tubes, which vibrate due to self-excitation independently of the neighbouring tubes. The added mass coefficient c_m and the natural frequency f_s of the tubes are calculated using the added mass coefficients for independently vibrating tubes in a bundle, experimentally determined by Moretti and Lowery (7). The maximum deviation between the calculated and measured frequencies is +16.2% and -10.7%. For the constants K and α, the conservative lower boundary

$$K = 3,0 \qquad \text{and} \qquad \alpha = 0 \qquad \text{for} \qquad m^* < 2,0 \quad (31)$$

is selected. The stability boundary function and the measured critical velocities are presented in the stability diagram in Fig 9. In Figs 8 and 9 no unanimous dependence of the reduced critical velocity on the mass damping number in the region of low mass damping numbers can be found. This result confirms the data of Weaver and Fitzpatrick (3), conversely to Chen (15), who has found a slight dependence. He suggested the use of exponents between $\alpha = 0.1$ and 0.15.

By using Equations 9, 24 and 29 and the corresponding empirical correlations for the influencing parameters, the amplitudes of tube vibrations in a tube bundle in crossflow in staggered arrangement can be approximately calculated. In Fig 10, the measured resulting amplitudes versus gap velocity of the first tube row are presented as a function of the reduced gap velocity. Also, the predicted amplitudes for periodical external excitation and for random external excitation and the critical velocity for which the danger of self-excitation with high amplitude vibrations is acute, are entered into the diagram.

The amplitudes of vibrations caused by periodical and random self-excitation can be predicted with good accuracy. The critical velocity and the greatest danger to the tube bundle can thus safely be avoided.

REFERENCES

(1) Owen, P.R. Buffeting excitation of boiler tube vibration. J. of Mechanical Engineering Science, 1965, 7, 4, pp. 431-439.

(2) Gog, W., Gelbe, H. Schwingungserregung in quer angeströmten Rohrbündeln mit Dreiecksteilung. Verfahrenstechnik, 1983, 17, 4, pp. 232-237.

(3) Weaver, D.S., Fitzpatrick, J. A. A review of flow induced vibrations in heat exchangers. Int. Conf. on Flow Induced Vibrations, Bowness-on-Windermere, England, 1987, Paper A1.

(4) Sandifer, J.B., Bailey, R. T. Turbulent buffeting of tube arrays in liquid crossflow. Symp. on Flow Induced Vibrations, ASME Winter Annual Meeting, New Orleans, USA, 1984, Vol. 2, pp. 211-226.

(5) Chen, S.S. Dynamics of heat exchanger tube banks. ASME-Paper No.76 - WA/FE-28, 1976.

(6) Hesse, F. Einfluß der Viskosität auf das Schwingverhalten einzelner Rohre in Rohrbündeln. Dissertation, Universität Hannover, 1987.

(7) Moretti, P.M., Lowery, R.L. Hydrodynamic inertia coefficients for a tube surrounded by rigid tubes. ASME-Paper No. Z 457 75-PVP-47, 1975.

(8) Magnus, K. Schwingungen. Teubner Studienbücher Mechanik, Verlag B.G. Teubner, Stuttgart, 3. Aufl. 1976.

(9) Stockmeier, D. Schwingungen in quer angeströmten Rohrbündeln - Einfluß der Viskosität der strömenden Flüssigkeit. Dissertation, Universität Hannover, 1990 (in preparation).

(10) Chen, S.S., Jendrzejczyk, J.A. Flow velocity dependence of damping in tube arrays subjected to liquid cross-flow. J. of Pressure Vessel Technology, 1981, 103, 2, pp. 130-135.

(11) Pettigrew, M.J., Rogers, R.J., Axisa, F. Damping of multispan heat exchanger tubes. Part 2: In liquids, Flow-Induced Vibration 1986, PVP-Conference, Chicago, USA, 1986, PVP-Vol.104, pp.89-98.

(12) Richter, A. Fluctuating forces on a circular cylinder rigidly supported in a narrow flow passage. Int. Symp. on Vibration Problems in Industry, Keswick, UK, 1973, Session 1, Paper 115.

(13) Blevins, R.D., Flow Induced Vibrations. 1977, Van Nostrand Reinhold Co., New York.

(14) Axisa, F., Antunes, J., Villard, B., Wullschleger, M. Random excitation of heat exchanger tubes by crossflow. Symp. on Flow Induced Vibrations, ASME Winter Annual Meeting, Chicago, USA, 1988, Vol. 2, pp. 23-46.

(15) Chen, S.S. Guidelines for the instability flow velocity of tube arrays in crossflow. J. of Sound and Vibration, 1984, 93, 3, pp. 439-455.

(16) Connors, H. J., jr. Fluidelastic vibration of tube arrays excited by crossflow. ASME Winter Annual Meeting, New York, USA, 1970, pp.42-56.

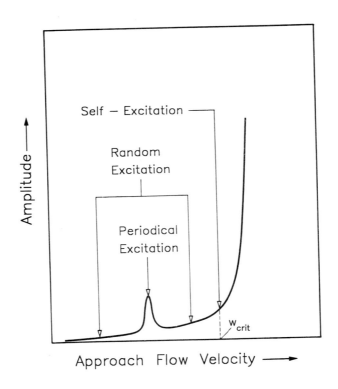

Fig 1. Qualitative diagram of the vibration amplitudes versus flow velocity in tube bundles in liquid flows.

Normal Square Array

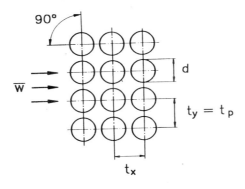

$$t_x = t_y = t_p$$

$$\tau_p = \frac{t_p}{d} = 1.28$$

Normal Triangular Array

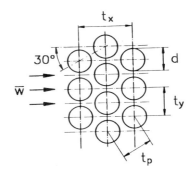

$$t_y = t_p$$

$$\tau_p = \frac{t_p}{d} = 1.28$$

$$\tau_x = \frac{t_x}{d} = 2.22$$

Fig 2. Investigated tube arrangements.

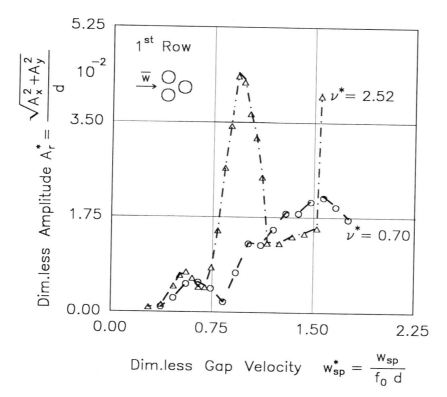

Fig 3. Dimensionless resulting vibration amplitudes in the first tube row versus the reduced gap velocity for two different viscosities of the streaming liquid; staggered tube bundles.

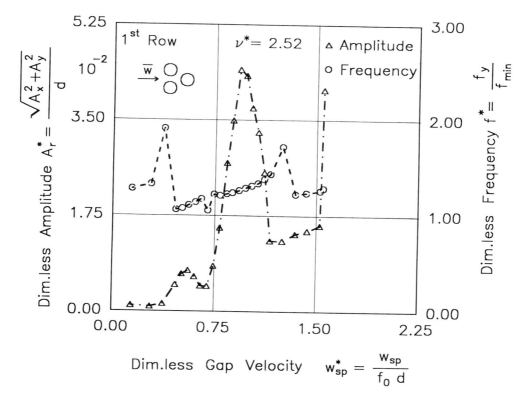

Fig 4. Dimensionless resulting amplitudes and dimensionless frequency of vibrations in the first tube row versus the reduced gap velocity; staggered tube bundles.

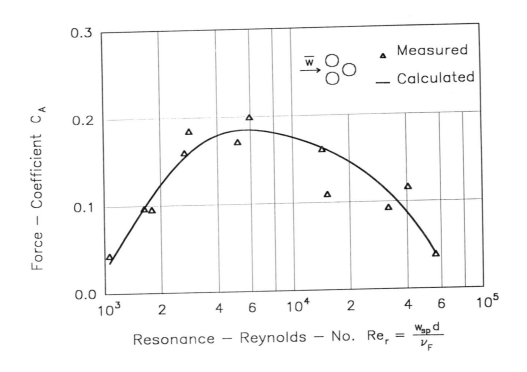

Fig 5. Measured force coefficients versus the resonance Reynolds number.

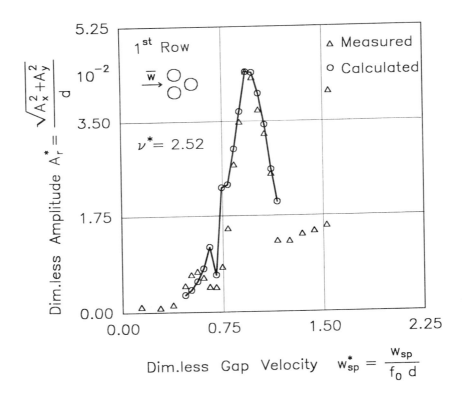

Fig 6. Comparison of measured vibration amplitudes and vibration amplitudes calculated by using measured frequency data and measured values of force coefficients.

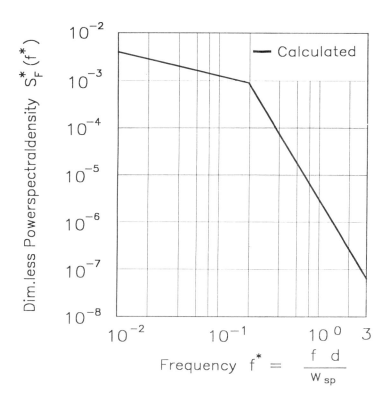

Fig 7. Diagram of the nondimensional power spectrum of the random excitation force versus the dimensionless frequency (14).

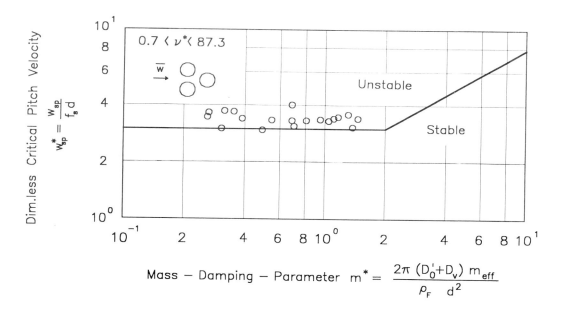

Fig 8. Stability diagram obtained from own experimental data for a tube bundle in staggered arrangement.

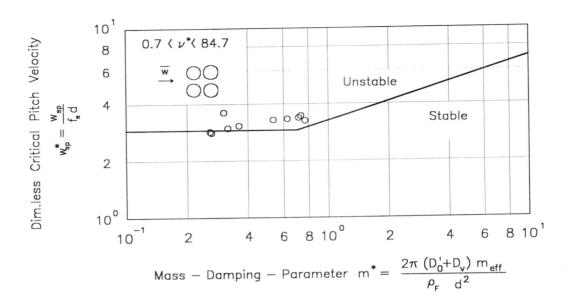

Fig 9. Stability diagram obtained from own experimental data for an
in-line tube bundle.

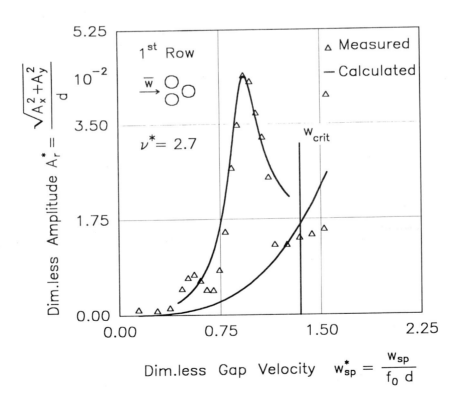

Fig 10. Comparison of measured and calculated vibration behaviour of
tubes in the first row in the staggered tube arrangement.

C416/057

Flow vizualization in a 1.5 pitch-to-diameter rotated square array of cylinders subject to cross-flow

S J PRICE, BSc, PhD, MASME, MAIAA M P PAIDOUSSIS, PhD, CEng, FIMechE, FRSC, FASME, FCSME, MIAHR and W N MUREITHI, MEng
Department of Mechanical Engineering, McGill University, Montreal, Quebec, Canada
B MARK, BEng, MEng, CSME
Pratt and Whitney, Longueuil, Canada

SYNOPSIS Flow–visualization experiments have been conducted in the interstitial flow passages of a rotated square array of cylinders, with $P/d = 1.5$, in water flow. The Reynolds number, Re, based on cylinder diameter and upstream flow velocity, was in the range 80 to 1 300. At low Reynolds numbers, symmetric attached vortices were observed forming behind cylinders in all rows of the array. At a critical Reynolds number, the exact value depending on the particular row, the dividing line between the symmetric vortices becomes unstable and folds up on itself, resulting in alternate vortex shedding. Also, the vortical motions from the upstream cylinders impinge on the downstream ones producing even more vortical motion behind these cylinders.

1   INTRODUCTION

It is generally accepted that there are three distinct mechanisms leading to vibrations of cylinder arrays in cross–flow (1–3), these being: random forced excitation due to turbulence in the flow; resonance between a structural natural frequency and a flow periodicity in the interstitial gap–flow; and self–excited fluidelastic instability. Turbulent excitation is easily understood physically. For the last two mechanisms, however, there are still a number of basic questions relating to the phenomena which are not understood.

The flow periodicity producing the resonance is usually referred to as "vortex shedding"; however, bearing in mind the closeness of cylinders in the array (P/d between 1.3 and 2.0) and the highly turbulent nature of the interstitial flow, it would be somewhat surprising if vortices, akin to those generated behind an isolated bluff body, could develop deep in the array. Indeed, some authors have stated that vortices cannot develop in an array of cylinders (4). However, there is considerable experimental evidence, from both interstitial flow and vibration measurements, that a fairly sharply–defined flow periodicity, with a constant Strouhal number, does exist in some arrays of cylinders (1–3, 5, 6). On the other hand, for other arrays with different geometrical patterns, there is equally compelling experimental evidence that no flow periodicity exists (7). Thus, two questions immediately spring to mind: firstly, what is the phenomenon producing the flow periodicity in cylinder arrays and is it related to classical vortex shedding; and secondly, why does this phenomenon occur in some arrays and not in others?

Fluidelastic instability has been the subject of a considerable amount of theoretical and experimental work; on one level, at least, it is reasonably well understood. It being generally accepted that the vibration is due to two different instability mechanisms: a single degree–of–freedom mechanism associated with the phase lag between cylinder motion and the resulting fluid forces (8–12),

and a coupled-mode stiffness–controlled binary flutter mechanism requiring motion in at least two degrees–of–freedom (8, 10, 11). What is not so well understood for these instability phenomena is the fluid dynamics producing the phase lag and/or the aerodynamic force field.

In an attempt to understand the fluid dynamics discussed in the foregoing, a program of flow visualization in the core of cylinder arrays subject to cross–flow has recently been initiated at McGill University, and some preliminary results are presented in this paper.

Although there are many excellent flow visualization studies for isolated bluff bodies, (e.g., References (13, 14)), much less work has been done when there are multiple bluff bodies in close proximity to one another; the only examples known to the authors being given in References (15–20).

Wallis (15) used a shallow water tank to observe the free surface flow pattern around groups of cylinders using aluminum dust particles sprinkled on the surface of the water. He observed the flow pattern in many different cylinder arrays, with Re (based on free stream velocity and cylinder diameter) in the range 135 to 2 700. Wallis' photographs show that for all the arrays tested, eddies are formed in the wake regions of the cylinders, but that they appear to remain attached to the cylinders and not to interact with the mean gap flow between the cylinders.

Bradshaw (16) used smoke to observe the wake patterns downstream of a row of cylinders ($P/d = 1.7$) in air flow with Re = 1 500. His photograph shows jets emerging from the cylinder gaps and then coalescing into stable "cells" downstream of the row. There appears to be some vortical motion within these cells.

Weaver et al. (17, 18) used aluminum particles to visualize the flow in a square array of cylinders with $P/d = 1.5$ and a rotated square array with $P/d = 1.41$ — Re in these experiments was in the range 100 to 1.1×10^4. In both cases the visualization was carried out with at least one cylinder free to vibrate. While they did observe vortical patterns behind the cylinder, in all cases these coincided with large amplitude vibrations of the flexible cylinder; it is debatable whether these vortical patterns are associated with cylinder motion, or whether they exist independently of it.

Cheng and Moretti (19) used coloured dyes to visualize the water flow through several arrays (in–line, rotated and normal triangular and rotated square) with $1.25 \leq P/d \leq 1.4$. Reynolds numbers are quoted as being of order 3 000 based on the gap velocity; thus, Re (based on free stream velocity) is probably of order 500. They concentrated mainly on examining the various mean flow patterns through the array and, although their visualization photographs show some examples of downstream gap flows coalescing, similar to Bradshaw's observations (16), there is no evidence of any vortical motion in the interstitial gaps.

Andjelić, Austermann and Popp (20) used a sheet of laser light to illuminate smoke particles in air flow for a normal triangular array with $P/d = 1.25$ and Re = 1 139. They observed small regions of attached recirculating flow behind the cylinders with a laminar gap flow weaving around these recirculating regions.

In the present paper the authors investigate the flow pattern in a rotated square array with $P/d = 1.5$. The cylinders in the array are essentially rigid, thus any flow patterns that are observed are "true" flow patterns and are not due to motion of the cylinders in the array. One of the reasons for choosing this array is that flow periodicities in its interstitial gaps had previously been measured with hot–wire anemometry; also, the vibration of a flexibly mounted cylinder in different rows of the array has been monitored (6). This work suggested that there is a flow periodicity in the array, at least for the first few rows; thus, it was hoped to link together the previous hot–wire and vibration measurements with the present flow visualization results to yield a more complete understanding of the flow in this array.

2 EXPERIMENTAL APPARATUS

The experiments were conducted in a closed section water tunnel, with a 260 mm square working section; the tunnel sides, top and bottom are all made of plexiglas — making this an ideal tunnel for flow visualization. An especially designed cylinder array, made totally of plexiglas, was inserted into the tunnel working section such that it spanned the height and width of the working section; the long cylinder axes being in the vertical direction. The cylinders were 12.7 mm (1/2 in.) in diameter and were rigidly supported at both ends so that the array may effectively be considered as being rigid. The array was seven rows deep with each row consisting of either 8 or 9 cylinders, with half cylinders being placed on the water tunnel side walls if necessary to produce a homogeneous resistance to the flow across the tunnel. The cylinders were arranged in a rotated square pattern with pitch–to–diameter ratio, P/d, equal to 1.5; see Fig. 1.

The interstitial flow in the array was visualized via two differently coloured dyes; the dyes were either injected into the flow from a streamlined probe upstream of the array or from holes on the cylinder surface within the array.

The position of the upstream probe could be adjusted such that the dye impinged on any desired part of the array. Two dyes were used: mixtures of water and Rhodamine, and of water and Fluorescein, which respectively appear orange–yellow and bright green when subject to ultraviolet light. Use of the two dyes enabled greater detail of the flow pattern in the array to be visualized. The relative concentration of the two dye mixtures was made such that the two mixtures produced approximately the same intensity of fluorescence; otherwise one of the dyes would appear underexposed while taking photographic records of the flow. The two dye mixtures were stored in reservoirs with a pressure head greater than the tunnel pressure; the flow of dye was adjusted via a valve such that the dyes were emitted into the water–flow with as little disturbance as possible.

The interstitial flow was illuminated from the side via two Xenon arc lamps, which produced primarily white light but also provided sufficient ultraviolet light to cause fluorescence of the dyes. The lamps were positioned such that they illuminated the array along diagonal paths between the cylinders, see Fig. 1. Because of the denseness of the cylinder array, the interstitial flow could only be illuminated through the cylinders; although the cylinders were made of plexiglas they did refract the light from the light source and thus, the lighting in the array was not totally homogeneous — producing some light or dark spots in the array.

Photographic records of the flow were taken from below the tunnel working section using a JVC KY-25 video camera with a 16 to 1 zoom lens and shutter speed of up to 1/1000 of a second. The video signals were recorded in S–VHS format. Hard copies of individual frames of the video could be obtained either via a video frame-grabber board linked to a HP RS/20C computer (then printed using a laser printer) or, as done for the photographs presented in this paper, printed directly via the video printer.

Using the present experimental apparatus the dyes tended to diffuse very rapidly in the interstitial flow; this was especially so deeper in the array than the second row. This effectively limited the maximum velocity to approximately 0.04 m/s for visualization deeper than the second row and 0.1 m/s for the first two rows. For velocities less than 0.01 m/s it was not possible to control the water tunnel and maintain a constant velocity. Thus, the experiments reported in this paper are for Re (based on upstream velocity and cylinder diameter) in the range 80 to 500 for rows deeper than row 2 and 80 to 1 300 for the first two rows. The velocity was measured using a calibrated turbine flow meter; this was judged to be accurate to within approximately 5%.

3 RESULTS AND DISCUSSION

Vortical motion was observed behind the cylinders in all rows of this array. However, the specific nature of the vortical motion was very dependent on Reynolds number, with two distinctly different flow patterns occurring for different ranges of Re. The flow corresponding to these two ranges of Re will be discussed separately in the following sections.

© IMechE 1991 C416/057

3.1 Low Reynolds number range (symmetric shedding)

In this low Re range, small symmetric attached vortices are formed behind the cylinders in all rows of the array. As will be discussed later in this section, the upper value of Re at which this range closes depends on the specific row. An example of a sequence of photographs, for one period of the evolution of these vortices, is shown in Fig. 2 for the wake flow behind a cylinder in row 1 with Re = 165. These vortices are not steady but oscillate together in the in-flow direction; the period of oscillation for the example of Fig. 2 is approximately 0.7 to 0.8 s, corresponding to a Strouhal number of approximately 1.3. During this time the vortices initially form very close to the base region of the cylinders and then begin to extend further downstream; possibly by being dragged along by the gap flow. As they extend downstream the vortices narrow down and the tips of the vortices appear to diverge from the centreline separating the two. Eventually, at a time of between 0.5 and 0.6 s for the example of Fig. 2, the vortices shed some of their vorticity and begin to contract, leaving a certain amount of fluid on the centreline. The remaining vorticity is then concentrated in the near wake region of the forming cylinder (at approximately 0.7 to 0.8 s for Fig. 2), and the process begins over again.

As previously stated, the attached vortices and associated extension and contraction of them occurs, at sufficiently low Re, for all rows of the array. Furthermore, preliminary results suggest that for all cylinders in the same row the motion of the extension and contraction is in-phase.

It should be noted that apart from the periodic motion associated with the extension and contraction of the vortices, there is also a periodic motion of the recirculating flow within the vortex. Measurement of this period proved much more difficult than the one due to the extension and contraction, but, for the example of Fig. 2, this period was estimated at 5 ± 1 s. Thus, the Strouhal number of this recirculating motion is approximately 0.2.

As the free stream velocity is increased, the area occupied by the symmetric vortices increases and eventually this is accompanied by an oscillation, in the direction normal to the flow, of the centreline dividing the two vortices. An example of this is shown in Fig. 3 for the wake region behind a cylinder in row 1 at Re = 280. It should be noted that even though the dividing line between the two vortices is oscillating normal to the flow, the vortices in the near wake region are still symmetric. The Reynolds number at which this oscillation starts depends on the row in which the cylinder is positioned as summarised in Table 1.

Table 1   Summary of the Reynolds number at which oscillation of the dividing streamline between the symmetric vortices begins.

Cylinder row	1	2	3	4	5
Reynolds number	215	150	—	130	130

One final point concerning this low Reynolds number range is that no flow can cross the dividing centreline between vortices. Thus, there is no motion of the flow along diagonal paths between cylinders and any flow particle

which enters the array in one streamwise open channel between cylinders will exit the array in the same channel.

3.2 Higher Reynolds number range

As shown in Fig. 3 the breakdown of the low Re range is characterized by an oscillation of the downstream part of the dividing line between symmetric quasi-attached vortices. As the Reynolds number is further increased the oscillation of this dividing line increases and the point of reattachment of the dividing line on the downstream cylinder also appears to oscillate, see Fig. 3. As this oscillation builds up, the dividing line starts to fold up on itself, possibly due to its becoming unstable, and some of the gap flow between rows is entrained into this folding process. The vortical motion of fluid on either side of the line is no longer symmetric but now begins to oscillate in an antisymmetric manner; possibly, the vortical motion is now being driven by the oscillation of the dividing line. This folding or instability of the dividing line could be characterized as the start of the alternating periodicity in the wake flow as is shown in Fig. 4 for the flow behind a cylinder in row 3 at Re = 180.

Although not apparent from any of the still photographs shown in this paper, the video film demonstrated that the oscillation of the dividing line would build up to some maximum value and then decay to a minimum, before starting to build up again. Possibly there is a characteristic period associated with this build up and decay, but, as yet, this has not been measured; it may, however, yield some clue to the multiple Strouhal numbers previously measured in this array (6).

The folds of the dividing line wrap themselves around the downstream cylinder and the vorticity is then convected further downstream, contributing to the vortex formation process on this downstream cylinder. Thus, there is considerable difference in the formation process between vortices originating behind an interior row in the array (any row deeper than row 2) and an upstream row (row 1 or 2). For example, even at a relatively high Re of 1 000 the vortices behind a cylinder in row 1 are formed in the near wake region, see Fig 5. While for much lower Re the vortices behind interior rows are formed in the region just behind the maximum width of the cylinder. Thus, it is apparent that the vortex formation process on cylinders in the interior rows is aided by the vorticity convected downstream from the upstream rows. Hence, at any particular Reynolds number the vortices behind the downstream rows are much better developed than those behind the corresponding upstream row.

For some cases in this velocity range, hot-film measurements were taken simultaneously with the flow visualization. Using a system of mirrors it was possible to show both the signal from the hot-film and the dye trace on the video; examples of this are presented in Fig. 6 showing the vortices being shed from a cylinder in row 3 with Re = 230. It is apparent from Fig. 6 that the hot-film signal and the flow visualization are recording the same periodic phenomenon. It can also be observed that a peak in the hot-film signal corresponds very closely to a vortex being sheared away from the upper surface of the cylinder. Unfortunately, with the present experimental set-up, it is not possible to vary the position of the hot-film probe and so the exact relationship between the vortex shedding and interstitial velocity measurements could not be established.

In this higher Reynolds number range, experiments were done with dyes of two different colours and it was apparent that there is considerable mixing between the flow of adjacent through–channels in the array; this mixing being driven by the vortex shedding from the cylinders. For example, consider Fig. 7 where the leading cylinder in the photograph is a cylinder in row 3 of the array with Re = 215. As the vortex forms in the wake of the row–3 cylinder, it wraps itself around the row–5 cylinder, and a significant portion of it is swept downstream in the upwards diagonal direction of the figure. Also, as the vortex formed in the wake of the row–4 cylinder it wraps itself around the row–6 cylinder and a portion of it is swept downstream in the downwards diagonal direction. This mixing of the channel flows, driven by the vortex shedding, is much more apparent in the video film, where it is much easier to observe the mixing of the different coloured dyes.

3.3   Unsteadiness of the flow

In some cases the alternate vortex shedding described above for rows 2 and 3 was perturbed by brief periods of symmetric shedding. Furthermore, in between the periods of alternate and symmetric shedding, there were other equally brief periods where the flow does not seem to have any dominant structure. An example of this is shown in Fig. 8 for the flow behind row 3 at Re = 405. Fig 8(a) shows what is clearly symmetric vortex shedding. This symmetric shedding, however, is very different from that occurring in the low velocity range; the vortices discussed here originate close to the maximum width of the cylinder, not in the base region as they do in the low velocity range. In Fig. 8(b) it appears that the upper of the two vortices is starting to break up and in Fig. 8(c) the two vortices have been totally destroyed. This is then followed by alternate vortex shedding very similar to that shown in Fig. 4. It is interesting that if the hot–film probe is placed in the flow during this switch from symmetric to alternate vortex shedding, or vice versa, then the vortex break–up is characterized by a non harmonic signal. See, for example, Fig. 9(a) where a typical hot–film signal is shown during a break–up of the vortices, as opposed to that measured a little later when alternate vortex shedding is occurring, as shown in Fig. 9(b).

It should be stressed that this break–down of the alternate vortex shedding is not the normal state of affairs. For the vast majority of the flow visualization records obtained in the higher Re region alternate vortex shedding occurred.

3.4   Strouhal numbers

Based on all the flow visualization experiments done to date, values of the period associated with the shedding phenomena were obtained for all rows of the array as a function of Re. These were obtained by counting the number of frames from the video film before the periodic flow started to repeat itself (typically this was done using several periods, not just one). The associated Strouhal numbers, S_t, based on free stream velocity, are presented in Fig. 10. Ignoring the two very low Strouhal numbers obtained behind row 5 for very low Re, it is apparent that S_t does not depend on the specific row from which the vortices are shed; this is in agreement with previous measurements (6). It is also apparent that in this Reynolds number range there is no dramatic change in S_t with Re. There is a gradual increase in S_t as Re is increased, but

bearing in mind that the range of Re shown in Fig. 10 covers both the symmetric (low Re) and alternate types of vortex shedding it is surprising that there is so little effect of Re. In the previous interstitial flow measurements (6), average Strouhal numbers throughout the array of 0.72 and 1.3 were obtained in water flow (in this case, the range of Reynolds number was approximately 1 300 to 10 000). The Strouhal number of 1.3 agrees reasonably well with the values presented here — obtained from the flow visualization study, although the latter does not show any trace of a periodicity with $S_t = 0.72$; thus, it is still uncertain what the origin of this lower Strouhal number is.

4.   CONCLUSIONS

Based on the results presented in this paper and on other flow visualization experiments not reported here, the following conclusions can be made for a rotated square array with $P/d = 1.5$ subject to cross flow in the Reynolds number range 80 to 1 300.

At low Reynolds numbers, symmetric attached vortices are formed behind all cylinders in the array. The vortices extend and contract, leaving a dividing line between them. At a certain critical Reynolds number this dividing line starts to oscillate, possibly because it becomes unstable, forming itself into alternately shed vortices. The value of Reynolds number at which this occurs depends on which row the cylinder is in, but in these experiments was in the range of 130 to 215. The alternate vortices then wrap themselves around the immediately downstream cylinder causing more vorticity to be shed from the downstream cylinders. Part of the shed vorticity is swept downstream along a diagonal path causing a mixing of the flow between different channels in the array; this is very different to what occurs in the low Reynolds number type flow where there is no mixing between the gap flows.

For rows two and three of the array, it appears that this alternate vortex shedding can occasionally become unsteady for short periods and break down into symmetric vortex shedding, although of a different type to that at low Reynolds numbers.

Strouhal numbers were obtained for the flow behind the first five rows of the array indicating that the Strouhal number does not appear to change from one row to another. There does seem to be a weak effect of Reynolds number on the Strouhal number, with Strouhal numbers tending to increase as the Reynolds number increases. However, the Strouhal numbers obtained here are in reasonably good agrement with those previously measured at much higher Reynolds numbers (6).

At present, because of the diffusion problem of the dye in the array, the authors are unable to say anything about what happens for Re greater than 1 300; however, new experiments are planned in the future to investigate this higher Reynolds number range.

ACKNOWLEDGEMENTS

The authors gratefully acknowledge the financial support of the Natural Sciences and Engineering Research Council of Canada and Le Fonds FCAR of Québec.

REFERENCES

(1) PAÏDOUSSIS, M.P., Flow–induced vibrations in nuclear reactors and heat exchangers: practical experiences and state of knowledge. In *Practical Experiences with Flow–Induced Vibrations*, (eds Naudascher, E. and Rockwell, D.), Berlin:Springer–Verlag, 1980, pp. 1–81.

(2) WEAVER, D.S. and FITZPATRICK, J.A., A review of cross–flow induced vibrations in heat exchanger tube arrays. *Journal of Fluids and Structures*, 1988, 2, 73–93.

(3) PAÏDOUSSIS, M.P. and PRICE, S.J., Dynamics and stability of cylinder arrays in cross–flow: New results and new questions. *AIAA/ASME/SIAM/APS 1st National Fluid Dynamics Congress*, Cincinnati, 1988, paper number AIAA–88–3688–CP, pp. 1127–1133.

(4) OWEN, P.R., Buffeting excitation of boiler tube vibration. *Journal of Mechanical Engineering Science*, 1965, 7, 431–439.

(5) PRICE, S.J., PAÏDOUSSIS, M.P., MACDONALD, R. and MARK, B., The flow–induced vibration of a single flexible cylinder in a rotated square array of rigid cylinders with pitch–to–diameter of 2.12. *Journal of Fluids and Structures*, 1987, 1, 359–378.

(6) PAÏDOUSSIS, M.P., PRICE, S.J., NAKAMURA, T. MARK, B. and MUREITHI, W.N., Flow–induced vibrations and instabilities in a rotated square cylinder array in cross–flow. *Journal of Fluids and Structures*, 1989, 3, 229–254.

(7) PRICE, S.J. and PAÏDOUSSIS, M.P. The flow–induced response of a single flexible cylinder in an in–line array of rigid cylinders. *Journal of Fluids and Structures*, 1989, 3, 229–254.

(8) CHEN, S.S., Instability mechanisms and stability criteria of a group of circular cylinders subjected to cross flows; Part 2: Numerical results and discussions. *ASME Journal of Vibration, Acoustics, Stress and Reliability in Design*, 1983, 105, 253–260.

(9) LEVER, J.H. and WEAVER, D.S., A theoretical model for fluid–elastic instability of heat exchanger tube bundles. *ASME Journal of Pressure Vessel Technology*, 1982, 104, 147–158.

(10) PRICE, S.J and PAÏDOUSSIS, M.P., An improved mathematical model for the stability of cylinder rows subject to cross–flow. *Journal of Sound and Vibration*, 1986, 105, 121–142.

(11) PRICE, S.J. and PAÏDOUSSIS, M.P., A single–flexible–cylinder analysis of the fluidelastic instability of an array of flexible cylinders in cross–flow. *ASME Journal of Fluids Engineering*, 1986, 108, 193–199.

(12) PAÏDOUSSIS, M.P. and PRICE, S.J., The mechanisms underlying flow–induced instabilities of cylinder arrays in crossflow. *Journal of Fluid Mechanics*, 1988, 107, 45–59.

(13) ZDRAVKOVICH, M.M., Smoke observations of the formation of a Kàrmàn Vortex street. *Journal of Fluid Mechanics*, 1969, 37, 491–496.

(14) GERRARD, J.H., The wakes of cylindrical bluff bodies at low Reynolds number. *Philosophical Transactions of the Royal Society of London*, Series A, 1978, 289, 351–382.

(15) WALLIS, R.P., Photographic study of fluid flow between banks of tubes. *Engineering*, 1939, 148, 423–426.

(16) BRADSHAW, P., The effect of wind–tunnel screens on nominally two–dimensional boundary layers. *Journal of Fluid Mechanics*, 1965, 22, 679–687.

(17) WEAVER, D.S. and ABD–RABBO, A., A flow visualization study of a square array of tubes in water cross flow. *ASME Journal of Fluids Engineering*, 1985, 107, 354–362.

(18) ABD–RABBO, A. and WEAVER, D.S., A flow visualization study of flow development in a staggered tube array. *Journal of Sound and Vibration*, 1986, 106, 241–256.

(19) CHENG, M. and MORETTI, P.M., Flow instabilities in tube bundles. In *Flow–Induced Vibration* (eds Au–Yang, M.K., Chen, S.S., Kaneko, S. and Chilukuri, R.) ASME: New York, 1989, pp. 11–16.

(20) ANDJELIĆ, M., AUSTERMANN, R. and POPP, K., Multiple stability boundaries of tubes in a normal triangular cylinder array. In *Flow–Induced Vibrations*, (eds Chen, S.S., Fujita, K. and Au–Yang, M.K.) ASME: New York, 1990, pp. 87–98.

FLOW DIRECTION

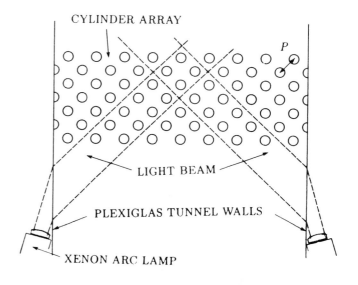

Fig 1   Schematic drawing of the cylinder array and visualization equipment.

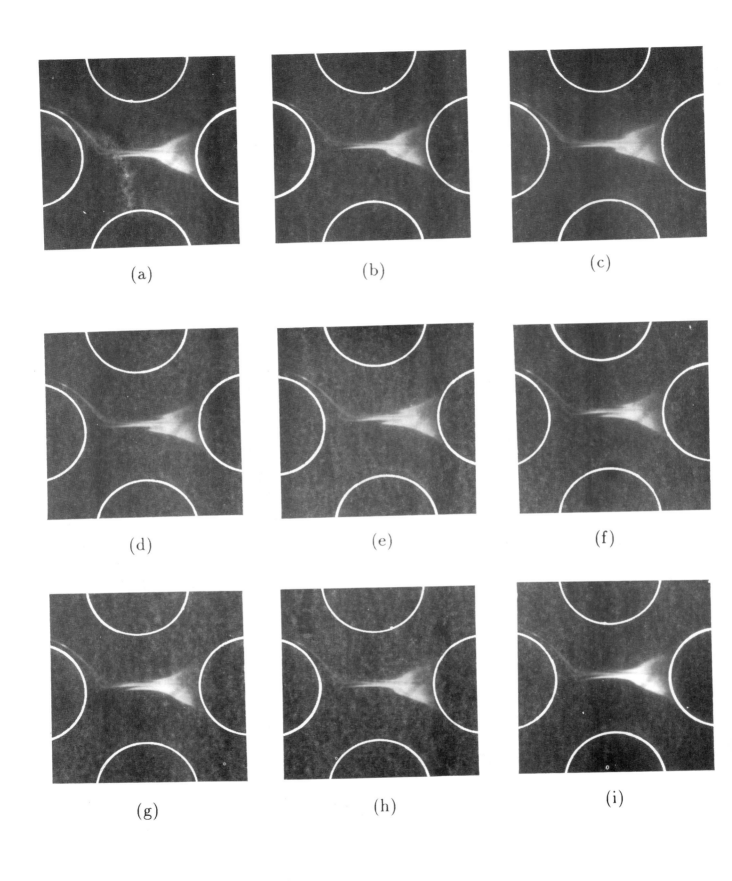

Fig 2   Formation of symmetric vortices behind a cylinder in row 1 at Re = 165.   (a) time, t = 0.0 s;   (b) t = 0.1 s;
(c) t = 0.2 s;   (d) t = 0.3 s;   (e) t = 0.4 s;   (f) t = 0.5 s;   (g) t = 0.6 s;   (h) t = 0.7 s;   (i) t = 0.8 s.

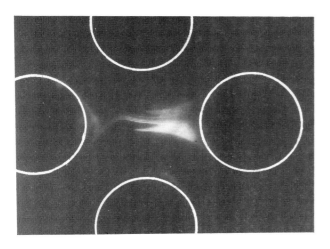 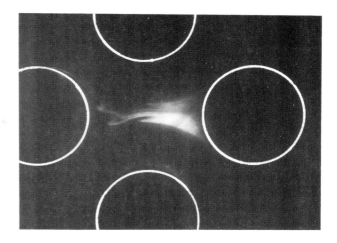

Fig 3   Two examples of oscillation of line dividing vortices behind a cylinder in row 1 at Re = 280.

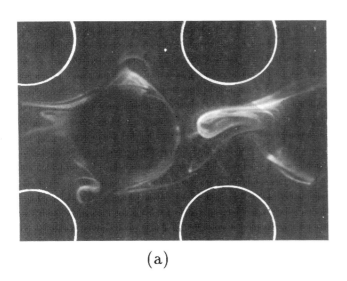 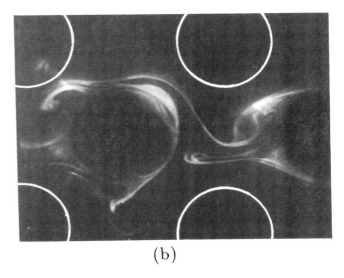

(a)   (b)

Fig 4   Formation of alternating vortices behind a cylinder in row 3 at Re = 180.   (a) t = 0.0 s; (b) t = 0.5 s.

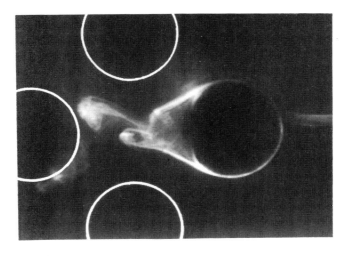

Fig 5   Formation of symmetric vortices behind a cylinder in row 1 at Re = 1 000.

 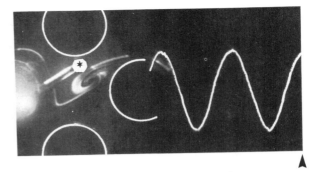

TIME OF VIDEO FRAME   TIME OF VIDEO FRAME

Fig 6   Two examples of the formation of alternating vortices behind a cylinder in row 3 for Re = 230 with the hot–film signal superimposed. * Marks the location of the hot–film probe.

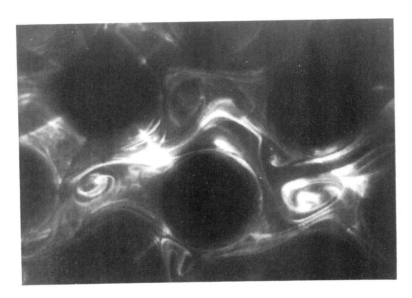

Fig 7   Alternate vortex shedding behind cylinders in rows 3 to 7 for Re = 215.

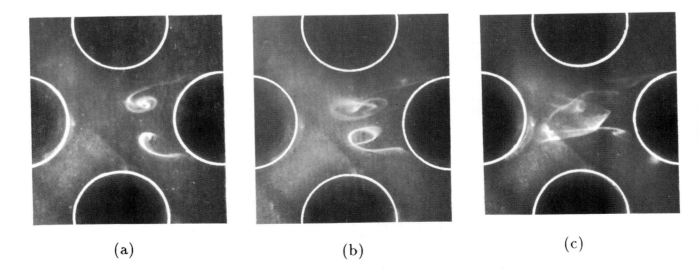

(a)   (b)   (c)

Fig 8   Switch from symmetric to alternate vortex shedding for the flow behind a cylinder in row 3 with Re = 405. (a) t = 0.2 s; (b) t = 0.3 s; (c) t = 0.4 s.

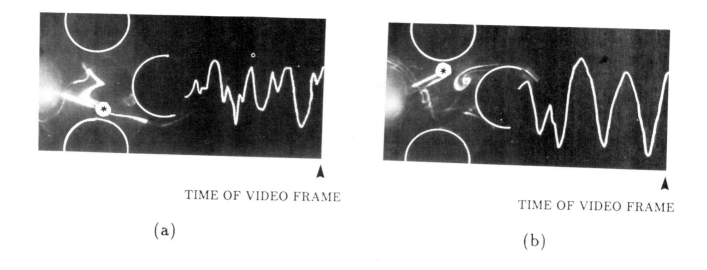

TIME OF VIDEO FRAME

(a)

TIME OF VIDEO FRAME

(b)

Fig 9   Comparison of hot–film signals obtained behind a cylinder in row 3 for Re = 370. (a) Non–harmonic signal corresponding to the vortex break–up; (b) harmonic signal corresponding to alternate vortex shedding. * Marks the location of the hot–film probe.

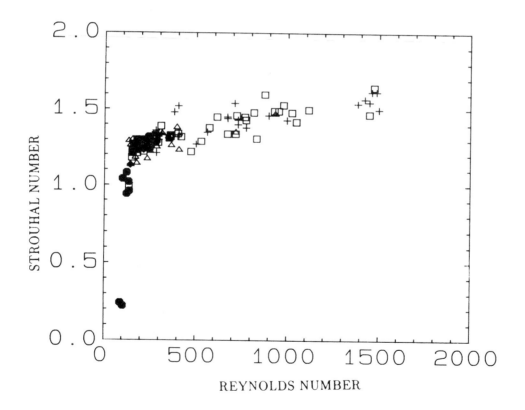

Fig 10   Summary of all values of Strouhal number obtained from the flow visualization experiments as a function of Reynolds number. + row–1; □ row–2; △ row–3; ◆ row–4; ● row–5.

The numerical prediction of vibrations in tube bundles induced by cross-flow turbulence

E DE LANGRE and B BEAUFILS
CEA, Saclay, France
J ANTUNES
LNETI, Sacavem, Portugal

SYNOPSIS. The methodology developed at CEA Saclay for the predictive analysis of tube bundles vibrations induced by cross-flow turbulence is presented here. Special attention is paid to its practical use for typical problems in linear and non-linear analysis.

NOTATION

a_i, a_n	modal correlation coefficient
A	damping operator
A_n	modal damping
c_F	adherence damping coefficient
D	tube diameter
D_o	reference tube diameter
e	tube thickness
E	Young's modulus
f, f_1, f_n	frequency and modal frequency
f_{rn}	reduced frequency
f_e^n, f_I^n	external and impact generalized forces
g	gap width
k	wear coefficient
K	stiffness operator
K_n	modal stiffness
K_c, K_F	impact and adherence stiffness
L, L_o	tube length and reference tube length
L'	scale of variation
M, M_n	mass operator and modal mass
$r(s)$	fluid volumetric mass profile
R	tube radius of curvature
s	location along the tube
S_n	PSD of banded white noise
T_1, T_2	integration time limits
$u(s)$	flow velocity profile
V, $\bar{V}$	flow velocity and mean flow velocity
x	distance between tube location and support limit
$\vec{X}$, $\dot{\vec{X}}$	tube displacement and velocity
$\vec{X}_N$, $\vec{X}_T$	normal and tangential tube displacement
$\dot{W}$	wear work rate
α	AVB position angle
δ	Dirac Delta function
ρ, $\bar{\rho}$	fluid volumetric mass and mean volumetric mass
λ_c	correlation length
ζ_i	modal damping
ε	statistical error
Δt	time-step size
σ	r.m.s displacement
φ	modal shape
Φ_F	cross-correlation spectrum
$\tilde{\Phi}_F$, $\tilde{\Phi}_F^c$	dimensionless and equivalent cross-correlation spectrum
μ	dry friction coefficient
$\langle\ \rangle$	positive part
τ_1, τ_2	integration time

1. INTRODUCTION

In shell and tube heat exchangers, flow-induced vibrations may be the cause of excessive wear and damage [1]. Fluid elastic instability may lead to failures on a short term basis. For this reason, most of the general interest was focused on this mechanism.

However, random excitation of tubes due to cross-flow turbulence may produce progressive damage at the supports through fretting wear and fatigue. Predictive analysis of vibrations due to this mechanism is therefore quite important in practice, in particular in the case of PWR Steam-Generators.

In fact, most of the work published in the recent years concerning cross-flow turbulence was focused on the experimental measurement of the fluctuating forces induced by the flow [2-4]. Work on various aspects of the numerical computation of the tube response under such excitation was also presented [5-9, 14].

The aim of this paper is to present several aspects of the practical use of the methodology developed at CEA, see [2, 5, 6, 8, 9], and implemented in the code GERBOISE, developed by CEA and FRAMATOME, for PWR Steam Generator tubes wear risk assessment.

2. TURBULENT FORCES IN SINGLE PHASE FLOW

The fluctuating pressure at the tube walls due to external cross-flow induces fluctuating lineic forces along the tube. Because of the random nature of turbulence, these forces are random functions of time and space. The formulation for the description of such forces, as detailed in [2] is summarized below.

The random force per unit length is entirely characterized by its cross-correlation spectrum

$$\Phi_F(s_1, s_2, f) = \left(\frac{1}{2}\bar{\rho}\,\bar{V}^2 D\right)^2 \frac{D}{\bar{V}} r(s_1) r(s_2) u^2(s_1) u^2(s_2)$$

$$e^{-\frac{|s_1 - s_2|}{\lambda_c}} \frac{L}{\lambda_c} \frac{D}{D_o} \frac{L_o}{L} \tilde{\Phi}_F^c(f_r) \qquad (1)$$

where s_1 and s_2 define locations along the tube and f is a given frequency. In the above equation, D and L are the tube diameter and length, $\bar{\rho}$ and $\bar{V}$ denote the mean values along the tube of the fluid density ρ and of the gap flow velocity V respectively with $V = V_o \frac{p}{p - D}$, p being the array pitch and V_o being the upstream velocity.

Functions $u(s)$ and $r(s)$ are the normalized flow and density profile defined as :

$$u(s) = V(s) / \bar{V} \quad , \quad r(s) = \rho(s) / \bar{\rho} \quad (2)$$

Moreover, the space dependence of the cross-spectrum is modelized through the correlation length λ_c, and $\tilde{\Phi}_F^e$ is an equivalent auto-spectrum, function of reduced frequency $f_r = f\, D/\bar{V}$, L_o and D_o being reference tube length and diameter associated with the spectrum.

Experimental evidence gathered in [2] showed that :

(a) the correlation length λ_c was found not to exceed a few tube diameters, or even less. As will be shown in section 3, exact knowledge of λ_c is not required for most practical applications.

(b) an envelope auto-spectrum $\tilde{\Phi}_F^e$ could be derived from a large set of experiments on various tube arrays. It is defined as :

$$\begin{cases} \tilde{\Phi}_F^e = 4\ 10^{-4}\ f_r^{-0.5} & .01 < f_r < .2 \\[2mm] \tilde{\Phi}_F^e = 3\ 10^{-6}\ f_r^{-3.5} & .2 < f_r < 3 \quad (3) \\[2mm] L_o = 1\ m\ ,\ D_o = .02\ m \end{cases}$$

However, numerical calculations presented here were performed by using a spectrum obtained through experiments on a U-bend bundle, see [2, 10] :

$$\begin{cases} \tilde{\Phi}_F^e = 4\ 10^{-7}\ f_r^{-2.7} & .1 < f_r < 2 \\[2mm] L_o = 1\ m\ ,\ D_o = .019\ m \end{cases} \quad (4)$$

3. RESPONSE OF A TUBE WITH LINEAR BOUNDARY CONDITIONS

3.1. Application of random linear vibration theory

If fixed linear boundary conditions are assumed at the supports, the tube response can be derived by using the classical random linear vibration theory :

$$\sigma_i(s) = \frac{1}{2}\ \bar{\rho}\ \bar{V}^2\ D\ \frac{L}{8\ \Pi^{3/2}\ m_i\ f_i^2\ \zeta_i^{1/2}}$$

$$(5)$$

$$\varphi_i(s) \left[f_{r_i}\ a_i\ \frac{D}{D_o}\ \frac{L_o}{L}\ \tilde{\Phi}_F^e\left(f_{r_i}\right) \right]^{\frac{1}{2}}$$

where σ_i denotes the r.m.s displacement along the tube, $\varphi_i(s)$, m_i, f_i, f_{r_i}, ζ_i are modal shape, mass, frequency, reduced frequency and damping respectively. The modal correlation factor a_i is defined as :

$$a_i = \frac{1}{\lambda_c\ L} \int_0^L \int_0^L \varphi_i(s_1)\ \varphi_i(s_2)\ r(s_1)\ r(s_2)$$

$$(6)$$

$$u^2(s_1)\ u^2(s_2)\ e^{-\dfrac{|s_1 - s_2|}{\lambda_2}}\ ds_1\ ds_2$$

The total r.m.s displacement along the tube is obtained through modal superposition :

$$\sigma^2(s) = \sum_{i=1}^{N} \sigma_i^2(s) \quad (7)$$

where N is the number of modes used.

3.2. Computationnal methods

The computation of the tube response requires only the calculation of the modes of the system and a numerical integration in equ (6). In practice, several methods may be used to perform this integration.

Method (a) Two dimensional quadrature.
The a_i coefficients are computed by using a two dimensional quadrature. The $[0, L] \times [0, L]$ domain is discretized in an adequate number of elements. Let L' be a typical scale of variation of the function $\varphi_i(s)\ r(s)\ u^2(s)$. The number of elements N_e needed to ensure a correct integration is expected to increase with decreasing values of $'L'$.

Method (b) One dimensional quadrature with λ_c dependence.
If the ratio λ_c/L' is much smaller than 1, eq (6) may be approximated as :

$$a_i = \frac{1}{\lambda_c\ L} \left[\int_0^L \int_0^L e^{-\dfrac{|s_1 - s_2|}{\lambda_c}}\ ds_1\ ds_2 \right]$$

$$(8)$$

$$\left[\int_0^L \varphi_i(s)\ r(s)\ u^2(s)\ ds \right]$$

which yields :

$$a_i = 2\left(1 - \frac{\lambda_c}{L}\left(1 - e^{-L/\lambda_c} \right) \right)$$

$$(9)$$

$$\frac{1}{2} \int_0^L \varphi_i(s)\ r(s)\ u^2(s)\ ds$$

The computation of the above formula only requires a one - dimensional quadrature and a much smaller computation time than in method (a) will be needed.

Method (c) One dimensional quadrature.
Due to the fact that λ_c is not well known, it is quite convenient to consider the case where λ_c/L is much smaller than 1. Eq (9) then becomes :

$$a_1 = \frac{2}{L} \int_0^L \varphi_1(s)\, r(s)\, u^2(s)\, ds \qquad (10)$$

The computation of the tube response, eq (5) does not require, in that case, any knowledge of λ_c.

These methods were tested on the case of a straight tube with pinned conditions at both ends. The flow velocity and density were assumed to be uniform along the tube, so that eq (6) becomes :

$$a_1 = \frac{1}{\lambda_c L} \int_0^L \int_0^L \sin\left(i\, \Pi\, \frac{s_1}{2}\right) \sin\left(i\, \Pi\, \frac{s_2}{2}\right)$$

$$\qquad (11)$$

$$e^{-\dfrac{|s_1 - s_2|}{\lambda_c}} \; ds_1\, ds_2$$

The exact solution is then :

$$a_1 = \frac{1 + i^2 \Pi^2 \,(\lambda_c/L)^2 \left[1 + (2\,\lambda_c/L)\left(1 - (-1)^i e^{-L/\lambda_c}\right)\right]}{\left[1 + i^2\, \Pi^2\, (\lambda_c/L)^2\right]^2} \qquad (12)$$

Method (a) was used with a Gaussian quadrature and 2000 elements over the domain.

The results of methods (b) and (c) were obtained through an analytical quadrature of the one dimensional integral, which is quite straightforward in that particular case.

Results are shown in table 1 for several values of λ_c/L and mode numbers. The reduced parameter λ_c/L', where L' here is the modal wave length, is also given.

From a practical point of view, it can be concluded from these results that :

(a) Obviously, method (a) gives very accurate results, independently of λ_c/L and λ_c/L'. However, the computation becomes too expensive if L' becomes very small. The use of this method for the analysis of the U-bend tube of Section 5 showed that for typical Steam-Generator parameters, a 5 % accuracy could be expected on the a_1 factor with 2000 elements, requiring about 1 second of CRAY CPU time.

(b) Method (b) gives a satisfactory approximation of the a_1 factor up to $\lambda_c/L' \simeq .2$ and for the case of large L'/L values, independently of λ_c/L. It may therefore be used for the analysis of the small radius tubes in a U-bend bundle.

(c) Method (c) also gives satisfactory approximation of the a_1 factor, but up to $\lambda_c/L' \simeq .1$ only and provided that λ_c/L remains much smaller than 1. The λ_c parameter being of a few diameters or less, this method is quite adequate for the large radius tubes of a Steam-Generator but is questionable for the smallest bends.

4. RESPONSE OF A TUBE WITH NON LINEAR BOUNDARY CONDITIONS

4.1. Computation of the tube dynamics

In the case of loose supports, the equations of motion of the tube are to be considered in the time domain :

$$M\ddot{X} + A\dot{X} + KX = F_e + F_1(X, \dot{X}) \qquad (13)$$

where M, A and K denote mass, damping and stiffness operators respectively, X is the tube displacement, F_e is the random external force due to turbulence and F_1 represents the impact forces at the loose supports. It was found quite convenient, [5], to use a projected form of eq (13) on the modal basis of the system :

$$M_n\, \ddot{q}_n + A_n\, \dot{q}_n + K_n\, q_n = f_e^n + f_1^n \qquad (14)$$

where M_n, A_n and K_n are modal mass, damping and stiffness respectively, q_n being the generalized displacement ant f_e^n, f_1^n being the modal projection of external and impact forces. Note that the supports which are considered as loose, through the use of F_1, are not to be taken into account when calculating the modal basis.

The solution of the set of equations made up of eq (14) written for each mode, is then done with the use of a time-stepping algorithm.

A Devogelaere explicit algorithm [7] is considered. A typical time step value to ensure stability and a few percent accuracy on average values, regardless of statistical effects considered in section 4.4, was found to be about :

$$\Delta t = \frac{1}{10\, f_n} \qquad (15)$$

where f_n is the frequency of the highest mode retained in the modal basis.

4.2. Random force simulation

The generalized force associated to cross-flow turbulence, f_e^n eq (14), may be computed directly from its formulation defined in equ (1). On each mode, $f_e^n(t)$ is such that, if there were no impact, the steady state modal response obtained by time-stepping integration would be that of eq (5). This condition yields that $f_e^n(t)$ is a banded white noise with spectral density :

$$S_n = \left(\frac{1}{2}\bar{\rho}\,\bar{V}^2\, D\right)^2 \frac{D}{\bar{V}} L^2 \frac{D}{D_o} \frac{L_o}{L}\, a_n\, \tilde{\Phi}_F^e\left(f_{r_n}\right) \qquad (16)$$

To ensure a correct decorrelation between drag and lift random forces, three samples of banded white noise, $B_x(t)$, $B_y(t)$, $B_z(t)$ are computed using a reference spectral density :

$$S_1 = \left(\frac{1}{2}\bar{\rho}\,\bar{V}^2\, D\right)^2 \frac{D}{\bar{V}} L^2 \frac{D}{D_o} \frac{L_o}{L}\, a_1\, \tilde{\Phi}_F^e(fr_1) \qquad (17)$$

The value of the generalized force on each mode is then :

$$f_e^n(t) = \sqrt{\frac{a_n \, \tilde{\Phi}_n^e \, (f_{r_n})}{a_1 \, \tilde{\Phi}_F^e \, (f_{r_1})}}$$

(18)

$$\left[\gamma_n^X \, B_X(t) + \gamma_n^Y \, B_Y(t) + \gamma_n^Z \, B_Z(t) \right]$$

where γ_n^X, γ_n^Y, γ_n^Z are modal directionnal weighting factors defined as :

$$\gamma_n^{X^2} = \frac{\int_0^L \left(\vec{\varphi}_n(s) \cdot \vec{i}_X \right)^2 ds}{\int_0^L \vec{\varphi}_n(s) \cdot \vec{\varphi}_n(s) \, ds}$$

(19)

$\vec{i}_X$ being the unit vector in the X direction. γ_n^Y and γ_n^Z are defined by the same formula using $\vec{i}_Y$ and $\vec{i}_Z$ vectors respectively.

4.3. Impact forces

The impact dynamics of a Steam-Generator tube on its supports is commonly modelled through :

(a) an elastic impact force, function of the tube normal displacement, see fig. 1 :

$$\vec{F}_N = K_c \, \langle \, \vec{x} \cdot \vec{n} \, \rangle \, \vec{n}$$

(20)

where K_c is the impact stiffness, $\vec{x}$ is the instantaneous distance between the tube external wall and the support wall, $\langle \, \rangle$ denotes the positive part and $\vec{n}$ is the vector normal to the support.

(b) a frictional force modelled by Coulomb's equations :

$$\vec{F}_T = - \mu(F_N)\frac{\vec{\dot{X}}_T}{\|\vec{\dot{X}}_T\|} \quad \text{if} \quad \vec{\dot{X}}_T \neq 0 \quad \text{(sliding)}$$

(21)

$$\vec{\dot{X}}_T = 0 \quad \text{and} \quad \|\vec{F}_T\| < \mu\|\vec{F}_N\| \quad \text{(adherence)}$$

(22)

where μ is the coefficient of friction and $\vec{\dot{X}}_T$ denotes the tangential velocity.

As wear rate is analysed by using Archard's equation, the instantaneous wear work rate is defined as :

$$\dot{W}(t) = F_N(t) \, \dot{X}_T(t)$$

(23)

Typical values of the impact parameters are [5, 6] :

$$K_c = 1.9 \, \frac{E \, e^2}{D} \sqrt{\frac{e}{D}}$$

(24)

$$\mu = .4$$

(25)

where e is the tube thickness and E is Young's modulus. Actually, as was shown in [8], a change of an order of magnitude in K_c induces only a 20 per cent error on average wear work rate, for systems such as those considered in the present paper.

The number of modes to be retained in the modal basis depends on the impact stiffness. A correct representation of the impact time-history is ensured if :

$$\frac{\varphi_N^2 \, (P)}{K_N} \simeq \frac{1}{K_c}$$

(26)

where N is the highest mode retained and P is the impact location.

In the time-stepping integration of eq (14), the computation of generalized impact forces $f_i^n(t)$ is done as follows. At each time step, displacement and velocities at the impact locations only are computed through modal superposition. The impact forces $F_i(X, \dot{X})$ may then be evaluated using eq (20) to (22). While the elastic impact force is quite straight-forward to calculate, the frictional force needs an adequate numerical scheme when adherence is involved [6]. The tangential force used to ensure zero velocity in that case is :

$$F_T = - K_F \left(X_T - X_T^o \right) - C_F \, \dot{X}_T$$

(27)

where K_F and C_F are adherence stiffness and damping respectively, X_T^o being the zero velocity tangential displacement. Typical values of K_F and C_F are :

$$K_F = 10 \, K_c$$

(28)

$$C_F = (K_F \, M_N)^{\frac{1}{2}}$$

(29)

However, these figures are not critical [6].

Once the impact forces are computed at all loose supports they are projected on the modes to derive $f_i^n(t)$.

4.4. Time averaging

For wear prediction, it is necessary to perform time averages of instantaneous displacements, impact forces and wear work rate which are produced by the time-stepping integration. Let the average wear work rate be defined as :

$$\overline{W} = \frac{1}{T_2 - T_1} \int_{T_1}^{T_2} \dot{W}(t) \, dt$$

(30)

where T_1 and T_2 denote the limit of the averaging interval.

An adequate choice of T_1 and T_2 is quite important in practice, because it has much influence on the wear rate predictions. Three aspects of the dynamics of the system must be considered.

(a) averaging must be done on the steady state regime. If the system were linear, the transient part of the response would be less than 2 per cent after :

$$T_1 = \frac{1}{\Pi \, f \, \zeta}$$

(31)

where f and ζ are modal frequency and damping. Actually, for a non-linear system, the transient response was found to vanish much more quickly, due to the strong influence of impact forces on the tube dynamics.

(b) the random nature of the turbulent forces makes the results of the averaging dependent on $T_2 - T_1$, regardless of the linear or non-linear nature of the system.

(c) the steady state regime of a forced non-linear system is quite complex, even for an harmonic excitation. Low frequency variations and even chaotic motions may be found in such cases [12]. The averaging duration $T_2 - T_1$ must therefore be chosen such that the response signal is sufficiently well sampled.

4.5. Numerical tests

The general considerations of the preceding sections are illustrated by performing computations on the case of a straight tube with pinned conditions at both ends, fig. 2a. The tube has length L = 2.26 m, diameter D = 22.2 mm, thickness e = 1.27 mm, Young's modulus $E = 2 \, 10^{11}$ Pa and equivalent lineic density $m_c = .885$ kg m^{-1}. Its natural modes have frequencies $f_N = N^2 \times 10$ Hz. A common value of ζ = .01 was arbitrarily assumed for modal damping rates.

To check the turbulent forces representation described in section 4.2, a linear case was computed using two methods :

(a) the analytical solution for linear systems, eq (5),

(b) the time stepping solution described above.

Four modes are considered, with a time-step $\Delta t = 10^{-3}$ s. The turbulent forces spectrum is that of eq (4), with a uniform flow velocity $\bar{V} = 2$ m/s and a fluid density $\bar{\rho} = 170$ kg m^{-3}.

Parameter T_1 is taken as zero, due to the value of T_2 used, compared to the T_1 value of eq (31). The r.m.s displacement σ at midspan versus $N_c = T_2 f_1$, the number of cycles of the fundamental frequency, is shown in table 2.

It is seen that the time-stepping solution clearly converges towards the analytical solution. A sufficient accuracy is achieved after 100 cycles of the fundamental frequency.

A non linear system is now considered in order to study the influence of several parameters on the accuracy of the averaging process, for a given value of T_2. The beam is now assumed to have loose supports at midspan and quarter span, fig. 2b.

The impact stiffness is $K_c = 10^6$ N m^{-1} and no dry friction is considered here, as it was found to have no critical effects on the aspects studied here. The modal basis is now made of 7 modes in each transverse directions, and the time step is $\Delta t = 2.44 \, 10^{-4}$ s. The parameters which are varied are :

- the support gaps, g_1 and g_2, fig. 2b,
- the shape of the support, fig. 3,
- the flow velocity.

The average impact force $\bar{F}_N$ is considered here for two values of T_2, assuming T_1 to be zero. The variation of F_N with T_2, noted ε, and the number of impacts per second, N_i, are also given for comparison. The results are gathered in table 3.

Let system 1 be taken as a reference. The variation of $\bar{F}_N$ is only 1.5 per cent between T_2 = 30 s and T_2 = 60 s. If the support gap is increased, system 2, the influence of T_2 is seen to be much bigger. This is also the case when the flow velocity is decreased, system 3. This may be understood by considering the number of impacts per second N_i, and the time histories of the impact force, fig. 4. Clearly, the time between impacts is much longer for systems 2 and 3, thus requiring a longer averaging time T_2 to ensure good accuracy.

Still considering system 1 as a reference, it is seen that introducing a new loose support, system 4, also increases the error ε. It is also the case when the support shape becomes circular, system 5. This effect is not due to the reduction in the number of impacts as above. It seems to be related to the increase in the number of possible dynamical regimes associated with the increase in the number of non linearities.

4.6. Pratical rules

From these results, confirmed by other calculations done by the authors, the following practical rules may be proposed

1. When simulating turbulent excitation of Steam Generator tubes with loose supports, it is of major importance to choose a convenient duration of the simulated signal. A compromise must be achieved between averaging errors and computation cost.

2. To ensure a given accuracy, the required duration of the signal will depend on the excitation amplitude and gap width, on the number and on the type of loose supports.

3. At the present time, there is no practical means of a priori estimating the duration of the signal which is necessary for a given case. Several calculations are needed to check the accuracy of the results.

4. Finally, it has to be emphasized that an accuracy of a few per cent concerning the dynamical averaged parameters, in particular wear work rate, is felt to be quite sufficient at the present time. This is related to the presence of many other uncertainties concerning other parameters which control the wear rate, in particular the wear coefficient. Indeed, up to now, such a coefficient is only known within an order of magnitude.

5. APPLICATION TO THE ANALYSIS OF A U-BEND TUBE

The methodology presented above has been implemented in a specific code, named GERBOISE, developed by CEA and FRAMATOME for PWR Steam Generator wear risk assessment. It is aimed at parametric analyses with linear and non-linear support conditions, and is associated with a data base containing flow profiles, turbulence spectra and wear coefficients. The code is coupled with CEA codes CASTEM 2000 for general purpose mechanics and GENEPI for Steam-Generator thermohydraulics [13].

GERBOISE is applied here to the analysis of a U-bend tube, with anti-vibratory V bars (AVB), fig. 5. The tube characteristics are those of the preceding section, its radius of curvature is R = 1 m, the angle of aperture of the AVBs being named α. The tube is assumed to be clamped at both ends.

Considering the AVB supports as linear (pinned conditions), a first analysis is made to study the influence of the angle of aperture α on the tube r.m.s displacement under turbulent excitation. The effect of the flow profile is also investigated considering a uniform profile, and a more realistic one, fig. 6. Using the methodology presented in section 3, the maximum r.m.s out of plane displacement along the tube is computed for several values of α and for the two profiles, with a mean flow velocity $\bar{V}$ = 4 m/s, and 5 modes.

The result of GERBOISE is shown in fig. 7. It clearly points out the fact that a good knowledge of the flow velocity profile is quite important for the optimization of α and for the values of displacement associated with it. Indeed, this analysis should include flow calculations [13] to correctly take into account the effect of the AVB location on the flow profile.

A second analysis is performed considering the AVB as loose supports. The influence of the tube-AVB gap on wear work rate is investigated. The non-uniform flow profile, fig. 6 is considered, with an angle of aperture α = 55°. With the use of the methodology presented in section 3, the parameters for the non-linear calculation are chosen to be :

- impact stiffness K_c = 10^6 N m^{-1}
- adherence stiffness K_f = 5 10^6 N m^{-1}
- adherence damping C_F = 5 10^3 N m s^{-1}
- time step Δt = 3 10^{-4} s
- averaging time T_1 = 0 T_2 = 10 s

A modal basis with 13 modes, ranging from 9.4 to 300 Hz is used with a common value of damping rate ζ = 10^{-2}. Fig. 8 displays wear work rate versus tube-support gap. It is seen that :

(a) for gaps up to g = 10 μm, the wear work rate is almost constant.

(b) for higher gaps, g > 10 μm, the wear work rate steeply decreases. This clearly is the consequence of the reduction of impact force. For g = 1 mm, there is no impact and therefore no wear work rate. These

results are quite consistent with those of [5].

These applications show that the use of the method for analyses at an industrial stage is today quite feasable with the help of GERBOISE. Such parametric studies required a total computing time of only about 15 minutes of CRAY-2 CPU.

6. CONCLUSION

There is an actual practical interest in performing predictive analysis of vibration and wear risks in tube bundles subjected to cross-flow turbulence.

The methodology developed at CEA Saclay for turbulent cross-flow analysis of linear and non linear systems has now reached a stage of industrial use and is implemented in the code GERBOISE.

On the basis of the present study, the following concluding remarks may be done on the method and it use.

(a) there is a strong consistency between the formalism used to represent random turbulent forces on linear and non linear systems.

(b) the use of a modal basis projection for the solution of the non linear equations of motion is both effective and convenient, in terms of the reduction in the number of degrees of freedom and for the representation of the spectral content and the spatial correlation of turbulent forces.

(c) the accuracy of wear work rate numerical predictions is quite sensitive to characteristics of the non linear system (gaps, number of supports, ..). An adequate choice of averaging duration in the statistical process is of major importance.

(d) the application of the method for Steam-Generators U-bend tubes is today quite feasable with the help of GERBOISE.

REFERENCES

[1] PAIDOUSSIS, M.P. Flow-induced vibrations in nuclear reactor and heat exchangers. IAHR-IUTAM Symposium on practical experiences with Flow-induce vibrations, Karlsruhe, Germany, 1979.

[2] AXISA, F., ANTUNES, J. and VILLARD, B. Random Excitation of heat exchangers tubes by cross-flows. Journal of Fluids and Structures, 1990, 4, 321-341.

[3] CHEN, S.S., and JENDRZEJCZYK, J.A., Fluid excitation forces acting on a square tube array. ASME Journal of fluids engineering, 1987, 109, 415-423.

[4] GRANGER, S. A global model for flow-induced vibrations of tube bundles in cross flow. ASME Pressure vessel and

Piping Conference, Nashville, 1990, 189, 139-152.

[5] AXISA, A., ANTUNES, J., and VILLARD, B. Overview of Numerical methods for predicting flow induced vibrations, ASME Journal of Pressure Vessel Technology, 1988, 10, 6-14.

[6] ANTUNES, J., AXISA, F., BEAUFILS, B., and GUILBAUD, D. Coulomb Friction Modelling of multispan tube bundles. Journal of Fluids and Structures, 1990, 4.

[7] ROGERS, R.J., and PICK, R.J. Factors associated with support forces due to heat exchanger tube vibration contact. Nucl. Eng. and Design, 1977, 44, 247.

[8] ANTUNES, J. Contribution à l'étude des vibrations de faisceaux de tubes en écoulement transversal. Thesis, 1986, Université de Paris VI.

[9] BEAUFILS, B. Contribution à l'étude des vibrations et de l'usure des faisceaux de tubes en écoulement transversal. Thesis, 1990, Université de Paris VI.

[10] ANTUNES, J., VILLARD, B., and AXISA, F. Cross-Flow induced vibration of U-bend tubes of Steam-Generators. 8th SMIRT Conference, Bruxelles, 1985, paper F 16/9.

[11] ARCHARD, J.F., and HIRST, M.E. The wear of metals under unlubricated conditions. Proceedings of the Royal Society of London, 1956, A 236, 397.

[12] De LANGRE, E., DOVEIL, F., PORCHER, G., and AXISA, F. Chaotic and Periodic motion of a non linear oscillator in relation with flow-induced vibrations of loosely supported tubes. ASME Pressure Vessel and piping Conference, Nashville 1990, 189, 119-127.

[13] OBRY, P., CHEISSOUX, J.L., GRANDOTTO, M., GAILLARD, J.P., De LANGRE, E., and BERNARD, M. An advanced Steam generator design 3D Code. Thermal hydraulics of advanced nuclear steam generators, ASME Winter Annual Meeting, Dallas, 1990.

[14] FISHER, N.J., OLESEN, M.J., ROJERS, R.J., KO, P.L. Simulation of tube-to-support dynamic interaction in heat exchange equipment. ASME Journal of Pressure Vessel Technology, 1989, 111, p 378-384.

TABLE 1

Computation of the modal correlation factor a_i

λ_c/L	Mode number i	λ_c/L'	a_i			
			Method (a)	Method (b)	Method (c)	Exact
.01	1	.01	1.01	.99	1.00	1.00
	2	.02	1.01	.99	1.00	.99
	5	.05	.99	.99	1.00	.99
.1	1	.1	.94	.90	1.00	.93
	2	.2	.78	.90	1.00	.76
	5	.5	.35	.90	1.00	.33
1.	1	1.	.32	.37	1.00	.32
	2	2.	.055	.37	1.00	.055
	5	5.	.018	.37	1.00	.015

TABLE 2

Linear system under turbulent excitation

Time stepping solution				Exact solution
N_2	100	500	1000	
σ (μm)	116.	111.	114.	113.

TABLE 3

Effect of averaging time

System	g_1 (mm)	g_2 (mm)	V(m/s)	Support Shape	$\bar{F}_N$ (N)		ϵ (%)	N_i
					T_2 = 30 s	T_2 = 60 s		
1	∞	.1	4	FLAT	1.42	1.40	1.5	82
2	∞	1.	4	FLAT	.152	.165	8	7
3	∞	.1	2	FLAT	.044	.049	9	13
4	.1	.1	4	FLAT	1.06	1.01	5	69
5	∞	.1	4	CIRCULAR	4.92	5.26	7	108

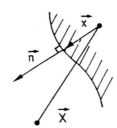

FIGURE 1 - Tube-support impact parameters

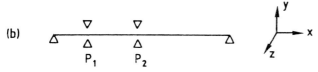

FIGURE 2 - Straight tube for linear
analysis (a) and non linear
analysis (b)

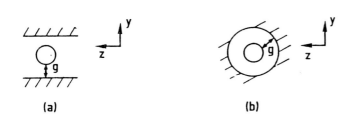

FIGURE 3 - Support shape (a) Flat (b) Circular

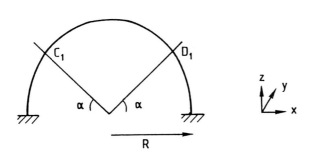

FIGURE 5 - U tube model with Antivibratory bars

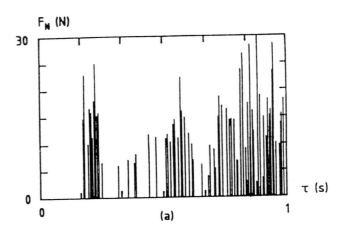

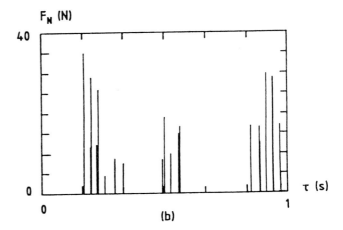

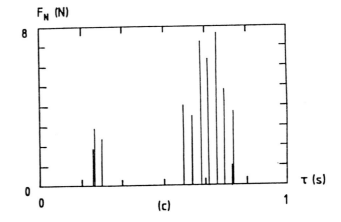

FIGURE 4 - Impact force time history

(a)	g = .1 mm	V = 4 m/s
(b)	g = 1 mm	V = 4 m/s
(c)	g = .1 mm	V = 2 m/s

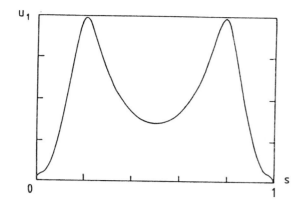

FIGURE 6 - Non-uniform flow velocity profile

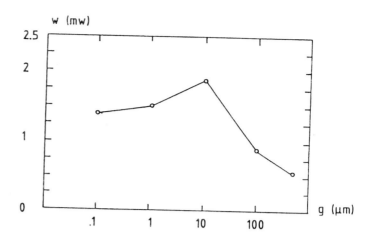

FIGURE 8 - Wear work rate as a function of tube-support gap

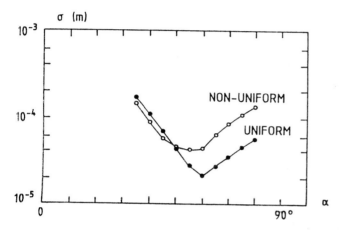

FIGURE 7 - Maximum R.M.S displacement along the tube as a function of AVB angle

Combined boundary integral equation and null-field equation method for hydrodynamic effects of two-dimensional exterior wave problem

I-T HWANG, MSc and C-N FAN, PhD
Institute of Nuclear Energy Research, Taiwan, People's Republic of China

SYNOPSIS

The purpose of this paper is to study the added mass and damping arising from a tube which vibrates in a compressible inviscid fluid by using the combined boundary integral equation and null- field equation method. The irregular frequencies can be eliminated and provide a unique solution. Several numerical examples are presented in this paper, the results show good agreement with analytical solution for regular geometries which can be analyzed by the seperational variable method. For arbitrary geometry of tubes are also discussed in this paper.

1 INTRODUCTION

The radiation and scattering of waves by rigid objects in fluid is one of the major problems in acoustics. Boundary integral equation method (BIEM) has been widely used to solve the fluid-structure interaction problems. BIEM has several advantages compared with finite element method or other numerical methods, for it, only the surfaces or boundaries are need to be discritized and analyzed. In addition, for exterior problems, the radiation condition is incorporated analytically in the integral formulation, (unlike the finite element method) it is not the problem that how far is enough to stop the discretization.

However, BIEM yields integral equations which have unique solutions, except at certain wavenumbers (irregular values). For the exterior Neumann problem, the irregular wavenumbers are corresponding to the eigenfrequencies of the interior Dirichlet problem; while for the exterior Dirichlet problem, the irregular wavenumbers are corresponding to the eigenfrequencies of the interior Neumann problem. Several methods have been developed to guarantee uniqueness of the integral equations over a range of wavenumbers or at all wavenumbers. (1) Null-field equation method ,leading to the T-matrix method for a scattering problem (2) Combined Helmholtz integral equation formulation (CHIEF) method (3) Helmholtz gradient formulation (HGF) method and (4) Combined integral equation formulation and null-field method. The null-field method was first derived by Waterman [1] in 1965, it has been discussed by many authors [2-4]. The rate of convergence of this method deteriorates very rapidly with increasing aspect ratio. CHIEF method was derived by Schenck [5] in 1968. Schenck used the Helmholtz integral equation with interior points in boundary of object as a constraint, lead to equations of overdetermined system and may then be solved by a least-square procedure. But when some of the related interior points coincide with a nodal surface of the related interior problem, CHIEF may not work. The selection of the interior points is a potentially serious shortcoming to CHIEF, since (i) the nodal surfaces are not usually known a priori, (ii) the eigenfrequencies and the nodal surfaces of the related interior problem become more closely spaced as the frequency increase, (iii) no criterion for the selection of the number and location of the interior points have been given. For low or moderately high

frequencies, CHIEF is successful.

Meyer et al.[6] implemente the method proposed by Burton and Miller [7] which Seybert and Rengarajan called Helmholtz gradient formulation (HGF), In HGF, a new integral equation is formed by adding to the usual Helmholtz integral equation. Although each of the two integral equations has a set of irregular wavenumbers, these sets are distinct; and HGF will theoretically yield unique solution for all wavenumbers. But Tobocman [8] show that HGF method converges more slowly than CHIEF method, and this method seems to give no satisfactory results at intermediate high wavenumbers. Stupfel et al. [9] implemented the method derived from D.S.Jones [2], the null-field and integral equations are coupled to solve the exterior Neumann problem, and the irregular wavenumber are eliminated up to a given irregular frequency through the use of M additional null-field equations. Stupfel et al. show that Jones' method is efficient for solving the radiating or scattering of objects of high aspect ratio and/or in the high frequency range. The paper of Stupfel are specialized to axisymmetrical problems. This paper implement Jones' method and numerical scheme of Stupfel et al. to analyze the radiation problem of 2-D object in fluid.

2 FORMULATION

In the exterior boundary-value problems of acoustics, one is concerned with finding solution of the Helmholtz equation,

$$(\nabla^2 + k^2)\Phi(r) = 0 \qquad (1)$$

where $\Phi(r)$ is the pressure in the infinite domain D exterior to a finite body B with surface S; k is the wavenumber ω/c, c is the speed of sound and ω is the frequency.

To find a potential $\Phi(r)$ satisfying the Helmholtz equation in D, the radiation condition must satifies

$$r^{1/2}\left(\frac{\partial\Phi(r)}{\partial r} - ik\Phi(r)\right) \to 0, \qquad r \to \infty \qquad (2)$$

For the Neumann problem, a boundary condition on S is

$$\frac{\partial\Phi(r)}{\partial n} = f(r) \qquad (3)$$

For the Dirichlet problem, it is

$$\Phi(r) = g(r) \qquad (4)$$

The formulation of the methodology in this paper is dedicated for Neumann problem, the same methods can be modified to solve the Dirichlet problem.

Let $G(P,Q)$ is the free-space wave source, which satisfies the Helmholtz equation in D and the radiation condition in infinity;

$$G(P,Q) = \frac{i\pi}{2} H_0^{(1)}(k \mid r_P - r_Q \mid) \qquad (5)$$

where $H_0^{(1)}$ denotes the Hankle function of the first kind.

Applying Green's identity in D, we obtain the corresponding Helmholtz integral equation;

$$C(P)\Phi(P) = \int_S [-\Phi(Q)\frac{\partial G}{\partial n}(P,Q) + G(P,Q)\frac{\partial \Phi}{\partial n}(Q)]dS(Q) \qquad (6)$$

where n is the unit normal on S directed away from D into B, and the coefficient

$$C(P) = 2\pi \qquad , P \in D \qquad (7)$$

$$C(P) = 0 \qquad , P \in inside B \qquad (8)$$

$$C(P) = \beta \qquad , P \in S \qquad (9)$$

where β is the solid angle, if the surface is smooth where the field point located, $\beta = \pi$.

For the Neumann problem, use (3) and (9) in (6) yields

$$\pi\Phi(p) + \int_S \Phi(Q)\frac{\partial G}{\partial n}(P,Q)dS(Q) = \int_S G(P,Q)f(Q)dS(Q) \qquad (10)$$

This integral equation posseses a unique solution unless the corresponding homogeneous integral equation;

$$\pi\Phi(P) + \int_S \Phi(Q)\frac{\partial G}{\partial n}(P,Q)dS(Q) = 0 \qquad (11)$$

has a non-trivial solution.

It is known that [2] when k is an eigenvalue of the interior Dirichlet problem, (11) has non-trivial solutions. At or in the neighborhood of these corresponding wavenumbers k, the coefficient matrix is ill conditioned, that causes the integral equation (1) does not have a unique solution for general $f(Q)$.

The nonuniqueness is a purely mathematical problem, no phisical meaning is encountered. It may be overcome by introducing the bilinear expansion for the fundamental solution $G(P,Q)$ and this will be discussed following.

2.1 NULL FIELD EQUATION

The fundamental solution may be written as [10];

$$G(P,Q) = \frac{i\pi}{2} \sum_{m=0}^{\infty} \sum_{l=1}^{2} \varepsilon_m \psi_m^l(Q)\varphi_m^l(P) \qquad (12)$$

for $r_Q > r_P$, where

$$\psi_m^l(Q) = H_m^{(1)}(kr_Q)E_m^l(\theta_Q)$$
$$\varphi_m^l(P) = J_m(kr_P)E_m^l(\theta_P)$$
$$E_m^1(\theta) = cos m\theta, E_m^2(\theta) = sin m\theta$$
$$\text{and, } \varepsilon_m = \begin{cases} 1 & , m = 0 \\ 2 & , m > 0 \end{cases}$$

Let P lies inside B and q lies on S (where $r_P < r_q$), by substituting (8),(12) into (6) to give [2-4]:

$$\sum_{m=0}^{\infty} \sum_{l=1}^{2} \varepsilon_m \varphi_m^l(P) \int_S [\Phi(q)\frac{\partial \psi_m^l}{\partial n}(q) - \frac{\partial \Phi}{\partial n}(q)\psi_m^l(q)]dS(q) = 0 \qquad (13)$$

Since φ_m^l are orthogonal, we obtain

$$\int_S [\Phi(q)\frac{\partial \psi_m^l}{\partial n}(q) - \frac{\partial \Phi}{\partial n}(q)\psi_m^l(q)]dS(q) = 0 \qquad (14)$$

$$\text{for } l = 1,2$$
$$m = 0,1,2,3,\ldots$$

(14) are so-called "null-field equations", the infinite set of null-field equations posseses the important property to be uniquely solvable, ie, the completeness of the infinite set of functions $\psi_m^l(q)$ on S ensures that $\Phi(q)$ is unique almost everywhere on S.

The null-field equations (14) for the exterior Neumann problem may be written as

$$\int_S [\Phi(q)\frac{\partial \psi_m^l}{\partial n}(q)]dS(q) = f_m^l \qquad (15)$$

where, $f_m^l = \int_S f(q)\psi_m^l(q)dS(q)$, $f(q) = \frac{\partial \Phi}{\partial n}(q) = \rho\vec{\lambda}$, ρ is the mass density of fluid and $\vec{\lambda}$ is the normal component of acceleration at point q. $\Phi(q)$ is the hydrodynamic pressure on S to be determined. If S is circle, then (15) can be easily solved by Fourier synthesis. For any other geometry,(15) must be solved numerically.

To implement numerically the null-field equations in the case of 2-D exterior Neumann problem, the surface pressure $\Phi(q)$ can be expanded as

$$\Phi(q) = \sum_{n=0}^{N} \phi_n(q) \qquad (16)$$

$$,N \rightarrow \infty$$

where the set of the functions $\phi_n(q)$ is required to be complete over S.

The choice of the $\phi_n(q)$ determines the numerical efficiency of the method. Different authors have advocated different choices for $\phi_n(q)$. However, to the authors' knowledge, there are not a satisfactory criterion for choosing the set of functions $\phi_n(q)$ at present. In this paper, $\phi_n(q)$ are chosen to be:

$$\phi_n(q) = \sum_{l=1}^{2} a_n^l E_n^l(\theta_q) \qquad (17)$$

where the angle θ_q is defined in Fig.1

By substituting (16),(17) into (15), we obtain

$$\sum_{n=0}^{N} \sum_{l=1}^{2} a_n^l \int_S E_n^l(\theta_q)\frac{\partial \psi_m^l}{\partial n}(q)dS(q) = f_m^l \qquad (18)$$

$$l = 1,2$$
$$m = 0,1,2,3,\ldots,M$$
$$M, N \rightarrow \infty$$

(18) is an infinite system of the unknown coefficient a_n^l; can be written in matrix form:

$$L_{m \times n}^l a_n^l = f_m^l \qquad (19)$$

where, $L_{m \times n}^l = \int_S \phi_n(q)\frac{\partial \psi_m^l}{\partial n}(q)dS(q)$, $f_n^l = \int_S f(q)\psi_m^l(q)dS(q)$, $m = 0,1,2,\ldots,M$ $,n = 0,1,2,\ldots,N$

We may solve (19) numerically by truncating this system for M and N are finite numbers. For $M > N$, (19) will lead to overdetermined linear system, and may be solved by the least-square method. But Stupfel et al. [9] show that $M > N$ gives no better results. Therefore, we may take $M = N$ and solve (19) by standard procedure.

Since $H_m(kr) = J_m(kr) + iY_m(kr)$, $J_m(kr)$ and $Y_m(kr)$ are the Bessel function of order m of 1st and 2nd kind, respectively. As $m \rightarrow \infty$, $J_m(kr) \rightarrow 0$ for larger m, but $Y_m(kr)$ is a rapidly increasing function of m for larger m; the asymptotic function of $Y_m(kr)$ is

$$Y_m(kr) \approx -\sqrt{\frac{2}{\pi m}}(\frac{2m}{ekr})^m \qquad (20)$$

$$,m \rightarrow \infty$$

So as $n \to \infty$, $H_m(kr) \approx iY_m(kr)$. Owning to the undesirable numerical behavior of $Y_m(kr)$ for small values of kr and/or large values of m, the null-field method gives undesirable results at these corresponding values. Therefore a "renormalization" procedure must be made to remove the large term $(2m)^m$ and to minimize the variations of r^{-m} along S.

If 10^A is the greatest number accepted by the computer, then M cannot be larger than $\overline{M}$ defined by

$$\sup_{r \in S} log \mid Y_{\overline{M}}(kr) \mid < A \tag{21}$$

For $m \geq \overline{M}$, $Y_m(kr)$ is replaced by $\overline{Y}_m(kr)$;

$$Y_m(kr) = -\sqrt{\frac{2}{\pi m}} \left(\frac{2m}{ek\bar{r}}\right)^m \overline{Y}_m(kr) \tag{22}$$

where, $r_{min} \leq \bar{r} \leq r_{max}$, r_{min} and r_{max} being the minimum and maximum values of $r_q, r_q \in S$. From the relation of the ascending recursion of Bessel function;

$$Y_{m+1}(kr) = \frac{2m}{kr} Y_m(kr) - Y_{m-1}(kr) \tag{23}$$

(22) set into (23), we obtain the ascending recursion of normalized Bessel function $\overline{Y}_m(kr)$;

$$\overline{Y}_{m+1}(kr) = e\left(\frac{\bar{r}}{r}\right)\left(\frac{m}{m+1}\right)^{m+1/2} \overline{Y}_m(kr)$$
$$-\left[\frac{ek\bar{r}}{2(m+1)}\right]^2 \left(\frac{m-1}{m+1}\right)^{m-3/2} \overline{Y}_{m-1}(kr) \tag{24}$$

Any order of $\overline{Y}_m(kr)$ are computed through (24), the same accuracy can be reached as the $Y_m(kr)$. Substituting (22) in (19), dividing $\bar{L}_{mn}^l$ and f_m^l by $i\sqrt{\frac{2}{\pi m}}\left(\frac{2m}{ek\bar{r}}\right)^m$, we have

$$\bar{L}_{mn}^l a_n^l = \bar{f}_m^l \tag{25}$$

where, $\qquad \bar{L}_{mn}^l = L_{mn}^l, \bar{f}_m^l = f_m^l, m < \overline{M}$

$$\bar{L}_{mn}^l = \int_S \phi_n(kr)\{[\frac{m}{kr}\overline{Y}_m(kr) - \sqrt{\frac{m}{m+1}}\frac{2}{ek\bar{r}}(\frac{m+1}{m})^m$$

$$(m+1)\overline{Y}_{m+1}(kr)]E_m^l(\theta)\frac{\partial(kr)}{\partial n} + \overline{Y}_m(kr)\frac{\partial E_m^l}{\partial n}(\theta)\}dS \tag{26}$$

$$\bar{f}_m^l = \int_S f(q)\overline{Y}_m(kr)E_m^l(\theta)dS \tag{27}$$

$$,m \geq \overline{M}$$

the differential form of Bessel function $\frac{dY_m}{dZ} = \frac{m}{Z}Y_m - Y_{m+1}$ has been used in (26).

If the smallest and greatest numbers accepted by the computer are 10^{-A} and 10^A, since from (20) and (22):

$$\mid \overline{Y}_m(kr) \mid \approx (\frac{\bar{r}}{r})^m, \text{as} \quad m \to \infty$$

the greatest value M can achieve must verify

$$(M)log(\frac{\bar{r}}{r_{max}}) \geq -A$$

$$(M)log(\frac{\bar{r}}{r_{min}}) \leq A$$

We can choose $\bar{r}$ to optimize M, by letting $\bar{r} = \sqrt{r_{max}r_{min}}$:

$$M \leq \frac{2A}{log(\frac{r_{max}}{r_{min}})} \tag{28}$$

If P is the number of siginificant digits allowed by the computer, for M is sufficiently large ,M must verfy:

$$log \mid \frac{Y_M(kr_{min})}{Y_M(kr_{max})} \mid \leq P \tag{29}$$

By using (20), we obtain another inequality;

$$(M)log\frac{r_{max}}{r_{min}} \leq P, \qquad \text{ie,}$$

$$M \leq \frac{P}{log(\frac{r_{max}}{r_{min}})} \tag{30}$$

By comparing (28) and (30), since $P \leq 2A$, in order not to loss of numerical accuracy in the computations of $\bar{L}_{mn}$ and $\bar{f}_m$, (30) is the dominant inequality for M.

However, even if M satifies (30),the calculated $\Phi(r)$ on the surface are loss of accuracy at points far from the origion. It is because the function we choose (17) to define the surface pressure on S is not accurate enough. Till now, it is a difficult work to choose a well defined functions to represent the surface pressure for objects of high aspect ratio and/or nonregular geometry. And that is why the null-field method fails in some cases.

According to Jones' idea, null-field method can be improved by coupling with the boundary integral equation.

2.2 COMBINED INTEGRAL EQUATION AND NULL-FIELD EQUATION METHOD

From (6) and (9), if we divide the boundary S into L straight line segment, we can write (6) for the pressure $\Phi(P)$ and its gradient $\frac{\partial \Phi}{\partial n}(P)$ of representative nodal point on the jth boundary element;

$$\beta_i \Phi_i + \sum_{j=1}^{L} \int_{S_j} \Phi_j \frac{\partial G}{\partial n}(i,j)dS_j = \sum_{j=1}^{L} \int_{S_j} G(i,j)\frac{\partial \Phi_j}{\partial n}dS_j \tag{31}$$

Now, by taking the field point sucessively to all the nodal points on the boundary, (31) can be converted into a $L \times L$ linear system;

$$\mathbf{H}\boldsymbol{\Phi} = \mathbf{G}\frac{\partial \boldsymbol{\Phi}}{\partial \mathbf{n}} \tag{32}$$

the coefficients of $\mathbf{H}$ and $\mathbf{G}$ can be computed from standard boundary integral procedure.

From Jones' idea, the integral equation (32) and the null-field equation (25) can be coupled to solve the hydrodynamic pressure $\Phi(P)$. In (25), the unknowns are a_n^l, in order to solve (25)and (32) simultaneously, a_n^l need to be expressed in terms of the nodal pressure Φ_j. From (16),(17), the coefficients a_n^l are expressed by standard Fouries series procedure;

$$a_0^1 = \frac{1}{2\pi}\int_0^{2\pi}\Phi(r,\theta)d\theta$$

$$a_0^2 = 0$$

$$a_n^1 = \frac{1}{\pi}\int_0^{2\pi}\Phi(r,\theta)cosn\theta d\theta$$

$$a_n^2 = \frac{1}{\pi}\int_0^{2\pi}\Phi(r,\theta)sinn\theta d\theta \tag{33}$$

If we divide the boundary S into L straight line elements, the values of $\Phi(r,\theta)$ at any point on the element can be defined in terms of their nodal values and two linear interpolation functions. Thus (33) can be expressed in matrix form;

$$\mathbf{a} = \mathbf{S}\boldsymbol{\Phi} \tag{34}$$

where,$\mathbf{a}$ is a $(2N+2) \times 1$ matrix, $\mathbf{S}$ is a $(2N+2) \times L$ matrix and $\boldsymbol{\Phi}$ is a $L \times 1$ matrix. (34) set into (25), we have

$$\mathbf{T}\boldsymbol{\Phi} = \bar{\mathbf{f}} \tag{35}$$

where $\mathbf{T} = \bar{\mathbf{L}} \times \mathbf{S}$ is a $(2N+2) \times L$ matrix. From (32) and (35), we obtain an overdetermined $(L+2N+2) \times L$ linear system;

$$\left[\frac{\mathbf{H}}{\mathbf{T}}\right]\{\boldsymbol{\Phi}\} = \left\{\frac{\mathbf{G}\frac{\partial \boldsymbol{\Phi}}{\partial n}}{\mathbf{f}}\right\} \tag{36}$$

We can solve (36) by using least-square method to solve the hydrodynamic pressure Φ on S. The hydodynamic force Φ_F will be obtained by integrating Φ over the surface of the tube.

3 NUMERICAL EXAMPLE

In this paper, we present the numerical results of the combined integral equation and null-field equation method for the 2-D exterior acoustic problem, all calculations are carried out using VAX/750. We consider the radiation problem of (1) circular tube, and (2) rectangular tube. Assume Ψ is the hydrodynamic force of the tube induced by excitation of unit acceleration, then

$$\Phi_F = \Psi \times \ddot{\lambda}$$

where $\ddot{\lambda}$ is the acceleration of the tube. Since Φ_F is complex, so is Ψ, let Ψ_R and Ψ_I be the real and imaginary part of Ψ, respectively.

$$\Phi_F = (\Psi_R + i\Psi_I) \times \ddot{\lambda} = \Psi_R \times \ddot{\lambda} + i\Psi_I \times \ddot{\lambda}$$

Since $\ddot{\lambda} = -i\omega\dot{\lambda}, \dot{\lambda} = \bar{\lambda}e^{-i\omega}t$, then;

$$\Phi_F = \Psi_R\ddot{\lambda} + \omega\Psi_I\dot{\lambda}$$

ie, the real part of the hydrodynamic force is inphase with the acceleration of tube and introduce the inertia effect called the added mass, while the imaginary part of the hydrodynamic force is in phase with the velocity of tube and introduce the damping effect called the radiation damping.[11] The hydrodynamic forces are discussed following;

1. **Circular tube**

   The surface of the circular tube is divided into $n = 32$ linear elements, the calculated real and imaginary part of normalized hydrodynamic forces $\overline{\Phi}_F = \Phi_F/\pi R^2$ acting on the tube are shown in Fig.2.a,2.b. The forces are comparing with the analytical solution and the solution by standard boundary integral equation methods, we can see from these figures that the irregular wavenumbers $kR \approx 3.7, 6.9$, boundary integral equation method has undesirable results at these wavenumbers , if we use combined integral equation and null-field equation method, the irregular ones are eliminated. Good correlations can be obtained by comparing with the analytical solution [12]. In this calculation, the additional equation $M = 0$ is sufficient to reach the required accuracy.

2. **Rectangular tube**

   In order to test the ability of the present works for the tubes of high aspect ratio, we present some numerical results for rectangular shape of aspect ratio $a/b = 1,2,6$, all the surface of the rectangulars are divided into $n = 128$ linear elements, the direction of excitation is along x-direction (Fig.3). The calculated real and imaginary part of the normalized hydrodynamic forces are shown in Fig.3,4,5, with additional equations $M = 8$ are used (notice that the renomalized procedure has been done to meat the maximun and minimum number accepted by the computer) to eliminate the irregular wavenumbers.

   In our calculations show that, if $M > 8$, the calculated forces are diverged and give no better results. This is because (30) plays an important role to restrict the maximum number of M.

4 CONCLUSIONS

In this paper, we present a method to analyze the problems of radiating tubes of arbitrary shape in compressible inviscid fluid. The numerical implementations of the combined integral equation and null-field equation method show that it is efficient to solve the radiating tubes and the irregular wavenumbers can be eliminated in all the high frequency range.

The calculated hydrodynamic forces are complex, they can be separated into two parts: real part and imaginary part. The real part is in phase with the acceleration of the tube and introduce the inertia effect called the added mass term, while the imaginary part is in phase with the velocity of the tube and introduce the damping effect called the acoustic radiation damping term. This is different from the case of the fluid is incompressible, the calculated hydrodynamic forces are always real and constant to the excited frequencies and the damping terms are zero.

The method present here so far is only restricted to the problem of one tube. It is difficult to analyze the radiation phenomena of two or more tubes of arbitrary shapes surrounding by compressible fluid, to the authors' knowledge, there is no contribution analyze this problem yet. It is hope to solve this problem in the future.

REFERENCE

(1) WATERMAN, P. C., J. acoust. Soc. Am., 1969, 45, 1417-1429.
(2) JONES, D. S., *Integral equations for the exterior acoustic problem*, Q. Jl Mech. appl. Math., 1974, 27, 129-142.
(3) MARTIN, P. A., *On the null-field equations for the exterior problems of acoustics*, Q. Jl Mech. appl. Math., 1980, 33, 385-396.
(4) COLTON, D., KRESS, R., *The unique solvability of the null field equations of acoustics*, Q. Jl Mech. appl. Math., 1983, 36, 87-95.
(5) SEYBERT, A. F., RENGARAJAN, T. K., *The use of CHIEF to obtain unique solutions for acoustic radiation using boundary integral equations*, J. acoust. Soc. Am., 1987, 81, 1299-1306.
(6) MEYER, W. L., BELL, W. A., ZINN, B. T., STALLYBRASS, M. P., *Boundary integral solutions of three-dimensional acoustic radiation problems*, J. acoust. Soc. Am., 1978, 59, 245-262.
(7) BURTON, A. J., MILLER, G. F., *The application of integral equation methods to the numerical solutions of some exterior boundary value problems*, Proc. R. Soc. London Ser., 1971, A323, 201-210.
(8) TOBOCMAN, W., *Comparison of the T-matrix and Helmholtz integral equation methods for wave scattering calculations*, J. acoust. Soc. Am., 1985, 77, 369-374.
(9) STUPFEL, B., LAVIE, A., DECARPIGNY, J. N., *Combined integral equation and null-field method for the exterior acoustic problem*, J. Acoust. Soc. Am., 1988, 83, 927-941.
(10) MORSE, P. M., FESHBACH, H., *Methods of theoretical physics (McGrawHill New York, 1953)*, Vol II.
(11) LIN, W. H., CHEN, S. S., *On the added mass and radiation damping of rod bundles oscillating in compressible fluids*, J. Sound and Vibration, 1981, 74, 441-453.
(12) CHEN, S. S., *Flow-induced vibration of circular cylindrical structures*, Argonne National Laboratory, Hemisphere Publishing Co., 1987, 25-30.

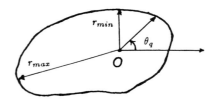

Fig.1 Symbols definition on object

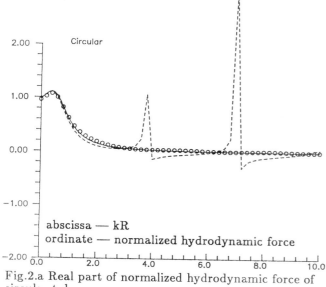

Fig.2.a Real part of normalized hydrodynamic force of circular tube
— Analytical solution
∘ Present
...B.I.E method

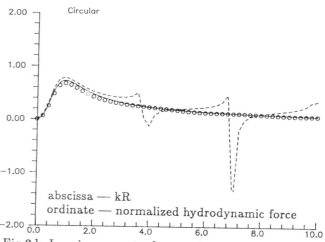

Fig.2.b Imaginary part of normalized hydrodynamic forces of circular tube
— Analytical solution
∘ Present
...B.I.E method

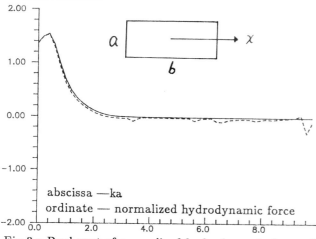

Fig.3.a Real part of normalized hydrodynamic force of rectangular tube ($a/b = 1$)
— Present
...B.I.E method

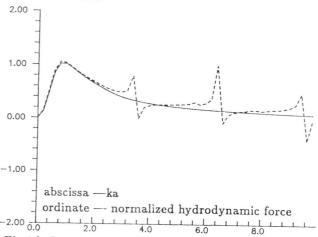

Fig.3.b Imaginary part of normalized hydrodynamic force of rectangular tube ($a/b = 1$)
— Present
...B.I.E method

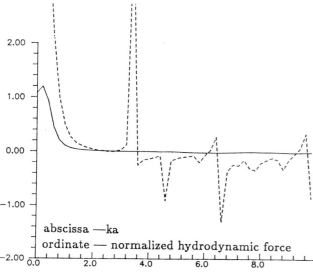

Fig.4.a Real part of normalized hydrodynamic force of rectangular tube ($a/b = 2$)
— Present
...B.I.E method

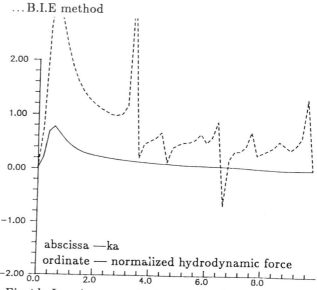

Fig.4.b Imaginary part of normalized hydrodynamic force of rectangular tube ($a/b = 2$)
— Present
...B.I.E method

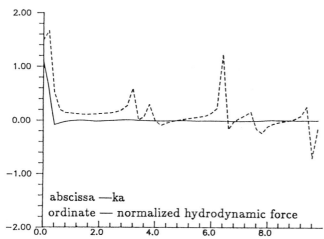

Fig.5.a Real part of normalized hydrodynamic force of rectangular tube ($a/b = 6$)
— Present
...B.I.E method

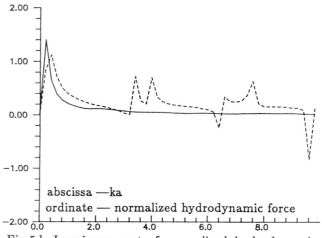

Fig.5.b Imaginary part of normalized hydrodynamic force of rectangular tube ($a/b = 6$)
— Present
...B.I.E method

C416/049

Internal and annular flow induced instabilities of clamped-clamped or cantilevered cylindrical shells in coaxial conduits

M P PAÏDOUSSIS, PhD, CEng, FIMechE, FRSC, MASME, MCSME, MIAHR
A K MISRA, PhD, MASME and V B NGUYEN
Department of Mechanical Engineering, McGill University, Montreal, Quebec, Canada

SYNOPSIS This paper presents a study of the effect of some of the system parameters on internal–and annular–flow–induced instabilities of clamped–clamped or cantilevered cylindrical shells in coaxial conduits; the parameters considered are shell thickness, length of the shell, annular width, and relative directions of the inner and annular flows. Shell motions are described by Flügge's shell equations and the unsteady fluid dynamic forces are evaluated by means of potential–flow theory. The time–averaged viscous loads on the shell due to flow pressurization and surface traction as well as internal damping of the shell material are also taken into account. Solutions are obtained with the aid of the Fourier–transform technique.

It is found that in both systems of clamped–clamped and cantilevered shells, where steel shells and water as the working fluid were used, a reduction in the annular width or in the shell thickness destabilizes the system while a reduction in the length of the shell stabilizes it. Clamped–clamped and cantilevered coaxial shells lose stability at lower annular–flow velocities when subjected concurrently to both internal and annular flows; this is more pronounced for counter– as opposed to co–current flows for clamped–clamped shells.

1 INTRODUCTION

The stability of systems of coaxial cylindrical shells subjected to annular and/or internal flows has been the subject of investigation of several recent papers. The study of such systems not only has a great academic appeal, but is also of considerable practical interest since such configurations are frequently found in heat exchangers, certain designs of nuclear reactors, large jet pumps, and so on. A complete literature review on the subject has recently been given by Païdoussis, Nguyen & Misra [5], and hence only a brief outline of the previous work most closely related to the present paper will be presented here.

In the above–mentioned studies [1–5], shell motions were described by Flügge's shell equations, modified to take into account steady viscous effects [2] due to flow pressurization and surface traction, while the unsteady fluid dynamic forces were determined by means of inviscid, potential–flow theory. For the system of clamped–clamped shells, although the effect of some system parameters on the critical flow velocity associated with a particular circumferential mode of the shells has been investigated [1–4], the influence of these parameters on the overall (i.e. lowest) critical flow velocity, which is in fact the most important from a practical viewpoint, has never heretofore been reported. It is clearly also of interest to study the stability of the system when subjected to counter–current flows, since so far only the case of co–current flows has been considered.

For the system of cantilevered shells, it has been found [5] that steady viscous forces strongly destabilize the system, and the overall critical flow velocity is greatly dependent on the amount of internal damping present in the shell material, assumed to be purely hysteretic. However, only limited calculations into the effect of system parameters have been conducted in this case also; for instance, investigations on how such an important parameter as the annular gap affects the stability of the

system have up until now been carried out by means of inviscid theory only and, as a result, the dynamical behaviour of the system has not been quantitatively predicted with reasonable accuracy.

This paper completes the first cycle of these studies. It is concerned with the system of a clamped–clamped or cantilevered cylindrical shell in a coaxial conduit conveying internal and/or annular incompressible, viscous flow. Attention is first given to the influence of such system parameters as shell thickness, length of the shell and annular width on the overall critical flow velocity. Steady viscous effects are then examined when the system is subjected to counter–current, as opposed to co–current, flows in the case of a clamped–clamped shell and to co–current flows in the case of a cantilevered shell.

2. FORMULATION OF THE ANALYTICAL MODEL

2.1. System definition and assumptions

Shown in Figure 1 is a system of coaxial cylinders of length L. The outer cylinder is rigid and is assumed to be infinitely long. A portion of the inner cylinder is flexible and thin enough to be considered a shell; at its upstream end, i.e. $x = 0$, the shell is assumed to be connected (clamped) to a semi–infinite rigid cylinder of the same radius and wall thickness as the shell; at the downstream end, $x = L$, the shell is either clamped onto another semi–infinite rigid cylinder (clamped–clamped shell) or unsupported (cantilevered shell).

The inner and outer cylinders have mean radii a and b. The shell has thickness h such that $h/a << 1$, and is assumed to be elastic and isotropic with Young's modulus E, density ρ_s, and Poisson's ratio ν. Incompressible fluid is generally flowing both inside the shell and in the annulus of densities ρ_i and ρ_o and with flow velocities U_i and U_o, respectively.

Shell motions are considered to be small, so that linear shell theory may be utilized and the shell–motion–induced perturbations to the flow may be derived from linearized theory. As mentioned earlier, these perturbations will be obtained from potential–flow theory, thus not accounting for unsteady viscous effects. Nevertheless, the flows are considered to be viscous, in the steady sense, and hence pressurization, necessary to overcome pressure drop, and traction effects on the shell are indeed taken into account. Finally, it is assumed that flow perturbations vanish far upstream and downstream of the flexible shell.

2.2 Equations of motion

The theory to be presented herein is based on a more general theory where both inner and outer cylinders may be flexible shells [5]. Shell motions are described by Flügge's shell equations [6], modified by Païdoussis, Misra & Chan [2] to take into account the stress resultants due to steady viscous effects. The equations of motion for the shell are given by

$$u'' + \frac{1}{2}(1-\nu)u^{\cdot\cdot} + \frac{1}{2}(1+\nu)v^{\cdot\prime} + \nu w'$$
$$+ k\left\{\frac{1}{2}(1-\nu)u^{\cdot\cdot} - w''' + \frac{1}{2}(1-\nu)w^{\cdot\cdot\prime}\right\}$$
$$+ [q_1 u'' + q_2(v^{\cdot} + w)]$$
$$+ q_3(u^{\cdot\cdot} - w') - \gamma\left[\frac{\partial^2 u}{\partial t^2}\right] = 0,$$

$$\frac{1}{2}(1+\nu)u^{\cdot\prime} + v^{\cdot\cdot} + \frac{1}{2}(1-\nu)v'' + w^{\cdot}$$
$$+ k\left\{\frac{3}{2}(1-\nu)v'' - \frac{1}{2}(3-\nu)w''^{\cdot}\right\}$$
$$+ [q_1 v'' + q_3(v^{\cdot\cdot} + w^{\cdot})] - \gamma\left[\frac{\partial^2 v}{\partial t^2}\right] = 0,$$

$$\nu u' + v^{\cdot} + w + k\left\{\frac{1}{2}(1-\nu)u''^{\cdot} - u'''\right.$$
$$- \frac{1}{2}(3-\nu)v''^{\cdot} + \nabla^4 w + 2w^{\cdot\cdot} + w\right\}$$
$$- [q_1 w'' + q_3(u' - v^{\cdot} + w^{\cdot\cdot})]$$
$$+ \gamma\left[\frac{\partial^2 w}{\partial t^2} - \frac{q}{\rho_s h}\right] = 0, \qquad (1)$$

where

$$(\ )' = a\frac{\partial(\ )}{\partial x}, \quad (\ )^{\cdot} = \frac{\partial(\ )}{\partial\theta}, \quad k = \frac{1}{12}\left(\frac{h}{a}\right)^2,$$

$$\gamma = \frac{\rho_s a^2(1-\nu^2)}{E}, \quad \nabla^2 = a^2\frac{\partial^2}{\partial x^2} + \frac{\partial^2}{\partial\theta^2},$$

and u, v and w are the axial, circumferential and radial displacements of the middle surface of the flexible shell, respectively; q_1, q_2, q_3 denote the nondimensional forces associated with steady viscous effects and $q = (P_i - P_o)|_{r=a}$ is the difference between the perturbation pressures in the inner and annular flows, q thus representing the unsteady radial force on the shell.

Shell motions must satisfy the following boundary conditions [6]: (i) at the upstream end (clamped), u, v, w and $\partial w/\partial x$ all vanish; (ii) at the downstream end, if the shell is also clamped, then u, v, w and $\partial w/\partial x$ again equal zero; but if the shell is unsupported, then the normal force N_x, the bending moment M_x, and Kirchhoff's effective shearing stress resultants $Q_x - (\partial M_{x\theta}/\partial\theta)/a$ and $N_{x\theta} - M_{x\theta}/a$ all vanish or, equivalently, in terms of shell displacements

$$u' + \nu v^{\cdot} + \nu w - kw'' = 0,$$
$$u^{\cdot} + v' + 3k(v' - w'^{\cdot}) = 0, \qquad (2)$$
$$w'' + \nu w^{\cdot\cdot} - \nu v^{\cdot} - u' = 0,$$
$$-w''' - (2-\nu)w'^{\cdot\cdot} + \left(\frac{3-\nu}{2}\right)v'^{\cdot} - \left(\frac{1-\nu}{2}\right)u^{\cdot\cdot} + u'' = 0.$$

2.3 Perturbation pressures and solution of the equations

For the purpose of satisfying equations (1), the shell displacements are expressed in the following functional forms:

$$\left\{\begin{array}{c} u \\ v \\ w \end{array}\right\} = \sum_{m=1}^{\infty} \left\{\begin{array}{c} aA_m \cos n\theta(\partial/\partial x) \\ B_m \sin n\theta \\ C_m \cos n\theta \end{array}\right\} \Phi_m(x)e^{i\Omega t}, \quad (3)$$

where n is the circumferential wave number, A_m to C_m are constants to be determined, and $\Phi_m(x)$ are appropriate admissible functions for the x–variations of shell displacements, here taken to be the eigenfunctions of a clamped–clamped beam if the shell is clamped at both ends, or of a cantilevered beam if one end of the shell is unsupported.

To facilitate the solution of equations (1), it is useful to define the following reference velocity:

$$\mathcal{U} = \left[\frac{E}{\rho_s(1-\nu^2)}\right]^{1/2}, \qquad (4)$$

and to introduce the following dimensionless parameters:

$$\overline{U}_i = \frac{U_i}{\mathcal{U}}, \quad \overline{U}_o = \frac{U_o}{\mathcal{U}}, \quad \overline{\Omega} = \frac{\Omega a}{\mathcal{U}},$$
$$\epsilon = \frac{r}{L}, \quad \epsilon_i = \frac{a}{L}, \quad \epsilon_o = \frac{b}{L}, \quad \xi = \frac{x}{L}, \qquad (5)$$
$$\overline{A}_m = \frac{A_m}{L}, \quad \overline{B}_m = \frac{B_m}{L}, \quad \overline{C}_m = \frac{C_m}{L},$$

where Ω is the radian frequency, which will be a function of m and n for any given physical system.

For the system involving a clamped–clamped shell, the method of solution, based on Galerkin's method, is identical to that given by Païdoussis, Chan & Misra [1]. Thus, for brevity, only the final results for the unsteady force, q, acting on the shell are given below:

$$q = \sum_{m=1}^{\infty} Q_m(\xi)\cos n\theta e^{i\Omega t}, \qquad (6)$$

where

$$Q_m(\xi) = \frac{\mathcal{U}^2\overline{C}_m}{2\pi}\int_{-\infty}^{\infty}\frac{1}{\overline{\alpha}}\left\{\rho_i W_{1n}(\overline{\alpha}, \epsilon_i)\left[\frac{\overline{\Omega}}{\epsilon_i} - \overline{U}_i\overline{\alpha}\right]^2\right.$$
$$\left. - \rho_o W_{2n}(\overline{\alpha}, \epsilon_i)\left[\frac{\overline{\Omega}}{\epsilon_i} - \lambda\overline{U}_o\overline{\alpha}\right]^2\right\}\Phi_m^{\star}(\overline{\alpha})e^{-i\overline{\alpha}\xi}\mathrm{d}\overline{\alpha},$$

$$W_{1n}(\overline{\alpha}, \epsilon) = \frac{I_n(\overline{\alpha}\epsilon)}{I_n'(\overline{\alpha}\epsilon_i)},$$

$$W_{2n}(\overline{\alpha}, \epsilon) = \frac{I_n'(\overline{\alpha}\epsilon_o)K_n(\overline{\alpha}\epsilon) - I_n(\overline{\alpha}\epsilon)K_n'(\overline{\alpha}\epsilon_o)}{I_n'(\overline{\alpha}\epsilon_o)K_n'(\overline{\alpha}\epsilon_i) - I_n'(\overline{\alpha}\epsilon_i)K_n'(\overline{\alpha}\epsilon_o)}.$$

In the above expressions, $\overline{\alpha}$ is the non–dimensional Fourier–transform variable and the asterisk denotes a transformed quantity; I_n and K_n are, respectively, the modified Bessel functions of the first and second kind, and $I'_n(z) = \mathrm{d}I_n(z)/\mathrm{d}z$; $\lambda = 1$ if the flows are co–current or -1 if the flows are counter–current, assuming that the annular fluid flows in the negative x–direction. It should be noted here that in the case of counter–current flows, it makes no difference whatsoever as to which fluid flows in the negative x–direction if both ends of the shell are clamped.

For the case of the cantilevered shell, the method of solution is based on the extended form of Galerkin's method, as has been utilized by Païdoussis, Nguyen & Misra [5]. The unsteady radial force, q, on the shell is found to be

$$q = \sum_{m=1}^{\infty} Q_m(\xi) \cos n\theta e^{i\Omega t}, \qquad (7)$$

with

$$Q_m(\xi) = \frac{\mathcal{U}^2 \overline{C}_m}{2\pi} \int_{-\infty}^{\infty} \frac{1}{\overline{\alpha}} \left\{ \rho_i W_{1n}(\overline{\alpha}, \epsilon_i) \left[\frac{\overline{\Omega}}{\epsilon_i} - \overline{U}_i \overline{\alpha} \right]^2 \right.$$
$$\left. - \rho_o W_{2n}(\overline{\alpha}, \epsilon_i) \left[\frac{\overline{\Omega}}{\epsilon_i} - \overline{U}_o \overline{\alpha} \right]^2 \right\}$$
$$\times \left\{ \Phi_m^{\star}(\overline{\alpha}) + R_m^{\star}(\overline{\alpha}) \right\} e^{-i\overline{\alpha}\xi} \mathrm{d}\overline{\alpha},$$

where $R_m(x), L \leq x \leq L'$, is an extension of the beam eigenfunctions $\Phi_m(x), 0 \leq x \leq L$, representing the manner in which the flow perturbations beyond the free end of the shell decay; $L' \sim O(3L)$ denotes the distance beyond which $R_m(x) = 0$ for $L' \leq x < \infty$. A number of so-called out–flow models have been proposed [7,8], giving functional forms for $R_m(x)$, and a full discussion on the importance of $R_m(x)$, both physically and mathematically, as well as the effectiveness of some such models may be found in Reference [5].

2.4. Steady viscosity – related stress resultants

The viscous nature of the fluid results in both steady (time–independent) and unsteady (time–dependent) viscosity-related loads being exerted on the shell, the latter of which are neglected in this paper. The steady loads have already been determined from the time–mean Navier–Stokes equations [9] for both systems of clamped–clamped shells [2] and clamped–free shells [5]. Again, for brevity and completeness, only the final results for the steady radial differential pressure, $\overline{P}_{rI}$, and the corresponding surface traction, $\overline{P}_{xI}$, on the shell will be given here.

In the case of co–current flows, the steady radial and axial loads on the shell are found to be

$$\overline{P}_{rI} = \left\{ \frac{2b}{b^2 - r_m^2} \rho_o U_{\tau oo}^2 - \frac{2\rho_i}{a} U_{\tau i}^2 \right\} x$$
$$+ P_i(0, a) - P_o(0, a), \qquad (8)$$
$$\overline{P}_{xI} = \rho_i U_{\tau i}^2 + \rho_o U_{\tau oi}^2. \qquad (9)$$

In the above expressions, $U_{\tau oi}$ and $U_{\tau oo}$ are the shear velocities of the annular flow at the inner and outer cylinder surfaces, and $U_{\tau i}$ is the shear velocity of the inner flow at the inner cylinder surface; $P_i(0, a)$ and $P_o(0, a)$ are the inner and annular fluid pressures at the position $x = 0$, $r = a \pm h$; r_m is the radius at which the mean velocity is maximum.

In the case of counter–current flows, which is herein considered for the system of a clamped–clamped shell only, after some coordinate transformations the steady loads on the shell may be shown to be

$$\overline{P}_{rI} = -\left\{ \frac{2\rho_i}{a} U_{\tau i}^2 + \frac{2b}{b^2 - r_m^2} \rho_o U_{\tau oo}^2 \right\} x$$
$$+ \left(\frac{2b}{b^2 - r_m^2} \right) \rho_o U_{\tau oo}^2 L + P_i(0, a) - P_o(L, a), \qquad (10)$$
$$\overline{P}_{xI} = \rho_i U_{\tau i}^2 + \rho_o U_{\tau oi}^2, \qquad (11)$$

where it is assumed that the annular fluid flows in the negative x–direction; $P_i(0, a)$ and $P_o(L, a)$ are the entrance static pressures of the inner and annular flows, respectively.

It is noted that in order to determine the differential pressures $\Delta P = P_i(0, a) - P_o(0, a)$ in equation (8) and $\Delta P = P_i(0, a) - P_o(L, a)$ in equation (10), the static pressures of both flows at either end of the shell have to be known. In the case of a cantilevered shell, where the inner and annular fluids flow co–currently and merge into each other at the free end of the shell, the exit pressures of the two flows are essentially the same. In the case of a clamped–clamped shell, where the two flows can be either co–current or counter–current and are separated throughout, it is assumed that the exit pressures of the flows are also equal. This assumption by no means changes the nature of the system; the only advantage resulting thereby is that the radial differential pressure $\overline{P}_{rI}$ depends only on the pressure drops of the two flows along the shell. For both types of flows, the foregoing reasoning effectively leads to

$$\Delta P = \frac{2\rho_i}{a} U_{\tau i}^2 L - \frac{2b}{b^2 - r_m^2} \rho_o U_{\tau oo}^2 L. \qquad (12)$$

3. RESULTS

In this Section, the effects of varying length L, thickness h, and annular gap $(b - a)$ on the stability of both clamped–clamped and cantilevered shell systems are discussed. In most cases to be considered, the internal fluid is stagnant, i.e. $\overline{U}_i = 0$. The analysis also covers the stability of the system of a clamped–clamped shell subjected to counter–current flows and the stability of the system of a cantilevered shell conveying co–current flows.

Calculations were conducted with the series in equation (3) truncated at $m = 3$ for the case of a clamped–clamped shell [1] and $m = 6$ for the case of a cantilevered shell [5]. For convenience, the material properties (steel shells and water as the working fluid) and the geometric dimensions of the cylinders are the same as had been used previously [1–5]. Although not appearing in equations (1), the shells were additionally considered to be subjected to internal dissipation which may be approximated by a hysteretic model [5]. However, here, for convenience, an equivalent viscoelastic model will be utilized instead, whereby E in equations (1) is replaced by $E(1+i\chi\Omega)$.[1] Thus, calculations were performed with the following set of parameters:

---

[1] It is worthwhile to point out that this model has the advantage, over the hysteretic one, that it does not increase the stiffness of the system and does not destroy the self–adjoint character of the problem.

$$E = 2.0 \times 10^{11} \text{ N/m}^2, \quad \nu = 0.3, \quad \rho_s = 7.8 \times 10^3 \text{ kg/m}^3,$$

$$\rho_i = \rho_o = 10^3 \text{ kg/m}^3, \quad \chi = 5 \times 10^{-6} \text{ s},$$

$$a = \frac{1}{11} \text{ m}, \quad b = \frac{1}{10} \text{ m}, \quad h = 0.5 \times 10^{-3} \text{ m}, \quad L = 1.0 \text{ m};$$

in studying the effects of system parameters, a was held fixed, while b, h or L could be varied.

Since the theory is linear, the results to be presented are correct only within the framework of linear theory. It is well known (Evensen [10]) that shells are subject to important softening type nonlinearities. Hence, although the results are expected to be physically correct for sufficiently small amplitude perturbations, the physical reality of the intricate behaviour predicted beyond the first loss of stability is questionable. The system of a clamped–clamped shell will be considered first, followed by the system of a cantilevered shell.

3.1. Stability of the system of a clamped–clamped shell

3.1.1. Effect of shell length

Shown in Figure 2 are the results for $\overline{U}_{oc}^*$ as a function of the ratio L/a in a $\frac{1}{10}$-gap system (i.e., $[b-a]/a = 1/10$), where $\overline{U}_{oc}^*$ denotes the overall (lowest) critical flow velocity whereas $\overline{U}_{oc}$ refers to the critical flow velocity associated with some particular n. Two variants of the theory have been used to calculate $\overline{U}_{oc}^*$; in the inviscid variant, the fluid is assumed to be purely inviscid, while in the viscous variant, steady viscous effects of the flow(s) are taken into account. The values of $\overline{U}_{oc}^*$ predicted by the viscous variant of the theory is of the order of three to six times smaller than that by the inviscid counterpart as L/a is varied from 5 to 20. Such a destabilizing trend of the steady viscous forces is not surprising since, as has already been pointed out [5], the destabilizing effect of the crushing compressive load q_3 appearing in equations (1) is in fact proportional to L; nevertheless, these results quantify the influence of this parameter on stability. In general, as L/a is increased, $\overline{U}_{oc}^*$ decreases and so does the circumferential mode associated with $\overline{U}_{oc}^*$. Thus, if L is large enough, the shell will eventually lose its stability by divergence in the $n = 1$ (beam) mode. This observation is similar to that made earlier by Païdoussis & Denise [11] for the system of an unconfined clamped–clamped shell conveying internal flow.

3.1.2. Effect of shell thickness

The variation of $\overline{U}_{oc}^*$ with the shell thickness, expressed nondimensionally as h/a, is plotted in Figure 3. Again, the steady viscous forces have a destabilizing effect on the system. As may be seen from the figure, $\overline{U}_{oc}^*$ increases with h/a, whereas the circumferential mode n associated with $\overline{U}_{oc}^*$ decreases. The effect of h/a on $\overline{U}_{oc}^*$ and n may be understood by considering the strain energies resulting from circumferential bending and stretching of the shell.

If the strain energies are plotted against the circumferential wave number n, it will be observed that the bending energy E_b increases with n while the stretching energy E_s varies in the reverse manner, resulting in a curve for the total strain energy E_t (i.e. $E_t = E_b + E_s$) of quasi-parabolic form [12]. Now considering an element of the shell, so small as to be approximated as a plate of

thickness h, it has been shown [13] that for such a plate E_b is proportional to h^3 while E_s is proportional to h. As h is increased, both E_b and E_s increase but E_b increases much faster than E_s, resulting in a shift of the minimum value of E_t towards a lower n. Meanwhile, the energy E_f required to overcome E_t and hence to collapse the shell comes from the centrifugal fluid–dynamic force, which is known to be proportional to U^2 according to inviscid theory. Implicitly, E_f is also proportional to U^2,

$$E_f = U^2 f(n),$$

where $f(n)$ is some function of the circumferential wave number n. It is apparent that the system loses stability when

$$E_t - E_f = E_t - U^2 f(n) = 0,$$

which implies that $\overline{U}_{oc}^*$ will become higher if there is an increase in $(E_t)_{\min}$ due to increasing h.

3.1.3. Effect of annular gap

Figure 4 shows how $\overline{U}_{oc}^*$ varies with the annular gap, expressed in the dimensionless form $(b-a)/a$. As might be expected, for both cases of inviscid and viscous flows, the system becomes unstable at lower flow velocities as the annular gap gets narrower. This phenomenon has been well explained in previous studies [1–5]. Firstly, the reduction in the annular gap results in a corresponding increase in the virtual or added mass of the annular fluid; the increase in added mass is associated with higher fluid dynamic forces and hence causes an effective reduction in the stiffness of the shell and a diminution of $\overline{U}_{oc}^*$. Secondly, in the case of a viscous fluid, a higher upstream pressure is required to push the fluid through a narrower annular gap, thus resulting in a larger pressure drop along the shell and a stronger destabilizing effect due to pressurization. Once again, however, these effects are here quantified explicitly, and the effect on the *overall* stability is given. Another observation from Figure 4 is that for the range of gap sizes considered the circumferential mode n associated with $\overline{U}_{oc}^*$ remains unchanged, at least for the parameters being studied.

It should be reiterated here that the results presented in Figures 2, 3 and 4 were obtained for a system with annular flow and a stagnant inner fluid (i.e., $\overline{U}_i = 0$).

3.1.4. System with counter–current flows

Figure 5 compares the results for $\overline{U}_{oc}$ as a function of n, obtained with the viscous variant of the theory for two types of flows: co– and counter–current flows. In both cases, the internal flow velocity was constant and taken to be $\overline{U}_i = 0.010$. It may be seen from this figure that the system subjected to counter–current flows loses stability at lower flow velocities than for co–current flows. The difference between the two types of flows in terms of $\overline{U}_{oc}$ ranges from virtually 0% (with respect to $\overline{U}_{oc}$ for co–current flows) at $n = 1$ to 10.7% at $n = 6$. As far as the overall critical flow velocity $\overline{U}_{oc}^*$ is concerned, which happens to be associated with $n = 4$, the difference is 8.3%.

The reduction in $\overline{U}_{oc}$ for all n when the system is subjected to counter–current flows can be accounted for by the fact that the axial loads generated by the internal flow shear the shell forward (in the positive x-direction) whereas the annular flow does just the opposite (in the negative x-direction), thus partially cancelling out the axial tension in the shell created by the internal flow, thereby reducing the stiffness of the shell. The radial loads on the shell also play an important role in determining the magnitude of $\overline{U}_{oc}$. In the case of counter–current flows, in the vicinity of the upstream end of the shell (i.e. $x = 0$) the hoop stress in the shell wall is tensile because the entrance pressure of the internal flow is higher than the exit pressure of the annular flow; on the other hand, in the vicinity of the downstream end (i.e. $x = L$) the hoop stress in the shell wall is compressive since the entrance pressure of the annular flow is higher than the exit pressure of the internal flow. Consequently, if the upstream differential pressure is larger than its downstream counterpart, and therefore the hoop stress in the shell is mostly tensile, the reduction in $\overline{U}_{oc}$ will be small; on the contrary, if the upstream differential pressure is smaller than its downstream counterpart, and hence the hoop stress in the shell becomes mostly compressive, the reduction in $\overline{U}_{oc}$ will be large.

3.2. Stability of the system of a cantilevered shell

3.2.1. System with co-current flows

Figure 6 presents the results obtained for $\overline{U}_{oc}$ as a function of n for two cases of flows, $\overline{U}_i = 0$ and $\overline{U}_i = \overline{U}_o$, for which only the viscous variant of the theory was used. In all circumferential modes considered, except $n = 1$, flutter of coupled-mode type (solid curves) is preceded by divergence (broken curves) at a much lower flow velocity.

As far as the first loss of stability (divergence) is concerned, the system becomes unstable at a slightly higher flow velocity when $\overline{U}_i = \overline{U}_o$ ($\overline{U}_{oc}^* = 0.003311$, $n = 4$) than when $\overline{U}_i = 0$ ($\overline{U}_{oc}^* = 0.003206$, $n = 4$), although in the scale of the figure the two broken curves appear to be coincident. The stabilizing effect as a result of $\overline{U}_i = \overline{U}_o$ may be attributed to the fact that the steady viscous forces due to the internal flow increase the axial tension in the shell and reduce the compressive hoop stress in the shell wall caused by the annular flow, thus resulting in an increase in the stiffness of the shell, thereby stabilizing the system. It is recalled, furthermore, that the inviscid results obtained by Païdoussis, Nguyen & Misra [5] also showed a similar effect when $\overline{U}_i = \overline{U}_o$. There is no doubt that the presence of internal flow in the present case would give rise to an increase in $\overline{U}_{oc}^*$, albeit small. It may be expected that a stronger stabilizing effect would have resulted if $\overline{U}_i$ had been taken to be larger, say $\overline{U}_i > \overline{U}_o$ (provided, of course, $\overline{U}_i$ remained smaller than the critical value for instability by the internal flow alone).

Another observation from Figure 6 that should be touched upon here is that the internal flow has a post–divergence destabilizing effect on the system. Nevertheless, as has been mentioned earlier, any predictions beyond first loss of stability by the present linear theory are questionable, in the sense that they may not occur in reality; hence, physical explanations for such post–divergence behaviour of the system may not be too meaningful and are not attempted. The results are nevertheless still of academic interest and are therefore presented (here and in subsequent figures).

3.2.2. Effects of shell thickness, length, and annular width

Figure 7 shows the results for $\overline{U}_{oc}^*$ as a function of the shell thickness h/a for two different lengths of the shell,

$L/a = 5$ and $L/a = 10$. Although the type of instability is flutter preceded by divergence, the stability of the system is affected by the parameters pretty much in the same way as in the case of clamped–clamped shells considered earlier. In other words, $\overline{U}_{oc}^*$ increases and the circumferential mode n associated with $\overline{U}_{oc}^*$ decreases with increasing h/a; furthermore, for a given thickness of the shell, both $\overline{U}_{oc}^*$ and its associated n decrease as L/a goes up.

Figure 8 is similar to Figure 7 in the sense that it shows the variation of $\overline{U}_{oc}^*$ with h/a, but now for two different annular widths. Again, similarly to what was observed for the system of a clamped–clamped shell, the smaller the annular width, the lower the overall critical flow velocity $\overline{U}_{oc}^*$; in addition, the circumferential mode n associated with $\overline{U}_{oc}^*$ remains almost unchanged as the annular width is varied. It may be worth reiterating once more that the results presented in Figures 7 and 8 (unlike some in Figure 6) were obtained for the system with annular flow and a stagnant inner fluid.

4. CONCLUSION

Instabilities of the system involving a cylindrical shell contained in a coaxial, infinitely long conduit conveying internal and/or annular flows have been studied. The shell was either clamped at both ends or cantilevered. In both cases, the effects of such important system parameters as shell thickness, length of the shell, and annular width on the stability of the system were investigated. Further considered was the stability of the system subjected to counter–current flows in the case of a clamped–clamped shell and to co–current flows in the case of a cantilevered shell. The analysis was carried out with steady viscous effects of the flows as well as internal (viscous) damping of the shell material taken into account.

It was shown that the system parameters have similar effects on the stability of clamped–clamped or cantilevered shells. As the shell gets longer, the overall critical flow velocity and its associated circumferential wave number decrease, and eventually the shell will lose stability in the beam mode. An increase in the shell thickness stabilizes the system and lowers the circumferential mode associated with instability. A reduction in the annular width results in an increase in the effective mass of the fluid as well as in the upstream pressurization, both of which tend to reduce the stiffness of the shell and hence to destabilize the system. Some of these effects are of course qualitatively predictable by physical reasoning alone or by some isolated calculations conducted previously. However, the results presented in this paper systematically quantify the importance of the influence of these parameters on overall (as opposed to modal) system stability.

When subjected to counter–current flows, the system of a clamped–clamped shell was found to become unstable at a lower critical flow velocity. The destabilizing effect of this type of flow is attributed to the viscous effects of the two flows; it depends strongly not only on the relative pressure drops along the shell, but also on the differential pressures at the upstream and downstream ends of the shell. The system of a cantilevered shell, on the other hand, loses stability at a lower critical flow velocity when subjected co–currently to both flows; the reduction in the critical flow velocity becomes larger as the internal flow velocity gets higher.

ACKNOWLEDGEMENT

The authors gratefully acknowledge the support by the Natural Sciences and Engineering Research Council of Canada and Le Fonds FCAR of Québec, which has made this research possible.

REFERENCES

(1) PAÏDOUSSIS, M.P., CHAN, S.P. and MISRA, A.K. Dynamics and stability of coaxial cylindrical shells containing flowing fluid. *Journal of Sound and Vibration*, 1985, 97, 201–205.

(2) PAÏDOUSSIS, M.P., CHAN, S.P. and MISRA, A.K. Dynamics and stability of coaxial cylindrical shells conveying viscous fluid. *Journal of Applied Mechanics*, 1985, 52, 389–396.

(3) EL CHEBAIR, A., PAÏDOUSSIS, M.P. and MISRA, A.K. Experimental study of annular–flow–induced instabilities of cylindrical shell. *Journal of Fluids and Structures*, 1989, 3, 349–364.

(4) EL CHEBAIR, A., MISRA, A.K. and PAÏDOUSSIS, M.P. Theoretical study of the effect of unsteady viscous forces on inner– and annular–flow–induced instabilities of cylindrical shells. *Journal of Sound and Vibration*, 1990, 138, 457–478.

(5) PAÏDOUSSIS, M.P., NGUYEN, V.B. and MISRA, A.K. A theoretical study of the stability of cantilevered coaxial cylindrical shells conveying fluid. *Journal of Fluids and Structures*, 1991 (in press).

(6) FLÜGGE, W. *Stresses in Shells*, 1960 (Springer–Verlag, Berlin).

(7) SHAYO, L.K. and ELLEN, C.H. Theoretical studies of internal flow–induced instabilities of cantilevered pipes. *Journal of Sound and Vibration*, 1978, 54, 463–474.

(8) PAÏDOUSSIS, M.P., LUU, T.P. and LAITHIER, B.E. Dynamics of finite–length tubular beams conveying fluid. *Journal of Sound and Vibration*, 1986, 106, 311–331.

(9) LAUFER, J. The structure of turbulence in fully-developed pipe flow. NACA Technical Note 2954, 1953.

(10) EVENSEN, D.A. Nonlinear vibrations of circular cylindrical shells. In *Thin–Shell Structures: Theory, Experiment, and Design* 1974, 133–155 (eds Y.C. Fung and E.E. Sechler, Prentice Hall, New Jersey). (Also NASA TN D-4090, 1967.)

(11) PAÏDOUSSIS, M.P. and DENISE, J.P. Flutter of thin cylindrical shells conveying fluid. *Journal of Sound and Vibration*, 1972, 20, 9–26.

(12) ARNOLD, R.N. and WARBURTON, G.B. Flexural vibrations of the walls of thin cylindrical shells having freely supported ends. *Proceedings of the Royal Society of London*, 1949, 197, 238–256.

(13) TIMOSHENKO, S. and WOINOWSKY–KRIEGER, S. *Theory of Plates and Shells*, 2nd edition, 1959 (McGraw–Hill Book Co., New York).

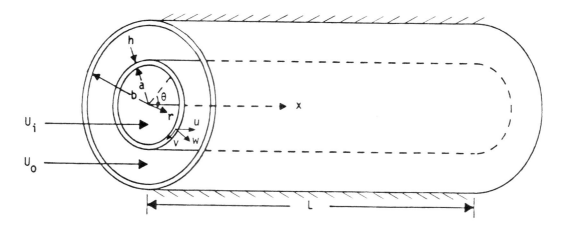

Figure 1. Schematic of the system under consideration.

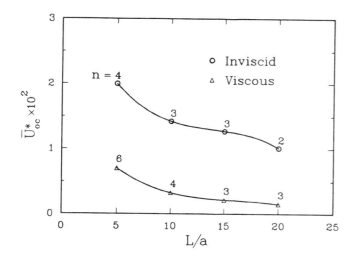

Figure 2. The overall (lowest) critical dimensionless annular flow velocity, $\overline{U}_{oc}^*$, in the $\frac{1}{10}$-gap system as a function of the dimensionless length of the shell L/a, with the circumferential mode, n, associated with first loss of stability indicated in the figure; $\bigcirc$, inviscid flow; $\triangle$, with steady viscous effects taken into account. The shell is clamped at both ends and the inner fluid is stagnant.

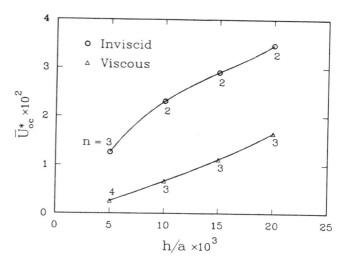

Figure 3. The overall critical dimensionless annular flow velocity, $\overline{U}_{oc}^*$, in the $\frac{1}{10}$-gap system as a function of the dimensionless wall–thickness of the shell h/a, with the circumferential mode, n, associated with first loss of stability indicated in the figure; $\bigcirc$, inviscid flow; $\triangle$, with steady viscous effects taken into account. The shell is clamped at both ends and the inner fluid is stagnant.

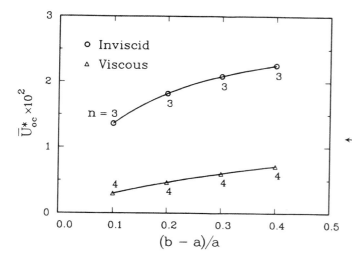

← Figure 4. The overall critical dimensionless annular flow velocity, $\overline{U}_{oc}^*$, as a function of the dimensionless annular gap $(b-a)/a$, with the circumferential mode, n, associated with first loss of stability marked in the figure; $\bigcirc$, inviscid flow; $\triangle$, with steady viscous effects taken into account. The shell is clamped at both ends and the inner fluid is stagnant.

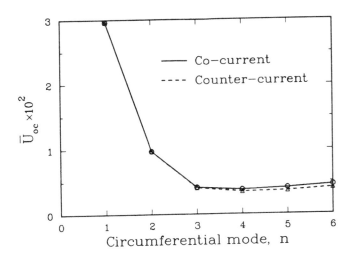

Figure 5. The critical dimensionless annular flow velocity, $\overline{U}_{oc}$, in the $\frac{1}{10}$-gap system as a function of the circumferential mode, n; ———, flows in the same direction; - - - -, flows in opposite directions. The shell is clamped at both ends and the inner flow velocity is constant ($\overline{U}_i = 0.01$).

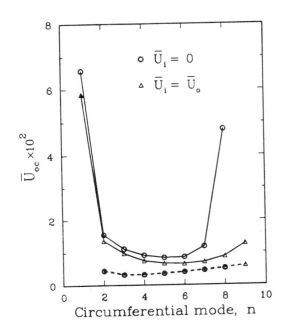

Figure 6. The critical dimensionless annular flow velocity, $\overline{U}_{oc}$, in the $\frac{1}{10}$-gap cantilevered system as a function of the circumferential mode, n, for two different inner flow velocities; ◯, $\overline{U}_i = 0$; △, $\overline{U}_i = \overline{U}_o$; - - - -, divergence boundary; ———, flutter boundary. The divergence boundaries for the two values of $\overline{U}_i$ are generally coincident.

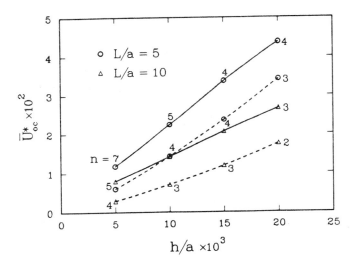

Figure 7. The overall critical dimensionless annular flow velocity, $\overline{U}_{oc}^*$, in the $\frac{1}{10}$-gap system as a function of h/a for two different shell lengths, with the circumferential mode, n, associated with first loss of stability marked in the figure; ◯, $L/a = 5$; △, $L/a = 10$; - - - -, divergence boundary; ———, flutter boundary. The shell is cantilevered and the inner fluid is stagnant.

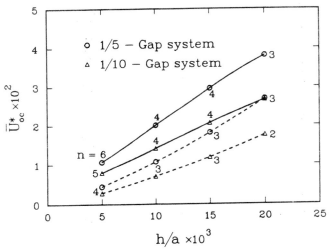

Figure 8. The overall critical dimensionless annular flow velocity, $\overline{U}_{oc}^*$, as a function of h/a for two different annular widths ($L/a = 10$), with the circumferential mode, n, associated with first loss of stability marked in the figure; ◯, $(b - a)/a = 1/5$; △, $(b - a)/a = 1/10$; - - - -, divergence boundary; ———, flutter boundary. The shell is cantilevered and the inner fluid is stagnant.

On the hydroelasticity of one-span pipelines with initial imperfections

D S DERMENDJIAN-IVANOVA, Dipl-Eng
Institute of Mechanics and Biomechanics, Bulgarian Academy of Sciences,
Sofia, Bulgaria

SYNOPSIS Using Bubnov-Galerkin's variational method a dynamical behaviour of one - span pipe is investigated. Initial deflections are due to tube plus liquid own weight. The movement of pipe and resonance appearing are shown.

NOTATION

$w_1(x,t)$	elastic line of vibrating tube
$w_0(x)$	initial sag
EI	cross-section rigidity
p_0	initial pump pressure
A	cross-section area
M	liquid mass per unit length
$\bar{m}$	tube mass per unit length
U	liquid flow velocity
t	time
σ	natural frequency of the system

1 INTRODUCTION

Pipes are universal structural components used in many technologies as transporting means for gases, liquids and powders, (e.g. aircraft and ship structures, off-shore structures, nuclear power technology, etc.). In most cases of aforementioned technologies the complicated isometry is main characteristic of the pipings, (e.g. the multitude of elbows, one-span sections, different supportings, etc.).

1.1. Initial imperfections

It is impossible to produce any structures without imperfections. They have different origins: (i)mistakes in the technological process; (ii)imperfections due to the gravity field (saging from liquid and pipe own weight).

The first type imperfections have random distribution. They have to be minimized due to the technological process. The second group of imperfections are inevitable and in the present paper their influence is taken into account.

1.2. Assumptions.

Tube: (i)the tube material is accepted as lineary elastic one; (ii)the cross-section A is ideal circular; (iii)five schemes of supporting are accepted as it is shown on Fig.1. Liquid: (i)the liquid is accepted as inviscid, compressible and heavy one; (ii)the velocity of the flow is one and same in all points of an arbitrary cross-section; (iii)the flow is potential one. Fluid-structure interaction: (i)the cross-section do not change its circular form and remains plane during tube vibration; (ii)the small dynamical deflections generate small perturbations of the initial potential liquid motion. So the perturbation can be described keeping in mind only the liquid motion along the neutral tube axis x.

2 THE PROBLEM

2.1. Physical description

On Fig.2(a) a straight line pipe is shown. Inner statical pressure p_0 is constant along the span due to the assumption that the liquid is ideal. When the pipe is without any motion and has no imperfections taking into account the fluid movement,[2],dynamical pressure of the fluid creates longitudinal force (MU^2). On Fig.2(b) the deformation (f_{ov}) due to tube and liquid own weight is shown. Then the force (MU^2) creates a moment $(MU^2 f_{ov})$ and it gives rise to an additional deflection of tube axis (f_{ov}) shown on Fig.2(c).

2.2. Mathematical description

Let us introduce an actual elastic line

$$W_{act} = W_{act}(x,t) \qquad (1)$$

Then

$$W_1(x,t) = W_0(x) + W_{act}(x,t) \qquad (2)$$

Following [1],[3] the differential equation of vibrating tube is

$$(EI) \frac{\partial^4 W_{act}}{\partial x^4} + MU^2 \frac{\partial^2 W_1}{\partial x^2} + 2MU \frac{\partial^2 W_{act}}{\partial x \partial t} + (\overline{m}+M) \frac{\partial^2 W_{act}}{\partial t^2} = 0 \qquad (3)$$

Transfering to the right-hand side the terms depending on x only and substituting

$$\xi = \frac{x}{L} \;, \quad q = L^2 \frac{MU^2}{EI} \;, \quad K = L^3 \frac{2MU}{EI} \;,$$

$$\Omega^4 = L^4 \frac{\overline{m}+M}{EI} \qquad (4)$$

we obtain the finally form of the differential equation

$$\frac{\partial^4 W_{act}}{\partial \xi^4} + q \frac{\partial^2 W_{act}}{\partial \xi^2} + K \frac{\partial^2 W_{act}}{\partial \xi \partial t} + \Omega^4 \frac{\partial^2 W_{act}}{\partial t^2} = -q \frac{d^2 W_0}{d \xi^2} \qquad (5)$$

We obtain partial differential equation versus span length and time, which is nonhomogenious one. The difficulties of its solving origins from the third term in left-hand side. We choose Bubnov-Galerkin's variational method for solving the problem as most successful about this type of equations.

3 SOLUTION

3.1. Solution of the homogenious equation

$$W_{act}(\xi,t) = \overset{\circ}{W}_{act}(\xi,t) + \overline{W}_{act}(\xi,t) \qquad (6)$$

- $\overset{\circ}{W}_{act}(\xi,t)$ is solution of the homogenious equation

$$\frac{\partial^4 W_{act}}{\partial \xi^4} + q \frac{\partial^2 W_{act}}{\partial \xi^2} + K \frac{\partial^2 W_{act}}{\partial \xi \partial t} + \Omega^4 \frac{\partial^2 W_{act}}{\partial t^2} = 0 \qquad (7)$$

The solution of Eq.(7) has been investigated in previous author's work,[1] . For the five basic supporting cases they are

A) $\overset{\circ}{W}_{act}(\xi,t) = \sum_m A_m \, SIN(m\pi\xi) \cdot e^{i\sigma t}$;

B) $\overset{\circ}{W}_{act}(\xi,t) = \sum_m A_m [SIN(K_m\xi)/COS(K_m) - K_m\xi] \cdot e^{i\sigma t}$;

$K_1 = 4.493$; $K_2 = 7.7252$; $K_3 = 10.904$;...

C) $\overset{\circ}{W}_{act}(\xi,t) = \sum_m A_m [COS(2m\pi\xi)-1] \cdot e^{i\sigma t}$;

D) $\overset{\circ}{W}_{act}(\xi,t) = \sum_m A_m [COS(m\pi\xi)-1] \cdot e^{i\sigma t}$;

E) $\overset{\circ}{W}_{act}(\xi,t) = \sum_m A_m [COS(m\pi\xi/2-1] \cdot e^{i\sigma t}$, $m = odd$; $\qquad (8)$

where A_m is indeterminate constant.

3.2. Solution of the nonhomogenious equation

- $\overline{W}_{act}(\xi,t)$ is partial solution of the nonhomogenious equation. It is chosen to have the type of the right-hand side term of Eq.(5), which is

$$-L^2 \frac{MU^2}{EI} \cdot \frac{d^2 W_0}{d\xi^2} \qquad (9)$$

Pinned-pinned pipe:

$$W_0(\xi) = \sum_n f_{on} \, SIN(n\pi\xi) \qquad (10)$$

Then the right-hand side of Eq.(5) is

$$+L^2 \frac{MU^2}{EI} \sum_n f_{on} (n\pi)^2 SIN(n\pi\xi)$$

and

$$\overline{W}_{act} = \sum_n C_{1n} f_{on} (n\pi)^2 SIN(n\pi\xi) \qquad (11)$$

Substituting this term in Eq.(5) we will obtain

© IMechE 1991 C416/017

$$C_{1n} = \cfrac{1}{(n\pi)^2 \left[\cfrac{(n\pi)^2 EI}{L^2 MU^2}\right] - 1}$$

Substituting

$$P_{n\,EuL}^{(a)} = \frac{(n\pi)^2 EI}{L^2}, \quad P_{n\,EuL}^{(b)} = \frac{(Kn)^2 EI}{L^2},$$

$$P_{n\,EuL}^{(c)} = \frac{(2n\pi)^2 EI}{L^2}, \quad P_{n\,EuL}^{(d)} = P_{n\,EuL}^{(a)}, \quad P_{n\,EuL}^{(e)} = \frac{(n\pi/2)^2 EI}{L^2}$$

and doing the same operations for another supporting cases we obtain

Pinned-pinned pipe:

$$Wact(\xi,t) = \sum_m A_m \sin(m\pi\xi).e^{i\sigma t} +$$

$$+ \sum_n \frac{f_{on}}{P_{n\,EuL}^{(a)}/MU^2 - 1} \sin(n\pi\xi) \quad (12)$$

Pinned-clamped pipe:

$$Wact(\xi,t) = \sum_m A_m [\sin(Km\xi)/\cos(Km) - Km\xi].$$

$$e^{i\sigma t} + \sum_n \frac{f_{on}}{P_{n\,EuL}^{(b)}/MU^2 - 1} \cdot \frac{\sin(Kn\xi)}{\cos(Kn)}$$

Clamped-clamped pipe:

$$Wact(\xi,t) = \sum_m A_m [\cos(2m\pi\xi) - 1].e^{i\sigma t} +$$

$$+ \sum_n \frac{f_{on}}{P_{n\,EuL}^{(c)}/MU^2 - 1} \cos(2n\pi\xi)$$

Clamped-clamped pipe with Q-apparatus:

$$Wact(\xi,t) = \sum_m A_m [\cos(m\pi\xi) - 1].e^{i\sigma t} +$$

$$+ \sum_n \frac{f_{on}}{P_{n\,EuL}^{(d)}/MU^2 - 1} \cos(n\pi\xi)$$

Cantilevered pipe:

$$Wact(\xi,t) = \sum_m A_m [\cos(m\pi\xi/2) - 1].e^{i\sigma t} +$$

$$+ \sum_n \frac{f_{on}}{P_{n\,EuL}^{(e)}/MU^2 - 1} \cos(n\pi\xi/2)$$
$$(m,n = odd)$$

4 NUMERICAL INVESTIGATION ON PINNED-PINNED PIPE

4.1. Initial conditions

$$Wact(\xi,0) = W_o(\xi) - \sum_n f_{on} \sin(n\pi\xi) \quad (13)$$

After substituting of this condition in (12) and doing orthogonalization we will

obtain

$$A_S = f_{oS} \left[1 - \frac{MU^2}{P_{S\,EuL}^{(a)} - MU^2}\right]$$

and the term of vibration's form will occur

$$Wact(\xi,t) = \sum_S f_{oS} \sin(S\pi\xi).$$

$$\left[e^{i\sigma t} + \frac{MU^2}{P_{S\,EuL}^{(a)} - MU^2} \cdot (1 - e^{i\sigma t})\right] \quad (14)$$

4.2. Data

Outer diameter 2R=200mm; Inner diameter 2r=190mm; Inertia momentum of the cross-section $I = 1.48395 \times 10^{-5} m^4$; Cross-section rigidity $EI = 3056.937 kNm^2$; Tube mass per unit length $m = 0.024498 kNs^2/m^2$; Liquid mass per unit length $M = 0.028902 kNs^2/m^2$.

4.3. Calculations

Natural frequencies of the hydroelastic system have been determined from the second approximation of Bubnov-Galerkin's method solving the equation

$$\begin{vmatrix} a_{11} & a_{12} \\ a_{21} & a_{22} \end{vmatrix} = 0 \quad (15)$$

where

$$a_{11} = 0.5 \left[\pi^4 - \frac{MU^2}{EI} L^2 \pi^2 - \frac{\bar{m} + M}{EI} L^4 \sigma^2\right],$$

$$a_{22} = 0.5 \left[(2\pi)^4 - \frac{MU^2}{EI} L^2 (2\pi)^2 - \frac{\bar{m} + M}{EI} L^4 \sigma^2\right],$$

$$a_{12} = -8/3 (MU^2/EI) L^3 \sigma i, \quad a_{21} = -a_{12}, \quad i^2 = -1.$$

Substituting these terms in Eq.(15) a biquadratic equation versus σ is obtained. Let us write it like this

$$h_1(U)\sigma^4 + h_2(U)\sigma^2 + h_3(U) = 0$$

Introducing $\omega = \sigma^2$ we will obtain a quadratic equation versus ω.
To be σ only real one (see Eq.(14)), ω must be real positive number. The limit case will create the following dependence

$$-h_2(U) \pm \sqrt{D} = 0 \quad (16)$$

where

$$D = h_2(U)^2 - 4h_1(U) \cdot h_3(U)$$

Equations (16) are quadratic equations versus velocity value U. Solving these equations and choosing the smaller positive value of U we will obtain the critical flow velocity Ucr. for a linear pipe. Graphic dependence Ucr.=Ucr.(L) is drawn down on Fig.3. The liquid plus tube own weight is $v=(m+M)*g=0.52385kN/m$. It produce in point (x=L/2) a moment $Mmax=0.52385*L^2/8kNm$ and vertical deflection $f_{ov}=5*v*L^4/(384*EI)$. In addition MU^2 produce $Mmax=MU^2*5*v*L^4/(384*EI)$ and vertical deflection $f_{ou}=25*L^6*v*MU^2/(18432*EI^2)$. The full deflection of pipe middle point is $f_{o1}=f_{ov}+f_{ou}$. It takes part in the expression of vibrating tube. On Fig.4 the vertical deflections of pipe's middle point j are shown. They depend on span length L and flow velocity U. The first five seconds of vibrating process are considered. The resonance appearing for every one span length (and corresponding critical flow velocity) is shown. Finally, on Fig.5 a space graphic of the vertical deflections of the tube middle point j is shown. It is done for a pipe with span length L= 9 m, because in this case the resonance appearing is most visible.

REFERENCES

(1) DERMENDJIAN-IVANOVA, D.S., V.A. DZHU-
    PANOV, "Spatial representation of the
    stability domains of one-span pipings",
    "Pipes & Pipelines International",
    Beaconsfield, England, (in print).

(2) SEDOV, L.I., "Mechanics of continuo-
    us media", Vol.1, Moskow, "Nauka",
    1973.

(3) VOLMIR, A.S., "Stability of elastic
    systems", Moskow, "Nauka", 1963.

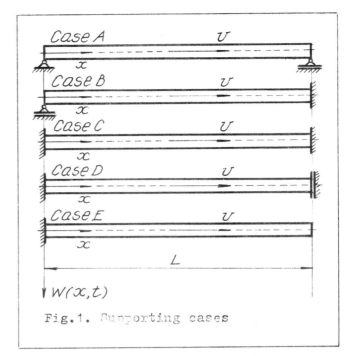

Fig.1. Supporting cases

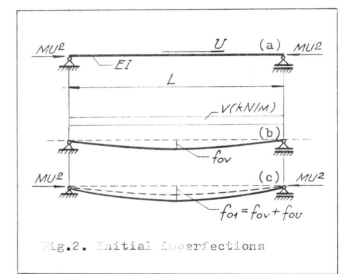

Fig.2. Initial imperfections

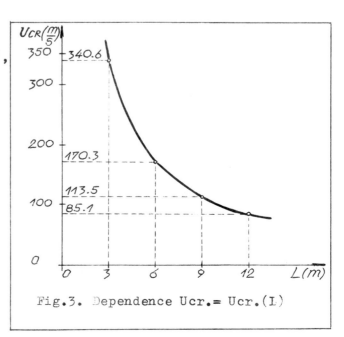

Fig.3. Dependence Ucr.= Ucr.(L)

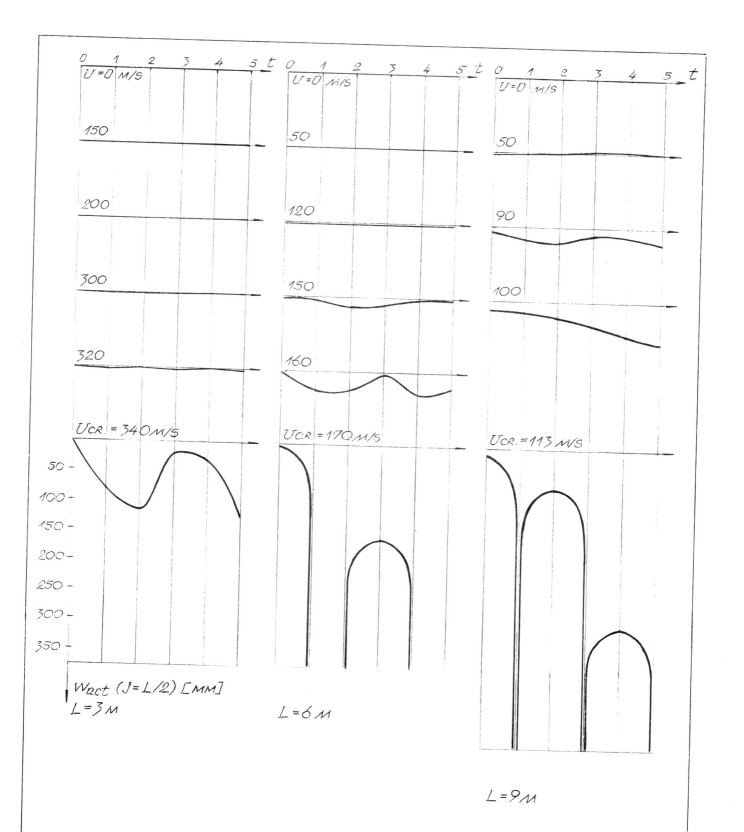

Fig.4. The vertical deflection $w_{act.}$ of tube middle point "j" (x=L/2) versus span length L(m), flow velocity U(m/s) and the time t(s) for a pinned-pinned pipe.

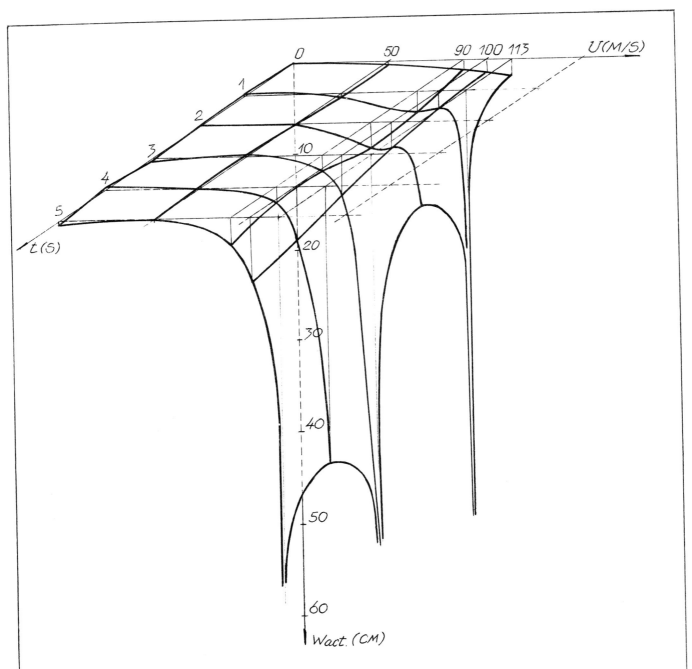

Fig.5. Space graphic representation of the vertical deflection of the
tube middle point "j"(x=L/2) for a pinned-pinned pipe.

C416/041

A boundary layer time delay model for the streamwise vibration of an isolated cylinder by vortex shedding

A LOWDON, BSc, PhD, GIMA
British Gas Engineering Research Station, Newcastle upon Tyne
N TONKS, BSc, MSc, PhD, CEng, FIMA, MRAeS
Department of Mathematics and Statistics, Newcastle upon Tyne Polytechnic
T S WILKINSON, BSc, FIMA
NEI Parsons Limited, Newcastle upon Tyne

SYNOPSIS In the laminar régime, the flow field around an isolated cylinder may be modelled as two regions - a boundary layer near to the cylinder surface and a potential flow region outside of this layer. Any disturbances that travel through the flow field are transmitted by waves that travel at the speed of sound relative to the fluid. The disturbances are also convected by the fluid at a much lower speed. In the boundary layer the convection will be slower still due to the slow moving fluid in this region. The resulting time delay in the transportation of the disturbances may affect the force experienced by the cylinder. A boundary layer model for the streamwise vibration of an isolated cylinder by vortex shedding is presented in momentum-integral form. The model is solved using a finite difference method and a boundary layer time delay is established.

1 INTRODUCTION AND THEORETICAL BACKGROUND

When an isolated cylinder is exposed to a perfectly uniform, non-turbulent incident flow, the wake behind the cylinder can develop an instability due to periodic vortex shedding. The vortices are shed alternately from opposite sides of the cylinder leading to fluctuating lift and drag forces on the structure. The fluctuating lift force has a frequency equal to the vortex shedding frequency, whereas the frequency of the fluctuating drag force is twice the vortex shedding frequency.

If the cylinder is flexible, or flexibly mounted, the usual response to this forcing is for the cylinder to vibrate transversely to the flow when the value of the reduced velocity is close to $1/S$ where S is the Strouhal number $f_s d/U_\infty$, f_s is the Strouhal shedding frequency, d is the tube diameter and U_∞ is the distant approach velocity of the fluid. If the body is lightly damped *lock-in* can occur, whereby the frequency of vortex shedding becomes locked in to the vibrational frequency of the body. **Bishop and Hassan (1)** showed that during lock-in, a circular cylinder experiences a substantial increase, not only in the oscillatory lift force, but also in the mean drag force. As a result, both transverse and (especially for high density fluids) streamwise vibrations can occur.

The flow field around an isolated cylinder may be modelled as two regions - a boundary layer near to the cylinder surface in which all of the viscosity of the fluid may be assumed to be concentrated and a potential flow region outside of this layer where the flow may be assumed to be inviscid and moving with steady velocity.

Within the boundary layer, the velocity of the fluid drops from the free stream value at the edge of the layer, to zero at the surface of the cylinder. As a result, steep velocity gradients exist in the boundary layer which give rise to frictional forces at the cylinder surface (skin friction) and consequently a source of vorticity.

Any disturbances that travel through the flow field are transmitted by waves that travel at the speed of sound relative to the fluid. The disturbances are also convected by the fluid at a much lower speed. Moreover, in the boundary layer region, the convection will be slower still due to the slow moving fluid in this region. The resulting time delay in the transportation of the disturbances may affect the force experienced by the cylinder.

The force acting on a cylinder in a transverse fluid flow is the sum of the force normal to the surface (pressure) and the integral of the shearing force tangential to the surface (viscous drag). The latter is very much less than the former because in a steady flow the boundary layer tends to separate from the surface of the cylinder at about 105^0 from the upstream stagnation point, and a wake comparable in width to the diameter of the cylinder results. The position of the separation point thus determines the magnitude of the lift and drag forces. Therefore, movements in the points of separation will be responsible for fluctuations in the pressure acting on the cylinder and fluctuations in the lift and drag forces will occur. Such movements will, of course, be associated with the growth and detachment of vortices.

Consequent changes in the free stream velocity distribution will cause movements of the position of the upstream stagnation point. If flow velocities are everywhere low compared with the speed of sound in the fluid, changes can be assumed to be instantaneous compared with changes of incidence as communicated by the boundary layer. This would further suggest the importance of the boundary layer time delay.

Separation of a boundary layer in a steady flow occurs when the product of the boundary layer thickness and the (adverse) pressure gradient is equal to some value that depends upon Reynolds number, free stream turbulence, surface roughness etc. Suppose, however, that the free stream velocity is suddenly changed (as in the case of an oscillating cylinder). The pressure gradient - in effect imposed by the potential field - will respond immediately, whereas the thickness will take some time to change. Therefore, if the change to the free stream velocity is such that the adverse pressure gradient is increased, the separation point will immediately move forward to a position where, at that time, the boundary layer thickness is appropriate. Some time later, when the thickness has increased to its equilibrium value, the separation point will move forward still further. The behaviour on the other side of the cylinder will be similar except that the separation point will move rearward.

Wilkinson and Ilett (2) carried out preliminary investigations into boundary layer time delays for both transverse and streamwise vibrations of an isolated cylinder. They suggested that solving the momentum integral boundary layer equation subject to an appropriate free stream velocity distribution would yield important information about boundary layer time delays. **Tonks (3)** postulated the existence of a boundary layer time delay mechanism for the transverse vibration of an isolated cylinder and calibrated the resulting mathematical model using the experimental data of **Gerlach and Dodge (4)**. The model yielded regions of instability consistent with experimental observations.

The current paper presents the first stage of an investigation to validate the hypothesis of **Tonks (3)**. The existence of a boundary layer time delay, for the streamwise vibration of an isolated cylinder in an otherwise steady flow, is established by solving numerically the momentum-integral form of the Prandtl boundary layer equations subject to appropriate free stream velocity and skin friction representations.

2 STREAMWISE VIBRATION OF AN ISOLATED CYLINDER

2.1 Introduction

Investigations of streamwise cylinder vibration in the Reynolds number range 10^2 to 10^5, have been carried out by a number of authors including **Tanida et al. (5)**, **Griffin and Ramberg (6)** and **Armstrong et al. (7)**. These authors have all concentrated on small amplitude vibrations.

If it is assumed that the cylinder undergoes small amplitude vibrations relative to the cylinder's diameter, then to model this behaviour, it is possible to consider the cylinder as stationary and to treat the free stream velocity as a mean flow with a superimposed oscillatory perturbation. This is completely equivalent to the cylinder vibrating in a mean flow as long as the acoustic wavelength of the perturbation is large compared with the diameter of the cylinder (**Lighthill (8)**). In this paper it is assumed that this condition is satisfied.

If the cylinder suddenly acquires an instantaneous velocity in opposition to the mean flow (as is the case for one half of the streamwise oscillation cycle), then the boundary layer on the cylinder will thin quickly and the separation point will move downstream. Over the second half of the cycle, the boundary layer will subsequently increase in thickness and the separation point will occur earlier once more. There is likely to be a time delay associated with the separation point returning to its equilibrium position. This could manifest itself by the boundary layer profile at the stagnation and separation points being out of phase at any instant of time. In the following analysis a mathematical model is established that predicts such a boundary layer time delay mechanism for the streamwise vibration of an isolated cylinder.

2.2 The mathematical model

Consider the flow over the curved surface in Fig 1. If the radius of curvature R is everywhere large compared with the boundary layer thickness $\delta(x)$, then without loss of generality, the x coordinate can be taken in the direction of the cylinder surface. The y coordinate is taken perpendicular to the cylinder surface. The x coordinate is made non-dimensional with respect to the radius of the cylinder, a, under the transformation $x \rightarrow x/a$ so that x is an angle in radians measured clockwise from the stagnation point. In the analysis that follows, all variables appear in their non-dimensional form, the details of which are given in the nomenclature.

Since it is the global properties of the boundary layer that are of interest, it is convenient to adopt an integral representation of the layer as suggested by **Wilkinson and Ilett (2)**. The integral representation is given by the momentum integral boundary layer equation:

$$\frac{\partial(U\delta_1)}{\partial t} + \frac{\partial(U^2\delta_2)}{\partial x} + U\delta_1 \frac{\partial U}{\partial x} = C_f \qquad (1)$$

where

$$\delta_1 = \int_0^\infty \frac{(U-u)}{U} dy \qquad (2)$$

and

$$\delta_2 = \int_0^\infty \frac{(U-u)u}{U^2} dy \qquad (3)$$

are the *displacement* and *momentum thicknesses* respectively, C_f is the skin friction, U is the free stream velocity and u is the x component of velocity within the boundary layer.

It is convenient to link together δ_1 and δ_2 through a *shape factor* H. For laminar boundary layers, we may assume that

$$H = \frac{\delta_1}{\delta_2} \qquad (4)$$

where H takes the values 2.3 at the stagnation point ($x = 0$) and 2.554 at the highest point on the cylinder ($x = \frac{\pi}{2}$) (**Schlichting (9)**). **Saatci (10)** represented the shape factor by the equation

$$H = K_1 \frac{dU_0}{dx} + K_2 \qquad (5)$$

where K_1 and K_2 are constants and U_0 is the mean flow velocity at the edge of the boundary layer. Using the above conditions on H gives $K_1 = -0.127$ and $K_2 = 2.554$.

Inserting equation (4) into equation (1) gives, for steady H

$$H(U \frac{\partial \delta_2}{\partial t} + \delta_2 \frac{\partial U}{\partial t}) + \delta_2(H+2)U \frac{\partial U}{\partial x} + U^2 \frac{\partial \delta_2}{\partial x}$$
$$= C_f \qquad (6)$$

Equation (6) is the governing **momemtum integral boundary layer equation**.

2.3 Free stream velocity and skin friction

The free stream velocity and skin friction representations characterise the flow. For the streamwise vibration of an isolated cylinder, the free stream velocity and skin friction as given by **Lighthill (8)** are

$$U(x,t) = U_0(x)(1 + \epsilon e^{i\omega t}) \qquad (7)$$

and

$$C_f = \begin{cases} \overline{C_0}(1 + \frac{3\epsilon e^{i\omega t}}{2}) + \frac{\epsilon}{2} e^{i\omega t} i\omega U_0 H \overline{\delta_2} \\ \quad \text{if } \omega < 10 \\[2ex] \overline{C_0} + \epsilon U_0 \sqrt{\omega} e^{i\omega t + \pi/4} \\ \quad \text{if } \omega > 10 \end{cases} \qquad (8)$$

where $U_0(x)$ is the mean flow, ω is the circular natural frequency of the imposed oscillation, $i = \sqrt{-1}$, ϵ is a small perturbation parameter, the overbar denotes a steady value and we attach meaning only to the real part. From potential flow theory

$$U_0(x) = 2\sin x \qquad (9)$$

$\overline{C_0}$ is available from **Schlichting (9)** in the form

$$Ax^2 + Bx$$

where A $(=-2.206)$ and B $(=4.405)$ are coefficients obtained from a quadratic fit to the Schlichting data.

2.4 Discretisation

To solve equation (6) a two-dimensional finite difference scheme is used as shown in Fig 2. Under discretisation, the point (x,t) is represented by $(i\Delta x, n\Delta t)$ where Δx and Δt are the discretised length and time steps respectively and i and n take appropriate integer values. The spatial and temporal derivatives $\frac{\partial \delta_2}{\partial x}$ and $\frac{\partial \delta_2}{\partial t}$ are approximated by

$$\frac{\partial \delta_2}{\partial x} \approx \frac{\delta_{2_i}^n - \delta_{2_{i-1}}^n}{\Delta x} \tag{10}$$

$$\frac{\partial \delta_2}{\partial t} \approx \frac{\delta_{2_i}^{n+1} - \delta_{2_i}^n}{\Delta t} \tag{11}$$

Choosing these finite difference approximations allows a time step to be specified for a numerically stable solution. From a *von Neumann* stability analysis of equation (12), a numerically stable solution is assured if

$$\Delta t \leq \frac{H_{min} \Delta x}{1 + \epsilon}$$

where H_{min} is the minimum value of H. The explicit appearances of δ_2 in equation (6) are replaced by $\delta_{2_{i-1}}^n$ in the discretised version. This is in keeping with the convective nature of the problem.

Inserting equations (10) and (11) into equation (6) yields

$$\delta_{2_i}^{n+1} = \delta_{2_i}^n (1 - \frac{U \Delta t}{H \Delta x})$$
$$+ \delta_{2_{i-1}}^n (\frac{U \Delta t}{H \Delta x} - \frac{\partial U}{\partial x} \frac{\Delta t (H+2)}{H} - \frac{\Delta t}{U} \frac{\partial U}{\partial t}) \tag{12}$$
$$+ \frac{\Delta t C_f}{H U}$$

This is the discretised version of the momentum integral boundary layer equation. The variables contained within the parentheses are evaluated at node i. However, the term

$$\frac{\Delta t C_f}{H U} = \frac{\Delta t C_f}{H U_0 (1 + \epsilon \cos(\omega t))} \tag{13}$$

is singular at the stagnation point $x = 0$. This problem is dealt with in subsection 2.5.

2.5 Initial and stagnation conditions

It is sufficient to initialise δ_2 to zero throughout the whole computational domain. This allows the solution to evolve in time and attain full periodicity. Graphs of steady δ_1 and δ_2 as a function of x are given by **Schlichting (9)**. The functions have a zero gradient in the vicinity of the origin which must, therefore, be preserved at each time level. Imposing $\frac{\partial \delta_2}{\partial x} = 0$ at node one gives

$$\frac{\delta_{2_1}^n - \delta_{2_0}^n}{\Delta x} = 0$$

i.e.

$$\delta_{2_1}^n = \delta_{2_0}^n \tag{14}$$

The *stagnation equation* evaluated at $x = 0$ is thus

$$\delta_{2_0}^{n+1} = \delta_{2_0}^n (1 + \frac{\Delta t \omega \epsilon \sin(\omega t)}{H (1 + \epsilon \cos(\omega t))}$$
$$- \frac{\Delta t U_0' (H+2)(1 + \epsilon \cos(\omega t))}{H}) \tag{15}$$
$$+ \frac{\Delta t C_f}{H U_0 (1 + \epsilon \cos(\omega t))}$$

where the dash denotes the total derivative with respect to x. As mentioned above, the term

$$\frac{\Delta t C_f}{H U_0 (1 + \epsilon \cos(\omega t))}$$

is singular at $x = 0$. Furthermore,

$$\lim_{x \to 0} \frac{\Delta t C_f}{H U_0 (1 + \epsilon \cos(\omega t))}$$

is indeterminate. Using L'Hôpital's rule, it can be shown that

$$\lim_{x \to 0} \frac{\Delta t C_f}{H U_0 (1 + \epsilon \cos(\omega t))}$$
$$= \frac{\Delta t (A x_p + B)(1 + 3\epsilon/2 \cos(\omega t))}{2 H_{min} (1 + \epsilon \cos(\omega t))} \tag{16}$$

where x_p ($= 2\Delta x$) is the value of x at which the condition $\frac{\partial \delta_2}{\partial x} = 0$ ends. Removing the singularity using the above substitution makes the problem fully computational.

3 COMPUTATIONAL ASPECTS

3.1 Approximate method of Waltz

To check the finite difference calculations, the approximate formula of Waltz is used. In dimensionless form this is

$$\delta_2^2 = \frac{0.470}{U^6} \int_0^x U^5 dx' \tag{17}$$

Substituting equation (7) into the above equation and integrating yields

$$\delta_2 = \sqrt{\frac{0.470}{2 \sin^6 x (1 + \epsilon \cos(\omega t))}}$$
$$* (\frac{8}{15} - \cos x + \frac{2}{3} \cos^3 x - \frac{1}{5} \cos^5 x)^{\frac{1}{2}} \tag{18}$$

The momentum thickness is computed at each grid point (other than $x = 0$) using both the finite difference scheme and the above equation and the results are compared; the finite difference calculations are thus checked. Table 1 gives a sample comparison for the case $\omega = 5\pi, \epsilon = 0.02, t = 5.0$.

Table 1 Comparison of the finite difference method and Waltz' approximate formula. $\epsilon = 0.02, \omega = 5\pi, t = 5.0$

Node	δ_2 :Finite diff.	δ_2 :Waltz
1	0.179	0.184
2	0.182	0.185
3	0.189	0.191
4	0.200	0.204
5	0.210	0.211
6	0.222	0.221
7	0.228	0.230
8	0.235	0.233
9	0.242	0.244
10	0.251	0.251
11	0.264	0.266
12	0.279	0.278
13	0.299	0.295
14	0.323	0.329
15	0.355	0.356
16	0.395	0.392
17	0.447	0.452

3.2 Discretisation parameters

From the literature, the boundary layer separation point for the steady flow around an isolated cylinder lies, approximately, between 1.79 and 1.9 radians, measured from the upstream stagnation point. As the approximations used in deriving the boundary layer equations are only valid for thin layers - effectively until separation occurs - the maximum (computational) value of x is conservatively taken as 1.8 radians. The region $0 \leq x \leq 1.8$ is then split into a grid of 17 equal intervals so that $\Delta x = 0.1059$. The restriction on Δt has already been stated earlier in the paper.

It should be noted that in this paper the term 'separation point' is only a nominal term used to signify the end of the computational domain. No part of the analysis is given to locating the true separation point $\frac{\partial u}{\partial y} = 0$.

4 RESULTS AND DISCUSSION

The results from the computer program written to solve the preceding mathematical model are contained in Table 2, for values of the perturbation frequency, ω, in the range $\frac{\pi}{32}$ to 15π. The time delay column represents the time difference between the momentum thicknesses at the separation and stagnation points attaining their respective maximum values once the solution has become steady periodic. The delay is measured to an accuracy of one time step Δt. All computations were carried out on a DEC VAX 8700 mini-computer at Newcastle upon Tyne Polytechnic.

Figs 3a to 6a show the variation of momentum thickness with time between the stagnation and separation points for one oscillation cycle over a range of values of ω, each solution having become steady-periodic . Features to note are the amplification of the perturbation as the separation point is approached and the phase difference (time delay) between the extrema of the stagnation point and separation point momentum thicknesses. The latter is further illustrated in Figs 3b to 6b.

For small values of ω the momentum thickness at the stagnation and separation points is approximately half a cycle out of phase. For large values of ω the time delay is negligible, presumably due to the inertia of the fluid.

Due to computational restrictions, the smallest tabulated value of ω is $\frac{\pi}{32}$. This represents a non-dimensional period of oscillation of 64. Since the solution must evolve in time to become steady-periodic, and since this can take upwards of five cycles to achieve, it is evident that a high demand is placed upon c.p.u. time. Typically, with values of Δt and Δx of 0.02 and 0.1059 respectively, upwards of 250 000 iterations are required. The size of ω must, therefore, be restricted.

5 CONCLUSIONS

A mathematical model for the streamwise vibration of an isolated cylinder has been presented using the momentum-integral form of the Prandtl boundary layer equations and assuming small amplitude vibrations of the cylinder. The existence of a boundary layer time delay has been established by analysing the momentum thickness profiles at the stagnation and separation points. The time delay tends to a fixed value for small values of the perturbation frequency, ω, whereas, for large values of this parameter, the delay is negligible.

Lowdon (11) has developed the model further to investigate the transverse vibration of an isolated cylinder. The resulting boundary layer time delay correlates well with that of Tonks (3).

The results from the analysis of an isolated cylinder have direct application in many fields of engineering e.g. heat exchanger tube vibration, the galloping of overhead power lines, the vibration of offshore risers and the flow around turbine blades.

Table 2 Time delay characteristics for the streamwise vibration of an isolated cylinder. $\epsilon = 0.02, 0.0 \leq x \leq 1.8$

ω	Period (P)	Time delay (T)	(T/P)*100
$\pi/32$	64	29.88	48.20
$\pi/16$	32	14.90	46.25
$\pi/8$	16	6.92	43.25
$\pi/4$	8	2.91	36.50
$\pi/2$	4	1.00	25.00
π	2	0.25	12.50
2π	1	0.03	3.00
3π	2/3	0.01	1.50
5π	2/5	0.00	0.00
7π	2/7	0.00	0.00
10π	1/5	0.00	0.00
15π	2/15	0.00	0.00

REFERENCES

(1) **BISHOP, R.E.D and HASSAN, A.Y** *The lift and drag forces on a circular cylinder oscillating in a flowing fluid.* Proc. Royal Society London, 1964, A227, pp 51-75.

(2) **WILKINSON, T.S. and ILETT, M.J.** *The excitation of cylinder vibration by cross flow.* NEI Parsons Ltd., 1973, Report CAP73-31.

(3) **TONKS, N.** *A theoretical analysis of flow induced vibrations of tube arrays in heat exchangers.* PhD Thesis, 1984, Newcastle upon Tyne Polytechnic.

(4) **GERLACH, C.R. and DODGE, F.T.** *An engineering approach to flow induced vibrations.* ASME Symposium on Flow Induced Vibrations in Heat Exchangers, Winter Annual Meeting, Dec.1970, Chicago, pp 18-26.

(5) **TANIDA, Y., OKAJIMA, A. and WATANABE, Y.** *Stability of circular cylinders oscillating in uniform flow or in a wake.* J. Fluid Mechanics, 1973, Vol. 61, pp 769-784.

(6) **GRIFFIN, O.M. and RAMBERG, S.E.** *Vortex shedding from a cylinder vibrating in-line with an incident uniform flow.* J. Fluid Mechanics, 1976, Vol. 75, pp 257-271.

(7) **ARMSTRONG, B.J., BARNES, F.H. and GRANT, I.** *The effect of a perturbation on the flow over a bluff cylinder.* Physics of Fluids, July 1986, Vol. 29, pp 2095-2102.

(8) **LIGHTHILL, M.J.** *The response of laminar skin friction and heat transfer to fluctuations in the stream velocity.* Proc. Royal Society London, 1954, A224, pp 1-23.

(9) **SCHLICHTING, H.** *Boundary layer theory.* 1979, McGraw-Hill, New York.

© IMechE 1991 C416/041

(10) **SAATCI, N.** *The basic theory of image plane representation of boundary layers and wakes and some possible extensions.* NEI Parsons Ltd., 1968, Report CAP68-52.

(11) **LOWDON, A.** *Flow induced vibrations of tube arrays in heat exchangers.* PhD Thesis, 1989, Newcastle upon Tyne Polytechnic.

NOMENCLATURE The important non-dimensionalisations are

$$t \rightarrow t\frac{U_\infty}{a}$$

$$x \rightarrow \frac{x}{a}$$

$$u \rightarrow \frac{u}{U_\infty}$$

$$U \rightarrow \frac{U}{U_\infty}$$

$$C_f = \frac{\tau\sqrt{Re}}{\rho U_\infty^2}$$

$$y \rightarrow \frac{y\sqrt{Re}}{a}$$

where τ = dimensional skin friction, Re = Reynolds number $\frac{U_\infty a}{\nu}$, ρ = fluid density and ν = coefficient of kinematic viscosity

The symbol $\rightarrow$ indicates the direction of the transformation to the dimensional variable i.e. the left hand side is transformed into the right hand side.

ACKNOWLEDGEMENTS

The authors would like to thank Newcastle upon Tyne Polytechnic for their support of the research project and NEI Parsons Ltd. for their collaboration. In addition, Dr. Lowdon would like to thank British Gas for their support in producing this paper and Dr. S. Bates, British Gas, for his comments and suggestions. The points of view expressed in the paper are solely those of the authors and not those of British Gas p.l.c. or NEI Parsons Ltd.

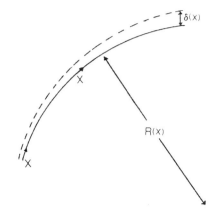

Fig 1   Boundary layer on a curved surface

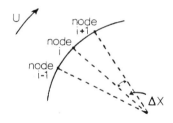

Fig 2   Finite difference discretisation

$\omega = \pi/4$

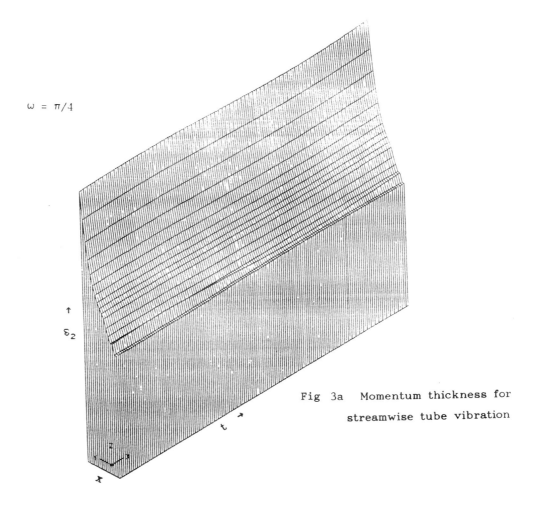

Fig 3a   Momentum thickness for
streamwise tube vibration

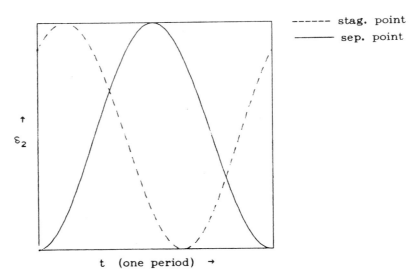

------ stag. point
—— sep. point

t (one period) →

Fig 3b   Comparison of momentum thickness at
the stagnation and separation points

288

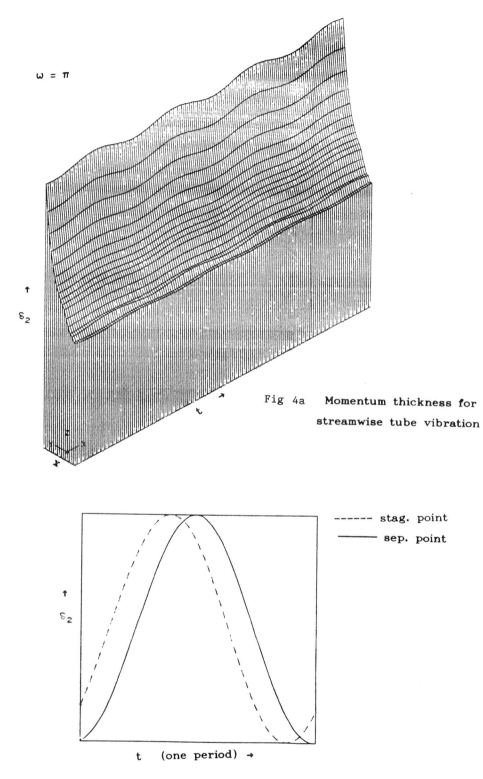

$\omega = \pi$

δ_2

Fig 4a   **Momentum thickness for**
streamwise tube vibration

------ stag. point
——— sep. point

δ_2

t   (one period) →

Fig 4b   Comparison of momentum thickness at
the stagnation and separation points

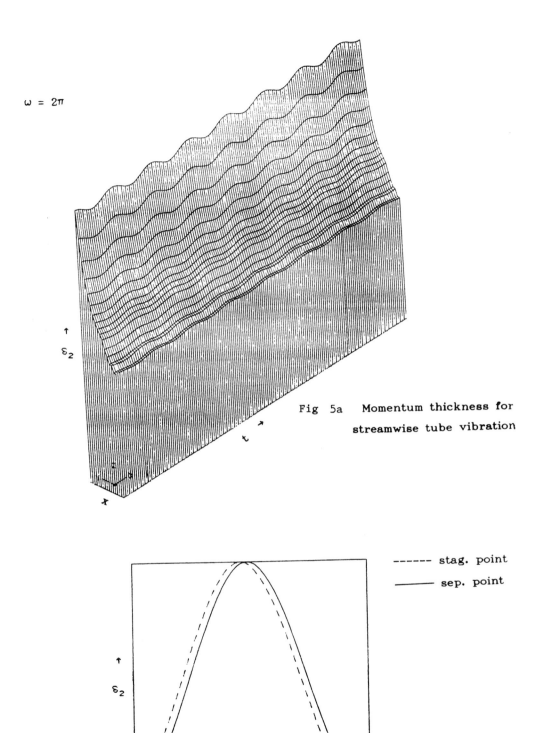

$\omega = 2\pi$

ε_2

Fig 5a   Momentum thickness for
streamwise tube vibration

------ stag. point

—— sep. point

ε_2

t (one period) →

Fig 5b   Comparison of momentum thickness at
the stagnation and separation points

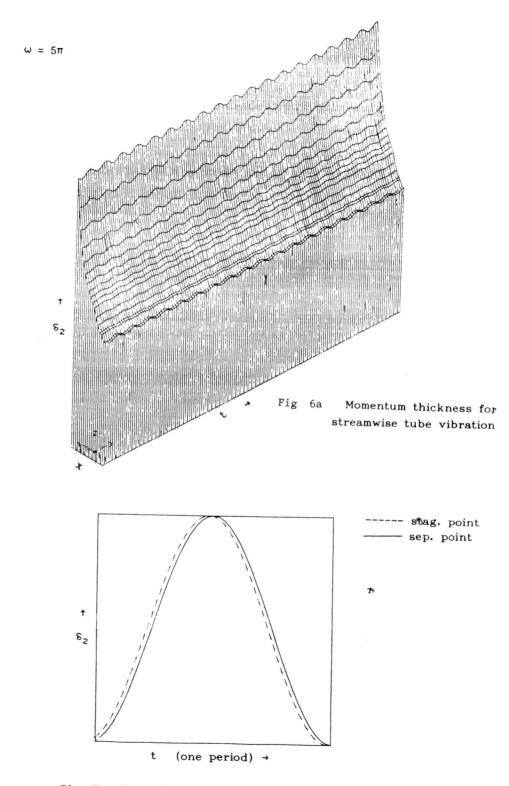

$\omega = 5\pi$

Fig 6a   Momentum thickness for streamwise tube vibration

----- stag. point

—— sep. point

Fig 6b   Comparison of momentum thickness at the stagnation and separation points

C416/001

Modelling the interaction of compressor surging with ductwork fluid compressibility and inertia

Eur Ing A ANDERSON, BSc(Eng), PhD, CEng, MIMechE and K SUWAN, BEng, PhD
Department of Mechanical, Materials and Manufacturing, University of Newcastle upon Tyne

SYNOPSIS   Developments in pump or compressor surge prediction tend to concentrate on the turbo-machines rather than the associated ductwork, which is conventionally restricted to incompressible flow or plenum models. Adapting the Method Of Lines gives a new lumped parameter duct flow model combining their features, but which remains appropriate for standard stability analysis procedures for self-excited vibrations. Recorded surge frequencies for a centrifugal compressor with both suction and discharge ductwork suggest dependence on acoustic standing waves. Eigenvalue or Routh-Hurwitz stability analysis using the proposed formulation shows potential in such situations.

NOTATION

A	pipe flow cross-sectional area
a	disturbance propagation wavespeed
$c_{ik,j}$	coefficients and order of polynomial, equations (9-10)
D,f	pipe equivalent diameter, Darcy friction factor
$\underline{E},\underline{X}$	coefficient matrix and state vector, equation (20)
G_i	gradient of performance character-istic, equation (10)
H_i,Q_i	for shorthand convenience, equations (25) and (16)
i,n	solution node index, number of nodes (Fig.1-3)
K	control valve loss coefficient, equations (9) and (26)
L	length of pipe segment (Fig.1-3)
MOC/L	Method of Characteristics/Lines
$\dot{m},\dot{m}_o$	mass flow rate and steady-state value
p,p_d,p_u	fluid static pressure, downstream and upstream of internal boundary condition
t	time (independent variable)
$\underline{R},\underline{S},\underline{U}$	coefficient vector and matrix with state vector, equations (1-5)
w^+,w^-	Riemann dependent variables, equation (4)
x,Δx	distance along pipe, discrete pipe segment (Fig.2-3)
$\Delta\dot{m},\Delta p$	small perturbations about steady-state, equation (19)
ρ	fluid density

1   INTRODUCTION

Flow-induced vibrations are generally associated with either resonant or self excited phenomena. For the latter there exist well-established techniques, the application of which to flow-induced vibrations extends back to eg, Thoma's use of the Routh-Hurwitz criteria for surge shaft stability by 1910 (1). However, the exploitation of standard Routh-Hurwitz, eigen-value, phase plane topology, Liapunov, etc stability analyses (2-6 et al) requires flow modelling with effectively lumped parameter systems represented by ordinary differential

equations in time. Consequently, these techniques apparently do not lend themselves to fluid systems in which wave propagation is significant and hence the transient flow partial differential equations are hyperbolic in character. Eg, hydro power system stability studies either adopt a transfer function corresponding to only incompressible pipe flow (7-8) or fall back instead on inspection of time-domain simulations obtained by a Method Of Characteristics (henceforth abbreviated to MOC) numerical solution (9-10).

Pump or compressor surging exhibits the classic features of self-excited vibration, being induced by an interaction of the flow characteristics of the turbomachine with those of the associated ductwork, while the external power input and pressure boundary conditions remain steady and provide no excitation to the system (11-12 et al). However, conventional surge prediction has been restricted to either incompressible pipe flow (6,13) or plenum (14-15 et al) models. Neither would be fully appropriate for a system (Fig.1) which surged at frequencies related to acoustic wave propagation in the ducts (Table 1).

The present objective is to adapt a numerical technique known as the Method of Lines (henceforth MOL) for a lumped parameter representation of compressible unsteady pipe flow (16-17) and to illustrate the application of this to surge prediction for a compressor/duct system (Fig.1) using conventional linearised (small amplitude) eigenvalue or Routh-Hurwitz stability analysis. However, as a preliminary it was found necessary to critically review application of the MOL to fluid transients. When the intention is to identify physical instabilities it is especially important that the formulation be free from not only gross simulation errors but also mathematical instabilities.

2   MOL REPRESENTATION OF TRANSIENT DUCT FLOW

The MOL is usually applied to parabolic problems (18-19) but has been used (intentionally or otherwise) for waterhammer (20-22) or other

pressure transients (23-25) and appears to lend
itself to lumped parameter representation of
distributed fluid systems (16-17,26).

Essentially, where partial differential
equations in time (t) and space (x) can be
written in terms of a state vector ($\underline{U}$) in the
form:

$$(\partial\underline{U}/\partial t) + \underline{S}(\partial\underline{U}/\partial x) = \underline{R} \qquad (1)$$

then, though there may be advantages for
simulation in a serial Continuous Space/
Discrete-Time boundary-value approach (19,27,28),
for stability analysis a parallel Continuous-
Time/Discrete-Space initial-value formulation
is preferred:

$$(d\underline{U}/dt) \simeq \underline{R} - \underline{S}(\Delta\underline{U}/\Delta x) \qquad (2)$$

where, for (n-1) space segments Δx, functions
fitted to values of the dependent variables ($\underline{U}$)
surrounding a general point (i) at any time
(Fig.2) can be differentiated to give
$(\Delta\underline{U}/\Delta x) \simeq (\partial\underline{U}/\partial x)$.

The intention is to avoid simulation, for
which in practice there is rarely any reason
not to use the MOC. However, to ensure adequate
representation of the fluid system before
proceeding to stability analyses, possible MOL
variants were compared empirically with the MOC
for time-domain simulation. The simplest
possible system with time-invariant boundary
conditions (Fig.3) was adopted (17,29). MOL
and MOC numerical solutions were compared
directly, both for a sharp transient initiated
by instantaneous downstream valve closure and,
(most importantly for stability analysis) trying
to hold an initial steady-state (30-31). These
suggested that existing implementations (16-17,
20-26) could be inappropriate unless the
following were considered.

2.1 Form of state vector $\underline{U}$

For investigation of asymptotic stability in
unsteady, one-dimensional duct flows where
disturbance propagation speeds do not vary
significantly, flow velocities are relatively
low and moving shocks do not occur, it is
convenient to assume that convective
accelerations and pressure-induced fluctuations
in fluid density (ρ), duct cross-sectional area
(A) and wavespeed (a) are numerically (if not
physically) negligible (30). Momentum and
continuity equations can then be written as in
equation (1) with (16,31):

$$\underline{U} = \begin{bmatrix} \dot{m} \\ (Ap/a) \end{bmatrix} \quad \underline{S} = \begin{bmatrix} 0 & \rho Aa \\ \rho Aa & 0 \end{bmatrix} \quad \underline{R} = \begin{bmatrix} -(f/2\rho AD)\dot{m}|\dot{m}| \\ 0 \end{bmatrix}$$

$$(3)$$

where the dependent variables are mass flow
rate ($\dot{m}$) and pressure (p), hydrostatic pressures
are neglected, f is Darcy friction factor and D
the duct equivalent diameter.

The MOL has been implemented with these
primitive variables (17,20-24) but for hyperbolic problems this results in the spurious
transients superimposed over the basic MOC

solution observed elsewhere (17,31). These
can be avoided by adopting instead
characteristic Riemann or Allievi dependent
variables (27-28,31-32):

$$W^{\pm} = [\dot{m} \pm (Ap/a)] \qquad (4)$$

giving, in place of equation (3):

$$\underline{U} = \begin{bmatrix} W^+ \\ W^- \end{bmatrix} \quad \underline{S} = \begin{bmatrix} \rho Aa & 0 \\ 0 & -\rho Aa \end{bmatrix}$$

$$\underline{R} = -(f/8\rho AD)(W^++W^-)|W^++W^-| \begin{bmatrix} 1 \\ 1 \end{bmatrix} \qquad (5)$$

2.2 Choice of discrete space interpolating polynomial

One supposed advantage of the MOL appears to be
that high-order methods can be used for both
integration in time (17,23,26,33) and interpolation in space (17,21-23,33-34).However,while
appropriate for parabolic equations,with hyperbolic equations this violates the domain of
dependence and again produces spurious parasitic
transients (31).

Hyperbolic continuous systems are
restricted to first-order linear interpolation
because they exhibit Lipschitz (bounded)
discontinuities in first or higher-order
derivatives across the characteristic curves
(35). Unlike the primitive variables (20,26),
the characteristic variables of equations
(4-5) define the correct match of variable
with forward and backward differences to
preserve the directionality of disturbance
propagation and boundary information:

$$(\partial W_i^-/\partial x) \simeq (W_{i+1}^- - W_i^-)/\Delta x \text{ for } i = 1 \text{ to } (n-1)$$

$$(6)$$

$$(\partial W_i^+/\partial x) \simeq (W_i^+ - W_{i-1}^+)/\Delta x \text{ for } i = 2 \text{ to } n$$

The necessary boundary conditions are solved
for W_1^+ and W_n^-, leaving (2n-2) ordinary
differential equations for the remaining
(2n-2) variables (Fig.2).

2.3 Representation of the pipe friction term

Some discrete representations of the Darcy-
Weisbach friction term may give rise to
instabilities (29,31,36), eg with the MOL
(17,22):

$$\dot{m}_i|\dot{m}_i| \simeq \dot{m}_c|\dot{m}_c| = (1/4)(W_c^++W_c^-)|W_c^++W_c^-| \qquad (7)$$

where the subscript C denotes evaluation for
node i on the known initial time line (Fig.2).
Frictionless implementations (23,32) avoid
this problem but are inappropriate for self-
excited oscillations which may depend on fluid
damping. An unconditionally stable linear
approximation can be adapted (31) from the
MOC (29,36):

$$\dot{m}_i|\dot{m}_i| \simeq \begin{cases} (1/4)(W_A^+ + W_A^-)|W_P^+ + W_P^-| & \text{for } W^+ (i=1 \text{ to } n-1) \\ \\ (1/4)(W_B^+ + W_B^-)|W_P^+ + W_P^-| & \text{for } W^- (i=2 \text{ to } n) \end{cases} \quad (8)$$

where the subscript P denotes evaluation for node i on the solution time line (Fig.2).

3 APPLICATION OF MOL TO COMPRESSOR SURGE

3.1 Basis of model

Where a pump or compressor performance characteristic (Fig.4) exhibits a negative slope, operation is usually stable, but where the slope is positive surge may occur, depending on its interaction with the duct system (11-15 et al). As the present objective is to illustrate modelling of the compressible unsteady duct flow, rather than the complex unsteady compressor internal flow (11-12,14-15), consequently the simplest possible represent- ation of the internal valve and compressor boundary conditions is adopted. Ignoring hysteresis, impedance and capacitance, then pressure difference characteristics can be represented simply by time-invariant polynomials in local discharge $\dot{m}_i$:

$$p_{di} - p_{ui-1} \simeq c_{io} + c_{i1}\dot{m}_i + c_{i2}\dot{m}_i^2 + \cdots + c_{ij}\dot{m}_i^j \quad (9)$$

Thus the local gradient G_i of the character- istic is simply:

$$G_i = d(p_{di} - p_{ui-1})/d\dot{m}_i = c_{i1} + 2c_{i2}\dot{m}_i + \cdots + jc_{ij}\dot{m}_i^{j-1} \quad (10)$$

Though the MOL allows as many degrees-of- freedom as desired, Table 1 suggests that in this particular case it should be sufficient to adopt the minimum two nodes for each pipe segment (ie one at each boundary with no internal nodes) giving $\Delta x = L$ (Fig.1). Thus at the two external boundary nodes with p_{d1} = constant and p_{u5} = constant (Fig.1) the proposed MOL formulation gives:

$$(d\dot{m}_1/dt) + Q_1 = 0 \quad (11)$$

$$(d\dot{m}_5/dt) + Q_{(5-1)} = 0 \quad (12)$$

and at each of the three internal boundary nodes (i = 2,3,4 on Fig.1), using equation (10) to specify the component in terms of the gradient of its performance characteristic:

$$(d\dot{m}_i/dt) + (A_{i-1}/a_{i-1})(dp_{ui}/dt) + Q_{i-1} = 0 \quad (13)$$

$$(dp_{di}/dt) - (dp_{ui}/dt) = G_i(d\dot{m}_i/dt) \quad (14)$$

$$(d\dot{m}_i/dt) - (A_i/a_i)(dp_{di}/dt) + Q_i = 0 \quad (15)$$

where (for shorthand convenience):

$$Q_{i-1} = +(a_{i-1}/L_{i-1})(\dot{m}_i - \dot{m}_{i-1}) + (A_{i-1}/L_{i-1})$$
$$(p_{ui} - p_{di-1}) + (f_{i-1}/2\rho_{i-1}A_{i-1}D_{i-1})\dot{m}_{i-1}|\dot{m}_{i-1}| \quad (16)$$

$$Q_i = -(a_i/L_i)(\dot{m}_{i+1} - \dot{m}_i) + (A_i/L_i)(p_{ui+1} - p_{di})$$
$$+ (f_i/2\rho_i A_i D_i)\dot{m}_i|\dot{m}_i| \quad$$

For comparison, an incompressible flow analysis assuming uniform instantaneous mass flow $\dot{m}_i$ throughout L_{i-1} would give flow inertia without compressibility:

$$(d\dot{m}_i/dt) + (A_{i-1}/L_{i-1})(p_{ui} - p_{di-1}) + (f_{i-1}/2\rho_{i-1}$$
$$A_{i-1}D_{i-1})\dot{m}_i|\dot{m}_i| = 0 \quad (17)$$

whereas treating the pipe as a plenum, with the friction losses lumped as a single orifice loss at one boundary (and the wavespeed a_{i-1} acting as an equation of state relating density and pressure changes) would give compressibility without inertia:

$$(A_{i-1}/a_{i-1})(dp_{ui}/dt) + (a_{i-1}/L_{i-1})(\dot{m}_i - \dot{m}_{i-1}) = 0 \quad (18)$$

3.2 Linearised equations for eigenvalue stability analysis

Prediction of surge behaviour beyond the stability limit is of considerable practical importance. However, since the simplified compressor model of equations (9-10) is adopted, then in this instance, a small perturbation analysis with the equations linearised about a steady-state will be used simply to determine surge inception (itself an important practical consideration).

Equations (11-16) are locally linearised (5) for small deviations ($\Delta\dot{m}_i$, etc) about a particular steady-state condition ($\dot{m}_o$, etc):

$$\dot{m}_i = \dot{m}_o + \Delta\dot{m}_i, (d\dot{m}_i/dt) = (d\Delta\dot{m}_i/dt),$$
$$\dot{m}_i|\dot{m}_i| = \dot{m}_o|\dot{m}_o| + 2\dot{m}_o\Delta\dot{m}_i \quad (19)$$

For linear homogeneous first-order equations:

$$d\underline{X}/dt = \underline{E}.\underline{X} \quad (20)$$

in which all the elements of $\underline{E}$ are locally constant and $\underline{X}$ is the state vector, eg (Fig.1):

$$\underline{X} = [\Delta\dot{m}_1, \Delta p_{u2}, \Delta\dot{m}_2, \Delta p_{d2}, \Delta p_{u3}, \Delta\dot{m}_3, \Delta p_{d3}, \Delta p_{u4},$$
$$\Delta\dot{m}_4, \Delta p_{d4}, \Delta\dot{m}_5] \quad (21)$$

then any standard software (37) can find the eigenvalues of the coefficient matrix $\underline{E}$. Such a system is stable if and only if all the eigenvalues of $\underline{E}$ have negative real parts and the frequencies of the system can be calculated in the usual way from the imaginary parts (14).

At the external boundaries, equations (11-12) are in the appropriate form and at internal boundaries algebraic rearrangement of equations (13-15) is straightforward (31):

$$(dp_{ui}/dt) = H_i\{Q_{i-1}(1-G_iA_i/a_i)-Q_i\} \qquad (22)$$

$$(d\dot{m}_i/dt) = H_i\{(A_i/a_i)Q_{i-1}+(A_{i-1}/a_{i-1})Q_i\} \qquad (23)$$

$$(dp_{di}/dt) = H_i\{Q_{i-1}-(1-G_iA_{i-1}/a_{i-1})Q_i\} \qquad (24)$$

where (for shorthand convenience):

$$H_i=(a_{i-1}/A_{i-1})(a_i/A_i)/[G_i-(a_{i-1}/A_{i-1})-(a_i/A_i)] \qquad (25)$$

4 DISCUSSION OF RESULTS

4.1 Prediction compared with experiment

Table 2 shows combinations of control valve settings for a fixed compressor speed, holding the upstream valve in a fixed position and varying downstream valve position and vice versa. Table 3 shows behaviour variation over the peak of the compressor performance characteristic (Fig.4) for different compressor speeds. In summary:

(a) All unstable operating regions where surging occurs experimentally are predicted, though the correct surge frequency may not be identified in all cases.

(b) The model is conservative, in that it may predict surging where none occurs, but only in operating regions where there is rough running experimentally.

It is possible that the simplified compressor representation does not allow all interactions to be modelled and this will be the subject of further investigation.

In this example, with its relatively short ducts, a conventional plenum model (14-15 et al) will perform similarly but incompressible pipe flow (6-8) does not predict surging at these frequencies related to acoustic wave propagation (Table 1). The real benefit of the proposed model should arise with longer ducts where both elastic and inertia effects are significant, eg (6-10, 16, 32 et al). Experimental comparisons for such cases are harder to come by and are also the subject of further investigation.

4.2 Sensitivity of formulation

Table 3 confirms normal expectations with the surge line located not at but to the left of the performance characteristic peak (Fig.4). Because reliable data are notoriously difficult to obtain for valve loss coefficients (K2,K4) and, even more so, slopes of the compressor performance characteristic (G3), Table 4 shows the sensitivity of the model to these crucial factors. The actual slope G3 of the characteristic (low sensitivity in Table 4) is less important than the relative position on the characteristic which defines discharge $\dot{m}_0$ (as in Table 3). The discharge directly influences the system characteristic, as does the control valve loss coefficient and Table 4 clearly

shows sensitivity to this.

Sensitivity to the system characteristic is also illustrated in this application by problems experienced with the rather over-simplified treatment of the two valve internal boundary conditions (i = 2 and 4) which are the dominant resistances. The usual expression for valve pressure drop in terms of duct dynamic pressure gives in equation (9):

$$c_{i2}=K_i/(2\rho_iA_i^2) \text{ and } c_{ik}=0 \quad (k=0,1,3 \text{ to } j) \qquad (26)$$

Appropriate values (38-39) of the valve loss coefficients (K2,K4) can be used directly in equations (10) and (14) or, alternatively, these can be set to zero and the valve losses combined with the pipe friction losses (which also include other local losses such as duct elbows) on either side of the compressor. Though further study is clearly called for, the latter procedure was adopted to make the treatment of these local losses consistent with that of friction losses, cf equations (8) and (11-15).

This treatment of the valves also subsequently allowed direct comparison with an even cruder model taking only three nodes to represent only two pipes (L1+L2) and (L3+L4). Table 2 confirms that this causes no gross change in predicted behaviour. Because this minimal discretisation can predict only the 23.75 Hz surge frequency (Table 1), it gives instability with no frequency (ie imaginary part of eigenvalue zero with real part positive) where either the experimental instability is at a higher frequency (53 Hz) or where the model predicts instability but only rough running is observed.

4.3 Approach to model

Two aspects seem to demand general comment. Firstly this is a "lumped parameter" as opposed to a "distributed" model (5). With the latter, either of the impedance or transfer matrix approaches widely used for pipe resonance problems can be adapted for analysis of self-excited oscillations by solving for r to obtain stability bounds from the assumed time variations in $\exp(j\omega+r)t$. However, the distributed approach is restricted to linearised problems in which the principle of superposition applies. While the application illustrated here is similarly linearised, the general advantage of the lumped parameter approach is that future development to non-linear stability analysis is possible. In addition, the lumped parameter approach allows the fluid ducting to be handled by the same standard methods (2-6 et al) as other components of the overall system (1,6,7,10 et al) and is directly related to other models previously used for turbomachine surging (13-15 et al).

Secondly, if a lumped parameter approach is chosen, as here, then the question of the appropriate degree of discretisation arises. A common rule-of-thumb is "ten lumps per wavelength" (eg 5 et al). For the shortest wavelength at the higher observed significant frequency (Table 1), equations (9-18) are based conveniently on eight "lumps" (Fig.1).

More lumps can easily be incorporated, eg taking a single internal node in each of the four pipes would increase this to twelve lumps, etc. The former is illustrated in this paper for both brevity and also, in particular, to allow direct comparison with previous lumped parameter models (5,13-15 et al), ie equations (17-18) above. The influence of degree of discretisation is the subject of further investigation (particularly for longer ducts) but, as noted in Section 4.2 above, the approach is apparently robust to under-discretisation.

5 CONCLUSIONS

It is believed that the limitations of the surge predictions arise from the modelling of the control valves and compressor. In contrast, it has been demonstrated that it is feasible to represent elastic-column pipe flows by lumped-parameter ordinary differential equations which contain terms additional to either of the corresponding conventional rigid-column or plenum approaches. This has been based on the MOL but it has been found necessary to modify implementations in the literature in order to obtain satisfactory results for either simulation or stability analysis. Even at a very crude level of discretisation, this seems to work satisfactorily for linearised small amplitude stability analysis where instabilities are associated with elastic-column effects. It thus has potential for vibration analysis of quite complex pipe systems in which self-excited fluid oscillations may occur, either for surge predictions as here, or for, eg, the design of vibration absorber elements (16), etc.

REFERENCES

(1) THOMA,D. Zur Theorie des Wasserschlosses bie selbsttätig geregelten Turbinenlagen, 1910 (Oldenbourg, Munich).

(2) DEN HARTOG,J.P., Mechanical vibrations, 4th edn, 1956 (McGraw Hill, New York).

(3) TIMOSHENKO,S.and YOUNG,D.H., Vibration problems in engineering, 3rd edn, 1955 (van Nostrand, Princeton, NJ).

(4) ATHERTON,D.P., Stability of nonlinear systems, 1981 (John Wiley, Chichester).

(5) DOEBELIN,E.O., System modelling and response: theoretical and experimental approaches, 1980 (John Wiley, New York).

(6) ANDERSON,A. Surge shaft stability for pumped-storage schemes. Chap 4 of CHEREMISINOFF,P.N. et al (eds), Civil Engineering Practice, 1988, 5, 97-137 (Technomic, Lancaster Pa).

(7) Power System Engineering Committee. Dynamic models for steam and hydro turbines in power system studies. In BYERLY,R.T. and KIMBARK,E.W. (eds), Stability of large electric power systems, 1974, 128-139 (IEEE Press, New York).

(8) SUCENA PAIVA,J.P. and BETAMIO DE ALMEIDA,A. Estabilidade da regulacao carga-velocidade em centrais hidroelectricas. Congresso 77, Ordem dos Engeneiros, Lisbon,1977, Sect 8, Paper 11.

(9) BRUNELLE,P.E. La simulation des transitoires dans les systemes hydroelectriques avec chambre d'equilibre et regulateur de vitesse lors de variations de la demande, IAHR Hydraulic Symposium, Bucharest, 1976, 151-162.

(10) SMITH,J.R.et al. Assessment of hydro-turbine models for power-systems studies. IEE Proceedings, Part C, 1983 130(1),1-7.

(11) KOLNSBERG,A. Reasons for centrifugal compressor surging and surge control. Journal of Engineering for Power, ASME, 1979, 101 (1), 79-86.

(12) STENNING,A.H. Rotating stall and surge. Journal of Fluids Engineering, ASME, 1980, 102 (1), 14-20.

(13) ROTHE,P.H. and RUNSTADLER,P.W. First-order pump surge behaviour. Journal of Fluids Engineering, ASME, 1978, 100, 459-466.

(14) GREITZER,E.M. The stability of pumping systems. Journal of Fluids Engineering, ASME, 1981, 103, 193-242.

(15) BRONS,M. Bifurcations and instabilities in the Greitzer model for compressor system surge. Mathematical Engineering in Industry, 1988, 2 (1), 51-63.

(16) ANDERSON,A. Interaction of surge shafts and penstocks. 4th International Conference on Pressure Surges, Bath, 1983, 297-312 (BHRA, Cranfield).

(17) MAUDSLEY,D. Errors in the simulation of pressure transients in a hydraulic system. Transactions, Institute of Measurement and Control, 1984, 6 (1), 7-12.

(18) HOLT,M. Numerical methods in fluid dynamics, 2nd edn, 1984 (Springer,Berlin).

(19) REKTORYS,K. The method of discretization in time and partial differential equations, 1982 (Reidel, Dordrecht).

(20) GALLER,B.A.and WESTERVELT,F.H. The digital computer for fluid-flow calculations. Section 25 of STREETER,V.L. (ed),Handbook of fluid dynamics, 1961, 19-22 (McGraw-Hill, New York).

(21) THIRRIOT,C. et al. Simulation numerique des ecoulements permanents et transitoires dans les systemes d'alimentation en eau, 13th IAHR Congress, Kyoto, 1969, 1,533-542.

(22) WOOD,D.J. Waterhammer analysis by analog computers. Journal of the Hydraulics Division, ASCE, 1967, 93 (HY1), 1-11.

(23) LAKSHMINARAYANAN,P.A. et al. A finite difference scheme for unsteady pipe flows. International Journal of Mechanical Sciences, 1979, 21 (9), 557-566.

(24) DIGERNES,T. Real-time failure detection and identification applied to supervision of oil transport in pipelines. Modelling Identification and Control, 1980, 1 (1), 39-49.

(25) OSIADACZ,A.J. Simulation and analysis of gas networks, 1987 (Spon, London).

(26) BHARATH,S. et al. A distributed mathematical model for pressure transient analysis in a railway brake pneumatic system. International Journal of Mechanical Sciences, 1990, 32, (2), 133-145.

(27) OOSTERVELD,M.and ADAMOWSKI,K. Hybrid computer model of St.Venant equations. Journal of the Hydraulics Division, ASCE, 1976, 102 (HY10), 1491-1501.

(28) VICHNEVETSKY,R. Hybrid computer integration of hyperbolic partial differential equations by a method of lines. 4th Australian Computer Conference, Adelaide, 1969, 457-461.

(29) HOLLOWAY,M.B.and CHAUDHRY,M.H. Stability and accuracy of waterhammer analysis. Advances in Water Resources, 1985, 8, 121-128.

(30) WYLIE,E.B. et al. Discussion and closure on fundamental equations of waterhammer. Journal of Hydraulic Engineering, ASCE, 1985, 111 (8), 1185-1200.

(31) SUWAN,K. The method of lines applied to waterhammer computation. PhD Thesis, 1989, University of Newcastle upon Tyne.

(32) DONDOE,S.and HALANAY,A. Stability of hyperbolic systems with controlled boundary conditions. Applications to governors for hydraulic devices. IAHR Hydraulic Symposium, Bucharest, 1976, 313-318.

(33) NOUGARO,J. et al. Critique des methodes numerique de calcul des intumescences et examen d'une nouvelle methode. L'Energia Elettrica, 1967, 85-93.

(34) COLLINS,J.I.and FERSHT,S.N. Mixed technique for computing surges in channels. Journal of the Hydraulics Division, ASCE, 1968, 94 (HY2), 349-362.

(35) JEFFREY,A. Quasilinear hyperbolic systems and waves, 1976 (Pitman, London).

(36) WYLIE,E.B. The microcomputer and pipeline transients. Journal of Hydraulic Engineering, ASCE, 1983, 109 (12),1723-1739.

(37) NAG Library. Fortran Mark 7, Routine FO2AGF, NAGFLIB, 1975, 3 (MK5),987/623 (Numerical Algorithms, Oxford).

(38) MILLER,D.S. Internal flow systems, 1978 (BHRA, Cranfield).

(39) LEVIN,L. Formulaire des conduites forcées, oleoducs et conduits d'aeration, 1968 (Dunod, Paris).

Table 1   Association of surge and acoustic natural frequencies

Observed surge frequencies F(Hz)	Associated length (L) of ductwork		
	Calculated from observed F (L=a/4F) (m)	Existing on apparatus	
		Measured length L (m)	Pipe combination (Fig.1)
23.75	3.58	3.58	$L_1+L_2+L_3+L_4$
$53.00^{+0.50}_{-0.00}$	1.60	1.61	L_2+L_3
$71.00^{+0.25}_{-0.00}$	1.20	1.23	L_1+L_2
$94.75^{+0.25}_{-0.00}$	0.90	1.03	L_3

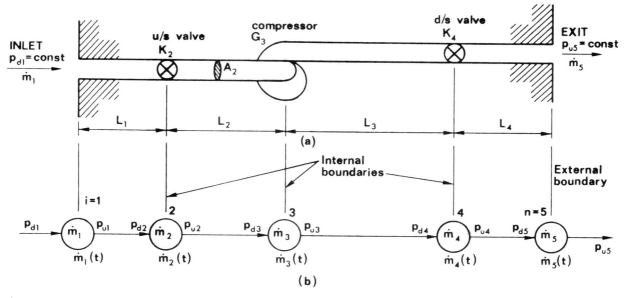

Fig.1. Compressor system tested: (a) schematic, (b) lumped-parameter model.

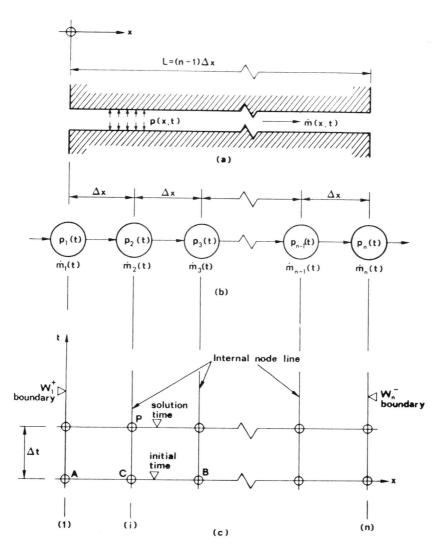

Fig.2. MOL applied to pipe element: (a) schematic, (b) lumped-parameter model, (c) finite-difference grid.

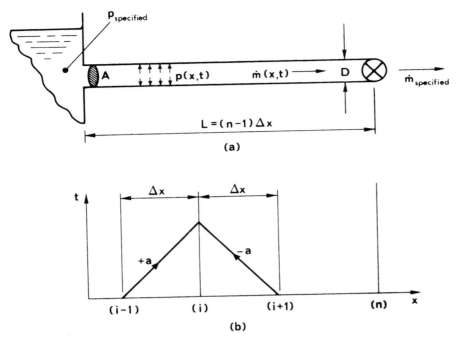

Fig.3. Pipe system to test transient solution techniques:
(a) schematic, (b) characteristics in space/time plane

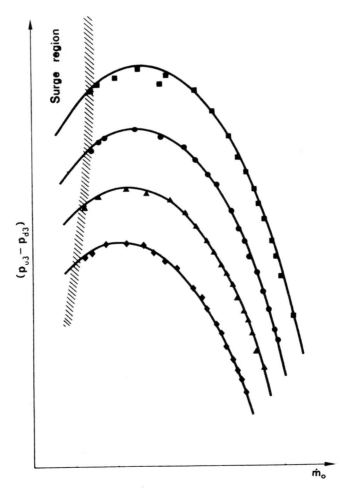

Fig.4. Performance characteristic for compressor (pressure rise/mass discharge at constant speed)

Table 2   Comparison of predicted with experimental (Fig.5) surge inception over full ranges of control valve settings (90° = fully open, 0° = shut):

S = Stable
R = Stable but Rough Running
U = Unstable (with lowest surge frequency, Hz)

| Case: Valve opening (degrees) | | Experiment 21600 rev/min (Fig.5) | Prediction | |
Upstream	Downstream		Four-pipe model (Fig.1)	Two-pipe model
>36°	>29°	S	S	S
	<29°	U (23.75)	U (23.75)	U (23.75)
≈36°-30°	>29°	S	S	S
	<29°	R	U (23.75)	U (0.00)
<20°	>37°	R	U (23.75)	U (23.75)
	<37°	U (53.00)	U (23.75)	U (0.00)
>27° <27°	>50°	S	S	S
		R	U (23.75)	U (23.75)
>27° <27°	≈34°-40°	S	S	S
		R	U (53.00)	U (23.75)
>27° <27°	≈34°-30°	S	S	S
		R	U (53.00)	U (0.00)
>33° <33°	<20°	U (23.75)	U (53.00)	U (23.75)
		U (53.00)	U (53.00)	U (0.00)

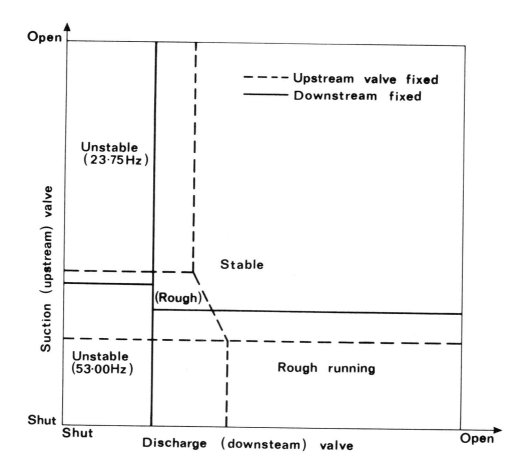

Fig.5.   Surge map for Table 2.

Table 3 Comparison of predicted with experimental surge inception (influence of slope of compressor characteristic):

S = Stable
R = Stable but Rough Running
U = Unstable (with lowest surge frequency, Hz)

Compressor speed (rev/min)	Valve opening (degrees) ±½° upstream	downstream	Steady discharge (kg/s)	Slope of characteristic G_3 (Ns/m²kg)	Experiment	Prediction
21600 (Table 2)	27.0	70	0.042	+3.75	R	U (23.75)
	31.0		0.070	+2.00	S	S
	36.0		0.105	0	S	S
	38.5		0.140	−2.00	S	S
	70	25.5	0.052	+3.33	U (23.75)	U (23.75)
		31.1	0.068	+2.00	S	S
		36.5	0.115	0	S	S
		39.0	0.150	−3.00	S	S
23400	70	26.5	0.058	+3.33	U (23.75)	U (23.75)
		34.5	0.090	+1.00	S	S
		37.0	0.119	0	S	S
		41.5	0.187	−4.62	S	S
25200	70	26.5	0.065	+10.00	U (23.75)	U (23.75)
		34.5	0.090	+2.00	S	S
		37.5	0.127	0	S	S
		41.5	0.190	−5.00	S	S
27000	70	27.5	0.068	+5.00	U (23.75)	U (23.75)
		35.5	0.100	+1.67	S	S
		38.0	0.135	0	S	S
		41.0	0.180	−2.00	S	S

Table 4 Sensitivity of prediction to control valve loss coefficient and slope of compressor characteristic at 21600 rev/min with upstream valve 70° and downstream 25.5° open ($\dot{m}_o$ = 0.052 kg/s)

Factor	Assumed test value (Tables 2-3)	Variation values for sensitivity analysis	Calculated lowest surge frequency (Hz)
Slope of compressor characteristic G_3 (Ns/m²kg)	+3.33	+5.00	23.75
		+4.00	23.75
			23.75
		+2.00	23.75
		+1.00	23.75
Downstream valve loss coefficient K_4 (38-39)	111.4	130	26.71
		120	25.24
			23.75
		100	21.36
		90	18.65

© IMechE 1991 C416/001

C416/093

The effects of turbulence and damping on pipeline acoustic resonance

P N LAMOUREUX, MEng, MASME, CPPA
Structural Dynamics Research Corporation, Ontario, Canada
D S WEAVER, PhD, FASME
McMaster University, Hamilton, Ontario, Canada

SYNOPSIS

Pipeline acoustic resonance has become an important problem in the oil and gas, energy and pulp and paper industries. The objective of this study was to investigate how acoustic response was affected by source turbulence and response damping. The experimental system consisted of airflow through an acrylic pipeline with a centrally located cavity formed by two closely spaced orifice plates. Turbulence conditioning resulted in an increase in the resonance lock-in regions of the pipe modes and an increased formation of higher shear layer oscillation modes. An increase in acoustic damping caused a shift in response away from lock-in regions about acoustic natural frequencies and towards a natural shear layer response.

NOTATION

f	frequency Hz
U	airflow velocity at convergence exit
L_p	cavity length
d	orifice diameter
m	shear layer oscillation stage number
N	pipeline acoustic mode number
v	kinematic viscosity
P	acoustic pressure
$Re = Ud/v$	Reynolds number
$St = fd/U$	Strouhal Number

1. INTRODUCTION

Acoustic resonance within pipelines excited by flow instabilities is a particular class of problem which has not received a great deal of attention from the scientific community despite the fact that we see common occurrences of this phenomenon throughout industry. Hartlen and Jaster reported severe vibrational amplitudes caused by acoustic resonance in the main steam piping of Ontario Hydro's nuclear generating facilities forcing the utility to derate their units from 791 MW to 650 MW [1]. Hassouneh [2] reported at the same time that the Oil and Gas industry experienced similar problems of acoustic and mechanical coupling in their piping systems which caused excessive vibrational amplitudes leading to degradation of system efficiency. In the pulp and paper industry, the occurrence of acoustic resonance in the main stock approach system can cause excessive pulsations leading to unstable stock flow delivery which ultimately affects paper quality.

All of the above mentioned cases are ones in which fluid instabilities, generated by flow separation within the pipeline from a plethora of discontinuities, organise themselves to excite plane wave acoustic pipe modes. This is referred to as an acoustic resonant system. In contrast to the attention given to the above mentioned mechanism is that given to the class of problems defined as flow resonant. A variety of flow conditions and geometries have been studied in this class of problems including the edgetone [3], the holetone and ringtone [4] and the platetone [5,6]. As well, the above configurations with adjacent cavities have also been extensively studied by various researchers [7-10] culminating in excellent reviews by Rockwell and Naudascher [11,12] and again by Rockwell [13]. In the particular class of problem investigated in the present study there has been some previously reported work by Schachenmann and Rockwell [14,15] and by Nomoto and Culick [16]. Distinction of the above two classes of problems can be made by comparing the wavelength of the separated flow zone to the acoustic wavelength of excitation. In the class of problem studied in this report, the acoustic wavelength is much longer than the separated flow zone (cavity length).

The objective of the present study was twofold. The first was to understand how the response of the shear layer is affected by upstream flow conditioning. Upstream flow conditioning was changed by adding a converging nozzle just before the cavity. The second objective of the study was to observe how the self-excited nature of the shear layer can be altered by changing the acoustic characteristics of the system. The ability of the shear layer to organise itself and oscillate around the pipeline acoustic modes is a function of how much influence the acoustic resonant frequencies have. This influence was altered by increasing the amount of acoustic damping in the system and thereby decreasing its resonant behaviour.

2. EXPERIMENTAL SYSTEM AND INSTRUMENTATION

Figure 1 shows the experimental system used throughout the test program. The bellmouth is at the entrance to a 1.40 meter acrylic pipeline of 0.14 meters in diameter

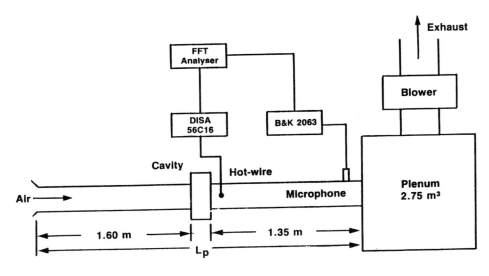

Figure 1 Experimental Facility

and was designed to reduce entrance flow noise without an appreciable alteration of the entrance impedance. The converging section was installed just after the inlet pipe section before the cavity. This section had an area ratio of 2:1 with a very smooth transition over 0.20 meters. The converging section closely followed design specifications of Morel [17] to offset adverse pressure gradients and to produce low turbulence and a flat velocity profile at the exit plane. The cavity was 0.075 meters long and was installed near the centre of the pipeline for all of the tests. The cavity was formed by placing two orifice plates, with an area ratio of 2:1, back to back with a 0.075 meter pipe section between. The exit section was constructed of acrylic 1.35 meters in length and of 6 mm thickness. For the damping tests, the exit section was replaced by a 1.35 meter long perforated pipe with the same inside diameter as the entrance section. The perforations provided an effective open area of 50 per cent made up of 12.7 mm diameter holes. The perforated pipe was wrapped with fibreglass insulation (glass wool) and was bound with a heavy plastic sheet. The glass wool provided varying degrees of system damping for the experimental study depending upon the density with which it was wrapped.

The entire piping section was connected to a plenum as shown in Figure 1. The plenum, installed between the suction pump and the exit pipe, was lined with sound absorbing foam and was shown to effectively isolate the test section acoustically from the pump. The suction pump was a positive displacement type capable of producing a high suction head with a minimum of pressure pulses. A 20 h.p. continuously variable d.c. motor drove the pump and allowed for a continuous variation in free stream velocity. The pump outlet was exhausted to outside of the building to minimize blower noise from entering via the upstream bellmouth. It also served to exhaust the smoke generated when using the flow visualization apparatus.

The acoustic response of the system was measured at a location capable of capturing all flow excited acoustic modes of interest by means of B&K 6.35 mm condenser microphones. All information was analyzed on line using a Nicolet 660B spectrum analyzer. Information collected on the Nicolet could be transferred to a VAX 730 for data reduction and display. Flow velocity was measured

at the location of the pipe centreline 0.01 meters behind the cavity section using DISA Type 55 constant temperature hot wire anemometers. Although local atmospheric conditions of temperature and density were not measured, the temperature did not vary significantly from 21 degrees celcius during the tests.

Determination of acoustic natural frequencies and damping was done without flow by means of external speaker excitation. The speaker placement, directly in front of the bellmouth, along with the band limited white noise excitation ensured excitation of all pipe modes present under investigation.

Flow visualization was accomplished by adding a smoke tracer to the flow just upstream of the cavity. The smoke was produced by mixing together anhydrous ammonia and sulphur dioxide. The percentage of each used was varied until the desired mixture producing adequate resolution was achieved. Since in many cases the phenomena to be visualized was very unsteady a single pulse strobe technique was used. This consisted of taking a picture of the flow through the cavity with an open shutter in complete darkness by providing a high intensity single strobe pulse. By varying the f-stop on the camera the desired image was captured.

3. FUNDAMENTAL FEATURES OF SELF-EXCITED SYSTEMS

The above mentioned classes of systems are ones in which an inherently unstable shear layer is enhanced by a feedback mechanism which controls the oscillatory behaviour of the fluid. The operating mechanism which controls the fluid mechanics of the shear layer is displayed in Figure 2. A shear layer, defined as a region between fluids of dissimilar velocity, is a fundamentally unstable system. This unstable system, if unimpeded, will exhibit growth and expansion in the streamwise and transverse direction to the flow until eventual breakdown into random turbulence. Alternatively, if an impingement surface is placed in the path of the flow, the shear layer will organise itself into discrete concentrations of vorticity producing pressure and velocity fluctuations which are ultimately the cause of acoustic excitation and mechanical vibration. The shear layer oscillations are self-sustaining, that is, they extract

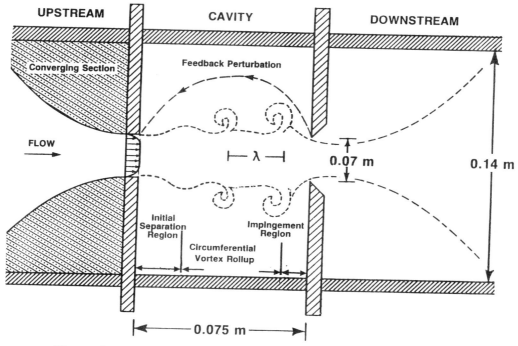

Figure 2 Schematic of Cavity and Cycle of Events for
Shear Layer Oscillations

the energy for motion from the flow itself. A number of events must take place for this to occur. First, the vorticity fluctuations inherent in the shear layer travel downstream and impinge upon a flow boundary. Pressure and velocity fluctuations created at this point are fed upstream to the sensitive region of the shear layer at separation. This causes enhanced growth of subsequent shear layer vorticity which then travels downstream to complete the cycle. This behaviour continues up to some periodic limit cycle.

Two criteria must be satisfied for the system to be self-sustaining, one concerns phase, the other amplitude. Concerning the phase, it can be said that the fluctuation feedback from the point of flow impingement to separation will enhance those shear layer perturbations which are in phase with it. That is, the shear layer oscillations which are most unstable are those receiving in phase enhancement from the feedback perturbations. Concerning amplitude, one can say that a minimum amount of energy must be available to sustain the motion since the system is self-excited. There must therefore be some minimum distance after separation for the shear layer to grow.

With the above two criteria satisfied we have a system which is self-sustaining, sensitive to flow velocity, impingement length and adjacent resonators. Figures 3a and 3b show schematically the general behavioral characteristics of this type of system with variations of flow velocity and impingement cavity length.

For the case of constant cavity length and varying flow velocity, a minimum flow velocity will be necessary to create and maintain stage 1 oscillations in the shear layer (one vortex between separation and impingement), designated A in Figure 3a. As the flow velocity is increased for the system, the band of selectively amplified frequencies in the shear layer also increases. As such, the selectively amplified frequency will vary in a linear manner as the flow velocity increases up to point

B. At this point the stage 1 operation of the shear layer can no longer excite the selectively amplified frequency and the system jumps to point C where the shear layer experiences stage two operation. The slope of the frequency-velocity characteristics of the system is now twice that found for stage 1 operation because the shear layer now has two complete cycles between separation and impingement. Stage 2 operation again continues up to its limitation at which point the system experiences another jump to stage 3 operation, point D to E. The variation in flow velocity is essentially a variation of phase since the bulk flow velocity convects the shear layer vorticity, which creates the feedback disturbance.

With constant flow velocity and varying cavity length, the system will respond as indicated in Figure 3b. In this case the successively higher stages of operation correspond to longer impingement lengths. Again, a satisfaction of the phase criteria requires an increase in the wavelength of the instability as the impingement length is gradually increased. Within stage 1 operation, this will cause the frequency of instability to gradually decrease as the distance between separation and impingement increases. With a uniform flow velocity, the selectively amplified frequency of the shear layer is fixed and effective over a very narrow band. Hence, at some impingement length, point A of Figure 3b, stage 1 operation can no longer excite this narrow band frequency and remain locked in, so the shear layer adds a second cycle between separation and impingement and jumps to stage 2 operation but remains within the narrow band of selectively amplified frequencies. With further increases in impingement length, stage 2 operation will continue until a jump to stage 3 operation is experienced, point C to D.

For those systems influenced by adjacent resonators, the system will experience lock-in regions. In these regions the shear layer oscillations will be much stronger and more coherent. A variation in flow velocity for this type

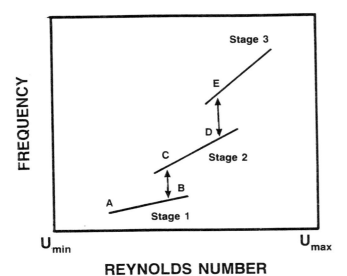

Figure 3a Frequency vs Reynolds Number
Fluid Resonant System

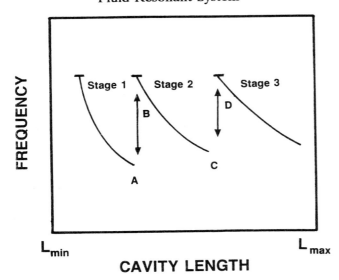

Figure 3b Frequency vs Cavity Length
Fluid Resonant System

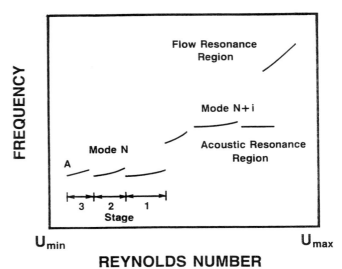

Figure 4a Frequency vs Reynolds Number
Acoustic Resonant System

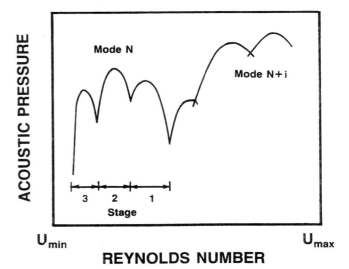

Figure 4b Acoustic Pressure vs Reynolds Number
Acoustic Resonant System

of system, where the frequency of shear layer excitation is influenced by the surrounding acoustic resonator, will be as displayed in Figure 4a. Here the resonant modes of the system dominate the frequency-velocity characteristics. It can be seen that, as the flow velocity is varied, the system passes through regions where acoustic modes control the shear layer oscillations. Each of these steps corresponds to a region of high acoustic output as displayed in Figure 4b. This is in contrast to the regions of fluid resonant response where the frequency varies in a linear fashion with respect to the flow velocity. In these regions the levels of acoustic energy emitted are very much lower.

In this study, flow visualization photos were taken in regions where the shear layer was influenced by the acoustics modes of the pipeline as well as areas where the natural flow instability dominated. Figure 5a shows a region of flow instability at a Reynolds number of 8 000. This photo clearly shows stage 1 operation of the shear layer corresponding to the low flow region of Figure 3a. At this flow velocity the system is not influenced by the pipeline acoustics and the natural flow

instability dominates. This region corresponds to stage 1 operation of Figure 3a which is expected to be functional before any acoustics begin to dominate the shear layer operation. If the flow velocity continues to increase, point A in Figure 4a is reached where the enhancement of the shear layer is influenced by the acoustic frequencies of the system. The flow visualization photo of Figure 5b was taken in this region at a Reynolds number of 19 000. Clearly, the shear layer oscillations are in a multistage operation which is necessary to sustain the oscillations and remain locked in to the acoustic mode. Subsequent increases in flow velocity will alter the phase of the feedback perturbations as mentioned previously in this section. The adjustment of the shear layer will continue until it can no longer remain locked in and satisfy the phase and amplitude criteria, at which point a jump to a different acoustic mode becomes imminent. Many other regions of operation were studied using still photo and video flow visualization techniques. The results generally supported the discussion above and provided an excellent means of corroborating the experimental data and understanding the phenomena.

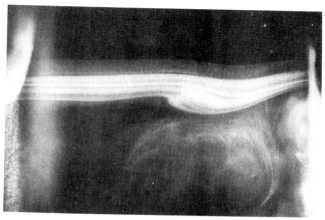

Figure 5a   Flow Visualization of Fluid Resonant Shear Layer

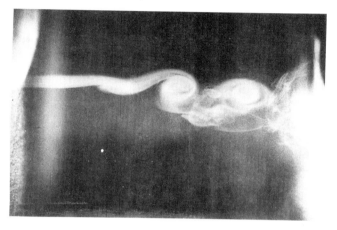

Figure 5b   Flow Visualization of Acoustic Resonant Shear Layer

4. ABATEMENT TECHNIQUES FOR FLUID/ACOUSTIC RESONANCES

In the past few years, a number of abatement or control strategies have been used by various researchers to reduce or eliminate the fluid loading on structures or to reduce the acoustic response of systems. Several of these studies concentrated on control of the free shear layer itself through active or passive techniques [18-22] while others took the approach of controlling the system response through stiffness or damping modifications [1,23]. The focus of the present study was the control of acoustic response through the addition of system damping.

In the passive techniques of controlling the fluid source instability [18-20], the intent is to break up the phase relationship between the instability wave and the feedback perturbations at separation. This has successfully been accomplished through the addition of vortex generators and slots at the separation point which are carefully designed and constructed to disturb the coherence of the organised shear layer. At the opposite end of the cavity the impingement point may be modified as a ramp in the streamwise direction which would create multiple impingement points for each location of contact of the shear layer. In this configuration each location of contact will require a

unique phase relationship for the feedback to be effective. As such, the selectively amplified frequency of the shear layer would have more difficulty growing to its maximum response. The active techniques of source control [21,22] apply an external response of opposite phase to that which controls the selectively amplified shear layer. This can be applied through acoustic [21] or mechanical [22] means and as with the naturally occurring feedback, it has been shown that a minimum gain is necessary before the external stimulus becomes effective.

5. EXPERIMENTAL RESULTS

5.1 Basic System Response

As described in Section 3, the acoustic feedback enhancement of the shear layer is affected by the acoustic natural frequencies of the system. There were three systems used in the present experimental program, (a) the acrylic pipeline described in Section 2 without the convergence, (b) the acrylic pipeline with the convergence added just before the cavity and (c) the same length pipeline with the convergence but also with the perforated pipe added downstream. Figures 6a and 6b show the no flow transfer function of acoustic response of the system to white noise excitation both with and without added damping. The response without added damping was for the pipeline with the convergence. For the pipeline without the convergence,

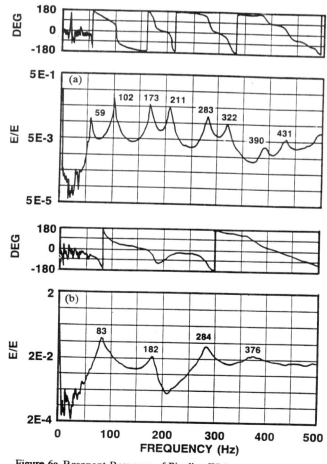

Figure 6a Resonant Response of Pipeline Without Added Damping
Figure 6b Resonant Response of Pipeline With Added Damping

the no-flow transfer function was very similar and is not shown here. The system resonances in the transfer function are easily distinguished by the 180 degree phase shift through resonance between excitation and response. White noise excitation of the system will excite all of the acoustic modes. In operation though, as mentioned in the introduction, it is largely those modes which possess a velocity anti-node at the cavity location which are excited by the unsteady shear layer. This is due to the action of the separated shear layer producing a large velocity disturbance within the cavity. For the system without added damping and the cavity installed near the center of the pipeline, the flow excited resonances are generally the even modes which possess a pressure node or velocity anti-node at the cavity location. For the case of added damping, the perforated pipe section was added downstream from the cavity which created an asymmetrical pipe geometry. As such, one would not expect to excite just the even or odd harmonics of the system but perhaps all pipe modes.

5.2 System Response Without Added Damping

Figures 7a and 7b display respectively the frequency and acoustic pressure as a function of Reynolds number for the case of no added damping and no convergence. Figure 7c is a waterfall display which shows the entire history of evolution of the pipeline excitation. At a Reynolds number of about 19 000 there is a distinct peak present at a frequency coincident with the first even acoustic mode of the pipeline at 109 Hz. This is consistent with the expectation of the cavity acting as a velocity source and, as such, for the geometry under investigation here, exciting the even acoustic modes of the pipeline. At this point, the acoustic pressure within the pipeline is expectedly quite low. The Strouhal number, while not displayed here, has a value of about 1.5, based upon cavity length. A Strouhal number of about 0.5 is expected for stage 1 operation. Therefore, the value of 1.5 is consistent with stage 3 operation for the shear layer. This was corroborated with flow visualization. Upon further increases in Reynolds number the frequency remains locked-in to the N=2 acoustic mode while the acoustic pressure gradually increases. At the same time, the Strouhal number decreases indicative of a shift in the stage of operation of the shear layer. It can be seen in Figure 7a that, at a Reynolds number of about 36 000, a flow dependency of the shear layer begins to dominate. In this region, the frequency of excitation increases linearly with flow velocity. A characteristic of the flow dependent region is the reduced output levels of acoustic pressure in Figure 7b. This observation has been mentioned by other researchers [24] where in regions of off resonance, that is, regions where the shear layer was not locked-in to the system acoustic modes, the acoustic output is substantially reduced. In this region, many harmonics of the fundamental flow dependent frequency can be present as can higher system modes at substantial amplitudes due to the shear layer non-linearity. Without conditions of phase and amplification satisfied, the harmonic oscillations will not dominate the shear layer. Instead, with further increases in flow velocity the shear layer adjusts its stage of operation from an m=2 to an m=1, thereby allowing the shear layer to remain locked-

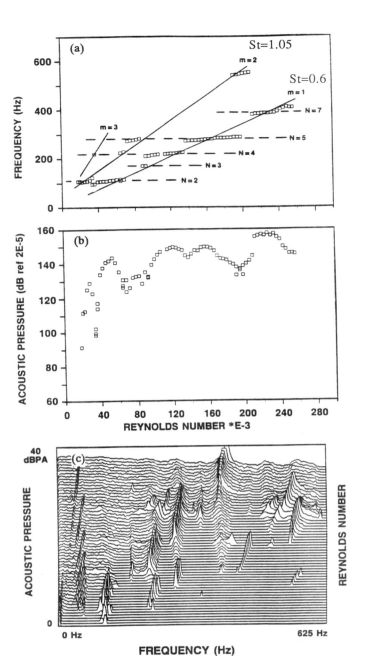

Figure 7 System Without Convergence and No Added Damping
a) Frequency vs Reynolds Number
b) Acoustic Pressure vs Reynolds Number
c) Waterfall Display of System Response

in to the N=2 acoustic mode. The flow dependent frequency is no longer present. The shear layer stage 1 lock-in at system mode N=2 remains very strong from a Reynolds number of 40 000 to about 70 000. Throughout this range, the acoustic pressure continually increases to a maximum and then gradually falls off. This behaviour within the lock-in region is consistent with the observation made by Schachenmann and Rockwell in their pipeline experiments [14]. The fall off in acoustic pressure is indicative of an imminent jump to a different mode of excitation of the system. Within this region, many interesting things can occur. The non-linearity of the shear layer excites many harmonics of the existing mode of operation. Also, flow dependent frequencies begin to appear. In these regions, Schachenmann and Rockwell [14] have described jumps in system operation which may occur in two ways. One

© IMechE 1991 C416/093

is by a continuous transfer of energy between the existing mode of operation and the subsequent sounding mode. The second allows a "dead-zone" to exist where no acoustic output is present between the existing and subsequent modes. In the present study, observations have revealed a continuous transfer of energy between modes with the existing mode decaying in strength as the next sounding mode continues to increase. This is evident throughout the entire range of operation in the waterfall plot of Figure 7c. Also, along with the system modes which grow and decay in these regions, there may be flow dependent frequencies of similar amplitude which are present. This characteristic reveals how complex the operation of the shear layer is in these regions, being able to support oscillations from up to two or three frequencies which are not harmonically related and requiring a different stage of operation of the shear layer.

With further increases in Reynolds number the shear layer eventually locks-in to the N=5 mode at Re=70 000. This remains for a short period of time until the shear layer jumps to the N=4 system mode at Re=90 000 only to jump back to the N=5 mode at Re=140 000. This exchange throughout this Reynolds number range provides a good example of how the change in flow velocity, which changes the convection velocity of the shear layer oscillations, can alter the phase relationship between separation and impingement. In the first occurrence of lock-in to the N=5 mode at Re=70 000 the shear layer was operating in an m=2 stage, that is two vortices between separation and impingement. Increasing the flow velocity increased the convection velocity of the shear layer oscillations thereby altering the phase which allowed an m=1 operation to excite the N=4 acoustic mode at a Reynolds number of about 90 000. But further increases in flow velocity have altered the phase to a point where the shear layer can no longer support the N=4 mode with one complete cycle between separation and impingement, hence the mode of excitation has to jump to N=5 to maintain m=1 oscillations. The waterfall plot elucidates the exchange in this region where the subsequent mode of operation gradually increases as the flow velocity increases. With each increase in flow velocity, the satisfaction of phase criteria for that mode is closer to being fulfilled, and as such, the amplitude of the next sounding mode steadily increases to a point where it begins to dominate and locks-in.

5.3 System Response With Converging Section

Figures 8a, 8b and 8c shows similarly, the frequency and acoustic pressure as a function of Reynolds number and the waterfall plot for the same pipeline but with the convergence added just before the cavity. The convergence was very carefully designed to provide a separation free boundary for the flow upstream of the upstream orifice plate. It is the expectation that with the acceleration of the flow through the convergence a more uniform flow velocity profile would exist. Also, one would expect lower turbulence levels and a flow which is no longer contracting between the orifice plates. In looking at Figure 8a one can see the excitation of higher shear layer modes at Reynolds numbers as high as 100

000. This is in contrast to the study without the convergence installed. This characteristic is the result of the energy conserving ability of the convergence as opposed to the cavity arrangement with dual orifice plates which dissipated energy in the flow. Also, when the frequency/Reynolds number data for the systems with and without convergence are compared for the N=2 mode (first sounding mode) one finds that the range over which this mode is excited is much longer for the system with the added convergence. For the cavity with the added convergence the N=2 mode is excited until a Reynolds number of almost 100 000 as shown in Figure 8a, whereas the cavity without the convergence has the N=2 lock-in region extending to a Reynolds number of only 70 000. Also, for the cavity with convergence added, the lock-in region for the N=4 mode is quite substantial being excited from Re=125 000 to Re=215 000. Additionally, in comparing each of the systems one

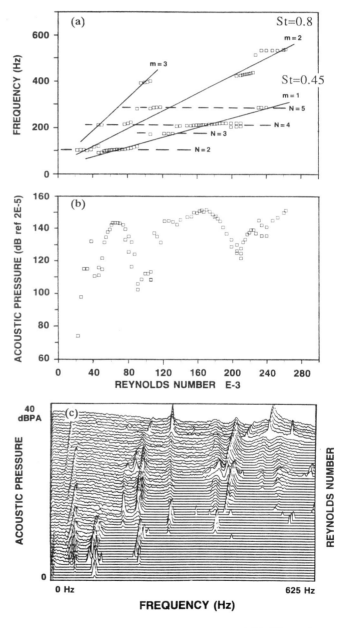

Figure 8 System With Convergence and No Added Damping
a) Frequency vs Reynolds Number
b) Acoustic Pressure vs Reynolds Number
c) Waterfall Display of System Response

finds that equivalent levels of acoustic output are attained within each lock-in region. This result is not entirely surprising since the acoustic pressure peak at resonance should only be limited by the damping of that mode. The no flow damping measured by the half-power point method showed very similar results for the pipeline with and without convergence present.

In summary, the system response has been altered with the convergence added. The changes that are apparent in the frequency/Reynolds number plots can be directly attributed to the effect of upstream flow conditioning on the shear layer by the converging section. It seems that the shear layer is more easily organised with the convergence added, creating a stronger feedback and thereby enhancing the self-excitation of the shear layer. This has allowed extended lock-in regions and the excitation of higher shear layer modes in the cavity.

5.4 System Response With Added Damping

As mentioned in the introduction, the objective of the study was to not only observe the changes in the system response to turbulent conditioning of the shear layer, but also to compare the changes in response due to an increase in system damping. For the case of added damping the same parameters were measured, those being the frequency and acoustic output pressure as a function of Reynolds number. Figures 9a and 9b are respectively the frequency and acoustic pressure as a function of Reynolds number. Also, displayed in Figure 9c is the waterfall plot showing the evolution of system response over the entire flow velocity range studied. In comparing the features of Figure 9 to that of Figures 7 and 8 for the systems without added damping it is clear that the frequency response of the system with added damping is much more flow velocity dependent. This response is characteristic of a flow resonant system as opposed to an acoustic resonant system which were distinguished from one another in Section 3. Although the resonant response of the system displayed earlier in Figure 6b does show some resonance peaks, they are so heavily damped that they do not strongly influence the response of the system under flow conditions. At a Reynolds number of about 20 000 in Figure 9a some periodicity is evident in the response spectrum at the N=1 pipe mode. The characteristics within this first lock-in region are very similar to that in Figures 7 and 8 for the other systems studied. Midway through the lock-in region there is an increase in frequency, followed by a decrease in acoustic pressure. In this region the shear layer, being influenced by the acoustic mode, adjusts its stage of operation to remain locked-in to the N=1 mode. With further increases in flow velocity, the shear layer adjusts to an m=1 mode of operation coincident with a steady rise in acoustic pressure throughout the range of lock-in. After the first lock-in region, the acoustic modes of the system no longer affect the shear layer operation to the same extent. As such, the system response is a strong function of flow velocity with a linear increase in frequency as the flow velocity is increased. An explanation for this behaviour could be that the acoustic damping of each mode increases with an increase in flow velocity. Therefore, although the higher velocities are necessary for excitation of the higher pipeline modes, the

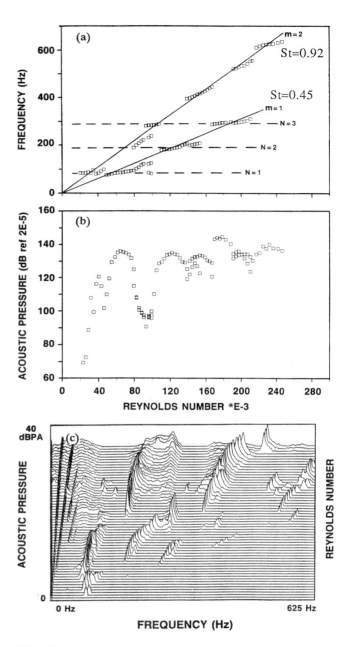

Figure 9 System With Convergence and With Added Damping
a) Frequency vs Reynolds Number
b) Acoustic Pressure vs Reynolds Number
c) Waterfall Display of System Response

damping level of the acoustic modes necessary to sustain the lock-in regions has increased to such a level that excitation of that mode is no longer possible. Extending further this hypothesis, if we create a system with a flat resonant response in the frequency range of interest, then there would be no lock-in regions and hence throughout the flow velocity of concern the frequency should increase in a linear manner. It also follows logically that without enhancement around certain acoustic modes the shear layer should simply adjust itself to maintain fluid resonant oscillations within the cavity which is characteristic of a cavity flow without an adjacent resonator.

The flow dependence of the frequency response for the system is clearly evident in the waterfall display of Figure 9c. One can see though that, since we do have some heavily damped acoustic modes, then as the flow velocity comes into the range of maximum phase amplification for those modes that the system has a tendency to lock-in. Generally though, the response of the system has a heavy dependence on the flow velocity with the exception of the N=1 mode. One further explanation for this behaviour is the very broad resonance peak due to the high modal damping. With this characteristic, the tendency would be for the system to respond well before the frequency at which the maximum of the resonance occurs. This behaviour would continue up to the resonance peak and beyond as long as phase and minimum amplification criteria are fulfilled.

In comparing the system with added damping to the systems without damping, one finds that, throughout the flow range tested, the acoustic output levels are reduced by 10 -15 decibels as shown in Figure 10. By adding the perforated pipe section, not only have we totally changed the acoustic resonance characteristics of the pipeline by reducing the number of frequencies in the range of interest, but, by adding the passive element, we have subsequently increased the energy dissipating ability of the pipeline. The result of this was a reduction in the ability of the shear layer to remain locked-in to any of the pipeline acoustic modes. Therefore, we have been able to alter the system from one that controls the shear layer through acoustic feedback to one which now has little or no influence resulting in a more natural shear layer behaviour.

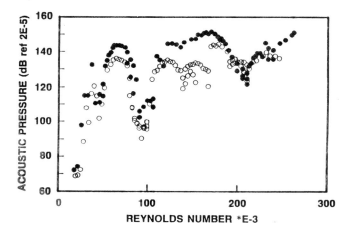

Figure 10 Comparison of Acoustic Pressure vs Reynolds Number
● System Without Added Damping
O System With Added Damping

6. CONCLUSIONS

The acoustic resonance characteristics of a pipeline excited by an unstable free shear layer has been studied by altering the physical system. The parameters studied were changes in the system acoustic response due to upstream flow conditioning of the shear layer and the changes in response due to increased levels of acoustic damping.

Flow conditioning was created by adding a converging nozzle just upstream of the cavity which allowed the flow to contract smoothly into the cavity without separation. This created a more uniform flow velocity profile for the shear layer which reduced the contraction of the flow

into the cavity and reduced turbulence. Upstream flow conditioning apparently increases the lock-in regions of the shear layer and permits higher shear layer oscillation modes to be excited. This implies that the shear layer is more susceptible to self-excitation and that the self-excited modes are more stable over a wider Reynolds number range.

The system damping was increased by adding a perforated pipe section downstream of the cavity. This dissipative energy element apparently reduces the acoustic feedback enhancement of the shear layer creating instead a more natural constant Strouhal number behaviour in the shear layer.

The implication of this study is that increased turbulence and damping will reduce the tendency to higher acoustic resonant pressures and extended lock-in regions.

REFERENCES

1. Hartlen, R. T., Jaster, W., Main Steam Piping Vibration Driven by Flow-Acoustic Excitation, in Proceedings IAHR/IUTAM Symposium Practical Experiences With Flow Induced Vibrations, editors E. Naudascher and D. Rockwell, Springer-Verlag, Berlin, 1979, pp 144-152

2. Hassouneh, M. A., Vibrations in Pipeline Systems, in Reference 1, editors E. Naudscher and D. Rockwell, pp 156-159

3. Powell, A., On the Edgetone, Journal of the Acoustical Society of America, 1961, Vol. 33, No. 4, pp 395-409

4. Chanaud, R. C., Powell, A., Some Experiments Concerning the Hole and Ring Tone, Journal of the Acoustical Society of America, 1965, Vol. 37, No.5, pp 902-911

5. Ho, C-M., Nossier, N.S., Dynamics of an Impinging Jet. Part 1. The Feedback Phenomenon, Journal of Fluid Mechanics, 1981, Vol. 105, pp 119-142

6. Nossier, N.S., Ho, C-M., Dynamics of an Impinging Jet. Part 2. The Noise Generation, Journal of Fluid Mechanics, 1982, Vol. 116, pp 379-391

7. Bilanin, A.J., Covert, E.E., Estimation of Possible Excitation Frequencies for Shallow Rectangular Cavities, AIAA Journal, 1973, Vol. 11, No. 3, pp 347-352

8. Heller, H.H, Bliss, D.B., The Physical Mechanism of Flow Induced Pressure Fluctuations in Cavities and Concepts For Their Suppression, AIAA Journal Paper N075-491, 1975

9. Rockwell, D., Prediction of Oscillation Frequencies for Unstable Flow Past Cavities, Journal of Fluids Engineering, June 1977, pp 294-300

10. Tam, C.K.W., Block, P.J.W., On the Tones and Pressure Oscillations Induced by Flow Over Rectangular Cavities, Journal of Fluid Mechanics, 1978, Vol. 89, Part 2, pp 373-399

11. Rockwell, D., Naudascher, E., Review-Self-Sustaining Oscillations of Flow Past Cavities, Journal of Fluids Engineering, June 1978, Vol 100, pp 152-165

12. Rockwell, D., Naudascher, E., Self-Sustained Oscillations of Impinging Free Shear Layers, Annual Review of Fluid Mechanics, 1979, Vol. 11, pp 67-94

13. Rockwell, D., Oscillations of Impinging Shear Layers, AIAA Journal, 1983, Vol. 21, No. 5, pp 645-662

14. Schachenmann, A., Rockwell, D., Self-Sustained Oscillations of Turbulent Pipe Flow Terminated By An Axisymmetric Cavity, Journal of Sound and Vibration, 1980, Vol. 73, No. 1, pp 61-72

15. Rockwell, D., Schachenmann, A., Self-Generation of Organized Waves In An Impinging Turbulent Jet At Low Mach Number, Journal of Fluid Mechanics, 1982, pp 425-441

16. Nomoto, H., Culick, F.E., An Experimental Investigation of Pure Tone Generation By Vortex Shedding In A Duct, Journal of Sound and Vibration, 1982, Vol. 84 No. 2, pp 247-252

17. Morel, T., Comprehensive Design of Axisymmetric Wind Tunnel Contractions, Journal of Fluids Engineering, 1975, Vol. 97, pp 225-233

18. Karadagon, H., Rockwell, D., Toward Attenuation of Self-Sustained Oscillations of Turbulent Flow, Journal of Fluids Engineering, 1983, Vol. 105, pp 335-340

19. Ziada, S., Buhlmann, E.T., Bolleter, U., Flow Impingement as an Excitation Source in Control Valves, Journal of Fluids and Structures, 1989, Vol. 3, pp 529-549

20. Harris, R. E., On the Generation of Acoustic Pipeline Resonance, PhD Thesis, McMaster University, Aug. 1987

21. Huang, X. Y., Weaver, D.S., A Flow Visualization Study of the Active Control of Free Shear Layers, ASME Pressure Vessels and Piping Conference, 1990, Nashville, USA

22. Kaykayglu, C.R., Active Control of a Mixing Layer by Upstream Influence, Journal of Fluids and Structures, 1989, Vol. 3, pp 1-16

23. Lamoureux, P.N., The Effects of Damping on a Pipeline Acoustic Source, MEng. Thesis, McMaster University, May 1988

24. Shakkottai, P., Kwack, Y.I., Cho, Back, L.H., High-Intensity Tone Generation By Aeroacoustic Sources, Journal of The Acoustical Society of America, December 1987, Vol. 82, No. 6, pp 2075-2085

Orifice plates as a source of vibrations in piping systems

F AXISA, PhD and H HASSIS, PhD
CEN Saclay, Gif sur Yvette, France

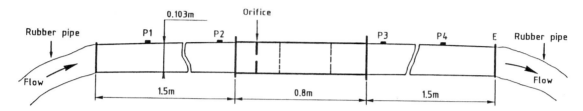

Fig. 1-a : test section

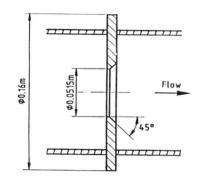

Fig. 1-b : circular orifice

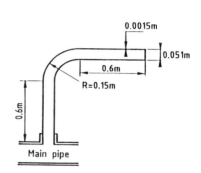

Fig. 1-c : bended pipe

Fig. 1 : Experimental rig.

1. INTRODUCTION

Industrial piping systems can experience severe low frequency vibration caused by internal flow of the conveyed fluid, see in particular Hartlen (1) and Chadha (2). Then, predictive methods are needed to design costly piping systems against such risks. Gibert (3) evidenced by experiment that the source of vibration is often related to the unsteady turbulent flow which occurs at any pipe component inducing sudden changes either in the area or in the direction of the permanent flow. Pressure fluctuations arising from such flow singularities can be separated into two quite distinct components :

1) In a region of a few tube diameters, downstream from the singularity, the fluctuations are dominated by an unsteady turbulent field. Usually, pipe deformation of the first vibratory modes can be safely ignored at such a scale length. Integration of the fluid momentum equation over the turbulent region shows that no resultant force is produced at the undeformed tube walls. Then, the unsteady turbulent field cannot excite by itself any low frequency vibration of the piping system.

2) Acoustic pressure fluctuations are present in the whole circuit as a system of standing waves which fluctuates randomly in time. At sufficiently low frequencies, only the plane waves have to be considered. Such waves are interacting with the walls wherever there is a change either in the area or in the direction of the tubes. Thus, they are able to excite random vibration of the whole piping system.

Gibert (3) developed an experimental method to measure the spectral properties of the sources of such acoustic internal noise. The author made use of a few scaling factors related to the geometry and to the permanent flow through the singularity, to produce normalized spectra which, in principle, depend only upon the nature of the singularity. Gibert (4) and Axisa (5) developed numerical methods, based on the finite element technique, to compute the acousto-mechanical response to such sources in piping systems of arbitrary geometries.

This paper describes experimental work recently carried out at C.E.N.S. concerning circular orifice plates as a source of vibrations in piping systems. Such simple components are frequently used in practice and are quite convenient to carry out extensive laboratory studies. Furthermore, information thus provided may be relevant, at least qualitatively, for more complex singularities such as valves and other flow-rate restricting devices.

Because of lack of space only the major results of this study can be reported here. More detailed information can be found in Hassis (6).

2. EXPERIMENTAL CONSIDERATIONS

The experimental rig is schematically shown in Fig. 1a. It is made of a straight stainless steel tube with internal diameter D = 103 mm, thickness e = 2 mm and total length L = 3.8 m. Sound velocity of water is 1114 m/s, instead of 1500 m/s in unconfined liquid. Actually, the tube is made of three parts to ease mounting and dismounting of the orifices. The latter are inserted in the central part 0.8 m long wich is extended at each end by tubes 1.5 m long. The bevel edged orifices are machined in circular steel plates 6 mm thick. Geometry is given in Fig. 1b. The opening ratio is d/D = 0.5 as referred to the diameter d of the smallest aperture. The latter can be located on the upstream or the downstream side. For convenience, the first case is called a direct and the second one a reversed layout. When not specified the experimental data presented here are referring to a direct layout. To prevent undesirable vibration the test section is clamped to the floor of the laboratory. At each end, the pipe is connected to a forced water flow loop through rubber tubes flexible enough to isolate efficiently the test section from external acoustical and mechanical sources. Water is almost saturated with air and its temperature is maintained at 20°C. Flexible bent tubes were designed to perform flow-induced vibration studies, see Fig. 1c. They can be mounted on the main pipe at locations noted P1 to P4 on Fig. 1a. They are made of a stainless steel tube 1.5. mm thick and external diameter 5 cm. The radius of curvature of the 90° elbow is 15 cm. The latter is extended at each end by a straight part 0.6 m long. One end of the bent tube is screwed to the main pipe to achieve a rigid T junction. The other is obturated by a rigid disk, provided with a drain cock. Thus, when mounted on the rig the bent pipes can be filled with water, with no air pocket or bubble left inside. The closed end is not supported. Flow and acoustic studies were carried out with bent tubes removed and orifices P1 to P4 obturated.

Steady hydraulic parameters of the loop are measured in a classical way to determine flow-rates and steady pressure profiles, along the unsteady turbulent region. Kistler 2501 sensors are mounted at the walls to measure the fluctuating pressure at various locations along the pipe. Finally, ENDEVCO 224 C accelerometers, fixed at the free end of the bent tubes are used for the vibration tests. Spectral analysis of the fluctuating signals was carried out by using a HP 3582A analyser connected to a HP 9000 microcomputer for final data processing, aimed in particular at providing dimensionless acoustic source spectra.

3. SINGLE ORIFICE IN NON CAVITATING FLOW

3.1. Permanent flow through the orifice

Fig. 2 shows a set of measured steady pressure profiles downstream of the orifice, for six values of pressure Pd at the downstream pipe end. Here, flow-rate is 40 l/s, leading to a steady flow velocity Vd = 19,2 m/s through the smallest orifice aperture. Position along the pipe is normalized by using D-d as a scaling factor. As expected, pressure drops abruply from the upstream value Pu, down to a minimum value Pmin, then it increases steadily up to Pd. Degassing and cavitation is observed to occur as soon as Pmin becomes less than about 0.1 PMa, see section 5.The measured head loss coefficient is in fair agreement with the empirical relationship given by Idel'Cick (7)

$$(1) \quad \zeta = \Delta P / \left(\frac{1}{2} \rho \, V_d^2 \right) = \left(1 + 0.707 \sqrt{1 - \left(\frac{d}{D} \right)^2} - \left(\frac{d}{D} \right)^2 \right)$$

where $\Delta P = P_u - P_d$.

Pmin roughly agrees with the empirical formula

$$(2) \qquad P_u - P_{min} = \Delta P / (1 - (d/D)^2)$$

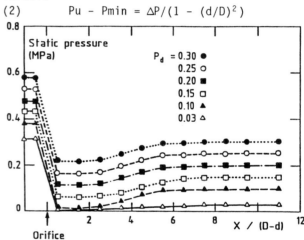

Fig. 2 : steady pressure profiles downstream of the orifice at fixed downstream pressure P_d. Flow rate 40 l/s, pressure drop $\Delta P = 0,278$ MPa.

3.2. Unsteady turbulent fluctuations

Fig. 3a is a plot of the rms values of pressure versus position downstream of the orifice.

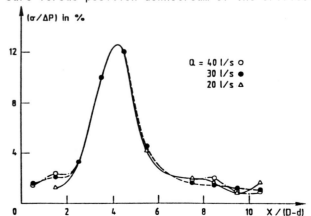

Fig. 3-a : profile of the reduced rms value of turbulent pressure fluctuations along the tube, downstream the orifice.

Experimental data have been conveniently norma-lysed by using ΔP and D-d as physically relevant scaling factors. Indeed, the reduced data are found to collapse satisfactorily on a single curve. The latter displays a well marked maximum of about 13 %, at 4 (D-d) from the orifice. The level becomes barely significant at distances larger than about 9 (D-d). Fig. 3b shows a set of dimensionless PSDs of pressure measured at 3.5 (D-d). The reduced frequency is

(3)
$$f_R = f(D-d) / V_c$$

and the spectral level is reduced according to

(4)
$$\tilde{\Phi}(f_R) = \frac{V_c}{(\Delta P)^2 \ (D-d)} \Phi(f)$$

where V_c is the steady flow-velocity through the vena contracta, given by $V_c = 1.67 \ V_d$, according to Idel'Cick (3). Again relevance of

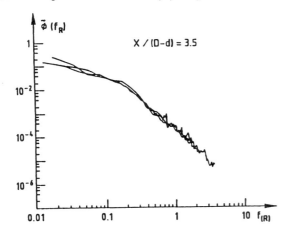

Fig. 3-b : dimensionless spectra of the turbulent fluctuations from measu-rement at 20, 30 and 40 l/s.

the selected scaling factors is confirmed by the collapsing of the reduced data to a unique broadband turbulent spectral profile. Tests performed on another similar orifice with d/D = 0,7 produced essentially the same results. Coherence and phase plots were also analysed leading to a very small correlation length of about D-d, and to a convective velocity of the turbulent structures of about 0.4 V_d. However such figures can be taken as rough estimates only because coherence was observed to drop quickly with distance and phase plots displayed irregular changes depending on the frequency.

3.3. Acoustic waves

Fig. 4 illustrates the spectral properties of pressure, when measured upstream and just downstream from the unsteady turbulent region. The PSD plots, see Fig. 4a, refers to positions 28 cm upstream and 35 cm downstream of the orifice. In the upstream spectrum several resonant peaks are clearly present at harmonic frequencies. It was verified that the frequencies of such peaks do not depend upon the steady flow velocity. The downstream spectrum is clearly of the turbulent type and its level is much higher than that of the former one. Fig. 4b is a plot of the observed coherence related to a pair of sensors located 0.3 and 3.6 m from the pipe inlet. Its value is practically one, except near a few discrete frequencies at which the PSD level itself is becoming negligibly small at least at one

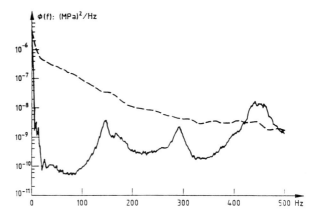

Fig. 4-a : comparison of acoustic and turbulent spectra :
- full line : acoustic spectrum measured 28 cm upstream of the orifice
- dashed line : turbulent spectrum measured 35 cm downstream of the orifice.

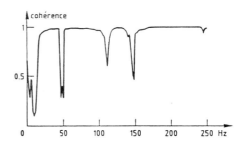

Fig. 4-b : coherence plotted us frequency between two acoustic transducers.

location. Fig. 4c shows the corresponding phase plot. It displays clear steplike changes from 0 to ± 180°.

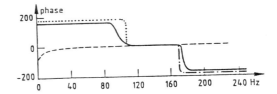

Fig. 4-c : phase plotted Vs frequency between two acoustic transducers.

—— full line : experimental data
····· dotted line : analytical prediction for a pressure source
– – – – dashed line : analytical prediction for a mass flow rate source.

Phase plots related to a pair of sensors located at s_1 and s_2 on the same side of the source allow to measure the equivalent acoustic impedance at the corresponding pipe end. Phase is given analytically by considering the corre-lation product

(5) $p(s_1,w)p^*(s_2,w) = \left(\frac{c}{A} q\right)^2 T(\lambda, \mu)$

$$T(\lambda,\mu) = (\lambda^2 + \mu^2)(\cos\beta_- + \cos\beta_+)$$

$$+ 2\lambda \sin\beta_+ + \cos\beta_- - \cos\beta_+ + 2i\mu \sin\beta_-$$

where p^* denotes the complex conjugate of p,q is the flow-rate at position of impedance

$$\alpha = \lambda + i\mu \quad \text{and} \quad \beta_+ = \frac{\omega}{c}(s_1 + s_2),$$

$$\beta_- = \frac{\omega}{c}(s_2 - s_1).$$

Provided dissipation remains sufficiently small $\mu = 0$ and phase displays steplike changes from 0 to $\pm 180°$, as actually observed in the present experiment. Thus, λ can be obtained by using the simplified relationship

$$(6) \qquad \lambda = \pm \cot g(\beta_2 - \beta_1)$$

$$\beta_1 = \omega_0 s_1 / c \qquad \beta_2 = \omega_0 s_2 / c$$

where ω_0 is the circular frequency of the first observed step in the phase plot. Finally, the position of the equivalent impedance is given by

$$(7) \qquad \beta_1 \text{ or } \beta_2 = \pi/2$$

Here, the method provided practically $\lambda = \mu = 0$. Thus, as desired a priori for sake of simplicity, the rubber tubes connected to the steel pipe are flexible enough to impose that pressure nodes are located near the pipe ends. The measured position is 15 cm away from the main pipe. As a consequence, central frequencies of the acoustic peaks are expected at harmonics of $f = c/2L = 135$ Hz, in close agreement with the measured values : 130, 256, and 396 Hz.

Coming back to the phase plot of Fig. 4c, the dotted curve superimposed on the experimental one (full line) is calculated by assuming a pressure source located at the orifice. It can be verified that it is in fact the case at least at sufficiently low frequencies. Similar plots were analysed up to 1 kHz. As a result, the presence of an additional acoustic flow-rate source was evidenced above about 400 Hz. The presence of two sources makes the determination of the source spectra more difficult, because a system with multiple inputs and outputs has to be analysed. Here, the study is restricted to the pressure source at frequencies below 250 Hz.

Fig. 5 shows the dimensionless spectrum obtained from several measurements at different locations and flow-rates. The data were reduced according to the same scaling factors as already used for the turbulent spectra. It can

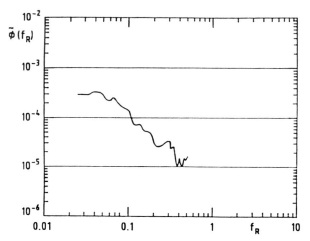

Fig. 5 : dimensionless spectrum of the pressure source as derived from several measurements.

be reasonably well fitted to the analytical profile.

$$(8) \qquad \tilde{\Phi}_{(f_R)} = 10^{-4} \left(\frac{f_R}{f_{Rc}}\right)^{-\gamma}$$

with

$$\gamma = 0.91 \qquad \text{if} \qquad f_R < f_{Rc} = 0.1$$

$$\gamma = 1.41 \qquad \text{if} \qquad f_R > f_{Rc}$$

Other measurements carried out with a similar orifice with $d/D = 0.7$ instead of 0.5 produced essentially the same spectrum. Finally an orifice $d/D = 0.5$ was also tested in a reversed layout. Results can be summarized as follows :

The loss of head coefficient is reduced by a factor of about 2, in fair agreement with Idel'Cick (7). The general shapes of the steady pressure profiles downstream the orifices are similar in both cases. However, the pressure acoustic source due to the reversed orifice displays a reduced spectrum which can be fitted to

$$(9) \qquad \tilde{\Phi}_{(f_R)} = 2 \; 10^{-5} \left(\frac{f_R}{f_{Rc}}\right)^{-\gamma}$$

$$\gamma = + 1.2 \qquad f_R \leqslant f_{Rc} = 0.1$$

$$\gamma = 2.2 \qquad f_R > f_{Rc}$$

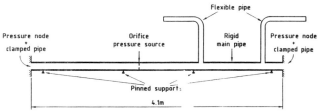

Fig. 6-a : model of experimental rig.

Differences between eqs. (8) and (9) are pointing out that turbulent and acoustic fluctuations can be sensitive even to relatively small changes in the geometry of the flow-singularity.

3.4. Vibratory response of the bent pipes

Fig. 6a shows a configuration of the test rig used to perform flow-induced vibration studies. Fig. 6b displays the displacements of the first four acousto-mechanical modes, vibrating in the plane of the bends, as computed by CASTEM (8). Modal shapes are normalized to a unitary maximum displacement. Out of plane modes are not considered here. Indeed, as expected from theory and then checked by experiment they are not excited by the flow singularity. Pressure profiles associated with the in plane modes are shown in Fig. 6c. As expected their slope displays abrupt changes at the bend and at the T junction related to the acousto-mechanical coupling terms. The flow-induced spectral response of accelerometers located at the free end of the bent pipes were used to determine the reduced damping of the in plane modes. Damping values were found to be small, typically 0.5 % and practically independent of the flow-rate. Then, theoretical response spectra of the accelerometer were computed by using CASTEM, according to the general formalism outlined in (4), for comparison with the experimental data set.

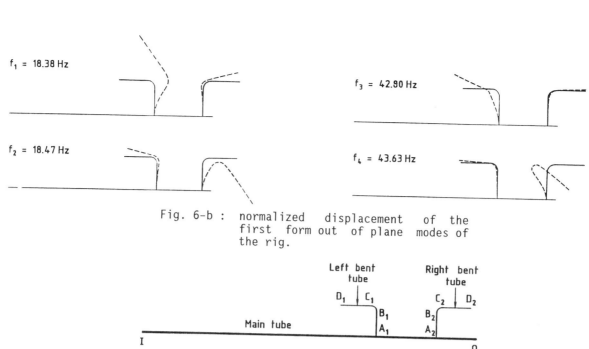

$f_1 = 18.38\,Hz$

$f_2 = 18.47\,Hz$

$f_3 = 42.80\,Hz$

$f_4 = 43.63\,Hz$

Fig. 6-b : normalized displacement of the first form out of plane modes of the rig.

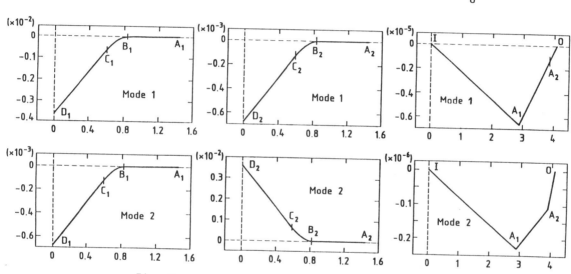

Fig. 6-c : pressure profiles associated to in-plane modes.

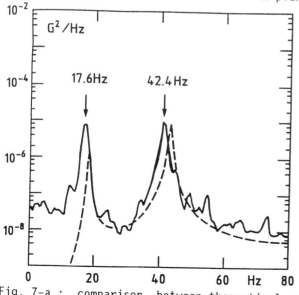

Fig. 7-a : comparison between theoretical and experimental response spectra of the accelerometer at the extremity of the left bent pipe.

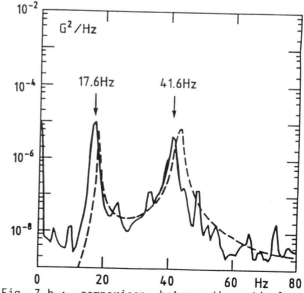

Fig. 7-b : comparison between theoretical and experimental response spectra of the accelerometer at the extremity of the right bent pipe.

Fig. 7 shows a typical example of the data fitting which was achieved. The source spectrum considered here refers to the reversed orifice. This and other similar tests performed with different orifice and flexible pipe arrangements provided satisfactory agreement between theory and experiment : relative discrepancy was less than 5 % on the natural frequencies and less than 15 % on the rms values of the mechanical response.

4. PAIR OF IDENTICAL ORIFICES IN NON CAVITATING FLOW

Series of tests were carried out by inserting a pair of identical orifices. The relative distance between the orifices was systematically varied from 2 (D-d) up to 17 (D-d). The resulting loss of head coefficient was found to vary steadily from the value for a single orifice to two times this value. Indeed, at small distances most of the pressure drop takes place at the upstream orifice and at sufficiently large distances flow is reestablished before reaching the downstream orifice.

5. SINGLE ORIFICE IN CAVITATING FLOW

Series of tests were performed with a single orifice d/D = 0.5 and flow-rates of 30 and 40 l/s, the downstream static pressure having been parametrically varied from 0.3 to 0.03 MPa. For practical convenience, a cavitation index was defined as follows,

(10) $\qquad \sigma_c = (Pmin - Pv) / \Delta P$

where Pv is the pressure of saturated vapor and Pmin is the minimum pressure which would be reached in absence of cavitation, given by the simplified empirical relation (2). No local measurements of the two-phase flow which is taking place just downstream from the orifice were available. Some flow visualisation was performed by using a transparent central tube. As soon as σ_c became lower than about 0.5 the presence of numerous small gas bubbles was clearly evidenced and an external noise was perfectly audible, as a series of bursts. It is believed that the cavitation which was observed is mainly due to water degassing, giving rise to a non uniform bubbly flow extending about ten D-d downstream the orifice.

Acoustic resonances of the piping system were

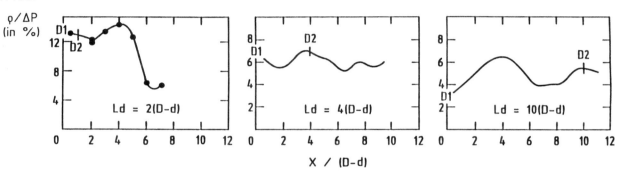

Fig. 8 : pair of identical orifices : reduced profiles of the turbulent pressure fluctuation.

Acoustic peaks were clearly observed, even in the unsteady turbulent spectra. Spatial distribution of the turbulent component is drastically changed in comparison with the single orifice configuration, as shown in Fig. 8 where the rms values of the fluctuations, referred to the total loss of head, are plotted versus distance. As a consequence of such profiles large pressure fluctuations are present at the walls of the two orifices.

The spectra of the acoustic pressure source are very sensitive to the distance between the orifices : at 17 (D-d) the spectrum is only somewhat higher than that of a single orifice whereas at 2 (D-d) it becomes roughly similar to that of the turbulent fluctuations at their maximum. Thus, acoustic spectral levels can be increased roughly by a factor of one hundred when two orifices are present instead of one. This fact was also confirmed by analysing the vibratory responses of bent pipes. This is likely a consequence of the surface source term due to wall effects. Thus, most of the acoustic noise would be produced by the pressure fluctuations at the walls of the pair of orifices. Such observations can have important practical consequences, in the design of multistage orifices which are not too noisy.

observed to decrease drastically with the cavitation index, as shown in Table 1. A reasonable fit to the experimental resonances was achieved by modelling the cavitating fluid as a column of two phase flow extending from the orifice to about 4 (D-d) downstream of it, having a characteristic homogeneous void fraction α_H increasing from 0 up to 6 % when σ_c varies from 0.5 and above to -0.24. Accordingly, at σ_c = -0.24 sound velocity in the two-phase column would be 55 m/s, leading to a Mach number of 0.6 when referred to the steady flow velocity across the vena contracta. This point was successfully checked by analysing the phase plot of two acoustic sensors located on both sides of the orifice.

Cavitation is also modifying the low frequency acoustic sources in several important ways. At first, even at the lowest frequencies of a few Hz it becomes necessary to take into account the presence of a mass-flow-rate source mixed with a pressure source. This is likely another consequence of the enhanced compressibility of the cavitating medium. Rough estimates of the spectral levels of these sources are sufficient to point out that the low frequency noise in a pipe can be considerably enhanced when cavitation occurs. In our tests, increases of PSDs as large as tow orders of magnitude were observed.

Consequently, the rms amplitude of the induced vibrations can be enhanced by a factor ten. This was also successfully checked by experiment.

6. CONCLUDING REMARKS

The experimental study described here provided several important results to validate the simplified theoretical approach outlined in (4). It also produced new information concerning the turbulent and the acoustic pressure fluctuations generated by circular orifices.

Furthermore, the experimental results are putting in evidence two points which are of considerable importance for practical applications :

(1) Plane wave acoustic sources generated by a flow-singularity can be greatly enhanced when large turbulent fluctuations are present at flat walls normal to the pipe axis.

(2) Plane wave acoustic sources generated by a flow-singularity can be greatly enhanced when cavitation occurs. Thus, cavitation may be a cause of severe low frequency vibrations of piping systems.

It is believed that the last two conclusion are of relevance for other pipe components also.

TABLE 1 - Relative change of acoustic natural frequencies with cavitation index σ_c

σ_c	Mode 1	Mode 2	Mode 3
-0.24	0.14	0.21	0.27
-0.17	0.15	0.29	0.40
0.00	0.27	0.62	0.70
0.16	0.67	0.96	0.82
0.33	0.87	0.98	0.91
0.49	1.00	0.99	1.00
0.66	1.00	1.00	1.00

REFERENCES

[1] R.T. Hartlen, W. Jaster. 1979 "Main Steam Piping Vibration Driven by Flow-Acoustic Excitation". Symposium on Practical Experiences with Flow-Induced Vibrations, Karlsruhe, Germany, Sept. 3-6, 1979.

[2] J.A. Chadha, D.E. Hobson, A. Marshall and D.H. Wilkinson. 1980 "Acoustic source Properties of Governor Valves". ASME PVP Conference San-Francisco U.S.A. August 12-15 1980, Vol. 41, pp. 125-138.

[3] R.J. Gibert. 1975 "Etude expérimentale de deux singularités d'un circuit". Note CEA N 1735.

[4] R.J. Gibert, F. Axisa and B. Villard. 1978 "Flow Induced Vibrations of Piping Systems : Vibration Sources-Mechanical Response of the Pipes".

B.N.E.S. International Conference on Flow-Induced Vibration in Nuclear Power Plants, Keswick U.K. 1978, paper 6:2.

[5] F. Axisa and R.J. Gibert. 1982 "Non Linear Analysis of Fluid-Structure Coupled Transients in Piping Systems". ASME PVP Conference, Orlando, U.S.A. June 1982 PVP Vol. 63 pp. 151 165.

[6] H. HASSIS 1990 "Contribution à l'Etude des Lignes de Tuyauteries Excitées par des Singularités d'Ecoulement en Régime Monophasique ou Cavitant. Thèse de Doctorat de l'Université de Paris 6.

[7] I.E. IDEL'CICK 1986 "Memento des Pertes de Charge. Edition Eyrolles Paris.

[8] A. HOFFMANN et Al. Système CASTEM - Programme TEDEL. Rapport CEA EMT/77-64.

C416/043

A study of cylindrical shell vibrations in fluid

J R MAGUIRE, BSc, PhD, CEng, MICE, MIStructE,
Lloyd's Register Industrial Division, Croydon, Surrey

SYNOPSIS This paper describes an experimental and theoretical investigation into the behaviour of a tall cantilevered thin cylinder. This investigation was to look at how frequencies, mode shapes and damping were affected by fluid level variations. The cylinder was studied empty, fluid - surrounded (simulating a dam intake tower) and fluid filled (simulating a tall tank). The results provide a study against which fluid-structure interaction computer programs may be verified. A comprehensive review carried out by Leissa (1) and subsequent review by the author (2) have shown that very few circular cantilevered shell tests have been carried out (even fewer with fluid-coupling considered) and consequently this study would seem to be warranted.

1. INTRODUCTION

During recent research studies (2) it was necessary to investigate the dynamic characteristics of a dam intake tower (3). As it was not possible to carry out tests on a full-scale structure, a laboratory investigation was planned into the behaviour of a cantilevered cylinder. This investigation was to look at how frequencies, mode shapes and damping were affected by fluid level variations for a fluid-surrounded cylinder (simulating a dam intake tower). At the same time it was felt to be worthwhile to look at the behaviour of a fluid-filled cylinder (simulating a tall tank). A tall thin stainless steel cylinder (of aspect ratio not dissimilar to that of a dam intake tower) was available at the University of Bristol, and was used for these tests.

There were two additional reasons for carrying out tests on a cantilevered cylinder. Firstly, in the design of a dam intake tower, or tall tank, it is useful to be able to calibrate a theoretical model against a known experimental solution ("benchmark"). Each of these types of structure may be idealised as a cylindrical cantilevered shell, either empty, fluid-filled or fluid surrounded. In a comprehensive review, Leissa (1) showed that very few circular cantilevered shell tests have been carried out (even fewer with fluid-coupling considered), and so carrying out a further study seemed to be warranted. The second additional reason for testing was that the Karadenitz axi-symmetric shell analysis program (4) had been checked against a number of "squat" shells, but not against a tall thin shell.

This extra check was felt to be a necessary prerequisite prior to using this program for prototype dam intake tower analysis which is likely to be undertaken by the University of Bristol in the future.

2. DESCRIPTION OF THE CYLINDER

The geometry of the stainless steel cylinder and its baseplate are shown in Fig.1. The principal dimensions are: length 1350 mm, radius 76.54 mm ($\pm$1.5 mm) and thickness 2.286 mm ($\pm$0.180 mm). The variation of radius ($\pm$2%) was visually apparent and this imperfection is thought to be of some significance (see later).

Before fixing the cylinder to its baseplate, the mass per unit length was measured as 8.631 kg/m. For theoretical analysis, the dynamic Young's modulus was assumed to be 200 kN/mm^2, and Poisson's ratio to be 0.30.

For the fluid-filled cylinder tests, the baseplate was securely bolted onto a steel plate set into a solid concrete block of dimension 1m x 1m x 1m. For the fluid-surrounded tests, the cylinder was centrally fixed inside a reservoir of plan dimension 2.5m x 1.7m, of sufficient depth to allow the water to rise to a level covering 90% of the height of the cylinder. The experimental setup is described in more detail in Section 4.

3. GENERAL THEORETICAL CONSIDERATIONS

The theory of thin cylindrical shell behaviour has already been discussed (2,5-12 incl.) as has the Karadenitz axi-symmetric shell analysis program (2,4). This program was used for the analysis of the cylinder behaviour, the number of shell and fluid elements chosen being described in later sections. A brief description of the fluid element used is given in Fig. 2. The theoretical mode shapes for empty cylinder vibration are shown in Fig. 3.

Boundary conditions are an important theoretical consideration (13). At the cylinder base, full fixity cannot be guaranteed, but the arrangement chosen (Fig.1) is thought to be close to an encastre condition. The effect of the reservoir wall on fluid-surrounded cylinder behaviour is discussed in a later section.

The effect of the radial imperfections on the cylinder behaviour was thought to be significant. Experiences with cooling towers (14,15,16,17) and full-scale tanks (18,19) have shown that response may be dominated by out of round imperfections. Some unusual vibrational behaviour was therefore anticipated.

4. GENERAL EXPERIMENTAL CONSIDERATIONS

A two stage testing procedure was adopted for all the cylinder tests. Firstly, hammer tests were carried out to determine frequencies and damping values using a small hand-held instrumented hammer, accelerometers, charge amplifiers, spectrum analyser and tape recorder. The cylinder was hit with the hammer either at 50 mm from the free end or at mid-height. At the 50 mm level and at mid-height, two accelerometers were mounted horizontally to measure the response. The frequencies and damping values (derived from the transfer functions) were then noted. A range of 0-2000 Hz was investigated, in 200 Hz intervals, using a nylon-headed hammer containing a Bruel and Kjaer type 8200 force transducer. The accelerometers used were the very light (mass = 2 grammes) Bruel and Kjaer type 4375. The second stage of the test procedure was to evaluate the mode shapes.

This was done by attaching a single electro-magnetic vibrator (Ling type V201) to a small perspex block glued 50 mm from the free end of the cylinder. The vibrator was then driven by a signal generator at each frequency derived from the hammer tests. The mode shapes were to be evaluated at each frequency by detecting the number and position of nodes. This was done by moving a microphone (Radio Spares type Electret Condensor) across the surface of the cylinder. As nodes occur at positions of zero vibration, these were visually detectable on an oscilliscope connected to the microphone. The number and position of circumferential and meridional nodes were then compared to Fig. 3 to determine which mode corresponded to each frequency.

5. TESTS ON THE EMPTY CYLINDER

5.1 Theoretical Investigation

The cylinder was idealised as an axi-symmetric cantilevered thin shell, the geometric and physical properties of which are given in Section 2. For the empty case, a number of finite element (F.E.) analyses (using the Karadenitz program) were made, using 5, 10, 20, 40 and 80 elements to model the cylinder. It was found that the 5 and 10 F.E. models did not contain sufficient elements to model the behaviour accurately enough (for the number of modes of interest) and that either a 20, 40 or 80 F.E. model should be used for this cylinder. As 85 was the largest number of structural elements that could easily be handled by the Karadenitz program, an 80 F.E. model was used. The frequencies from this model are given in Table 1. The damping value for this type of steel cylinder was expected to be in the range 0.05-1.00% critical in the fundamental mode (20).

5.2 Experimental Investigation

Hammer tests were carried out on the empty cylinder, hitting and measuring at both 50 mm from the free end and at mid-height. A coherence of better than 0.95 was regularly achieved at spectral peaks after 5 averages. The analysis interval chosen was 200 Hz, leading to a resolution of 0.4 Hz. Typical transfer functions and coherences are shown in Figure 4. The peaks at the natural frequencies are sharp, due to the low damping associated with stainless steel. Also noticeable are several distinct troughs in the coherence values, which sometimes seem to indicate where a mode is not being excited by the hammer. A summary of frequencies and damping values is presented in Table 2. It should be noted that most of the measured mode shapes were found to correspond to those shown in Fig. 3. The exception to this was for the modes marked m-1A and M=1B in Table 2. These "distorted" mode shapes are shown in Fig.5.

5.3 Comparisons and Conclusions

Comparing the theoretical frequencies in Table 1 with the experimental frequencies in Table 2, good agreement may be seen for the modes m=2, 3 and 4. This indicates that the finite element model and Karadenitz program are correctly predicting these modes. However, theoretical mode m=1 was not detectable during experimental tests; instead, distorted modes m=1A and m=1B appeared, at frequencies lower than those expected for m=1. This is thought to be due to the effect of the imperfections in the cylinder (Section 3), which would be expected to reduce the sectional stiffness and correspondingly reduce the measured frequencies. It might be hypothesised that m=1 mode exists, and that the hammer is not exciting it. In this case, a trough in the coherence would be expected at 82Hz, but from Fig 4(a) no such trough appears implying that mode m=1 does not exist. Measured damping values for modes m=2, 3 and 4 lie between 0.008% and 0.202%, which are at the lower end of the expected range (Section 5.1). For the distorted modes m=1A and m=1B the damping is significantly higher, ranging from 0.209% to 0.784%, which is still within the expected range.

In conclusion, it was felt that an 80 finite element model in connection with the Karadenitz program could accurately predict the "undistorted" frequencies and mode shapes of this tall empty circular cantilevered cylinder. As expected, imperfections in the cylinder seem to be significant, apparently causing distortions to mode m=1 and a reduction in corresponding frequencies. However, modes m=2, 3 and 4 seem to be unaffected by the same imperfections. Experimentally, single point excitation with the hammer seems to be adequate to excite all of the modes of interest of this cylinder.

6. TESTS ON THE FLUID-FILLED CYLINDER

6.1 Theoretical Investigation

As has been stated previously the maximum number of structural elements (seven degrees of freedom per node) that may be easily handled by the Karadenitz program is 85. This number must be reduced once fluid elements (one degree of freedom per node) are also taken into consideration. Fig.6 shows the structure and fluid mesh chosen for the analysis of the fluid-filled cylinder. Once four fluid elements across the radius had been chosen (see later) the maximum allowable number of fluid and structural elements vertically was 39. This number (39= approx 40) has already been shown to give an adequate number of structural elements (Section 5.1). Four fluid elements across the radius were chosen based on meshes successfully used by Karadenitz (4). In addition, increasing the number of structural elements to 20 showed little change in frequency values, thereby indicating that 4 fluid elements were sufficient. The Karadenitz program was run for a number of water levels, modelling the behaviour at water levels of 0%, 30%, 60% 70%, 80%, 90%, and 100% (0, 48, 92, 108, 124, 140 and 156 fluid elements respectively). A selection of results is given in Table 3. The variation of frequency value against water level is plotted later (Section 6.3).

Hydrodynamic damping was expected to slightly increase the measured damping as the fluid level rose (1,21); a number of authors have examined this particularly in the offshore engineering field (22,23,24). It has been shown that hydrodynamic damping is frequency dependant and also dependant on whether the fluid is flowing (relative to the structure) or still (25,26).The increase in damping due to hydrodynamic effects was expected to be about 0.5% (26) for the fundamental mode of this cylinder, though a simplified formula (21) suggests an increase of 3%.

The variation of mode shape with increasing water level was also investigated. Fig.7 shows the expected variation in meridional mode shape, the circumferential (cos mθ) mode shape remaining unchanged. As may be seen, very little change in theoretical mode shape occurs.

6.2 Experimental Investigation

Hammer tests and mode shape definition (with microphone and electro-magnetic vibrator) were carried out as described in earlier sections. A selection of experimental frequencies is given in Table 4. Only modes which were clearly distinguishable are shown. The variation of frequency value against water level is plotted later (Section 6.3). Experimental mode shapes (as defined by the positions of the nodes) varied very little, matching the slight variations shown in Fig.7. Damping was found to vary slightly with rising water level, the difference between the 0% and 100% water levels being an increase of 0.03% (critical damping) for m=2, an increase of 0.06% for m=3 and a reduction of 0.11% for m=1A and m=1B.

6.3 Comparisons and Conclusions

For the fluid-filled cylinder, a typical variation of frequency with water level is shown in Figures 8. The full set of variations show good agreement between theoretical and experimental frequencies for modes m=2 and m=3, but a poorer correlation between the theoretical m=1 modes and experimental modes m=1A and m=1B. This indicates that the Karadenitz program incorporating fluid coupling can predict the modal values for an undistorted fluid-filled cylinder (such as an undistorted tall tank). The experimental change in frequency due to fluid coupling is significant, with an average maximum reduction (compared to the empty cylinder frequencies) of 40% for m=1A and 1B, 38% for m=2 and 33% for m=3. The corresponding theoretical reductions were 41% for m=1, 38% for m=2 and 32% for m=3. Experimental and theoretical mode shapes agreed well, bearing in mind that these were only defined by node positions. The experimental change in damping due to hydrodynamic effects was small (even less than was expected).

7. TESTS ON THE FLUID-SURROUNDED CYLINDER

7.1 Theoretical Investigation

For the fluid-surrounded cylinder, a regular fluid mesh was constructed (for ease of data preparation), and this is shown in Fig.9. To give regularly shaped elements, the number of fluid elements was reduced from 156 (fluid-filled) to 80, and the number of structural elements was chosen to be 40. The fluid elements are closely packed at the structure-fluid interface and subsequently spaced out. The Karadenitz program was again run for water levels of 0%, 30%, 60% 70%, 80%, 90% and 100% (0, 24, 48, 56, 64, 72 and 80 fluid elements respectively). A selection of results is given in Table 5. The variation of frequency against water level is plotted later (section 7.3). As in the case of the fluid-filled cylinder, the increase in damping due to hydrodynamic effects was expected to be 0.5%. The variation of mode shape with increasing water level was also investigated. The variation in meridional mode shape was almost identical to that shown in Fig. 7, the circumferential (cos mθ) mode shape remaining unchanged. As may be seen, very little change in theoretical mode shape occurs.

Boundary conditions are an important theoretical consideration. Pressure-wave reflections from the reservoir wall may have a significant influence on dynamic behaviour, and this needs investigating. Usually in the experimental analysis of dams a boundary is deemed to have little effect if it is placed at least 3 times the dam height away from the dam face (27,28). For this cylinder the fluid mesh shown in Fig.9 was varied in width from a minimum width of 35 mm to a maximum width of 2700 mm. Changes in frequency for various m and n values (and different water levels) were plotted. These showed little boundary wall effect if the wall is placed at greater than 460 mm (3 times the cylinder diameter) away from the cylinder face. As both the theoretical and experimental boundaries were mainly at a greater distance away from the cylinder than 460 mm, pressure-wave reflections were not expected to cause any significant modifications to the dynamic behaviour.

7.2 Experimental Investigation

Hammer tests and mode shape definition (with a microphone and an electro-magnetic vibrator) were carried out as described in earlier sections. A selection of experimental frequencies is given in Table 6. Only modes which were clearly distinguishable are shown. It should be noted that frequencies at a water level of 100% of the cylinder height could not be achieved, as this would have resulted in a submerged vibrator. Instead, 100% values were estimated from a smooth curve drawn through the 70%, 80% and 90% frequencies. The variation of frequency value against water level is plotted later (Section 7.3). Experimental mode shapes (as defined by the positions of the nodes) varied very little, matching the slight variations shown in Fig 7.

Damping was found to vary slightly with rising water level, the difference between the 0% and 90% water levels being an increase of 0.06% (critical damping) for m=2, an increase of 0.16% for m=3, and an increase of 0.25% for m=1A and m=1B.

7.3 Comparison and Conclusions

For the fluid-surrounded cylinder, a typical variation of frequency with water level is shown in Figure 10. The complete set (2) show a reasonable agreement between theoretical and experimental frequencies for modes m=2 and m=3, but a poorer correlation between the theoretical modes m=1 and the experimental modes m=1A and m=1B. This indicates that the Karadenitz program incorporating fluid-coupling can predict the modal values for an undistorted fluid-surrounded cylinder (such as an undistorted intake tower). It is interesting to note that there is generally a closer experimental/theoretical agreement on frequencies for the fluid-filled cylinder than for the fluid-surrounded cylinder. This might in part be due to base fixity and/or boundary wall effects in the case of the fluid-surrounded cylinder. The experimental change in frequency due to fluid-coupling is significant, with an average maximum reduction (compared to empty cylinder frequencies) of 39% for m=1A and m=1B, 37% for m=2 and 31% for m=3.

The corresponding theoretical reductions were 47% for m=1, 38% for m=2 and 32% for m=3. Experimental and theoretical mode shapes agreed well. The experimental change in damping due to hydrodynamic effects was small (even less than expected).

8. CONCLUSIONS

Theoretical frequencies and mode shapes have been presented for a tall undistorted cylinder including fluid-structure coupling effects. Experimental frequencies, mode shapes and damping values have been presented for a tall slightly distorted cylinder including fluid-structure coupling effects. The small imperfections in the experimental cylinder have been seen to give rise to unusual dynamic behaviour, particularly in the fundamental mode. This change in behaviour could be of importance for a dam intake tower (or tall tank) subject to earthquake and should be researched further.

Fluid coupling effects have been seen to affect the cylinder frequencies significantly, with a reduction of up to 40% measured during fluid-filling or fluid-surrounded. At the same time, limited measurements have shown that the mode shapes remain practically unchanged. The added damping due to hydrodynamic effects has been seen to be very small for this particular cylinder in still water. Finally, the experimental results provide a study against which new analyses and experimental work may be compared.

9. ACKNOWLEDGEMENTS

The majority of this work was carried out whilst the author was carrying out research at Bristol University under the supervision of Prof. R.T. Severn. The financial assistance of the Science and Engineering Research Council under Grant No. GR/C/08497 is gratefully acknowledged.

10. REFERENCES

(1) LEISSA A.W. "Vibrations of Shells" N.A.S.A. SP-288, Washington D.C., 1973.

(2) MAGUIRE J.R. "The Dynamic Characteristics of Elevated Tanks and other Selected Protype Structures", Ph.D.Thesis, Bristol University, 1984.

(3) SEVERN R.T., Professor of Civil Engineering (University of Bristol), Private communication, June 1983.

(4) KARADENITZ H. "The Theoretical and Experimental Dynamic Analysis of Thin Shells of Revolution" Ph.D. Thesis, University of Bristol, May 1976.

(5) WARBURTON G.B. "The Dynamical Behaviour of Structures" 2nd. edition, Pergamon, 1976.

(6) BAKER E.H. et al "Structural Analysis of Shells" McGraw-Hill, New York, 1962.

(7) DONNELL L.H. "Beams, Plates and Shells" McGraw-Hill, New York, 1976.

(8) SEIDE P. "Small Elastic Deformations of Thin Shells" Noordhoff, Leyden, 1975.

(9) WARBURTON G.B. "Dynamics of Shells" Univ. of Toronto, Dept. of Mech. Eng., Technical Publication TP7307, 1973.

(10) NOVOZHILOV V.V. "The Theory of Thin Shells" Noordhoff, Groningen, 1959.

(11) FLUGGE W. "Stresses in Shells" 2nd edition, Springer-Verlag, Berlin, 1970.

(12) SANDERS J.L. Jnr. "An Improved First Approximation Theory for Thin Shells" N.A.S.A. TR R-24, 1959.

(13) LYSMER J., KUHLEMEYER R.L. "Finite Dynamic Model for Infinite Media" J. Eng. Mech. Div., A.S.C.E., Vol.95, No.EM4, Aug. 1969.

(14) AL-DABBAGH A., GUPTA A.K. "Meridional Imperfections in Cooling Tower Design" A.S.C.E., J. Struct. Div., June 1979, Vol.105, No.ST6, pp.1089-1102.

(15) CROLL J.G.A., KALELI F., KEMP K.O., MUNRO J. "A Simplified Approach to the Analysis of Geometrically Imperfect Cooling Tower Shells" Eng. Struct., Vol. 1, No.2, Jan.1979, pp.92-98.

(16) DONNELL L.H., WAN C.C. "Effects of Imperfections on Buckling of Thin Cylinders and Columns under Axial Compression" A.S.M.E. Transactions, Vol.72, J. of Appl. Mech.,Mar.1950

(17) ELLINAS C.P., CROLL J.G.A., KEMP K.O."Cooling Towers with Circumferential Imperfections" A.S.C.E., J. Struct. Div., Dec 1980, Vol. 106,No.ST12.

(18) CLOUGH D.P., CLOUGH R.W. "Earthquake Simulator Studies of Cylindrical Tanks" Nuclear Eng. and Design, Vol.46, No.2, April 1978, pp. 367-380.

(19) CLOUGH R.W., NIWA A., CLOUGH D.P. "Experimental Seismic Study of Cylindrical Tanks" Proc. A.S.C.E., ST12, Dec.1979

(20) HALLAM M.G., HEAF N.J., WOOTON L.R. "Dynamics of Marine Structures" Report UR8, 2nd. edition, CIRIA Underwater Engineering Group, Oct.1978.

(21) HERON "Structural Damping" Vo.22, No.4, 1977, published by H. Van Goyden.

(22) KIRK C.L. "Dynamic Analysis of Offshore Structures" CML Pubs., Southampton,1982.

(23) RUHL J.A. "Offshore Platforms : Observed Behaviour and Comparison with Theory" J. Petrol. Tech., April 1978, pp.638-648.

(24) VUGTS J.H. HAYES D.J. "Dynamic Analysis of Fixed Offshore Structures" Eng. Struct., Vol. 1, No.3, April 1979.

(25) DUNCAN W.J., THOM A.S., YOUNG A.D. "Mechanics of Fluids" 2nd. edition 1970.

(26) FISH P. and RAINEY R., Paper 50 in B.O.S.S. 1979, London, Vo.2, pp43-60.

(27) ALTINISIK D. "Aseismic Design of Concrete Dams" Ph.D. Thesis, University of Bristol, Oct. 1980.

(28) BRAHTZ H.A., HEILBRON C.H. "Discussion of Water Pressure on Dams during Earthquakes by Westergaard"Trans. ASCE., V.98, 1933.

Table 1 - Empty Cylinder - Theoretical Frequencies (Hz) from an 80 finite element solution

n	m=1	m=2	m=3	m=4	m=5
1	82	256	717	1374	2219
2	460	305	727	1382	2232
3	1126	509	765	1401	2252
4	1898	853	853	1429	2255
5	2693	1287	1009	1486	2300
6	3442	1775	1233	1568	2345
7	3976	2293	1511	1684	2405
8	4102	2818	1830	1835	2483
9	4639	3335	2177	2018	2580
10	4667	3819	2542	2231	2698

m = circumferential mode number
n = meridional mode number

Table 2 - Empty Cylinder - Summary of Experimental Frequencies and Damping Values

(a)   Frequencies (Hz)

n	m=1	m=2	m=3	m=4	m=1A	m=1B
1	–	247.5	696.9	1336	57.4	65.2
2	–	291.3	706.6	1344	383.0	402.7
3	–	484.2	741.0	1359	–	–
4	–	832.8	827.5	1390	–	–
5	–	1252	983.8	1442	–	–

NOTE: mode shapes m=1A and m=1B shown in Fig.5.

(b)   Damping Values (Per cent of Critical)

n	m=1	m=2	m=3	m=4	m=1A	m=1B
1	–	0.040	0.014	0.019	0.784	0.729
2	–	0.069	0.014	0.007	0.209	0.211
3	–	0.155	0.027	0.022	–	–
4	–	0.138	0.091	0.011	–	–
5	–	0.202	0.071	0.008	–	–

Table 3 - Fluid-Filled Cylinder Theoretical Frequencies (Hz) (39 structural elements/up to 156 fluid elements)

(a)   Water level 0 per cent

n	m=1	m=2	m=3	m=4
1	82.2	255.8	710.9	1370
2	460.7	304.9	716.3	1394
3	1133	509.1	758.1	1411
4	1928	853.6	836.7	1496
5	2779	1290	1005	1499

(b)   Water level 60 per cent

n	m=1	m=2	m=3	m=4
1	75.1	197.1	492.4	985.9
2	321.3	262.2	561.7	1018
3	817.0	386.5	698.0	1088
4	1392	640.7	726.1	1219
5	1944	943.9	817.8	1370

(c)   Water level 100 per cent

n	m=1	m=2	m=3	m=4
1	48.3	158.6	481.6	983.4
2	274.3	190.2	491.9	992.0
3	682.6	318.4	515.7	1004
4	1172	536.7	577.0	1027
5	1694	815.7	684.3	1076

Table 4 - Fluid-Filled Cylinder Experimental Frequencies (Hz)

(a)   Water level 0 per cent

n	m=1	m=2	m=3	m=1A	m=1B
1	–	247.5	696.9	57.4	65.2
2	–	291.3	706.6	383.0	402.7
3	–	484.2	741.0	–	–
4	–	832.8	827.5	–	–
5	–	–	983.8	–	–

(b)   Water level 60 per cent

n	m=1	m=2	m=3	m=1A	m=1B
1	–	–	–	46.3	52.1
2	–	252.0	520.0	270.2	280.6
3	–	361.6	–	–	–
4	–	616.6	–	–	–
5	–	–	795.9	–	–

(c)   Water level 100 per cent

n	m=1	m=2	m=3	m=1A	m–1B
1	–	153.9	465.9	35.0	40.3
2	–	182.1	475.3	229.9	240.7
3	–	304.5	502.3	–	–
4	–	517.7	558.4	–	–
5	–	–	660.9	–	–

Table 5 - Fluid-Surrounded Cylinder
Theoretical Frequencies (Hz)
(40 structural elements/up to 80 fluid elements)

(a) Water level 0 per cent

n	m=1	m=2	m=3	m=4
1	82.3	255.8	711.0	1370
2	461.6	305.0	716.2	1391
3	1135	509.8	758.3	1394
4	1930	855.0	837.2	1419
5	2783	1292	1006	1570

(b) Water level 90 per cent

n	m=1	m=2	m=3	m=4
1	42.2	136.7	398.9	824.2
2	303.0	200.1	457.7	859.3
3	892.0	404.7	576.2	942.5
4	1354	618.3	736.8	1081
5	1962	959.8	804.8	1262

Table 6 - Fluid-Surrounded Cylinder
Experimental Frequencies (Hz)

(a) Water level 0 per cent

n	m=1	m=2	m=3	m=1A	m=1B
1	–	247.6	697.1	51.8	58.2
2	–	291.3	706.8	365.2	382.1
3	–	484.1	741.5	–	–
4	–	817.4	832.2	–	–
5	–	–	984.3	–	–

(b) Water level 90 per cent

n	m=1	m=2	m=3	m=1A	m=1B
1	–	160.0	479.9	34.7	38.8
2	–	205.5	531.9	242.1	252.6
3	–	330.2	540.0	–	–
4	–	545.9	618.7	–	–
5	–	–	719.5	–	–

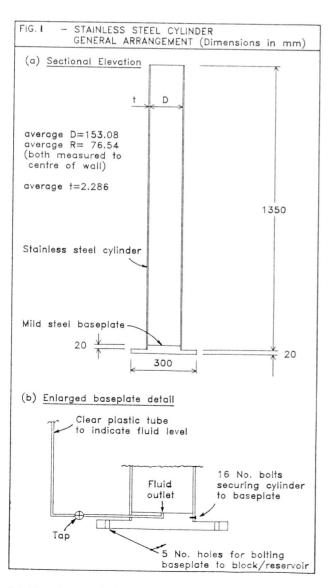

FIG. 1 – STAINLESS STEEL CYLINDER
GENERAL ARRANGEMENT (Dimensions in mm)

(a) Sectional Elevation

average D=153.08
average R= 76.54
(both measured to centre of wall)

average t=2.286

Stainless steel cylinder

Mild steel baseplate

(b) Enlarged baseplate detail

Clear plastic tube to indicate fluid level

Fluid outlet

16 No. bolts securing cylinder to baseplate

Tap

5 No. holes for bolting baseplate to block/reservoir

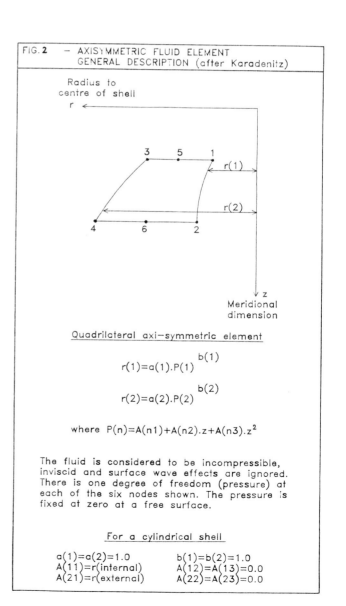

FIG. 2 – AXISYMMETRIC FLUID ELEMENT
GENERAL DESCRIPTION (after Karadenitz)

Radius to centre of shell
r

Meridional dimension

Quadrilateral axi-symmetric element

$$r(1)=a(1).P(1)^{b(1)}$$

$$r(2)=a(2).P(2)^{b(2)}$$

where $P(n)=A(n1)+A(n2).z+A(n3).z^2$

The fluid is considered to be incompressible, inviscid and surface wave effects are ignored. There is one degree of freedom (pressure) at each of the six nodes shown. The pressure is fixed at zero at a free surface.

For a cylindrical shell

a(1)=a(2)=1.0	b(1)=b(2)=1.0
A(11)=r(internal)	A(12)=A(13)=0.0
A(21)=r(external)	A(22)=A(23)=0.0

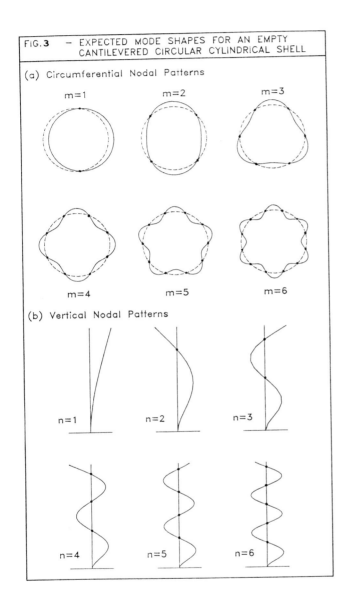

FIG.3 — EXPECTED MODE SHAPES FOR AN EMPTY
CANTILEVERED CIRCULAR CYLINDRICAL SHELL

(a) Circumferential Nodal Patterns

m=1   m=2   m=3

m=4   m=5   m=6

(b) Vertical Nodal Patterns

n=1   n=2   n=3

n=4   n=5   n=6

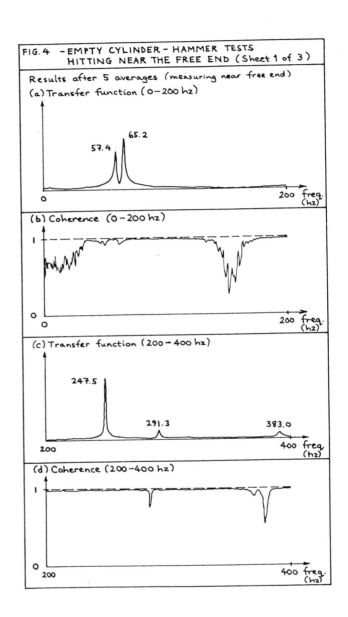

FIG.4 — EMPTY CYLINDER – HAMMER TESTS
HITTING NEAR THE FREE END (Sheet 1 of 3)

Results after 5 averages (measuring near free end)
(a) Transfer function (0–200 hz)

57.4   65.2

0   200 freq.
                         (hz)

(b) Coherence (0–200 hz)

1

0
0   200 freq.
                         (hz)

(c) Transfer function (200–400 hz)

247.5

291.3   383.0

200   400 freq.
                         (hz)

(d) Coherence (200–400 hz)

1

0
200   400 freq.
                         (hz)

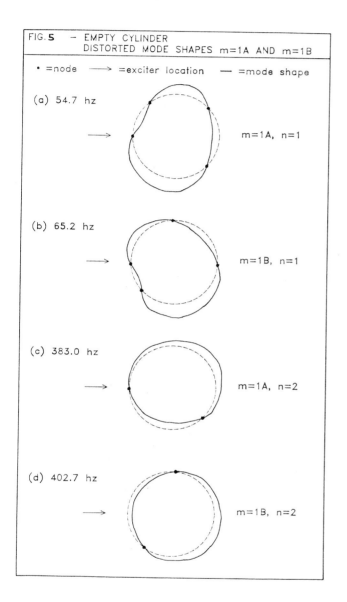

FIG. 5 – EMPTY CYLINDER
         DISTORTED MODE SHAPES m=1A AND m=1B

• =node   ⟶ =exciter location   — =mode shape

(a) 54.7 hz   m=1A, n=1

(b) 65.2 hz   m=1B, n=1

(c) 383.0 hz   m=1A, n=2

(d) 402.7 hz   m=1B, n=2

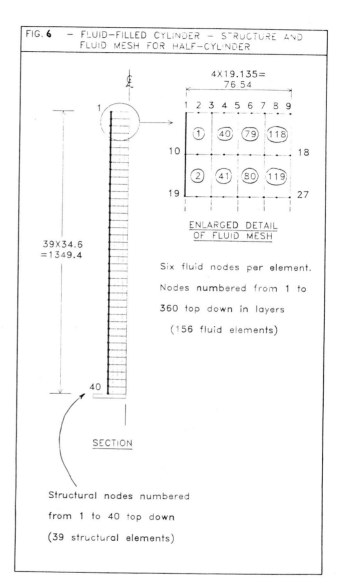

FIG. 6 – FLUID-FILLED CYLINDER – STRUCTURE AND
         FLUID MESH FOR HALF-CYLINDER

4X19.135=
76.54

39X34.6
=1349.4

ENLARGED DETAIL
OF FLUID MESH

Six fluid nodes per element.

Nodes numbered from 1 to

360 top down in layers

(156 fluid elements)

SECTION

Structural nodes numbered

from 1 to 40 top down

(39 structural elements)

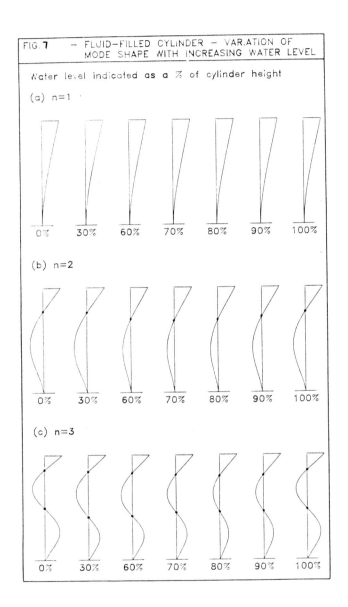

FIG. 7 — FLUID-FILLED CYLINDER — VARIATION OF MODE SHAPE WITH INCREASING WATER LEVEL

Water level indicated as a % of cylinder height

(a) n=1

0%   30%   60%   70%   80%   90%   100%

(b) n=2

0%   30%   60%   70%   80%   90%   100%

(c) n=3

0%   30%   60%   70%   80%   90%   100%

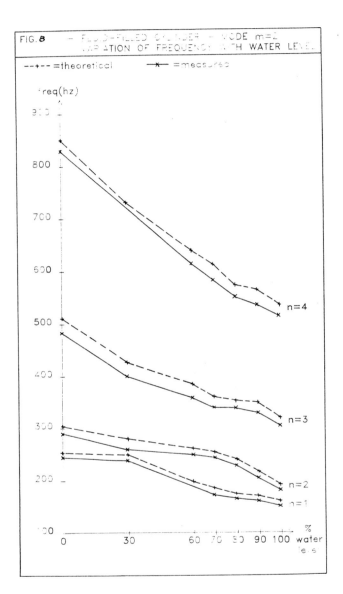

FIG. 8 — FLUID-FILLED CYLINDER — MODE m=2 VARIATION OF FREQUENCY WITH WATER LEVEL

--+-- =theoretical   --*-- =measured

freq(hz)

n=4
n=3
n=2
n=1

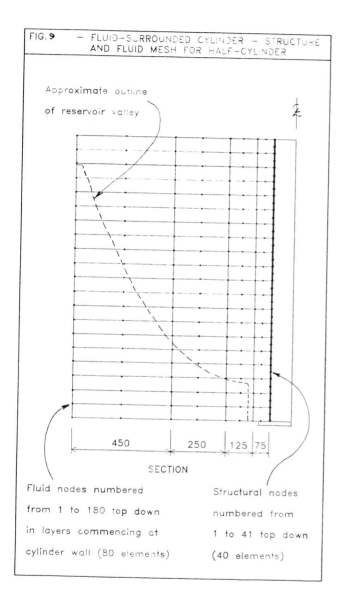

FIG. 9 — FLUID-SURROUNDED CYLINDER — STRUCTURE AND FLUID MESH FOR HALF-CYLINDER

Approximate outline of reservoir valley

450 | 250 | 125 | 75

SECTION

Fluid nodes numbered from 1 to 180 top down in layers commencing at cylinder wall (80 elements)

Structural nodes numbered from 1 to 41 top down (40 elements)

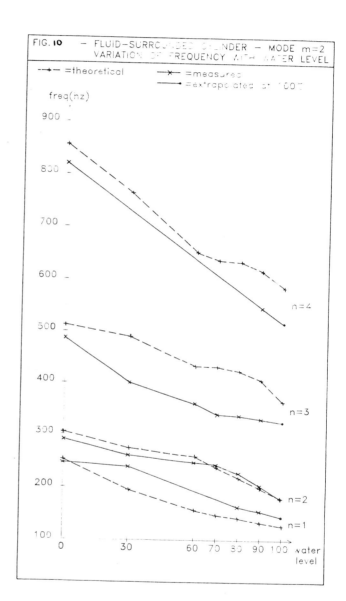

FIG. 10 — FLUID-SURROUNDED CYLINDER — MODE m=2 VARIATION OF FREQUENCY WITH WATER LEVEL

--+-- =theoretical   --x-- =measured
——•—— =extrapolated at 100%

freq(hz)

n=4
n=3
n=2
n=1

water level

C416/023

A computational model of wave induced response of a compliant cylinder

J M R GRAHAM, MA, PhD and B DJAHANSOUZI, BSc(Eng), PhD
Department of Aeronautics, Imperial College of Science, Technology and Medicine, London

SUMMARY

A vortex method which includes the effects of viscous diffusion is used to simulate wave flows past a compliant circular cylinder. Two-dimensional computations are carried out for a section of the cylinder, whose mechanical response is assumed to be represented by a linear spring-mass system with zero damping and two degrees of freedom, in-line and transverse to the flow. Two different frequency ratios and a range of Keulegan-Carpenter numbers up to 12 are investigated and some comparisons made with experimental measurements. The computations were carried out for Reynolds numbers in the range 1 - 2 x 10^3.

NOTATION

A_j	Element of cross-sectional area
C_D	Drag Coefficient
C_L	Lift Coefficient
C_M	Inertia Coefficient
d	Diameter of circular cylinder
f, f_a, f_w	Natural frequency (Hz) of cylinder, in air, in water
f_v	Natural frequency of vortex shedding
F_X, F_Y	In-line force per unit length of cylinder, transverse force
K_C	Keulegan-Carpenter number UT/d
m, m_w	Mass per unit length of cylinder, added mass in water
S	Strouhal number for cylinder $f_v d/U$
t, T	time, time period of incident flow
U, U_0	Incident flow velocity, amplitude
x, y	In-line, transverse coordinate directions and cylinder displacements
β	Stokes beta parameter $d^2/\nu T$
Γ_j	Element of circulation
ζ	Damping as a fraction of critical
ν	Kinematic viscosity of water
ρ	Density of water
ϕ	Phase constant in transverse force equation
ψ	Stream-function
ω	Vorticity

1 INTRODUCTION

Recent experimental work at both laboratory scale (1, 2, 3, 4, 5) and large scale (6) has indicated that compliant cylinders respond strongly in both the in-line and transverse directions when subjected to waves or similar oscillatory incident flows. In this context, a compliant cylinder is one which due, either to its support conditions or to its own elastic behaviour in bending, has its lowest natural frequencies of response in water of similar order to the wave or incident flow frequency. High frequency vibrations of, for example, the cylinder surface and low frequency slow drift motions are excluded. Interest in this type of response of, in particular, circular cylinders exists because of the need to predict the behaviour of riser pipes, pipelines and other relatively long unsupported tubular sections exposed to oscillatory flows in offshore oil production. Recent designs of significantly lighter weight jacket structures for direct lift installation have also tended to introduce much longer, slenderer structural elements than hitherto. The lowest natural frequency of these elements is still high compared with relevant flow induced frequencies, except for wind induced effects which are becoming a problem prior to installation. However the trends in design, which are continuing to lower the natural structural frequencies, imply that wave-current induced vortex shedding effects may become a problem for structural members in the future.

The study of compliant cylinder response in steady incident flows is well established. Two main modes of vibration have been observed to be associated with vortex shedding. A maximum in the transverse vibration occurs at reduced velocities Ud/f in the region of 5 for circular cylinders in subcritical flow, when the vortex shedding locks on to the cylinder motion and the frequency of the transverse force induced by the shedding is close to the natural frequency of the cylinder. The amplitude of the response and the velocity range over which it occurs, decrease rapidly with increase in the damping ζ. At lower reduced velocities in-line vibration may occur, depending again on ζ. In this case, the double frequency of the vortex shedding present in the drag force induces the motion. For significant amplitudes of motion the vortex shedding may also change from an antisymmetric to a symmetric mode. Other forms of flow induced vibration such as galloping, (associated with mean force characteristics giving negative fluid damping), and random buffeting may occur.

In oscillatory flow with no significant mean component, such as that induced by waves, there are important differences in the character of the unsteady forces. First of all a large oscillatory in-line force occurs under all conditions. This force has components at the fundamental and higher harmonics of the incident flow. Harmonics occur even when the incident flow is sinusoidal, because of the quadratic nature of the drag term in the Morison loading. For a compliant cylinder the amplitude of motion of the response may lead to velocities comparable to those in the incident flow. In that case the in-line loading

should be approximated by Morison's equation based on the relative motion:

$$F_X(t) = \pi/4 \, \rho d^2 \left\{ C_M (\dot{U} - \ddot{x}) + \ddot{x} \right\} + 1/2 \, \rho d \, C_D (U - \dot{x}) |U - \dot{x}| \quad (1)$$

where F_X is the in-line force per unit length on the circular cylinder, with in-line displacement x. When the incident velocity is sinusoidal:

$$U = U_0 \sin(2\pi t / T)$$

then clearly F_X contains components at odd multiples of the base frequency and the cylinder will respond in-line when its natural frequency is close to one of these components, but principally at the fundamental frequency.

Prediction of the transverse force, induced by vortex shedding on a cylinder in oscillatory flow, can be obtained from the equation:

$$F_Y(t) = 1/2 \, \rho d C_L U^2 \exp\left\{ i \, S/d \int U \, dt + \phi \right\} \quad (2)$$

proposed by Bearman et al. (7), and in a different form by Verley (8), and applied on a half cycle mode basis. C_L is a lift coefficient evaluated from the data, depending strongly on Keulegen-Carpenter number, S is the Strouhal number, and ϕ is a phase which is typically close to 0 or π. If U is sinusoidal, then F_Y has a multi-line spectrum with power at multiples of the incident velocity frequency. These frequencies are therefore not directly related to the "Strouhal frequency" US/d although the envelope of the line spectrum does peak in the vicinity of $\pi/4 \, (U_0 S/d)$. Hence, significant transverse response of a compliant cylinder will not be concentrated at one particular range of reduced velocity, but may be expected to occur at a large number of discrete reduced velocities, the region with peak response being dependent on the Keulegen-Carpenter number.

If the cylinder is free to respond both in-line and transversely, then the forcing equation for transverse response should probably be modified from the form of (2), to reflect the effect of the in-line motion x. However, experimental validation of this is not yet complete, and it is also clear from laboratory experiments (9), that the response of a compliant cylinder in oscillatory flow cannot be predicted by a straightforward application of (2). For this reason, in parallel with laboratory experiments on elastically mounted cylinders, bottom pivotted cylinders and analysis of the large scale compliant cylinder data (6), numerical flow models have been run, to attempt to predict response (for example, Vada and Skomedal, 10). The present paper describes the application of such a model, based on the discrete vortex method, to the response of an elastically mounted section of a circular cylinder in oscillatory flow. A two-dimensional flow is simulated with some of the parameters, (frequency ratio, Keulegen-Carpenter number), similar to those in the experimental tests (6), but at a comparatively low Reynolds number (10^3) with laminar flow assumed.

2 COMPUTATION OF THE FLOW FIELD

The flow computations have been carried out using a two-dimensional unsteady viscous flow solver, based on a discrete vortex method. In this method, the Navier Stokes equations are solved in the vorticity-streamfunction form with a split time-step for convection and diffusion:

$$\omega_t + \psi_y \omega_x - \psi_x \omega_y = 0 \qquad (3)$$

$$\omega_t - \nu \omega_{xx} - \nu \omega_{yy} = 0 \qquad (4)$$

$$\psi_{xx} + \psi_{yy} + \omega = 0 \qquad (5)$$

where (3) and (4) are solved in sequence, and ν is the kinematic viscosity. Convection of vorticity, equation (3), is carried out by convecting particles (vortices) carrying circulation $\Gamma_j = \iint_{A_j} \omega \, dA$, where A_j is an element of area associated with the cross-section of the jth fluid particle.

The streamfunction field and its derivative the velocity, is computed on a fixed, (in the present case log-polar), mesh surrounding the cylinder. For the calculations shown here, the mesh had 256 x ~100 elements, with a submesh system, used to provide greater resolution near the cylinder surface. The streamfunction field was computed from equation (5), using a fast Fourier transform in the direction around the cylinder and Gaussian elimination of the resulting tridiagonal matrix radially. Diffusion, equation (4), was computed on the fixed mesh by a semi-implicit finite difference method, and involved forward and backward projection of the vorticity between the array of moving vortex points and the nodes of the fixed mesh. This process was carried out on the vorticity change due to diffusion in each time step, in a way which minimised the numerical diffusion. A first order boundary condition for vorticity on the cylinder surface, rather than a second order one, was used for stability reasons and an explicit first order time stepping scheme was used for convection. The viscosity was assumed to take its molecular value throughout the computations reported here; i.e. turbulence was not modelled. Further details of the method are given in reference (11).

3 FLUID-STRUCTURE COUPLING

The section of the compliant cylinder was modelled as a single degree of freedom spring-mass system, with similar frequency ratio to the oscillatory flow as the full scale cylinder tests (6). The response is given by:

$$x(t) = A(t) \sin(2\pi ft) - B(t) \cos(2\pi ft) \qquad (6)$$

where:

$$A(t) = 1/(2\pi mf) \int_0^t F(\tau) \cos(2\pi f\tau) \, d\tau$$

$$B(t) = 1/(2\pi mf) \int_0^t F(\tau) \sin(2\pi f\tau) \, d\tau$$

and F(t) = the appropriate external loading force at time t.

The velocity and acceleration of the cylinder can then be expressed for each direction respectively as:

$$\dot{x}(t) = 2\pi f\{A(t)\cos(2\pi ft) + B(t)\sin(2\pi ft)\} \qquad (7)$$

$$\ddot{x}(t) = -4\pi^2 f^2 \{A(t)\sin(2\pi ft) - B(t)\cos(2\pi ft)\} + F(t)/m \qquad (8)$$

The external loading force F(t) in the above equations represents the in-line and the transverse force for the in-line and transverse components of motion respectively. These are given by eqn (1), and eqn (2) modified by the Froude-Krylov force $\{\pi/4\ d^2\ \rho\ddot{y}\}$ to take account of the transverse acceleration of the moving cylinder. The flow computation is performed in a reference frame fixed in the cylinder, with the incident velocity input adjusted to take account of the cylinder motion.

4   TEST CASES

The case of oscillatory flow past a flexible cylinder was considered for a range of Keulegan Carpenter numbers (K_C = 6, 8, 10 and 12) at a single value (196) of the β-parameter (d^2/vT), to allow direct comparison with previously computed fixed cylinder cases. To determine the structural response, data regarding the natural period of vibration and the mass of the flexible cylinder were required. Frequency data for various modes of the Christchurch Bay Compliant cylinder, have been measured in both air and water. The mass of the cylinder was not known exactly but could be estimated on the basis of available frequency data.
In air f_a = 0.66 Hz ,

while in water f_w = 0.49 Hz
and it follows that

$$m\ =\ m_w\ /\ \{\ (f_a/f_w)^2\ -\ 1\ \}$$

where $m_w\ =\ \pi/4\ \rho d^2$, the added mass due to the water. Thus, for example, for the fully compliant mode (F6), the estimated mass per unit length, m = 222.2 kg/m.

The program was set up and run for two simulated ratios of cylinder natural frequency in water, to the planar incident oscillatory flow frequency simulating the wave:

$f_w.T$ = 2.0   and   6.0.

These corresponded to cases F6 (cylinder fully free) and F1 (cylinder fully locked) respectively. The value of $f_w.T$ = 2.0 was used because this was a value in the region of which a large cylinder response was obtained

at a Keulegan-Carpenter number of 8 in the compliant cylinder tests.

5   RESULTS AND DISCUSSION

Figure 1 shows the time history of in-line and spanwise force, and Figure 2 is the vortex distribution at t/T = 4.5 for K_C = 6. In this case the frequency ratio $f_w.T$= 6.0, so that the cylinder is equivalent to the fully locked mode. During the run, the maximum displacements were small, 0.025d and 0.005d in the in-line (x) and transverse (y) directions respectively. The vortex patterns and force histories for this case at K_C = 6 are not visibly different from those for the rigid cylinder at the same K_C .

Figures 3 and 4 show the time history of loading and the vortex distribution at t/T = 6.75 for the case of K_C = 6, at a frequency ratio of $f_w.T$ = 2.0 for the fully compliant mode. The force history shows minimal transverse loading over the first 3 cycles consistent with negligible transverse motion of the cylinder shown in Figure 5. Thereafter, the cylinder begins to respond, reaching x = 0.25d and y = 0.23d, and leading to a rapid increase in the loading on the cylinder. It is clear that for a full assessment of the effect of cylinder response on loading in this case the run should have been continued longer. However this was difficult to achieve at the time on the workstation used for these computations.

For K_C = 8, 10 and 12 with $f_w.T$ = 2.0, the results are shown in Figures 6, 7, 8, and 9. In these cases, the cylinder response starts much earlier, is stronger and becomes fully developed over the period of the run, as indicated in Figures 8 and 9. The loading on the compliant cylinder is significantly increased compared with the rigid cylinder at the same values of K_C . Maximum displacements are seen to reach x/d = 1.31 and y/d = 0.66 at K_C = 12. The time histories of response also show the increasing influence of the higher frequencies generated by the vortex shedding from the cylinder. The transverse response is not surprisingly dominated by components from the vortex induced lift spectrum, but the in-line response also shows strong evidence of influence from these components.

© IMechE C416/023 1991

The full set of results which were obtained from the computations are summarised in Figure 10. This shows the inertia and drag coefficients computed from the time histories, ignoring the first period of each computation during which the cylinder response was still small. These coefficients are compared with the values obtained for a rigid cylinder using the same computational method with the same values of the numerical discretisation parameters. In the lower part of the same figure the response of the cylinder in the in-line and transverse directions is also shown. The force coefficients for the case $f_w.T = 6$ and $K_C = 6$ are not shown since they were indistinguishable from the rigid cylinder results. It is clear from these results that the increasing response of the cylinder is accompanied by an increase in the drag coefficient above the rigid cylinder value at the same value of K_C. The inertia coefficient is similarly increased except at $K_C = 6$, where it apparently decreases. However this anomolous behaviour may be due to error in the values of the force coefficients which were obtained from an insufficient duration of the flow computation, as noted above.

The large scale tests in the DHL flume (6) also suggested a monotonic increase in drag coefficient with displacement, given very approximately in the above K_C range by:

$$C_D = C_D(rigid) + 2.5 \ y_{RMS}/d$$

This result for the large scale cylinder starts from a much lower, probably supercritical, value of $C_D = 0.4$. By comparison the best fit to the present results gives, for a subcritical β parameter of 196:

$$C_D = C_D(rigid) + 1.75 \ y_{RMS}/d$$

in the KC range studied, over which $C_D(rigid)$ varies but is always > 1.0. However, experiments carried out on a small scale pendulum mounted cylinder in a U-tube (9) show that when the cylinder was constrained to move transversely only the response, for a frequency ratio of 2.0 as in the computations, peaked in the region of $K_C = 8.0$ to 10.0 depending on the level of damping, which was very low in this experiment, with the peak value in the region of $y_{RMS}/d = 0.3$. But this

frequency ratio did not give the largest response, a significantly larger one being obtained at the non-integral frequency ratio of 2.72. Force measurements from these compliant cylinder experiments do also indicate a large increase in $C_{F\ RMS}$ with cylinder displacement for the latter frequency ratio. But the increase is much larger than that indicated by the linear relation suggested above based on the computed results.

The differences between the large scale experimentally measured results and the small scale computed results may be associated with the apparently earlier onset with increasing K_C of significant asymmetry and hence transverse force in the large scale cases, both rigid and compliant. Separation on the large scale section is likely to occur at considerably different locations compared with the sub-critical cases.

The computations also show a significant increase in C_M with transverse displacement at $K_C = 10$ and 12. This is not apparent in the large scale measurements (6). However, this effect coupled with the smaller increase in the computed values of C_D with displacement compared with the large scale, means that the increase in $C_{F\ RMS}$ with transverse displacement is similar in the two cases. It is therefore possible that the main difference between the two cases at small and large Reynolds number may be a change in the phase of the force increase with displacement. But this conclusion can only be tentative because phase is quite sensitive to the way in which the force coefficients are calculated from the time histories and there is a suggestion with some of the present computations that the runs have not been continued for a sufficiently long time after the impulsive start.

The computed results show a possible indication of y_{RMS} peaking in the neighbourhood of $K_C = 10 - 12$ at a value of somewhat less than 0.3 diameters, in qualitative agreement with the measured results. But computations at higher K_C, which should be carried out in the future, would be necessary to confirm this.

The in-line response is predicted by the

computations to rise continuously with increasing K_C, which agrees with the measured data. However the rate of rise is quite rapid above $K_C = 6$ giving larger in-line responses than measured. This might be explained in the case of the large scale compliant cylinder in waves by the mode shape and wave velocity profile which cause sections of the cylinder at different depths to see different relative in-line velocities. But the predicted in-line displacements are also larger than those measured on the pendulum mounted cylinder (9) undergoing rigid translatory motion in a U-tube with a uniform incident flow. In this case the main difference is that in the computations two degrees of freedom, in-line and transverse occur together, whereas in the experiment the cylinder was constrained to perform in-line motion only.

6 CONCLUSIONS

The computations show a significant increase in the in-line flow induced forces, due to an oscillatory flow acting on a cylinder when it is free to move in-line and transversely, compared with the case when it is rigid. The results are qualitatively similar to those measured at low Reynolds number in a water tunnel and to those obtained on a large scale compliant cylinder experiment in waves. But there is not the same clear evidence of the response peaking which is seen in the measurements and the predicted levels of response and increase in C_D are smaller. An increase in C_M with transverse displacement is also predicted by the numerical simulation which is not apparent in the measured data. In-line response is predicted to increase with K_C, but the predicted increase is larger than that measured.

7 ACKNOWLEDGEMENT

This work was carried out with the support of SERC through MTD Ltd, and of the Offshore Industry.

REFERENCES

1. Sarpkaya T. Hydroelastic response of cylinders in harmonic flow. Proc. RINA. Spring Meeting, 1979.
2. Bearman P.W. and Hall P.F. Dynamic response of circular cylinders in oscillatory flow and waves. Proc. Int. Conf. Flow Induced Vibrations, Bowness-on-Windermere, 1987, p183, BHRA.
3. Maull D.J. and Kaye D. Oscillations of a flexible cylinder in waves. Proc. 5th Int. Conf. Behaviour of OffShore Structures, Trondheim, 1988, p535, Tapir.
4. Borthwick A.G.L. and Herbert D.M. Loading and response of a small diameter flexibly mounted cylinder in waves. Jnl. Fluids Structures, Vol. 2, No. 5, 1988, p479.
5. McConnell K.G. and Park Y.S. The frequency components of fluid lift forces acting on a cylinder oscillating in still water. Experimental Mechanics, Vol.22, No. 6, 1982, p216.
6. Bearman P.W. Wave loading experiments on circular cylinders at large scale. Proc. 5th Int. Conf. Behaviour of OffShore Structures, Trondheim, 1988, p471, Tapir.
7. Bearman P.W., Graham J.M.R. and Obasaju E.D. A model equation for the transverse forces on cylinders in oscillatory flow. App. Ocean Res. Vol. 6, 1984, p166.
8. Verley R.I.P. Oscillations of cylinders in waves and currents. PhD. Thesis, Loughborough Univ., 1980.
9. Bearman P.W. and Mackwood P. Hydroelastic response in oscillatory flow. Final report on Project A04, MTD Fluid Programme 87/89, 1989
10. Skomedal N.G., Teigen P. and Vada T. Computation of vortex induced vibration and the effect of correlation on circular cylinders in oscillatory flow. Proc. 8th Int. Conf. OMAE., The Hague, 1989, p311.
11. Graham J.M.R. Computation of viscous separated flow using a particle method. Num. Meth. for Fluid Dyn. III, Ed. Morton W. and Baines M., Oxford Science Pub.,1988.
12 Bearman P.W., Chaplin J.R., Graham J.M.R., Kostense J.-K., Hall P.F. and Klopman G. The loading on a cylinder in potential flow beneath periodic and random waves. Proc. 4th Int. Conf. Behaviour of OffShore Structures, Delft, 1985, p213, Elsevier.

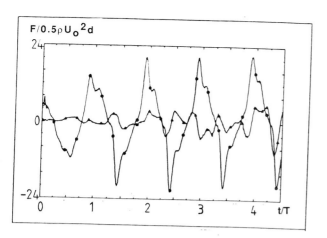

Fig. 1   Time history of in-line and transverse forces, K_C = 6, $f_w.T$ = 6.0, β = 196.   In-line = O, transverse = Δ

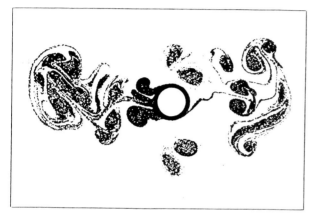

Fig. 2   Vortex distributions at t/T = 4.5, as fig. 1.

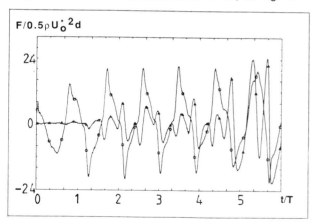

Fig. 3   (as fig. 1) with $f_w.T$ = 2.0

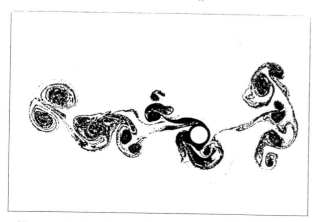

Fig. 4   Vortex distributions, as fig. 3.   t/T = 6.75

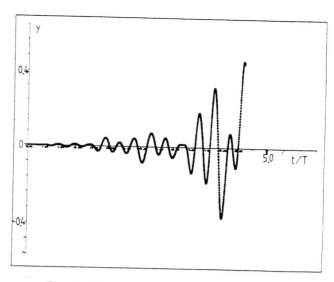

Fig. 5   Time history of tranverse displacement of cylinder, as fig. 3.

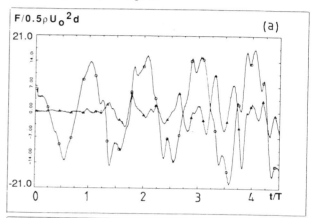

(a)

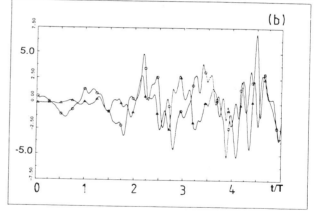

(b)

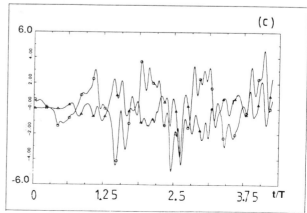

(c)

Fig. 6   (as fig. 1) with $f_w.T$ = 2.0, (a) K_C = 8, (b) K_C = 10, (c) K_C = 12

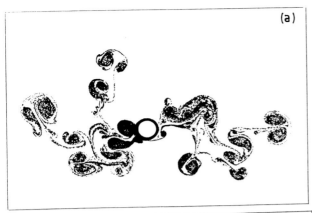

(a)

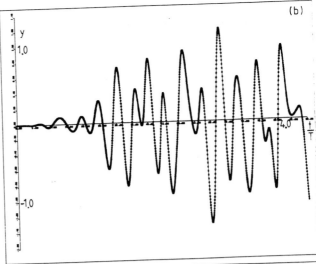

(b)

(b)

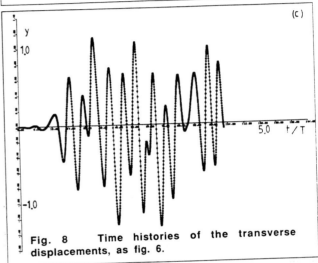

(c)

Fig. 8 Time histories of the transverse displacements, as fig. 6.

(c)

Fig. 7 Vortex distributions as fig. 6, at (a) $K_C = 8$, $t/T = 4.5$, (b) $K_C = 10$, $t/T = 4.5$, (c) $K_C = 12$, $t/T = 4.05$.

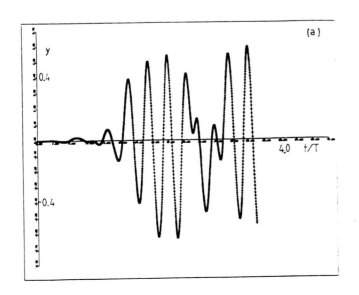

(a)

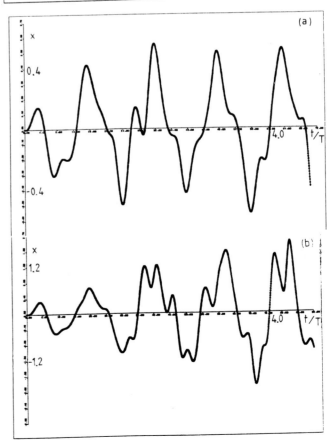

(a)

(b)

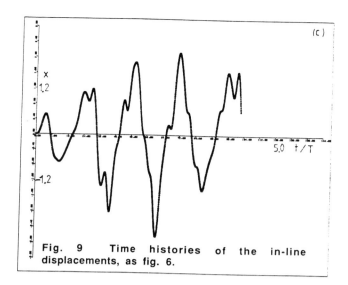

Fig. 9 Time histories of the in-line displacements, as fig. 6.

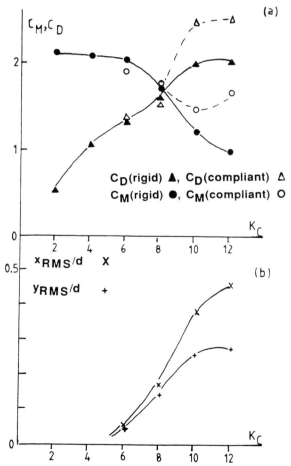

Fig. 10 (a) Drag and Inertia coefficients for the rigid and compliant cylinders and (b) in-line and transverse displacements for the compliant cylinder as functions of K_C.

Thermoelastic instabilities of fast reactor fuel pins

J HEINECKE, Dipl-Ing and G WEBER, Dipl-Ing
Interatom GmbH, Bergisch Gladbach, Germany

SYNOPSIS   The phenomenon named thermo-elastic instability leading to fuel pin oscillations in sodium cooled fast reactors is desribed. The computer code PATT developed to analyse the problem and it's application on in-pile and out-pile experiments is outlined. Technical solutions to avoid these oscillations are presented.

1   Introduction

In fuel subassemblies irradiated in the German experimental sodium cooled fast reactor KNK II/2 at the Karlsruhe Research Center, operating with it's second core since June 1983, wear on fuel pins and spacer grids has been observed in the course of the post irradiation examinations: Due to mechanical interaction between fuel pins and spacer grids the clad thickness of the pins has been reduced up to 50 % and the thickness of the spacer straps has been partly reduced to such amount, that some grid cells have been broken; the axial distribution of wear intensity, common for all the pins, starts in the heated fuel zone, increases steadily to its maximum at the upper part of the heated zone and decreases towards the top of the pin; the intensity of wear decreases from the center of the pin bundle with 127 pins arranged in a triangular array towards the peripheral pins. Although a certain small amount of wear is well known being caused by flow induced vibrations of the fuel pins and is usually tolerated, the observed behaviour seemed to be in contradiction to the results of numerous outpile tests performed on a variety of subassemblies in sodium and water.

A detailed analysis of all experimental findings revealed that this wear is not caused by flow induced vibrations but by "pin movements due to fluid-thermoelastic coupling". This phenomenon is characterized by low-frequency oscillations of the fuel pins within their grid cell clearances initiated by lateral movements of the pins. Along the heated length of 600 mm the temperature of the coolant increases by about 230 K. Due to the clearances between pins and grids and the free axial span between spacers the pins have the freedom to move and to bow. This leads to a coolant flow redistribution around the circumference of the pins and subsequently to a new coolant temperature distribution and a new temperature gradient field developing along the pins. These temperature gradients induce new pin bowing and new deflections, which produce a new temperature field again. Depending on the conditions concerning geometry, power and flow this process can lead to thermo-elastic instabilities and permanent oscillations.

This paper describes in detail the phenomenon and the calculational route of the computer code PATT developed to analyse the problem. By postprocessing the results of PATT the oscillating pin can be visualized on the screen of a personal computer. The results of investigations to identify the key parameters controlling the process of oscillation are explained. The calculational results are compared with in-pile experimental results of the CABRI-test-facility and out-pile experimental results of the THIBO-test-facility. Finally technical solutions, which are forseen for the new KNK II fuel subassemblies to avoid the occurance of this phenomenon, are presented.

2   Experimental results

An experiment, where temperature oscillations and pin movements have been measured, was a LOF test (Loss Of Flow) with an irradiated single fuel pin in the CABRI-test-facility. The pin of 7.6 mm diameter was fixed at the bottom in a tube of 12 mm inner diameter and was suggested to be centered inside the tube by spacers at different axial levels. Of course, as the pin has been irradiated, the gaps between the bowed and enlarged pin (by irradiation induced swelling and creep) and the spacers have been designed with relative large clearances, so that the pin had some freedom to move by bowing. The upper three spacer were designed with flexible dimples but zero clearance in order to have contact with the pin in any case.

At the start of the test the fuel pin was in a stable position. But as the coolant flow has been reduced, leading to a rise of the temperature increase, coolant temperature oscillations in the range of maximum ± 70 K occured, once the temperature increase had passed a certain threshold. It was clear, that these temperature oscillations were caused by pin movements, as they could clearly be identified with a hodoscope measuring the fuel movements. The experimentators called these pin movements "pin warping", the same effect, which is named here "thermo-elastic instabilities". The pin warping resembled an upwards directed wave, with a wave length of about 50 cm and period of about 4 to 5.5 s. The amplitudes of the motion were larger than the spacer clearances. From this, it was concluded that the tube with the attached spacers performed some warping too.

There was another experiment in the CABRI-test-facility which showed also pin warping, indicated by temperature oscillations. But, as this TOP experiment (Transient Over Power) was designed for a fresh fuel pin, the clearances between pin and spacer could be kept small, so that the measured temperature oscillations were much smaller than in the experiment mentioned above.

This arrangement of a single pin in a tube seemed to be a simple geometric configuration for further studies both from the theoretical and experimental point of view. So an out-pile experiment was decided upon to demonstrate the thermo-elastic instabilities.

This experiment was performed at the Karlsruhe Research Center. It was named THIBO (THIBO is the German acronym for: thermohydraulisch-induzierte Brennstaboszillationen, which means: thermohydraulic induced fuel pin oscillations) (1,2).

Both the CABRI experiment and the THIBO experiment have been investigated using a theoretical model, to identify the physical effects and to find the key parameters gouverning the process of pin movements due to thermo-elastic instabilities.

3 Theoretical model

The theoretical considerations start from a very simple model to get a clear insight into the phenomenon of the thermo-elastic instabilities. An internally heated pin, being fixed in tube at two axial spacer levels, is cooled by longitudinal flow. The pin is loaded with a certain temperature difference along it's circumference developing along it's length. This temperature difference will lead to pin bowing, which increases the temperature difference and consequently enhances the bowing. In this simple model the bowing will increase and increase for a spacer distance larger than a critical value. Real fuel pins in the reactor are of course not fixed in two axial spacer levels only, but in up to about ten or even more spacer levels and the heated zone covers only a part of the total pin length.

3.1 Simple model

A first model, in which simplified functional relationships between temperature difference and bowing, respectively bowing and temperature difference, were incorporated, considering the whole pin length with different axial levels of spacers, results in bowing deflections and temperature differences which never correspond to each other. A new calculated temperature difference based on the old bowing deflection always changes the bowing deflection and consequently the temperature difference. This iterative process did never converge in this

simple model. But, as for simplification no clearances between spacers and pins have been taken into account, this process works only, if unrealistic amplification factors for the feed-back function between temperature difference and bowing deflection are considered. For physically realistic factors, the process, being started by means of an artificial bowing, stops immediately after some iterations leading to a straight pin and no temperature differences. An iterative procedure is absolutely necessary, as a closed solution for cases with more than two spacer levels cannot be found.

The results obtained with this first simple model revealed that fuel pins can be subjected to thermo-elastic instabilities as stable solutions could not be found. But, of course, a more sophisticated theoretical model is to be used, especially to model more realistic cases with pins spaced by a series of grids which have clearances between their dimples and the pins. These clearances introduce a larger degree of freedom for the pin by allowing a lateral movement of the pin in addition to the bowing of the pin.

3.2 Detailed model

In order to limit the effort for developing a new model, it was decided to use computer codes, which are already established in the core design, to solve the problem in a short time. Two codes have been selected, see Fig 1: The subchannel analysis code C3CLM for the thermohydraulic calculations and the core restraint code FIAT for the mechanical calculations.

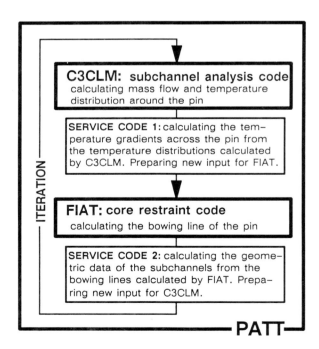

Fig 1 Iterative scheme of C3CLM and FIAT

C3CLM (3) is an improved version of the well known steady-state and non-steady-state subchannel code COBRA IIIC adapted to liquid metal applications. It is used to calculate the temperature distribution in the coolant and the pin all along it's length and circumference taking into account changes of the coolant channel geometry, as caused by the bowing and lateral movement of the pin, developing along the pin length.

FIAT (4), originally developed to solve static core restraint problems, is used to calculate the bowing line of the pin on basis of the temperature field produced by C3CLM. The bowing calculation is restricted to a two-dimensional model.

In a first step these two codes have been applied successively in an iterative scheme linked together via small service codes to manage the data transfer from code to code.

The non-steady-state option of C3CLM has not yet been used. The purpose of these calculations was to find out, if stable solutions could be found, where bowing deflection and temperature difference fit together. It was assumed, that a case without stable solution is a probable candidate for thermo-elastic instabilities.

This model, of course, was checked by calculations using the non-steady-state option of C3CLM, i.e. the transient development of the temperature field around the pin was taken into account. The pin bowing itself was assumed to follow the temperatures instantaneously. This required, that the essential parts of FIAT and the the service codes had to be implemented in C3CLM forming a new code called PATT. (PATT is the German acronym for: Programm zur Analyse des thermischen Taumelns, which means: code for the analysis of thermal staggering. Moreover PATT is the German word for stalemate). Due to the required very small time steps leading to very large code running times, these check calculations have been restricted to few cases.

Most progress in the "theoretical understanding" of the thermo-elastic instability problem hase been made by performing calculations using the steady-state option seeking for the stable solutions.

Two other approaches to solve the problem of pin movements due to thermo-elastic instabilities have been presented in (5,6).

The application of these tools on the experiments and on the KNK II subassembly design will be shown in the following.

4   Evaluation of experiments

4.1   CABRI-experiments

Fig 2 shows the radial layout of the calculational model used for the evaluation of the CABRI-experiment.

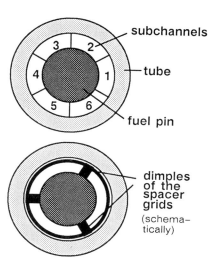

Fig 2   Radial layout of the CABRI-experiment

The thermohydraulic solution considers all six subchannels around the pin, taking into account turbulent and diversion crossflows and heat conduction between them. The bowing deflection is calculated in one azimutal plane only, as the mechanical code is restricted to a 2d-solution. This 2d-model has the advantage, that calculational results can be interpreted much easier than the results of a 3d-model. On the other hand, if one obtaines thermo-elastic instabilities already in a 2d-model, it is expected, that this is even more likely to happen using a three dimensional model, as the degree of freedom of the pin is higher when adding the third dimension.

Fig 3 gives a description of the details of the figures following later in the text:

-   On the left side the length of the pin and the position of the heated zone is indicated.

-   The thin line represents the axis of the straight pin.

-   The thick line represents the axis of the bowed pin. The deflection is scaled up in comparison to the pin length.

-   The black triangles indicate the positions of the dimples of the spacers, the distance between triangles and the thin axis is a measure for the clearance between pin and dimples of the spacers.

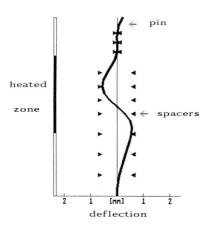

Fig. 3 Description of the details of the figures

Fig 4 shows the results of the first 14 iterations of the C3CLM-FIAT iterative scheme of the CABRI-LOF-experiment seeking for a stable solution using the steady-state option of C3CLM.

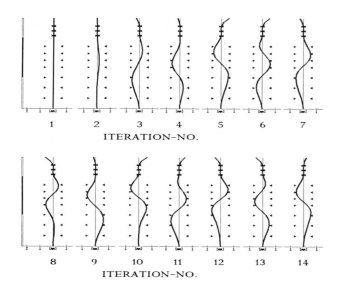

Fig 4   CABRI, C3CLM-FIAT iterative scheme

The iteration starts with a straight pin, for which the thermohydraulic calculation results in a small temperature difference, as the channel obstructions due to the spacing grids are not symmetrical around the pin. This small temperature difference is sufficient large enough to start the bowing process. Already after three iterations, the bowing line is fully developed and from iteration to iteration new bowing lines are created, which contours really shift upwards like a wave. This phenomenon, which was measured in the experiment, can be calculated by the model in spite of the simplification by restricting to the steady-state option.

To handle the large amount of resulting data from the calculations, an animation code was developed, which shows the development of the bowing lines from iteration to iteration. Using an interpolation scheme a continuously moving pin is visualized on the screen of a small personal computer.

Temperature oscillations and pin movements are calculated with the model very similar to the experimental observations. What couldn't be calculated, was the start of the oscillation after a certain threshold of the temperature increase of the coolant has been exceeded. The theoretical model predicted oscillations for any value of the temperature increase, only amplitudes of the deflections and the temperature oscillations were changing with changing temperature increase. It must be remembered, that the CABRI-LOF-experiment was performed with an irradiated pin, which distortion was not taken into account in the calculation. It may be, that the irradiation induced bowing of the pin has led to a clamping of the pin inside the tube, which could be overridden only, if a threshold of the temperature increase has been exceeded.

The presence of the smaller temperature oscillations, which has been observed during another CABRI-TOP-experiment with a fresh fuel pin and much smaller clearances between pin and spacers, has been confirmed by the calculations.

4.2   THIBO-experiments

The THIBO-Experiment was built up on purpose very similar to the CABRI-geometry. An electrically heated pin with a diameter of 7.6 mm and an axial length of 1510 mm was placed in a tube with a diameter of 12 mm. The pin is fixed at the bottom and spaced radially by 8 spacers with adjustable dimples. The spacer levels are arranged as in the KNK-reactor, the adjustable dimples allow to simulate different clearances between pin and dimples. The experimental results are presented in detail in (1,2).

The operational data like power, mass flow rate and temperature are taken close to the data in the reactor. It took some time, to generate conditions leading to thermo-elastic instabilities. Calculations which were performed, revealed, that the experiment set-up has to be built very accurately to get the pin oscillating. Temperature gradients coming from non-symmetrical heat losses of the test facility or a pre-bowed pin resulting from the fabrication process can introduce forces in the pin-spacer system, being so large, that movements of the pin due to small changes of temperature gradients, created by the pin itself, are prevented.

But after some modifications and additional tests a configuration with large clearances of about 0.5 mm between pin and spacer was found, which showed the expected pin movements. Only the spacers at the top and at the bottom of the pin had a smaller clearance of about 0.05 mm. The experimental findings were very similar to the CABRI-test. Below a temperature increase between inlet and outlet of the tube of 110 K no thermo-elastic instabilities were observed. Only above this "critical" temperature increase the pin started to move. This could be repeated as often as wanted.

Both, the measured temperatures and the measured pin movements (measured with an X-ray image intensifier system coupled to a video recorder) show a very good agreement to the calculated values. Typical calculational results are shown on the next figures.

Fig 5 shows the bowing line for 0.55 mm clearance between pin and spacer (except for the lower and the last but one of the upper grid with a smaller clearance) calculated with the steady-state option of C3CLM.

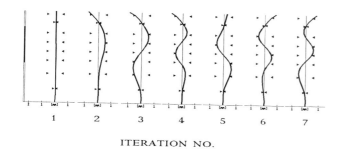

ITERATION NO.

Fig. 5   THIBO,   C3CLM-FIAT iterative scheme

Fig 6b shows the bowing line for an increased clearance of 1.0 mm calculated (this should simulate the possibility of the pin to move inbetween 2 of the 3 dimples located each 120°) calculated with the non-steady-state option, in comparison with the result of the steady-state option, Fig 6a, i.e. iteration no 4 of Fig 5.

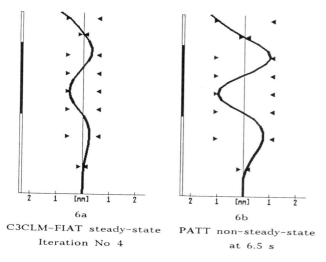

6a	6b
C3CLM-FIAT steady-state	PATT non-steady-state
Iteration No 4	at 6.5 s

Fig. 6   THIBO,   Comparison of steady-state and non-steady-state solutions

The calculation was run with 400 time steps of 0.05 s each, so covering a problem time of 20 s. The calculated frequency was 1 Hz. It can be seen from the comparison of the two figures, that the iterative scheme of the steady-state option gives more or less the same result as the non-steady state option. The lower measured frequency of 0.2 Hz may be explained by the restriction to the two-dimensional bowing model in the calculation and and the fact, that the housing tube of the test section has been found oscillating, too.

5   KNK II calculations

After having checked the model against these two types of experiments it has been applied to the KNK II/2 geometry, where the thermo-elastic instabilities have been observed. The calculations have been performed simulating the fabricational clearance between pin and spacer. The clearance was considered in the two-dimensional bowing model being on one side 0.1 mm in the direction towards the spacer dimples and to be 0.2 mm on the other side in the direction inbetween two spacer dimples placed in a angle of 120°, cf Fig 2.

For this layout the steady-state and non-steady-state option have been applied.

Fig 7 shows the first 14 iterations using the steady-state-option.

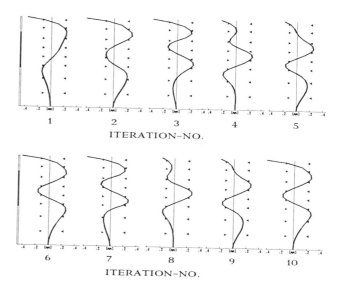

ITERATION-NO.

Fig 7   KNK II/2,   C3CLM-FIAT iterative scheme

Fig 8 shows the comparison of the steady-state solution with the non-steady-state solution.

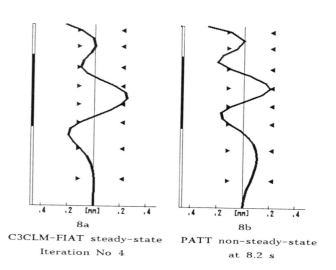

8a	8b
C3CLM-FIAT steady-state	PATT non-steady-state
Iteration No 4	at 8.2 s

Fig. 8   KNK II/2, Comparison of steady-state and non-steady-state solutions

Both solutions result in a permanent pin movement like waves going from the bottom to the top of the pin. The non-steady-state solution shows more pronounced bowing lines. The calculated frequency was about 2.5 Hz.

6 Improved subassembly design for KNK II

As already indicated when describing the experiments, measures to avoid this thermo-elastic instabilities could be:

- to limit the freedom of the pin to move
- to restrain the pins inside the spacer grids

Both measures have been adopted to improve the design of the KNK II subassemblies.

6.1 Flexible dimples

The freedom of the pin to move has been restricted with flexible dimples of the spacers avoiding any clearances. This keeps pin in the centered position if the compliance of the stiffness of the dimples is larger than about 100 N/mm.

The result is given in Fig 9. It should be mentioned, that the dimples shown here do not represent the tips of the flexible part of the dimples but the rigid stops, which limit the displacements to 0.1 mm.

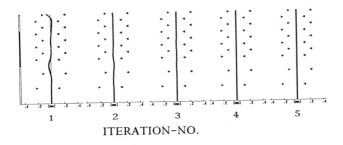

ITERATION-NO.

Fig. 9   KNK II/3   Flexible dimples

Already after four iterations, a given artificial disturbance (temperature gradient of about 20 K) is reduced to zero and the pin is calculated being straight. The bowing of the pin, resulting from the temperature gradient, produces forces, which are too small to create significant bowing of the flexible dimples. So bowing is not increasing from iteration to iteration. On the contrary the flexible dimples enforce the pin to be straight already after 4 iterations.

6.2   Displaced spacers

To restrain the pin by the spacers, the spacers have been displaced at successive axial levels in different directions. The spacer have been displaced in direction of the corners of the hexagonal wrapper tubes and the angle of displacement has been changed from spacer to spacer by 60°. This forces the pin into a spiral shape, to follow the displaced spacers.

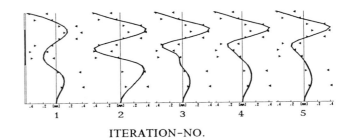

ITERATION-NO.

Fig. 10   KNK II/3   Displaced spacers

The bowing line of the pin resulting from the displacement of the spacers only is shown on Fig 10, iteration No 1. As mentioned, due to the change of the angle of displacement, the pin shows some kind of spiral bowing line, drawn in this 2d-model as wave. Despite the presence of temperature gradients, the pin keeps in general the bowing line forced upon by the spacer displacements. The additional forces created by the restraint bowing due to the temperature gradient are too small to override the mechanical pre-bowing of the pin due to the spacer displacement. A stable situation is achieved.

REFERENCES

(1)   Bojarski, E. et al.   Experimente zu thermohydraulisch induzierten Brennstaboszillationen (THIBO) in natriumgekühlten Reaktoren, Jahrestagung Kerntechnik '89, Düsseldorf, Mai 1989

(2)   Bojarski, E. et al.   THIBO-experiments: thermohydraulically induced fuel rod oscillations in sodium cooled reactors, B.N.E.S. International Conference on Fast Reactor Core and Structural Behaviour, Inverness, June 1990

(3)   Rowe, D.S.   COBRA IIIC, A digital computer program for steady state and transient thermal-hydraulic analysis of rod bundle nuclear fuel elements, BNWL 1695, March 1973

(4)   Urban, K.   Analysis of bowed reactor cores using the FIAT-Program, 4th SMiRT-Conference, San Francisco, 1977

(5)   Preumont, A.   Thermoelastic oscillations of FBR fuel pins. Transactions of the 10th International SMiRT-Conference, Los Angeles, August 1989

(6)   Fabry, J.P. et al.   SATIN, a computer model for the analysis and prediction of thermoelastic vibrations in FBR gridded subassemblies, Transactions of the 10th International SMiRT-Conference, Los Angeles, August 1989

C416/052

Fluid-elastic instability of heat exchanger tube bundles: review and design recommendations

M J PETTIGREW, MASME and C E TAYLOR, MSc, MCSME, MASME
Atomic Energy of Canada Limited, Chalk River Laboratories, Ontario, Canada

ABSTRACT Fluidelastic instability is the most important vibration excitation mechanism for heat exchanger tube bundles subjected to cross-flow. Most of the available data on this topic have been reviewed from the perspective of the designer. Uniform definitions of critical flow velocity for instability, damping, natural frequency and hydrodynamic mass were used. Nearly 300 data points were assembled. We found that only data from experiments where all tubes are free to vibrate are valid from a design point of view. In liquids, fluid damping is important and should be considered in the formulation of fluidelastic instability. From a practical design point of view, we conclude that fluidelastic instability may be expressed simply in terms of dimensionless flow velocity and dimensionless mass-damping. There is no advantage in considering more sophisticated models at this time. Practical design guidelines are discussed.

NOTATION

c_m	—	confinement coefficient
D	—	tube diameter (m)
D_e	—	equivalent diameter (m)
f	—	tube frequency (Hz)
K	—	fluidelastic instability constant
L	—	tube length (m)
L_e	—	tube length subjected to cross-flow
m	—	total tube mass per unit length (kg/m)
P	—	tube pitch (m)
U	—	flow velocity (m/s)
ζ	—	damping ratio
ρ	—	fluid density
ν	—	kinematic viscosity

Subscripts

a	—	air (damping)
c	—	critical
h	—	hydrodyamic (mass)
r	—	reference gap
s	—	structural (damping)
p	—	pitch
t	—	tube (mass)
t	—	total (damping)
v	—	viscous (damping)

1. INTRODUCTION

There are several flow-induced vibration excitation mechanisms that could cause excessive vibration in shell-and-tube heat exchangers. These are: fluidelastic instability, periodic wake shedding resonance, turbulence-induced excitation and acoustic resonance. Of these, fluidelastic instability is by far the most important. In our experience, most heat exchanger tube vibration problems are related to fluidelastic instability.

Excessive vibration due to fluidelastic instability may cause tube failures either by fatigue or by fretting-wear. To avoid such problems, it is necessary to perform a thorough flow-induced vibration analysis at the design stage. This requires sound information and design guidelines on fluidelastic instability.

This paper addresses the question of fluidelastic instability of heat exchanger tube bundles subjected to single-phase cross-flow. Single-phase flow means here both liquid and gas flow. Fluidelastic instability of tube bundles subjected to two-phase (i.e., liquid-vapour) cross-flow is treated in a separate paper (Pettigrew et al. 1989b).

2. NATURE OF FLUIDELASTIC INSTABILITY

Generally in a tube bundle, the fluid forces on one tube are affected by its motion and the motion of neighbouring tubes. This creates an interaction between fluid forces and tube motion. Fluidelastic instability is possible when the interaction between the motions of individual tubes is such that it results in fluid force components that are both proportional to tube displacements and in-phase with tube velocities. Instability occurs when, during one vibration cycle, the energy absorbed from the fluid forces exceeds the energy dissipated by damping. Then, the vibration amplitude of the tube increases rapidly and, in theory, would become extremely large. In practice, the vibration amplitude is limited by the presence of surrounding tubes or by other non-linearities such as clearance hole type support plates.

Figure 1 shows a typical vibration amplitude vs flow velocity relationship for a tube bundle in cross-flow. Beyond a given threshold velocity, the vibration amplitude becomes very large and the tube bundle becomes unstable. The threshold velocity is usually called the critical velocity for fluidelastic instability, U_c.

Fluidelastic instability is very distinct from periodic wake shedding resonance. Periodic wake shedding resonance occurs when the flow velocity is such that the frequency of vortex shedding coincides with the natural frequency of the tube. Such a resonance would disappear if the flow velocity is increased significantly, as shown in Figure 1. This does not happen in the case of fluidelastic instability. A significant increase in flow velocity would simply result in more violent vibration.

During instability, the motion of one tube is somewhat related to the motion of neighbouring tubes. There is usually an organized pattern of tube motion within the tube bundle. This pattern is sometimes called bundle vibration mode. There are many possible modes of vibration for a given bundle, depending on the relative motion and phase of the tubes. Thus, fluidelastic instability may be possible for several bundle modes of vibration. In some cases, the tube motion is mostly in the lift direction, in others, in the drag direction and, sometimes, the motion is orbital. From a practical point of view, the specific bundle mode at which instability is taking place is not important as long as instability is avoided.

The presence of fluidelastic instability is usually characterized by the following features. As already discussed, a sudden large increase in vibration amplitude with increasing flow velocity indicates instability. The motion between adjacent tubes is usually well correlated, suggesting strong hydrodynamic coupling. Also, a sudden change in vibration pattern within the tube bundle is indicative of instability. Finally, the tube vibration response spectra are significantly different during instability. The response peak becomes much narrower, giving the appearance of much reduced damping. This behaviour indicates coupling between fluid forces and tube motion, which is characteristic of fluidelastic instability phenomena. Not all the above characteristics are necessarily present in practical cases, due to a variety of reasons, such as non-linearities. From a practical point of view, we define fluidelastic instability as severe vibration that is not due to periodic wake shedding resonance or to turbulence-induced excitation.

3. FLUIDELASTIC INSTABILITY: EXISTING MODELS

Since the mid 1960's, several models and theories have been proposed to formulate fluidelastic instability in tube bundles subjected to cross-flow. In the simplest theory, fluidelastic instability is expressed in terms of a dimensionless velocity, U/fD, and a dimensionless mass-damping term, $2\pi\zeta m/\rho D^2$, thus:

$$\frac{U_c}{fD} = K\left(\frac{2\pi\zeta m}{\rho D^2}\right)^b \qquad (1)$$

where U_c is the critical velocity for fluidelastic instability, f the tube natural frequency, D the tube diameter, ζ the damping ratio, ρ the density of the fluid, and m the tube mass per unit length, which includes the hydrodynamic mass and the mass of the fluid inside the tube. In the simplest model, the exponent b is 0.5. The fluidelastic instability constant K is usually determined experimentally.

Roberts (1966) was probably the first to discuss fluidelastic instability in cross-flow. He studied the aeroelastic behaviour of a row of cylinders of pitch to diameter ratio P/D of 1.5 in a wind tunnel. He identified the above dimensionless parameters as dominant in the formulation of fluidelastic instability. Although Roberts' expression is somewhat more complicated, an approximate simplified expression

$$\frac{U_{pc}}{fD} = 9.8\left(\frac{2\pi\zeta m}{\rho D^2}\right)^{0.5}$$

may be deduced from his experimental data. In this expression, U_p is the pitch velocity which is defined as:

$$U_p = \frac{U_\infty P}{(P-D)} \qquad (2)$$

where U_∞ is the free stream velocity or the velocity, that would prevail if the tubes were removed.

Connors (1970) was probably the first to study fluidelastic instability in heat exchanger tube bundles. He did his experimental work in a wind tunnel. He proposed a quasi-static model to describe fluidelastic instability. This work led to the formulation of Equation (1) in which $b = 0.5$. Connors reported a fluidelastic instability constant $K = 9.9$ for a tube row of $P/D = 1.41$, which is in agreement with Robert's findings. Unfortunately, because of the lack of other data at the time, the value of $K = 9.9$ was used for tube bundles by some designers.

In the early 1970's, a comprehensive program was undertaken at Chalk River Laboratories to study flow-induced vibration of nuclear heat exchangers. This work was done in collaboration with Canadian industries and universities. Realistic tube bundles of both triangular and square configurations of P/D between 1.23 and 1.57 were tested in liquid flow. This work led to the recommendation of

$$\frac{U_{pc}}{fD} = 3.3\left(\frac{2\pi\zeta m}{\rho D^2}\right)^{0.5} \qquad (3)$$

as a design guideline to avoid fluidelastic instability in heat exchangers. Details may be found in Gorman (1976), Pettigrew et al. (1978) and Pettigrew and Gorman (1978).

Since circa 1975, a number of researchers have studied fluidelastic instability in tube bundles. Several new models have been proposed and a number of design guidelines have been recommended. It is not the purpose of this paper to review all this work in detail. However, we shall discuss some of the more interesting models and in particular, those that are directly relevant to the formulation of practical design guidelines. For additional information, the reader is referred to some excellent reviews by Païdoussis (1983), Chen (1984) and Weaver and Fitzpatrick (1987).

Generally, the research work on fluidelastic instability falls in two categories. The first is aimed at obtaining a basic understanding of fluidelastic instability. This work is usually done on well defined and well instrumented arrays of cylinders, often in wind tunnels because of simplicity, often with only one flexible cylinder in an otherwise rigid array of cylinders, often with externally added damping, sometimes with a single row of cylinders and most of the time with cylinders with well defined support conditions.

The second category, on the other hand, is aimed at producing design information. This type of work is usually done on realistic heat exchanger tube bundles, often in liquid flow, in a few cases in two-phase flow, sometimes with replicated heat exchanger tube support conditions, sometimes on complete, or on sections of, real heat exchangers and mostly in large scale test facilities. While the latter category is much less elegant, it often provides information that is much closer to real heat exchanger designs.

At this time, it is important to review some typical models and design guidelines that have been proposed for fluidelastic instability. These are outlined in Table 1. As already discussed, the simplest model is of the form:

$$\frac{U}{fD} = K\left(\frac{2\pi\zeta m}{\rho D^2}\right)^{0.5} \qquad (4)$$

Based on this model, Pettigrew and Gorman (1978) have recommended $K = 3.3$ as a design guideline for all tube bundle configurations; Chen (1984) recommended $K = 2.35$ for normal square (90°) tube bundles of $(2\pi\zeta m/\rho D^2) > 0.7$ and $K = 2.8$ for rotated triangular (60°) tube bundles of $(2\pi\zeta m/\rho D^2) > 1.0$. A slight variation of this model is:

© IMechE 1991 C416/052

$$\frac{U}{fD} = K\left(\frac{2\pi\zeta m}{\rho D^2}\right)^b \qquad (5)$$

which has been used by Weaver and Fitzpatrick (1987) to recommend: K = 2.5 and b = 0.48 for normal square (90°) tube bundles, K = 4 and b = 0.48 for rotated square (45°) tube bundles, K = 3.2 and b = 0.40 for normal triangular (30°) tube bundles and K = 4.8 and b = 0.3 for rotated triangular (60°) tube bundles in all cases for $(2\pi\zeta m/\rho D^2) > 0.3$; and, b = 0 and K = 1.4, 2.2, 2.0 and 1.0 for the 90°, 45°, 30° and 60° tube bundles, respectively, for $(2\pi\zeta m/\rho D^2) < 0.3$. Chen (1984) used the same formulation to make the recommendation K = 2.1 and b = 0.15 for square bundles below $(2\pi m\zeta/\rho D^2) < 0.7$ and K = 2.8 and b = 0.17 for rotated triangular bundles below $(2\pi m\zeta/\rho D^2) < 1.0$.

A somewhat more sophisticated model has been proposed by several researchers (Chen et al. 1983, Gibert et al. 1977 and Tanaka et al. 1981):

$$\frac{U}{fD} = K(2\pi\zeta)^a \left(\frac{m}{\rho D^2}\right)^b \qquad (6)$$

In this model, the mass term and the damping term are separated. For example, Tanaka et al. (1981) suggested a = 0.20 and b = 0.33 for heavy fluids (liquid) based on testing a square tube bundle of P/D = 1.33.

The addition of a dimensionless parameter including the term P/D has also been proposed by Païdoussis (1981) and Chen (1984), thus:

$$\frac{U}{fD} = K(2\pi\zeta)^a \left(\frac{m}{\rho D^2}\right)^b \left(\frac{P}{D} - C\right)^c \qquad (7)$$

Based on Equation (7), Païdoussis (1981) suggested a design guideline where K = 5.8, a = 0.4, b = 0.4, c = 0.5 and C = 1. Similarly, Chen (1984) proposed K = 3.54, a = 0.5, b = 0.5, c = 1.0 and C = 0.5 for rotated square tube bundles.

Teh and Goyder (1988), and Lever and Weaver (1986) proposed a slightly different version of Equation (5):

$$\left(\frac{U}{fD}\right) = F\left(\frac{2\pi\zeta m}{\rho D^2}\right)^b \qquad (8)$$

where F is a function of several parameters such as Reynolds Number, P/D, tube bundle configuration, turbulence level, etc. The function F is obtained experimentally by Teh and Goyder (1988). It is derived analytically in the case of the Lever and Weaver model.

Not surprisingly, the designer is now confused by the abundance of models and design guidelines. It is the purpose of this paper to review this work and arrive at simple and practical design guidelines.

4. APPROACH

Since our aim is to formulate practical design guidelines, our approach has to be very pragmatic. We have reviewed most of the available data from the literature and some unpublished data from our laboratories. Nearly 300 data points were gathered in a comprehensive database. The experimental parameters extracted from the references are outlined in Table 2. Typical data points from the database are illustrated in Table 3.

The data were compared against the available models to select the most appropriate. Then, conservative but realistic design guidelines were derived from the best fit of the available data to the chosen model. More weight was given to data originating from realistic heat exchanger configurations. Obviously, practical design guidelines must not contradict experience on real heat exchangers.

5. IMPORTANT DEFINITIONS

Inconsistent definition of terms is a significant difficulty in reviewing data from other researchers. Flow velocity, damping, frequency, threshold velocity for instability, etc. are often defined differently. Sometimes important information was missing. Some assumptions were necessary. In other cases, missing parameters could be deduced by calculation. Such assumptions or calculations are noted in Table 3. Uniform definitions of important parameters were adopted in this document, as discussed below. Often the data of a given researcher had to be normalized or corrected to be compatible with the uniform definitions.

5.1 Tube Bundle Configurations

Most heat exchange tube bundles are either of triangular or square configuration. For each configuration, there are two principal tube bundle orientations: normal (30°) and rotated (60°) for triangular bundles, and normal (90°) and rotated (45°) for square bundles. The angle pertains to the flow direction relative to the tube orientation, as shown in Figure 2. In practice, it is very difficult to predict the exact flow direction everywhere in a shell-and-tube heat exchanger. In fact, all flow directions are usually possible in a given heat exchanger. Practical design guidelines must cover the worst tube bundle orientation. Thus, in this document, we often consider the two principal bundle orientations together. This leads to only one set of design guidelines without concern for bundle orientation.

5.2 Flow Velocity Definition

Throughout our research program, we have been using a so-called "reference gap velocity", U_r, to present our results. Many other researchers (e.g., Chen 1984, Weaver and Fitzpatrick 1987) are now using the same velocity definition, although they do not call it reference gap velocity. Pitch velocity has been used recently. Since it is shorter and equally meaningful, we propose to use it in this paper. Thus, regardless of tube bundle configuration or orientation, the reference gap velocity, U_r, or pitch velocity, U_p, is defined as

$$U_r = U_p = U_\infty P/(P-D) \qquad (9)$$

where P is the pitch of the tube bundle and U_∞ the free-stream flow velocity. The so-defined pitch velocity is the true gap velocity for both normal triangular and normal square configurations. It is not for the rotated triangular and the rotated square configurations. For the latter, the pitch velocity is only an indication of the flow velocity between the tubes.

This definition of the velocity has two advantages. Firstly, it enables the designer to compare directly the two principal orientations of a tube bundle from a vibration viewpoint. As already discussed, flow in all directions is usually possible in one or another region of actual heat exchangers. Secondly, vibration excitation forces appear related to the flow velocity between the tubes, and thus, to the pitch velocity.

Some designers use a gap velocity, U_g, in heat transfer and pressure drop calculations. Gap velocity definitions are shown in Figure 2. The pitch velocity can easily be deduced from the gap velocity.

5.3 Critical Velocity for Fluidelastic Instability

Different researchers often use different criteria to determine the critical velocity for fluidelastic instability. For example, Heilker and Vincent (1981) used the velocity at which tube rattling occurred as a criterion, while Soper (1983) used the point at which a tangent to the post-critical response intersected the velocity axis, whereas Teh and Goyder (1988) took the velocity at which the damping appears to be nil. These differences are a great source of disparity in the data. Here again we take a very practical approach. When the instability threshold is well defined, we simply take the flow velocity at which it occurs as the critical instability velocity (see Figure 3a). When it is not well defined, we take the velocity at which excessive vibration amplitude occurs (see Figure 3b). This amplitude is normally between 250 and 750 μm RMS, depending on tube frequency and tube size (i.e., span length and flexural rigidity). Such vibration levels are not normally acceptable in heat exchangers. In our data base development, we have attempted to normalize the results of other researchers to our definition of fluidelastic instability. This was not always easy or even possible because of lack of information.

In cases where the tubes are partially subjected to cross-flow, the flow velocities were normalized to obtain the equivalent uniformly distributed velocity as outlined in Pettigrew et al. (1978).

5.4 Damping

Damping is a great source of controversy for two reasons. Firstly, damping is difficult to measure accurately, particularly in tube bundles. Secondly, different damping definitions have been used by different researchers to analyse their own results (i.e., damping in air, damping in still liquid and damping in flowing fluids). In gases, damping values in air are acceptable since fluid damping is not significant. In liquids, we use damping values in still liquids. The reasons for this will be discussed in the next section of this paper. Since damping values in liquids were not always available, it was sometimes necessary to calculate liquid damping to complete the database, as shown in Table 3. This was done using the damping formulation of Pettigrew et al. (1986).

5.5 Tube Frequency

To analyze the data, the tube frequency in air was used in gases; the tube frequency in still liquid was used in liquids. When the tube frequency in liquid was not given, it was calculated by taking into account the effect of hydrodynamic mass as formulated by Pettigrew et al. (1989a).

6. PARAMETRIC DEPENDENCE STUDY

The purpose of this section is to identify the more important parameters by correlating them against the available data. This will lead to the formulation of the most suitable practical model for fluidelastic instability.

6.1 Flexible vs Rigid Tube Bundles

Some experiments were done with realistic tube bundles where all the tubes were free to vibrate. Other more fundamental experiments were done on one flexible tube in an otherwise rigid array of tubes. Are the latter experiments appropriate to generate design data? Gorman (1977) was probably the first researcher to look at this question. He tested brass tubes, which are more flexible, in an array of steel tubes in liquid flow. He found that instability occurred at an effectively 20% greater flow velocity for the single flexible tube. Recently, we have completed a series of experiments on both flexible tube bundles and single flexible tubes in rigid arrays (Pettigrew et al. 1989). We found instability took place at a slightly higher flow velocity (i.e., ≈10% higher) for the single flexible tube experiments. Teh and Goyder (1988) have conducted elegant experiments on a single flexible cylinder constrained to vibrate in the lift direction only. The single flexible cylinder was installed in several otherwise rigid arrays of different configurations subjected to air flow in a wind tunnel. He found reasonable agreement with the results of Soper (1983) in similar arrays of flexible cylinders in the same wind tunnels. Thus, it can be said that in some cases, the difference is not large.

On the other hand, some researchers have reported considerable differences in behaviour between single and multiple flexible cylinder arrays. For example, Figure 4 compares the vibration response of one flexible tube to that of seven flexible tubes for a rotated triangular array (Lever and Rzentkowski, 1988). The critical velocity for fluidelastic instability is significantly different. Andjelic and Popp (1989) arrived at similar conclusions for a normal triangular array.

In Figure 5a, we present all the fluidelastic instability data for bundles with all flexible tubes in terms of the dimensionless critical velocity, U_{pc}/fD, and the mass-damping parameter, $2\pi\zeta m/\rho D^2$. A line at K = 3.0 and b = 0.5 has been drawn to represent the overall trend in the data for further comparison. Figure 5b presents Teh and Goyder's data for a single flexible cylinder in normal triangular tube arrays. Price and Païdoussis' (1987) results for a single flexible cylinder in a normal square rigid array of P/D = 1.5 are shown in Figure 5c. Comparison of Figure 5a against 5b and 5c clearly indicates that the fluidelastic instability behaviour is generally different for flexible tube bundles than for a single flexible tube in an otherwise rigid array of tubes. For the latter tube arrays, the relationship between dimensionless flow velocity and dimensionless mass-damping is far from simple and is somewhat discontinuous between liquid flow and gas flow regions. Thus, for the purpose of formulating design guidelines, only the data for all flexible tube bundles are considered.

6.2 Damping

In gases, structural damping (mostly friction and impact damping at the support) is the dominant energy dissipation mechanism, Pettigrew et al. (1986). Fluid damping is not significant except perhaps for very dense gases. Thus, we generally use damping values in air for data analysis.

Fluid damping is much more important in liquids. Some researchers do not consider fluid damping in their analysis. A possible reason is that it is very difficult to measure in tube bundles because of hydrodynamic coupling, etc. Another reason is that, at fluidelastic instability, damping appears very small, which is characteristic of fluidelastic instability phenomena. However, this is not necessarily a valid reason to ignore fluid damping. Looking at the problem a different way, it can be said that, below critical flow velocities for instability, the tube bundle is stable largely because of fluid damping. Thus the latter may very well be a governing parameter in fluidelastic instability phenomena.

© IMechE 1991 C416/052

Some researchers have reported that the exponent, b, in Equation (5) becomes smaller for lower values of the mass-damping parameter (see Table 1). This trend has been observed in particular by Tanaka et al. (1981) for data points below $2\pi\zeta m/\rho D^2 < 0.2$ while testing a square tube array in water flow. Structural damping only was used in their analysis of these data. We have calculated the still fluid damping for this case using the formulation of Pettigrew et al. (1986). The fluidelastic instability results considering fluid damping are compared to the original analysis in Figure 6a. Interestingly, the results now fit well around a straight line of exponent b = 0.5.

In Figure 5a, all the data for flexible tube bundles are presented in terms of the mass-damping parameter $2\pi\zeta m/\rho D^2$ in which the damping ratio, ζ, includes still fluid damping. The same data are compared to that considering structural damping only in Figure 6b. It shows that the data collapse better around a straight line when fluid damping is considered. Thus, it is desirable to consider fluid damping in the formulation of fluidelastic instability. We also arrived at the same conclusion while analysing fluidelastic instability data for two-phase flow, Pettigrew et al. (1989).

Flow dependent damping is another aspect of the damping question. It is not normally a dominant damping mechanism under heat exchanger conditions. Chen (1981) has shown that it is directly related to the dimensionless flow velocity, U_p/fD, and that it is practically insignificant for the tube bundles he has tested for $U_p/fD < 3.0$, which is the range of interest for heat exchangers in liquids. Furthermore, it is very difficult to differentiate energy dissipating fluid forces from fluidelastic excitation forces, particularly near instability. Thus, we assume that flow dependent damping is part of the fluidelastic instability phenomenon, since both are related to flow dependent fluid dynamic forces.

It should be pointed out that in fundamental experiments in wind tunnels, the mass-damping parameter is often changed by changing damping. In real heat exchangers, fluid density governs the mass-damping parameter. For example, in high pressure steam, the density may be 100 kg/m^3, whereas in power condensers it may be 0.01 kg/m^3. This is a factor of 10^4, which is simulated in wind tunnel studies by similarly changing damping. Thus, laboratory conditions may be very different than realistic heat exchanger operating conditions (e.g., fluid density, viscosity, Reynolds Number). This should be carefully considered in applying laboratory data to heat exchanger design. For example, data from tests in wind tunnels may not necessarily apply to condensers.

6.3   Pitch-to-Diameter Ratio

Some researchers found the pitch-to-diameter ratio P/D to have a significant effect on fluidelastic instability for some tube bundle configurations. For instance, both Hartlen (1974) and Soper (1983) found the instability factor, K, to increase with P/D for normal triangular and rotated square tube bundles. On the other hand, they found no significant effect of P/D for normal square and rotated triangular tube bundles. Unfortunately, the designer can not take advantage of the effect of P/D, since it does not apply to all tube bundle orientations. In practice, all orientations are possible in a given heat exchanger tube bundle.

The fluidelastic instability factor is plotted against P/D for all the available data in Figure 7a, 7b, 7c and 7d for the normal triangular, rotated triangular, normal square and rotated square tube bundles, respectively. It shows that, although there is a trend with P/D in some cases, the trend is not general and, thus, cannot be used for practical design guidelines. Thus, P/D is not taken into account in the recommended fluidelastic instability formulation.

6.4   Fluidelastic Instability Formulation

Figure 5a would suggest a fluidelastic instability formulation of the form

$$\frac{U_p}{fD} = K\left(\frac{2\pi\zeta m}{\rho D^2}\right)^{0.5}$$

The exponent b = 0.5 seems very appropriate as it follows the data reasonably well over values of the mass-damping parameter covering some five decades.

An attempt was made to explore the suitability of more sophisticated models. As discussed in Section 3, several authors suggested a model of the form:

$$\frac{U_p}{fD} = K(2\pi\zeta)^a \left(\frac{m}{\rho D^2}\right)^b$$

Values of the damping exponent a between 0.2 and 0.3 have been suggested. Thus, the model

$$\frac{U_p}{fD} = K(2\pi\zeta)^{b/2} \left(\frac{m}{\rho D^2}\right)^b$$

was tried on the data as shown in Figure 8. A line with the slope of b = 0.5 has been drawn as a lower envelope of the data. This corresponds to a damping exponent a = 0.25. Generally, the agreement with the data is no better than for the simpler model. The more sophisticated model may fit some of the data better, as suggested by several researchers. However, this is not generally true. Thus, we have no reason at this time to recommend more sophisticated models. Also, as shown in Figure 9 and 10, a mass-damping parameter exponent of b = 0.5 generally fits the data well. Thus, we recommend the simple fluidelastic instability formulation

$$\frac{U_{pc}}{fD} = K \left(\frac{2\pi\zeta m}{\rho D^2}\right)^{0.5}$$

as a practical design guideline. We now have to choose an appropriate value for the instability constant, K, as discussed next.

7.   DEVELOPMENT OF DESIGN GUIDELINES

The data are presented in terms of dimensionless flow velocity and dimensionless mass-damping in Figure 9 for both triangular and square tube bundles. We now have to choose an appropriate instability constant K as a design guideline. To take a lower envelope of all data would be unrealistic and overly conservative. The scatter in the data is often due to unrepresentative laboratory conditions (very high or low damping, etc.) or to non-uniform definitions of terms, as already discussed. Thus, to avoid unduly penalizing the designer with extreme data points, we propose to take roughly a "lower decile" line through the data. We believe this is a conservative and realistic approach.

This approach leads to an instability constant K = 3.0, as shown in Figure 9a and 9b, for triangular tube bundles and in Figure 9c and 9d for square tube bundles. It may be deduced from Figure 9a and 9b that twelve data points out of 108 are below the K = 3.0 line for triangular tube bundles. Thus roughly 90% of the data is above K = 3.0, which corresponds to the lower decile line. Similarly for the square tube bundles, five data points out of 93 are below the K = 3.0 line (see Figures 9c and 9d). Thus more than 90% of the data are above K = 3.0.

The data of Chen and Jendrzejczyk (1981), shown in Figure 9c, were not considered in the above analysis, since most of these data are for rectangular (not square) arrays. However, had it been considered, it would not have changed the above guideline. Some results by Hartlen (1974) were also not considered, since they were qualified by the author as being preliminary and tentative. These results were obtained with plastic tubes with very high damping. However, all other results by Hartlen (1974) were considered.

All the data points for all tube bundles are presented in Figure 10. The "lower decile", K = 3.0, design guideline is also shown. Only 17 out of 200 points are below that line. All these seventeen data points may be put in question for a variety of reasons, such as insufficient information, unrealistic damping and ill-defined critical velocity for instability. However, they are not necessarily in error. On the other hand, all data points from realistic situations, such as Halle's (1986 and 1988) data on real multispan heat exchanger tube bundles, Godon's (1988) data on real condenser configurations in steam flow, Gorman's (1976) and Pettigrew and Gorman's (1978) data on realistic tube bundles in liquid flow and Eisinger's (1980) data on actual steam reheaters, are above K = 3.0.

Interestingly, Figure 10 covers a range of mass-damping parameters from 5×10^{-2} to 5×10^3, which is a factor of 10^5! It includes data from highly damped light cylinders in liquid flow, heat exchanger tubes in liquid flow, tube bundles in high pressure high density steam flow, tube bundles in wind tunnels and condenser tube bundles in very low pressure, low density steam flow.

Since the mid-seventies, hundreds of heat exchangers for the Canadian nuclear industry have been designed following similar guidelines (i.e., K = 3.3). These guidelines are also used for non-nuclear heat exchangers by most Canadian manufacturers and by many manufacturers in the USA and elsewhere. To our knowledge, none of the heat exchangers designed according to the above guidelines have failed, and all those that did fail did not satisfy the above guidelines.

The performance of ten operating heat exchangers was reviewed and compared against the above design guidelines, Pettigrew and Campagna (1979). Both failure histories and satisfactory performances were considered, as shown in Figure 11. It confirms that the above design guidelines are a reasonable design criterion. Many more such comparisons have been done since that time with similar results.

8. CONCLUDING REMARKS

Most of the available data on fluidelastic instability in tube bundles subjected to single phase cross-flow have been reviewed. These data were compared against the existing expressions to formulate fluidelastic instability. From a practical design point of view, it is concluded that:

1) Fluidelastic instability may be expressed in terms of dimensionless flow velocity, U/fD, and dimensionless mass-damping $2\pi\zeta m/\rho D^2$.

2) A simple expression of the form:

$$\frac{U_{pc}}{fD} = K \left(\frac{2\pi\zeta m}{\rho D^2}\right)^{0.5} \text{ is appropriate for design}$$

purposes.

3) A fluidelastic instability constant K = 3.0 is a reasonable design criterion for both square and triangular tube bundles.

4) Although the effect of pitch-to-diameter ratio, P/D, is significant in some cases, the trend is not general. Thus, the term P/D could not be included in the fluidelastic instability expression.

5) Fluid damping should be included in the mass-damping parameter.

6) At the present time, there is no advantage in considering more sophisticated fluidelastic instability models.

ACKNOWLEDGEMENTS

The authors have benefitted from discussions with Prof. D.S. Weaver of McMaster University, Canada. The Heat Transfer and Fluid Flow Service (HTFS), the CANDU Owners Group (COG) and Atomic Energy of Canada Limited have supported this work. Their contributions are gratefully acknowledged. Prof. D.J. Gorman of the University of Ottawa greatly contributed to our initial experimental program.

REFERENCES

Abd-Rabbo, A. and Weaver, D.S. (1986) "A Flow Visualization Study of Flow Development in a Staggered Tube Array", *Journal of Sound and Vibration, Vol. 106*, pp. 241-256.

Andjelic, M., and Popp, K. (1989), "Stability Effects in a Normal Triangular Cylinder Array", *Journal of Fluids and Structures 3*, 165-185.

Axisa, F., Villard, B., Gibert, R.J., Hetsroni, G., and Sundheimer, P., (1984), "Vibration of Tube Bundles Subjected to Air-Water and Steam-Water Cross-Flow: Preliminary Results on Fluidelastic Instability", *Proceedings of ASME Symposium on Flow-Induced Vibrations, Vol. 2*, pp 269-284, New Orleans.

Bai, D., (1982), "Flow-Induced Vibrations of Multi-Span Tube Bundles of Large Condensers" Experimental Studies on Full-Scale Models in Steam Cross-Flow", *Vol. 1, Proceedings of the Third Keswick International Conference on Vibration on Nuclear Plant*, Keswick, G.B., pp 217-230.

Carlucci, L.N., and Brown, J. (1983), "Experimental Studies of Damping and Hydrodynamic Mass of a Cylinder in Confined Two-Phase Flow", ASME J. of Vibration, Acoustics, Stress and Reliability in Design, Vol. 105, 83-89.

Chen, S.S. (1981) "Fluid Damping for Circular Cylindrical Structures", *Journal of Nuclear Engineering and Design, Vol. 63*, pp. 81-100.

Chen, S.S. (1984) "Guidelines for the Instability Flow Velocity of Tube Arrays in Crossflow", *Journal of Sound and Vibration, Vol. 93*, pp. 439-455.

Chen, S.S., and Jendrzejczyk, J.A., (1981), "Experiments on fluidelastic instability in tube banks subjected to liquid cross-flow", *Journal of Sound and Vibration, Vol. 78 (3)*, pp 355-381.

Chen, S.S. and Jendrzejczyk, J.A. (1983), "Stability of Tube Arrays in Cross Flow", *Journal of Nuclear Engineering and Design, Vol. 75*, No. 3, June, pp. 351-373.

Connors, H.J. (1970), "Fluidelastic Vibration of Tube Arrays Excited by Cross Flow", *Flow-Induced Vibration in Heat Exchangers*, ASME-WAM New York, pp. 42-56.

Connors, H.J. (1978), "Vibration of Heat Exchanger Tube Arrays", *ASME Journal of Mechanical Design, Vol. 100,* April, pp. 347-353.

Connors, H.J. (1980), "Fluidelastic Vibration of Tube Arrays Excited by Non-uniform Cross-Flow", *Flow Induced Vibration of Power Plant Components, ASME Publication PVP-41,* August, pp. 93-107.

Eisinger, F.L., (1980), "Prevention and Cure of Flow-Induced Vibration Problems in Tubular Heat Exchangers", *ASME Journal of Pressure Vessel Technology, Vol. 102,* pp 138-145.

El-Kashlan, M. (1984) "Array Geometry Effects on Vortex Shedding and Instability in Heat Exchanger Tube Bundles", *Ph.D. Thesis,* McMaster University, Canada.

Gibert, R.G., Chabrerie, J., and Sagner, M. (1977) "Vibrations of Tube Arrays in Transversal Flow", Paper F 6/3, *Transactions of the 4th International Conference on Structural Mechanics in Reactor Technology,* San Francisco, USA, August 15-19.

Godon, J.L., (1984), "Flows and Flow Induced Vibrations in Large Condensers", *Vol. 3 - Vibration in Heat Exchangers,* ASME Winter Annual Meeting, New Orleans, USA, pp 1-16.

Godon, J.L., and Lebret, J., (1988), "Influence of the Tube Support Plate Clearance on Flow-Induced Vibration in Large Condensers", *Vol. 5 - Flow-Induced Vibration in Heat Transfer Equipment,* ASME Winter Annual Meeting, Chicago, USA, pp 177-186.

Gorman, D.J., (1976), "Experimental Development of Design Criteria to Limit Liquid Cross-Flow-Induced Vibration in Nuclear Reactor Heat Exchange Equipment", *J. Nuclear Science and Engineering, Vol. 61,* pp 324-336.

Gorman, D.J. (1977) "Experimental Study of Peripheral Problems Related to Liquid Flow-Induced Vibration in Heat Exchangers and Steam Generators", Paper F6/2, *Proceedings, 4th International Conference on Structural Mechanics in Reactor Technology,* San Francisco, USA.

Halle, H., Chenoweth, J.M., and Wambsganss, M.W., (1986), "Shellside Flow-Induced Tube Vibration in Typical Heat Exchanger Configurations; Overview of a Research Program", *Flow-Induced Vibration - 1986, PVP-Vol. 104, Proceedings of ASME-PVP Conference,* Chicago, USA, pp 161-169.

Halle, H., Chenoweth, J.M., and Wambsganss, M.W., (1988), "Shellside Waterflow-Induced Tube Vibration in Heat Exchanger Configurations with Tube Pitch-to-Diameter Ratio of 1.42", *Vol. 5 - Flow-Induced Vibration in Heat Transfer Equipment,* ASME Annual Meeting, Chicago, USA, pp 1-16.

Hartlen, R.T. (1974), "Wind-Tunnel Determination of Fluid-Elastic Vibration Thresholds for Typical Heat-Exchanger Tube Patterns", *Ontario Hydro Research Report 74-309-K,* August.

Heilker, W.J., and Vincent, R.Q., (1981), "Vibration in Nuclear Heat Exchangers Due to Liquid and Two-Phase Flow", *ASME Journal of Engineering for Power, 103,* pp 358-365.

Johnson, D.K. and Schneider, W.G. (1984), "Flow-Induced Vibration of a Tube Array with an Open Lane", *Proceedings of ASME Symposium on Flow-Induced Vibrations, Vol. 3, Vibration in Heat Exchangers,* December, New Orleans, pp. 63-72.

Lever, J.H. and Rzentkowski, G.(1988), "An Investigation into the Post-Stable Behaviour of a Tube Array in Cross-Flow, *Proceedings of the International Symposium on Flow-Induced Vibration and Noise, Vol. 3,* pp. 95-110, ASME-WA Meeting, Chicago, USA.

Lever, J.H. and Weaver, D.S. (1986) "On the Stability of Heat Exchanger Tube Bundles, Part I: Modified Theoretical Model", *Journal of Sound and Vibration, Vol. 107,* No. 3, pp. 375-392.

Lubin, B.T., Letendre, R.P., Quinn, J.W., and Kenny, R.A., (1986), "Comparison of the Response of a Scale Model and Prototype Design Tube Bank Structure to Cross-Flow Induced Fluid Excitation", *Flow Induced Vibration - 1986, PVP-Vol.104, Proceedings of ASME PVP Conference,* Chicago, pp 171-177.

Minkami, K., and Ohtomi, K., (1987), "Flow Direction and Fluid Density Effects on the Fluidelastic Vibrations of a Triangular Array of Tubes", *Paper B2, International Conference on Flow Induced Vibrations,* Bowness-on-Windermere, England, pp 65-75.

Nakamura, T., Yamaguchi, N., Tsuge, A., Fujita, K., Sakata, K., and Saito, I., (1986a), "Study on Flow Induced Vibration of a Tube Array by a Two-Phase Flow (1st Report: Large Amplitude Vibration by Air-Water Flow)", *Trans. of Japanese Society of Mechanical Engineers, Vol. 52,* No. 473, C.

Nakamura, T., Fujita, K., Kawanishi, K., and Saito, I., (1986b), "A Study on the Flow Induced Vibration of a Tube Array by a Two-Phase Flow (2nd Report: Large Amplitude Vibration by Steam-Water Flow), *Trans. of Japanese Society of Mechanical Engineers, Vol. 52,* C.

Païdoussis, M.P. (1981) "Fluidelastic Vibration of Cylinder Arrays in Axial and Cross-Flow: State of the Art", *Journal of Sound and Vibration, Vol. 76,* pp. 329-360.

Païdoussis, M.P. (1983) "A Review of Flow-Induced Vibrations in Reactors and Reactor Components", *Journal of Nuclear Engineering and Design, Vol. 74,* No. 1, January, pp. 31-60.

Pettigrew, M.J., and Campagna, A.O. (1979), "Heat Exchanger Tube Vibration: Comparison Between Operating Experiences and Vibration Analyses", *Proceedings IAHR-IUTAM Symposium on Practical Experiences with Flow-Induced Vibrations,* Karlsruhe, Germany, September 3-6, also *Atomic Energy of Canada Limited Report AECL-6785.*

Pettigrew, M.J. and Gorman, D.J. (1977) "Experimental Studies on Flow-Induced Vibration to Support Steam Generator Design, Part III: Vibration of Small Tube Bundles in Liquid and Two-Phase Cross Flow", Paper No. 424, *International Symposium on Vibration Problems in Industry,* Keswick, U.K., also *Atomic Energy of Canada Limited Report AECL-5804.*

Pettigrew, M.J. and Gorman, D.J. (1978) "Vibration of Heat Exchange Components in Liquid and Two-Phase Cross-Flow", *Proceedings of the B.N.E.S. Conference on Vibration in Nuclear Plant,* Keswick, U.K., Paper 2:3, also *Atomic Energy of Canada Limited Report AECL-6184.*

Pettigrew, M.J., Kim, B.S., Taylor, C.E., and Tromp, J.H. (1987), Unpublished Chalk River Laboratory data.

Pettigrew, M.J., Rogers, R.J. and Axisa, F. (1986) "Damping of Multispan Heat Exchanger Tubes - Part 2: In Liquids", *Symposium on Special Topics of Structural Vibration, Vol. 104,*
pp. 89-98, ASME Pressure Vessels and Piping Conference, Chicago, July.

Pettigrew, M.J., Sylvestre, Y., and Campagna, A.O. (1978) "Vibration Analysis of Heat Exchanger and Steam Generator Designs", *Nuclear Engineering and Design, Vol. 48*, pp. 97-115.

Pettigrew, M.J., Taylor, C.E. and Kim, B.S. (1989a) "Vibration of Tube Bundles in Two-Phase Cross-Flow - Part 1: Hydrodynamic Mass and Damping", *ASME J. of Pressure Vessel Technology, Vol. 111,* pp. 466-477.

Pettigrew, M.J., Taylor, C.E., Tromp, J.H. and Kim, B.S. (1989b) "Vibration of Tube Bundles in Two-Phase Cross-Flow - Part 2: Fluidelastic Instability", *ASME J. of Pressure Vessel Technology, Vol. 111,* pp. 478-487.

Price, S.J. and Païdoussis, M.P. (1987) "The Flow-Induced Response of a Single Flexible Cylinder in an In-line Array of Rigid Cylinders", *Proceedings of International Conference on Flow-Induced Vibrations*, Bowness-on-Windermere, England, May, pp. 51-63.

Remy, F.N. (1982) "Flow Induced Vibration of Tube Bundles in Two Phase Cross Flow", BNES Internaitonal Conference on Vibration in Nuclear Plant, Keswick, U.K., Log No. 68.

Remy, F.N. and Bai, D. (1982) "Comparative Analysis of Cross-Flow Induced Vibrations of Tube Bundles", Paper F3, *International Conference on Flow-Induced Vibrations in Fluid Engineering*, Reading, England, September 14-16.

Roberts, B.W. (1966) "Low Frequency, Aeroclastic Vibrations in a Cascade of Circular Cylinders", Mechanical Engineering Science, Monograph No. 4, September, pp. 1-29.

Scott, P.M., "Flow Visualization of Cross-Flow Induced Vibration in Tube Arrays", *M. Eng. Thesis*, McMaster University, Hamilton, Ontario, 1987 April.

Soper, B.M.H. (1983) "The Effect of Tube Layout on the Fluid-Elastic Instability of Tube Bundles in Cross-flow", *ASME Journal of Heat Transfer, Vol. 105*, pp.744-750, November.

Tanaka, H. and Takahara, S. (1981) "Fluidelastic Vibration of a Tube Array in Cross-Flow", *Journal of Sound and Vibration, Vol. 77*, pp. 19-37.

Teh, C.E. and Goyder, H.G.D. (1988) "Data for the Fluidelastic Instability of Heat Exchanger Tube Bundles", *Vol. 3 - Flow-Induced Vibration and Noise in Cylinder Arrays*, ASME-WAM, Chicago, pp. 77-94.

Weaver, D.S. and Abd Rabbo, A. (1985) "A Flow Visualization Study of a Square Array of Tubes in Water Cross-Flow", *ASME J. Fluids Engineering, Vol. 107*, pp. 354-363.

Weaver, D.S., and El-Kashlan, M., (1981), "The Effect of Damping and Mass on Flow-Induced Response of Various Tube Arrays in Water", Journal of Sound and Vibration, Vol. 76, pp. 283-293.

Weaver, D.S. and Fitzpatrick, J.A. (1987) "A Review of Flow Induced Vibrations in Heat Exchangers", *Proceedings of the International Conference on Flow Induced Vibrations*, Paper A1, Bowness-on-Windermere, England, pp. 1-17.

Weaver, D.S., and Grover, L.K. (1978) "Cross-Flow Induced Vibrations in a Tube Bank-Turbulent Buffeting and Fluid Elastic Instability", *Journal of Sound and Vibration, Vol. 59,* No. 2, pp. 277-294.

Weaver, D.S. and Koroyannakis, D. (1982) "The Cross-Flow Response of a Tube Array in Water - A Comparison with the Same Array in Air", *ASME Journal of Pressure Vessel Technology, Vol. 104*, pp. 139-104.

Weaver, D.S. and Koroyannakis, D. (1983) "Flow Induced Vibrations of Heat Exchanger U-Tubes, A Simulation to Study the Effects of Asymmetric Stiffness", *Journal of Vibration, Stress and Reliability in Design, Vol. 105*, pp. 67-75, also ASME Paper 81-DET-20.

Weaver, D.S. and Yeung, H.C. (1984) "The Effect of Tube Mass on the Flow Induced Response of Various Tube Arrays in Water", *Journal of Sound and Vibration, Vol. 93(3)*, pp. 409-425.

TABLE 1: TYPICAL FLUIDELASTIC INSTABILITY MODELS AND SUGGESTED DESIGN GUIDELINES

Fluidelastic Instability Model	Author	Suggested Design Guidelines					Applicability		Comments
		K	a	b	c	C	$\left(\dfrac{2\pi\zeta m}{\rho D^2}\right)$	Bundle Type	
$\dfrac{U}{FD} = K\left(\dfrac{2\pi\zeta m}{\rho D^2}\right)^b$	Pettigrew and Gorman (1978)	3.3	-	0.5	-	-	All	All	
	Connors (1978)	2.9	-	0.5	-	-	All	90°	P/D = 1.42
	Chen (1984) " " "	2.35 2.80 2.10 2.80	- - - -	0.5 0.5 0.15 0.17	- - - -	- - - -	> 0.7 > 1.0 < 0.7 < 1.0	90° 60° 90° 60°	
	Weaver and Fitzpatrick (1987) " " " " " " "	2.5 4.0 3.2 4.8 1.4 2.2 2.0 1.0	- - - - - - - -	0.48 0.48 0.40 0.30 0 0 0 0	- - - - - - - -	- - - - - - - -	> 0.3 > 0.3 > 0.3 > 0.3 < 0.3 < 0.3 < 0.3 < 0.3	90° 45° 30° 60° 90° 45° 30° 60°	
$\dfrac{U}{FD} = K(2\pi\zeta)^a\left(\dfrac{m}{\rho D^2}\right)^b$	Tanaka et al. (1981) "	- -	- 0.2	0.5 0.33	- -	- -	< ~ 2.0 < ~ 2.0	90° 90°	P/D = 1.33 P/D = 1.33
$\dfrac{U}{FD} = K(2\pi\zeta)^a\left(\dfrac{m}{\rho D^2}\right)^b\left(\dfrac{P}{D} - C\right)^c$	Paidoussis (1981)	5.8	0.4	0.4	0.5	1	All	All	
	Chen (1984) " "	3.54 3.58 6.53	0.5 0.1 0.5	0.5 0.1 0.5	1.0 1.0 1.0	0.5 0.9 0.9	All < 2.0 > 2.0	45° 30° 30°	
	Connors (1978)	1.76	0.5	0.5	1.0	- 0.21		90°	P/D > 1.41
$\dfrac{U}{FD} = F(...)\left(\dfrac{2\pi\zeta m}{\rho D^2}\right)^b$	Lever and Weaver (1986)	-	0.5	0.5	-	-			F (...) is derived analytically
	Teh and Goyder (1988)	-	0.5	0.5	-	-			F (...) is obtained experimentally

TABLE 2: SUMMARY OF REFERENCES AND TUBE BUNDLE GEOMETRIES

Test Series	Reference	Bundle Orientation (degrees)	P/D	L (m)	(Le) (m)	D (mm)	t (m)	Material	m_t (kg/m)	End Condition †
Remy82	Remy (1982) Remy & Bai (1982)	90	1.44	1.0	(0.144)	10.0	1.0	304 L	0.220	1
						19.05	1.0	S S	0.720	7
Nak86a	Nakamura (1986a)	90	1.42			19.05	1.0	S S	0.720	7
Nak86b	Nakamura (1986b)	90	1.42			19.05	2.0	acrylic	0.278	5
Sop83	Soper (1983)	30, 60 45, 90	1.25, 1.27 1.35, 1.52, 1.78	0.456		25.4, 25.0			0.177	
Axisa84	Axisa et al. (1984)	90	1.44			19.05	1.09	I600	0.492	1
H&V81	Heilker & Vincent (1981)	30, 60 45, 90	1.33, 1.36 1.41, 1.50	0.914		22.0, 19.05 22.2	1.2, 1.22 1.27	I800 I600	0.631, 0.577 0.706	4
P&G77	Pettigrew & Gorman (1977)	30, 60, 90	1.5 1.47	1.22 0.914	(0.051) (0.051)	12.7 12.9 13.0	0.76 1.12 1.07	S S I600 S S	0.319 0.439 0.330	4 5
Pett87	Pettigrew et al. (1987)	30, 60 45, 90	1.22, 1.35 1.47	0.6						4
Chen81	Chen & Jendrzejczyk (1981)	90, 60	1.35, 1.52 1.5, 1.6	0.914	(0.305)	15.90	3.18	Brass		
Con78	Connors (1978)	30, 60, 90	1.41, 1.69, 2.12			18, 24				7
Con80	Connors (1980)	30, 60	1.32, 1.25			24				7
J&S84	Johnson & Schneider (1984)	60	1.5			15.9				4
Lub86	Lubin et al. (1986)	90	1.55	0.325		17.0	3.5	S S		1
W&K82	Weaver & Koroyannakis (1982)	60	1.375	0.305		25.4	1.02	Al	0.367	2
W&K83	Weaver & Koroyannakis (1983)	60	1.375	0.305		25.4		acrylic	0.607	2
W&AR85	Weaver&AbdRabbo (1985)	90	1.50	0.305		25.4		acrylic	0.607	2
AR&W86	AbdRabbo & Weaver (1986)	45	1.41	0.305		25.4		acrylic	0.607	5
Scot87	Scott (1987)	45, 90 30, 60	1.7, 1.33, 1.5 1.375, 1.73	0.305		25.4			0.607	2
W&G78	Weaver & Grover (1978)	60	1.375	0.305		25.4			0.115	2
W&EK81	Weaver & ElKashlan (1981)	60	1.375	0.305		25.4	0.38, 1.65 1.25, 2.41, 3.05	Al, SS Brass	0.157, 0.325 0.889, 1.18 0.151, 1.78	2
W&Y84	Weaver & Yeung (1984)	90, 45 30, 60	1.5	0.316		12.7		acrylic, Al, Brass		2
M&O87	Minkami & Ohtomi (1987)	30, 60	1.3	0.335	(0.20)	12.0		S S	0.920	5
Gor76	Gorman (1976)	30, 60 90, 45	1.33, 1.54 1.36, 1.3	0.94		19.05 13.0	1.17 1.68	S S		6
P&G78	Pettigrew & Gorman (1978)	30, 60 90, 45	1.57, 1.23 1.47, 1.50	0.94		19.05 13.0	1.17 1.68	S S		4
Hal86	Halle et al. (1986)	30, 60 90, 45	1.25			19.05	1.2			9
Hal88	Halle et al. (1988)	30, 60 90, 45	1.42			19.05	1.2			9
Eis80	Eisinger (1980)		1.25, 1.3							9
God88	Bai & Godon (1982), (1984), (1988)	30	1.37, 1.42 1.31, 1.41, 1.33			19.0, 26.0 17.0, 18.0	0.4 to 1.0	Ti, Ad/Br Fe/St	0.3 to 1.122	9
Har74	Hartlen (1974)	30, 60 45, 90	1.25, 1.375 1.5, 1.28, 1.4, 1.53	0.762	(0.610)	12.7 12.5 12.2			0.092 0.0565 0.083	1
Tan81	Tanaka & Takahara (1981)	90	1.33	0.3		30			1.62, 1.98	8

† End Conditions:
1) Clamped-Clamped (C-C)
2) One tube plus neighbours are Clamped-Free and all other tubes are C-C
3) One tube is flexible in lift direction and all other tubes are C-C
4) Pinned-Pinned
5) Clamped-Free
6) Clamped-Pinned
7) Clamped-Clamped with piano wire (translation)
8) Unknown
9) Multispan Heat Exchanger Tubes

TABLE 3: TYPICAL DATA POINTS FROM DATABASE ON FLUIDELASTIC INSTABILITY OF TUBE BUNDLES IN SINGLE PHASE CROSS-FLOW

Test Series	Orient.	P/D	Tube Dia mm	Tube Mass kg/m	Mass Freq (air) Hz	Damp Rat (air) %	Density kg/m3	Freq Hz	Damp Rat (tot) %	Tot Mass kg/m	Crit Vel m/s	Mass Damping	Reduced Crit. Vel	FEI Constant	Comments	Footnotes
NakB6a'	90	1.420	19.05	0.720	15.2	0.640	1000.00	12.3	0.990	1.100	0.60	1.89E-01	2.56E+00	5.90		1,2,3,4
NakB6a'	90	1.420	19.05	0.720	25.0	0.610	1000.00	20.2	1.460	1.100	1.45	2.78E-01	3.77E+00	7.15		
NakB6a'	90	1.420	19.05	0.720	30.0	0.740	1000.00	24.3	1.200	1.100	1.92	2.29E-01	4.15E+00	8.68		
AxisaB4'	90	1.440	19.05	0.492		0.200	1000.00	51.0	0.700	0.492	1.10	5.96E-02	1.13E+00	4.64		
AxisaB4'	90	1.440	19.05	0.492		0.200	1000.00	51.0	0.700	0.492	1.60	5.96E-02	1.65E+00	6.74		
AxisaB4'	90	1.440	19.05	0.492		0.200	1.20	75.0	0.200	0.492	21.00	1.42E-01	1.47E+01	3.90		
Pett87'	30	1.220	13.000	0.330		0.200	1000.00	25.4	1.020	0.560	0.68	2.12E-01	2.06E+00	4.47		
Pett87'	60	1.220	13.000	0.330		0.200	1000.00	25.4	1.020	0.560	0.63	2.12E-01	1.91E+00	4.14	not	
Pett87'	45	1.220	13.000	0.330		0.200	1000.00	25.9	0.930	0.540	0.83	1.87E-01	2.47E+00	5.70	published	
Pett87'	90	1.220	13.000	0.330		0.200	1000.00	25.9	0.930	0.540	0.81	1.87E-01	2.41E+00	5.57		
Pett87'	30	1.350	13.000	0.330		0.200	1000.00	25.9	0.940	0.540	0.78	1.89E-01	2.32E+00	5.33		
Pett87'	60	1.470	13.000	0.330		0.200	1000.00	26.2	0.890	0.530	1.10	1.75E-01	3.23E+00	7.71		
Pett87'	90	1.470	13.000	0.330		0.200	1000.00	26.2	0.890	0.530	0.63	1.75E-01	1.85E+00	4.42		
Pett87'	30	1.470	13.000	0.330		0.200	1000.00	26.5	0.840	0.510	0.87	1.59E-01	2.53E+00	6.33		
Con80'	30	1.320	24.00		19		1.20					1.00E+01	1.04E+01	3.29		
Con80'	60	1.250	24.00		19		1.20					1.00E+01	1.45E+01	4.59		
J&S84'	60	1.500	15.90		61.8	0.900	1000.00	44.0	1.650	0.620	1.32	2.54E-01	1.89E+00	3.74		
Lub86'	90	1.550	17.00	0.367	720.0	0.040	1000.00	647.0	0.056	1.330	24.20	2.24E-02	2.20E+00	14.70		
W&K82'	60	1.375	25.40	0.607	40.0	0.140	722.50	22.5	1.100	1.160	0.75	1.24E-01	1.31E+00	3.72		3,4,6
W&K83'	60	1.375	25.40	0.607	21.7		1000.00	15.1	0.645	1.290	0.58	8.10E-02	1.51E+00	5.31		
W&AR85'	90	1.500	25.40	0.607	25.5	0.220	1000.00	16.9	0.590	1.257	1.05	1.07E-01	2.45E+00	7.50		
AR&W86'	45	1.410	25.40	0.607	27.5	0.240	1000.00	16.4	0.600	1.707	1.42	9.77E-02	3.41E+00	10.79		1,3,8
Scot87'	45	1.700	25.40		24.8	0.810	1000.00	16.1	2.100	1.140	0.97	2.33E-01	2.37E+00	4.91		1,3,8
Scot87'	90	1.330	25.40		24.6	0.920	1000.00	16.2	2.700	1.290	0.86	3.39E-01	2.09E+00	3.59		8
Gor76'	30	1.330	19.05				1000.00	40.0	1.000	1.160	3.08	2.01E-01	4.04E+00	9.02		
Gor76'	60	1.330	19.05				1000.00	40.0	1.000	1.160	1.83	2.01E-01	2.40E+00	5.36		6,8
Gor76'	30	1.540	13.00				1000.00	30.0	1.130	0.520	1.36	2.18E-01	3.49E+00	7.46		
Gor76'	60	1.540	13.00				1000.00	30.0	1.130	0.520	1.00	2.18E-01	2.56E+00	5.49		
Hal86'	60	1.250	19.05				1000.00	22.9	3.000	1.030	1.08	5.66E-01	2.48E+00	3.29	multispan	
Hal86'	45	1.250	19.05				1000.00	23.5	3.000	1.030	1.03	5.35E-01	2.30E+00	3.15	baffled	
Hal86'	30	1.250	19.05				1000.00	22.9	3.000	1.090	1.33	5.66E-01	3.05E+00	4.05	tubes	
Hal86'	30	1.250	19.05				1000.00	37.2	3.000	1.090	2.55	5.66E-01	3.60E+00	4.78		6,7

1. m_h was calculated using Equation (11) of Pettigrew et al. (1989a)
2. f or m_h was calculated using equation (2) of Carlucci and Brown (1983)
3. ζ_v was calculated using Equation (1) of Pettigrew et al. (1986)
4. ζ_t was calculated using $\zeta_v + \zeta_s f/f_a$
5. m was calculated from the given mass ratio $(m/\rho D^2)$
6. ζ or m was calculated from the mass-damping parameter $(2\pi \zeta_s m/\rho D^2)$
7. f_a was calculated using beam theory
8. ζ was measured in a still fluid and/or using a single tube
9. c_m was calculated using 1. and 2. above

VIBRATION AMPLITUDE (mm RMS)
PITCH FLOW VELOCITY (m/s)
0
0.5
1.0
1.5
0
1.0
2.0
3.0
INSTABILITY
WAKE-SHEDDING RESONANCE
THRESHOLD
TURBULENCE INDUCED VIBRATION

Figure 1: Vibration Response of a Normal Triangular Tube Bundle of P/D = 1.33 Showing Fluidelastic Instability and Periodic Wake Shedding Resonance, Gorman (1976).

FLOW VELOCITY
NORMAL TRIANGLE (30°)
$U_p = U_g = \frac{U_\infty P}{(P-D)}$
ROTATED TRIANGLE (60°)
$U_g = \frac{3}{2} U_\infty \frac{P}{(P-D)}$
NORMAL SQUARE (90°)
$U_p = U_g = \frac{U_\infty P}{(P-D)}$
ROTATED SQUARE (45°)
$U_g = \frac{U_\infty}{\sqrt{2}} \frac{P}{(P-D)}$
FLOW
P
D

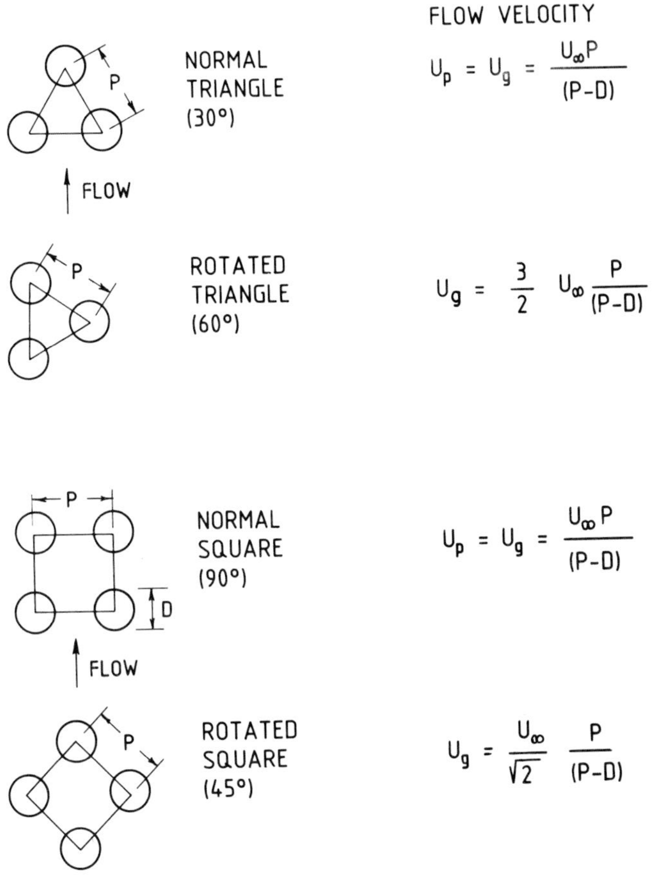

Figure 2: Principal Tube Bundle Configurations

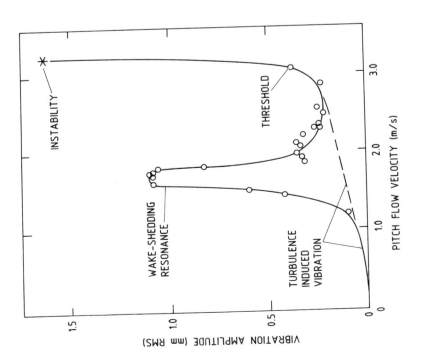

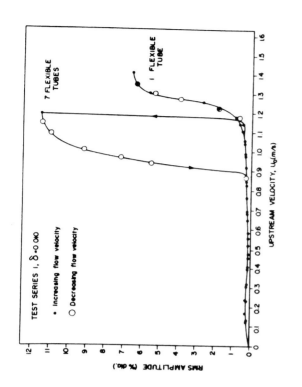

Figure 4: Vibration Response of One Flexible Tube vs Seven Flexible Tubes in 60° Array, Lever and Rzentkowski (1988).

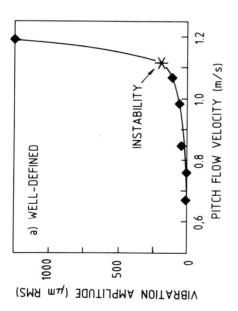

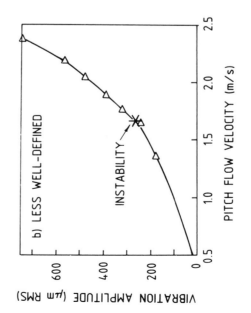

Figure 3: Fluidelastic Instability Thresholds

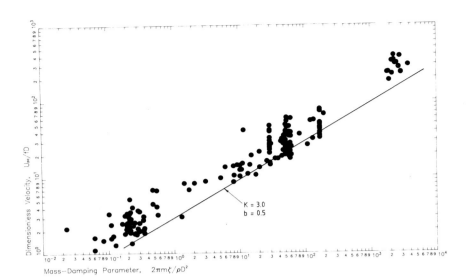

a) All Flexible Tubes

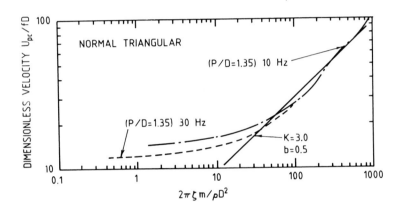

b) A Single Flexible Tube in Normal Triangular Rigid Arrays Subjected to Gas Flow, Teh and Goyder (1988)

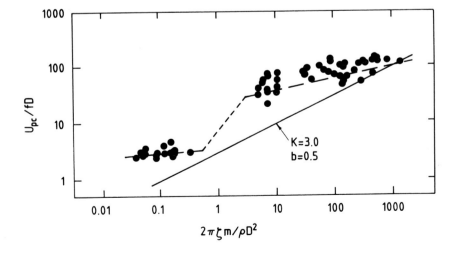

c) A Single Flexible Tube in a Normal Square Rigid Array of P/D = 1.5 Subjected to both Liquid and Gas Flow, Price and Païdoussis (1987)

Figure 5: Effect of Flexible vs Rigid Tube Bundles on Fluidelastic Instability

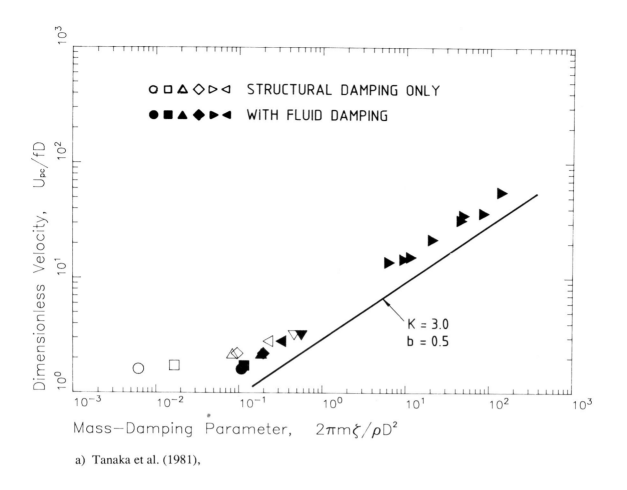

a) Tanaka et al. (1981),

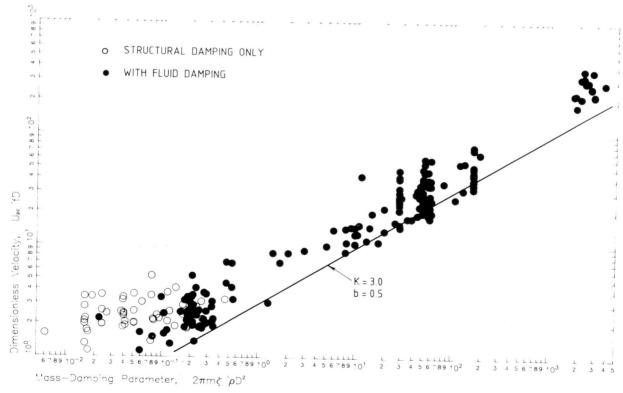

b) Data for Flexible Tube Bundles

Figure 6:   Comparison of Fluidelastic Instability Results with and without Fluid Damping

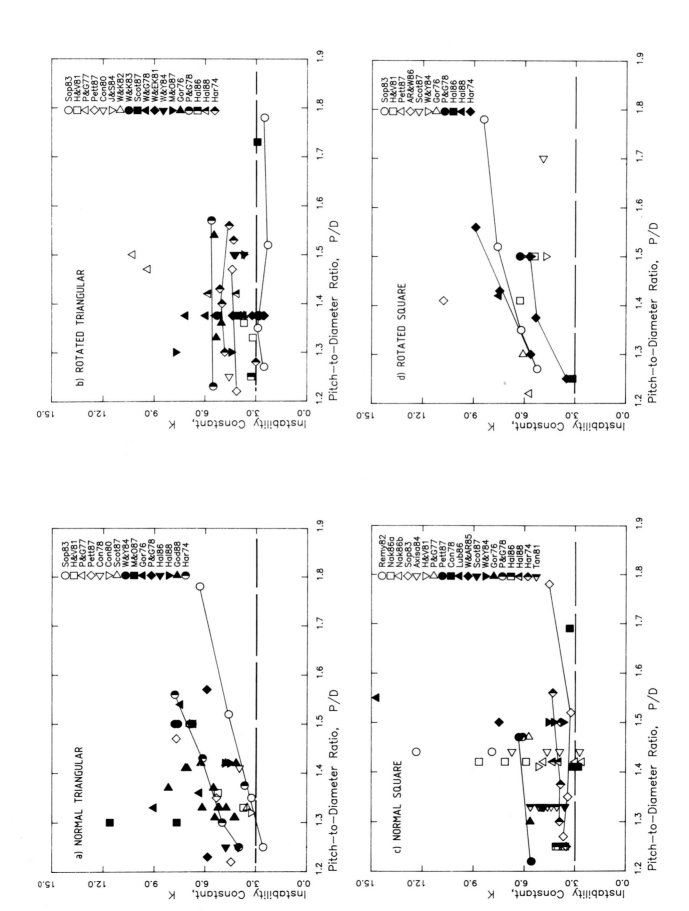

Figure 7: Effect of Pitch over Diameter Ratio on Fluidelastic Instability Constant

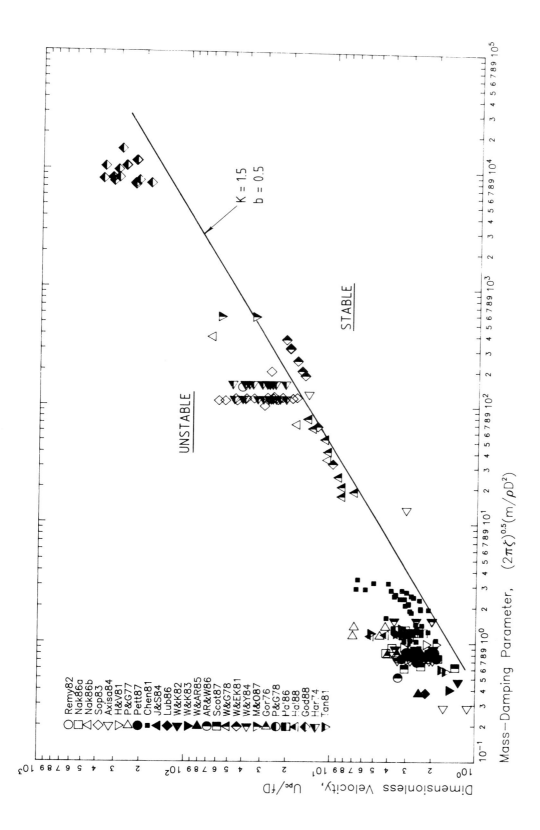

Figure 8: Fluidelastic Instability Data Presented in Terms of Modified Mass-Damping Parameter $(2\pi\zeta)^{0.5} (m/\rho D^2)$

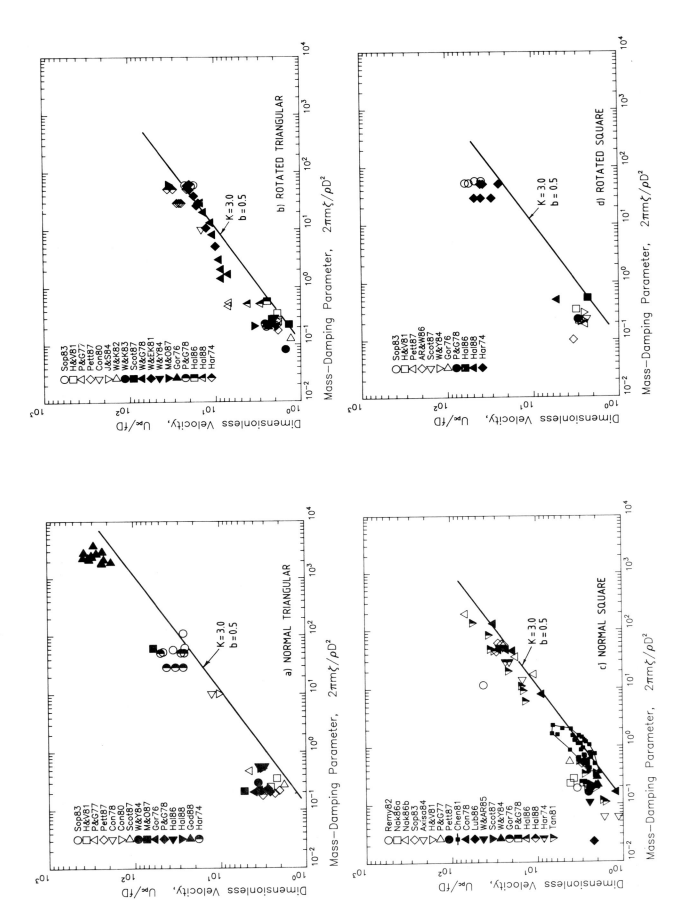

Figure 9: Fluidelastic Instability Data for Different Tube Bundle Geometries:

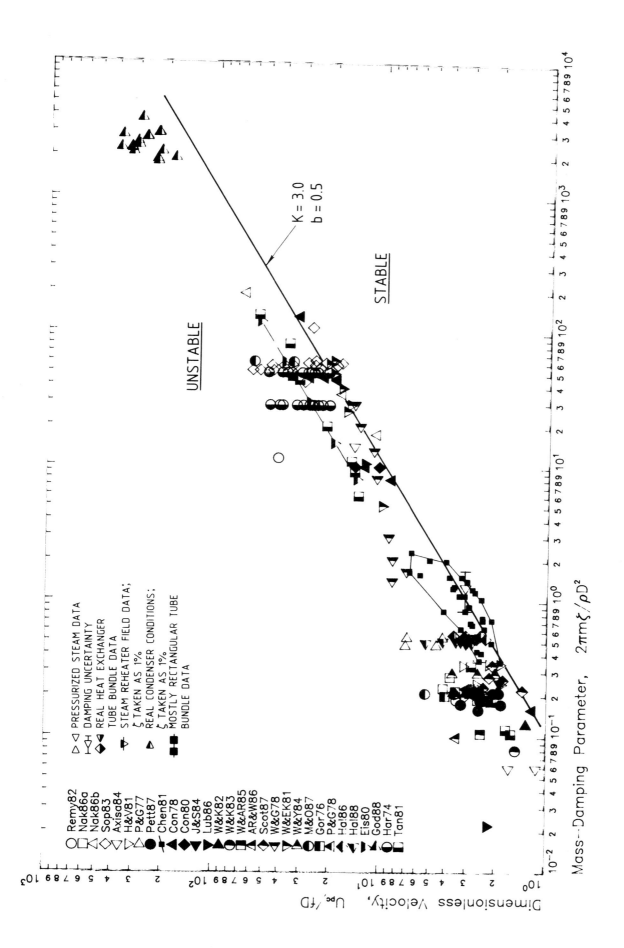

Figure 10: Summary of Fluidelastic Instability Data for All Flexible Tube Bundles Showing Recommended Design Guidelines of K=3.0

CASE NO.	COMPONENT TYPE	REGION	P/D	D (mm)	MODE ORDER	f (Hz)	$\frac{2\pi\zeta m}{\rho D^2}$	$\frac{u_p}{u_{pc}}$
NPSG-1	Steam Generator	Inlet	1.50	12.7	1st	42.5	0.44	1.36
NPSG-2	" "	Outlet	1.50	12.7	1st	48.9	11.75	0.85
DPSG-1	" "	U-tube	1.38	12.7	1st	11.4	16.2	2.27
						53.9		1.24
DPSG-2	" "	U-tube	1.38	12.7	1st	30.2	20.4	0.11
PASG	" "	U-tube	1.50	12.7	1st	17.0	10.4	1.30
							23.2	0.87
BASG	" "	U-tube	1.57	13.0	1st	35.5	16.2	0.49
DPBC-1	Cooler	Outlet	1.50	12.7	1st	103	0.156	0.77
DPBC-2	"	Inlet	1.50	12.7	1st	87.1	0.181	0.75
DPBC-3	"	Interior	1.50	12.7	1st	104	0.152	0.76
PASC-1	"	Outlet	1.26	12.5	1st	62.1	0.256	1.73
PASC-2	"	Outlet	1.26	12.5	3rd	209	0.076	1.74
PAMX-1	Heat Exchanger	Interior	1.50	12.7	1st	37.1	0.43	2.04
PAMX-2	" "	Interior	1.50	12.7	1st	134	0.12	1.07
GBHX-1	" "	Inlet	1.25	19.1	1st	17.7	0.751	0.70
GBHX-2	" "	Inlet	1.25	19.1	8th	42.7	0.311	1.37
GBHX-3	" "	Inlet	1.25	19.1	8th	69.2	0.192	0.35
GBCX-1	Cooler	Inlet	1.25	19.1	1st	18.1	0.581	1.71
PHRC-1	"	Inlet	1.33	19.1	15th	177	0.050	1.55

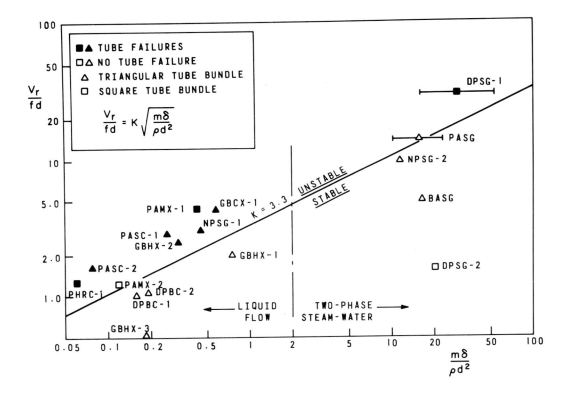

Figure 11: Fluidelastic Instability Analyses of Real Heat Exchangers: Comparison of Operating Experience vs Fluidelastic Instability Constant K=3.3, Pettigrew and Campagna (1979)

C416/025

Two-phase flow unsteady dynamic forces acting on a single row of vibrating circular cylinders

F HARA, PhD, MJSME, MASME
Department of Mechanical Engineering, Science University of Tokyo, Japan

SYNOPSIS This paper examines experimentally, together with flow visualization, the characteristics of the unsteady dynamic forces of two-phase flow, acting on a single row of vibrating circular cylinders which are installed at the pitch-to-diameter ratio of 1.33. The fluid forces acting on the center cylinder, forced to oscillate sinusoidally, are evaluated to show the incoherent feature to the sinusoidal oscillatory displacement of the cylinder due to strong random disturbance generated by air bubbles in the flow. This incoherent character due to air bubbles is, in addition to the increase in damping, concluded to be one of the major causes to suppress the fluidelastic instability occurred at the critical flow velocity in the single-phase water cross flow.

1. INTRODUCTION

Experimental data of two-phase cross-flow induced fluidelastic vibrations in tube arrays have been accumulated in the course of works done by Pettigrew and Gorman (1), and Heilker and Vincent (2). Recently, Pettigrew et al (3) (4) and Axisa et al (5) (6) reported refined experimental data and demonstrated a good relationship between the critical reduced velocity and mass-damping parameter similar to that obtained for a single-phase water cross flow. Yoshikawa and Hara (7), and Nemoto and Hara (8) showed that air bubbles in the water cross flow suppressed or destabilized the vibration of a single row of circular cylinders, depending on the flow velocity and void fraction. Hara (9) revealed a more complicated structure of the vibrational instability in two-phase flow using a five-circular-cylinder row. Using more complicated tube array, Goyder (10) demonstrated the importance of two-phase flow buffeting vibration.

The present understanding of two-phase flow induced vibrations in tube arrays is still at primitive stage due to a very complicated flow behavior around vibrating tubes as well as a complexity of dynamic interaction between tubes and two-phase flow. To understand more clearly the characteristics of two-phase flow induced vibrations and the mechanisms governing the vibrational instability, the flow behavior around a simple array of circular cylinders such as a single row of circular cylinders and characteristics of unsteady fluid forces acting on them are needed to be investigated. This paper thus deals with the investigation to the unsteady fluid force and the flow behaviors to demonstrate the mechanisms to suppress the vibrational instabiltiy by adding air bubbles in the flow using a single row of circular cylinders. The instability occurs in the water flow at the reduced velocity of about 3 where three central

cylinders of a single row of five cylinders oscillate at a large amplitude and out-of-phase to each other. Air bubble effects on this instability is found to generate the incoherent structures of fluid dynamic coupling between each cylinder and to result, thereby, in producing rather random, not large unsteady fluid forces on the cylinders. In addition to the increase in damping of two-phase flow, these effects of air bubbles in the flow may be one of the major causes to suppress the fluidelastic instability.

2. EXPERIMENTAL SETUP AND PROCEDURE

Three circular cylinders were installed horizontally with flat springs in a row within a 200 mm x 60 mm rectangular test channel to investigte the vibrational instability of the cylinder system when subjected to water cross flow. For this experiment, three central test cylinders were free to vibrate only in the lift direction because the instability mode for a row of three cylinders in water cross flow was dominated in the lift direction (11). This was beneficial to avoid unnecessary complexity in

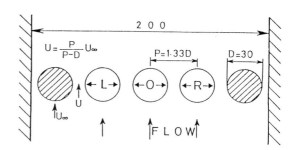

Fig. 1 Three-test cylinder configuration used in experiments, where the O, L and R cylinders are free to vibrate in the lift direction.

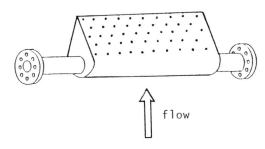

Fig. 2 The detail of air injection manifold
having 96 circular holes of 1 mm
in diameter

experiments. The test cylinders were 30 mm in diameter and 58 mm long, and the aspect ratio of the test cylinder was about 2, which was small. Note that this small aspect ratio was due to the limitation in the cross sectional area of the test channel to produce a homogeneous air-bubble two-phase flow. The gap between test cylinders was 10 mm and thus the pitch-to-diamter ratio was 1.33. Fig. 1 is a schematic drawing of the experimental test section and test cylinder configuration. The major parameters for the vibration of the test cylinders were as follows: natural frequency in air = 3.6 Hz and mass-damping ratio = 0.45 to 0.66 when defined as $\delta_m = 2\pi\zeta \ m/\rho D^2$, where ζ = damping ratio in air, D = cylinder diameter, m = mass of cylinder per unit length, and ρ − water density.

To produce rather homogeneous air bubbles in the test channel, air was injected through an air injection manifold in the water flow at the upstream nozzle attached to the downstream end of the test channel. The manifold had 96 circular holes of 1 mm in diameter in each side-plate as shown in Fig. 2.

For measuring the unsteady dynamic forces acting on the cylinders, only the center cylinder (O cylinder) was replaced with a cylinder of the same size, but fixed with springs much stiffer than the original ones. The cylinder was then forced to oscillate sinusoidally in the lift direction at the natural frequency (3.33 Hz in water) of the remaining two cylinders (L and R cylinders). Note that the mass-damping parameter of the L and R cylinders was about 0.8 for the unsteady fluid force measurement experiment.

The flow inside the test channel was veritically upward and the maximum Reynolds number attained by this test channel was 7.2 x 10^4 based on the test cylinder's diameter D, and the approaching velocity of a single-phase water flow U_∞. We defined the gap velocity U as P/(P´- D) x U_∞, where P is the pitch, and U_∞ the approaching flow velocity. Reduced velocity was thus defined as U/fD, f being the natural frequency of the test cylinder freely vibrating in air. The void fraction α was defined as $Q_a/(Q_a + Q_w)$, where Q_a is air flow rate and Q_w water flow rate. Q_a was measured by a float-type air flow meter, and Q_w by an orifice.

For the vibrational characteristics experiment, the accelerations of the O, L, and R cylinders were measured only in the lift direction by accelerometers attached inside each test cylinder and they were recorded on magnetic tape. Data of three accelerations were then digitized by an A/D converter with a sampling period of 0.02 s to evaluate their magnitude in terms of root mean square (RMS) and the correlation between them. This measurement was done for reduced velocity U/fD up to about 22 and the void fraction α from 1.5% to 70%. The average bubble size was measured using a photograph of air bubbles in the flow and found 6.5 mm in diameter, and thus the flow regime was homogenously bubbly.

For the fluid force measurement, first we examined wake flow patterns behind the row of cylinders when the center cylinder was forced to oscillate sinusoidally, and determined the oscillation frequency at which a wake pattern generated was very similar to that in the vibrational characteristics test. The frequency was 3.33 Hz. Changing the flow velocity, oscillation amplitude and void fraction, we measured the vibrational strain of the stiff, flat spring attached to the O cylinder and the L and R cylinders' accelerations. The unsteady fluid force F was then evaluated as

$$F = F_s - (2\pi f)^2 \ m_o X_o$$

where F_s is the force measured by the strain gage pasted to the stiff spring, f the frequency of the center cylinder oscillation, m_o mass of the center cylinder in air and X_o the displacement of the O cylinder oscillation. The structural damping effect on measuring the unsteady fluid force was neglected not only because of the small value of the damping ratio but also due to the small relative velocity of the center cylinder. The error generated by neglecting the structural damping effect was estimated as about 0.4% of the force F_s.

Two 500w, direct-current electric lamps were installed above the upper tank attached to the test channel to light the test cylinders from the top. The light was passed through the test channel due to a sharp edge of the test section's exit, and thus the test cylinders were exposed to the light parallel to the flow. The water flow was seeded with aluminum particles which provided maximum reflection at about 90 degrees to the incident light, however the two-phase flow was not seeded because air bubbles in the flow reflected the incident light effectively. The observation and photographing were done from the side of the test section. The jet and wake patterns in both water and two-phase flows were recorded using a press camera and a high sensitivity film (400 ASA). The patterns of jet and wake around the test cylinders in the water flow were observed for the following two conditions: 1) all five circular cylinders were rigidly fixed at the pitch-to-diameter ratio of 1.33, and 2) reduced velocity U/fD of 2.9 at which three central cylinders underwent the out-of-phase mode instability. The two-phase flow patterns were examined first for the case of all five test cylinders being rigidly fixed, and then for the case where the air bubbles in the flow suppressed the unstable vibration.

3. AIR BUBBLE EFFECTS ON VIBRATION

Typical acceleration waveforms of each test cylinder obtained at the reduced velocity U/fD of 2.9 showed that three circular cylinders O, L, and R vibrated almost sinusoidally at the frequency of 3.8 Hz, a bit larger than 3.6 Hz due

© IMechE 1991 C416/025

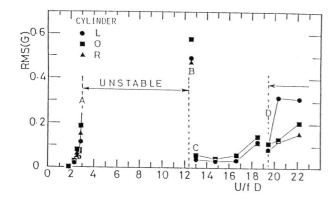

Fig. 3 RMS values of vibrational accelerations against the reduced velocity

to a steady fluid force, in the lift direction and their phase relation was apparently out-of-phase or of 180 degree difference. Calculating the RMS values of these accelerations, we plotted the magnitude of each vibrational acceleration against the reduced velocity as shown in Fig. 3. When the reduced velocity became about 3, the cylinders exhibited unstable vibration, and the critical reduced velocity of 3 was perfectly in agreement with Chen's result (11) for a mass damping parameter of about 0.5. They kept colliding constantly with each other for the reduced velocities up to about 12. The cylinder's acceleration became very large due to collision and off-scaled for the range of reduced verocity from 3 to 12. (At the reduced velocity of 12.6, we observed a different, almost in-phase mode of vibration in the three cylinders, where the vibration frequency was 4.7 Hz, which was rather large compared to that of the out-of-phase mode vibration, and then the cylinders became rather quiet for reduced velocities from 13 to 19 as shown in Fig. 3.) Over the reduced velocity of 20, two of the three cylinders buckled and remained almost still while the remaining cylinder vibrated strongly, and its amplitude was very large.

The effects of air bubbles were investgated for the reduced velocity range from 1.9 to 3.3, which corresponded to the out-of-phase mode instability. Fig. 4 is the O cylinder's acceleration in RMS plotted against the void fraction. For a small reduced velocity at which no instability occurred, increase in void fraction made the vibration gradually to grow for

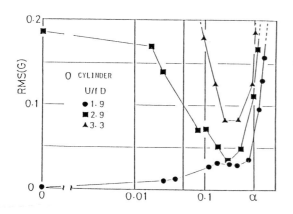

Fig. 4 Effects of void fraction on O cylinder for reduced velocity from 1.9 to 3.3

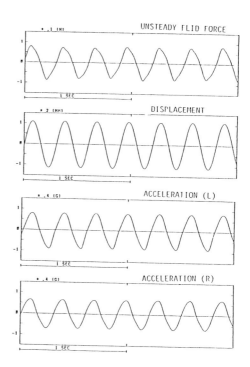

Fig. 5 Timewise waveforms of unsteady fluid force and displacement of O cylinder, and L and R cylinders accelerations for U/fD = 3.6 and γ = 0.075

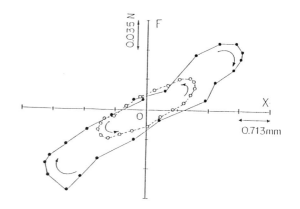

Fig. 6 Lissajous orbits between the unsteady fluid force and displacement of O cylinder for U/fD = 3.0 and γ = 0.038 (O) and U/fD = 3.6 and γ = 0.075 (●)

void fractions up to 30% and further increase in void fraction excited the vibration violently. At the reduced velocity of 2.9 where the out-of-phase mode instability was found in water cross flow, air bubbles in the flow suppressed the unstable vibration effectively under the void fraction of about 20%, however the vibration was again excited for higher void fractions than 20%.

4. FLUID FORCE IN WATER CROSS FLOW

4.1 General feature

Fig. 5 shows the waveforms of the unsteady fluid force, the displacement of the center cylinder, and accelerations of the L and R cylinders when U/fD = 3.6 and the ratio of the dispacement to the diameter γ = 0.075. Fig. 5 shows clearly the definite phase-lead of the unsteady fluid force to the displacement, and a very small phase-lag between the L cylinder acceleration to the 0 cylinder displacement. These features are described on a condensed form of the Lissajous orbits in Fig. 6. Figs. (5) and (6) show that, when the row of three cylinders was vibrationally unstable at the reduced velocity of 3.6, the three cylinders were completely out-of-phase, meaning that the L and R cylinders vibrated at a 180° phase difference with respect to the center cylinder's oscillation.

4.2 Fluid force magnitude and phase difference

The RMS values of the unsteady fluid force and the accelerations of the L and R cylinders were calculated for the two reduced velocityies of 3.0 and 3.6, corresponding, respectively, to a small vibration level and an unstable vibration in the cylinder row. The magnitude of unsteady fluid force was plotted against the amplitude ratio γ in Fig. 7, where the ordinate is the RMS value of the fluid force (N). The unsteady fluid force increased linearly with the oscillation amplitude for U/fD = 3.0, because the fluid force was majorly due to the effect of added mass and was then proportionally related to $(2\pi f)^2 \gamma D$. For U/fD

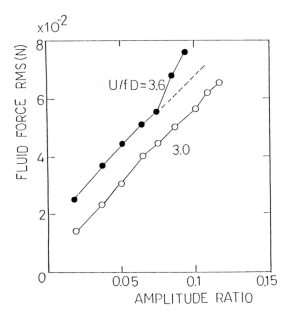

Fig. 7 RMS values of the unsteady fluid force of 0 cylinder plotted against the amplitude ratio γ

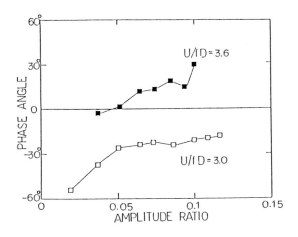

Fig. 8 Phase angle between the unsteady fluid force and displacement of 0 cylinder plotted against γ

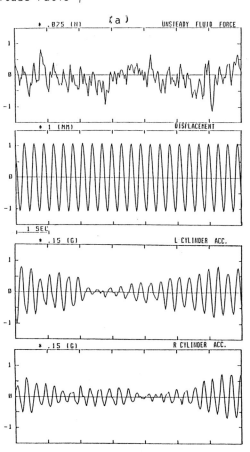

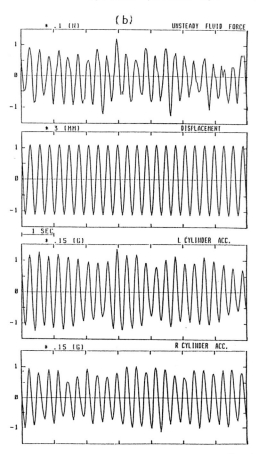

Fig. 9 Typical waveforms of two-phase flow unsteady force and displacement of 0 cylinder, and the accelerations of L and R cylinder for U/fD = 3.6, (a) γ = 0.037 and (b) γ = 0.113

= 3.6, it became rather large at the oscillation amplitude ratio of γ = 0.075, when compared to the trend for smaller amplitude ratios. Fig. 8 shows the relationship of the phase angle of the unsteady fluid force to the displacement of the O cylinder with respect to the amplitude ratio for the cases of U/fD = 3.0 and 3.6. For the reduced velocity of 3.6, the phase angle was almost zero for a small amplitude ratio and increased with it to almost 30° when the oscillation amplitude became about 10.5 % of the cylinder diameter. This indicates that the unsteady fluid force produces a negative damping in the central, oscillating cylinder (14).

5. TWO-PHASE FLOW UNSTEADY FLUID FORCE

5.1 General feature

Figs. 9 (a) and (b) are the typical waveforms of the two-phase flow unsteady force, the displacement of the center cylinder, and the accelerations of the L and R cylinders when reduced velocity U/fD = 3.6 and void fraction α = 19%. The amplitude ratio γ is 0.037 and 0.113 for (a) and (b) in Fig. 9, respectively. Clearly, the unsteady fluid force in two-phase flow was very random and small even when the center cylinder oscillated sinusoidally at a small amplitude. When γ = 0.113, corresponding to a large amplitude oscillation of the center cylinder, the two-phase flow unsteady force acting on the harmonically oscillating center cylinder was rather random and still not large. The vibrational accelerations of the L and R cylinders were also rather random and not large compared with those in Fig. 5.

5.2 Fluid force magnitude

The RMS values of the two-phase flow unsteady force and the accelerations of the L and R cylinders were calculated for the two cases of reduced velocity and void fraction, i.e., U/fD = 3.0 and α = 21%; and U/fD = 3.6 and α = 19%. They were plotted against amplitude ratio γ together with the results for the single-phase water flow in Fig. 10. The two-phase flow unsteady force

increased with the amplitude ratio for both reduced velocities. However, comparing with those in water flow, the magnitude of the two-phase flow unsteady force was rather small even when the amplitude ratio γ was large. For small γ, the unsteady fluid force was not much different for both under-critical and critical reduced velocities; but for large γ, the fluid force showed a markedable difference between two reduced velocities U/fD = 3.0 and 3.6.

Fig. 11 shows the RMS values of the acceleration of the L cylinder plotted against the amplitude ratio γ for both the cases U/fD = 3.0 and α = 21%; and U/fD = 3.6 and α = 19%, together with those for water flow. For both reduced velocities, the vibration magnitude of the L cylinder was almost same level and had a weak dependency on the amplitude of O cylinder's oscillation. This fact means that the fluid dynamic influence of the O cylinder oscillation on the adjacent cylinders was blocked by the air bubbles passing through the gaps between the O cylinder and L and/or R cylinders. Their vibration seemed to be caused mostly by the random buffeting force due to the air bubbles in the narrow gaps between cylinders. This may leads to the discussion that the vibrations of the O, L and R cylinders are not well coherent and the structure of the fluid dynamic coupling between the three cylinders becomes incoherent due to a strong disturbance generated by the air bubbles passing through the gaps.

5.3 Correlation and coherence

Fig. 12 shows the correlation coefficient between the unsteady fluid force and O cylinder's oscillatory displacement, plotted against the amplitude ratio for U/fD = 3.6 and α = 19%. Let us recall the correlation in the case of a single-phase water flow, which was almost 1.0, as seen in Fig.5, due to a highly coherent fluid dynamic interaction between the water flow and oscillating cylinders. But for the case of the two-phase flow, it was found that, when the amplitude ratio γ was small, e.g. γ ≤ 0.05, the correlation coefficient was not equal to 1.0 but smaller than 0.7. This means that the unsteady

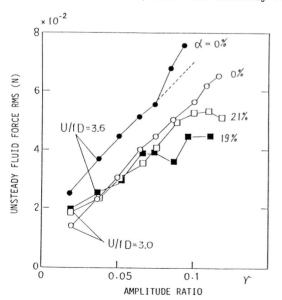

Fig. 10 RMS values of two-phase flow unsteady force plotted against the amplitude ratio γ

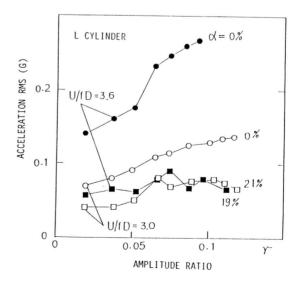

Fig. 11 RMS values of the acceleration of L cylinder plotted against the amplitude ratio γ

C416/025 © IMechE 1991

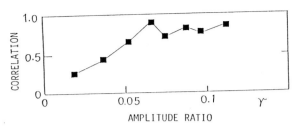

Fig. 12 Correlation coefficient of two-phase
flow unsteady force and displacement
of O cylinder plotted against the
amplitude ratio γ

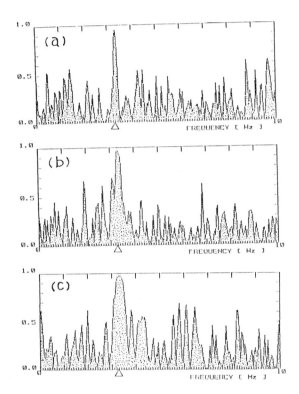

Fig. 13 Coherence between two-phase flow
unsteady force and displacement of O
cylinder, (a) γ = 0.037, (b) γ =
0.075, and (c) γ = 0.113

Fig. 14 Photograh of jets and wakes in the
five fixed test cylinders (U = 0.31 m/s)

Fig. 15 Oscillating jets and wakes under the
out-of-phase mode instability in
water flow (U/fD = 2.9)

correlation to the O cylinder's oscillation.

6. FLOW VISUALIZATION

6.1 Water flow wake pattern

Fig. 14 is a photograph of jet and wake flows
behind the rigidly fixed five circular cylinders
subjected to an upward water cross flow. The gap
velocity U was 0.31 m/s. The wakes behind the
cylinders were medium, small, large, small, and
medium from left to right, which is in good
agreement with Bradshaw's result (12) (13). The
tail of each small wake located in both sides of
the large one was found to oscillate at a high
frequency, but this oscillation was not
condsidered as the Karman vorticity. Note that
the wake flow pattern shown in Fig. 14 was
switched to another one due to flow disturbance,
and we found totally four patterns.

Fig. 15 is the oscillating jets and wakes at
the reduced velocity of 2.9 where the out-of-
phase mode instability was found in the test
cylinder system. The arrows indicate the
direction of the cylinder's motion. Fig. 15 shows
that when the O cylinder moved to the right, the
L and R cylinders proceeded to the left. As the
adjacent two cylinders approached each other, a
frontal jet passing through the gap between them
was developed and curved outward, reducing the
rearward jet. According to this jet pattern, the
separation points of the O cylinder were not
symmertically located, i,e., the separation point
at right was positioned rather downstream to the

fluid force acting on the sinusoidally
oscillating O cylinder was rather random compared
to the purely sinusoidal motion of the O
cylinder. This seemed to be caused by the
incoherent buffeting of air bubbles on the
oscillating cylinders. For large γ, the
correlation was still not large, which indicates
that the fluid force was also strongly influenced
by the air bubbles passing through the gaps.

Fig. 13 shows the coherence of the unsteady
fluid force to the O cylinder oscillation
(displacement) for various amplitude ratios at
U/fD = 3.6 and α = 19%. The symbol Δ on the
frequency axis indicates the O cylinder's
oscillation frequency of 3.33 Hz. In each figure
almost 1.0 coherence was obtained at this
oscillation frequency, but at other frequencies
than 3.33 Hz, the fluid force was found to have
the force components uncorrelated to the O
cylinder's oscillation. This is consistent to
that in Fig. 12, indicating that the two-phase
flow unsteady force did not have a strong

Fig. 16 Two-phase flow jet and wake pattern in the fixed test cylinders (U = 0.31 m/s, α = about 20%)

Fig. 17 Two-phase flow jet and wake patterns observed at U/fD = 2.9 and α = 20%, where the vibration was suppressed

cylinder and the one at left upstream. The separation points were found to oscillate in accordance with the cylinder's oscillation (14).

6.2 Two-phase flow wake pattern

Fig. 16 is a two-phase flow pattern produced by rigidly fixed five test cylinders at the gap velocity of water U = 0.31 m/s and void fraction α = about 20 %, and shows that the jet and wake pattern was very similar to that obtained in a single-phase water flow (Fig. 14). The wake containing many air bubbles and located behind the 0 cylinder was large, and a small wake was generated behind each of L and R cylinders. The medium wake located behind the most left and right cylinders. The wake configuration was, thus, the same as that in Fig. 14. Note here that the wakes behind each cylinder contained air bubbles almost homogenously.

At the small reduced velocity of 2.9, air bubbles were found to suppress the out-of-phase mode instability in the test cylinders when the void fraction was about 20 %. A typical flow pattern observed for the above condition is shown in Fig. 17, where air bubbles flew along the jets passing the gaps between test cylinders. There existed a water region, containing no air bubbles, behind each test cylinder and its size changed randomly from small to medium, medium to large and vise versa. For instance the water region behind the 0 cylinder is large and the two behind the L and R cylinders small in Fig. 17. Comparing the two-phase flow wake pattern with that of a single-phase water flow for the rigidly fixed five cylinder array (Fig. 14), we find that the air bubbles in the flow does disturb the coherent fluid dynamic interaction between cylinders. This may result in producing the same jet and wake pattern as that in the fixed cylinders, and then in suppressing the unstable fluidelastic vibration.

7. DISCUSSION

7.1 Incoherenct structure of two-phase flow fluid force

The unsteady fluid force generated in the row of cylinders subjected to water cross flow was found (14) very coherent to the motion of the cylinder row and it had a phase-lead to the oscillatory cylinder-displacement as seen in Fig. 8. The magnitude of the fluid force was also quite coherent with the amplitude of the 0 cylinder's

oscillation (Fig. 7). This coherent strucutre of the unsteady fluid force generated in the water flow was concluded in Ref. 15 to generate a negative damping effect on the vibration of a single row of cylinders, which causes the cylinder row vibrationally unstable.

However, when the flow was two-phase bubbly, the unsteady fluid force was found very incoherent to the 0 cylinder's oscillation especially for the amplitude ratio small (Figs. 11 and 12). The magnitude of the unsteady fluid force of two-phase flow was, too, small compared with that of the water flow at the small amplitude ratio (Fig. 10). Furthermore the fluid dynamic interaction between the cylinders in the single row arrangement was blocked by air bubbles passing through the gaps, which seems to weaken the fluid dynamic coupling between the cylinders. This is also a candidate to cause the two-phase flow unsteady force to be incoherent to the oscillatory motion of the cylinders.

When the cylinder row is unlocked by air bubbles from the high coherent coupling between the cylinders in the water flow, the vibration may suddenly become small, and the two-phase flow unsteady fluid force consequently becomes small and incoherent to the motion of cylinders, namely random. Thus the cylinder row is kept vibrating randomly with a small amplitude. This small vibration is observed as the suppression of the unstable, out-of-phase vibration by the two-phase flow.

7.2 Flow pattern

We found different jet and wake patterns in both single-phase water and two-phase mixed flows depending on reduced velocity. The one was that appeared typically for the rigidly fixed cylinders, and the second the pattern appeared at the small reduced velocity of about 3 in water flow where the three test cylinders underwent the out-of-phase mode instability.

For the rigidly fixed cylinder system used, the jet and wake pattern is practically the same in both water flow and two-phase flow as shown in Figs. 14 and 16. This means that air bubbles do not influence the jet and wake pattern substantially for the single row of the five cylinders when rigidly fixed. At the reduced velocity of 2.9 in water flow, the jet and wake pattern shown in Fig. 15 was particular among the those observed in both water and two-phase flows, and strongly related to the out-of-phase mode instability in the cylinder system. A small amount of air bubbles in the water flow having the reduced velocity U/fD = 2.9 seemed not to change the jet and wake pattern from that in water flow, because the vibration magnitude in the two-phase flow was found comparable to that obtained in water flow.

For the reduced velocity U/fD = 2.9, if the flow contained air bubbles so many as that of void fraction α = about 20%, the out-of-phase mode vibration was suppressed, and the jet and wake pattern changed from the one particular to the out-of-phase mode instability in the water flow to that obtained by the rigidly fixed cylinders. Note here that the correlation coefficients between the accelerations of the O and L cylinders, and those of the L and R cylindes were almost zero for the two-phase flow of U/fD = 2.9 and α = 20% (7). This means that the O, L, and R cylinders vibrated randomly at a small amplitude.

The out-of-phase mode instability of the test cylinder system is caused by the special unsteady fluid force acting on the cylinders. The force is found to be phase-lead to the cylinder's motion, and also to be strongly related to the oscillation of the flow separation points on each cylinder (14) (15). The jets containing air bubbles are generated in the convergent regions formed by the upstream frontal surfaces of each cylinder (Fig. 17), and the air bubbles in the jets are evidently elongated by the flow accaleration due to the shrinkage of flow passages. Thus the flow boundary layer of the cylinder is likely interacted with air bubbles and the flow in the cylinder's boundary layer is therefore disturbed strongly. This results in the intervention to the coherent motion of the separation points. The phase-lead unsteady fluid force might then disappear in the cylinder-two-phase flow interacting system, which is considered as one of the major mechanisms to unlock and suppress the out-of-phase mode instability. Adding to the mechanism speculated above, the two-phase bubble flow produces a rather high damping in vibrating cylinders (16), which seems also to contribute to the vibration suppression.

Once the vibration system is unlocked from the out-of-phase mode instability due to the mechanisms examined above, the vibration amplitude becomes small, thereby the jet and wake pattern is set to that observed for the rigidly fixed cylinder row. Then the two-phase flow generates rather random fluid forces on the test cylinders due to buffeting of two-phase bubbly fluid, and also producing a rather high damping on vibrating cylinders (16). Then the cylinder-row system is likely kept under a small random vibration.

8. CONCLUSION

This paper demonstrated experimentally the incoherent structure of the two-phase flow unsteady fluid force acting on a vibrating cylinder, in the lift direction, in a single row of three circular cylinders. One major mechanism to suppress the out-of-phase mode instability was discussed from the incoherent characteristics of the unsteady fluid forces due to the air bubbles added in the flow.

The measurement of two-phase flow unsteady fluid force, its comparison to that in water flow, and the visualization of flows passing the gaps between vibrating circular cylinders were done for the typical reduced velocity of 3.6 in both water and two-phase flows. The following major results were obtained for the characterisitcs of the unsteady fluid force acting on the row of three circular cylinders subjected to two-phase cross flows:

(1) The unsteady forces of the two-phase flow were rather small compared with that in water flow, random and not well coherent to the sinusoidal oscillation of the test cylinder when U/fD = about 3 and void fraction = 20%. However the unsteady fluid force in water flow was very coherent to the test cylinder's motion to generate the destabilizing force on the cylinder system.
(2) While the jets passing along the gaps between the vibrating cylinders oscillated in harmony with the cylinder's oscillation in the single-phase water flow of U/fD = about 3, the pattern of two-phase-flow jets was similar to that generated by the rigidly fixed cylinders in water flow, and the cylinder vibrations were almost suppressed by the two-phase flow of α = about 20%.
(3) The incoherent structure of the two-phase flow unsteady forces seemed to be one of the major causes to suppress the unstable, out-of-phase mode vibration in a single row of cylinders. However the increase in damping of two-phase flow must be also recognized as another cause to suppress the unstable, out-of-phase mode vibration.

ACKNOWLEDGEMENTS

The author is grateful to the Toray Foundation for partial aid in the research, and wishes thanks to go to Mr. Norio Yoshikawa for assisting in experiments.

REFERENCES

(1) Pettigrew, M. J. and Gorman, D. J., "Vibration of Heat Exchange Components in Liquid and Two-Phase Cross Flow", Atomic Energy of Canada Limited, AECL-6184, 1978, pp 1 - 20
(2) Heilker, W. J. and Vincent, R. Q., "Vibration in Nuclear Heat Exchangers Due to Liquid and Two-Phase Flow", ASME Journal of Engineering for Power, Vol. 103, 1981, pp. 358 - 366
(3) Pettigrew, M. L. et al, "Vibration of Tube Bundles Subjected to Two-Phase Cross-Flow", ASME Symposium on FIV, Vol. 2, 1984, pp.251 - 268
(4) Pettigrew, M. L. et al, "Vibration of Tube Bundles in Two-Phase Cross Flow: Part 2 - Fluidelastic Instability", ASME Symposium on FIV and Noise, Vol. 3, 1988, pp.159 - 179
(5) Axisa, F. et al, "Vibration of Tube Bundles Subjected to Air-Water and Steam-Water Cross-Flow: Preliminary Results on Fluidealstic Instability", ASME Symposium on FIV, Vol. 2, 1984, pp. 269 - 284
(6) Axisa, F. et al, "Vibration of Tube Bundles Subjected to Steam-water Cross Flow", 8th SMiRT Trans., Vol. B, 1985, B1/2
(7) Yoshikawa, N. and Hara, F., " A Study of Vibrations of a Single Row of Circular Cylinders Subjected to Two-Phase Cross Flow", JSME Trans. Vol. 51, No. 470 - c, 1985, pp. 2487 - 2496

(8) Nemoto, A. and Hara, F., " An Experimental Investigation of Fluid-Elastic Instability for a Single Row of Tubes Subjected to Two-Phase Cross Flow", JSME Trans, Vol. 52, No. 481 - c, 1986, pp. 2366 - 2342

(9) Hara, F., "Vibration of Single Row of Circular Cylinders Subjected to Two-Phase Bubble Cross-Flow", Proc. Inter. Conf. on Flow Induced Vibrations, Bowness-on-Windermere, 1987, pp. 203 - 210

(10) Goyder, H. G. D., "Two-Phase Buffeting of Heat Exchanger Tubes", Proc. Inter. Conf. on Flow Induced Vibrations, Bowness-on-Windermere, 1987, pp. 211 - 219

(11) Chen, S. S. and Jendrezejczyk, J. A., "Stability of Tube Array in Cross Flow", Nuc. Eng. and Design, Vol. 75, No. 3, 1983, pp. 351 - 373

(12) Bradshaw, P. J., "The Effect of Wind-Tunnel Screens on Nominally Two-Dimensional Boundary Layers", J. Fluid Mechanics, Vol. 22, No. 4, 1965, pp. 679 - 688

(13) Ishigai, S. and Nishikawa, E., "A Study of Cross Flow Strctures in Tube Arrays", Trans. JSME, Vol. 40, No. 337, 1974, pp. 2599 - 2608

(14) Hara, F., "Unsteady Fluid Dynamic Forces Acting on a Single Row of Cylinders Vibrating in a Cross Flow", J. of Fluids and Structures, Vol. 3, 1989, pp. 97 - 113

(15) Tanaka, H. and Takahara, S., "Fluid Elastic Vibration of Tube Arrays in Cross Flow", J. of Sound and Vibration, Vol. 77, No. 1, 1981, pp.19 - 37

(16) Hara, F. and Kohgo, O., "Numerical Approach to Added Mass and Damping of a Vibrating Circular Cylinder in a Two-Phase Bubble Fluid", Computational Mechanics '86, Springer-Verlag, Vol. 2, 1986, pp.VII-255 - 260

C416/032

A study on random fluid forces acting on a tube in parallel two-phase flow

F INADA, PhD, MJSME, K KAWAMURA, MSc, MJSME and A YASUO, MSc, MJSME
Central Research Institute of Electric Power Industry, Tokyo, Japan

SYNOPSIS   The secondary coolant in a steam generator is a parallel two-phase flow, which can induce lateral vibration of the heat transfer tubes. In this report, the statistical properties of the fluid forces acting on a tube in a water-air, two-phase flow, such as power-spectral-density and cross-spectral-density, were investigated experimentally.   It was found that the fluid forces were hardly affected by the jet flow from the orifice (48% constriction ratio) or the system pressure. By applying the statistical properties of fluid forces, the amplitude of the tube vibration was also estimated.

NOTATION

f frequency
f_0 maximum value of frequency range
F fluid forces acting on a tube per unit length
$\tilde{F}$ fluid forces acting on a force transducer
l length of the force transducer
P system pressure
$R_{FF}(z,z',\tau)$ cross-correlation function of the random fluid force field
$S_{FF}(z,z',f)$ cross-spectral density of random fluid force field
t time
U homogeneous flow velocity
V_c propagating velocity of random fluid force field(eq.(4))
y tube displacement
z,z' coordinate (see Fig.2)
α nozzle-opening ratio
$(=\dfrac{\text{cross-sectional area of the nozzle}}{\text{cross-sectional area of flow path}})$
ε_g homogeneous void fraction
$(=\dfrac{\text{volumetric flow rate of vapor phase}}{\text{total volumetric flow rate}})$
ξ reducing rate of random fluid force magnitude (eq.(5))

1. INTRODUCTION

The characteristics of random fluid forces acting on tubes in a parallel two-phase flow were investigated experimentally.

Many heat transfer tubes are installed in PWR steam generators. The secondary coolant flowing outside of the tubes forms steam-water two-phase flow, and the flow conditions vary along the vertical axis of the tubes, as the flow is constricted where the tube is supported and becomes a jet flow. The turbulence of the two-phase flow can induce tube vibration, which in turn can cause fretting damage to the tubes.

The characteristics of tube vibration in a parallel two-phase flow were investigated in the case of an air-water, two-phase flow by Hara & Yamashita(1) and Kawamura(2), and in the case of a steam-water, two-phase flow, which was the same pressure condition of the actual steam generator, tested by Pettigrew & Gorman(3) as well as Carlucci(4) and Carlucci & Brown(5) measured hydrodynamic mass and damping of a tube in air-water, two-phase flow. It was shown by Pettigrew & Gorman(3) that the tube vibration amplitude decreased with increasing system pressure in the case of steam-water two-phase flow.

If the tube-vibration amplitude is estimated from the random pressure field characteristics, tube-vibration amplitude is generally estimated in the case that the tube span, i.e., the tube's natural frequency, is varied. Chen & Wambsganss (6) and Wambsganss & Zaleski(7) estimated tube vibration from the pressure field characteristics. In an air-water, two-phase flow, Gorman(8) investigated the pressure acting on tubes, and estimated the tube-vibration amplitude; but the effect of natural frequency, the shape of the flow path and system pressure on the fluid force characteristics were not sufficiently understood.

In this report, not pressure on a tube but the fluid force acting on a tube in an air-water, parallel two-phase flow was measured since Gorman(8) showed that the pressure fluctuations were much more highly correlated in the peripheral direction for a two-phase flow, and only the pressure difference between any two diametrally opposite points on the tube caused tube vibration. The cross-spectral density of a random fluid force field was obtained. Using the characteristics of random fluid force, the amplitude of a simply supported tube was estimated in the case that the natural frequency of the tube was varied. The effects of the flow-path constriction of tube-support plates and system pressure change on tube vibration in the case of air-water two-phase flow were also investigated.

2. EXPERIMENTAL SETUP AND PROCEDURE

As shown in Fig.1, the water which is pumped up by a pump flows through a surge tank, flow meters and valves, and flows into an air-water mixer. The air which is compressed by a screw compressor flows through a drier, a filter, valves and flow meters, and also flows into the air-water mixer.

Then, water and air are mixed, and after that air-water two-phase flow flows through the test section, which has an approach section 1m in length at the upstream end, and flows into an air-water separator. Air and water separated in the separator are drawn into a tank installed at floor level, depressurized at valves and discharged to the atmosphere and the water tank, respectively.

Fig.2 shows the test section. A tube 22mm in outer diameter and 0.8m in total length made of aluminum alloy is inserted in the center of an acrylic tube 40mm in inner diameter. An orifice is installed at 0.15m downstream from the upstream end of the tube to investigate the effect of flow constriction. The random fluid forces acting on the tube segments for fluid force measurement of 50mm length, the center of which is located at 0.1m, 0.3m and 0.5m downstream from the orifice, were measured. These tube segments are supported by plate springs at the ends of the tube support segments, which are held securely by pins. Semiconductor strain gauges, which can detect random fluid forces, are installed on plate springs. The natural frequency of these fluid force measurement systems is 250Hz.

The inner diameter of the orifice was set at 32mm in order to make the nozzle-opening ratio α almost equal to that of the actual steam generator, and 40mm, which was without constriction. When the homogeneous flow velocity was fixed at U, the relation of the homogeneous void fraction and the characteristics of random fluid forces acting on the tube were investigated. The pressure was set at 2×10^5, 3×10^5 and 4×10^5Pa in order to investigate the effect of system pressure change on the characteristics of random fluid forces.

3. EXPERIMENTAL RESULTS

3.1 Power spectral density of fluid force field

Fig.3 shows an example of power spectral density $S_{FF}(z,z,f)$ of random fluid forces acting on a tube per unit length in the case of nozzle-opening ratio $\alpha=1$, homogeneous void fraction $\varepsilon_g=0.4$, system pressure $P=4\times10^5$Pa and homogeneous flow velocity $U=1.9$m/sec. In a typical steam generator, the range of U and ε_g is from $U=0.4$m/sec and $\varepsilon_g=0$ to $U=4$m/sec and $\varepsilon_g=0.9$. It is shown that the power spectral density was independent of frequency at below 20Hz. The power spectral density showed a similar tendency in the case that ε_g was from 0 to 0.95 and in the case that $U=3$m/sec.

Fig.4 shows the square root of the average power spectral density below 20Hz$(=f_0)$. The values measured at the force transducers located at $z=0.1$m, 0.3m and 0.5m are indicated, but in the case of $\alpha=1$, the average values of the three measured points are indicated because they were close to one another. The tendency of the curve of $\alpha=0.48$ and $z=0.1$m was different from that of $\alpha=1$, but that of $\alpha=0.48$ and $z=0.3$m, 0.5m was similar to that of $\alpha=1$. In the case of $\alpha=0.48$, the flow constriction hardly influenced the fluid forces more than 0.3m downstream of the orifice. Since the span length of the actual steam generator is 1.283m and is sufficiently larger than 0.1m, the jet flow from the tube support hardly affects the tube vibration. The average power

spectral density of $U=3$m/sec was slightly larger than that of $U=1.9$m/sec in the range of $\varepsilon_g<0.2$ and was almost same in the range of $\varepsilon_g>0.2$.

Fig.5 shows the effect of system pressure change in the case of $\alpha=1$. It is shown that the power spectral density of fluid force was hardly influenced by the system pressure change.

3.2 Cross-spectral density, auto-correlation function and cross-correlation function of the fluid force

The cross-spectral density $S_{FF}(z,z',f)$ of a random fluid force field in the case of $\alpha=1$ is shown in Fig.6, which is an example of the case of $z=0.3$m, $z'=0.5$m, $U=1.9$m/sec, $P=4\times10^5$Pa, $\varepsilon_g=0.4$. The absolute value was independent of the frequency, as shown in Fig.6(a). The phase was proportional to the frequency, as shown in Fig.6(b) when the cycle of 2π was considered. Figs.7(a)(b) show the auto- and cross-correlation functions, which were obtained when a reverse Fourier transformation of power-spectral density (Fig.3) and the cross-spectral density (Fig.6) was performed, where the component of power- and cross-spectral density above 20Hz was assumed to be zero. The auto-correlation function took a peak value at $\tau=0$, and approached zero when τ was not close to zero. The cross-correlation function took a peak value at $\tau=\tau_c$ which was larger than zero and approached zero when $|\tau-\tau_c|$ was not close to zero.

3.3 Formulation of random fluid force characteristics

Based on the above results, the general formula of the cross-spectral density of a fluid force field was written in the form,

$$S_{FF}(z,z',f)=\frac{\overline{F^2}}{f_0}exp(-\xi|z'-z|)exp(-j\frac{2\pi f(z'-z)}{V_c})$$
$$(|z'-z|<0.4m,\ f<20Hz)........(1)$$

where $\overline{F^2}$ stands for the mean square value of F.

Equation (1) expresses that the random fluid forces generated at all locations in a two-phase flow are propagated downstream at velocity V_c, with a reduction in magnitude. The rate of decrease in the magnitude is $e^{-\xi}$ per unit length.

In this paper, the cross-correlation function $S_{FF}(z,z',f)$ in Eq.(1) was obtained from the cross-correlation function $S_{\tilde{F}\tilde{F}}(z,z',l,f)$ of the fluid force measured at the force transducers of $l(=50mm)$ length centered at z and z', in the form,

$$S_{FF}(z,z',f)\approx S_{\tilde{F}\tilde{F}}(z,z',l,f)/l^2 \qquad ...(2)$$

In this case, if l was infinitesimally small, $S_{FF}(z,z',f)$ would be obtained exactly, but l has a finite value, so the high-frequency characteristics become worse. So the measurement was taken at below 20Hz. When the cross-spectral density $S_{FF}(z,z',f)$ of the random fluid force is expressed in Eq.(1), the cross-spectral density $S_{\tilde{F}\tilde{F}}(z,z',l,f)$ of the fluid force acting on force transducers of l length at z and z' is obtained in the form,

$$S_{\tilde{F}\tilde{F}}(z,z',l,f)=S_{FF}(z,z',f)l^2\psi(\xi l,\frac{2\pi fl}{V_c})\ldots(3-1)$$

where

$$\psi(\eta,S_t)=\int_0^1\int_0^1 exp[-\eta(u'-u)]exp[-jS_t(u'-u)]du'du$$
$$(z'-z>l)$$
$$=\int_0^1\int_0^1 exp[-\eta|u'-u|]exp[-jS_t(u'-u)]du'du$$
$$(z'=z)$$
$$\eta=\xi l,\quad S_t=\frac{2\pi fl}{V_c}\qquad\ldots\ldots(3-2)$$

If ψ is nearly equal to unity, then eq.(3-1) becomes eq.(2). In the low-frequency range, ψ is nearly equal to unity, but ψ decreases with increasing frequency. In the frequency range below 20Hz, ψ is larger than 0.6, so that errors remain less than 40%.

The parameter $\sqrt{\overline{F^2}}/f_0$ in Eq.(1) was obtained as shown in Fig.4-5 in section 3.1. The parameters ξ and V_c are obtained from the peak value of the auto- and cross-correlation functions and τ_c in the form,

$$V_c=\frac{z'-z}{\tau_c}\qquad\ldots\ldots(4)$$

$$\xi=-\frac{1}{z'-z}log_e[\frac{R_{FF}(z,z',\tau_c)}{R_{FF}(z,z,0)}]\qquad\ldots\ldots(5)$$

Since l has a finite value, the accuracy of the auto- and cross-correlation functions also becomes worse in cases in which the random fluid force includes a high-frequency component. When the cross-spectral density $S_{FF}(z,z',f)$ of the random fluid force field is expressed in Eq.(1), the cross-correlation function $R_{\tilde{F}\tilde{F}}(z,z',l,\tau)$ of the fluid force acting on the force transducers of l length at z and z' is obtained in the form,

$$R_{\tilde{F}\tilde{F}}(z,z',l,\tau)$$
$$=2l^2\overline{F^2}exp[-\xi(z'-z)]\mu(\xi l,\frac{2\pi f_0l}{V_c},(\tau-\frac{z'-z}{V_c})2\pi f_0)$$
$$\ldots\ldots(6-1)$$

where

$$\mu(\eta,S_{t0},\hat{\tau})$$
$$=\int_0^1\int_0^1 exp[-\eta(u'-u)]\frac{sin[S_{t0}(u'-u)-\hat{\tau}]}{S_{t0}(u'-u)-\hat{\tau}}du'du$$
$$(z'-z>l)$$
$$=\int_0^1\int_0^1 exp[-\eta|u'-u|]\frac{sin[S_{t0}(u'-u)-\hat{\tau}]}{S_{t0}(u'-u)-\hat{\tau}}du'du$$
$$(z=l)$$
$$\eta=\xi l,\quad S_{t0}=\frac{2\pi f_0l}{V_c},\quad\hat{\tau}=(\tau-\frac{z'-z}{V_c})2\pi f_0\ldots\ldots(6-2)$$

The function μ has a peak value at $\hat{\tau}=0$. If the peak value of μ is nearly equal to unity, then $R_{FF}(z,z',\tau)$ can be obtained from $R_{\tilde{F}\tilde{F}}(z,z',l,\tau)$ divided by l^2. In the low-frequency range, $\mu|_{\hat{\tau}=0}$ is nearly equal to unity, but $\mu|_{\hat{\tau}=0}$ decreases with increasing frequency. In the frequency range below 20Hz, $\mu|_{\hat{\tau}=0}$ is larger than 0.8, so that the errors are less than 20%.

3.4 The experimental results of parameter V_c and ξ

The experimental results of V_c are shown in Fig.8(a)(b). Fig.8(a) shows V_c as a function of the homogeneous void fraction ϵ_g in cases in which the nozzle-opening ratio α is unity, U is 1.9m/sec and the pressure P is 4×10^5Pa. The parameter V_c was about 2.8m/sec and almost constantly independent of ϵ_g. The parameter V_c in the case of $\alpha=0.48$, $z=0.3$m and $z'=0.5$m is shown in Fig.8(b). Fig.8(b) has a similar tendency as Fig.8(a), which also shows that the influence of the jet flow from the constriction of the flow channel on fluid force was small. In Fig.8(a)(b) the mean flow velocities of the vapor and liquid phases, u_g and u_l, which are calculated with Zuber-Findlay's correlation(9), assuming that the flow pattern is a slug flow, are also exhibited. It is shown that V_c had almost the same value as u_g. When U was 3m/sec, V_c was about 4.3m/sec and V_c had also almost the same value as u_g.

Even if the pressure P was varied to 2×10^5Pa or 3×10^5Pa, the pattern of Fig.8(a)(b) did not change.

The experimental result of parameter ξ is indicated in Fig.9. Fig.9(a) shows ξ as the function of ϵ_g in cases in which the nozzle-opening ratio α is unity and U is 1.9m/sec. The parameter ξ had a tendency to increase with the increasing homogeneous void fraction ϵ_g. Fig.9(b) shows ξ in a case in which the nozzle-opening ratio α is 0.48, $z=0.3$m and $z'=0.5$m. Fig.9(b) had a similar tendency as Fig.9(a), which also shows that the effect of the jet flow from the constriction of the flow channel on random fluid forces was small. When U was 3m/sec, ξ decreased by approximately one-half.

3.5 Estimation of tube-vibration amplitude

The amplitude of the vibration of a simply supported tube is estimated on the basis of the cross-spectral density, eq.(1). Equation (1) was obtained on the basis of the experimental data in the range of $|z'-z|<0.4$m. In this section eq.(1) is extrapolated to the range of $|z'-z|>0.4$m.

The power-spectral density of the tube-vibration displacement is expressed as

$$S_{yy}(\hat{z},f)\simeq\sum_{r=1}^{\infty}\int_0^1\int_0^1\frac{\phi_r(\hat{u})\phi_r(\hat{u}')\phi_r^2(\hat{z})}{m^2(2\pi f_r)^4}|H_r(jf)|^2$$
$$\times S_{FF}(\hat{u},\hat{u}',f)d\hat{u}'d\hat{u}\ldots\ldots(7)$$

where

$$\hat{u}=\frac{u}{L},\quad\hat{u}'=\frac{u'}{L},\quad\hat{z}=\frac{z}{L}\qquad\ldots\ldots(8)$$

The parameter m is the mass of the tube per unit length, f_r is the natural frequency of the r-th mode and L is the length of tube.

The r-th natural-mode function ϕ_r satisfies the following formula

$$\int_0^1\phi_r(\hat{u})\phi_s(\hat{u})d\hat{u}=\begin{cases}1(r=s)\\0(r\neq s)\end{cases}\qquad\ldots\ldots(9)$$

The frequency response of the r-th mode is expressed as

$$H_r(jf) = \cfrac{1}{\{1 - (\cfrac{f}{f_r})^2\} + 2j\zeta_r \cfrac{f}{f_r}} \qquad \dots\dots(10)$$

where ζ_r is the r-th mode-damping ratio.

The substitution of eq.(1) into eq.(7) yield

$$S_{yy}(\hat{z},f) \simeq \sum_{r=1}^{\infty} \frac{\phi_r^2(\hat{z})}{m^2(2\pi f_r)^4}|H_r(jf)|^2 \frac{\overline{F^2}}{f_0}\lambda(\xi L, \frac{2\pi fL}{V_c})$$

$$\lambda(\eta, S_t) = \int_0^1\int_0^1 \phi_r(\hat{u})\phi_r(\hat{u}')exp[-\eta|\hat{u}'-\hat{u}|]$$
$$\times exp[-jS_t(\hat{u}'-\hat{u})]d\hat{u}'d\hat{u}$$
$$\eta = \xi L, \quad S_t = \frac{2\pi fL}{V_c} \qquad \dots\dots(11)$$

Integrating eq.(11) in relation to f, the r.m.s.-value of the tube displacement is obtained as:

$$\sqrt{\overline{y^2}} = \sqrt{\int_0^{\infty} S_{yy}(\hat{z},f)df} \qquad \dots\dots(12)$$

Fig.10 indicates the r.m.s.-value of the vibration displacement of a simply supported tube at the center as a function of the natural frequency, which is varied with the tube-span length, where the mass per unit length of the tube is 1.25kg/m and the flexural rigidity of the cylinder is 987Nm². Fig.10 shows the response of only 1st mode to be simplicity. The damping ratio is assumed to be 0.02. $\sqrt{\overline{y^2}}$ varied in inverse proportion to the 2nd power of the natural frequency.

4. CONCLUSIONS

The cross-spectral density of the random fluid forces acting on a tube in a parallel air-water two-phase flow was investigated experimentally. The random fluid forces induced in a two-phase flow were propagated downstream at a velocity similar to the vapor phase with a reduction in magnitude. The reducing rate of the magnitude was $e^{-\xi}$ per unit length, and ξ was increasing with the increasing homogeneous void fraction of the two-phase flow. The vibration amplitude of a simply supported tube in a parallel two-phase flow was also estimated in the case the distance between the tube support was changed. The characteristics of the random fluid forces were hardly affected by the jet flow from the orifice at the nozzle-opening ratio of 48%. The characteristics of the random fluid forces were also hardly affected by the system pressure for the pressure range from 2×10^5Pa to 4×10^5Pa.

The method of extrapolation from air-water to steam-water is not yet fully understood. The result of air-water two-phase flow condition seems to be conservative, but the extrapolation method is the subject for a future study.

REFERENCES

(1) HARA, F. & YAMASHITA, T. Parallel two-phase-flow-induced vibrations in fuel pin model. Journal of Nuclear Science and Technology, 1978, 15, 346-354.

(2) KAWAMURA, K. Steam generator tube vibrations induced by two-phase jet flows from baffle plates, CRIEPI Report E282006, 1983.

(3) PETTIGREW, M. J. & GORMAN, D. J. Experimental studies on flow induced vibration to support steam generator design, AECL-4514, 1973.

(4) CARLUCCI, L. N. Damping and hydrodynamic mass of a cylinder in simulated two-phase flow, Trans. ASME Journal of Mechanical Design, 1980, 102, 597-602.

(5) CARLUCCI, L. N. & BROWN, J. D. Experimental studies of damping and hydrodynamic mass of a cylinder in confined two-phase flow, 1983, 105, 83-89.

(6) CHEN, S. S. & WAMBSGANSS, M. W. Response of a flexible rod to near-field flow noise, ANL-7685, 1970, 5-31.

(7) WAMBSGANSS, M. W. & ZALESKI, P. L. Measurement, interpretation and characterization of nearfield flow noise, ANL-7685, 1970, 112-140.

(8) GORMAN, D. J. An analytical and experimental investigation of the vibration of cylindrical reactor fuel elements in two-phase parallel flow, Nuclear Science and Engineering, 1971, 44, 277-290.

(9) ZUBER, N & FINDLAY, J. A. Average volumetric concentration in two-phase flow systems, Trans. ASME Journal of Heat Transfer, 1965, 87, 453-468.

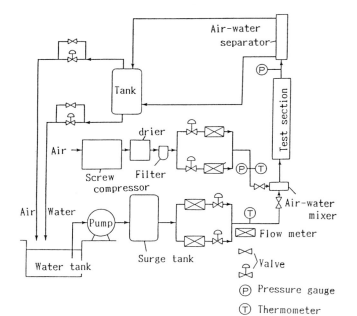

Fig.1 Schematic diagram of loop.

© IMechE 1991 C416/032

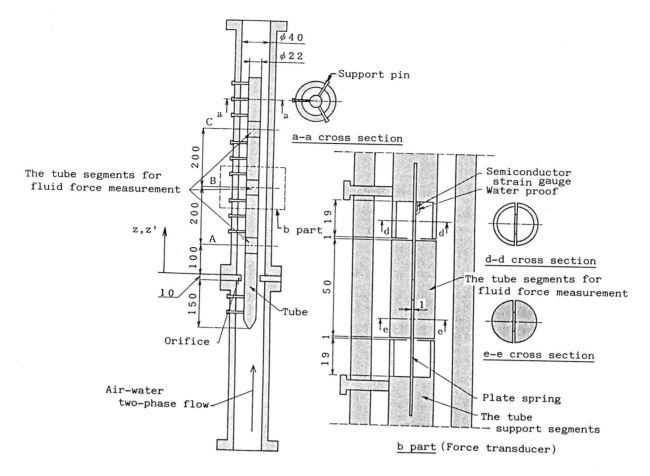

Fig.2 Test section.

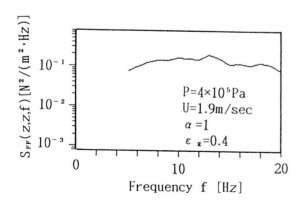

Fig.3 Power-spectral-density of fluid force field.

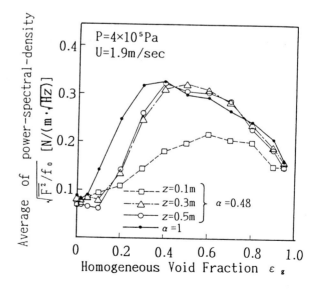

Fig.4 The square root of the average power spectral density below 20Hz (the effects of flow constriction).

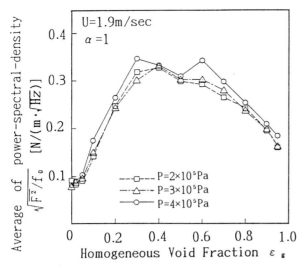

Fig.5 The square root of the average power spectral density below 20Hz(the effects of system pressure).

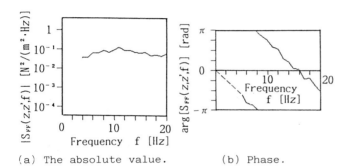

(a) The absolute value.　　(b) Phase.

Fig.6 Cross-spectral-density of fluid force field (P=4×10^{5}Pa, U=1.9m/sec, ε_g=0.4, α=1, z=0.3m, z'=0.5m).

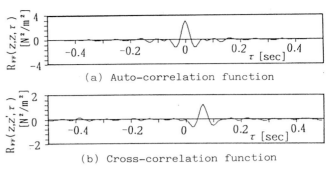

(a) Auto-correlation function

(b) Cross-correlation function

Fig.7 Auto-correlation function and cross correlation function of fluid force field (P=4×10^{5}Pa, U=1.9m/sec, ε_g=0.4, α=1).

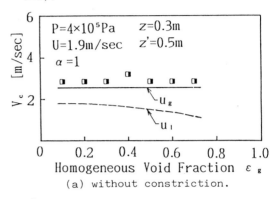

(a) without constriction.

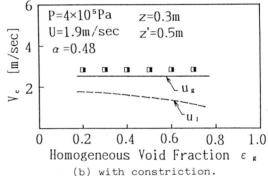

(b) with constriction.

Fig.8 Parameter V_c of eq.(1).

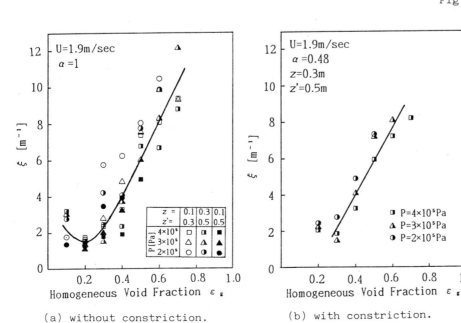

(a) without constriction.　　(b) with constriction.

Fig.9 Parameter ξ of eq.(1).

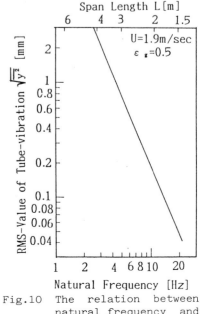

Fig.10 The relation between natural frequency and r.m.s.-value of tube vibration.

C416/105

Hanger cable oscillations on the Humber Bridge

M L STOCKWELL, CEng, MIStructE and R A EVANS, BSc, CEng, MICE. MCIT
Humber Bridge Board, Hull, North Humberside
N J CHERRY, BSc(Eng), PhD, MRAeS, DIC, ACGI *
Redland Technology Limited, Harsham, West Sussex

SYNOPSIS Large amplitude flow induced vibrations of the hanger cables on the Humber Bridge have been observed in winter when there was a significant build-up of snow and ice on the cables and deck, and also at other times of the year in rainy conditions. This paper gives a brief technical description of the bridge and its hanger cables and describes the nature of the oscillations and the circumstances in which they occur. Video recordings of the oscillations have been made using the TV monitoring system constantly operating on the bridge. It was possible to estimate typical ice shapes which have been observed on the cables. Wind tunnel tests, using a sectional model of the cables with these ice shapes modelled, confirmed galloping instability in conditions typical of those observed at full-scale. The oscillations in rainy conditions appear to be similar to those reported on cable stayed bridges. These probably occur on the Humber Bridge hanger cables because, unlike most suspension bridges, the hangers are inclined to the vertical. To date no wholly satisfactory solution has been found for either type of oscillation.

NOTATION

D	diameter of the hanger cables
f	natural frequency of fundamental mode of vibration
$L_{x,u}$	integral length scale of turbulence
m	mass per unit length of the hanger cable
Re	Reynolds number of the flow (UD/ν)
r	half spacing of model support springs (Figure 5)
U	approaching wind speed
$\sqrt{\overline{u^2}}/U$	longitudinal turbulence intensity in approach flow
δ	logarithmic decrement of damping
ν	kinematic viscosity of air
θ	approach angle of the wind, measured relative to the ice (Figure 6)
ρ	density of air

1 DESCRIPTION OF THE HUMBER BRIDGE

Designed to cross the last major unbridged estuary in Britain, the Humber Bridge (Figure 1) was opened to traffic in 1981. The design comprises a continuously welded closed box stiffening girder (as developed on the Severn and Bosporus bridges) supported from the main catenary cables by means of inclined hanger cables which have pinned connections top and bottom (Figures 2 & 3). With a main span of 1410m it has the largest bridge span in the world, 112m more than that of the Verrazano Narrows in New York. The main towers of the bridge are of reinforced concrete.

To accommodate deck movements arising from loading and temperature effects the three spans are supported at the towers and anchorages by A-frame rockers (Figure 4). The rockers permit longitudinal movements and small changes in gradient of the deck but constrain transverse movement. At the towers continuity of the road surface above the rockers is provided by a joint of the "rolling leaf" type which works after the fashion of a roll top desk (Figure 4). At the anchorages, where movements are smaller, a sliding steel joint with rubber seals is provided.

As with other long span bridges the structure is very flexible. Some of the principal movements under extreme conditions of load are (Reference 1):

a) Maximum tower top movement occurs at the Barton tower where, under the worst conditions of highway loading, the tower top deflects by 630mm.

b) The maximum vertical deflection at mid span due to the design traffic load is 3210mm; an increase of 20°C in the ambient temperature would increase the deflection by a further 1100mm.

c) The maximum transverse deflection of the deck mid-span due to winds of 48m/s at deck level is 4510mm; the main suspension cables would then move 4380mm.

2 HANGER CABLE OSCILLATIONS

In service (since 1981) the bridge hangers had generally been free from obvious oscillation with the exception of a few occasions on which oscillations of moderate amplitude (up to 0.3m on longer hangers) had been observed in rainy

* BMT Fluid Mechanics Ltd.
   (Now at Redland Technology Ltd.)

conditions. These events had been transitory and had been observed at wind speeds between 10 and 20m/s.

In December 1986 (and subsequently in January 1987) a previously unseen event of much grander proportions occurred. Following a snow storm in which cam-shaped flutes of wind driven snow had adhered to the hanger cables, violent wind induced fundamental mode hanger vibrations were observed. The cable movements were large, up to 1 metre amplitude on the longest (100 metre plus) hangers and rotation of the lower cable sockets on their pins (Figure 3) could be clearly observed, as could an unquantified deformation of the hanger cables themselves at the socket necks.

During this event a broad range of hanger lengths was simultaneously affected. When the phenomenon occurred the wind speed lay in the range 11 to 15m/s, and only occurred when the wind was in the eastern quarter. The ice flutes on the hangers were facing approximately ENE.

Following these events a series of wind tunnel tests were carried out and are described in Section 3. In January 1988, shortly after completion of these tests large amplitude oscillations of some of the longer hangers were again observed.

This event arose after a night of sporadic snow fall during which snow flutes had again formed on the hanger cables. While the hangers were moving the wind lay in the northern quarter (i.e. - running along the bridge) and its angle of approach to the snow flutes was estimated at about 25 degrees. The oscillations took place in bright sunshine between 09.40 hours and 10.10 hours and came to an abrupt end when, as a consequence of the combined effect of the rapid thaw and the violence of the hanger movements, the ice flutes were shaken loose and showered down onto the bridge.

Since 1988 the ice related phenomenon has not been observed but rain related oscillations have been observed from time to time. A typical event occurred in the spring of 1990, at a time when monitoring equipment was in place on one of the bridge hangers. The vibrations occurred during a rain storm, with a 10m/s wind blowing from the easterly quarter. Spectral analysis of the hanger movement record showed that the oscillation was mainly occurring at a frequency of 3.5Hz, i.e. the 5th mode of vibration of the hanger concerned, which had a fundamental natural frequency of 0.7Hz. Earlier occurrences were more noticeably in the fundamental mode.

Video recordings of both types of oscillation have been made using TV cameras permanently mounted on the bridge, for monitoring the carriageways. These recordings are to be shown and discussed.

3 WIND TUNNEL TESTS

Galloping instability was immediately suggested as the most likely explanation of the large amplitude oscillations with ice build-up, although other mechanisms were discussed and very largely dismissed. The oscillations in rain were assumed to be similar in mechanism to those reported on the inclined cables of some cable

stayed bridges (References 2 & 3). They appear to be related to the manner in which the water runs down the cable when there is a component of wind blowing onto the undersurface.

There are many reports in the literature of cable oscillations due to ice build-up. These are very often on overhead power lines (References 4-8 for instance), and less frequently on guyed masts and towers (Reference 9).

There are differences between the present situation and overhead power lines. Overhead power lines hang in a catenary, and as ice builds up this catenary swings or rotates due to the increased drag loading. This effect may be supplemented by a rotation of the iced section brought about by aerodynamic pitching moments. The combined effect is to change the angle at which the wind approaches the cable, until an unstable condition is approached. Large amplitude oscillations then result. In contrast, because these hanger cables are taut and near vertical they are not free to swing in the same manner. In addition they also have more torsional stiffness than power lines. As a result changes in wind angle are more likely to come from a change in wind direction, rather than a rotation of the cable. Also, being of steel the mass parameter ($m/\rho D^2 = 3900$) is somewhat larger than values commonly reported for overhead power lines.

It was decided to perform a series of sectional model tests in order to see if the full-scale behaviour of the cables with ice build-up could be reproduced in the wind tunnel. For these measurements the reported ice shapes were modelled. No efforts were made to model the rain induced oscillations.

3.1 Model details

The measurements were made using a sectional model and the wind tunnel mounting arrangement is shown in Figure 5. This allowed the sectional model to move in the across-stream and alongstream directions, and also in torsion, although in the event only across-stream motions were observed. In addition the approach angle of the wind to the cable, defined in Figure 6, could be adjusted, as could the level of structural damping incorporated into the mounting arrangement.

The tests were performed in BMT's No. 4 wind tunnel, which has a test section 2.14m square. In order that full-scale Reynolds numbers could be achieved, and that the model itself was both manageable and rigid over its length, a model scale of 0.6 was chosen. This gave a model scale diameter of 38.2mm compared with 63mm at full-scale. The dynamic properties of the model were chosen to model the fundamental mode of the long hangers (length of order 100m, natural frequency about 0.7Hz). With a model length of 2.1 metres, the model represented about 2 percent of the full-scale cable, taken out of the centre.

The model cable consisted of a length of steel tube with copper wire wound round it in a helical fashion. This was then given several coats of paint in order to partially fill in the indentations between strands as at full-scale. A strip of wood modelled the ice shape, based on eye witness accounts, together with measurements made on ice flutes which had fallen to the ground because of the large amplitudes of response. In order to check the sensitivity to the precise ice shape modelled, the initial shape suggested by the Humber Bridge Board was modified slightly by rounding the pointed nose. This shape was also tested, and is shown dotted in Figure 6. In practice there may be much larger differences in ice shape from one occurrence to another, although such effects were not studied.

3.2 Conditions for dynamic similarity

In addition to producing the correct cross-sectional shape of the cable, the reduced velocity (U/fD), the mass parameter ($m/\rho D^2$), the Reynolds number of the flow (UD/ν), and the logarithmic decrement of structural damping (δ) in the modes of interest, were all accurately reproduced. There were inevitably doubts as to the level of structural damping at full scale, and partly for that reason measurements were made over a range of values, in fact from $\delta = 0.005$ to $\delta = 0.15$. Later full scale measurements confirmed the actual value to be around $\delta = 0.02$, but the range tested gave a very useful indication of the effects of damping.

For the torsional behaviour to be correctly reproduced the non-dimensional mass moment of inertia and torsional stiffness must also be modelled. The mass moment of inertia of the model cable was slightly larger than the correct scaled value, whilst no information was available for the full-scale torsional stiffness. For this reason several different torsional stiffnesses were tested. Initially the model cable was mounted with a low torsional stiffness, although no specific full-scale value was modelled. Later sensitivity checks were performed, and showed that at likely full-scale damping levels the results were not sensitive to the precise stiffness, confirming that torsional effects were not important.

The 7° inclination of the long hangers from the vertical is of little consequence, and has been ignored in the modelling.

Clearly at the scale employed it was not possible to model the turbulence characteristics of the full-scale wind (longitudinal turbulence intensity, $\sqrt{u^2}/U$, about 11% and $L_{x,u}$ of the order of 150m at mid-hanger height). For that reason, in common with most other sectional model tests reported in the literature, the measurements were performed almost entirely in smooth flow. For the present geometry this is not seen as a serious limitation. At full-scale the size of typical energy containing eddies is very large compared with the cable diameter, such that each cross-section experiences a slowly changing velocity modelled by smooth flow.

A few measurements were also made in grid generated turbulence. This was a very poor representation of atmospheric turbulence ($\sqrt{u^2}/U = 6\%$, $L_{x,u} = 0.5m$ full-scale), and the precise interpretation of the results must be in doubt. However it is interesting to note that the results were not very different to those in smooth flow; the principal effect of the turbulence being to slightly increase the range of wind angles for which galloping was noted.

3.3 Wind tunnel results

Initially measurements were made at the lowest level of damping ($\delta = 0.005$) without the ice fitted. Only very low level wake induced oscillations were observed. (The critical wind speed for vortex shedding response would correspond with 0.32m/s at full-scale, although no response was observed).

The measurements were then repeated for a range of damping levels with the ice fitted. The ice shape was then modified as indicated in Figure 6, and key measurements were repeated. A few measurements were also repeated in grid generated turbulence, and also a few with different levels of torsional stiffness - most of the measurements having been performed at a low value. The torsional stiffness was varied by adjusting the spacing between the vertical spring supports (2r in Figure 5).

Key results with ice shapes fitted are summarised in Figures 7,8,9 & 10. Except for the results in Figure 10, all results were measured in smooth flow. Figure 7 is typical of all of the instabilities observed, with the onset being marked by an extremely violent increase in response, such that further increases in wind speed were not possible. The instabilities involved motion almost exclusively in the across-stream direction, there being virtually no along-stream or torsional response. Replacing the along-stream springs in Figure 5 by stiff wires, thus eliminating the possibility of streamwise motion had no effect on the observed response. Neither were the results strongly dependent upon the model being given an initial disturbance of moderate amplitude.

For both the original and modified ice shapes, Figure 8 shows that instability occurred (at wind speeds below the 21m/s full-scale top wind speed of the tunnel) for only a fairly narrow range of wind angles θ (labelled ice angle in Figures 8 & 10). This range corresponded with $26° \leq \theta \leq 31°$ for the original ice shape, and $29° \leq \theta \leq 35°$ for the modified ice shape, where theta is defined as in Figure 6. This range increased slightly when testing was performed in grid turbulence (Figure 10), at least in part because the cross-stream fluctuations in wind speed can themselves be regarded as a variation in approach wind angle.

Testing at different torsional stiffnesses produced similar results at dampings typical of full-scale (Figure 9), thus confirming that torsion does not play a significant role. Instead it is principally the wind vector which must rotate once ice formation has taken place.

As expected the level of structural damping had a significant effect upon the critical wind speed for the onset of instability. This is clearly evident in Figure 9, an increase in damping causing an increase in the critical wind speed. Damping measurements on the full-scale hangers showed values of logarithmic decrement of about $\delta = 0.02$, which is well towards the lower end of the range considered. The principal sources of damping are rotation of the cable fixings, and some relative sliding between adjacent wire strands within the cable.

3.4 Comparison between full-scale and model-scale behaviour

The wind tunnel results suggest that once the ice has formed, the wind must veer round before instability is likely to occur. The wind at the site is turbulent, with streamwise turbulence levels about 11 percent, and lateral turbulence levels about 8 percent, both at mid hanger height. Since turbulence causes fluctuations in wind angle, the shift in wind direction will not need to be as large as those noted from the wind tunnel tests, but would nevertheless be expected to be significant. Such a swing in direction was observed from the wind records measured on the bridge.

During the instance in January 1988 described in detail in Section 2, the wind direction was estimated to be about 25 degrees to the ice flutes. They built up during the early hours of the morning in light winds, and pointed roughly ENE. The oscillations took place between 09.40 hours and 10.10 hours during which period the wind direction had shifted to a more northerly direction. Subsequent examination of the records from the earlier instance in December 1986, which had prompted the study, showed that the ice flutes had built up whilst the wind was blowing fairly consistently from the ENE, and the oscillations occurred when it shifted to a more easterly direction. Again this is broadly consistent with the wind tunnel observations.

Having established similar trends in wind direction between the wind tunnel and full-scale observations, it is interesting to compare the wind speeds measured on site during these oscillations, with the critical wind speeds measured in the wind tunnel. During the oscillations of January 1988 the wind records showed that the oscillations coincided with an increase in wind speed from about 6-10m/s, to 12-15m/s. During the earlier instance of December 1986, the wind speeds prevailing during the oscillations were of similar magnitude at 11-15m/s. These were measured on an anemometer mounted 6.3m above deck level, on a mast along the span of the bridge. Assuming likely approach wind profiles, the approach wind speed at mid hanger height may be 15-20 percent higher than at anemometer level. However the anemometer wind speed indication is probably subject to an acceleration caused by the presence of the deck, which will absorb some of this difference. Nevertheless the wind speeds at mid hanger height will still be slightly higher than those measured by the anemometer.

Assuming a full-scale damping of $\delta = 0.02$ the wind tunnel suggests a critical wind speed for the onset of oscillations as low as 4m/s (Figure 9), although there is a significant increase away from the most susceptible wind angle (Figure 8). Given the various uncertainties in the modelling, including uncertainties as to the precise ice shape, and given that the wind may not have been approaching from the worst angle, and will not be as well correlated up the height of the cable at full-scale, this level of agreement is considered reasonable.

4 CLOSING REMARKS

Having confirmed that the large amplitude oscillations of the cables with ice build-up were due to galloping instability, some thought was given to possible solutions. To date (not surprisingly) no wholly satisfactory solution has been found (either for these or the rain induced oscillations).

The wind tunnel tests clearly showed the beneficial effect of increased structural damping for increasing the critical windspeed for the onset of instability with ice build-up, although this could not be used to suppress the galloping. If the critical wind speed were to be increased above a sensible design wind speed, then for the ice shape considered a damping level in excess of $\delta = 0.1$ would probably be required. Increased damping is used on many suspension and cable stayed bridges to eliminate aeolian oscillations in the higher modes of the cables. This has been achieved in several different ways: Stockbridge type dampers, car shock absorbers between the cables and the deck, and elastomer damping materials incorporated into the anchorages. These would not be sufficiently effective to suppress galloping oscillations.
A Stockbridge damper tuned to damp the fundamental mode would also be rather ungainly, and would be an eyesore mounted high up on the hangers.

Connecting the cables together thus eliminating the modes of concern would be more effective, and has been employed on some cable stayed bridges to eliminate rain induced oscillations. For the longest hangers several interconnections would be required to move the critical wind speed above the design wind speed. This would be costly, would create an eyesore, and would also raise quite substantial maintenance problems in its own right.

None of these suggestions attack the root of the problem - the build-up of ice, and there seems little prospect of doing so, short of heating the cables. It is fortunate that occurrences are comparatively rare.

Some consideration has been given to adding spiral protuberances to the cables to influence the manner in which water runs down them, in order to cure the rain induced vibrations. However the fear is that these could aggravate the ice problem.

5 ACKNOWLEDGEMENTS

The authors gratefully acknowledge the assistance of Mr. A.M. Elliott of BMT Fluid Mechanics Ltd. during the wind tunnel testing.

REFERENCES

(1) FISHER, D. Design and construction of the Humber Bridge. Physics Education, 17, 5th September 1982.

(2) HIKAMI, Y. and SHIRAISHI, N. Rain induced vibrations of cables in cable stayed bridges. Proc. of 7th Int. Conf. on Wind Eng., Aachen, July 1987.

(3) LANGSOE, H.E. and LARSEN, O.D. Cable stay oscillations caused by direct excitation of the stays by the wind (rain vibrations). Proc. of Int. Conf. on Cable Stayed Bridges, Bangkok, Nov. 1987.

(4) PARKINSON, G.V. Aeroelastic galloping in one degree of freedom. Proceedings of Conference on Wind Effects on Buildings & Structures. Held at NPL, June 1963.

(5) HOGG, A.D. and EDWARDS, A.T. The status of the conductor galloping problem in Canada. Proceedings of Conference on Wind Effects on Buildings & Structures. Held at NPL, June 1963.

(6) RICHARDSON, A.S. Jr., MARTUCCELLI, J.R. and PRICE, W.S. Research study on galloping of electric power transmission lines - Part I. Proceedings of Conference on Wind Effects on Buildings & Structures. Held at NPL, June 1963.

(7) BLEVINS, R.D. Flow Induced Vibration, Publ. Van Nostrand Reinhold.

(8) SMITH, I.P. The suppression of oscillations of overhead lines. CERL Report RD/L/N174/66.

(9) FISCHER, O. Vibration absorbers for the stays of guyed masts. Acta Technica CSAV, 1987, Vol. 32, No. 1, pp.95-111.

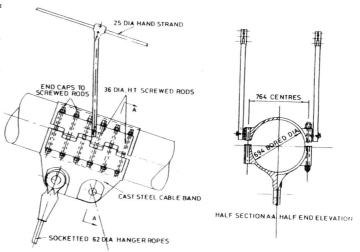

FIG 2 CABLE BAND DETAILS

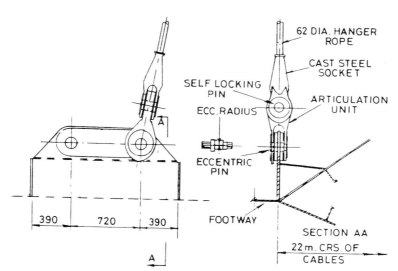

FIG 3. HANGER CONNEXION-DOUBLE PIN PLATE ARTICULATED SOCKET

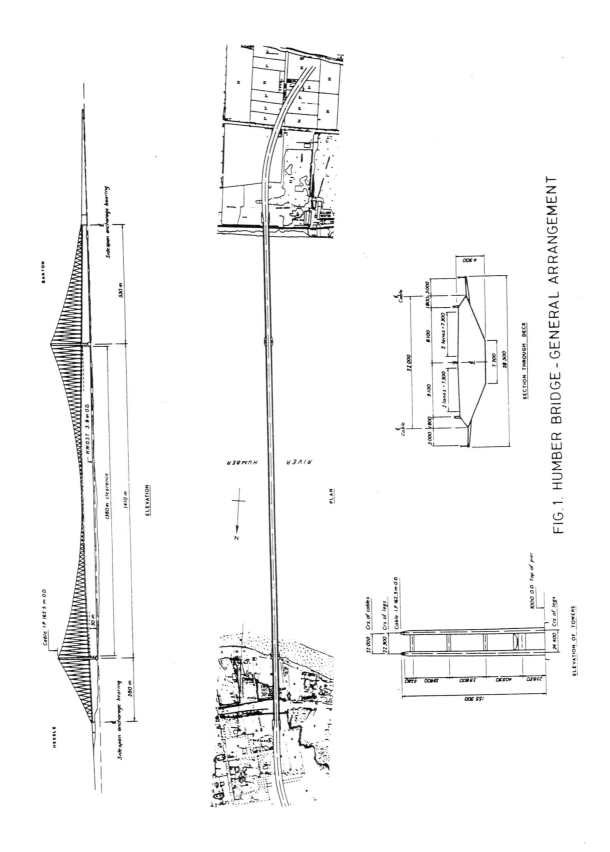

FIG. 1. HUMBER BRIDGE - GENERAL ARRANGEMENT

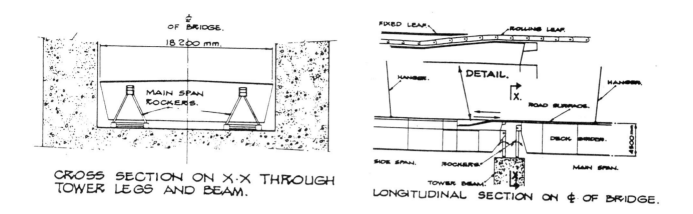

CROSS SECTION ON X·X THROUGH TOWER LEGS AND BEAM.

LONGITUDINAL SECTION ON ₵ OF BRIDGE.

FIG. 4. ROCKERS AND EXPANSION JOINTS

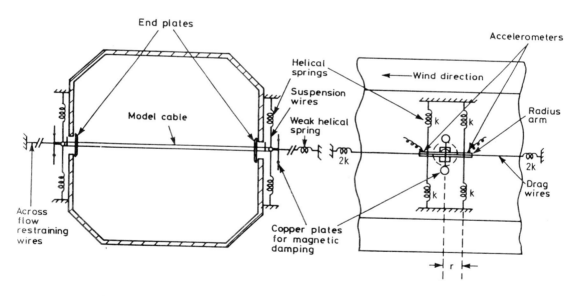

Fig 5 Diagrammatic sketch showing the dynamic rig for the model cable

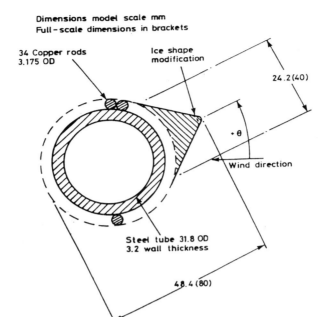

Dimensions model scale mm
Full-scale dimensions in brackets

34 Copper rods
3.175 OD

Ice shape
modification

24.2(40)

θ

Wind direction

Steel tube 31.8 OD
3.2 wall thickness

48.4 (80)

Fig 6 Construction of the model cable

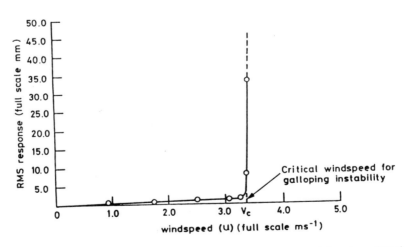

Critical windspeed for
galloping instability

Fig 7 Displacement response of the model cable: original ice shape (fig 1)
θ = 29 degrees, δ_s = 0.005

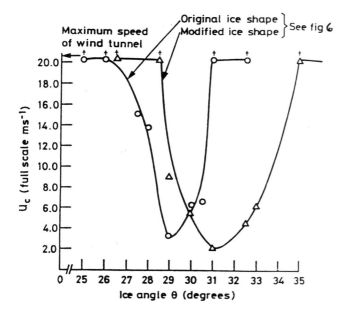

Fig 8 The effect of ice shape on critical windspeed for galloping instability, $r = 0.1$ m, $\delta_s = 0.005$

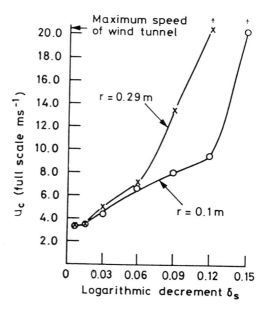

Fig 9 The effect of structural damping on critical windspeed for galloping instability : original ice shape (fig 1) $\theta = 29$ degrees

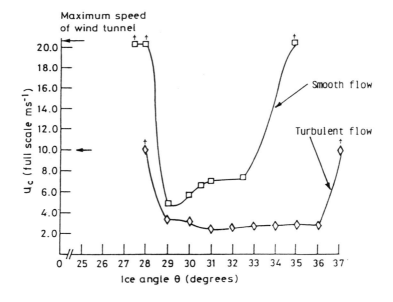

Fig 10 The effect of turbulence on critical windspeed for galloping instability :

C416/037

Countermeasures for rain–wind induced vibration from the viewpoint of aerodynamic stabilization

T KINOSHITA, H NAKANISHI, PhD and K-I SUGII
Kobe Steel Limited, Kobe, Japan

SYNOPSIS: Wind-tunnel tests for inclined cables with circular and polygonal cross-sections have been conducted to evaluate their oscillation characteristics due to wind and rain. From an aerodynamic point of view, except for a few cases using a hexagonal shape, the stability of polygonal shapes was much greater than that of the circular shape. The octagonal cross-section shows an especially high stability among polygonal shapes. Through experimental results and investigations, octagonal shaped cable is proposed as a countermeasure for rain-wind induced vibration in cable-stayed bridge has been proposed

NOTATION

α : horizontal angle of inclined cable
β : vertical angle of inclined cable
θ : angle of stagnation point from horizontal line
ξ : angle from stagnation point
δ : logarithmic decrement
ρ : density of air
A : oscillation amplitude
D : diameter of cylinder
U : mean velocity of wind
f_y : natural frequency
F_D : drag force
C_D : drag force coefficient
F_L : lift force
C_L : lift force coefficient
F_y : vertical force
C_y : vertical force coefficient

1. Introduction

From recent observations of the cables in cable-stayed bridges, it has been reported that an interesting vibration phenomenona, so-called "Rain-Wind Induced Vibration," arises under rainfall conditions.

Hikami[1] reported that the rain drops flow down the cable and two water rivulets are formed on the upper and lower side of the cable surface, and that the inclination of the cable is a critical factor in this phenomenon. Yamaguchi[2] proposed a 2-degree of freedom model consisting of the vertical motion of the cable and the circumferential vibration of the water rivulet. From this model he determined that the circumferential vibration of the water rivulet located on the upper side surface is important. Matsumoto, et al.,[3],[4] pointed out that there is an axial flow behind the inclined cable and the aerodynamic instability of the inclined cable is caused by this axial flow. However, it is not clear how the water rivulet affects the vibration of the cable.

The vibration of the cables of cable-stayed bridges raises the problem of fatigue at cable attachments, as well as the uneasiness of people on the bridge. Therefore, many countermeasures[5],[6],[7] have been proposed, such as mechanical dampers, oil dampers at the end of the cable, gear shaped cable, v-shaped channel cable or cable with spiral protuberances.

In this paper, the results of wind tunnel tests are presented, in which various cross-sectional shaped cable are examined in order to maximize aerodynamic stability in the inclined cables. Based on this study, countermeasures for this "rain-wind induced vibration" in cable-stayed bridges have been proposed and are presented herein. First, in order to determine the fundamental relation between separation points, position of rivulets and aerodynamic response, flow visualization and response measurements were conducted by placing artificial rivulets on the cable. Second, the cable was given various polygonal cross-sections. Water was sprinkled on the surface of these various shaped cross-sections, and it was found that rivulets were formed at a corner of the surface of the polygon, the location depending on the cable cross-sectional shape regardless of wind or amount of rainfall. Aerodynamic stability was achieved due to the polygonal shape. From these results, it can be seen that it is possible to choose cross-sectional shapes in such a way as to reduce vibration caused by wind and rain.

2. Aerodynamic Characteristics of Inclined Cables

2-1 Oscillation of Inclined Cables

In order to see how the water rivulets affect the vibration of the inclined cable, a fundamental experiment was conducted, where a string (diameter=1.0mm) was used as an artificial rivulet to replace the actual water rivulets. Using such artifical rivulets, characteristics of the vibration such as the amplitude of the cable and the separation point of the boundary layer of the flow were easily and accurately measured as a function of the position of the rivulet in conjunction with the wind direction.

An Eiffel type wind tunnel (1.2m height, 1.2m width) was used in this experiment. A polyvinyl-chloride pipe was employed as the cable model, and the model was placed just at the exit of the wind tunnel.

Figure 1 illustrates the experimental apparatus. Figure 2 shows the angle of inclination of the cable. Figure 3 defines the attack angle and shows aerodynamic forces on the cross-section of the cable with artificial rivulets. As shown in this illustration, vertical springs support the cable model and wire was used to prevent the cable from moving horizontally. The conditions of this experiment are shown in Table 1. Hikami[1] reported that the water rivulets were formed on the upper and lower surface of the cable when the inclination of the cable is $\alpha = \beta = 45°$, and the amplitude of the cable oscillation become larger compared with that of the cable with the other inclination. Matsumoto et al.[3] described that when the inclination of the cable is similar as the above ($\alpha = 45°$, $\beta = 42.5°$), the inclined cable is aerodynamic unstable and the vibration occurs. Therefore in order to raise the vibration phenomena the experiment was examed under the condition which is $\alpha = \beta = 45°$.

Table 1 Experimental Conditions

Cable model		
Material	Polyvinyl-Chloride Pipe	
Length	2.6	m
Diameter	0.165	m
Weight	3.9	kg/m
Natural frequency	fy = 1.17	Hz
Logarithmic decrement	δ = 0.005	
Wind velocity	U = 0 to 25	m/s
Horizontal angle	α = 45°	
Vertical angle	β = 45°	
Reynolds number	Re = ~2.57×10^5	

Before advancing to the experimental stage, we first considered where the artificial rivulets should be fixed so as to see how the rivulet position affects the vibration of the inclied cable. The position of the stagnation point on the inclined cable can be approximated from the following equation[4]:

$$\theta = 90° - \arccos\left\{ \frac{\sin\alpha \cdot \sin\beta}{(\sin^2\alpha + \cos^2\alpha \cdot \cos^2\beta)^{1/2}} \right\}$$

In addition, it has been reported by Hikami that water rivulets can be seen at two places, between 20° and 60°, and between 140° and 160° from the top of the cable. Therefore, we fixed the position of the artificial rivulets at the places shown in Table 2, where the location is described by the angle ξ between that and the stagnation point.

Table 2 Experimental Cases

Case	ξ
1.	75°
2.	85°
3.	95°

In the experiments, the wind velocity and the amplitude of the cable were measured, and the angle of the separation point from the stagnation point was observed using flow visualization techniques. Figure 4 shows the result of the measurements, in which the response of the cable is plotted against the wind velocity for positions of the artificial rivulets at $\xi = 75°$, 85°, 95°. It can be seen that large amplitudes appear in both $\xi = 85°$ and 95°, but the response is not as large for $\xi = 75°$. This indicates that the rivulet positions of $\xi = 85°$ and 95° were able to simulate rain-wind induced vibration. Figure 5 shows the relationship between the artificial rivulet point and the measured maximum amplitude. In this figure, the angle of the separation points is also shown. In addition, as well as shown in Ref. 8, it was observed that the angle of the separation point, ξ, is distributed from 75° to 80° in all three cases. It has been found that the rivulet position of $\xi = 75°$ is on up-stream side of the separation point, but those of $\xi = 85°$ and 95° are on the down-stream side of the separation point. In other words, it can be said that artificial rivulets make the inclined cable unstable only when their position is down-stream of the separation points.

3. Countermeasures for Rain-Wind Induced Vibration

From the results of the experiments of inclined cables with artificial rivulets described in the previous section, an important consideration for developing countermesures to "Rain-Wind Induced Vibration" was found. When artificial rivulets were located up-stream of the separation point, the cable response was small even under the cable inclination, $\alpha = \beta = 45°$.

For this reason, it can be considered that these special artificial rivulets acted as dampers to reduce the vibration due to rain and wind. In order to apply this concept to any wind direction, cables with polygonal cross-sections such as hexagonal, octagonal or decagonal can be considered as the cable for cable-stayed bridges.

3-1 Aerodynamic Force Coefficient of Polygonal Vertically Stayed Cable (2-Dimensional Model)

Aerodynamic force coefficients of these polygonal shapes have been measured in a two dimensional model constructed of wood and then painted. Table 3 shows the experimental conditions and the definition of attack angle and diameter.

Table 3 Experimental Conditions

Cable model		
Material	Wood	
Length	1.0	m
Diameter	0.165	m
Attack angle	η = -30° to 30°	
Wind velocity	U = 5, 10, 15	m/s
Reynolds number	Re = 5.14×10^4, 1.03×10^5, 1.54×10^5	

Definition of attack angle and diameter

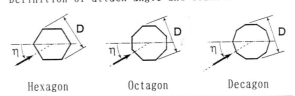

Hexagon   Octagon   Decagon

The static drag, F_D, and lift, F_L, were measured by a load-cell. The static drag coefficient, C_D, lift coefficient, C_L, and vertical force coefficient, C_y, were calculated by the following equations:

$$C_D = \frac{F_D}{\frac{1}{2}\rho U^2 D}$$

$$C_L = \frac{F_L}{\frac{1}{2}\rho U^2 D}$$

$$C_y = (C_L + C_D \tan\eta)\sec\eta$$

where ρ is the density of air, U is the mean velocity, D is the diameter and η is the angle of attack.

Figure 6 shows typical results of the experiments, where the aerodynamic coefficient is plotted against the angle of attack of the wind. The aerodynamic coefficient was almost independent of the Reynolds number, therefore this figure shows the

© IMechE 1991 C416/037

result under the condition of Re=1.03×10⁵. As is well-known, the result of the hexagonal cross-section shows aerodynamic instability, because dCy/dη < 0 at η =0°. However, octagonal and decagonal cross-sections show aerodynamic stability, as those aerodynamic coefficients increase monotonically in the range of −30° < η < 30°, though the rate of increase is small in the range of −10° < η < 10°.

3-2 Vibration Response of Polygonal Cross-Section Inclined Cable without Rain

Dynamic experiments on inclined cable with polygonal cross-sections were conducted. The method of supporting the cable model was the same as used in the cylindrical cable model. However, these experiments have been conducted at various horizontal angles of α =0°, 20°, 40° and 45°, and for hanging from the vertical spring at the corner and at the face. Cable models were constructed of wood and then painted, with the outer diameter, length and weight made equal to the cylindrical case (D=0.165 m, l=2.6 m, w=3.9 kg/m, and natural frequency of approximatly fy=1.17 Hz).

Typical results of the experiments are shown in Figure 7. Figure 7(a) shows the relationship between wind velocity and oscillation amplitude for horizontal angles of α = 0°, 20°, 40° and 45° for the octagonal cross-section cable. Figure 7(b) shows the results for a horizontal angle of α = 45° for the hexagonal, octagonal and decagonal cases. In addition, the results of the cylindrical cable tests with artificial rivulets are also shown on those figures. In figure 6, the negative slope of the Cy curve are recognized at the regions of η =±10° to ±15°. However it is considered that the vibration of large amplitude does not occur because the region of negative slope is small and the slope is not steep.

Through comparing the results of the polygonal cross-sectional cable with that of the cylindrical cable with rivulets, it was found that the amplitude of the polygonal type is always smaller than that of cylindrical type. Further, it can be seen that the amplitude of the octagonal cable is the smallest among the three types of polygonal cables. This result indicates that the octagonal cross-section cable is highly stable from an aerodynamic viewpoint.

3-3 Effect of Rain on Polygonal Cable

In order to determine the behavior of inclined octagonal cross-section cable under rain and wind condition, experiments utilizing a water spray from the top of model to simulate rainfall, were conducted.

Wind velocity and oscillation amplitude were measured and the formation of water rivulets on the surface of cable was observed. The method of supporting the cable model was the same as in the dynamic vibration experiment, and the octagonal cross-section model was used as a typical polygonal cross-sectional cable at an inclination of α =45°, β =45°.

The cable surface with water rivulets is shown in Photographs 1(a) and (b). The number and width of the water rivulets were due to both volume of water supply and wind velocity, but each water rivulet was located behind a corner on the surface of the cable.

Water was splashing from each corner on the bottom side of the cable. The separation point on the polygonal cable is fixed at a corner, hence the

position of the separation point is not changed by a water rivulet located at the corner.

Figure 8 shows the relationship between the wind velocity and the response of the amplitude of the cable with octagonal cross-section for both with and without water spray. As can be seen, water rivulets did not affect the behavior of cable by increasing the vibration. More precisely, the water rivulets function as a damper to reduce the vibration.

4. Conclusions

From the results of wind-tunnel tests on the aerodynamic stability of inclined cables, the following conclusion were obtained :

1) The inclined circular cable model that holds the artificial rivulets just behind the separation point of the boundary layer of the flow incurs intensive vibration.

2) When the artificial rivulets are located on the up-stream side of the separation point, the oscillation amplitude is fairly small compared with the above. In other words, the inclined cable with the separation point moved to the up-stream side of the original position, has the effect of atenuation of the vibration.

3) It is ascertained that the octagonal or decagonal cross-section cable is aerodynamically stable.

4) The rainfall does not affect the stability of the inclined cable with polygonal cross-section

5) Inclined cable with a polygonal cross-section has high aerodynamic stability. Octagonal cross-section cable is more aerodynamically stable than hexagonal or decagonal cable. Polygonal cross-section cable is easily manufactured because of its simplicity. Therefore it is proposed that octagonal cross-section cable be used as the countermeasure for "rain-wind induced vibration."

References

1) Hikami, U. :Rain Vibrations of Cables in Cable-Stayed Bridge, J. of Wind Engrg., No. 27, March 1986, pp17-28
2) Yamaguchi, H. :Analytical Study on Growth Mechanism of Rain Vibration of Cables, J. of Wind Engrg. No. 37, Oct., 1988, pp113-120
3) Matsumoto, M., N. Shiraishi, M, Kitazawa, C. Knisely, H. Shirato, Y. Kim and M. Tsujii:Aerodynamic Behavior of Inclined Circular Cylinders-Cable Aerodynamics:J. of Wind Engrg., No. 37, Oct., 1988, pp103-112
4) Matsumoto, M., N. Shiraishi, M. Tsujii and S. Hirai:On Aerodynamic Oscillation of Cables for Cable Stayed Bridges, J. of Japan Soc. of Civil Engrs., No. 416, 1990
5) Baba, K., T. Ohta and H. Katsuchi:Mechanical Damper for the Cables of Cable-Stayed Bridges, Honshi Technical Report, Vol. 12, no. 47, 1988, pp15-23
6) Miyazaki, M. and Y. Ohhashi:Experimental Study for Control of Wind-Induced Vibration of Cable-Stayed Bridge, Preprint of 43rd annual meeting of Japan Soc. of Civil Engrs., 1988, pp718-719
7) Miyazaki, M. and H. Kudo:Experimental Study for Reduction Effect of Vibration due to V-Stripe, Preprint of 44th annual meeting of Japan Soc. of Civil Engrs., 1989, pp-842-843
8) Nishimura, H and H. Nakanishi:Locations of Flow Separation Points under the Rain Vibration of Cables, J. of Wind Engneering, Vol. 30, 1989

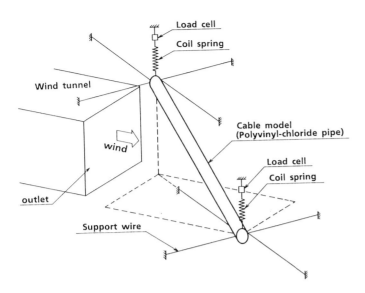

Figure 1 Experimental set-up of inclined cable.

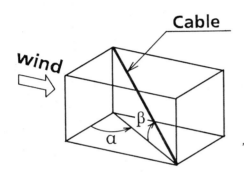

Figure 2 Inclination of cable against wind.

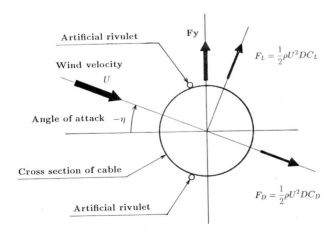

Figure 3 Definition of angle of attack and various aerodynamic forces on cross section with artificial rivulets.

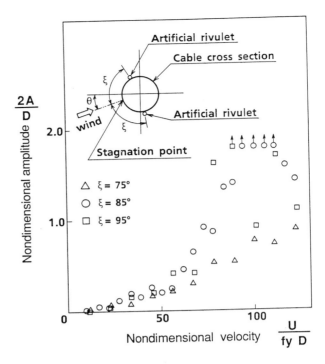

Figure 4 Relationship between wind velocity and oscillation amplitude of inclined cable with artificial rivulet attached at angle $\xi = 75°$, $85°$ and $95°$ from stagnation point.

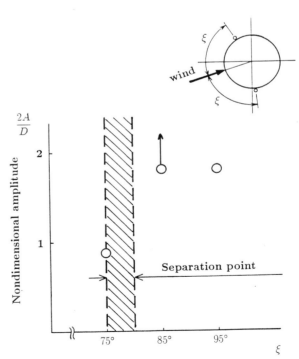

Figure 5 Relationship between position of artificial rivulet, maximum oscillation amplitude and separation point.

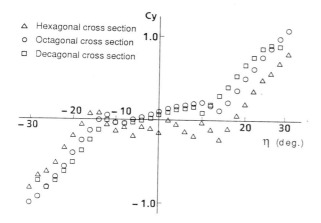

Figure 6 Aerodynamic coefficient as a function of angle of attack for hexagonal, octagonal and decagonal cross section.

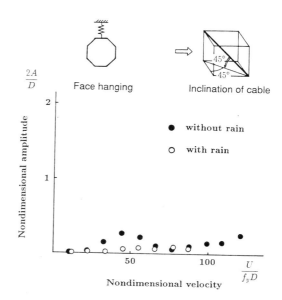

Figure 8 Effect of rain on inclined octagonal cable.

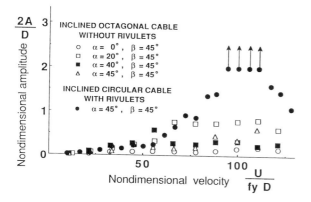

a. Velocity vs. Amplitude diagram for octagonal cable with various horizontal angles α. ($\beta = 45°$) (corner hanging)

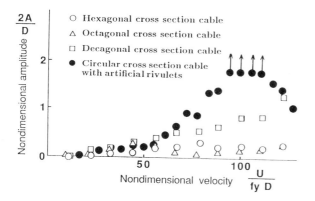

b. Velocity vs. Amplitude diagram for various polygonal cables at the same inclination as circular cable ($\alpha = 45°$, $\beta = 45°$). (face hanging)

Figure 7 Relationship between wind velocity and oscilation amplitude for inclined polygonal cable.

a. Upper surface of inclined octagonal cable. Wind blows from left hand side.

b. Lower surface of inclined octagonal cable. Wind blows from right hand side.

Photograph 1 Surface of inclined octagonal cable under rainfall conditions.

Streamwise galloping of a rough-walled circular cylinder

Y TOMONARI, PhD
Department of Aeronautical Engineering, Nippon Bunri University, Japan

SYNOPSIS Streamwise free-oscillations of an elastically suspended rough-walled circular cylinder in a uniform flow are examined both theoretically and experimentally. Attention is focussed on very slow and small-amplitude oscillations where aerodynamic forces are thought to be quasi-steady and linear. A quasi-steady linear theory is derived first, which gives a relationship that combines the drag coefficient of a stationary cylinder with the logarithmic decrement of free oscillations of the same cylinder. Experimental data both for stationary and oscillating cylinders are presented next for a range of the reduced velocity of the main flow (85-850), the Reynolds number (7500-75000) and the roughness ratio (0, 0.61-3.98 per cent). The data show disagreement of the relationship mentioned above. The disagreement occurs over a wide range of the Reynolds number across the critical regime and it becomes severe for the high roughness ratio. Finally some data are presented which are obtained by using a highly roughened cylinder subjected to forced oscillations with a constant amplitude. The data show a clear sign of the presence of an unusual phase difference between the velocity of the cylinder and its base pressure. This effect, a kind of hysteresis, can be the cause of the disagreement between the quasi-steady linear theory and experiments.

NOTATION

c	structual damping constant per unit span
C_D	drag coefficient; $D / (\frac{1}{2} \rho U^2 h)$
C_D'	derivative; dC_D / dR_v
D	drag force per unit span
f	frequency of oscillation
f_0	fundamental frequency of oscillation
h	cylinder diameter
k	spring constant per unit span
m	mass per unit span of a cylinder
r	roughness height
R_v	Reynolds number; $U h / \nu$
R_v	Reynolds number; $V h / \nu$
$R_{\dot{x}}$	Reynolds number; $\dot{x} h / \nu$
t	time
U	free stream velocity for a stationary cylinder
V	free stream velocity for an oscillating cylinder
x	streamwise displacement of a cylinder
$\dot{x}$	streamwise velocity of a cylinder
$\ddot{x}$	streamwise acceleration of a cylinder
$\emptyset$	phase difference of either base or stagnation pressures with respect to $\dot{x}$
δ	logarithmic decrement with a cylinder immersed in a uniform flow
δ_0	logarithmic decrement with a cylinder immersed in a vacuum
ν	kinematic viscosity of fluid
ρ	density of fluid

1 INTRODUCTION

The subject of flow-induced streamwise oscillations of an elastically suspended circular cylinder has been one of the topics of recent concern [1]. It seems, however, that streamwise oscillations in a high velocity range where the reduced velocity exceeds the order of 100 have not been studied except very few examples, though it is recognized that self-excited oscillations may take place there [2,3]. The present study aims to derive a basic relationship assuming quasi-steady and linear aerodynamic forces (§2) and also aims to examine how the theory agrees with the experiments (§3). The latter is accomplished with use of a circular cylinder fitted with surface roughness. Special attention was paid to critical Reynolds number ranges.

2 A QUASI-STEADY LINEAR THEORY OF STREAMWISE GALLOPING

A sketch of the present problem of streamwise oscillations is shown in Fig. 1(a), where a cylinder is exposed to a uniform flow and it is suspended elastically in the streamwise direction. We assume that the equation of motion is expressed as follows;

$$m\ddot{x} + c\dot{x} + kx = D, \tag{1}$$

and we will consider flows where the condition,

$$V/fh \gg 1, \tag{2}$$

is satisfied. The condition of Eq. (2) allows us to assume that the transient value of the drag force, D, which is shown in Fig. 1(a), should be equivalent to the steady value of the drag force which is shown with the same symbol, D, in Fig. 1(b), where U is a constant velocity given by a relative speed at an arbitrary instant as follows;

$$U = V - \dot{x}. \tag{3}$$

We can, therefore, introduce drag coefficient, as follows;

$$D = \frac{1}{2} \rho U^2 h C_D (R_v). \tag{4}$$

Note that the notation $C_D (R_v)$ means that C_D is a function of R_v. Since a relation, $R_v = R_v - R_{\dot{x}}$, holds (cf. Eq. (3)), we can expand $C_D (R_v)$ around R_v as follows;

$$C_D (R_v) = C_D (R_v) - C_D' (R_v) R_{\dot{x}}, \tag{5}$$

where $C_D (R_v)$ is given by $[C_D (R_v)]_{R_v = R_v}$ and $C_D' (R_v)$ is given by $[C_D' (R_v)]_{R_v = R_v}$. Higher order terms are neglected in Eq. (5) as we are considering the small-amplitude oscillations where

$$R_v \gg R_{\dot{x}} \tag{6}$$

holds. Substituting Eq. (5) and (3) into Eq. (4), together with a definition of $R_{\dot{x}} = \dot{x} h / \nu$, and again disregarding higher order terms with respect to $\dot{x}$, we obtain

$$D = \tfrac{1}{2} \rho V^2 h\, C_D\,(\,R_V\,)$$
$$- \rho V h\,(\ C_D\,(\,R_V\,)$$
$$+ \tfrac{1}{2}\,C_D'\,(\,R_V\,)\,R_V\,)\,\dot{x}. \quad (7)$$

Note that Eq. (7) has been made linear to $\dot{x}$, by abbreviation. Substituting Eq. (7) into Eq. (1), we obtain

$$m\ \ddot{x}\ +\ \{\,c\ +\ \rho V h\,(\ C_D\,(\,R_V\,)$$
$$+ \tfrac{1}{2}\,C_D'\,(\,R_V\,)\,R_V\,)\,\}\dot{x} + k\ x$$
$$= \tfrac{1}{2}\,\rho V^2 h\, C_D\,(\,R_V\,). \quad (8)$$

In order to eliminate the constant right-hand side of Eq. (8), we will adopt a new variable x_1 as follows;

$$x\ =\ x_1\ +\ (\ \tfrac{1}{2}\,\rho V^2 h\, C_D\,(\,R_V\,)\,)\,/\,k. \quad (9)$$

Substituting Eq. (9) into Eq. (8), we obtain

$$m\ \ddot{x}_1\ +\ \{\,c\ +\ \rho V h\,(\ C_D\,(\,R_V\,)$$
$$+ \tfrac{1}{2}\,C_D'\,(\,R_V\,)\,R_V\,)\,\}\dot{x}_1$$
$$+ k\ x_1\ =\ 0\,, \quad (10)$$

which has a form of a linear equation for damped oscillations. Based on general relations for damped oscillations, the coefficient of $\dot{x}_1$ in Eq. (10) can be connected to δ by the following equation if δ is small enough;

$$c\ +\ \rho V h\,(\ C_D\,(\,R_V\,)$$
$$+ \tfrac{1}{2}\,C_D'\,(\,R_V\,)\,R_V\,)\ =\ 2\,m\,\delta\,f_0. \quad (11)$$

For a special hypothetical case when the cylinder is immersed in a vacuum (ie. $\rho = 0$), Eq. (11) will reduce to

$$c\ =\ 2\,m\,\delta_0\,f_0. \quad (12)$$

Subtraction between Eq. (11) and (12) yields a relation,

$$C_D\,(\,R_V\,)\ +\ \tfrac{1}{2}\,C_D'\,(\,R_V\,)\,R_V$$
$$= 2\,(\,m\,/\,\rho h^2\,)(\,V\,/\,f_0\,h\,)^{-1}\,(\,\delta\ -\ \delta_0\,). \quad (13)$$

The value of the left-hand side of Eq. (13) would be given by stationary tests (§3.2(a)), while that of the right-hand side by free-oscillation tests (§3.2(b)). Q_1 and Q_2 will be refered to as the left- and the right-hand sides of Eq. (13), respectively.

3 EXPERIMENT

3.1 Experimental apparatus

(a) Wind tunnel
A closed loop low speed wind tunnel was used. The test section had a 40×40 cm cross section and a streamwise length of 66 cm. The r.m.s. turbulence level was 0.2 per cent and the maximum wind speed was 40 m/s, approximately.

(b) Model
A circular cylinder whose outer surface was roughened by densely distributed small particles with irregular shape was used as a model. The roughness size was varied from 0, 0.16 to 1.05 mm. The outer diameter of the smooth cylinder was 26.0 mm and that for roughened cases was 26.4 mm, approximately; the latter included the thickness of adhesive material which was stuck to the cylinder. The cylinder had a length of 382.5 mm and its spanwise axis was set perpendicular to the main flow and horizontal. End plates were attached to the cylinder; each plate had a diameter of 100 mm and a thickness of 1 mm, and was located 8.8 mm from each tunnel side wall. The cylinder was mounted on a centre rod; the latter passed through holes of the tunnel side walls and was connected to an oscillating system assembled outside.

(c) Oscillating system
The oscillating system consisted of four vertical plate-springs and a massive iron frame; the former suspended the latter. The frame, to which the centre rod of the cylinder was connected, was allowed to perform free or forced oscillations only in the direction of the main flow; for forced-oscillation tests a special driving unit was added. Adjustable-tension coil springs were also employed in order to cancel the mean drag force acting on the oscillating cylinder. A magnetic damper was also employed to suppress harmful oscillations; the damper also served as a generator of the signal of $\dot{x}$ while the signal of x was picked up by strain gauges stuck to the plate springs.

3.2 Experimental method

(a) Stationary tests to measure steady drag force
First, the strength of the magnetic damper for the oscillating system was adjusted to a maximum, in order to suppress all oscillations of the cylinder. Secondly, streamwise displacement of the cylinder was calibrated by applying a standard horizontal force, and finally, steady drag force was measured at various velocities of the main flow. The steady drag force acting on the end plates was subtracted.

(b) Free-oscillation tests to measure logarithmic decrement
At each velocity of the main flow, the time-averaged streamwise location of the cylinder was adjusted first to an original zero-position by controlling the tension of the coil springs. Secondly, small amplitude initial oscillations were given manually, and subsequent damped oscillations were recorded. The magnitude of δ was determined from the expression, $\delta = (n-1)^{-1}\log_e(a_1/a_n)$, where $n-1$ is the wave number included in the interval in which the amplitude decreases from a_1 to a_n; the ratio, a_1/a_n, was taken to be 3 and the initial relative amplitude, a_1/h, was set to be 0.48, approximately. This gave $\dot{x}_{max}/V = 0.035$-0.0035 (for $V/fh = 85$-850), which was small enough for Eq. (6) to be satisfied. The magnitude of δ_0 was determined by measuring δ at $V = 0$ m/s; the error of this simplified method was checked and judged to be negligible. Values, which should be inherent to the oscillating system, are as follows; $\delta_0 \doteqdot 0.051$, $f_0 \doteqdot f \doteqdot 1.79$ Hz, $m/\rho h^2 \doteqdot 2.28 \times 10^4$.

(c) Forced-oscillation tests to measure phase difference between $\dot{x}$ and either base or stagnation pressures
The oscillating system was arranged to allow forced oscillations at which the value of the relative amplitude, a/h, was fixed to 0.31, where a shows the amplitude which was adjusted to be equal to the mean amplitude for the free oscillation tests. The signal of $\dot{x}$ was taken from the coils attached to the magnetic damper (refer to §3.1(c)), while the signal of the base pressure was picked up by a 2 mm-diameter pressure tapping at the midspan of the cylinder; the base pressure was transmitted to a pressure-difference transducer to which another input of an averaged base pressure was given. The response of a combined series of the pressure measurement devices was checked in transient tests.

The signals both of $\dot{x}$ and the fluctuating component of the base pressure were fed to a computer to produce a cross-correlation function. An interval for 16 sinusoidal waves of $\dot{x}$ was assigned for the computation. The phase difference between the two signals was determined from the shift of the cross-correlation function along the time-axis. The stagnation pressure on the upstream side of the cylinder was measured by 180° rotation of the cylinder. An overall check of the measuring system was done using the signals of $\dot{x}$ and a sinusoidally varying reference pressure; the latter was taken by a cylinder-mounted Pitot tube protruding upstream. The error was negligible.

© IMechE 1991 C416/103

3.3 Experimental results

Figure 2 shows two series of measurements obtained by using stationary and oscillating cylinders for various roughness ratios. The results of the stationary tests are plotted in terms of C_D (R_V). A curve fitting technique was applied to the plots of C_D (R_V) based on a combined use of exponential and linear functions. The fitted function was used for producing a new function, Q_1, which is given in Fig. 2 by curves.

Other groups of the plots in Fig. 2 are of Q_2, which were obtained by the oscillating cylinder. About 10 data were used to obtain each plot of Q_2 including standard deviation. It is seen that the disagreement between Q_1 and Q_2 is larger for higher roughness ratios where Q_2 is appreciably smaller than Q_1.

Figure 3 presents the phase shift of the base and the stagnation pressures for a highly roughened case. About 6 data were used to determine each experimental point of ⊙, and 1-3 data for ◎; all the output signals for the latter were very stable. It is clear that the base pressure shows an unusual phase shift up to -90 degrees ie. the phase lag of 90 degrees with respect to $\dot{x}$. This implies that the drag force should also be hysteretic. The presence of the hysteresis might be the reason for the disagreement between Q_1 and Q_2 seen in Fig. 2, since Eq. 13 was derived by assuming that aerodynamic forces are quasi-steady ie. of no phase lag. Flow mechanism during the phase lag is, however, unknown in the present stage.

4 CONCLUSIONS

The results are as follows;
(1) A quasi-steady linear theory is derived for the present problem.
(2) Experimental check of the theory, using a rough-walled stationary and free-oscillating circular cylinders in a high reduced velocity range across the critical flow regime, shows that the theory disagrees with experiments and becomes inapplicable for the high roughness ratio.

(3) Forced oscillation tests using a highly roughened cylinder show that the base pressure has an unusual phase lag with respect to the velocity of the cylinder. It is suggested that this hysteretic effect can be the cause of the disagreement mentioned above since the quasi-steady theory is based on a hypothesis of no phase lag in aerodynamic forces.

A special investigation would be necessary for the critical Reynolds number range of a smooth cylinder, which was not included in the present experiment.

ACKNOWLEDGMENT

The author sincerely thanks Dr. M. M. Zdravkovich of University of Salford for the valuable advice and helping in English during the preparation of a manuscript. The author also sincerely thanks Dr. T. Mizota in Fukuoka Institute of Technology for valuable advice. Referees' valuable comments are also much acknowledged.

REFERENCES

(1) Naudascher, E. Flow-induced streamwise vibrations of structures, *Journal of Fluids and Structures*, 1987, Vol. 1, pp. 265-298.

(2) Toyoda, K. A consideration about the drag force on a sphere (an approximate translation), *Journal of the Japan Society of Mechanical Engineering*, 1967, Vol. 70, No. 579, pp. 6-8. (in Japanese)

(3) Lawson, T. V. Wind effects on buildings, Vol. 1, Design Applications, 1980, p. 110 (Applied Science Publishers LTD).

(4) Low, H. T., Chew, Y. T. and Tan, K. T. Streamwise oscillation of a cylinder at large reduced velocity, *Journal of Wind Engineering and Industrial Aerodynamics*, 1990, Vol. 33, pp. 531-549. (This paper was published after the completion of this work.)

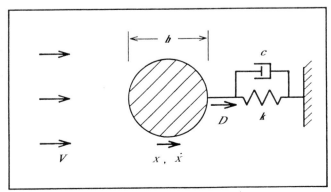

(a) Oscillating cylinder in a uniform flow.

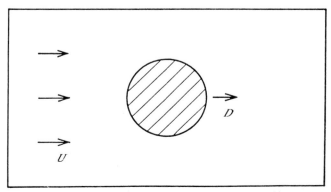

(b) Stationary cylinder in a uniform flow.

Figure 1. Conceptual sketch for quasi-steady streamwise oscillations.

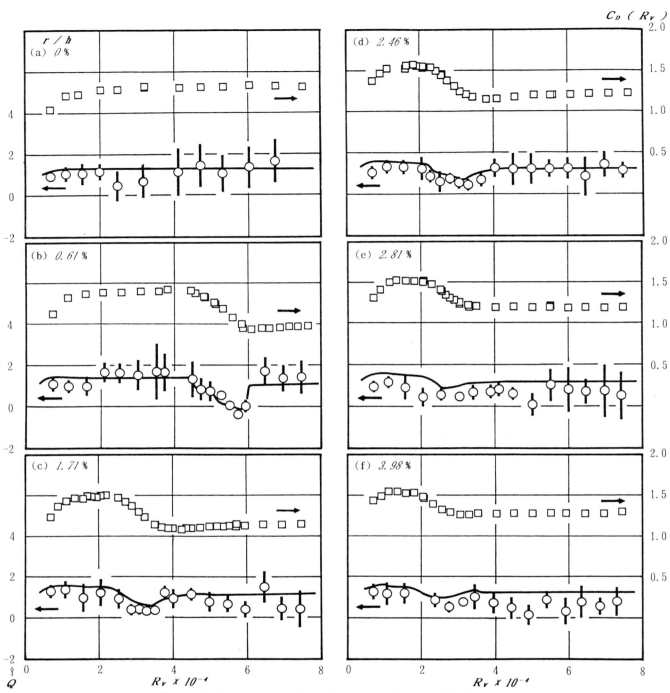

Figure 2. Measurements of stationary and free-oscillation tests.
□; C_D (R_V), ———; Q_1 , ○; Q_2 .(The symbol, ○, shows the mean value while the vertical thick lines show the magnitude of standard deviation.)

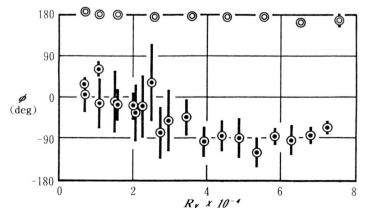

Figure 3. Measurements of forced-oscillation tests (r/h = 2.81 %). ◎; phase difference of stagnation pressure with respect to $\dot{x}$, ⊙; phase difference of base pressure with respect to $\dot{x}$. (The symbols, ◎ and ⊙ show the mean value while the vertical thick lines show the magnitude of standard deviation.)

C416/096

On the mechanism of self-excited vertical vibration of underflow gates

S KANNE, Dipl-Ing, E NAUDASCHER, Dr-Ing, VDI, IAHR, ASCE, ASEE
Institute of Hydromechanics, University of Karlsruhe, Germany
Y WANG
Yangtze River Scientific Research Institute, Hubei, People's Republic of China

SYNOPSIS The paper presents new experimental information on the self-excited vertical vibration of a submerged underflow gate as a function of gate geometry, gap width, damping, and submergence. It is shown that these vibrations are not excited by a galloping mechanism alone, i.e. by movement-induced changes in flow pattern producing fluid forces in the direction of the body velocity. The fluctuating gap width causes discharge variations and fluid-inertia effects which lead to additional excitation forces on the gate if the fluid separates at the upstream edge of the gate underside and the flow under the gate is submerged. These forces are distinct from those due to galloping in that they cannot be treated quasi-steadily.

NOTATIONS

a	amplitude of vibration
B	width of gate
c	damping constant
C_c	contraction coefficient
C_F	mean-lift coefficient
C_L	length coefficient
d	gate thickness
e	extension of gate lip
f, f_n	frequency, natural frequency in still water
k	spring constant
m	structural mass
Q	discharge
s	gap width
Sc	Scruton number = $4\pi m\beta/\rho d^2 B$
V	velocity of fluid (at vena contracta)
V_r	reduced velocity = $V/(f_n d)$
y	vertical displacement of gate
α	angle between velocity and relative velocity of the fluid (Fig. 1)
β	damping ratio
ν	kinematic viscosity of the fluid
ρ	fluid density

1. INTRODUCTION

Self-exitation or movement-induced exitation (MIE) has been classified by Naudascher & Rockwell [7] into different mechanisms:

(1) MIE not dependent on coupling,
(2) MIE involving coupling with fluid-flow pulsations,
(3) MIE involving mode coupling,
(4) MIE involving multiple-body coupling.

The gate investigated is a single-body oscillator with one degree of freedom, and therefore it cannot be excited by (3) or (4). Self-excited vertical vibrations of underflow-gates have been studied by Kolkman [2,3], Kolkman & Vrijer [4,5], Thang [17], Thang & Naudascher [19], and Vrijer [20]. In [17] and [19] galloping, a coupling-independent type of MIE, is assumed to be the main excitation mechanism. In [2,3,4,5,20] fluid-inertia effects caused by coupling with fluid-flow pulsations are supposed to be the main source of excitation, and a simplified linearized theory is presented to describe the behaviour of the gate. The galloping theory and Kolkman's theory on the fluid-inertia effects will be summarized in this paper.

1.1 Galloping

Since the galloping theory is well-known, only its formulation and some important conclusions are presented here. The basic equation of motion of a damped linear system used in the galloping theory is

$$m\ddot{y} + c\dot{y} + ky = F_y \qquad (1)$$

The fluid force in the direction of the body movement is

$$F_y = \frac{1}{2} C_{F_y} \rho V^2 B d \qquad (2)$$

For the definition of symbols see list of notations.

Novak [8,9,10,11,12] and Parkinson [13,15,16] have investigated the galloping of bluff bodies by using a quasi-steady analysis. In their study the authors measured experimentally the mean-lift coefficient C_{F_y} for a stationary cylinder. Since C_{F_y} is only a function of α, the angle between the velocity V and the relative velocity V_{rel}, (Fig. 1), C_{F_y} can be approximated by a polynomial over a finite range of α. When this polynomial is substituted into equation (2), the equation of motion can be solved and the following general conclusions characterizing the galloping of bluff bodies can be drawn:

- There is excitation from rest if

$$A_1 = \left. \frac{d\ C_{F_y}}{d\ \alpha} \right|_{\alpha=0} > 0 \qquad (3)$$

Equation (3) is known as the Den Hartog criterion.

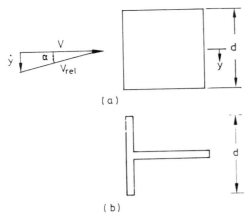

(a)

(b)

Fig 1 Cylindrical cross sections susceptible to galloping, and definition of symbols for quasi-steady analysis.

- A body is stable if

$$V_r < (V_r)_{cr} = \frac{2\,Sc}{A_1} \qquad (4)$$

where $V_r = V/f_n d$ is the reduced velocity and $Sc = 4\pi m\beta/\rho d^2 B$ the Scruton number.

- The amplitude a as a function of the reduced velocity V_r can be presented independently of the Scruton number Sc in a universal response diagram by making it dimensionless

$$\frac{a}{d}\frac{\pi}{Sc} = Fct\left(\frac{V_r}{2\,Sc}\right) \qquad (5)$$

- With $V_r \to \infty$ the response curve degenerates into a straight line going through the origin.

1.2 Coupling with fluid inertia by fluid-flow pulsations

The movement of a valve or a gate induces fluid-flow pulsations by the fluctuating gap width. Related to this are pulsations of the flow velocity and an acceleration or deceleration of the fluid immediately ahead of and behind the gate. For the system shown in Figure 2, Kolkman [2] has developed an equation which describes the magnitude of excitation and which can be used as a stability criterion for the gate. Figure 2 shows a system with one degree of freedom in the y direction and with a mass m, a spring constant k, and a damping constant c. The mass of the fluid coupled with the gate motion is approximated in [2,4] by an imaginary volume of height s and length $L = (C_{Lu} + C_{Ld} + d/s)\,s$, (see Fig. 2). If the gate is moving downwards, the flow will be decelerated because the gap width reduces. This means the pressure increases upstream of the point of separation and decreases downstream of it. For gate shapes with upstream point of separation as those shown in Fig. 2b,c,d, the pressure decrease causes a force acting on the gate in the direction of the movement of the gate thus transfering energy from the flow to the gate. Kolkman introduced a number of simplifying assumptions: the fluid is incompressible, viscosity has no effect, the length L is proportional to the inertia of the fluid, and the contraction coefficient C_c is constant. In the following equations, the

406

prime denotes the time-dependent part and the index o the mean value of a term.

- Discharge equation

$$Q = C_c\,s\,B\,\sqrt{2g\,\Delta H} \qquad (6)$$

- Equation of motion for the fluid mass

$$\Delta H' = -(C_{Lu} + C_{Ld} + d/s)\,\dot{Q}/g\,B \qquad (7)$$

- Equation of motion for the gate

$$F' = C_p\,\rho\,g\,d\,B\,\Delta H' = -m\ddot{y} - c\dot{y} - ky \qquad (8)$$

According to Kolkman [2], the time-dependent fluid force F' has two components. One is related to the time-dependent changes in the mean lift on the bottom surface of the gate $F'_1 = C_F (C_{Lu} + C_{Ld} + d/s)\,\rho\,d\,\dot{Q}$, where C_F is the mean-lift coefficient. The other is related to the time-dependent inertial force on the bottom surface of the gate $F'_2 = C_{Ld}\,\rho\,d\,\dot{Q}$. Using equation (7), the force coefficient C_p may be written as

$$C_p = C_F + C_{Ld}/(C_{Lu} + C_{Ld} + d/s) \qquad (9)$$

Equations (6), (7) and (8) can be combined into a third-order differential equation. The steady-state solution is obtained by introducing the harmonic motion with constant amplitude, $y = y_o\,e^{-i\lambda t}$. If it is assumed that

$$\frac{\sqrt{2g\,\Delta H_o}}{C_c\,(C_{Lo} + C_{Lu} + d/s)\,s\,c}\,\frac{m}{} \gg 1 \qquad (10)$$

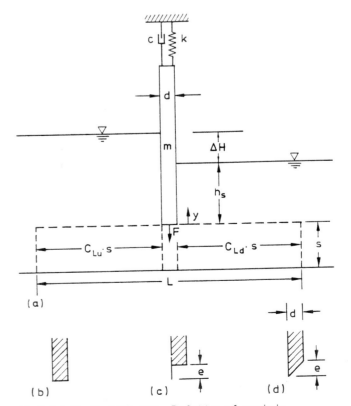

(a)

(b)   (c)   (d)

Fig 2 (a) Vertical lift gate. Definition of symbols.
(b,c,d) Investigated shapes of gate underside.

then the solution can be expressed as (11)

$$c = C_P \rho d B \sqrt{2g \Delta H_o} \; \frac{C_c (C_{Lo} + C_{Lu} + d/s)}{1 + 4\pi^2 C_c^2 (C_{Lo} + C_{Lu} + d/s)^2 (f s/V)^2}$$

Kolkman and Vrijer [7] determined the negative damping of a model lift gate and the corresponding values of c experimentally and compared the results with the prediction of eq. (11). The poor agreement they obtained does not appear surprising in view of the fact that they assumed C_c and C_F in eq. (11) to be constant. This assumption is reasonable only for extremely small relative gate amplitudes. Hence, eq. (11) is valid only near the critical velocity V_{cr}; it can be viewed as a stability criterion.

With the aid of the Scruton number, the reduced velocity, and $c = 2m\omega_n \beta$, equation (11) can be written in the dimensionless form (12)

$$Sc = (V_r)_{cr} \frac{C_P C_c (C_{Lo} + C_{Lu} + d/s)}{1 + 4\pi^2 C_c^2 (C_{Lo} + C_{Lu} + d/s)^2 (s/d)^2 [1/(V_r)_{cr}]^2}$$

According to this equation, one should expect the gate to behave as follows near vibration onset.

(a) Assuming that for a particular geometry of the system the coefficients C_c, C_{Lu}, and C_{Ld} are constant and that $C_F = 0$ for relative gap widths $s/d > 3$ (from [17]), eq. (12) can be written as

$$Sc = C_1 \frac{(V_r)_{cr}}{1 + C_2/(V_r)_{cr}^2}$$

with constants C_1 and C_2. In cases where $C_2/(V_r)_{cr}^2 \ll 1$, $(V_r)_{cr}$ changes linearly with Sc in analogy to galloping. In cases where $C_2/(V_r)_{cr}^2 \gg 1$, $(V_r)_{cr}$ is proportional to $Sc^{1/3}$. In the experiments reported below, $C_2/(V_r)_{cr}^2$ is larger than one. Hence one should expect $(V_r)_{cr}$ to grow more nearly with $Sc^{1/3}$.

(b) The coefficients C_c, C_{Lu}, and C_{Ld} change slowly with changing gap width, and the mean-lift coefficient C_F, entering eq. (12) by eq. (9), decreases with growing gap width ratio s/d or is constant ($s/d > 3$). With increasing s/d, hence, $(V_r)_{cr}$ should be expected to increase for a given value of Sc. This conclusion from eq. (12) is related to the fact that with increasing gap width, the relative fluid-flow variations, and thus the magnitude of excitation, decrease.

(c) Since $C_{Lu} \simeq C_{Ld}$, it can be assumed that $C_{Lu} = C_{Ld} = C_L$. In addition, $C_L \gg d/s$ for large s/d values [1], so ($C_{Lu} + C_{Ld} + d/s$) can be approximated by $2C_L$ in eq. (12). Thus, one obtaines, with eq. (9), (13)

$$Sc = (V_r)_{cr} C_c (2C_F + 1) \frac{1}{1/C_L + [4\pi C_c s/d \,(V_r)_{cr}]^2 C_L}$$

With this equation the effect of the submergence ratio h_s/d on $(V_r)_{cr}$ can be estimated as follows. With increasing h_s/d the volume of the coupled fluid mass will increase,

and with it C_L. Therefore $(V_r)_{cr}$ can be expected to increase with h_s/d, but only if

$$C_L > \frac{(V_r)_{cr}}{4\pi C_c} \frac{d}{s}$$ (14)

2. EXPERIMENTAL EQUIPMENT

The gate model is located in a 0.5 m wide water channel. The gate opening is varied by moving a false floor up and down. The gate is an aluminium plate and has attached to it brass fixtures of different shapes. The thickness of the gate is 1 cm, and there are small gaps between the gate and the sides of the channel of about 2 mm. The gate is held by horizontal wires such that the vertical motion of the gate is nearly frictionless. Vertical coil springs are used to suspend the gate elastically. The mass of the gate is 4.78 kg and the lowest damping ratio of the gate in air is $\beta = 0.001$ at a frequency $f_n = 3.6$ Hz. The damping can be increased by means of electromagnetic brakes. The displacement of the gate is measured with an inductive displacement transducer [1].

The level of turbulence in the oncoming flow was measured with a hot-film anemometer 2.5 m in front of the gate in one third of the water depth. At this location the turbulence level, at a gap ratio of $s/d = 10$, is $Tu = 0.08$. Because of the acceleration of flow under the gate, the turbulence level is much smaller there and it decreases with decreasing gap width. The damping ratio was measured in still water the depth of which was adjusted according to $h_d = s + h_s$, where h_s is the depth of submergence in the experiment (Fig. 2 a). The influence of h_s/d and the gap ratio s/d on the damping was eliminated using electromagnetic damping to keep the Scruton number constant.

Three different gate shapes were investigated (Fig. 2 b,c,d). Since the gate shapes (c) and (d) show similar response curves, only the results for gate shape (b) and (c) will be presented. The velocity-independent parameter $Re/V_r = fd^2/\nu$, at the frequencies $f = 2.7$ Hz and 3.6 Hz, was $fd^2/\nu = 270$ and 360, respectively.

3. RESULTS AND DISCUSSION

3.1 Characteristics of the response curve

Figures 3a,b show the response curves for two relative gap widths and two Scruton numbers. All measured curves show oscillation hysteresis with a soft-excitation range at low values of the relative amplitude a/d and a hard-excitation range at high values of a/d. The dashed line separating the two ranges indicates the threshold value of a/d that needs to be exceeded to obtain high amplitude vibration.

According to the galloping theory, soft excitation occurs only if the gradient of the mean-lift coefficient, A_1, satisfies eqs. (3), $A_1 > 0$, and (4), $A_1 = 2 Sc/(V_r)_{cr}$. Thang [17] has measured the mean-lift coefficient of a rectangular gate and deduced that A_1 approaches zero for a gap ratio of roughly s/d = 5 [19]. The fact that excitation from rest does occur for s/d = 5 and 10 (Figs. 3 a, b) proves that galloping cannot be the main reason for soft excitation of a gate.

With growing amplitudes, the shearlayers approach the gate underside due to increasing angles α of the relative velocity (Fig. 1). Under these circumstances the galloping mechanism can be expected to contribute more and more to the exciting forces even though the gate behaviour cannot be exactly predicted by the galloping theory. According to the latter, the response curve degenerates into a straight line going through the origin; this is in contrast to the experimental evidence (Figs. 3 a, b). Moreover, the gradient of the response curve at large amplitudes is larger than predicted by the galloping theory. A final proof that galloping cannot be the only

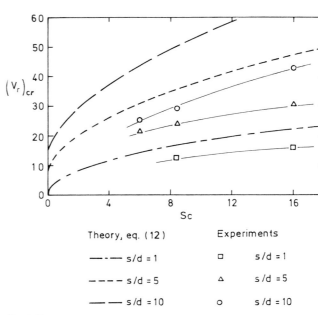

Theory, eq. (12)	Experiments	
— · — s/d = 1	□	s/d = 1
— — — s/d = 5	△	s/d = 5
— — s/d = 10	○	s/d = 10

Fig 4 Theoretical prediction of gate stability and comparison with experimental results.

mechanism of excitation is derived from a comparison of the lateral responses of a prism and a gate according to Figs. 1b and 2c, respectively. Whereas soft excitation is observed for the gate (Figs. 3 a, b), the corresponding prism shows galloping of the hard-excitation type only [7].

3.2 Effect of the Scruton number

Response curves of galloping-induced vibrations can be presented according to eq. (5) in a universal response diagram. In the case of the underflow gate this is not possible. The increase of the intensity of excitation with increasing reduced velocity is much stronger than described by galloping theory. Clearly, there exists an additional source of excitation due to fluid-inertia effects resulting from fluid-flow pulsations.

Because Kolkman's theory is limited to amplitude ratios $a/d \to 0$, only the critical reduced velocity $(V_r)_{cr}$ can be deduced from it. Figure 4 shows calculated and measured values of $(V_r)_{cr}$ as a function of Sc. The measured values were taken from the results for the gate with extended lip, because the galloping mechanism can be expected to have the least effect for this geometry at small amplitudes. The coefficients C_{Lu} and C_{Ld} were determined from [2] with the approximation $C_L \simeq C_{Lu} \simeq C_{Ld}$, and C_c is given the values 0.61, 0.62, and 0.63 for s/d = 1, 5, and 10, respectively (eq. (9) holds true in the case considered).

The trend of the measured curves in Fig. 4 agrees with the prediction, although the measured values of $(V_r)_{cr}$ are considerably smaller than the theoretical ones. This discreapancy may be due, in part, to the difficulties in determining C_L and Sc. The latter contains a damping ratio β measured in still water, which could be larger than the value representative to the case of flowing water. The increasing difference between measurement and computation with increasing gap width may stem, in part, from the different level of turbulence under the

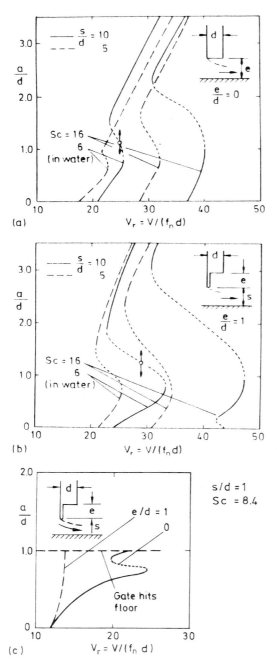

Fig 3 Effect of gap ratio, Scruton number, and gate shape on gate response. Submergence ratio $h_s/d = 14$. (a,b) s/d = 5 and 10; (c) s/d = 1.

gate resulting from different fluid accelerations. And, last but not least, the assumption that the pressure and velocity distributions in the gap are constant for large gap ratios is probably invalid since the local pressure fluctuations close to the gate are larger than the fluctuations averaged over the gap width.

3.3 Effect of gate shape and gap ratio

At large gap ratios ($s/d = 5$ and 10), the gate shape has little effect on the critical reduced velocity, although the distance between shearlayer and gate underside is different for the investigated shapes. This finding indicates that galloping is hardly the main cause for the onset of excitation at these gap ratios.

At large amplitudes, due to large shearlayer movements, the galloping mechanism does play a role as seen also from the effect of the gate shape on the response curves. For a gate with extended lip (shape 2, Fig. 2c), larger amplitudes are necessary for the shearlayers to approach the gate underside than for a gate without lip extension (shape 1, Fig. 2b). The triggering amplitude, therefore, is larger in the first case. Since shearlayer reattachment with accompanying reduction in galloping excitation is reached at smaller amplitudes in the latter case, moreover, vibration is more limited for shape 1 than for shape 2. This same effect is also the reason for the smaller amplitudes obtained at $s/d = 5$ in the upper part of the response curves for gate shape 1 as compared to $s/d = 10$. A similar trend does not occur for shape 2 because of the larger distance between shearlayer and gate underside in that case.

At $s/d = 1$, Fig 3c, the shearlayer is very close to the gate underside for gate shape 1. This fact, and a much stronger effect of the gate shape on the damping ratio, lead to different response curves in this case.

3.4 Effect of submergence ratio

Three different submergence ratios, $h_s/d = 8$, 14 and 20, were investigated for a damping ratio of $\beta = 0.007$. Figure 5 shows the results for the gap ratio $s/d = 5$. Clearly,

$(V_r)_{cr}$ increases with increasing submergence ratio. In other words, the magnitude of excitation decreases as the submergence is increased. A similar behaviour was observed for all gap ratios and gate shapes investigated [1]. This finding agrees with the prediction discussed in section 1.2, since eq. (14) holds true for all investigated conditions. However, the computation leads to a much lower increase in $(V_r)_{cr}$ with increasing h_s/d than that measured. The reason may be that variations in h_s/d change other parameters the influence of which were neglected in eq. (12). More importantly, the influence of a progressive surface wave downstream of the gate, moving in the downstream direction, has not been accounted for. Surface-wave effects are especially large in cases with large discharge and small submergence ratios, e.g., for $s/d = 10$ with $h_s/d = 8$, 14 and $s/d = 5$ with $h_s/d = 8$. The waves occur only at small amplitudes (i.e., in the range of soft excitation) and their frequency was observed to be exactly half the gate frequency [1].

3.5 Comparison with measurements of Thang

Thang [17] performed measurements with a gate of shape 1 (Fig. 2b) at $s/d = 5$. His model was the same as that used in the present study except that the profiles which were attached to the vertical aluminium plate were made of plexiglas whereas in this study they are of brass. The model was installed in a shorter channel, and the approach-flow conditions were different. Figure 6 contains results from [17] as well as results from the present study obtained with the same elastic and damping characteristics (i.e., same f_n and Sc).

In contrast to the present study, Thang did not detect a soft-galloping range at small amplitudes. Factors which possibly explain this discrepancy in results include the different approach flows in the two studies and the different materials of the gate profiles. The plexiglas model is less stiff than that made of brass; hence, increased gate bending and damping might have been present in Thang's experiments. Furthermore, Thang has shown that the ratio of the stiffness of the positioning device (consisting of wires and plate springs) to the

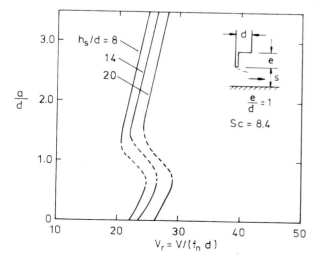

Fig 5 Effect of submergence ratio on gate response for $s/d = 5$.

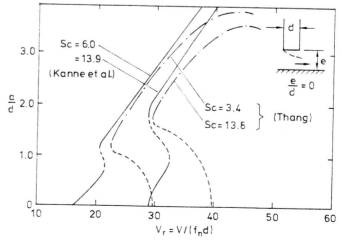

Fig 6 Comparison of experimental results of Thang [17] and Kanne et al. [1] for gate with flat bottom (Fig. 2b) at $s/d = 5$.

stiffness of the coil spring has an effect on the response curve of the gate. The main reason for this effect is the nonlinear relationship between the movements of the plate springs and the coil spring which suspend the gate. The relation between the coil-spring constant and the plate-spring constants can be affected by different tensions in the wires, for example. As the comparison of the results in Fig. 6 shows, the self-excited gate system is very sensitive to slight changes in the system design.

4. SUMMARY

At least two mechanisms of excitation have been identified to cause self-excited vertical gate vibrations: (a) coupling with fluid inertia by fluid-flow pulsations and (b) galloping. At small relative amplitudes a/d and large gap ratios s/d, (a) appears to be the major source of excitation, whereas at large values of s/d galloping effects become important. The gate with flat bottom is more susceptible to vibrations than the gate with extended lip. With flat bottom, the shearlayer approaches the gate underside more rapidly as amplitudes increase. With decreasing gap ratio, the danger of vibration increases mainly because of intensified fluid-inertia forces.

Kolkman's theory [2], which is based on mechanism (a), can be used to estimate qualitatively the influence of geometric parameters and Scruton number on the susceptibility of particular gate shapes to self-excited vibrations. In order to predict the critical reduced velocity and the amplitude of vibration, however, the combined effects of mechanisms (a) and (b) need to be taken into account. Investigating gate vibrations experimentally, one needs to pay attention to the approach-flow conditions and details of the vibrating system in addition to its geometric and damping conditions. A comparison of results obtained with the same experimental set-up but with slight differences in the details of the system dynamics has demonstrated that a transfer of experimental results to other conditions must be done very critically, simply because of the difficulties in reproducing prototype conditions related to, e.g., bearings and suspensions in the model.

ACKNOWLEDGEMENT

Financial support of the Sonderforschungsbereich 210, University of Karlsruhe, and its sponsor, the German Science Foundation (DFG), is gratefully acknowledged.

REFERENCES

[1]   KANNE, S. & E. NAUDASCHER, Y. WANG. Untersuchung von Schützschwingungen im Bereich grosser reduzierter Geschwindigkeiten. Report Nr. E/61, SFB 210, University of Karlsruhe, Germany, September, 1990.

[2]   KOLKMAN, P.A. Flow-Induced Gate Vibrations. Delft Hydraulics Laboratory, Publ. Nr. 164, 1976.

[3]   KOLKMAN, P.A. Development of Vibration-Free Gate Design: Learning from Experiences and Theory. See [5], 1979.

[4]   KOLKMAN, P.A. & A. VRIJER. Gate Edge Suction as a Cause of Self-Exciting Vertical Vibrations. Proceeding 17. IAHR Congress, Baden-Baden, 1977.

[5]   KOLKMAN, P.A. & A. VRIJER. Vertical Gate Vibrations by Galloping or by Fluid Inertia? Journal of Hydraulic Research, Vol. 25, No. 3, 1987.

[6]   NAUDASCHER, E. & D. ROCKWELL (eds.). IAHR/ IUTAM Symp. on Practical Experiences with Flow-Induced Vibrations, Karlsruhe 1979, (Springer 1980)

[7]   NAUDASCHER, E. & D. ROCKWELL. Flow-Induced Vibrations — An Engineering Guide. IAHR Monograph, Preprint Nr. A/63-66, SFB 210, University of Karlsruhe, Germany, June, 1990.

[8]   NOVAK, M. Aeroelastic Galloping of Prismatic Bodies. ASCE, J. Eng. Mech., Vol. 95, EM 1, 1969.

[9]   NOVAK, M. Aeroelastic Instability of Prismatic Bodies. Proceedings of the Conference on Tower-Shaped Structures, Int. Association for Shell Structures, Den Hague, April 1969.

[10] NOVAK, M. Galloping and Vortex Induced Oscillations of Structures. Proceedings 3. Int. Conference on Wind Effects on Buildings and Structures, Tokio, 1971.

[11] NOVAK, M. Galloping Oscillations of Prismatic Structures. ASCE, J. Eng. Mech., Vol. 98, EM 1; 1972.

[12] NOVAK, M. & A.G. DAVENPORT. Aeroelastic Instability of Prisms in Turbulent Flow. ASCE, J. Eng. Mech., Vol. 96, EM 1, 1970.

[13] PARKINSON, G.V. Aspects of the Aeroelastic Behaviour of Bluff Cylinders. Transactions of the Engineering Institute of Canada, Vol. 6, 1963.

[14] PARKINSON, G.V. Aeroelastic Galloping in One Degree of Freedom. Proceedings Int. Conference on Wind Effects on Buildings and Structures, Teddington, England, 1963.

[15] PARKINSON, G.V. & N.P.H. BROOKS. On the Aeroelastic Instability of Bluff Cylinders. ASME J. Applied Mechanics, June 1961

[16] PARKINSON, G.V. & J.D. SMITH. The Square Prism as an Aeroelastic Nonlinear Oscillator. Quart. J. Mech. and Applied Math., 1964.

[17] THANG, N.D. Strömungsbedingte Schwingungen unterströmter Schütze. Dissertation University of Karlsruhe, 1983.

[18] THANG, N.D. & E. NAUDASCHER. Approach-Flow Effects on Downpull of Gates. ASCE J. Hydr. Eng., Nov. 1983.

[19] THANG, N.D. & E. NAUDASCHER. Self-Excited Vibrations of Vertical-Lift Gates. Journal of Hydraulic Research, Vol. 24, No. 5, 1986.

[20] VRIJER, A. Stability of a Vertically Movable Gate. See [6], 1979.

C416/101

Surface pressure characteristics of a square prism under aerodynamic response control by boundary layer acceleration

Y KUBO, PhD, MJSCE and H YASUDA, MJSCE
Department of Civil Engineering, Kyushu Institute of Technology, Kitakyushu, Japan

SYNOPSES   The suppression of aerodynamic vibration of deflective structures such as pylons of long suspension bridges and high rise buildings, towers is very important for the construction of these structures. This paper deals with the suppression method of aerodynamic vibration of a square cylinder by controlling the surface boundary layer. The control of boundary layer is done by accelerating the separation flow from upstream corners by the rotating cylinders located at the upstream corner of the square prism. When the separation flow is accelerated, the surface pressure distribution on the body is different from the one without rotating cylinders. With increment of rotary surface velocity of the rotating cylinder, the surface pressure distribution comes to a similar pressure distribution of stream-line body. This means this device has the possibility of suppression of aerodynamic responses of a square cylinder.

NOTATIONS

P_m	mean surface pressure of the prism
P_∞	far upstream pressure
V_∞	far upstream wind velocity
ρ	air density
$\overline{C_p}$	coefficient of mean pressure
$\widetilde{C_p}$	coefficient of fluctuating pressure
V_U	ratio of surface velocity of upper rotating cylinder to the reference wind velocity
V_L	ratio of surface velocity of lower rotating cylinder to the reference wind velocity

1 INTRODUCTION

With increments of bridge length and of building height, the static deflections and dynamic response amplitudes of the structures due to wind action come to be much more serious problems for the construction of large structures. The pylons of the longest suspension bridge in the world under construction in Japan have 300 m height. The static and dynamic wind loads cause large bending moments at the root of the pylons. It is very important for the tall pylon to reduce the wind load and to reduce the static deflections and dynamic response amplitudes from the view point of structural design.

The vibrations of some pylons and buildings, chimneys have been suppressed by using an improved shape of structures to the wind action and by using the tuned mass damper (T.M.D.) or tuned liquid damper (T.L.D.). Two damping devices of T.M.D. and T.L.D. have the same mechanism for damping effect on the structures[1]. Their most effective parameter is the mass ratio of the damping device to the structure. Therefore, the larger mass is required for the larger structures. Adding, this device is effective only to one characteristic frequency of the structure, and there are difficulties in tuning the frequency of the devices to that of real structures.

Instead of these devices, the boundary layer control method has the merits to reduce the static and dynamic wind load and to be able to work under various wind speeds and wind directions by using an active control system. The present method is one of boundary layer control methods. This was proposed by V.J.Modi, University of British Columbia. He already applied his method, acceleration of boundary layer by rotating cylinders, on the high lift airfoil[2] and on the reduction of drag force of the trailer-trucks[3]. The authors are trying to apply his method on the suppression of aerodynamic vibration of bluff bodies.

2 EXPERIMENTS

The experiments were conducted by using the open circuit wind tunnel with test section of 1.1 x 1.1 x 8.2 m. The surface pressures of the cylinder at rest condition were measured to investigate the effectiveness of the rotating cylinders on the control of boundary layer on the surface of a square prism.

The model used in the present research is a 15 x 15 cm square prism with rotating cylinders driven by servomotor as shown in Fig.1. As the blockage ratio of the prism is 14%, the data measured by the present system include the blockage effects. However, it is supposed that there is no need worrying about the effectiveness of the rotating cylinders on suppression of aerodynamic responses. The size of the model was decided from the rotating cylinder diameter (d=15.3 mm) calculated to have rotating speed with 2 times of maximum approaching flow velocity of $V_\infty = 6$ m/s in relation with the effective revolution per minutes of the DC servomotors.

As the model will be used for dynamic response tests, it is difficult to attach end plates with enough size to exclude the end plate effects from the data. Therefore, the secondary end plates were used on the wind tunnel walls. Reference 4 describes the end plate effects in detail.

10 pressure taps are set on the each surface. The cylinder has totally 40 pressure taps to measure the surface pressure characteristics of the square prism. The pressure tubes are connected to the scanner which is driven by the stepping motor controlled by the micro computer as shown in the block diagram of measuring system of Fig. 2. The analog data measured by a pressure gauge is converted to digital data and processed by the FFT analyzer. The processed data are stored by the micro computer to

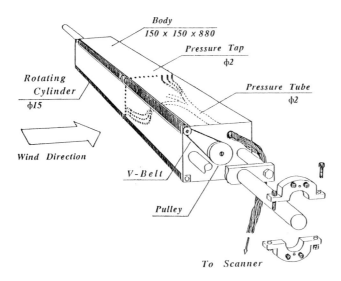

Fig 1 Experimental model for a square prism with rotating cylinders driven by DC servomotor set in the prism.

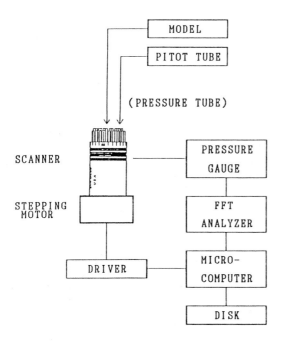

Fig 2 Block diagram for measuring system to measure the surface pressure on the square prism.

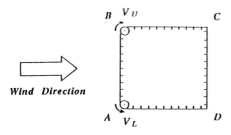

Fig 3 Definition of the pressure tap locations.

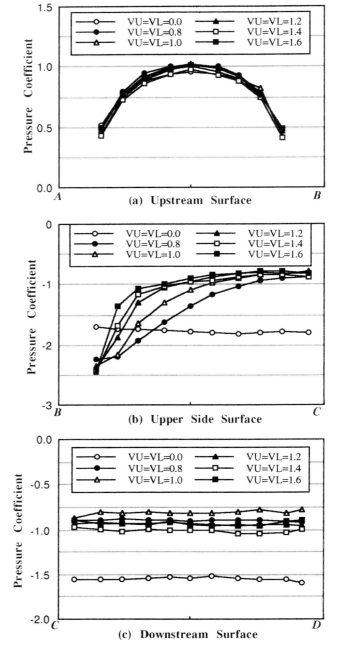

Fig 4 Mean pressure coefficient distributions of Case 1 ($V_U = V_L$).

magnetic floppy disks. The frequency response of the pressure transducer system is flat up to about 55 hz. The experiments for measuring surface pressure was conducted by means of varying the revolution per minutes of the rotating cylinders.

3 PRESSURE DISTRIBUTIONS

The surface pressure measurements were conducted to investigate the effects of rotating cylinder to the surface pressure distributions. The following shows the measured results of the mean pressure coefficients and the fluctuating pressure coefficients. The location of the pressure taps shows in Fig. 3.

Pressure coefficients are calculated by the following equations.

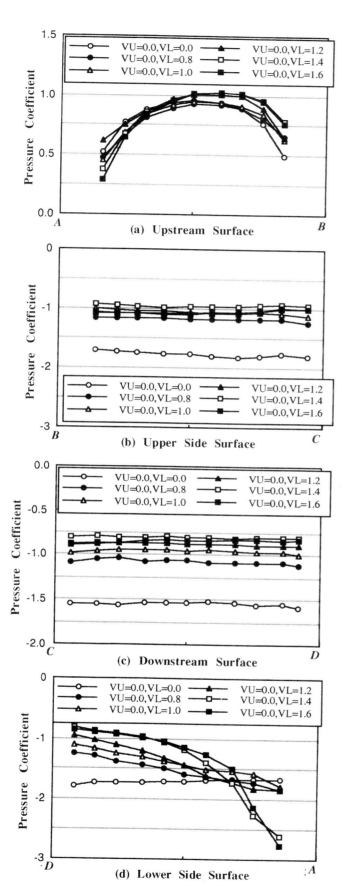

(a) Upstream Surface

Legend:
VU=0.0,VL=0.0 | VU=0.0,VL=1.2
VU=0.0,VL=0.8 | VU=0.0,VL=1.4
VU=0.0,VL=1.0 | VU=0.0,VL=1.6

(b) Upper Side Surface

(c) Downstream Surface

(d) Lower Side Surface

Fig 5 Mean pressure coefficient distributions of Case 2 ($V_U = 0.0$).

coeffient of mean pressure:

$$\overline{C_p} = \frac{P_m - p_\infty}{\frac{1}{2}\rho V_\infty^2} \quad\text{-----}(1)$$

coefficient of fluctuating pressure:

$$\widetilde{C_P} = \frac{R.M.S.}{\frac{1}{2}\rho V_\infty^2} \quad\text{-----}(2)$$

The results are classified into following 3 cases.
Case 1: upper and lower rotating cylinders have the same rotary surface velocity,
Case 2: upper rotating cylinder at rest and only lower rotating cylinder is driven with various revolutions.
Case 3: the rotary surface velocity of the upper rotating cylinder has $1.2V_\infty$ and lower rotating cylinder is driven with various revolution.

3.1 Mean pressure distributions

The mean pressure coefficients has the following characteristics.
•Case 1 ($V_U = V_L$)
Fig. 4 shows the distribution of the mean pressure coefficients of Case 1.
The mean pressure distribution of upstream surface AB perpendicular to the flow direction is not changed by the rotary surface velocity of the rotating cylinders. $\overline{C_p}$ takes the constant value of $\overline{C_p} = 1.0$ at the stagnation point to the variation of surface velocity of the cylinder. On the other hand, when the rotating cylinders are driven with the higher rotary surface velocity, the mean pressure on the downstream surface (base pressure) takes the larger values in the range smaller than approaching flow velocity, the values are $\overline{C_p} = -1.5$ for the case of no rotary surface velocity and $\overline{C_p} = -0.9$ for the case that the rotary surface velocity is 0.8 times as fast as approaching flow, $\overline{C_p} = -0.8$ for the case of the same rotary surface velocity as the approaching flow. According to the results, as the base pressure is recovered by the rotating cylinders by about more than 30%, it is supposed that the drug also is reduced by the same rate as the base pressure. The pressure distribution on the side surfaces (BC and AD surfaces in Fig.3) is strongly influenced by the rotary surface velocity of the cylinders. When the rotary velocity of the cylinder increases, the surface pressure on the upstream side surface takes smaller values and the smallest value at the upstream corners. Comparing with the shapes of pressure distribution on the side surface, the increment of rotary surface velocity of the cylinders leads high negative pressure on the side surface at the upstream corner. This fact means that the in increment of rotary surface velocity of the cylinders leads to improvement of the bluff shape to a stream-lined shape.
Above stated case is that the rotating cylinders work to generate symmetric flow. The following case is that the rotating cylinders work to generate the asymmetric flow pattern around the square prism. Figs. 5 and 6 show the results of the surface pressure distribution measured under the condition $V_U \neq V_L$.
•Case 2 ($V_U = 0.0$)
As the value of pressure coefficients near rotating cylinders comes to be smaller with increment of the rotary surface velocity of rotating cylinders, the pressure distribution on the upstream surface has not a symmetric form but a distorted form such as that lower pressure exists at near a rotating cylinder. The pressures on the side surfaces have also asymmetric distribution between lower and

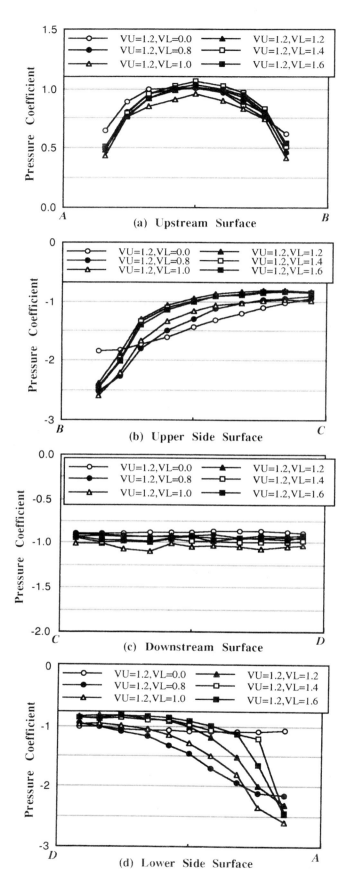

(a) Upstream Surface

(b) Upper Side Surface

(c) Downstream Surface

(d) Lower Side Surface

Fig 6 Mean pressure coefficient distributions of Case 3 (V_U = 1.2).

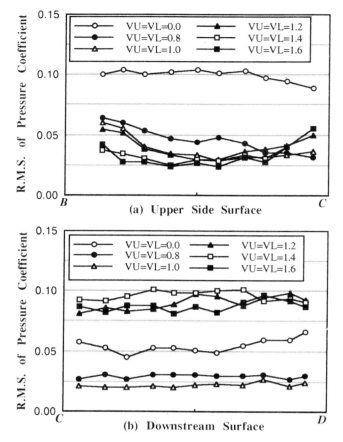

(a) Upper Side Surface

(b) Downstream Surface

Fig 7 Fluctuating pressure coefficient distributions of Case 1 ($V_U = V_L$).

upper side surfaces. The pressure distribution on the lower surface has similar formations of pressure distributions as those on the side surfaces of Case 1. The pressure on the upper surface takes almost an equal value from upstream edge to downstream edge, and the shape of pressure distribution on the upper surface is almost flat. The base pressure distribution also has a flat shape to the variation of lower rotary surface velocity.

•Case 3 (V_U = 1.2 V_∞)

In this case, the pressure distributions of upper and lower surfaces respectively depends on the surface velocity of the rotating cylinders. The pressure of the both sides has a little interference between both the rotary surface velocities of the rotating cylinders. This means that the aerodynamic response can be suppressed by the independent control of the rotary surface velocity of each rotating cylinder.

3.2   Fluctuating component of surface pressure

The mean pressure mainly causes static deflection of a structure. Instead of this, as the fluctuating component is related to the causes of the dynamic responses, it is very important to be able to reduce the value of fluctuating component of pressure for the aerodynamic design of structures.

•Case 1 (V_U = V_L)

Fig.7 shows the distribution of r.m.s. of fluctuating pressure coefficients for the case of V_U = V_L. The relation between r.m.s. distributions and the rotary surface velocity of rotating cylinder is shown in Fig.7(a). The r.m.s. for V_U = V_L=0.0 takes the value of

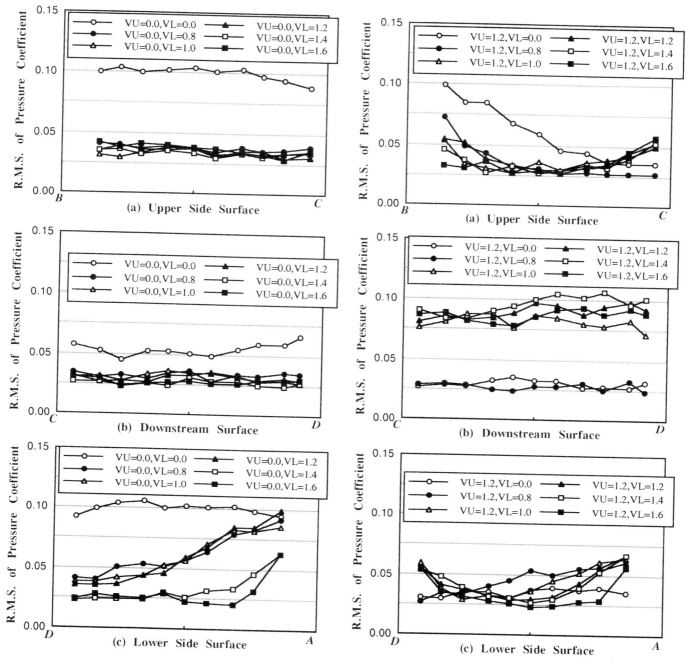

(a) Upper Side Surface

(b) Downstream Surface

(c) Lower Side Surface

Fig 8 Fluctuating pressure coefficient distributions of Case 2 ($V_U = 0.0$).

(a) Upper Side Surface

(b) Downstream Surface

(c) Lower Side Surface

Fig 9 Fluctuating pressure coefficient distributions of Case 3 ($V_U = 1.2$).

about 0.1 on the whole side surfaces BC and DA. The shape of r.m.s. distribution on the side surface changes with increment of rotary surface velocity of rotating cylinders. The r.m.s. values at the upstream point on the surface decrease with increment of the rotary surface velocity. But the values at downstream points increase in the higher rotary surface velocity of rotating cylinder than $1.2V\infty$. This means that the reduction of the fluctuation component on the surface pressure leads aerodynamic amplitude to its reduction. Therefore, the aerodynamic response amplitude is supposed to be suppressed in higher rotary surface velocity of rotating cylinders than $1.4V\infty$, because the r.m.s. value takes almost equal and small value in the range of higher rotary surface velocity than $1.4V\infty$. Fig.7(b) shows the r.m.s. distribution of the fluctuating pressure on the leeward surface. The r.m.s. of the base pressure fluctuation takes large values with increment of rotary surface velocity of

the rotating cylinders. The increment of the r.m.s. value due to the higher rotary surface velocity is considered as the result that the reattachment point of separation flow moves to the nearer upstream point with increment of the rotary surface velocity of rotating cylinders and as a result, the higher rotary surface velocity gives the same effects on the bluff body as that the bluff body is improved to the stream-lined body.

•Case 2 ($V_U = 0.0$)

Fig.8 is the results of the case 2. The r.m.s. of fluctuating component on the upper side surface is independent of the rotary surface velocity of lower side rotating cylinder. And the r.m.s. of base pressure also is a little influenced by the rotary surface velocity of the lower rotating cylinder. The most remarkable characteristics of the r.m.s. of pressure distributions in this case exists on the results of pressure fluctuation of the lower surface. The r.m.s. values in the range less than $V_L=1.2$ take almost same values and the r.m.s. values in the range larger than $V_{L=1.2}$ take half of the r.m.s. value in the range less than $V_{L=1.2}$. This case is considered to be most effective combination of rotary surface velocities of two rotating cylinders in the present experimental cases, because the r.m.s. value takes the least value.

•Case 3 ($V_U = 1.2$)
As shown in Fig.9 , the distribution of the r.m.s. value shows complicated patterns to the variation of rotary surface velocities of two rotating cylinders. But in the higher rotary surface velocity of rotating cylinders, the r.m.s. values of side surface take the smaller values and the r.m.s. values of base pressure take the larger values as same as the characteristics shown in the results of Cases 1 and 2.

4 FLOW VISUALIZATION

Photos 1 and 2 show the examples of the flow patterns around square prisms without and with rotating cylinders. Photo 1 is the flow pattern at the condition of $V_U = V_L = 0.0$ and Photo 2 is at $V_U = 1.5$ $V_L = 0.0$. According to these pictures, the upper stream line of Photo 2 comes up to the square prism surface. This means that the high rotary surface velocity causes the earlier reattachment and the earlier reattachment improves the square prism to a shallow rectangular cylinder in the sense of aerodynamic characteristics.

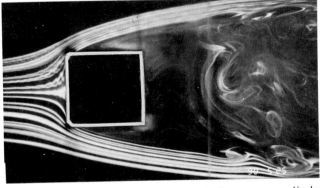

Photo 1 Flow visualization around square cylinder with rotating cylinders of $V_U = V_L = 0.0$.

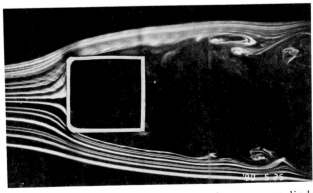

Photo 2 Flow visualization around square cylinde with rotating cylinders of $V_U = 1.5$, $V_L = 0.0$.

5 CONCLUDING REMARKS

The present research has been conducted to find the method how to apply the boundary layer control method on the suppression of aerodynamic responses of bluff bodies. The useful informations for suppression of aerodynamic responses of bluff body were obtained from the fundamental experiments of measuring surface pressure of a square prism with two rotating cylinders set on upstream corners.
(1) The mean and fluctuating pressures can be controlled by controlling the rotary surface velocity of the rotating cylinder
(2) The higher rotary surface velocity leads the bluff body to be more similar stream-lined body. In other words, the bluff body can be improved to the elongated body by accelerating the boundary layer by the rotating cylinder.
(3) The most effective combination of rotary surface velocities of two rotating cylinders in the present research is Case 2 that one is at rest and another is rotating with the velocity higher than $1.4V\infty$.
(4) The reduction of r.m.s. value of fluctuating surface pressure on the upper and lower side surfaces means the earlier reattachment of the separation flow by acceleration of boundary layer and it works out as to suppress the aerodynamic response of a bluff body.
The present research will be extended to the investigation of effectiveness for the suppression of aerodynamic responses by using the spring balance method. The authors have plans of 3 dimensional wind tunnel tests to apply this method on the suppression of real structures as tall buildings and tall pylons, bridge girders of super long suspension bridges. The full-scale application requires to solve the problem of Reynolds number influence and how to make the economical rotating cylinder system.

ACKNOWLEDGEMENT

The authors are much indebted to Prof. V.J. Modi for giving them the first hints to start the present research. This research is supported by Grant-in-Aid for General Scientific Research of the Japanese Ministry of Education.

REFERENCES

1) FUJINO. Y., PACHECO, B. M., CHAISERI, P., SUN, L. M., KOGA, K., Understanding of TLD properties based on TMD analogy, *Journal of Structural Engineering*, JSCE, 1990, Vol.36a, pp.577-590..
2) MODI, V. J., SUN, J. L. C., AKUTSU, T., LAKE, P., McMILLIAN, K., SWINTON, P.G., and MULLINS, D., Moving surface boundary layer control for aircraft operation at high incidence, *Journal of Aircraft*, AIAA, Nov. 1981, Vol. 18, No. 11, pp.963-968
3) MODI, V. J., FERNANDO, M. S. U. K., YOKOMIZO, T., Moving surface boundary-layer control as applied to two and three dimensional bluff bodies, Proceedings of 8th International Colloquium on Industrial Aerodynamics, 1989, Sept,.
4) KUBO, Y., MIYAZAKI, M., KATO, K., Effects of End Plates and Blockage of Structural Members on Drag forces, Journal of Wind Engineering and Industrial Aerodynamics, 1989, Vol.32, pp.329-342.

C416/010

Flow induced vibrations in long corrugated pipes

S ZIADA, MEng, PhD, MASME and E T BÜHLMANN, PhD
Laboratory for Vibrations and Acoustics, Sulzer Innotec, Winterthur, Switzerland

SYNOPSIS   Flow-induced vibrations of a 450 m long corrugated pipe are investigated experimentally. The vibrations are found to be caused by simultaneous resonance of two different modes, the first is an acoustical mode and the second is an axial (accordian) vibration mode of the pipe corrugations. Although the vibration occurs at a single frequency, the wavelengths of the resonant modes are different; both being however much smaller than the pipe length. This underscores the importance of the damping resulting from the interaction of the excited modes along the whole length of the pipe. This "mode interaction damping" seems to increase as the pipe length is reduced.

NOTATION

c	speed of sound
d	inner diameter
e	corrugation depth
f	frequency
L	total length of corrugated pipe
ℓ	corrugation pitch
p	amplitude of pressure pulsation
Q	flow rate
R	Reynolds number, $R = V\ell/\nu$
S	Strouhal number, $S = f\ell/V$
t	thickness of pipe wall
V	flow velocity
x	amplitude of axial vibrations of the pipe corrugations
λ	wavelength

1   INTRODUCTION

Corrugated pipes and metal bellows often experience vibration or noise problems, especially when the internal flow velocity is relatively high. These problems are usually the result of either acoustic resonances, as in the case of gas flows [1], or mechanical resonances of the corrugated pipe section, as in the case of liquid flows [2 - 6]. In either case, the resonance modes are excited by the unstable shear layers which separate from the tips of the pipe corrugations [7].

Although the excitation mechanism of corrugated pipes and metal bellows is not fully understood, several investigations have provided valuable information which can be used to assess the liability of a system to flow-induced vibrations. The vibration usually occurs over a certain range of Strouhal number, which is defined by

$$S = f_n \ell /V \qquad (1)$$

where, f_n is the frequency of the resonance mode n, ℓ is the corrugation pitch and V is the mean flow velocity at which mode n is excited. Weaver and Ainsworth [5] reported a Strouhal number of 0.45 for the maximum vibration amplitude. This value agrees with the results of Gerlach [2, 3], Bass and Holster [4] and Klaui [6].

Gerlach [2] developed a "stress indicator" which can be used to evaluate the fatigue life of metal bellows conveying water. He recognized that the upstream velocity profile has a strong effect on the vibrations, and therefore recommended an increase in the "stress indicator" by a factor of 2 when an upstream elbow is present. More recently, Weaver and Ainsworth [5] and Klaui [6] investigated the effect of the upstream flow conditions on bellows vibration. They reported a rather substantial increase in the Strouhal number at the onset of vibration when upstream flow distortions were introduced. This is important because in many industrial applications the approach flow is non-uniform. In these cases, the vibration will be initiated at flow rates which are lower than those of the corresponding ideal cases.

The present paper focuses on very long corrugated pipes for which the vibration frequency can be admissible to both the axial (i.e. accordian) vibration modes of the pipe wall and the longitudinal acoustic modes. The vibration and the acoustic modes can therefore be excited simultaneously. Such simultaneous excitation has not been investigated in previous papers because only short pipes or bellows were considered.

This work was initiated to investigate a vibration problem which arose in a district heating system. In this system, two corrugated pipes, each 450 meter in length, are used to transport hot water between a power station and a central heating unit. The vibration was so severe that the unit could not be operated at loads higher than 30% of its maximum capacity. Field measurements were conducted to diagnose the cause of the vibrations. Since those measurements were not sufficient to identify the type of the system resonator, additional measurements were carried out in the laboratory, but on a shorter pipe of smaller diameter.

First, the results of the field and the laboratory tests are presented. Thereafter, the excitation mechanism and the effect of the pipe length are discussed. Finally, the methods of curing the pipe vibration in the laboratory and in the heating unit are addressed.

2   TEST FACILITY AND INSTRUMENTATION

The tests were carried out on actual specimens of corrugated pipes such as those commonly used in district heating systems. The pipes have several layers of insulation to minimize the heat losses from the conveyed hot water. As shown in Fig. 1, a thick layer of insulation separates two corrugated pipes. Another two, but thinner layers are used to insulate the outer pipe. The inner pipe, which is in contact with the flowing water, is made of stainless steel. Its wall thickness and corrugation pitch are substantially smaller than those of the outer pipe. The geometrical parameters of the tested pipes are given in Table 1.

Table 1: Geometrical parameters of the tested pipes

Pipe used in	d (mm)	ℓ (mm)	e (mm)	t (mm)	L (m)
Heating unit	147	19.5	6.75	1.0	450
Laboratory	60.4	6.85	2.3	0.5	45

The pipe used in the district heating system had an inner diameter of d=147 mm and a corrugation pitch of ℓ=19.5 mm. The supply and return lines of this pipe, each has a length of 450m, transported water at about 95 °C between the power station and a central heating unit. Four Kistler pressure transducers were used to measure the pressure pulsations at the central heating unit.

The pipe tested in the laboratory was smaller in size (d = 60.4 mm, ℓ = 6.85 mm and L = 45 m). Water at room temperature was circulated through the pipe by means of a variable speed pump. The flow rate was measured with the aid of a standard orifice plate. As shown in Fig. 2, 11 measurement stations were distributed at equal distances along the middle section of the pipe. At each station, the insulation and the outer corrugated pipe were removed to attach pressure transducers (type Kistler) and accelerometers (type Brüel & Kjaer) directly to the inner corrugated pipe. The accelerometers were mounted with their axes parallel to the pipe centre line to measure the axial movements of the pipe wall. Their signals were integrated to record directly the vibration velocity. Multi-channels FM-recorders, UV-recorders and a real time analyser were used to record and analyse the signals.

3   FIELD MEAUSREMENTS

The system response as a function of the flow velocity V is shown in Fig. 3(a). In this figure, f and p are the frequency and the amplitude of the pressure pulsations, respectively. The Strouhal number S is based on the corrugation pitch ℓ .

At flow velocities less than 0.5 m/s, the amplitude of the pressure pulsations was very small and did not cause any problems. Above this critical flow velocity, large amplitude pressure pulsations occurred at a discrete frequency. This frequency increased in a step-like pattern as the flow velocity was increased. As shown in Fig. 3(a_2), the Strouhal number of the pressure pulsations remained within the range of 0.5 to 0.65. It should be noted that the measured amplitude p depends on the distance between the measurement location and the nearest pressure node. The values given in Fig. 3(a_3) are the highest values obtained from measurements at four different locations. They do not necessarily represent the maximum pulsation amplitudes that occur in the piping system.

Because of the high level of noise and vibration that was felt in the whole community served by the corrugated pipeline, the unit could not be operated at loads higher than 30 % (i.e. 0.5 m/s) of its nominal capicity. It was therefore necessary to reduce the vibration level so that the unit could be operated at full load.

The results shown in Fig. 3(a) suggested that several resonance modes of the system are excited consecutively as the flow velocity is increased. The excitation source is very likely to be the unstable shear layer which separates from the tips of the pipe corrugations.

© IMechE 1991 C416/010

The aspect which could not be clarified, however, concerned the nature of the excited modes. Whether they are acoustical modes of the piping system or axial vibration modes of the corrugated pipe wall could not be resolved. Thus, it was decided to carry out additional tests on a smaller size pipe, which could be accommodated in the laboratory.

4   LABORATORY TESTS

The goal of the laboratory tests was to clarify the nature of the excited resonance modes so that suitable counter-measures could be developed. A test loop in the laboratory would also allow one to test the effectiveness of any proposed counter-measure. In order to achieve these objectives, however, the vibration phenomenon must first be reproduced in the laboratory test facility !

When the laboratory test facility was being designed, it was clear that it was not necessary to construct a model dynamically similar to the central heating unit. This is because the vibration phenomenon was not a unique feature of a certain corrugated pipe or a piping system. Vibrations were observed in several other installations in which different corrugated pipes were used. The pipe chosen for the tests was therefore subject to the laboratory constraints alone, such as the available space and the maximum flow rate of the available pump. The tested pipe had an inner diameter of 60.4 mm and a length of 45 m.

The laboratory test results given in Fig. 3(b) show that the overall system response is similar to that of the heating unit. The frequency of the pressure pulsation increases in a step-like pattern, Fig. 3(b₁), and the Strouhal number remains in the range of 0.5 to 0.65, Fig. 3(b₂). However, the critical flow velocity and the pulsation frequency are substantially higher than those measured in the heating unit. This is because the laboratory test pipe is shorter than that used in the heating unit, see Table 1. Considering the similarities between the results shown in Figs. 3(a) and 3(b), it can be concluded that the vibration phenomenon observed in the heating unit is successfully reproduced in the laboratory test loop.

Fig. 4(a) shows time traces of the pressure signals recorded whilst the system was vibrating at 315 Hz. It is seen that the pulsation amplitude depends on the location of measurement, and that the phase difference between different signals is either 0 or 180°. These features characterize a standing pressure wave. The pattern of this wave is clearly depicted in Fig. 4(b), which shows the distribution of the pressure amplitude, measured from Fig. 4(a), along the pipe length. The distributions of the

pressure pulsations for the frequencies 327 and 455 Hz were also obtained in a similar way and are given in Figs. 4(c) and 4(d), respectively. They also clearly show a standing wave pattern.

Since the wavelength λ of the standing waves can be measured from Fig. 4, the speed of sound propagation in the flowing water can be estimated from the relationship $C = \lambda f$. The measured wavelengths give an average value of $C = 1036$ m/s. This value is relatively low because the pipe wall is very thin.

The effect of the pipe elasticity on the speed of sound propagation in water can be estimated from the formula:

$$C = C_o \, [1/(1+ (d/t) \, B/E)]^{1/2} \qquad (2)$$

where, C is the effective speed of sound; C_o is the reference speed of sound (1510 m/s at 30 °C); d and t are the pipe inner diameter and wall thickness, respectively; B is the Bulk modulus of elasticity for water; and E is the modulus of elasticity of the pipe material. The value calculated from equation (2), $C = 990$ m/s, is about 5 % lower than the average of the measured values. This difference, although small, may be caused by the stiffening effect of the pipe corrugations, which is not taken into account in equation (2).

Distributions of the pressure pulsation and the axial vibration velocity of the pipe wall for the frequency 410 Hz are given in Fig.5. Both distributions exemplify a standing wave pattern. Here again, the phase between the pressure and the vibration velocity signals was either 0 or 180°. This was independent of whether the signals corresponded to the same measurement location or not. The arrows given in Fig. 5(b) indicate the direction of the vibration velocity. The deflection pattern associated with the vibration mode given in Fig.5(b) is depicted (schematically and exaggerated) in Fig.5(c). It is divided into 4 sectors, each representing half a wavelength. The pipe corrugations are stretched along sectors 1 and 3 and are compressed along sectors 2 and 4. This pattern is reversed after half a cycle, i.e. the compressed parts become stretched and vice versa.

The above test results show that the observed vibration is caused by the simultaneous resonance of two different modes. The first is an axial vibration mode of the pipe wall whereas the second mode is an acoustic resonance mode of the associated piping system. Whether the excitation of both modes is a prerequisite for the occurrence of vibration is not clear.

The rather unexpected result that Fig. 5 reveals is that the wavelengths of the axial pipe vibration and the standing pressure wave are not equal.

This implies that the vibration velocity and the pressure pulsation are in phase over some portions of the pipe, and out of phase along the other portions. When they are in phase, the energy transferred from the fluid to the pipe will enforce the pipe vibration (i.e. a negative damping effect). When the pressure and the vibration velocity are out of phase, energy will be transferred from the pipe to the fluid and the vibration will be damped (i.e. a positive damping effect). The net energy transfer over the whole pipe length will therefore determine whether the system oscillation will be enhanced or damped out. This aspect is discussed further in the next section.

Since the vibration and the acoustic modes have different wavelengths, it is not likely that one causes the other. This leads to the supposition that both modes are excited independently by the shear flow over the corrugations.

5   DISCUSSIONS
5.1   Excitation mechanism

As mentioned earlier, the system vibration is excited by the unstable shear layer which separates from each corrugation tip. The impingement of this shear layer upon the following corrugation tip provides a feedback mechanism by which the shear layer oscillation is enhanced [8]. Although this feedback mechanism can cause serious vibration and noise problems in a wide variaty of engineering applications, it is very weak, or rather suppressed, in the case of corrugated pipes and metal bellows. This is because the separation and the impingement locations are rather undefined, due to the roundness of the corrugations, and also because the pipe flow is highly turbulent. In other words, the feedback mechanism does not materialize without the "help of an additional trigger". The response of a lightly damped resonance mode to broad band turbulence excitation can constitute this additional trigger, if its frequency is close to the frequency of the shear layer instability. Once the shear layer is triggered, the fluctuating energy injected into it at separation is amplified in the downstream direction. The subsequent impingement of the shear layer upon the tip of the downstream corrugation, feeds this energy back into the resonance mode.

Due to the above cycle of events, acoustic and mechanical resonances of corrugated pipes and metal bellows are often strongly excited. In the case of acoustic resonances, the shear layer is excited by the acoustic particle velocity of the resonating mode, whereas in the case of mechanical resonances, it is excited by the movements of the corrugation tips and/or by the periodic pumping of fluid from and into the "cavities" formed by the pipe corrugations.

Finally, a general feature of impinging shear layers is noteworthy. There is a minimum flow velocity below which the oscillation can not be self-sustained. This minimum velocity decreases as the corrugation pitch, i.e. the impingement length, is increased.

5.2   Strouhal number

The Strouhal number of the observed vibration is compared in Fig. 6 with that reported in the literature for metal bellows [5, 6]. The open data points correspond to tests with uniform approach flow, whereas the solid data are for cases of non-uniform approach flow. The data show clearly that the range of the vibration Strouhal number (based on the mean velocity) is substantially higher for non-ideal flow situations. The present results are closer to those for the non-ideal flow situations. This is logical since the investigated pipe contained several bends along its length.

Fig. 6 underlines an important fact; that is, when the approach flow is non-uniform, which is often the case in many industrial applications, the use of a Strouhal number determined from tests with uniform approach flow will overestimate the critical flow velocity. A non-conservative design may therefore result. For this reason, when the approach flow is non-uniform, a lower bound of S = 0.7 is recommended for design purposes.

5.3   Effect of the pipe length

Since the investigated pipes are much longer than the wavelengths of the excited vibration and acoustic modes, the interaction between these two modes along the whole length of the pipe is bound to have a considerable effect on the system oscillation. In this section, an effort is made to clarify this effect and its relation to the pipe length.

The results of the present tests, and others carried out in different installations, indicate that decreasing the length of the pipe increases the critical flow velocity, V_{cr}, and the frequency at which the vibration starts. Moreover, the mode which is excited first, i.e. at or just beyond V_{cr}, is by no means one of the lower system modes. For example, the lowest acoustic modes which were excited during the field and the laboratory measurements are the eighteenth and the twenty eighth, respectively. The increase in V_{cr}, consequent upon the reduction of the total pipe length, must be caused by an increase in the system damping. It is argued here that **the interaction between the pipe vibration and the acoustic pulsations is the main source of this increased damping.** This "interaction damping" seems to decrease as the wavelength of the system oscillation is decreased. In other words, resonances will be excited only if their wavelengths are much smaller than the total length of the pipe. This argument can be substantiated by the following example which is typical for long corrugated pipes.

Let us consider a pipe of length L_1, critical flow velocity V_{cr1} and frequency f_1 for the lowest excited mode. If the length of this pipe is halved, $L_2 = L_1/2$, the critical flow velocity and the frequency will increase to V_{cr2} and f_2, respectively. The critical velocity V_{cr2} cannot be regarded as the minimum velocity required to initiate the shear layer oscillations for this corrugation geometry. This is because V_{cr1}, which is smaller than V_{cr2}, is sufficiently high to excite the longer pipe. Thus, the damping of the mode f_1 must be higher for the shorter pipe. This increase in damping can not be attributed to the fluid damping because viscous losses per unit length have not been altered. However, the ratio of the total pipe length to the wavelength of the frequency f_1 has been reduced by shortening the pipe. It is this alteration that increases the damping at the frequency f_1. At a higher frequency, such as f_2, this ratio is increased again to a critical value and therefore the vibration can be re-established. It should be remembered that the pipe vibration and the acoustic pulsation are excited independently by the shear flow over the corrugations. Their co-existence will therefore depend on the damping resulting from their mutual interaction over the whole length of the pipe, which constitutes a large number of wavelengths. The present results indicate that this "interaction damping" decreases as the ratio between the wavelength and the total pipe length is decreased, i.e. as the number of wavelengths spanning the pipe length is increased.

6   COUNTER-MEASURES

After considering several alternatives and the feasibility of their implementation, it was concluded that damping the axial vibration of the pipe was the most promising and practical approach. The effect of two damping blocks was therefore investigated on the laboratory test loop. As shown in Fig. 7, the damping blocks consisted of two wooden pieces which were tightened around the inner pipe. Their locations, which are denoted by B_1 and B_2 in Fig. 2, divided the pipe into three equal portions. Two sets of blocks of different lengths were tested. The shorter set (H = 0.25 m) did not produce any improvement. The second set had a length of 0.5 m, which approximated one quarter of the vibration wavelength. As shown in Fig. 8, the use of one block of the longer set did not eliminate the vibrations. When the second block was tightened around the pipe,

the vibration was completely eliminated. The vibration reappeared as soon as one block was removed again. Clearly both blocks were necessary to eliminate the vibration.

The damping blocks influence the pipe vibration in one of two ways: i) they increase the damping along their length or ii) they can be considered as two solid pipes, or "rigid supports", which divide the whole pipe into three mechanically independent portions. Either way, the blocks clearly alter the pipe response substantially. From an acoustical point of view, the blocks have a negligible effect. Therefore, the elimination of the acoustic resonance as well, by using the blocks, must be attributed to the alteration of the pipe response and the resulting increase of the interaction damping which has been discussed in the previous section.

The above test results suggest that the vibration in the central heating unit may be eliminated by replacing several portions of the corrugated pipe with solid pipes. It was decided to carry out this alteration in stages so that the effect of every stage could be assessed. The first stage entailed replacing a piece 20 meter long in the middle of both the supply and the return pipes.

The test results of the first stage are compared with the original results in Fig. 9. For technical reasons, the flow rate could not be increased to its maximum value (100 m³/hr) in either tests. The replacement of the central portion of the pipe increased the critical flow rate from 30 m³/hr to 55 m³/hr (Fig. 9(c)). The vibration frequency was also increased from 17.5 Hz to 30.5 Hz (Fig. 9(a)), but the Strouhal number remained within the original range of 0.5 to 0.65 (Fig. 9(b)). Although the amplitude of the pressure pulsation was reduced from 1.0 bar to 0.35 bar, it was still unsatisfactory and additional counter-measures were necessary to facilitate the unit operation at full load.

Although the results of the first stage were very encouraging, the second and the third stages were altered due to practical considerations, such as costs, feasibility and for topographical reasons. Instead of replacing short pieces as was planned, long portions of the pipe were replaced by solid pipes.

In the second stage, 100 m of the pipe from the power station end was replaced by a solid pipe. The test data for this stage are presented in Fig. 9 by the square data points. The critical flow rate increased only slightly and all other variables, i.e. frequency, amplitude and Strouhal number, did not alter much. The similarity between the results of the first and second stages is due to the fact that the length of the corrugated pipe at the heating unit end was the same in both cases.

The third and final stage entailed replacing 170 m of the pipe at the heating unit end. The final geometry, starting from the heating unit, consisted of 170 m of solid pipe, 45 m of corrugated pipe, 20 m of solid pipe, 115 m of corrugated pipe, and finally 100 m of solid pipe. The amplitude of the pressure pulsation for this final geometry is shown in Fig. 9(c), and pressure spectra of stages 2 and 3 are compared in Fig. 10. For this final geometry, the system vibration was completely eliminated over the whole range of the unit operation.

7   SUMMARY AND CONCLUSIONS

A 450 m long corrugated pipe in a district heating system experienced vibration problems at loads higher than 30% of its full capacity. In order to investigate the excitation mechanism and possible means of its alleviation, a shorter pipe of smaller diameter was tested in the laboratory. The pressure pulsation and the pipe vibration were measured simultaneously at several locations to clarify the nature of the excited modes and possible means of their attenuation. The test results led to the following conclusions:

1. The critical flow velocity at which the vibration is initiated and the frequency of the initial vibration increase as the pipe is made shorter.

2. The observed vibrations are the results of simultaneous resonance of two modes. The first is a longitudinal acoustic mode whereas the second is an axial vibration mode of the pipe corrugations. Higher order modes are excited consecutively as the flow velocity is increased. The order of the lowest excited modes, however, is very high (higher than the fifteenth mode). This means that the wavelength of the excited modes is very short in comparison with the total pipe length.

3. The Strouhal number, based on the corrugation pitch, of all the observed vibrations is confined to the range of 0.5 to 0.65. This is similar to the Strouhal number range for metal bellows, and indicates that the excitation mechanism is similar in both cases. As suggested by Rockwell and Naudascher [7], the excitation source seems to be the impinging shear layer which separates from the tip of each corrugation and impinges on the tip of the following corrugation.

4. The acoustic and the axial vibration modes are found to be excited simultaneously. Although the frequencies of these two different type modes are equal, their wavelengths are not. This suggests that the two modes are excited independently by the shear layer.

5. It is argued that the co-existence of these two different modes depends on the damping resulting from their mutual interaction over the whole pipe length. The effect of this "interaction damping" seems to be very crucial in determining whether the resonant vibration will be damped out or excited. The test results suggest that the "interaction damping" of any mode decreases as the ratio of its wavelength to the total pipe length is decreaed.

6. The vibration can be eliminated by replacing portions of the corrugated pipe with solid pipes. The length of each solid pipe must be at least one quarter of the vibration wavelength. This seems to be the only recommendation that can be made at present.

REFERENCES

(1)   PETRIE, A.M. and HUNTLEY, I.D. The acoustic output produced by a steady airflow through a corrugated duct. Journal of Sound and Vibration, 1980, 70(1), 1-9.

(2)   GERLACH, C.R. Flow-induced vibrations of metal bellows. Journal of Engineering for Industry, 1969, 91(4), 1196-1202.

(3)   GERLACH, C.R. Vortex excitation of metal belows. Journal of Engineering for Industry, 1972, 94(1), 87-94.

(4)   BASS, R.L. and HOLSTER, J.L. Bellows vibration with internal cryogenic flows. Journal of Engineering for Industry, 1972, 94(1), 70-75.

(5)   WEAVER, D.S. and AINSWORTH, P. Flow induced vibrations in bellows. International Symposium on Flow-Induced Vibration and Noise. Chicago, 1988, 4, 205-214.

(6)   KLAEUI, E. Jet: vibration tests on calorimeter bellows. Report No. 3554/1512, Sulzer Bros. Ltd., Winterthur, Switzerland, 1987.

(7)   ROCKWELL, D. and NAUDASCHER, E. Self-sustaining oscillations of flow past cavities, Journal of Fluids Engineering, 1978, 100, 152-165.

(8)   ROCKWELL, D. Oscillations of impinging shear layers. AIAA Journal, 1983, 21(5), 645-664.

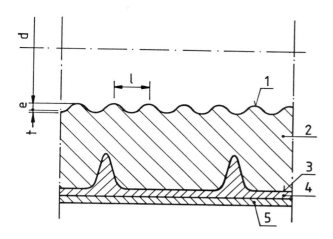

Fig 1 Schematic presentation of the corrugated pipe and the insulating layers. 1, inner pipe, stainless steel; 2, insulation, synthetic foam; 3, outer pipe, carbon steel; 4, insulation, bitumen; 5, insulation, rubber compound.

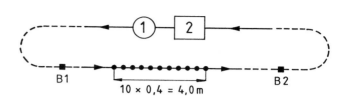

Fig 2 Schematic presentation of the Laboratory test loop. 1, variable speed pump; 2, tank; ●, locations of measurements; ■, damping blocks.

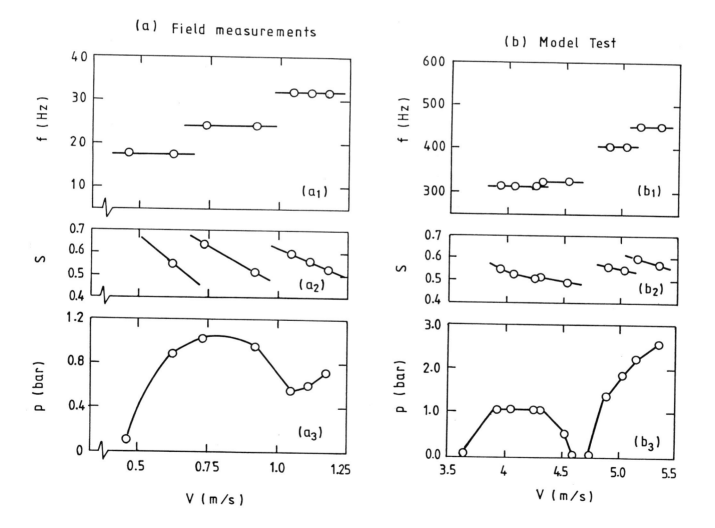

(a) Field measurements

(b) Model Test

Fig 3 Frequency, f, Strouhal number, S, and amplitude, p, of the pressure fluctuations as functions of the flow velocity, V. (a) results of field measurements, (b) results of laboratory tests.

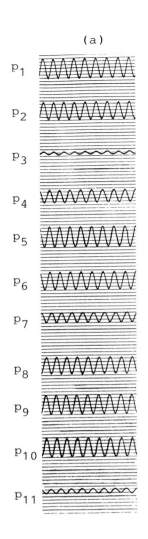

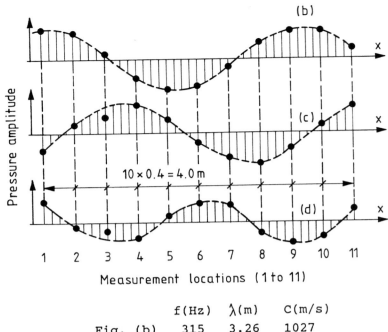

	f(Hz)	λ(m)	C(m/s)
Fig. (b)	315	3.26	1027
Fig. (c)	327	3.22	1053
Fig. (d)	455	2.26	1028

Fig 4 Time traces and axial distributions of the pressure pulsation measured during the laboratory tests.

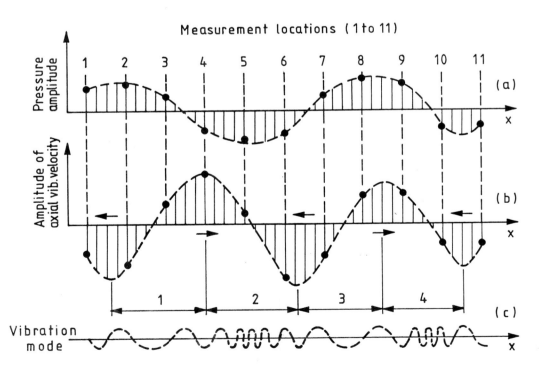

Fig 5 Axial distributions of (a) amplitude of pressure pulsations and (b) amplitude of axial vibration velocity of the corrugations. The vibration mode corresponding to the vibration distribution (b) is shown schematically in (c). Laboratory tests, f = 410 Hz.

424

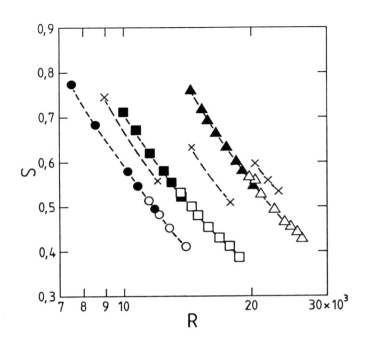

Fig 6 Comparison of the present Strouhal number for large amplitude vibration with those given in the literature for metal bellows. O,●, l = 4.2 mm, f = 328 Hz [6]; □,■, = 3 mm, f = 795 Hz [5]; △,▲, l = 3 mm, f= 1230 Hz [5]; X, l = 19.5 mm, f= 17-31 Hz, present field measurements. Open symbols, uniform flow; solid symbols, non-uniform flow.

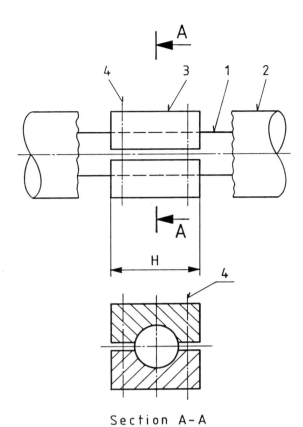

Section A-A

Fig 7 Geometry of the damping block. 1, inner pipe; 2, pipe with insulating layers; 3, wooden block; 4, clamp.

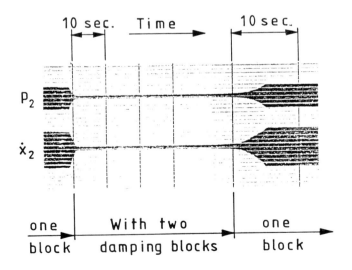

Fig 8 Vibration and pressure signals showing the elimination of vibration by means of two damping blocks.

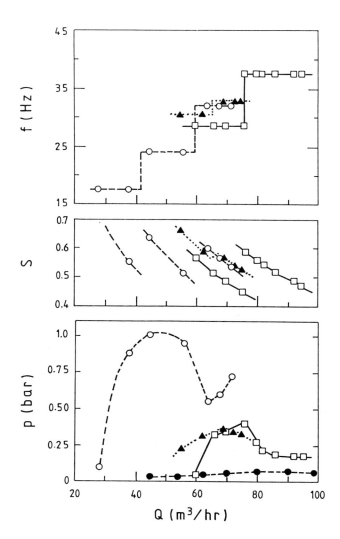

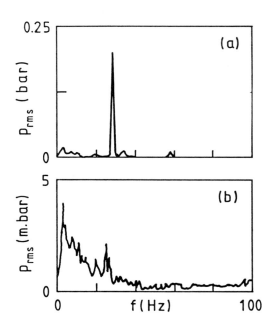

Fig 10 Typical pressure spectra of (a) the second stage and (b) the third stage. (a) Q = 65 m³/hr, (b) 100 m³/hr.

Fig 9 Results of the field measurements showing the effect of different stages of counter-measures. o, original pipe; ▲, first stage; □, second stage; ●, third stage.

Combustion air flow induced furnace vibration in an oil-fired utility boiler — a case study

F L EISINGER, MSc, PhD, MASME
Foster Wheeler Energy Corporation, Clinton, New Jersey, United States of America

SYNOPSIS Excessive furnace vibration was encountered when a burner air swirler was modified to reduce pressure drop. An investigation showed that the primary cause of the vibration was combustion air flow induced. The problem was overcome by a new low pressure drop swirler configuration and a modification of the fuel nozzles. The test and analysis program characterizing the problem and leading to its solution is described.

1 INTRODUCTION

Experience with utility steam generators indicates that furnace vibration is more likely to develop in units fired by oil or gas than in those fired by pulverized coal. It appears that the coal fires have greater inherent damping and are thus less prone to excite the furnace gases.

Strong furnace vibration is typically characterized by the presence of well developed standing waves in the furnace, generating high sound levels and causing structural vibration of the furnace walls. Because of noise considerations, as well as concern for the structural integrity of the unit, furnace vibration cannot be permitted to take place within the operating range of the steam generator.

The standing wave vibration is excited by burners. The vibration is considered a condition of resonant instability during which the excitation frequency(s) of the burner coincide with the standing wave frequency(s) of the furnace gases. Once initiated, a feedback mechanism typically occurs during which the pressure pulsation in the furnace has a modulating effect upon the burner(s). The standing wave vibration typically persists over a large range of boiler load. This is analogous to the lock-in regime of a vortex-excited vibration of tube bundles or cavities within the tube bundles, due to cross flow.

In the arrangement of pressure jet flame burners typically used in utility boilers, the causes of the pressure pulsation or velocity fluctuations are found either in the fuel supply or in the air supply needed for combustion, or in a combination of the two. Since the momentum of the fuel spray is generally small in comparison with the momentum of the air flow, the characteristics of the flame will depend more on the air flow pattern than on the fuel spray. However, in spite of the dominating effect of air flow, the influence of the mode of fuel injection on the air flow pattern and the combustion itself may be significant.

In this paper we are concerned with an oil-fired burner utilizing a conical oil jet spray issuing from a fuel nozzle. Swirling air flow is typically used in burners for stability and easy control of flame shape. One or more concentric swirling air jets, often with different swirling characteristics, and sometimes in combination with nonswirling axial jets, are used.

2 BRIEF REVIEW OF PUBLISHED WORK

A brief review of relevant literature on air flow and fuel injection configuration effects on combustion from the standpoint of burner-induced vibration follows:

Vonnegut [1] performed experiments on swirling flows in tubes where a discrete tone was generated at the tube exit. As the fluid approaches the tube exit plane, it becomes unstable and periodic fluctuations of motion are produced, generating sound. Vonnegut found that the frequency of the oscillation was directly proportional to flow rate. During observations of small air bubbles in water, the oscillations were visible as bubble precession around the tube axis, occurring at about the same frequency as the fluid rotational velocity.

Chanaud [2], in his experiments, extended Vonnegut's results showing that a smooth area increase at the exit of the tube promotes and enhances the axial periodicity. He also showed that the Strouhal number may be a function of flow rate and Reynolds number (based on tube diameter and axial flow velocity).

Chigier and Beer [3] have shown that an annular swirling jet establishes a recirculation zone, the strength of which is proportional to the degree of swirl. (A minimum swirl number of about $S = 0.6$ is required to initiate the formation of a recirculation zone). A divergent air nozzle increased the size and the strength of the internal vortex, and the maximum flow velocities were deflected outward to large radial distances.

Chanaud [4] has pointed to a spiral vortex-induced precession velocity superimposed upon the axial flow. The frequency of this vortex (called the precessing vortex core — PVC) increases with flow rate. The existence of the spiral vortex represents a structural change in the swirling flow (the vortex breakdown phenomenon). The existence of a reverse flow region is necessary for the generation of the PVC instability. The periodic motion of the PVC seems to be controlled by a feedback through the oscillation superimposed on the reversed flow, reminiscent of vortex-shedding. There is a critical Reynolds number corresponding to the initiation of the periodic motion, and a maximum Rossby number above which no periodic motion will occur.

Chigier et al [5] discuss the formation of the recirculation eddies in the wake of flameholders. This work is particularly relevant to one of the burner configurations reported in this paper where a swirler is located within a divergent section of an air register. In such a burner configuration, the length of the recirculation zone increases with the swirl number and decreases with the blockage ratio. A good sized recirculation zone (one which provides flame stability) thus requires an adequate swirl and a low blockage ratio. Chigier et al also show that a disc, instead of a swirler, can be used as a flame stabilizer, as it also promotes the development of a recirculation zone. This recirculation bubble, however, has somewhat different effects on the shape and stability of the flame; the main difference being that the recirculating bubble is stationary (nonrotating about the burner axis) unlike the zone behind a swirler.

Syred et al [6], in their experiments, showed that the shape and size of the recirculation zone are only slightly changed under combustion conditions compared to isothermal conditions. Under strong swirl conditions, aerodynamic forces are so dominant that little change occurs to flow fields as a result of chemical reaction in the flame.

Sarpkaya [7], in his experiments, also showed that the shape and size of the recirculation zone are only slightly reduced under combustion conditions compared to isothermal conditions. He also observed the vortex breakdown phenomenon in a mildly diverging cylindrical tube, which results in a double helix and spiral-type motion.

Syred and Beer [8] showed experimentally that true axisymmetric flow occurs only for very low swirl numbers. When the flow reaches a critical swirl number, an instability develops and the central forced vortex region of flow starts to precess about the axis of symmetry. The precessing vortex core lies on the boundary of the reverse flow region. On leaving the swirl generator, the PVC rapidly dissipates, and the mean flow becomes axisymmetric within less than one diameter downstream of the tube exit. The flow upstream is a three dimensional, time dependent turbulent flow.

While the interaction of the precessing vortex core and combustion is complex, a central axial fuel injection leads to the suppression of the precessing mode, and the flow reverts to a stable axisymmetric situation. At the other extreme, tangential fuel injection, the large precessing vortex core is still present, but with reduced amplitude and increased frequency.

Chigier [9] emphasized the role of the recirculating bubble as a constant heat source with reduced velocity requirements for flame stabilization. Due to a high turbulence intensity in the recirculating zone this well stirred region contributes beneficially to fuel mixing and chemical reaction.

Syred et al [10] demonstrated the existence of a longitudinal oscillation in a tube excited by PVC. Tangential fuel entry gives the strongest coupling between the PVC and a longitudinal excitation. It follows that swirl stabilized burners can generate resonance instabilities and excite furnaces due to the periodic fluctuations of velocity and pressure emanating from the burner. The methods of reduction of the excitation recommended are fuel entry on the axis of symmetry, sudden enlargement of flow area and of course separation of excitation frequencies from the furnace frequencies, if possible. He puts PVC into the category of vortex-shedding phenomena.

Chigier and Dvorak [11] have shown that the flow pattern changes under flame conditions; namely, the kinetic energy of turbulence per unit mass and the velocity fluctuation become higher than in the corresponding cold condition.

Syred et al [12] showed that in turbulent diffusion flames, the PVC is damped in comparison with the PVC in nonreacting flows. A first and second instability is referred to, respectively, for the initiation of the recirculating bubble and the establishment of the PVC. While the frequency of the PVC varies with the Reynolds number, its stability may be determined by the Rayleigh criterion [13] whereby it is

Stable if $\rho W r$ increases with r (solid body rotation)

Neutral if $\rho W r$ = constant (free vortex)

Unstable if $\rho W r$ decreases with r

where   r, W and ρ

are radial distance, tangential flow velocity and flow density, respectively.

It is further shown that for a lean fuel/air ratio (less fuel), the PVC is strong. For a rich ratio, the PVC is typically damped and therefore weaker.

Chen [14] confirmed that fuel injection in a gas burner can affect the PVC and burner stability. He found from his experience with swirling flows [15], that an oscillation frequency on the order of 20 to 40 per cent of the frequency of the swirling (rotating) flow will take place.

Further evidence of oscillation generated by swirling flow can be found for example in publications by Hosoi [16], Chen [15], Escudier [17], and Hayama [18].

A toroidal recirculating vortex region can also be generated by an annular axial jet (without swirl) resulting from shear effects [19]. This recirculation region has many attributes of the swirl–generated recirculation zone, such as—expansion, entrainment, velocity decay, and convergence toward axis. It appears, however, that no precessing vortex core is generated since no swirling conditions exist—as in the disc or cone flameholder cases.

3   DESCRIPTION OF PROBLEM

Furnace vibration occurred when the original burner swirler, (Configuration A, Fig 1), was changed to Configuration B, Fig 2. The furnace vibration was eliminated by a burner modification using a new swirler design (Configuration C, Fig 3).

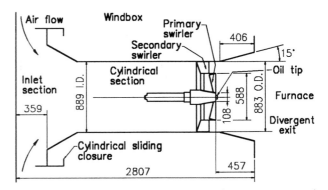

Fig 1   Original burner arrangement (Configuration A)

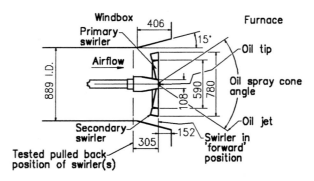

Fig 2   Modified burner arrangement causing furnace vibration, swirler in 'forward position' (Configuration B)

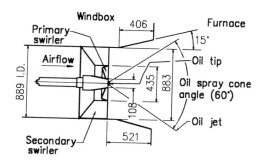

Fig 3 Final burner arrangement eliminating
furnace vibration (Configuration C)

3.1 Original burner arrangement (Configuration A)

Fig 1 shows the original burner configuration. The air register consisted of three sections:

(i) the 359 mm wide annular inlet section with radial air inlet

(ii) the cylindrical section which was 889 mm in diameter and 2042 mm long

(iii) The exit section 406 mm long, which diverged from the cylindrical section at an angle of 15° to a final exit diameter of 1107 mm.

The swirler was positioned inside the cylindrical section of the air register and mounted on the oil gun which was rigidly supported on the register axis. The front face of the primary center portion of the swirler was positioned 457 mm upstream of the exit plane of the air register.

There were eight burners at four elevations located at the rear wall of the furnace. The burner arrangement and the swirler orientation is shown in Fig 4. The eight cylindrical barrels were located inside a windbox which received air for all the burners from a forced draft fan.

Air flow through each burner was controlled by a cylindrical closure sliding over the annulus of the register inlet section.

The swirler consisted of a primary central section with a hub of 108 mm inside diameter and 588 mm outside diameter. The primary swirler had 24 blades at a 45° blade angle. The secondary section of the swirler with an outside diameter of 883 mm consisted of 24 blades with a blade angle of 30°. The central hub contained the oil spray nozzle which had 12 exit holes, each 4.73 mm in diameter and a spray cone angle of 80°. The oil nozzle had a steam atomizing chamber where the oil was atomized before exiting the nozzle.

The flow parameters of the burner were:

Burner full load capacity: 56 MW

Full load air flow at 10 percent excess air: 32.7 m³/s
(changes approximately linearly with load within a 50 percent - 100 percent load range).

Maximum air velocity in cylindrical portion of air register: 52.7 m/s

Air temperature: 305°C

Full load oil flow: 4733 kg/h

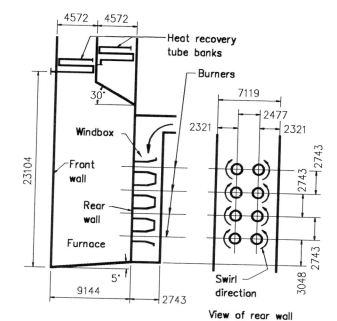

Fig 4 Schematic of furnace, windbox and burner arrangement

Oil pressure: 862 kPa
Oil temperature: 120°C
Atomizing steam flow: 474 kg/h
Atomizing steam pressure: 1034 kPa
Windbox pressure over atmospheric: 2.6 kPa
Furnace negative pressure: -0.125 kPa

3.2 Modified burner arrangement (Configuration B)

The type and position of the swirler was modified to reduce pressure drop through the swirler to increase capacity and flexibility of unit operation. Fig 2 shows the modified burner arrangement. The swirler was now located within the divergent portion of the air register. It was mounted on the oil gun which was rigidly supported along the register axis. The front of the swirler was positioned 152 mm upstream of the exit plane of the register.

The swirler consisted of a shrouded primary section with 24 blades at a 45° blade angle with an outside diameter of 590 mm. The secondary swirler had an outside diameter of 780 mm, with 24 blades at a 45° blade angle, and was unshrouded. As mentioned before, this burner configuration caused the excessive furnace vibration.

3.2.1 Standing wave frequencies of furnace gases and windbox air. The standing wave frequencies in an enclosure are given by the formula

$$f = \frac{c}{2}\left[\left(\frac{n_x}{l_x}\right)^2 + \left(\frac{n_y}{l_y}\right)^2 + \left(\frac{n_z}{l_z}\right)^2\right]^{1/2}$$

where

f - frequency of standing wave, Hz

c = speed of sound in air or gas, m/s

n_x, n_y, n_z = 0, 1, 2, 3,...modal coefficients, dimensionless

l_x, l_y, l_z = dimensions of enclosure in x, y, z, directions, m

The dimensions of the furnace and windbox used in the analysis are:

Furnace (average gas temperature, 1565°C)

  Depth: $l_x = 9.14\ m$

  Width: $l_y = 7.12\ m$

  Height: $l_z = 22.7\ m$

Windbox (average air temperature: 305°C)

  Depth: $l_x = 2.74\ m$

  Width: $l_y = 8.75\ m$

  Height: $l_z = 15.3\ m$

The first six modes of the standing wave frequencies in the furnace and windbox are given in Table 1.

Table 1 Standing wave frequencies in furnace and windbox

Mode			Standing wave frequency	
			In furnace	In windbox
0	0	1	18.1	15.8
1	0	0	45.0	27.6
1	0	1	48.5	31.8
0	1	0	57.8	88.0
0	1	1	60.6	89.4
1	1	0	73.3	92.2

3.2.2 Furnace vibration with modified burner arrangement (Configuration B)

Large furnace vibration occurred within the boiler operating range with the burners arranged per configuration B (Fig 2). To monitor the vibration, pressure pulsation inside the furnace was measured through pressure taps via piezoelectric pressure transducers inserted at different locations through the furnace walls. The dominant frequency of the pressure pulsation was in the range of 42 Hz – 45 Hz, corresponding to a standing wave frequency of the furnace gases in the front-to-rear direction (furnace depth = 9.14 m).

Fig 5 gives the pressure pulsation amplitudes in the furnace at the dominant frequency of 42 Hz - 45 Hz as a function of load and cone angle of oil spray. At each condition, the onset of vibration was sudden, resulting in large structural vibration of the furnace walls. The sound levels during this vibration were typically in the 110 dB – 130 dB range.

A clear relationship existed between the onset of the vibration and the angle of the oil spray cone, Fig 2. With a lowering of the spray angle the onset of vibration was delayed. Although with the reduced spray angle a substantial portion of the load range remained without vibration, operation was not possible at these conditions because of the flame becoming too long and smoky. This was particularly true at the 70° spray angle.

Detailed diagnostic testing of the boiler with this burner configuration was performed in order to assess the sensitivity of the vibratory condition to various burner operating parameters. The program included the testing of

- the effect of boiler load or air flow to burners
- the effect of oil spray nozzle configuration (spray angle, number and size of orifices)
- the effect of air swirler position (swirler in forward

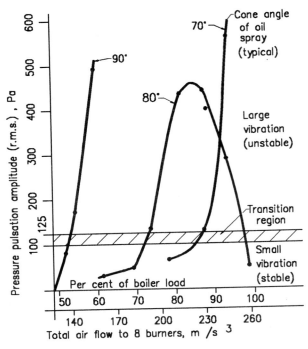

Fig 5 Pressure pulsation in furnace with burner Configuration B causing high furnace vibration at 42 to 45 Hz frequency measured at front wall. All eight burners in operation. Data taken at steady–state operating condition.

position and also pulled back by a maximum of 305 mm)
- the effects of parameter changes
  - fuel oil temperature
  - atomizing steam pressure
  - excess air levels
  - number of burners in operation

The fuel and atomizing steam supply lines were tested for possible pressure pulsations within the respective supply line systems. The pressure pulsation in the windbox was also monitored.

The results showed that air flow, oil spray angle, and swirler positions had a strong effect on vibration. Changes in the other parameters had relatively minor effects.

Possible burner–to–burner interactions were tested by taking some of the burners out of service. It was determined that burner interactions were minimal, as the vibration remained basically a function of air flow. (With fewer burners in service, the furnace vibration levels were commensurately reduced).

No pressure pulsation was detected either in the oil or in the steam supply line system. The pressure pulsation measured in the windbox showed qualitatively the same pulsation spectrum as that obtained in the furnace and there were no frequency components present which could be attributed to the windbox dimensions.

As a result of the testing, it was concluded that no adjustment of operating parameters with this burner configuration was possible which would eliminate the vibration within the load range of the boiler and at the same time maintain the necessary flame shape and quality.

© IMechE 1991 C416/095

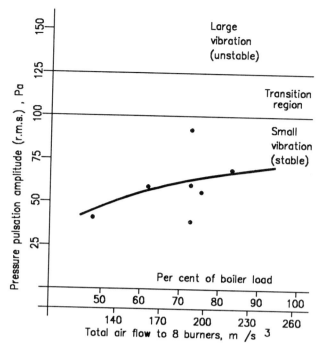

Fig 6 Pressure pulsation in furnace with burner Configuration A at 42 to 45 Hz frequency measured at front wall. All eight burners in operation. Data taken at steady–state operating condition.

4 TEST RESULTS WITH THE ORIGINAL BURNER CONFIGURATION (CONFIGURATION A)

As mentioned earlier, the boiler equipped with burners of the original configuration (Configuration A) did not experience furnace vibration. The typical pressure pulsation in the furnace at the 42 Hz - 45 Hz frequency, as measured at the front furnace wall with the original burners is shown in Fig 6. As expected vibration increases slightly with load, but remains stable and relatively low.

5 TEST PROGRAM OF VIBRATION ELIMINATION

5.1 Scaled burner model tests

A detailed analysis of the full scale test results, both with the original swirler configuration (A) and with the modified swirler (B), indicated that the vibration problem was primarily air flow related and therefore a modification of the air swirler would be necessary. Model tests in a test furnace were designed to provide sufficient data for a change in the air swirler design.

The test model burner was a one-half physical scaled version of the full size burner. The flow input (oil and air) to the burner and its heat release rate because of its half physical size was approximately one quarter of the full size burner.

The flow velocities of the test burner were approximately equal to the velocities of the full size burner, with approximately identical pressure drops across the test and full size burners. The test furnace dimensions were: 2.44 m in diameter, 8.23 m long.

A large number of air swirler and oil nozzle configurations were tested with the following main parameters investigated.

- flame pattern, size and quality
- air velocities through cylindrical section of burner and primary and secondary portions of swirler
- pressure drop through burner
- effect of oil spray nozzle parameters
- air swirler position
- pressure pulsation in furnace

The evaluation of the test results (including their correlation with the full scale test results) led to the selection of three additional air swirler configurations which were manufactured full size and individually tested in the boiler.

5.2 Full scale single burner tests

Four air swirler configurations were tested.

(1) 590 mm diameter shrouded primary swirler with 24 blades, 45° blade angle with a 780 mm diameter secondary swirler, 24 blades, 45° blade angle, no outside shroud (Configuration B-used a reference).
(2) Same primary swirler as per (1) with a 686 mm diameter secondary swirler, 24 blades, 45° blade angle, no outside shroud.
(3) Same primary swirler as per (1) with a 635 mm diameter secondary swirler, 24 blades, 45° blade angle, no outside shroud.
(4) 435 mm diameter shrouded primary swirler with 24 blades, 45° blade angle with a 883 mm diameter shrouded secondary swirler, 36 blades, 15° blade angle.

The burners were mounted in the boiler and tested one by one with oil firing using combustion air at ambient temperature with the boiler/turbine operating on bypass.

Partial, full load and overload conditions of the burners were simulated on the basis of fuel oil pressure and pressure differentials through the burners.

Pressure pulsation readings in the furnace were taken with different oil spray nozzles at three simulated loads (at 75, 100 and 125 percent of load).

Tests were conducted with the air swirlers in two positions: in the 'forward' position inside the divergent section and in the 'pulled back' position within the burner cylindrical section.

Figure 7 is a plot of the pressure pulsation amplitudes for each swirler as measured at the furnace target wall (front wall) (swirlers 1, 2 and 3 were positioned in the 'forward' position, swirler 4 in the 'pulled back' position).

Swirler No. 4 clearly produced the lowest pressure pulsation amplitudes in the furnace.

Figure 8 shows the pressure pulsation results of swirler No. 4 as a function of the oil tip spray angle. The best results were obtained with the 70° angle of the oil spray nozzle, the lowest angle tested.

Based on these single burner test results, swirler No. 4, was selected as giving the most favorable results among the four tested. These swirlers were manufactured and installed in all eight burners of the boiler.

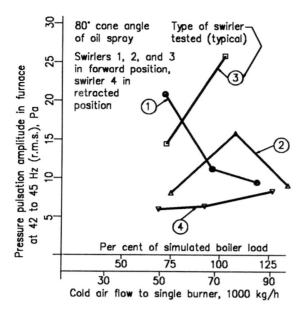

Fig 7 Full scale single burner tests
in boiler. Pressure pulsation
measurements at front wall.

6 FULL SCALE VIBRATION TESTING OF BOILER EQUIPPED WITH NEW SWIRLERS (CONFIGURATION C)

The best swirler (No. 4 from full scale single burner tests) was installed in all eight burners in the pulled back position (Configuration C, Fig 3) and the boiler was tested for vibration and flame quality.

Initial operation with these swirlers indicated a major improvement; however, some vibration was still in existence within a certain load range when the burners were equipped with 90°, 80° and 75° oil spray cone nozzles. Detailed vibration testing followed, resulting in the optimization of mode of fuel injection for complete elimination of the vibration problem.

The final testing included three different oil nozzles with 75°, 70°, and 60° oil spray angles and involved

- testing within a 66 percent to 100 percent load range
- changes in excess air
- testing for stability against vibration
    - taking burners out of service and returning them to service
    - opening and closing of air registers on burners out of service

The vibration test results, amplitude of pressure pulsation in the furnace as a function of load and oil spray cone angle are given in Fig 9.

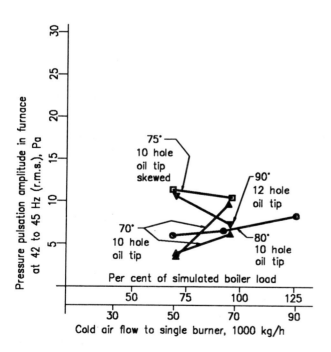

Fig 8 Full scale single burner tests
in boiler with swirler number 4
(Configuration C – Fig 3).
Effect of cone angle of
oil spray.

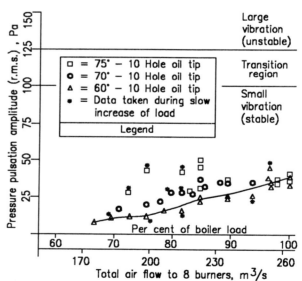

Fig 9 Pressure pulsation in furnace with final
burner arrangement (configuration C)
at 42 to 45 Hz frequency measured
at front wall. All eight burners in
operation. Data taken at steady–state
operating condition except as noted.

The best results were obtained with a 60° oil spray angle tip having 10 exit holes of 5.2 mm in diameter each. The maximum pressure pulsation in the furnace in the dominant 42 Hz - 45 Hz frequency range at full load was less than 0.05 kPa (r.m.s). This was significantly below the value of 0.1 to

0.125 kPa, the threshold value typically present at the onset of large furnace vibration.

With this burner configuration, a fully stable vibration resistant behavior and very good flame quality throughout the entire load range was achieved.

7 COMPARISON OF WINDBOX–TO–FURNACE PRESSURE DIFFERENTIALS IN BURNER CONFIGURATIONS A, B, AND C

The windbox-to-furnace pressure differential is basically governed by the pressure differential across the air swirler. Fig 10 gives the pressure differentials for the original (A), modified (B), an the final (C) swirler configurations. As mentioned before, the pressure differential through the burners was a design consideration. It was necessary to maintain the pressure drops in burner configuration C at or below the values of burner configuration B for flexibility of unit operation. This goal was achieved.

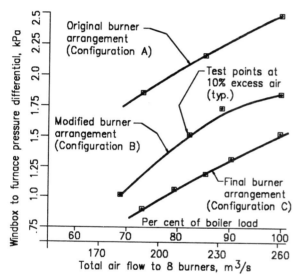

Fig 10   Windbox–to–furnace pressure differentials with all 8 burners in operation as a function of boiler load. Data taken at steady state operating conditions.

8 COMPARISON OF FURNACE VIBRATORY AND NON–VIBRATORY CONDITIONS (BURNER CONFIGURATIONS A, B & C)

The experimental results obtained during the full scale operational boiler testing have shown that only when the pressure pulsation inside the furnace reached a certain level (threshold), strong furnace vibration was initiated. After reaching this threshold, vibration amplitudes increased dramatically with load.

The transition region between the non-vibratory (small vibration) and the vibratory (large vibration) regions was experimentally established for the tested furnace to be about 0.1 kPa to 0.125 kPa (r.m.s.) at the first dominant mode frequency of 42 Hz - 45 Hz.

Above the transition region a fully established standing wave is present in the furnace, with flames and furnace gases fully coupled.

The region below the transition region represents the non-vibratory (small vibration) conditions. The small pulsations present within this region are primarily an expression of the flames' normal turbulent behavior (without coupling effects).

The maximum experienced pressure pulsation amplitudes in the furnace in the three burner configurations are given in Table 2.

Table 2 Maximum pressure pulsation amplitudes in furnace at full load at three burner configurations

Burner configuration	Pressure pulsation amplitude kPa (r.m.s.) at 42 Hz - 45 Hz	Note
A	0.09	Non-Vibratory Condition
B	0.6	Vibratory Condition
C	0.05	Non-Vibratory Condition

9 DISCUSSION OF RESULTS AND WORKING THEORY

The swirler positioned within the divergent portion of the air register, Fig 2, generates favorable conditions for a good and stable flame. The swirler by itself, having a swirl number of about 0.68, would promote a recirculation zone capable of sustaining a stable flame. Two additional factors (1) the strong axial annular flow around the swirler, and (2) the effect of the divergent air register, have a pronounced influence on further increasing the size and enhancing the strength of the recirculating zone downstream of the swirler, consistent with published data [3, 4]. The combined result leads to a substantial increase of the effective swirl number. These conditions helped to maintain a stable and good quality flame in the non-resonant operating range. The strong swirl brought about the development of a precessing vortex core [4, 8, 10], which was the apparent source of the front-to-rear standing wave inside the furnace, consistent with similar observations of Syred et al [10]. Although the change of the size of the recirculation zone due to combustion is known to be relatively small [6, 7], there is a damping effect due to combustion [12] when axial fuel injection is used [8, 12]. As our tests have shown, the damping of the PVC can be increased and its strength reduced by reducing the spray angle of oil injection. By optimizing the spray angle, both the damping of the PVC, as well as the enhancement of the recirculating eddy, can be achieved. This reduces the vibration potential and increases stability. Chen [14] has obtained similar results with gas burners.

It was the strength of the recirculation eddy in conjunction with the precessing vortex core, which prevented us from obtaining favorable results within the entire load range in burner Configuration B. Adjustments which were tested in this burner configuration resulted either in a vibratory condition or unacceptably long and smoky flames, or both.

In the final swirler configuration C, the essentially axial annular air jet (15° blade angle) in combination with the central swirling jet (swirl number of about 0.7) and the further enhancing effect of the low blockage ratio of 0.25, also resulted in a relatively strong recirculation zone with a PVC apparently present as well. The final adjustment of the mode of fuel injection to a 60° spray angle sufficiently damped the PVC and at the same time maintained the necessary strength of the recirculation zone for stability.

In the original burner configuration A, the high pressure drop through the burners had a beneficial effect on overall performance, consistent with the full scale and model scale test results.

We have seen that the burner exit conditions, both the effect of air leaving the air register through the flameholder as well as the mode of fuel injection, are the main factors determining the conditions for vibration excitation, with air flow having the principal role. Either a suppression of the excitation, or a separation between the burner excitation and furnace natural frequencies are needed to prevent furnace vibration.

10 SUMMARY AND CONCLUSIONS

It has been shown that strong swirling and axial jet air flows in a burner give rise to pressure and velocity fluctuations, the frequency of which is a function of flow in a Strouhal-like relationship. The source of the pulsation is primarily in the precessing vortex core which typically accompanies the flame stabilizing recirculation zone.

The original high pressure drop burner did not excite furnace vibration. It was only with the reduced pressure drop burner with the air swirler located in the divergent section of the air register that large furnace vibration occurred. The vibration was strong and could not be reduced or eliminated within the boiler load range by changes in operational parameters. Based on experimental testing, a new low pressure drop swirler was designed which, in combination with an experimentally optimized mode of fuel injection, eliminated the furnace vibration within the entire load range and at the same time provided flames of good quality.

The determination of burner excitation frequencies to prevent resonance with furnace cavity standing wave frequencies is of primary concern in the design stage. Sufficient flexibility for adjustments must be built into the burner design to prevent furnace vibration if resonant conditions cannot be fully predicted or avoided.

ACKNOWLEDGMENT

Many dedicated engineers participated in the solution of the vibration problem. The author is particularly indebted to Mike Claps for his tireless contribution during the full scale and model testing and his help throughout the entire program, to Berkeley Davis for his participation in the full scale tests, to Norman Buckland and Ruben Martin for performing the scaled model tests, and to Zenon Semanyshin, Steve DeDuck, Elias Gedeon, Larry White, Chien Pai and Bob Sullivan for carrying out the extensive test and analysis program.

The author gratefully acknowledges the permission of Foster Wheeler Energy Corporation to publish the results contained in this paper.

REFERENCES

[1] Vonnegut, B., A vortex whistle, Journal of the Acoust. Society of America 1954, 26, 18-20.

[2] Chanaud, R. C., Experiments concerning the vortex whistle, Journal of the Acoust. Society of America, 1963, 35, pp. 953-960.

[3] Chigier, N. A., and Beer, J. M., Velocity and static pressure distribution in swirling jets issuing from annular and divergent nozzles, Transactions of the ASME, J. of Basic Engineering, December 1964, pp. 788-796.

[4] Chanuad, R. C., Observations of oscillatory motion in certain swirling flows, 1965, J. Fluid Mech., Vol. 21, part 1, pp. 111-127.

[5] Chigier, N. A. and Gilbert, J. L., Recirculation eddies in wake of flameholders. Journal of the Institute of Fuel, 105, March 1968.

[6] Syred, N., Chigier, N. A. and Beer, J. M., Flame stabilization in recirculation zones of jets with swirl, 13th Symposium (International) on Combustion, The Combustion Institute, Pittsburgh, PA. 1971, pp. 617-624.

[7] Sarpkaya, T., Vortex breakdown in swirling conical flows, Sept. 1971, AIAA Journal, Vol. 9, No. 9, pp. 1792-1799.

[8] Syred, N. and Beer, J. M., The damping of vortex cores by combustion in swirl generators, 1972, Astronautica Acta, Vol. 17, pp. 783-801.

[9] Chigier, N. A., Gas dynamics of swirling flow in combustion systems, 1972, Astronautica Acta, Vol. 17, pp. 387-395.

[10] Syred, N., Hanby, V. I. and Gupta, A. K., Resonant instabilities generated by swirl burners, Journal of the Institute of Fuel, December 1973, pp. 402-407.

[11] Chigier, N. A., and Dvorak, K., Laser anemometer measurements in flames with swirl, 15th Symposium (International) on Combustion, The Combustion Institute, Pittsburgh, PA, 1975, pp. 573-585.

[12] Syred, N., Gupta, A. K., and Beer, M., Temperature and density gradient changes arising with the precessing vortex core and vortex breakdown in swirl burners, 15th Symposium (International) on Combustion, the Combustion Institute, Pittsburgh, PA. pp. 1975, pp. 587-597.

[13] Rayleigh, Lord, Proceedings of the Royal Society, London, 93, 148, 1916.

[14] Chen, Y. N., Studies into swirling flow in furnaces with view to flame stability (In German), Gaswarme International, Vulkan-Verlag, Heft 1, 1979, pp. 33-50.

[15] Chen, Y. N., Experiences with flow-induced vibrations at Sulzer, Practical Experiences with Flow-Induced Vibrations, Editors, E. Naudascher and D. Rockwell, Springer-Verlag, 1979 paper B7, pp. 265-278.

[16] Hosoi, Y., Characteristics of pressure surge due to whirling water from exit of water turbine runner, Bulletin of the JSME, Vol. 16, No. 93, March 1973, pp. 560-569.

[17] Escudier, M., Swirling flow induced vibrations in turbomachine exit chambers, Practical Experiences with Flow-Induced Vibrations, Editors, E. Naudascher and D. Rockwell, Springer-Verlag, 1979, paper B 10, pp. 287292.

[18] Hayama, S., Matsamura, Y., and Watanable, T., Swirling flow-induced resonant pressure pulsations in a pipe, 1990, Flow-Induced Vibration. The American Society of Mechanical Engineers, PVP—Vol. 189, pp. 295-300.

[19] Chigier, N. A., and Beer, J. M., The flow region near the nozzle in double concentric jets, Journal of Basic Engineering, Transactions of the ASME, December 1964, pp. 797-804.

C416/009

Multiple side-branches as tone generators

S ZIADA, MEng, PhD, MASME and E T BÜHLMANN, PhD,
Laboratory for Vibrations and Acoustics, Sulzer Innotec, Winterthur, Switzerland

SYNOPSIS   Complex piping systems with multiple side-branches are very liable to
flow-induced acoustic resonances. This is demonstrated by means of model tests of
two piping systems, one with a single side-branch the second containing two side-
branches. The acoustic response of these two systems is studied as the flow
velocity in the main pipe is increased. The influence of the distance between the
branches, the Reynolds number, the upstream turbulence level and the angle between
the branches is also investigated.

NOTATION

C	speed of sound
D	diameter of the main pipe
d	diameter of the branch pipe
f_n	frequency of the acoustic mode n
H	distance between orifice and upstream branch
L_1, L_2	branch length
ℓ	distance between branches
ΔL	$L_1 - L_2$
M	Mach number (V/C)
n	mode order
$\tilde{P}$	total rms amplitude of pressure pulsation
$\tilde{p}$	rms amplitude at the resonance frequency
$\tilde{p}_{max}$	maximum amplitude reached at resonance
P_s	static pressure in the main pipe
R	Reynolds number (Vd/γ)
S	Strouhal number ($S = fd/V$)
V	flow velocity in the main pipe
Θ	angle between branch pipes
λ	acoustic wavelength
ρ	density of the flowing medium

1   INTRODUCTION

Acoustic resonances of branch pipes are often strongly excited by the flow over the mouth of the branch. The resonant modes consist of odd numbers of a quarter wavelength along the branch pipe (see Fig. 1(a)). When a resonance occurs, the amplitude of the acoustic pressure pulsation can be several times higher than the dynamic head in the main pipe. This level is sufficiently high to cause severe noise and vibration problems in a wide variety of engineering applications [1 - 6].

The excitation mechanism of branch pipe resonances is similar to that causing acoustic resonances of deep cavities exposed to grazing flow. The latter case has received considerable attention in the literature due to its importance in aeronautical and marine applications [7 - 12]. Several reviews [13 - 15] summarize the present state of knowledge in the field.

Flow-induced resonances of deep cavities and branch pipes are classified by Rockwell and Naudascher [15] as fluid-resonant oscillations. These oscillations are self-sustained due to the coupling between the resonant acoustic field and the unstable shear layer which spans the mouth of the cavity. At the point of separation, the acoustic field induces velocity fluctuations in the shear layer. If the shear layer is unstable at the frequency of the acoustic field, it extracts energy from the mean flow to amplify the initial velocity fluctuations into large scale vortex-like structures. Further downstream, the interaction of the formed vortices with the acoustic field and the cavity downstream corner transfers the fluctuating energy of the shear layer back into the resonant acoustic field. This last event of the excitation mechanism is the most difficult to characterize. Considerable insight, however, has been provided in recent work by Welsh and his co-workers [16 - 18]. They used Howe's theory of aerodynamic sound [19] to show that acoustic energy can either be generated or absorbed by vortices convecting within an acoustic field. They were able to explain, by means of experiments and numerical simulations, why resonances occur over certain ranges of Strouhal number and why each range is characterized by the number of the vortices formed in the shear layer.

Although the excitation mechanisms for branch pipes and deep cavities in moving vehicles are basically similar, there are important geometrical and flow differences which preclude the applicability of the well documented data on cavity flow to industrial cases of branch pipes. Pipe flow past a branch is usually very turbulent, which is not the case in most of the cavity investigations. Moreover, the ratio between the branch and the main pipe diameters (d/D) is crucial in determining the pressure amplitude and, to a lesser extent, the Strouhal number of resonance [20]. Finally, the acoustic characteristics of the associated piping system must also be taken into account where branch pipes are concerned.

There is a paucity of published work on pipe branches [20-22] other than case histories [1-6]. Jungowski et al. [20] reported a substantial reduction in the pulsation amplitude when the diameter ratio (d/D) was increased. Erickson et al. [21] observed resonances at two different ranges of Strouhal number. Flow visualization of the shear layer revealed the formation of either a single vortex, during the lower Strouhal number resonance, or two vortices, during the higher Strouhal number resonance. The pulsation amplitude was substantially higher for the single vortex case.

The present investigation focuses on piping systems involving two branches in close proximity. It was motivated by field experiences which indicated that multiple branches are much more liable to flow-induced vibration than single branches. The cases which are of primary interest are shown in Fig. 1. They are classified according to the distance between the branches. This distance is much smaller than one half of the acoustic wavelength in case (b), approximates one half of the wavelength in case (c) and is zero in case (d). Since case (c) has been investigated in some detail by Bruggeman [22], it will not be considered here in any detail. Only cases (b) and (d) are investigated and compared with the case of a single branch, i.e. case (a). Several counter-measures which can be adopted to eliminate the observed resonances are also addressed.

2   EXPERIMENTAL FACILITY

A pressurized air test facility was used to carry out the tests. The facility is equiped with a filter, a low-noise pressure regulator, a silencer and a metering orifice plate. It has a maximum capacity of 1.8×10^3 kg/h and a maximum supply pressure of 5 bar (abs). All pipes, including the branches, were made of steel.

The tested geometries represented models of piping systems commonly used in power plants, such as the piping systems of turbine by-pass valves and safety valves. The inner diameter of the main pipe was D = 89 mm. The other test parameters (see Fig. 1 and the list of notation) were: d/D = 0.57; ℓ/d = 2.35 - 5.6; L = 0.61 - 2.0 m; R < 4 x 10^5 and M < 0.15. Unless otherwise stated, all the tests were carried out with two branches of equal length, i.e. $L_1 = L_2 = L$, see Fig. 1.

The first set of experiments was conducted at atmospheric pressure. In this case, Brüel and Kjaer 1/4" microphones were used to monitor the pressure pulsation in the main pipe and the closed ends of the branches. At a later stage, a throttle valve was installed at the end of the main pipe to pressurize the system. The main objective was to increase the Reynolds number without altering the Mach number. When tests were carried out at a high pressure, 4 bar (abs), Kistler pressure transducers were used instead of the microphones. Spectral analysis of the pressure signals was carried out by means of a Nicolet 444 A spectrum analyser.

3   TEST RESULTS

3.1   General system response

The geometry of two branches arranged in tandem, as shown in Fig. 1(b), was tested first. The pressure pulsations were measured at the closed end of the two branches as the flow velocity V in the main pipe was increased in steps. In all the tests reported upon here, the pressure pulsation in the downstream branch was about 10 % smaller than that in the upstream branch. The cause of this slight, but consistent, difference is not known and has not been investigated to date. All the results given hereafter were taken at the end of the upstream branch.

Fig. 2 shows the development of the pressure spectra as the mean flow velocity in the main pipe was increased from 10 to 86 m/s. The spectral peaks indicate the occurrence of resonances at the frequencies of the acoustic modes. These frequencies can be estimated from:

$$f_n = \frac{(2n-1)\ C}{4\ [L+(\ell/2)]} \qquad n = 1, 2, 3$$

where, n is the mode order and C is the speed of sound. It is noteworthy that the results given in Fig. 2 correspond to cases (b) and (c) of Fig. 1. At low velocities, the wavelength of the excited (lower) modes is much larger than the distance between the two branches, i.e. $\ell \ll \lambda/2$. In this case, the pressure pulsations at the ends of the branches must be out of phase. This was con-

© IMechE 1991 C416/009

firmed by observing the signals on a two channel oscilloscope. At high velocities, the frequencies of the excited modes became so high that one half of the acoustic wavelength approached the distance ℓ. As shown in Fig. 1(c), the pressure pulsations at the ends of the branches were found to be in-phase with one another. Note that there is an intermediate velocity range in Fig. 2 within which the acoustic modes were very weakly excited. This is because the wavelength corresponding to these modes does not satisfy either of the conditions $\ell << \lambda/2$ or $\ell \approx \lambda/2$.

The dominant frequency f, the rms amplitude p and Strouhal number S of the pressure pulsations are given in Fig. 3 as functions of the flow velocity. Two cases are given; $L_1 = L_2 = 2.0$ m and $L_1 = L_2 = 1.0$ m. The rms amplitude is non-dimensionalized by the dynamic head in the main pipe. The data given in the Strouhal number plots correspond to the pulsation amplitudes which exceeded about 10 % of the dynamic head.

As can be seen from Fig. 3, higher order modes are consecutively excited as the flow velocity is increased. The broken lines shown in Figs. 3 (a_1) and (b_1) are drawn through the data points of maximum pulsation amplitude. They yield a Strouhal number of S = fd/V = 0.45, which agrees very well with the value reported by Jungowski et al. [20] for a single branch with a diameter ratio of 0.52.

As shown in Figs. 3(a_2) and (b_2), the occurrence of large amplitude pressure pulsations is not associated with a single value of S but rather with a certain range. This range depends on the dynamic head available in the main pipe. Tests with higher pressures resulted in a resonance range of S = 0.27 to 0.55. A value of S = 0.55 is therefore recommended for design purposes. This value gives the maximum allowable flow velocity consistent with the avoidance of resonance.

The amplitude of the pressure pulsations for the case of a single branch was also measured and is given in Figs. 3 (a_4) and (b_4). It does not exceed 10 % of the dynamic head, which agrees with the results of Jungowski et al. [20]. The presence of the second branch is seen to increase the resonance amplitudes by more than one order of magnitude. These findings suggest that the results obtained from tests on single branches are not necessarily applicable to cases involving two branches.

3.2 Effect of Reynolds number

The effect of the Reynolds number was investigated by repeating the previous tests at a higher pressure, 4.0 bar (abs). This allowed the Reynolds number

at the resonance of any mode to be increased, while holding all other parameters, such as M and S, unchanged. Due to the increase in the flow density, the maximum flow velocity of the tests was limited to about 20 m/s.

The results of the high pressure tests are given in Fig. 4. Comparison of Figs. 3 and 4 shows that as the Reynolds number at the resonance of a certain mode is increased, the dimensionless amplitude of the pressure pulsation is also increased. In the case of L = 2.0 m for example, the first mode was hardly excited during the low pressure tests. When the Reynolds number is increased by a factor of about 4, the dimensionless amplitude of this mode is increased from 0.15 to 2.5, compare Figs. 3(a_3) and 4(a). Similar behaviour can be seen in the response of the other modes depicted in Fig. 4.

Further study of the results given in Figs. 3 and 4 leads to the following observations concerning the effect of the Reynolds number:

a) There seems to be a minimum Reynolds number which is required to excite the resonance. This can be seen clearly by comparing the response of the first mode, for L = 2.0 m, at low and high pressures.

b) Above this minimum Reynolds number, the dimensionless amplitude at resonance is smaller the higher the order of the mode is. The higher modes, however, have a wider range of lock-in. In other words, the range of the Strouhal number within which large amplitude pulsations occur is wider for the higher order modes, see Figs. 3(a_2), 3(b_2) and 4(a).

c) As the frequency of the first mode is increased, the dimensionless amplitude at resonance is also increased. This is due to the increase in the Reynolds number at resonance.

3.3 Effect of the distance between the branches

The effect of the distance between the two branches is shown in Fig. 5 for the case L = 1.0 m. The response amplitude of the first two modes is seen to decrease as the ratio ℓ/d is increased. At ℓ/d = 5.6 for example, the dimensionless amplitude becomes one order of magnitude smaller than that occurring at ℓ/d = 2.35. Another result of increasing the ratio ℓ/d is the increased liability of the higher modes to excitation. As shown in Figs. 5 (b_1) and (c_1), the resonance Strouhal number of the higher modes is about twice that of the lower modes. The resonance amplitude however is relatively small.

As mentioned in the introduction, the occurrence of resonance at twice the main Strouhal number has been observed for single branches as well. It is associated with the formation of two vortices in the shear layer [21]. The pulsation amplitude resulting from this shear layer mode is much weaker than that produced at the main Strouhal number [20]. These features of the single branch case agree with the present results for two branches.

Fig. 6 depicts the maximum dimensionless amplitude measured at the resonance of each mode as a function of the ratio ℓ/d. The amplitude is seen to become very small for sufficiently large values of the ratio ℓ/d.

The strong influence of the ratio ℓ/d can be clarified by considering its effect on the amplitude of the pressure pulsation at the mouth of each branch. Since the two branches are acoustically coupled, a pressure node is expected to exist in the main pipe at a distance of ℓ/2 from each branch mouth. As the distance ℓ (or the ratio ℓ/λ) is increased, the pressure amplitude at the branch mouth will be increased. This increases the dissipation of the acoustic energy into the main pipe and therefore, the system resonance is progressively suppressed as the distance ℓ is increased. When the distance ℓ becomes comparable to half of the acoustic wavelength, as in the case of a higher mode for example, a pressure anti-node is initiated in the main pipe between the branches as shown in Fig. 1 (c). Since each branch mouth becomes closer to a pressure node, the acoustic damping is decreased and the resonance is enhanced. The effect of ℓ/d discussed above can be seen clearly in Figs. 5 and 6.

3.4 Co-axial branches

The acoustic response of co-axial branches at atmospheric pressure is shown in Fig. 7. The overall system response is similar to that of the tandem branches discussed earlier, except that the dimensionless amplitude is higher and the lock-in range is wider for the case of co-axial branches. These findings are logical since the co-axial branches can be considered as a special case of zero spacing between the branches. As mentioned in the previous section, a reduction in the ratio ℓ/d reduces the acoustic damping. This increases the resonance amplitude and the lock-in range. In spite of this increase in the lock-in range, the Strouhal number of large amplitude pulsation did not exceed the recommended design value of 0.55.

It is noteworthy that the resonance amplitude in Fig. 7 (c) is about one order of magnitude higher than the dynamic head in the main pipe. This underscores the damaging potential of acoustic resonances in piping systems with multiple branches.

4 COUNTER-MEASURES

4.1 Effect of detuning the resonance frequencies

The resonance frequencies of the branches can be detuned by making one branch shorter (or longer) than the other. This would weaken the acoustic coupling between the branches and therefore the acoustic damping of the system would be increased drastically. The effect of making one branch (the downstream) 15 % shorter than the other is shown in Figs. 3 (a_5) and (b_5). The data points in these figures represent the rms amplitudes of the dominant frequency components in the pressure spectra. It is seen that detuning the resonance frequencies is a very effective way of eliminating the system resonance.

The detuning process however is not as simple as it seems, especially when the branches are relatively long and the operating velocity range is wide. In such cases, many resonance modes would be liable to excitation within the velocity range. To avoid the resonance of all modes, the ratios $\Delta L/L_1$, $\Delta L/\ell$ and $\Delta L/\lambda$ have to be carefully chosen. This aspect is being investigated further at present.

4.2 Effect of the distance between the branches

As mentioned in Sec. 3.3, the amplitude of the pressure pulsation at resonance can be reduced by increasing the spacing ratio ℓ/d. The results of the tests at atmospheric pressure (see Fig. 6) show that a value of ℓ/d $\approx$ 6 is sufficiently large in order to avoid large amplitude pulsations. However, current tests at higher pressures indicated the need for a substantially higher value of ℓ/d to suppress the pressure pulsation adequately. Large branch spacings also should be selected with care to avoid the excitation of a higher order mode when the distance between the branches approaches half of the acoustic wavelength [22].

4.3 Effect of the angle between the branches

Several tests were conducted to investigate the case whereby the two branches are not in the same plane, i.e. when the branches deviate from the tandem arrangement by an angle Θ. The main objective of introducing this angle is to weaken the fluid dynamic coupling between the branches by reducing the enhancement caused when the vortex formed at the upstream branch arrives at the downstream branch. The tests were carried out in steps of 45°, and at each step the maximum pressure amplitude at resonance was measured. As shown in Fig. 8, the resonance amplitude is progressively reduced as the angle θ is increased. The maximum reduction in the amplitude amounts to 30% at θ = 180°. This amount is clearly insufficient to warrant regarding this design modification as an effective counter-measure.

Since the angle θ has virtually no effect on the system acoustic damping, the reduction in the amplitude with the angle θ must be caused by the weakening of the fluid dynamic (or the vortex) coupling between the branches. The effect of this vortex coupling however seems to be minor because the reduction in the amplitude with the angle θ is only slight.

4.4   Effect of the upstream turbulence

It is well known that shear layer excitations can be weakened by breaking the two-dimensionality of the flow [15, 23, 24]. This may be achieved by increasing the turbulence level at the separation point of the shear layer [25]. In order to investigate this possibility, an orifice plate was introduced in the main pipe to increase the turbulence level in the approach flow. The distance H between the orifice plate and the upstream branch was varied to alter the turbulence level at the mouth of the branches. The area of the orifice was half that of the main pipe. The effect of varying the distance H was studied, but no measurements of the turbulence level were carried out.

As the distance H was reduced, the amplitude of the pressure pulsation became smaller, but the resonance peaks became wider. This trend continued until the system response reached its minimum at H = 5.5 D. Fig. 9 compares this minimum response with the response of the original system, i.e. without the orifice. The data points represent the total rms amplitude of the pressure pulsation over the frequency range 0 to 1.0 kHz. The resonance amplitudes of the first two modes are seen to be substantially smaller in the presence of the orifice.

As the distance H was further reduced to values less than 5.5 D, the pulsation amplitude started to increase again and the resonance peaks became much wider, i.e. large amplitude pulsations occurred over a wider velocity range. This indicated that the turbulence level produced by the orifice was so high that it excited the system resonances.

The reduction in the amplitude caused by the orifice plate is not related at all to any alteration in the system acoustic damping. The orifice plate is positioned in the main pipe in which the amplitude of the pressure pulsation is very small; about 50 times smaller than that in the branches. In addition, the area ratio of the orifice (0.5) is too large to cause any considerable change in the acoustic damping of the system, even in the presence of flow.

In summary, using an orifice plate upstream of the branches can substantially reduce the intensity of the system resonances. The orifice plate however should not be positioned too close to the branches, otherwise the turbulence generated by the orifice may become an excitation source in itself. A distance of 5.5 D was found to be an optimum upstream distance in the present tests.

5.   SUMMARY AND CONCLUSIONS

Flow-induced acoustic resonances of two side branches in close proximity have been investigated experimentally. The resonance of the two branches is found to be much stronger than that of a single branch. This difference is caused by the acoustic coupling between the two branches which drastically reduces the dissipation of the acoustic energy into the main pipe. Co-axial branches produce the strongest resonance because the dissipated energy becomes minimal in this case. Pulsation amplitudes up to 900 % of the dynamic head in the main pipe have been recorded. This value is about two orders of magnitude higher than that observed in the case of a single branch.

Several tests have been carried out to investigate the effect of the geometrical and the flow parameters on the acoustic response of the system. The main findings of these tests are summarized in the following:

(1)   The acoustic modes of the branches are excited consecutively as the flow velocity in the main pipe is increased. The resonances occur in the main within a Strouhal number range of 0.27 to 0.55. Resonances can also occur at a higher Strouhal number (≈ 0.9), but these resonances are much weaker than those occurring within the main Strouhal number range.

(2)   In all tests, the Strouhal number for large amplitude pulsations did not exceed 0.55. Acoustic resonances can therefore be avoided by keeping the Strouhal number, based on the first mode frequency and the maximum flow velocity, higher than 0.55.

(3)   The dimensionless amplitude at the resonance of a certain mode increases as the Reynolds number at resonance is increased.

(4) The dimensionless amplitude at the resonance of the higher modes decreases continually as the mode order is increased.

(5) The resonances become progressively weaker as the distance between the branches is increased. At sufficiently large distances, system resonances do not occur, thus resembling the case of a single branch. This means resonance at the lower modes can be avoided by increasing the distance between the branches.

(6) The angle Θ between the branches has only a minor effect on the system response. The pulsation amplitude decreases slightly as the angle between the branches is increased.

(7) Detuning the resonance frequencies of the branches, by making the branches different lengths from one another, is the most effective counter-measure.

(8) Increasing the turbulence level of the approach flow considerably reduces the pulsation amplitude. This attenuation effect vanishes as the turbulence level exceeds a certain limit and itself becomes an excitation source.

ACKNOWLEDGEMENTS

The work described in this paper forms part of the research project: Flow-Excited Resonances in Complex Pipe Systems. This project is jointly supported by "Nationaler Energie - Forschungs - Fonds" (NEFF) and Sulzer Brothers Limited. The authors are grateful to Messrs. A. Foude, R. Qian and M. El-Shazly for conducting some exploratory experiments during the initial period of the project.

REFERENCES

(1) COFFMANN, J.T., and BERNSTEIN, M.D. Failure of safety valves due to flow-induced vibration. *Journal of Pressure Vessel Technology*, 1980, 102, 112 - 118.

(2) BALDWIN, R.M., and SIMMONS, H.R. Flow-induced vibration in safety relief valves. *Journal of Pressure Vessel Technology*, 1986, 108, 267 - 272.

(3) CHEN, Y.N., and FLORJANCIC, D. Vortex-induced resonance in a pipe system due to branching. Conf. on Vibration and Noise in Pumps, Fan and Compressor Installations, University of Southampton, England, 1975, 79 - 86.

(4) CHEN, Y.N., and STUERCHLER, R. Flow-induced vibrations and noise in a pipe system with blind branches due to coupling of vortex shedding. Internoise 77, Zurich, 1977, B 189 - B 203.

(5) CHEN, Y.N., and ZIADA, S. "Störmungserregte Schwingungen infolge Wirbelkopplung in der HZUE-Leitung." Sulzer Bros. Ltd., 1982, Report No. 1512/2803.

(6) BERNSTEIN, M., and BLOOMFIELD, W. Malfunction of safety valves due to flow-induced vibrations. ASME Pressure Vessel and Piping Conference, Honolulu, 1989, 155 - 164.

(7) ELDER, S.A., FARABEE, T.M., and DE METZ, F.C. Mechanisms of flow-excited cavity tones at low Mach number. *Journal of the Acoustical Society of America*; 1982, 72, 532 - 549.

(8) TAM, C.K.W., and BLOCK, P.J.W. On the tones and pressure oscillations induced by flow over rectangular cavities. *Journal of Fluid Mechanics*, 1978, 89, 373 - 399.

(9) EAST, L.F. Aerodynamic induced resonances in rectangular cavities. *Journal of Sound and Vibration*, 1966, 3 , 227 - 287.

(10) ELDER, S.A. Self-excited depth-mode resonance for a wall-mounted cavity. *Journal of the Acoustical Society of America*, 1978, 64 (3), 877 - 890.

(11) PARTHASARATHY, S.P., CHO, Y.I., and BACK, L.H. Sound generation by flow over relatively deep cylindrical cavities. *Journal of the Acoustical Society of America*, 1985, 78 (5), 1785 - 1795.

(12) DE METZ, F.C., and FARABEE, T.M. Laminar and turbulent shear flow induced cavity resonances. American Institute of Aeronautics and Astronautics, 1977, Paper No. 77-1293.

(13) ROCKWELL, D. Oscillations of impinging shear layers. *American Institute of Aeronautics and Astronautics Journal*, 1983, 21, 645 - 664.

(14) ROCKWELL, D. Self-sustained oscillations of impinging free shear layers. *Annual Reviews of Fluid Mechanics*, 1979, 11, 67 - 94.

(15) ROCKWELL, D., and NAUDASCHER, E. Review-self sustaining oscillations of flow past cavities. *Journal of Fluids Engineering*, 1978, 100, 152 - 165.

(16) STONEMAN, S.A.T., HOURIGAN, K., STOKES, A.N., and WELSH, M.C. Resonant sound caused by flow past two plates in tandem in a duct. *Journal of Fluid Mechanics*, 1988, 192, 455 - 484.

(17) STOKES, A.N., THOMPSON, M.C., HOURIGAN, K., and WELSH, M.C. Numerical prediction and experimental measurement of acoustics and flow in a duct with baffles. 10th Australasian Fluid Mechanics Conference, Melbourne 1989.

(18) HOURIGAN, K., STOKES, A.N., THOMPSON, M.C., and WELSH, M.C. Flow-induced acoustic resonances for a bluff body in a duct: a numerical study. 9th Australasian Fluid Mechanics Conference, Auckland, 1986, 504 - 507.

(19) HOWE, M.S. Contributions to the theory of aerodynamic sound, with application to excess jet noise and the theory of the flute. *Journal of Fluid Mechanics*, 1975, 71, 625 - 673.

(20) JUNGOWSKI, W.M., BOTROS, K.K., and STUDZINSKI, W. Cylindrical sidebranch as tone generator. *Journal of Sound and Vibration*, 1989, 131 (2), 265 - 285.

(21) ERICKSON, D.D., DURGIN, W.W., MAQUIRE, C.F., and MOELLER, M.J. Shear layer coupling with sidebranch resonators. Forum on unsteady flow, ASME Publications FED 39, 1986, 43 - 45.

(22) BRUGGEMAN, J.C. Flow-induced pulsations in pipe systems. Doctoral Dissertation, Technische Universiteit Eindhoven, 1987.

(23) KARADOGAN, H., and ROCKWELL, D. Toward attenuation of self-sustained oscillations of a turbulent jet through a cavity. *Journal of Fluid Engineering*, 1983, 105, 335 - 339.

(24) ZIADA, S., BUEHLMANN, E.T., and BOLLETER, U. Flow impingement as an excitation source in control valves. *Journal of Fluids and Structures*, 1989, 3, 529 - 549.

(25) CRIGHTON, D.G. Acoustics as a branch of fluid mechanics. *Journal of Fluid Mechanics*, 1981, 106, 261 - 298.

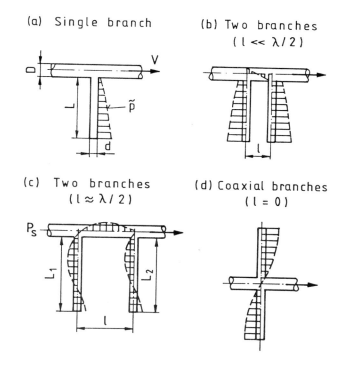

(a) Single branch   (b) Two branches ($l \ll \lambda/2$)

(c) Two branches ($l \approx \lambda/2$)   (d) Coaxial branches ($l = 0$)

Fig 1   Schematic presentation of typical geometries of side branches.

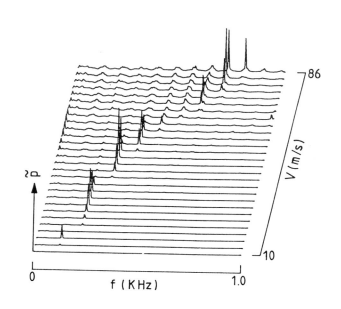

Fig 2   Development of the pressure spectrum measured at the closed end of the upstream branch as the flow velocity is increased. $L_1 = L_2 = 2$ m, $l/d = 2.35$, $P_s \approx 0.96$ bar (abs).

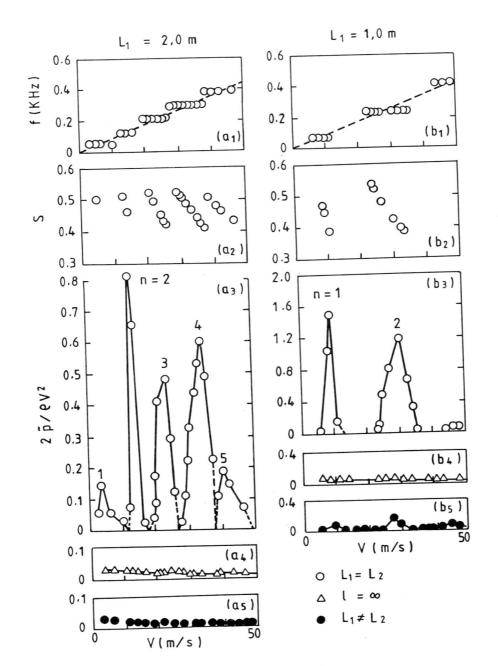

Fig 3 General response of two branches in comparison with that of a single branch and that of detuned (two) branches. $(a_1), (a_2), (a_3)$, two branches, $L = 2.0$m, $l/d = 2.35$; $(b_1), (b_2), (b_3)$, two branches, $L = 1.0$ m, $l/d = 2.75$; $(a_4), (b_4)$, single branch; $(a_5), (b_5)$, $(L_1 - L_2)/L_1 = 15\%$. $P_s = 0.96$ bar (abs).

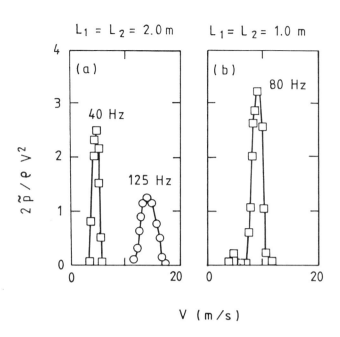

$L_1 = L_2 = 2.0\,m$ $L_1 = L_2 = 1.0\,m$

(a)   40 Hz   125 Hz

(b)   80 Hz

V (m/s)

Fig 4 Dimensionless amplitude of the pressure pulsation as a function of the flow velocity. P_s = 4 bar (abs), ℓ/d = 2.35 . (a), L = 2.0 m; (b), L = 1.0 m.

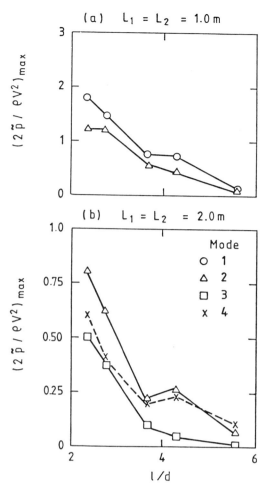

(a) $L_1 = L_2 = 1.0\,m$

(b) $L_1 = L_2 = 2.0\,m$

Mode
○ 1
△ 2
□ 3
× 4

l/d

Fig 6 Maximum amplitude measured at the resonance of each mode as a function of the spacing ratio ℓ/d. P_s = 0.96 bar (abs).

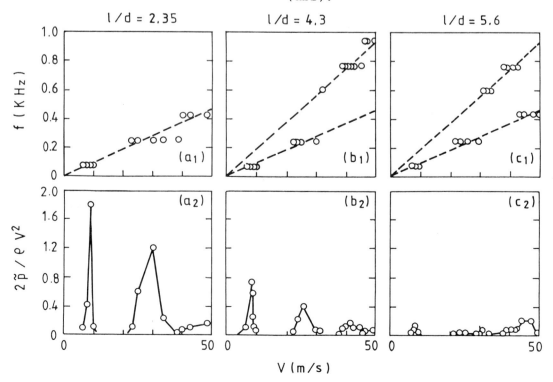

l/d = 2.35   l/d = 4.3   l/d = 5.6

(a_1) (b_1) (c_1)

(a_2) (b_2) (c_2)

V (m/s)

Fig 5 Frequency and amplitude of the pressure pulsation as functions of the flow velocity for three values of the spacing ratio ℓ/d. (a), ℓ/d = 2.35; (b), 4.3, (c), 5.6 . L = 1.0 m, P_s = 0.96 bar (abs).

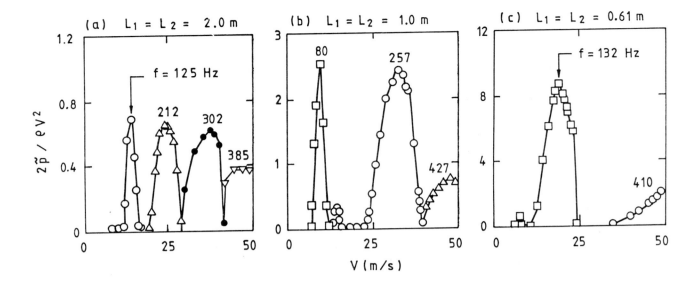

Fig 7 General response of the co-axial branches. (a), $L_1 = L_2 = L = 2.0$ m; (b), 1.0 m; (c), 0.61 m. □, mode 1; O, 2; △, 3; ●, 4; ▽, 5. $P_s = 0.96$ bar (abs).

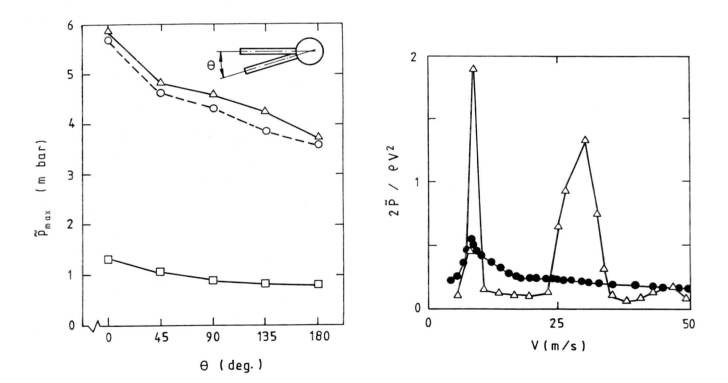

Fig 8 Effect of the angle between the branches on the maximum amplitude measured at resonance. $l/d = 2.75$, $P_s = 4.0$ bar(abs). △, L=1.0 m, mode 1, 80 Hz; □, L = 2.0 m, mode 1, 40 Hz; O, L=2.0 m, mode 2, 125 Hz.

Fig 9 Total rms amplitude of the pressure pulsation for the case of two branches with and without an orifice plate upstream of the branches. $L_1 = L_2 = 1.0$ m, $l/d = 2.35$, $P_s = 0.96$ bar (abs), H/D = 5.5 . △, without orifice; ●, with orifice.

© IMechE 1991 C416/009

An experimental investigation into flow induced acoustic resonances in an annular cascade

M L LEGERTON, BSc S A T STONEMAN, PhD, CEng, MIMechE, MIOA
and R PARKER, DSc, CEng, FIMechE, MRAeS, FIOA
Department of Mechanical Engineering, University College of Swansea, West Glamorgan

SYNOPSIS.

The effects of plate spacing on the acoustic resonances generated by vortex shedding from annular cascades of plates in tandem in a duct have been investigated. The plate spacing affected both the amplitude of the sound produced and the velocity range over which each mode was excited. The velocity range over which each mode was excited is thought to be influenced by both the natural shedding frequency and the interaction with the downstream plate.

NOTATION.

Symbol	Definition	Unit
e	extra distance	m
f	frequency of acoustic resonance	Hz
r	mean vortex convection velocity/free stream velocity	-
SPL	sound pressure level or dB(ref $2*10^{-5}$ Pa)	Pa(rms)
St	Strouhal number = frequency*plate thickness/velocity	-
t	time	s
v	free stream velocity	m/s
x	plate spacing	m
X	axial position of vortex	m
$\emptyset$	relative phase angle	cycles

1 INTRODUCTION.

Vortex shedding from bodies in ducted flow systems can excite acoustic resonances within the duct. These acoustic resonances can be accompanied by large amplitude vibration of the vortex shedding bodies and other bodies in the flow, which would not be present otherwise. These vibrations can sometimes lead to component failure.

Parker [1] showed that acoustic resonances are generated when vortex shedding from a cascade of flat plates locks onto one of the acoustic modes of the duct. By testing with plates of the same geometry, but made from different materials, he showed that the resonances are independent of the mechanical properties of the plate.

Subsequent investigations in rectangular ducts were usually confined to the excitation of the Parker β-mode [2] by vortex shedding from a single plate in a rectangular duct. The β-mode is a cross-mode of the duct. The height of the duct corresponds to one half wavelength of the standing wave. Pressure anti-nodes, with a phase difference of 180 degrees, exist at the top and bottom walls. Relatively large acoustic particle velocities are produced at the leading and trailing edges of plates at mid-height in the tunnel.

Cumpsty and Whitehead [3] later studied a single plate in a rectangular duct. They presented a theory which predicts the amplitude of the acoustic resonance from measurements taken in non-resonant conditions. This work was extended by Archibald [4] who developed a linear feedback model to predict the variation in phase between the vortex shedding and acoustic field, and change in frequency, with velocity in resonant conditions.

Welsh et al [5] proposed a mechanism by which the flow generates an acoustic resonance. Vorticity, acoustic particle velocity, and vortex convection speed were key elements of the explanation based upon Howe's [6] theory of aerodynamic sound. The analysis predicts an acoustic source to be just downstream of the trailing edge of a shedding plate.

Acoustic resonances have also been studied by Parker [7,8], Parker and Pryce [9], Parker and Stoneman [10,11], and Parker et al [12] in axisymmetric flow configurations such as annular cascades and axial flow compressors. These investigations showed that a series of circumferential modes in the annulus can be excited by vortex shedding from radial blades with semi-circular trailing edges. The modes are described by the mode number which defines the number of complete waves or lobes in the annulus. For example, mode four has four waves around the annulus. Modes can be either standing waves, or travelling waves propagating circumferentially. They also showed that the acoustic resonances can excite can significant structural vibration of the compressor blading. Parker and Pryce [9] found that the pressure drop across an annular cascade increases when acoustic resonances are excited by vortex shedding from the trailing edges of the cascade plates. The results of Parker and Stoneman [11] showed that the axial spacing between a vortex shedding row of inlet guide vanes and a downstream rotor has a marked effect on the velocity range over which each mode is excited. A simple model was proposed to predict this effect. This is based upon the premise that the maximum amplitude would occur when a vortex passed through a sound generating region at the downstream plate, at the same phase in the acoustic cycle that vortex shedding at the upstream plate generated sound.

The effects of plate spacing were further investigated by Stoneman et al [13] using two plates in tandem in a rectangular duct. They found that changing the plate spacing causes a shift in the velocity range over which the resonance is excited. Increasing the spacing between the plates at constant flow velocity causes the amplitude of the resonance to rise and fall in a series of peaks and troughs. At some spacings the resonance can be virtually eliminated. The effect of plate spacing at constant velocity was modelled using Howe's [6] theory of aerodynamic sound. The analysis showed that both the leading and trailing edge of the downstream plate can act as either a sound source or sink depending upon the phasing of a vortex passing through each region in relation to the acoustic field.

Carr [14] also investigated the effect of plate spacing on the generation of acoustic resonances in a rectangular duct. He found the same variation in the resonant velocity range with plate spacing for upstream plates of different chord. He was able to predict this variation using a similar model to that of Parker and Stoneman [11] based upon the phasing of the interaction between the vortices with the downstream plate and the acoustic field.

Legerton et al [15] also studied the generation of acoustic resonances with the tandem plate configuration. They showed that while the plate spacing influences both the resonant amplitude and the velocity range over which the resonance is excited, the downstream plate chord only influences the amplitude of the sound generated. The change in the mean of the velocity range over which the resonance is excited with plate spacing was empirically modelled. The model assumes that the conditions for resonance are influenced by both the natural shedding characteristics and the preference for phase matching between the vortex shedding and vortex impingement.

A study by Johnson and Loehrke [16] on the sound generated by vortex shedding from two plates located in tandem in an open jet, showed differences between laminar and turbulent wakes. The laminar wake produces frequency staging with increasing plate separation. This was interpreted as a feed back effect similar to that described by Rockwell and Naudascher [17]. No frequency staging is observed with a turbulent wake although the amplitude of the sound varies periodically with plate spacing. They concluded that in this case there is no feedback and that the variation in sound amplitude is produced by multiple sound sources which cancel or reinforce depending upon plate spacing.

The experimental study described in this paper extends previous work undertaken in rectangular ducts to an annular cascade, where a series of cicumferential modes may be excited. Investigations in an annular tunnel with two fixed rows of plates, are seen as a stepping stone to an understanding of the more complex case found in axial-flow turbomachinery, where the second row is both staggered and rotating. The results presented in this paper are restricted to configurations in which the second row of plates is directly behind the upstream row. There is a strong wake interaction in this arrangement which highlights any plate spacing effects. The predictions of the empirical model described by Legerton et al [16] were compared with the results from the annular rig.

2 EXPERIMENTAL APPARATUS AND PROCEDURE.

The test rig used in the investigation was a blow-down, open-circuit annular wind tunnel (Fig.1). Air was supplied from a two stage, centrifugal compressor. The air was passed into a chamber containing a baffle plate and eight swirl control vanes which, in other investigations have been used to produce up to forty degrees of swirl in the flow along the working section. These vanes were set so that the flow in the tunnel was purely axial. Two gauzes were installed in the upstream end of the working section which reduced the turbulence intensity from 8% to 4%.

The outer wall of the working section was made from 0.5" (12.7mm) thick perspex tubing of 10" (254mm) internal diameter. The inner wall was made from 6" (152.4mm) diameter steel tube.

Both upstream and downstream cascades consisted of fifteen steel plates. The two cascades were arranged in tandem (one behind the other). The upstream plates were of 2.75" (69.9mm) chord and 0.15" (3.8mm) thick with semi-circular leading and trailing edges. The downstream plates had a chord of 1.575" (40mm) and thickness of 0.12" (3mm) with semi-circular leading edges and 30 degree, asymmetrically bevelled trailing edges. The 30 degree bevel on the trailing edges was designed to prevent vortex shedding from the downstream plate. The downstream plates were mounted on an assembly which provided manual adjustment of the axial spacing between the two rows of plates. The variation in the axial spacing between pairs of plates was less than 0.003" (0.08mm). The axial spacing between the rows was measured by hand held digital calipers.

The sound generated in the tunnel was measured with a 0.5" Bruel and Kjaer microphone, flush mounted in the tunnel wall, at mid-chord and mid-pitch of the upstream plates. Parker and Pryce [9] showed in a similar annular cascade with one row of plates, the maximum SPL occurs at the plate midchord.

The acoustic mode numbers were identified by using one fixed microphone and another able to traverse around the circumference of

the duct. Both signals were displayed on an oscilloscope triggered by the stationary microphone signal. The number of 360 phase changes between the two signals could be counted, as one microphone was traversed around the duct for one revolution. This corresponded to the number of acoustic waves or lobes around the annulus, the mode number. If the phase changes occurred in 180 steps a standing wave was present. If however the phase change occurred continuously a travelling wave was present.

The velocity fluctuations in the wake were detected with a Dantec P11 hot-wire connected to a Dantec Anemometer (56C Series). The hot-wire was mounted on a right-angled probe holder so that the probe holder did not interfere with the wake of the plate being measured. No hot-wire measurements could be taken for spacings of zero to 3mm as the probe holder was of 4mm diameter. The hot-wire was positioned 2mm, 5mm, and 12mm downstream of the upstream plate trailing edge for axial spacings of 4mm to 8mm, 9mm to 14mm, and 15mm to 50mm respectively. The 12mm position was also used for the tests on the upstream row installed alone.

The steady flow velocity was measured using a pitot tube upstream of the plates. The total and static pressures were converted into analogue voltages by Furness Low Pressure Transducers (FC0 Series). A NiCr/NiAl thermocouple connected to a Comark Microprocessor Thermometer, Type 61100, measured the air temperature in the duct.

The signals from all the instrumentation were monitored by a Masscomp 5450 mini-computer incorporating an analogue to digital converter (ADC).

Plate spacings of zero to 50mm were tested in 1mm intervals. An additional test was carried out for comparison, with the upstream plates installed alone. Each plate configuration was tested over a velocity range of 5m/s to 45m/s in 1m/s steps with increasing velocity. 45m/s was close to the maximum attainable. Plate spacings of 6mm and 13mm, and the upstream plates installed alone were also tested over the same velocity range, but with decreasing velocity, in order to investigate any mode hysteresis effects. The tests on the single row were performed four times with increasing velocity and four times with decreasing velocity.

3 DATA PROCESSING AND PRESENTATION.

The output signals from the instrumentation were repeatedly sampled. Data was sampled at 10kHz, 1024 frames per sample. In order to account for variations in duct static pressure and temperature the Mach number at standard temperature and pressure (293 K, 1 atmos) was calculated for each required velocity. When the air Mach number, calculated from the pitot and thermocouple measurements, was within a range corresponding to ± 0.05m/s of the required velocity, the digitised signals from the microphone and hot-wire were stored in a file for that test, along with the mean values of the pressure transducer and thermocouple channels. Using Mach number as the controlling parameter instead of velocity ensured that the ratio of natural shedding frequency to the acoustic mode frequency was independent of changes in the air temperature delivered by the compressor. Results were plotted against velocity to aid comparison with previous work and ease the calculation of non-dimensional vortex shedding parameters.

The data files were processed by software developed in house which converted the dynamic microphone and hot-wire data into frequency spectra using a Fast Fourier Transform with a Hanning window. The results for each plate configuration were displayed in the form of Z-plots, one for the microphone signal and one for the hot-wire signal. An example of each is given in Fig.2, showing the Z-plot of the microphone and hot-wire signals with the upstream plate installed alone. The Z-plot comprises a series of vertical frequency spectra, one at each of the velocities tested. A horizontal line, proportional to the logarithmic amplitude is drawn for each frequency bin, provided the amplitude is above a threshold level. This line is centred on the velocity co-ordinate of that spectrum. For further discussion on the development and production of the Z-plots see Parker and Stoneman [10]. The amplitudes and frequencies of the ten largest peaks in each spectrum were found by interpolation using the method described by Parker and Stoneman [18].

The large number of Z-plots, and the difficulty in estimating amplitude levels from them, prompted further data processing. Input data for a proprietary contour plotting package was prepared by a program which extracted data relating to the highest peak for given velocity and frequency ranges, and a given list of plate configurations. For example, the peak amplitude from all spectra lying between 1390Hz and 1650Hz, and 15m/s and 45m/s, together with the corresponding velocity and plate spacing was placed in a file for subsequent input into the contour plotting facility. This particular frequency range restricted the data to that corresponding to the excitation of mode 4. The contour plotting routine used was part of the Unimap package on a Vax 8700.

4 RESULTS.

4.1 Upstream plates installed alone.

Z-plots of the upstream plates installed alone in the tunnel, with increasing velocity are shown for both the hot-wire and microphone in Fig.2. The hot-wire shows that from 5m/s to 8m/s and from 10m/s to 15m/s the vortex shedding exhibited normal, constant Strouhal number (St) behaviour with a Strouhal number of 0.26 based upon plate thickness. At 9m/s the vortex shedding frequency appeared to be less than the natural shedding frequency for this velocity. The shedding frequency was held at about 550Hz, later found to correspond to the frequency of mode 1. No sound above the background noise level was detected at this frequency.

Between 16m/s and 19m/s the vortex shedding then became locked to one of the resonant modes of the duct. This was subsequently identified as a travelling mode 2, i.e. two lobes around the annulus. It can be seen from the z-plot of the microphone signal that the locking of the vortex shedding to the second circumferential mode of the duct coincided with the production of sound at this frequency.

The vortex shedding then reverted to the Strouhal line at 20m/s before locking on to the third circumferential mode, a travelling mode 3, between 21m/s and 25m/s. This was again accompanied by the production of sound at the same frequency. The vortex shedding locked on to mode 4 between 27m/s and 30m/s, and then mode 6 between 31m/s and 38m/s. Mode 5 was missed out.

The final mode which was excited has been labelled as 7b, as later investigations with two rows of plates showed that there could be two modes both with seven standing waves around the annulus, but with a difference in frequency of about 50Hz between them. Mode 7b co-existed with mode 6 at some velocities, being exited at velocities between 36m/s and 42m/s. The vortex shedding then reverted to Strouhal like behaviour but at a slightly reduced Strouhal number. The change in the nature of the vortex shedding from being highly correlated when locked on to an acoustic resonance to broadband vortex shedding can be seen comparing the spectra at 42m/s and 43m/s.

The resonant frequency of each mode increased slightly with velocity.

The maximum SPL recorded was 1438Pa rms or 157.1dB for mode 6 at 34m/s.

Repeating the same test a further three times produced the same pattern of results on the z-plots with the various modes coming in and out at the same velocities.

Four similar tests were performed, but this time with decreasing velocity. A comparison between the results is shown in Fig.3. The results shown are an average of the four tests with increasing velocity and the four tests with decreasing velocity. It can be seen that there is very little inter-mode hysteresis.

4.2 Two rows of plates in tandem.

Inter-mode hysteresis effects were also studied with the second row of plates installed downstream, and in tandem with the first. The results with an axial spacing of 6mm are representative, and shown in Fig.4

and Fig.5. Both figures show that significant inter-mode hysteresis effects occurred when a second row of plates was installed downstream of the first. At this particular spacing of 6mm, the greatest hysteresis occurred between mode 4 and mode 6. Mode 5 was weakly excited, but always at levels much below mode 4 or 6. The maximum amplitude of mode 5 was 58Pa rms (129dB) at 34m/s with increasing velocity. With increasing velocity the switch from mode 4 to mode 6 occurred between 34m/s and 35m/s, whereas with decreasing velocity the change from mode 6 to mode 4 occurred between 31m/s and 30m/s.

Figure 4 shows that at velocities for which a particular mode was excited with both increasing and decreasing velocity, the amplitude of the sound was similar. Mode 7a was an exception to this, but even here the SPL's with increasing velocity were only 2.3dB to 6.5dB greater than those with decreasing velocity.

Figure 5 shows that once established a given mode was excited at the same frequency independent of whether the velocity was increasing or decreasing. The frequency of each mode increased with increasing velocity in the same manner as the results of the single row of plates.

The main objective of this work was to investigate the effect of the axial spacing between the plate rows on the resonances excited in an annular cascade. The diversity of the results obtained are illustrated in the series of z-plots for the microphone signal shown in Fig.6a to Fig.6d for axial spacings of 3mm,6mm,14mm and 18mm. All the results were obtained with increasing velocity.

The smallest axial spacing at which resonances were excited was 3mm (Fig.6a). Only the higher modes, from mode 4 upwards, were excited. Those which were excited were present over a wide range of velocities. The potential for the excitation of more than one mode at a time is clearly demonstrated in this plot. Mode 6 and 7b existing simultaneously from 32m/s to 44m/s.

Figure 6b shows the results for an axial spacing of 6mm. The increasing velocity data of Fig.4 and Fig.5 were obtained from this test. Some of the highest SPL's were generated at this spacing, at 39m/s mode 6 was excited at 2092Pa rms (160dB).

The z-plot from the data for an axial spacing of 14mm (Fig.6c) shows several interesting features. It was one of the spacings at which all modes were excited. Mode 1 was present at both 8m/s and 13m/s. Modes 1,2,3,4 and 6 were excited as travelling waves whereas modes 5,7a and 7b were excited as standing waves. It is not known why some modes are excited as standing waves and others as travelling waves. The difference in frequency between modes 7a and 7b can be seen by comparing the data at 34m/s and 35m/s. This plot is also a good example of a spacing at which two families of resonances could be observed. Modes 2,4 and 6 were all excited at large amplitudes over two distinct velocity ranges.

Figure 6d, the z-plot for a spacing of 18mm, has virtually lost the resonances generated at the higher velocity ranges and has only one family of resonances. All modes were again excited at this spacing. At velocities between 40m/s and 45m/s the production of low amplitude vortex sound was observed. This can just be seen in Fig.6d as broadband noise with a Strouhal number of 0.21.

By inspection of the whole series of z-plots, from zero to 50mm, a general pattern of was observed in the way the velocities at which each mode was excited changed with axial spacing. As the spacing was increased the mean of the velocity range over which each resonance was excited increased. Also, as the spacing was increased, the maximum amplitude of each resonance would rise to a peak and then tail off. As the SPL of the resonances decreased, a second family of resonances would come in at lower velocities. At certain spaces therefore, two distinct families of resonances co-existed, such as at a spacing of 14mm (Fig.6c). With a further increase in spacing the first family would disappear, leaving the second family on its own. This would then follow a similar pattern, to be replaced by a third family. Over the 50mm variation in range of axial spacing tested, three distinct families came and went.

This effect can be illustrated by considering one mode in isolation. Figure 7 is a contour plot of the SPL recorded at varying velocities and spacings for the fourth circumferential mode, mode 4. The three distinct families, and the start of the fourth can be seen. The increase in the mean of the velocity range with increasing spacing is also clearly shown. The pattern shown in Fig.7 for mode 4, was repeated by each of the other modes, although these were sometimes distorted by the presence of other modes.

A summary of the change in the velocity range with spacing over which each mode was excited is shown in Fig.8. Figure 8 is hand drawn, and is derived from inspection of the individual z-plots. The resulting image is somewhat complex, but the different shading used for each mode allows one to pick out individual modes. Modes 2 and 3 have the same basic pattern as mode 4. The higher modes, modes 5,6,7a and 7b, having less difference in frequency between them, interacted with each other to a greater extent. This produced a more complex picture at the higher velocities.

5 DISCUSSION.

5.1 Effect of plate spacing.

The somewhat complex picture of Fig.8 can be rationalised by plotting the data in reduced velocity format, as in Fig.9. The ordinate is still the axial spacing, but the abscissa has been changed to reduced velocity, or velocity divided by the frequency. The data were prepared by taking the spectra of every combination of spacing and velocity, and finding the peak amplitude. A dot was then plotted, with the reduced velocity being calculated from the flow velocity and the frequency of the resonance excited at that velocity. The density of the dot plotted was proportional to the SPL of the resonance. Plotting the data in this manner caused it to collapse into a similar pattern to the data of mode 4. The three families of resonances, and the change in the resonant velocity range with spacing, can again be observed.

Previous models of the effect of plate spacing on the velocity range over which the resonance has been excited have been based upon the technique known as a "reduced velocity analysis" (Parker & Stoneman [11], Carr [14]). This technique again proves useful in the analysis. The analysis does not require a knowledge of the mechanism by which sound is produced by vortex shedding from a bluff body or by the interaction of vortices with a downstream body. All that is required is the assumption that sound is generated at certain localities in the flow, say in the region of the upstream plate trailing edge and the downstream plate leading edge. The reduced velocity analysis calculates the separation between these two points in the flow, such that there is a vortex at each location, at the same phase of the sound field. The argument being that if the sound generated by the vortices is at the same phase relative to the sound field at each location, the net sound production will be a maximum.

Let t be the time and X(t) the axial position of a vortex with X(0)=0

$$t = X/(r.v) \qquad (1)$$

where   v = free stream velocity
and   r = vortex convection velocity / v

As the resonances occur at low Mach numbers the phase change in the axial direction is small and the phase of acoustic field is assumed dependant only upon time t. The phase change, $\emptyset$, expressed as fraction of 360 degrees ($\emptyset=1$ is equivalent to 360 degrees), from t = 0

$$\emptyset = t.f \qquad (2)$$

where   f = vortex shedding frequency = acoustic resonance frequency. Substituting for t from (1) gives

$$\emptyset = X.f/r.v$$

or $X = \emptyset.r.v/f \qquad (3)$

For maximum sound production $\emptyset = 0,1,2,...$ If

$$X = x+e$$

where x = plate spacing, and e = an "extra distance" to allow for the locations of sound production to be away from the exact positions of the upstream plate trailing edge and the downstream plate leading edge.

$$x+e = \emptyset.r.v/f \qquad (4)$$

Unknown parameters are "e" and "r". Parker and Stoneman [11] calculated the ratio of vortex convection velocity to free stream velocity, "r", to be 0.78 by estimating the vortex position from flow visualization on a plate in a rectangular wind tunnel, and measuring the wake profile with a hot-wire.

Legerton et al [15] considered various previously published hypotheses. These assumed that the shift in reduced velocity to produce the correct phasing of the vortex arrival at the downstream plate leading edge, is completely dominant over the propensity of the upstream plate to shed vortices at a specific Strouhal number or reduced velocity in the absence of an acoustic resonance. Legerton et al [15] proposed that these two influences on the non-dimensional shedding frequency during resonance are of similar strength, and the resultant reduced velocity is a compromise, lying between the values dictated by the natural shedding and the vortex phasing at the downstream plate. This hypothesis led to an empirical model which produced good agreement with the experimental results of tandem plates in a rectangular duct. The same method was used here to predict the variation in reduced velocity of the resonances with plate spacing. The model was graphically constructed in Fig.9 so that comparison can be made with the experimental results.

The variation in natural shedding frequency with plate spacing is shown as a dashed line. The data for this curve were scaled from Legerton et al [15] and Johnson and Loerhke [16]. Chain dotted lines of constant phase difference between vortex shedding and vortex interaction were plotted on the same axis. These were derived from the reduced velocity analysis described above. The ratio of vortex convection velocity to free stream velocity, r, was chosen to be the same as that estimated by Parker and Stoneman [11], 0.78. The "extra distance", e, was chosen to be a small negative number. This was because when a vortex is shed from the upstream plate it is already a short distance downstream of the trailing edge. At some small spacing therefore, the instant a vortex is shed, it also impinges on the downstream plate. This corresponds to a phase difference of zero, and will remain zero over the entire velocity range at which vortex shedding exists. The actual value of the "extra distance" was chosen to be -3mm, as the resonances were found to be excited over the largest velocity ranges at a spacing of 3mm. 3mm agrees well with the difference in plate spacing and vortex spacing shown in Stoneman et al's [13] Fig.11.

The hypothesis proposed by Legerton et al [15], was that the propensity of the upstream plate to shed vortices in the absence of an acoustic resonance, has an influence on the Strouhal number or reduced velocity during resonance, as well as the requirement for integer number of cycles phase difference between sound generating regions in the flow as described by the reduced velocity analysis. To illustrate this, solid lines have been drawn that pass through the points of intersection of the constant phase lines and natural vortex shedding line. The gradient of the lines were found by adding a vector at a tangent to the natural shedding curve to a vector in the direction of the constant phase lines. If the vortex shedding vector was approximately 1.6 times the magnitude of the phase vector the sum of the two produced a good fit to the experimental data. This factor of 1.6 is the same as that used by Legerton et al [15]. The gradient of the resultant line can be expected to continually change as the gradient of the natural vortex shedding curve also changes. To account for this the sum of the two vectors was recalculated for small increments in axial spacing. The gradient of the natural shedding line at the spacing of the point under consideration, and the gradient of the phase line at the same velocity as this point were used in the recalculation. Configurations with different shedding and impingement bodies may require the lines to be more heavily weighted one way or the other. These lines have been drawn to show that the change in reduced velocity with spacing, can be interpreted as the resultant of two influences trying to pull the reduced

448

velocity in different directions, as the spacing is varied.

6 CONCLUSIONS.

Vortex shedding from an annular cascade of plates in a duct can excite a series of circumferential acoustic modes within the duct. These modes can comprise of either standing or travelling waves.

The installation of a second row of plates in tandem, downstream of the vortex shedding plates, can change the velocity ranges over which each acoustic resonance is excited. The spacing also influences the SPL generated. Both effects vary cyclically with plate spacing. Inter-mode hysteresis was more pronounced with tandem plates than with a single row of plates.

The change in velocity range and SPL of the resonances with axial spacing are consistent with results previously obtained from tandem plates in a rectangular wind tunnel. This is particularly true for the lower modes. The higher modes have less difference in frequency between them. This results in greater interaction between the modes. However, when the data were plotted against reduced velocity, it was found that the change in resonant velocity range with spacing is again consistent with the tandem plate results.

A model which predicted the variation in the mean of the velocity range over which the resonance is excited in a rectangular duct, has been applied to the results obtained from the annular rig, used in this investigation. Good agreement was found between the model predictions and experimental results. This model assumed that both the preference for phase matching between the vortex shedding from the upstream plate and vortex interaction with the downstream plate, and the propensity of the upstream plate to shed vortices at a given Strouhal number, in the absence of an acoustic resonance, both influence the reduced velocity at which resonances are excited.

ACKNOWLEDGEMENTS.

The authors would like to express their gratitude to Rolls Royce for their continuing support of the research into flow induced acoustic resonance at the University College of Swansea.

REFERENCES.

1. Parker, R., Resonance effects in wake shedding from parallel plates: some experimental observations, J. Sound Vib., 4, 62-72, 1966.
2. Parker, R., Resonance effects in wake shedding from parallel plates: Calculation of Resonant Frequencies, J. Sound Vib., 5, 330-343, 1967.
3. Cumpsty, N.A. and Whitehead, D.S., The excitation of acoustic resonance by wake shedding, J. Sound Vib., 18, 353-369, 1971.
4. Archibald, F.S., Self excitation of an acoustic resonance by vortex shedding, J. Sound Vib., 38, 81-103, 1975.
5. Welsh, M.C., Stokes, A.N. and Parker, R., Flow-resonant sound interaction in a duct containing a plate. Part I. Semicircular leading edge. J. Sound Vib., 95, 305-323, 1984.
6. Howe, M.S., On the absorption of sound by turbulence, IMA J. Appl. Maths, 32, 187-209, 1984.
7. Parker, R., Resonance effects in wake shedding from compressor blading, J. Sound Vib., 8, 281-297, 1968.
8. Parker, R., An investigation of acoustic resonance effects in an axial-flow compressor stage, J. Sound Vib., 8, 281-297, 1968.
9. Parker, R. and Pryce, D.C., Wake excited resonances in an annular cascade: an experimental investigation, J. Sound Vib., 37, 247-261, 1974.
10. Parker, R. and Stoneman, S.A.T., An experimental investigation of the generation and consequences of acoustic waves in an axial flow compressor: large axial spacings between blade rows, J. Sound Vib., 99, 169-192, 1985.
11. Parker, R. and Stoneman, S.A.T., An experimental investigation of the generation and consequences of acoustic waves in an axial flow compressor: the effect of variations in the axial spacings between blade rows. J. Sound Vib., 116, 509-525, 1987.
12. Parker, R., Stoneman, S.A.T. and Carr, M.I., Excitation of blade vibration by flow induced acoustic resonances in axial-flow compressors, Symposium on Unsteady aerodynamics of turbomachines and propellers, Cambridge, pp. 579-600, September 1984.
13. Stoneman, S.A.T., Hourigan, K., Stokes, A.N. and Welsh, M.C., Resonant sound caused by flow past two plates in tandem in a duct, J. Fluid Mech., 192, 455-484, 1988.
14. Carr, M.I., The excitation of acoustic resonances in an axial flow compressor stage by vortex shedding from aerofoil section blading, Ph.D. Thesis, Dept. Mech. Eng., University College of Swansea, 1986.
15. Legerton, M.L., Stoneman, S.A.T. and Parker,R., The effects of plate spacing and downstream plate length on the acoustic resonance excited by flow past two plates in tandem in a duct, to be published.
16. Johnson, C.O. and Loehrke, R.I., An experimental investigation of wake edge tones, AIAA J., 22, 1249-1253, 1984.
17. Rockwell, D. and Naudascher, E., Self-sustained oscillations of impinging shear layers, Ann. Rev. Fluid Mech., 11, 67-94, 1979.
18. Parker, R. and Stoneman, S.A.T., On the use of the fast Fourier transform when high frequency resolution is required, J. Sound Vib., 104, 75-79, 1986.

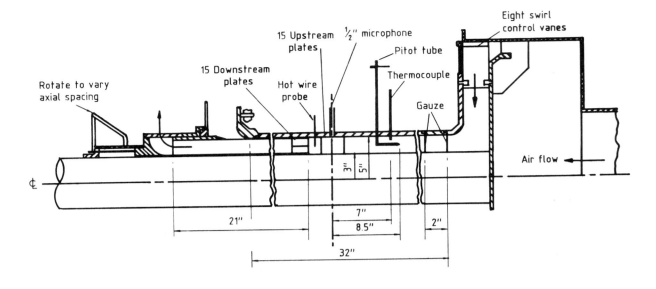

Figure 1. Schematic of annular wind tunnel and instrumentation.

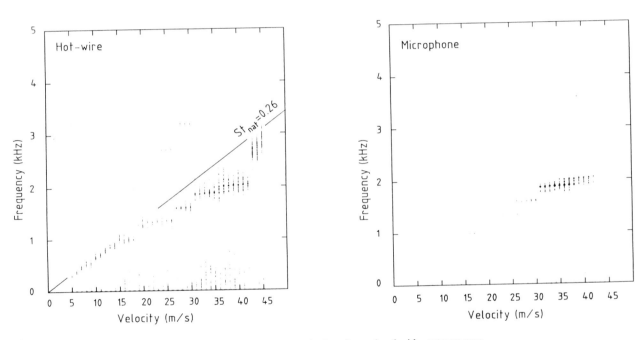

Figure 2. Z-plot of hot-wire and microphone signal with upstream row
of plates installed alone.

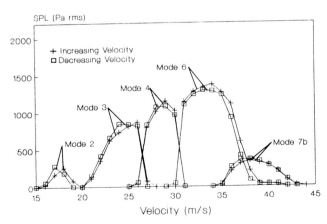

Figure 3. Single row of upstream plates. Variation in SPL with
velocity.

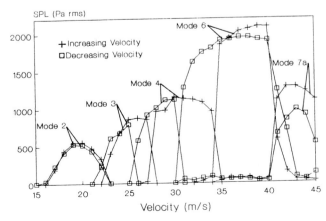

Figure 4. Tandem plates. Spacing = 6mm. Variation in SPL with
velocity.

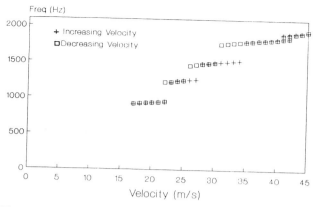

Figure 5. Tandem plates. Spacing = 6mm. Variation in resonant
frequency with velocity.

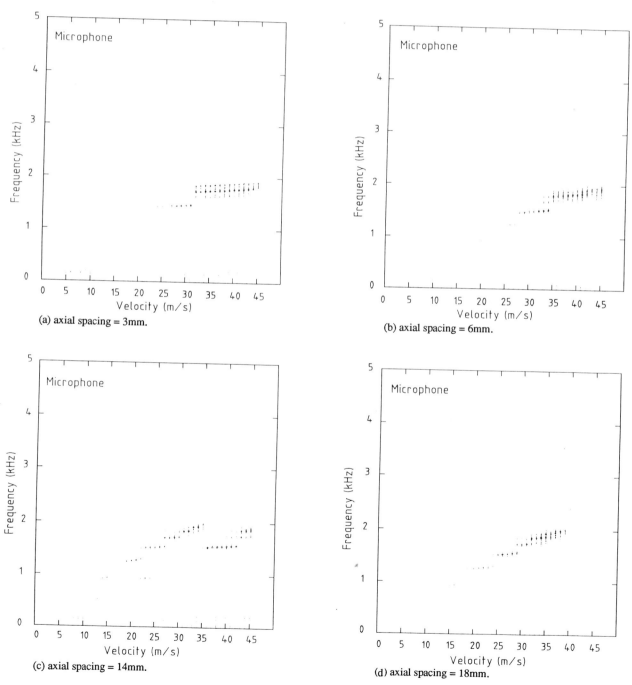

(a) axial spacing = 3mm.

(b) axial spacing = 6mm.

(c) axial spacing = 14mm.

(d) axial spacing = 18mm.

Figure 6. Z-plots of microphone signal with two rows of plates in
tandem.

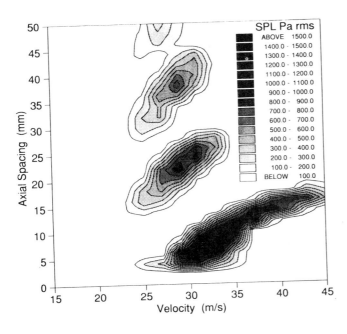

Figure 7. Variation in SPL of mode 4 with velocity and axial spacing.

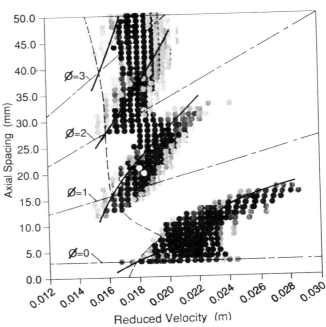

Figure 9. Reduced velocity plot. --- natural vortex shedding,-·——·-
constant phase lines, —— predicted variation in reduced
velocity with spacing. See Fig.7 for key.

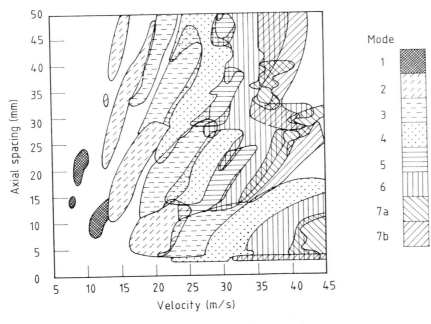

Figure 8. Variation in resonant mode with velocity and axial spacing.

C416/046

Galloping of rectangular cylinders: effects of downstream splitter plate

Y NAKAMURA, PhD, K HIRATA and T URABE
Research Institute for Applied Mechanics, Kyushu University, Kasuga, Japan

Synopsis: Galloping of rectangular cylinders with and without a splitter plate is investigated experimentally in low-speed wind tunnels. Particular emphasis is placed on galloping of rectangular cylinders with a splitter plate. The experiments are concerned with measurements on freely-oscillating rectangular cylinders with side ratios d/h=0.2 to 6.0 along with flow visualization on forced-oscillating rectangular cylinders with d/h=0.6, 1.0 and 2.0. The mechanism of galloping of rectangular cylinders with a splitter plate is proposed on the basis of the experimental findings. Close similarity between low-speed galloping of rectangular cylinders with and without a splitter plate is also mentioned.

Nomenclature

d = cylinder length paralell to the flow, mm
f_v = frequency of regular vortex shedding, Hz
f_y = frequency of body oscillation, Hz
h = cylinder length normal to the flow, mm
U = free-stream velocity, ms-1
$\bar{U}$ = reduced velocity = $U/f_y h$
$\bar{U}_r$ = vortex-resonance velocity = the inverse of the Strouhal number
β = log rate of growth of oscillation in wind
β_a = aerodynamic log rate of growth of oscillation
   = $\beta + \delta_s$
δ_s = structural damping

1. Introduction

Galloping, which is a single-degree-of-freedom flutter in translation in a cross-flow direction, is one of the most serious wind-induced vibrations of structures(1-3). This is one of a series of papers reporting our recent investigation on galloping of bluff bodies. The principal aim of the investigation is to elucidate the aerodynamic mechanism of galloping. The first paper(4) was concerned with experiments on oscillating rectangular cylinders. The experiments included measurements of the mean and fluctuating side-face pressures on forced-oscillating cylinders with d/h=0.4 and 0.6, where d is depth (streamwise cross-section dimension) and h is height (cross-flow dimension), along with measurements on freely-oscillating cylinders with d/h=0.2 to 1.0.

One of the most significant findings of the previous paper is that a galloping-like instability was observed at low speeds well below the vortex-resonance one on short rectangular cylinders for which high-speed galloping can not occur. The precise mechanism of low-speed galloping, as referred to in the paper, and a possible relation to the high-speed counterpart that can occur on long rectangular cylinders have remained unknown to date.

The present paper will report the results of galloping of rectangular cylinders in the presence of a splitter plate. It is concerned with free-oscillation experiments on cylinders over a range of d/h 0.2 to 6.0 in combination with flow visualization using smoke on force-oscillating cylinders with d/h=0.6, 1.0 and 2.0. The experiments also include measurements on cylinders without a splitter plate.

While a number of papers have been written on galloping of bluff bodies without a splitter plate, very few have been published on galloping of bluff bodies with a splitter plate. These include Nakamura & Tomonari (5) and a more recent one, Matsumoto et al. (6). Our previous paper (5) reported for the first time that galloping can occur on a variety of bluff bodies with a splitter plate including rectangular, D-section and circular cylinders. Matsumoto et al. (6) investigated galloping of a circular cylinder with a splitter plate.

2. Experimental arrangements

2.1. Free-oscillation experiment

The free-oscillation experiment was performed in a low-speed wind tunnel with a rectangular working section 3m high, 0.7m wide and 2m long. The tunnel could generate a very smooth flow with a turbulence intensity of about 0.12%. The rectangular-cylinder models used were constructed with light plastic plates and a metal backbone tube. The height h of the model was equal to 100mm while the depth d was widely varied. The resulting range of the side ratio d/h was about 0.2 to 2.0. As is shown in figure 1(a), the model had 350mm (=3.5h) square end plates with a separation of 650mm (=6.5h), and it was mounted horizontally in the working section with the front face normal to the flow.

A wooden splitter plate of 5mm (=0.05h) in thickness covering the model's full span was placed downstream of the model and fixed relative to the tunnel walls. The gap between the model and the splitter plate was 5mm (=0.05h) and several streamwise plate lengths up to a value of 2m (=20h) were examined in the experiment. The gap between the end plate and the splitter plate was made narrowest possible.

The model was supported with flexural and coil springs to move in a direction normal to the flow (figure 1(b)). The displacement of the model was sensed by strain gauges cemented on the flexual springs. The frequency and the logarithmic rate of growth or decay of oscillation at an amplitude of 0.1h on models in still air and in wind were determined from the displacement signals displayed on a pen-recorder. No systematic measurements of the steady-state amplitude, which could have often been much larger than 0.1h, were attempted because attention here was focused on the small-amplitude behaviour of galloping.

The reduced speed is defined by $\bar{U}=U/(f_y h)$, where U is the wind speed and f_y is the system natural frequency. The range of the wind speed was about 1.3 to 13.4ms-1, and the corresponding range of the Reynolds number, based on the height h, was $(1-10) \times 10^4$ approximately. Two different spring systems were chosen for the experiment, for which we obtained low and high values of the natural frequency, as are exemplified in Table 1. The resulting ranges of the reduced speed were respectively $\overline{U}=2$ to 14 and $\overline{U}=6$ to 40, approximately.

The values of the mass ratio $\mu = m/(\rho h^2)$, where m is the gross mass of the model per unit span and ρ is the air density, and the Scruton number defined by $S_c = 2\mu\delta_s$, where δ_s is the system damping, are listed in Table 1 for rectangular cylinders with d/h=0.6, 1.0 and 2.0. The experiments included tests on rectangular cylinders without a splitter plate. In the tests a constant-temperature hot-wire anemometer was used to detect the frequency of regular vortex shedding. The reduced vortex-resonance speed is defined by $\overline{U}_r = U/(f_v h)$, where f_v is the vortex-shedding frequency measured on a stationary cylinder.

2.2. Flow visualization

Flow visualization using liquid paraffin smoke was made on force-oscillating rectangular cylinders with d/h = 0.6, 1.0 and 2.0 with and without a splitter plate in a low-speed wind tunnel with a rectangular working section 2m high, 4m wide and 6m long.

The height of the model was h= 150mm for cylinders with d/h=0.6 and 1.0 and h=100mm for a cylinder with d/h=2.0. The splitter plate was 1.5m in length, and the gap between the model and the splitter plate was 5mm. The model was placed vertically in the working section, and oscillated sinusoidally in a direction normal to that of the free-stream with an electro-mechanical vibrator at an amplitude of 0.1h. The flow speed was constant and equal to about 0.8ms^{-1}. The frequency of oscillation was varied from about 1 to 3Hz to meet the range of the reduced speed obtained in the free-oscillation experiment.

3. The effect of splitter-plate length on galloping

All the galloping instabilities observed built up spontaneously from rest, and the amplitude of oscillation mostly increased far beyond 0.1h.

The galloping characteristics can be controlled by three parameters related to the splitter plate; the thickness and length of the plate, and the gap between the model and the plate. According to our previous experiments, no appreciable influence of reducing the plate thickness and the gap below 0.05h could be anticipated. On the other hand, the effect of varying the splitter-plate length on galloping can be considerable.

Figure 2 shows the aerodynamic rate of growth of oscillation β_a plotted against the reduced speed $\overline{U}$ on a rectangular cylinder with d/h=0.6 for four values of the plate length. β_a is defined by $\beta = \beta_a - \delta_s$, where β is the logarithmic rate of growth of oscillation in the free-oscillation experiment measured at an amplitude of 0.1h.

Figure 2 shows that the effect of the splitter-plate length is very significant in the high-speed range. Although we have high-speed galloping for long plates (15h and 20h), we have stable oscillations, at least in a limited range, for short plates (6.67h and 10h).

Further point of interest is that the cylinder response at low $\overline{U}$ is almost independent of the plate length. There is a critical $\overline{U}$ for each plate length below which the cylinder response is close to that corresponding to a very long plate. For example, the critical value for a 15h plate is about 30. On this basis, we adopted a 15h plate as a good substitute for a very long plate to investigate the galloping characteristics for $\overline{U}<30$. All the results that will be shown below are associated with a 15h plate.

4. Galloping of rectangular cylinder with a long splitter plate

The results of β_a for a rectangular cylinder with d/h=0.6 with a long splitter plate, i.e., a 15h plate, have been shown in figure 2. Figures 3 and 4 show the corresponding results for rectangular cylinders with d/h=1.0 and 2.0, respectively. The results for rectangular cylinders without a splitter plate are also included in figures 3 and 4.

As can be seen, the results for all the cylinders tested show common trends. Galloping can occur in the high-speed range, and as $\overline{U}$ is lowered from above, it becomes progressively weakened and eventually vanishes. With further decrease in $\overline{U}$, the stability of oscillation is increased rather rapidly, and after reaching a maximum, it reverses its direction.

Figure 5 shows the stability boundary for rectangular cylinders with a splitter plate. As can be seen, the critical $\overline{U}$ below which galloping vanishes increases with increasing d/h. To see when galloping vanishes at all, further experiment, specially designed for a high-speed range up to about $\overline{U} = 150$, was made using rectangular cylinders with d/h centred around 5.0 for which the height h was equal to 30mm and the length of a splitter plate was equal to 30h. As can be seen in the figure, galloping vanishes at a value of d/h between 5.0 and 6.0. This is in contrast to high-speed galloping of rectangular cylinders without a splitter plate which vanishes at around d/h = 3.0(1).

5. The results of flow visualization

Flow visualization showed that varying the reduced speed produced very similar changes in the flow pattern for rectangular cylinders with d/h = 0.6, 1.0 and 2.0 with a splitter plate. This is in accordance with the results of the free-oscillation experiment shown earlier. The long splitter plate caused the delay of the flow reattachment so that the flow pattern for any one of these three can be reasonably representative of those for galloping cylinders. Figure 6(a,b,c) shows smoke pictures for a square-section cylinder with a splitter plate oscillating at three different values of $\overline{U}$, i.e., $\overline{U}=12$, 7.0 and 5.0, respectively. Each picture has an illustration that points out some salient flow features. They are chosen to represent different states of a freely-oscillating cylinder; galloping (figure 6a), slightly damped (figure 6b) and heavily damped (figure 6c). All pictures shown were taken at an instant when the cylinder was moving downward at the neutral position, or in other words, at the maximum positive incidence relative to the flow.

6. Proposed mechanism of galloping of rectangular cylinders with a splitter plate

As mentioned in our previous paper (4), an oscillating bluff body produces undulating wake behind it. In general the flow just around an oscillating bluff body can be controlled directly by the instantaneous body motion and indirectly by the past body motion that has been imprinted in the undulating wake.

However, the results of the flow visualization shown in figure 6(a,b,c) suggest that the instantaneous body motion, or more precisely stated, the latest cycle of the body oscillation, has a dominant influence on the flow just around it. In the following we will see the sequence of events by lowering $\overline{U}$ from above.

At high $\overline{U}$ (figure 6a) where the shear layers are free from the direct interference of the trailing edges, the downward cylinder motion causes the lower shear layer to become closer to the side and hence more curved, while the upper shear layer becomes further away from it and hence less curved. As a result, a downward pressure force can be induced to augment the cylinder motion. This is why we call the instability under discussion exactly as galloping. Note that the splitter plate can prevent the upper and the lower flows from communicating with each other, and this is vital for the present mechanism to work effectively.

As $\overline{U}$ is lowered, the wave length of the wake undulation, or equivalently of the motion-dependent vortices, is progressively shortened and there comes a stage (figure 6b) at which the lower side now impedes the shear layer not to roll up freely. This is what we call the shear-layer/edge direct interaction (4). As can be seen in the picture, the curvature of the shear layer is reversed and at the same time the vortex B vanishes at this interaction. We should then expect that a reattachment-type pressure distribution be developed on the lower side, to act toward subsiding the cylinder motion rather than augumenting it. With further decrease in $\overline{U}$, the process progresses steadily (figure 6c).

The interpretation of the oscillating flow field given above may be too crude, but, for the moment, sufficient to understand the onset and suppression of the instability under discussion. We have made further measurement of the mean and fluctuating side-face pressures to support the hypothesis. However, the results have not been shown in this paper owing to the space limitation.

7. Low-speed galloping of rectangular cylinders without a splitter plate

Figure 7 shows the stability boundaries for galloping and vortex excitation on rectangular cylinders without a splitter plate, which is taken from (4). We see from the figure that apart from the well-known high-speed galloping occurring on long cylinders exceeding the critical, low-speed galloping can occur on short cylinders below the critical at reduced speeds much lower then the vortex-resonance speed.

We now compare the low-speed responses of rectangular cylinders with and without a splitter plate. In figure 4 for a rectangular cylinder with d/h=2.0, the response of the cylinder without a splitter for $\overline{U} < 9$, approximately, is close to that for the cylinder with a splitter plate. The experiment has shown that this holds true even with a rectangular cylinder with d/h=0.6 for $\overline{U} < 5$, approximately.

Figure 8(a,b) compares the flow patterns between rectangular cylinders with d/h=0.6 with and without a splitter plate oscillating at a very low reduced speed of $\overline{U} = 2.8$. They indicate surprisingly similar flow patterns. It follows that the flow just around an oscillating body at very low $\overline{U}$ is almost entirely determined by the instantaneous body motion, or more precisely stated, by the latest cycle of oscillation. In other words, no significant effects are present of the downstream wake undulation that is a product of the past body motion. This is one of the most outstanding features of the low-speed oscillating flow, as commented earlier (7). On this basis we can infer that low-speed galloping of rectangular cylinders without a splitter plate is similar to the galloping of rectangular cylinders with a splitter plate.

8. Conclusions

Galloping of rectangular cylinders with and without a splitter plate was investigated experimentally in low-speed wind tunnels. Particular emphasis was placed on galloping of rectangular cylinders with a splitter plate. The experiments were concerned with measurements on freely-oscillating rectangular cylinders with d/h = 0.2 to 6.0 along with flow visualization on forced-oscillating rectangular cylinders with d/h = 0.6, 1.0 and 2.0.

The experiments showed that rectangular cylinders with a splitter plate with d/h up to 5.0 are susceptible to galloping, and galloping vanishes at a value of d/h between 5.0 and 6.0. An interpretation of the mechanism of galloping of rectangular cylinders with a splitter plate was proposed on the basis of the new experimental findings.

The basic mechanism of excitation is such that at high reduced speed where the shear layers are free from the direct interference of the trailing edges, the downward cylinder

motion causes the lower shear layer to move closer to the side and hence more curved, while the upper shear layer becomes further away from it and hence less curved; as a result, a downward pressure force can be induced to augment the cylinder motion. The presence of a splitter plate is vital for such a mechanism to work effectively. As reduced speed is lowered, galloping is progressively weakened owing to the circulation lag caused by the downstream wake undulation. However, galloping vanishes at low reduced speeds primarily because of the onset of the shear-layer/edge direct interaction. With further decrease in reduced speed, the flow around a cylinder has become almost independent of the downstream wake undulation. For this reason, low-speed galloping of rectangular cylinders without a splitter plate is similar to the galloping of rectangular cylinder with a splitter plate.

A unified approach towards the aerodynamic mechanisms of galloping of rectangular cylinders with and without a splitter plate will be presented in a further paper.

References

(1) Parkinson, G.V. 1974 Mathematical models of flow-induced vibrations of bluff bodies. Flow-induced Structural Vibrations, ed. Naudascher, E., Springer, 81-127.
(2) Bearman, P.W. 1984 Vortex shedding from oscillating bluff bodies. Ann. Rev. Fluid Mech. 16, 195-222.
(3) Nakamura, Y. 1988 Recent research into bluff-body flutter. J. Wind Engng 137, 1-10.
(4) Nakamura, Y. and Hirata, K. 1990 Pressure fluctuations on oscillating rectangular cylinders with a long side normal to the flow. Submitted to J. Fluids and Structures.
(5) Nakamura, Y. and Tomonari, Y. 1977 Galloping of rectangular prisms in a smooth and in a turbulent flow. J. Sound and Vibration 52(2), 233-241.
(6) Matsumoto, M., Shiraishi, N., Kitazawa, M., Knisely, C., Shirato, H., Kim, Y. and Tsujii, M. 1988 Aerodynamic behavior of inclined circular cylinders - Cable aerodynamics. J. Wind Engineering, No.37, 103-112.
(7) Nakamura, Y. and Nakashima, M. 1986 Vortex excitation of prisms with elongated rectangular, H- and ⊢- cross-sections. J. Fluid Mech. 163, 149-169.

(a)

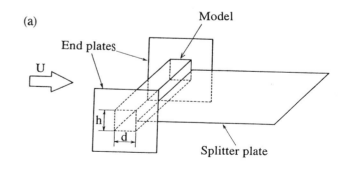

(b)

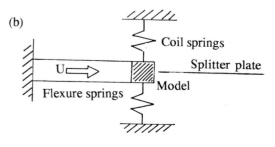

Figure 1. Rectangular-cylinder model with a splitter plate.

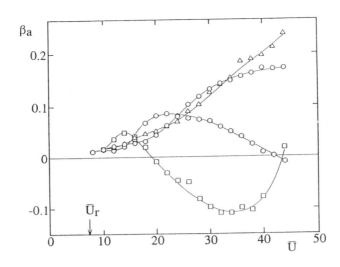

Figure 2. Effect of splitter-plate length on aerodynamic rate of growth of oscillation.
d/h=0.6; □ ,plate length = 6.67h; ⬡ ,10h; ○ ,15h; △ ,20h.

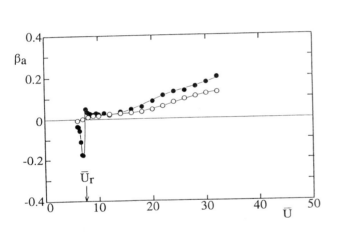

Figure 3. Aerodynamic rate of growth of oscillation. d/h=1.0;
● ,without splitter plate; ○ ,plate length = 15h.

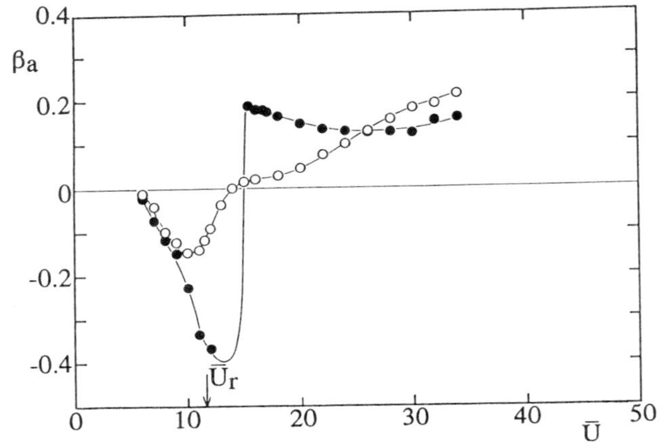

Figure 4. Aerodynamic rate of growth of oscillation. d/h=2.0;
● ,without splitter plate; ○ ,plate length = 15h.

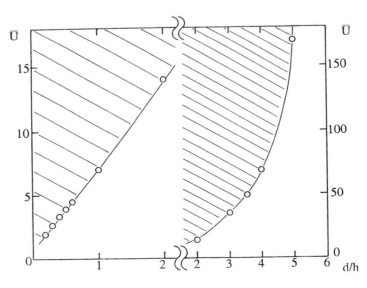

Figure 5. Stability boundary for galloping of rectangular cylinders with a splitter plate.

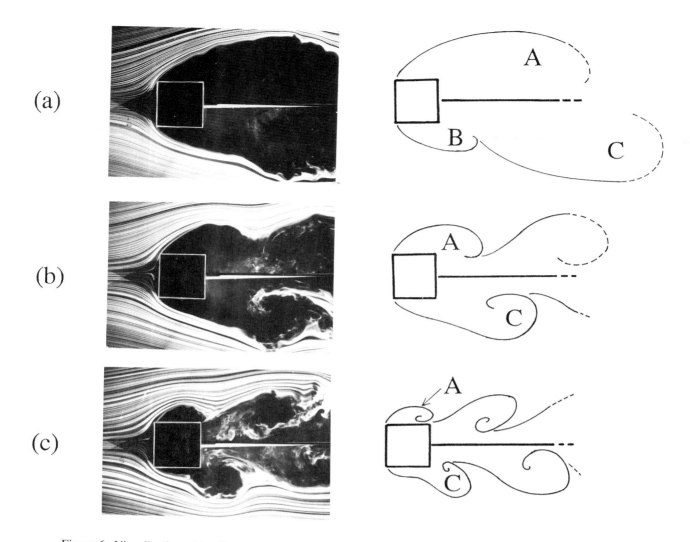

Figure 6. Visualization of the flow around an oscillating square-section cylinder with a splitter plate. Pictures correspond to an instant when the cylinder is moving downward at the neutral position.
(a) $\bar{U} = 12$; (b) 7.0; (c) 5.0

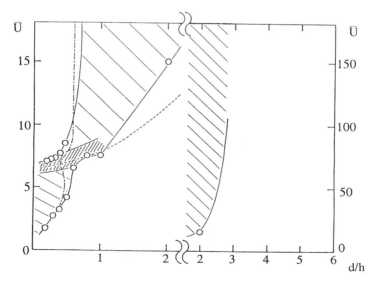

Figure 7. Stability boundaries for galloping and vortex excitation on rectangular cylinders without a splitter plate.
————, critical geometry; ------, vortex-resonance speed.

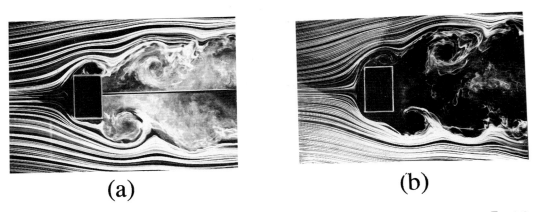

Figure 8. Visualization of the flow around a rectangular cylinder with d/h = 0.6 oscillating at $\overline{U}$ = 2.8. (a) with splitter plate; (b) without splitter plate.

Table 1. Some characteristic parameters for rectangular cylinders with d/h = 0.6, 1.0 and 2.0 in the free-oscillation experiment.

d / h	U (m s^{-1})		fy(Hz)	$\overline{U}$	μ	Sc
0.6	Low	2.4~11.2	8.00	3.5~14.0	170.8	1.09
	High	3.1~13.4	3.05	10.0~44.0	192.5	1.96
1.0	Low	1.3~7.0	6.70	2.0~10.5	234.4	3.38
	High	1.3~7.0	2.20	6.0~32.0	331.6	5.50
2.0	Low	1.3~7.0	5.20	2.5~13.5	389.1	6.07
	High	1.3~7.1	2.10	6.0~34.0	363.9	8.81

C416/030

Measurements of damping forces caused by flow between two concentric cylinders

D E HOBSON, MA, PhD
PowerGen, Ratcliffe-on-Soar, Nottinghamshire

SYNOPSIS The fluid damping forces acting on a vibrating cylinder and caused by annular flow have been measured directly over a range of frequencies and at Reynolds numbers ranging from 500 to 10 000. The results are compared with a theoretical analysis which makes simple quasi-steady assumptions about the behaviour of the frictional forces on the cylinder. The effects of surface roughness, eccentricity and high frequency parameter have also been explored either experimentally or theoretically.

NOTATION

$Cp(z)$	steady pressure coefficient, $(P-P_0)/\frac{1}{2}\rho U^2$	y	vertical displacement
$Cp'(\lambda,z)$	unsteady pressure coefficient, $(p'/h')(H/\frac{1}{2}\rho U^2)$	z	axial distance
		$\Re$	real part
		$\Im$	imaginary part
f	friction coefficient, $(-dP/dz)(2H/\frac{1}{2}\rho U^2)$	α	see text
F	force	β	$(Re')^{\frac{1}{2}}$
$g(\lambda)$	dynamic force coefficient, $(F'/h')(H/\frac{1}{2}\rho U^2 r^2)$	δ	eccentric displacement
		ϵ	length/radius ratio, L/r
h	annular clearance, $h=H+h'(z)$	θ	circumferential direction
H	mean annular clearance	λ	reduced frequency, $\omega r/U$
j	$\sqrt{-1}$	μ	dynamic viscosity;gap ratio
L	length of annulus	ρ	gas density
m	added mass per unit length	τ	skin friction
n	Reynolds number exponent	$\psi(z)$	mode or displacement shape
p	static pressure	$\phi(\beta)$	pressure multiplier
$P(z)$	steady pressure	ω	angular frequency
$P(\omega)$	pressure/displacement transfer function		
ΔP	overall pressure drop	Subscripts and superscripts	
r	mean annulus radius	z,θ	axial and circumferential directions
Re	Reynolds number, $\rho U(2H)/\mu$	$'$	perturbation quantity
Re'	frequency parameter, $(\rho\omega H^2)/2\mu$	t	based on conditions in the seal throat
t	time	o	atmospheric conditions downstream
u	axial velocity		
U	mean axial velocity	L	at position z=L
v	tangential velocity		
$X(\omega)$	force/displacement transfer function, $F'(\omega)/h'(L,\omega)$		
x	horizontal displacement		

1. INTRODUCTION

Failures associated with the excitation of structures by an axial flow between two cylinders have occurred in industrial plant over the past twenty years; there are examples of damage caused by these annular flows in valves, heat exchanger and nuclear reactor core components (Reference 1). Many of these problems have been unanticipated at the design stage because of a lack of appreciation of the excitation phenomena involved and the absence of any simple guidelines to indicate, for example, whether a particular component might be subject to oscillatory or divergent instability and the order of magnitude of the fluid forces involved. This is in marked contrast to the case of vortex shedding, for example, where accurate assessments of the fluid forces can generally be made.

Recently, to improve understanding of this type of flow-induced vibration, attempts were made to model the unsteady flows in the annulus caused by the vibrating cylinders and in particular to predict the self-induced positive and negative fluid damping; this led to a series of closed form analytic solutions for simple annular geometries (Reference 2) and later to a method of dealing with more complex cases where the centrebody vibrated in an arbitrary, piecewise linear mode shape and the annulus consisted of sections of constant diameter lengths connected by contraction or expansion components whose steady flow characteristics such as loss coefficient were prescribed (Reference 3). This approach has now been embodied in a user-friendly computer program ANNULUS and one of the purposes of this paper is to provide some validation, in particular of the way in which the program predicts the effects of skin friction on fluid damping.

This is accomplished by directly measuring the frequency dependent forces required to shake a lightweight centrebody surrounded by a narrow annulus down which air is blown at Reynolds numbers in the range 500 to 10 000. By comparison with the forces at zero flow and making an allowance for the viscous damping present in the annulus even when there is no flow, non-dimensional fluid coefficients are derived for comparison with theory.

In addition, the complicating effects of high eccentricity of the inner cylinder, which cannot be dealt with theoretically, are described as are the effects of a large increase in skin friction caused by non-isotropic roughness elements; the latter is a severe test of the model for the relationship between pressure gradients and instantaneous flow velocity in the annulus.

Finally, the quasi-steady assumptions made about the two-dimensional behaviour of the flow in the annulus when the frequency is high are examined and the effects on skin friction and the added mass parameter calculated.

2. SOURCES OF FLUID DAMPING

The method used for predicting the fluid forces has been set out elsewhere (Reference 4) and is based on the mass and momentum conversation equations for the flow down the annulus. An assumption is made that the annulus width H is narrow compared with the radius r and that the effects of any velocity variation across the annulus can be represented by a Reynolds number dependent friction factor f based on a mean velocity. It is assumed that the instantaneous skin friction τ lies parallel to the instantaneous velocity w which has a tangential as well as axial component, and that the same friction coefficient applies in all directions, i.e. the surface roughness is isotropic. This implies the following relationships between τ, its components τ_z and τ_e, the velocity components u,v in the axial and tangential directions and the pressure gradient dp/ds parallel to the w direction:

$$\tau = (H/2)dp/ds = (f/4)(\tfrac{1}{2}\rho w^2) \tag{1}$$

$$w^2 = u^2 + v^2 \tag{2}$$

$$\tau_z = \tau(u/w) \tag{3}$$

$$\tau_\theta = \tau(v/w) \tag{4}$$

Carrying out the linearisation, assuming $u=U+u'(z,\theta)\exp(j\omega t)$ etc the perturbation components of τ become:

$$\tau_z' = (f/4)\{(\rho U u')(1+m/2)+m((\tfrac{1}{2}\rho U^2)(h/H)\} \tag{5}$$

$$\tau_\theta' = (f/8)(\rho U v') \tag{6}$$

where n is the gradient of the friction factor versus Reynolds number relationship:

$$n = d(\log f)/d(\log Re) \tag{7}$$

and is equal to -1 for laminar flow and between zero and -0.25 for turbulent flow.

2.1 Infinitely long cylinders

Using these relationships it is a straightforward matter to derive formulae for the forces on the cylinder for the simple case of an infinitely long annulus and rigid body motion. Thus for zero flow the added mass per unit length m and frictional force per unit length become:

$$m = \rho\pi r^2(r/H) \tag{8}$$

$$F'/L = -12\pi\mu(\omega r^2/H^3).h' \tag{9}$$

where h' is the lateral displacement of the cylinder and μ the dynamic viscosity of the fluid. The negative sign in the latter expression indicates that the fluid damping on the structure is positive.

When the flow is non-zero the inertial term is unchanged but the frictional term becomes:

$$F'/L = -\pi(f/4)(\rho\omega r^3 U/H^2).h' \tag{10}$$

which for laminar flow i.e. f=96/Re is identical to equation (9).

Finally, for these infinite cylinders it should be noted that at zero frequency there are no restoring or divergent forces; this is not the case for finite length cases, nor for cases when the displacement or mode shape $\psi(z)$ of the cylinder is not constant.

2.2 Finite length cylinders - damping arising from boundary conditions

For an annulus of finite length the effects of inlet and outlet fluid boundary conditions must be taken into account; although these effects decay rapidly with distance from the boundaries as $\exp(-z/r)$, as pointed out in Reference 2 these boundary conditions can be important sources of both positive and negative damping. In the case of constant displacement shape h'(z)=h' and no frictional pressure drop, closed form analytic solutions have been obtained for several important cases. The first of these, and the simplest, is the so-called reference configuration of a loss-less, constant total pressure ΔP inlet followed by a frictionless annulus and terminated in an abrupt expansion where static pressure is held constant. Defining a non-dimensional fluid force coefficient $g(\lambda)$ and reduced frequency λ,

$$g(\lambda) = (F'/h')(H/\tfrac{1}{2}\rho U^2 r^2) \tag{11}$$

$$\lambda = \omega r/U \tag{12}$$

$$\Delta P = \tfrac{1}{2}\rho U^2 \tag{13}$$

expressions for the damping component $\Im(g)$ of $g(\psi)$ have been evaluated and this is given in full in the Appendix. Of particular importance is the upper limit for $g(\lambda)$ which applies when the annulus is very long, $\epsilon=L/r\to\infty$

$$\Im(g) = -2\pi\lambda \tag{14}$$

or

$$\Im(F'/h') = -\pi\rho\omega U r^3/H \tag{15}$$

The second important configuration is one where the annulus is partially blocked by a short upstream seal, leaving a gap in the annulus of μH and increasing the local mean axial velocity to $U_t = U/\mu$ and overall pressure drop to

$\Delta P = \frac{1}{2}\rho U^2_t$. Again the Appendix gives the result for the general case; most significant however is the case for an almost closed seal at the inlet of a long annulus, $\mu \to 0$, $\epsilon \to \infty$,

$$\Im(g_t) = +2\pi\lambda_t \qquad (16)$$

where both g_t and λ_t are now defined in terms of U_t instead of U (see equations 11 and 12). It is thought that this expression gives an upper bound to the negative damping caused by a flow in any annulus subject to a pressure differential of ΔP.

Similarly, for a downstream seal the upper bound on positive damping is

$$\Im(g_t) = -2\pi\lambda_t \qquad (17)$$

2.3 The general case - the program ANNULUS

ANNULUS, written in FORTRAN, is a user-friendly computer program which calculates the unsteady flows, pressures and forces for the general case of a cylinder whose displacement or mode shape can be approximated by piecewise linear sections; the annulus width, mean axial velocity and friction factor may vary in a piecewise constant manner but, at the junctions of the annular sections where the flow area changes, loss or pressure recovery coefficients must be specified. Further details of the mathematical model can be found in Reference 4.

In particular the program calculates, at a specified number of reduced frequencies, the distribution of (complex) non-dimensional pressure

$$Cp'(z) = (P'/h'(L))(H/\tfrac{1}{2}\rho U^2) \qquad (18)$$

at axial stations along the annulus and a force coefficient

$$g(\lambda) = (F'/h'(L))(H/\tfrac{1}{2}\rho U^2 r^2) \qquad (19)$$

for the structure as a whole, where in the case of the experiments to be described later, the reference displacement $h'(L)$ used in this

expression is located at the termination of the annulus, at $z=L$.

It is useful to note that $g(\lambda)$ may be regarded as the fraction of the force $\frac{1}{2}\rho U^2 r^2$ that a body would experience were it to vibrate with an amplitude equal to the full clearance, assuming linear behaviour.

The program has been used to predict the conditions prevailing in the rig used for the experiments to be described next. For this case the displacement shape is given by $\Psi(z) = .1 + z/L$ and the annulus width is constant with a loss-less inlet and sudden expansion at exit. Examination of the results of the calculations shows that $g(\lambda)$ and $Cp'(\lambda)$ can be closely approximated by the expressions

$$g(\lambda) = g(0)+j(dg/d\lambda)\lambda+d^2g/d\lambda^2(\lambda^2/2) \qquad (20)$$

and

$$Cp'(\lambda)=Cp'(0)+j(dCp'/d\lambda)\lambda+ \\ d^2Cp'/d\lambda^2(\lambda^2/2) \qquad (21)$$

for low values of λ, and it is these derivatives of g and Cp' which are compared with experiment.

In a separate exercise, ANNULUS was also used to predict the static sideloads acting on the centrebody, i.e. $g(\omega),\omega=0$. Examination of a wide range of situations in which displacement shape, skin friction coefficient and inlet and outlet boundary conditions were varied showed that $g(0)$ is closely associated with the maximum pressure drop ΔP occurring over an axial distance equal to the radius whether this arises from friction or a local area change, the overall pressure drop and length of the annulus being unimportant provided $L \gg r$. This leads to upper and lower bounds for $g(0)$,

$$-\pi < g(0) < +\pi. \qquad (22)$$

This implies that, assuming linear behaviour, the maximum sideforce F' attainable at maximum displacement $h'=H$ is simply

$$F' = \pm(\pi r^2)\Delta P \qquad (23)$$

3. MEASUREMENT OF FLUID DAMPING

The experimental work was carried out on the Annular Flow Rig which has been described in detail elsewhere (Reference 5); it is an unusual facility in that it was designed to measure directly the forces required to vibrate the structure over a range of frequencies simultaneously rather than at single resonant frequency. Fluid forces were determined by carrying out gas-off and then gas-on experiments and comparing them, a correction being made for the effects of the zero flow gas damping effects.

3.1 Rig design

The rig consisted of a 1.34m long, 119mm diameter, lightweight centrebody (Figure 1) which could be forced to vibrate as a rigid body, pivoted at one (upstream) end and attached to a large electromagnetic shaker at the other. Air was supplied from a centrifugal fan via an orifice plate into the settling chamber where upstream pressure was measured, and then flowed into the 2 mm wide annulus between the centrebody and the outer cylinder. The latter could be jacked horizontally or vertically so that the centrebody could be arranged to vibrate about a range of eccentric mean positions if necessary.

3.2 Instrumentation and data processing

A non-contacting displacement transducer measured vertical motion and a force transducer attached between the body and the shaker by a pivot arrangement was used to measure the forces required to shake the body. Pressure tappings at intervals along the outer cylinders were used to measure both steady and unsteady pressures.

The shaker was excited by a broad band signal from a signal analyser which was also used to perform the FFT analysis required to calculate the force and pressure/displacement transfer functions $X(\omega)$ and $P(\omega)$ used to calculate the derivatives needed for comparison with the theoretical predictions. Examples of these are shown in Figure 2 where both real and imaginary components of $P(\omega)$ and $X(\omega)$ are shown.

All rig operations, signal acquisition and data processing were carried out under computer control and the results stored for further analysis and plotting.

Figure 3 shows an example of the result of subtracting the gas-off transfer function from the gas-on value (Figure 2, bottom) and calculating the non-dimensional parameters λ and $g(\lambda)$. The real part of $g(\lambda)$ is negative and almost constant indicating that there is a positive (centralising) gas stiffness. The absence of significant curvature indicates that the gas-on added mass is little different from the gas-off value, a point confirmed by theory (for this geometry only).

According to theory the imaginary part should be a straight line at these low frequency parameters, with slope proportional to friction factor. In recognition of the fact that this is not quite the case, when results for $dg/d\lambda$ are presented both the initial slope and average over the full range available are plotted.

3.3 Checks on overall accuracy and repeatability

With no gas flow, the real part of the transfer function $X(\omega)$ was entirely inertial, representing the effective mass of the centrebody and the added mass effect of the air in the annulus which together amounted to 1.6kg. Overall repeatability was checked, therefore, by measuring $X(\omega)$ in the range 5-25 Hz and calculating the combined mass; in all 90 tests were carried out over a period of three days and all results found to be within ±0.4% of the mean value.

The absolute accuracy was determined by

attaching a 200gm mass to the centrebody close to the annulus exit; comparison of transfer functions both with and without the mass and calculation of the extra inertial term showed that there was a systematic error of -4.5% with a standard deviation over eight tests of ±2.4gm. It was calculated that, when the same technique was used to measure the additional forces due to fluid effects, the random error in the damping was no more than ±6% at 25 Hz and zero flow, increasing inversely with decreasing frequency but decreasing with increasing flow.

4. EXPERIMENTAL VALIDATION

4.1 Unsteady pressure measurements

Measurements of unsteady pressure can be used in their own right to validate the computer program but they are also needed to ensure that the zero flow correction factor applied to all the results to correct for the (laminar) gas damping is accurate. This correction factor is calculated to be:

$$dg/d\lambda = -24585/Re \qquad (24)$$

for this rig and is obtained by integrating the pressure field taking due account of the displacement shape $\psi(z/L)$. Figure 4 therefore shows how measured values of the derivatives of Cp' compare with theory and it can be seen that agreement is very good. It can also be seen that, for this geometry, local pressures are approximately proportional to local displacements (a straight line through $z/L = -0.1$) except near the inlets and outlets $z/L = 0,1.0$.

Figure 5 shows similar results for the laminar flow case, Re = 2000 and the turbulent flow case Re = 10,000 which have very similar friction factors (see next section) but different Reynolds number exponent n. Again the theory is close to the experimental values lending confidence to the mathematical models used.

4.2 Steady flow measurements

Perturbations about a known steady flow form the basis for all the theoretical methods described here and a knowledge of the friction factor and its Reynolds number dependence is necessary in order to provide input to the program ANNULUS before predictions of force coefficient $g(\lambda)$ are possible.

Measurements of the axial distribution of static pressure were therefore taken with the centrebody held rigid and concentric and the friction factor f calculated over a range of Reynolds numbers from 500 to 10,000. At Reynolds numbers below about 4000 the pressure gradient along the annulus was constant and the friction factor close to its theoretical value for laminar flow, 96/Re (Figure 6). At higher turbulent Reynolds numbers, however, the slope over the upstream third of the annulus was less than over the remainder, possibly due to entrance effects or differences in surface roughness. This presented no difficulty for ANNULUS however since it can deal with such piecewise constant friction factors.

4.3 Measurements of unsteady force coefficients

Figure 7 shows the experimental results for the first derivative of the force coefficient $g(\lambda)$, which is proportional to fluid damping, after the correction for zero flow damping (Equation 24) had been made. It can be seen that agreement with theory is very good, the only significant errors occurring at Re = 7000, just beyond transition, where there were significant differences between the initial and average slopes of $dg/d\lambda$. Furthermore, the general similarity of Figures 6 and 7 demonstrates quite clearly the close relationship between skin friction and fluid damping, at least when the walls of the annulus are smooth.

5. EFFECTS OF NON-ISOTROPIC ROUGHNESS

To test this link further a centrebody was constructed with circumferential ridges formed on the surface; these were 0.35mm high and spaced at 2.5mm, a distance close to the optimum value for obtaining a maximum increase in skin friction. Figure 8 shows that, at low Reynolds numbers, the effect on the (laminar skin friction was very small but transition to turbulent flow occurred very early, at Re = 1000; turbulent friction factors were an order of magnitude higher than for the smooth centrebody.

Interesting, however, the predicted increase in damping did not occur and the values for $g(\lambda)$ were only slightly greater than the smooth cylinder results (Figure 9). This casts doubt on the model used for relating instantaneous pressure gradients and skin friction with flow velocity used to predict the behaviour of a smooth surface.

6. EFFECTS OF ECCENTRICITY

In many practical cases, the mechanical constraints on the inner cylinder may be insufficient to hold the body in a concentric location; indeed the gas forces may cause the body to diverge to an equilibrium position closer to the wall in which case it may experience damping very different to that when it is concentric with the outer cylinder.

To illustrate the effects, which cannot be predicted at present, the experiments on the smooth centrebody were repeated with its axis still located parallel with the outer cylinder but displaced 1.5mm either in the vertical or horizontal directions, i.e. with 75% eccentricity. Force measurements showed that, at zero flow, the damping increased by about a factor of three (Figure 10) but that the increase due to flow was roughly the same as for a smooth cylinder. At the maximum flow tested, this resulted in a 20% increase in damping when the cylinder was displaced vertically (i.e. vibrating perpendicular to the nearest wall) and 75% when displaced horizontally (vibrating parallel to the nearest wall).

7. EFFECTS OF HIGH FREQUENCY PARAMETER

The model used so far for the detailed flow in the annulus assumes, effectively, that there is no local interaction between the inertial pressure fields and the frictional pressure terms and that the velocity profile is flat. The pressure gradient down the annulus can then be written

$$dp/dx = -\rho du/dt - (f/d).\tfrac{1}{2}\rho u^2 \qquad (25)$$

or, for oscillatory laminar flow

$$dp/dx = j\omega\rho u - 12\mu u/H^2 \qquad (26)$$

where u is taken to be the average velocity across the annulus.

Non-dimensionalising dp/dx using the inertial part $-j\rho\omega u$ and introducing a frequency parameter Re', a pressure factor $\phi(\beta)$ can be defined for this simple case for comparison with the more accurate analysis described next:

$$\phi(\beta) = (dp/dx)/(-j\omega\rho u) \qquad (27)$$

Combining with Equation 26, this is equivalent to

$$\phi(\beta) = (1-6j/\beta^2) \qquad (28)$$

where

$$\beta^2 = Re' \qquad (29)$$

$$Re' = (\rho\omega H^2/2\mu) \qquad (30)$$

Now, starting from the equations describing the unsteady two-dimensional flow of a viscous fluid between two flat plates, see for example Reference 6, a more accurate solution can be obtained for $\phi(\beta)$; this is given in the Appendix and shown graphically in Figure 11. It can be seen that, at low frequencies, Re'<10, $\Im(\phi)$ is very close to the steady flow value -6/Re', implying that the velocity profile is still essentially parabolic and that the unsteady pressure drop relationship is the same as the steady one. Above Re' = 10 there are considerable deviations, however, and for Re'>100, $\Im(\phi) \rightarrow -\sqrt{Re'}$; this is a factor $\sqrt{Re'}/6$ greater than the steady value and varies as $\omega^{1/2}$.

Examination of the solution for the velocity profile would show that, as Re' increases, the profile changes from a parabolic shape to one where the velocity is flat over the centre on the annulus, variations being confined to increasingly thin shear layers adjacent to the walls where skin friction is very high. It is not surprising therefore that the inertial term in Equation 25, which is based on the assumptions that the velocity is everywhere equal to the mean flow, becomes increasingly accurate and that $\Re(\phi) \rightarrow 1.0$. However, at low frequencies, $\Re(\phi)$ assumes a value of 6/5 whereas the approximation Equation 28 tends to unity.

This is an unexpected result which has implications for the added mass relationship (Equation 8, for example) for structures vibrating in narrow clearances at values of Re' less than about 100, and when the mean flow is zero or laminar. In the case of turbulent flow, where the underlying steady velocity profile is flatter, the effect would be less.

7. DISCUSSION

The experiments have shown that the gas forces on vibrating concentric cylinders of simple geometry are well predicted by the theory and it is worth discussing whether the approach used here can be used to provide some general guidelines for determining the stability of annular geometries.

It is proposed firstly that the concentric results give some indication of the minimum positive damping experienced by more complex, possibly eccentric geometries; this together with the expression for the maximum negative damping might form the basis for a first, rapid evaluation of the total fluid dynamic damping and the potential for oscillatory instability of this type of structure.

A second rule for determining stability might stem from examination of the decentralising forces; in recognition that in eccentric configurations there is only a very poor knowledge of instability mechanisms it is suggested that, if the static destabilising force given by Equation 23 is sufficient to displace the centrebody significantly, say by more than 10% of the clearance H, then the structure should be regarded as 'floppy' and potentially prone to self-induced vibration. Further theoretical or experimental work would then be needed to prove stability or otherwise.

8. CONCLUSIONS

1. Damping of cylindrical structures due to an annular flow arises from inlet or outlet region effects and from frictional effects in the annulus, both effects increasing with velocity.

2. The damping forces and pressure distribution along the annulus are well predicted by making simple assumptions about the unsteady flow in the annulus.

3. The inertial or added mass effects are unaffected by the flow in the cases considered here and again are accurately predicted by theory.

4. A cylinder with a circumferentially ribbed surface was only twice as heavily damped as a smooth cylinder in spite of a ten-fold increase in friction factor; this results casts doubt on the mathematical models employed when the surface roughness is highly non-isotropic.

5. A modification to the theory which takes account of interactions between fluid acceleration and the viscous forces, when the mean flow is laminar or zero, predicts a large increase in friction factor at high frequencies and a 20% increase in the added mass or inertial effect at low frequencies. It was not possible

to confirm this experimentally however.

6. Simple expressions based on the models used here are given for the positive damping due to annular flow. In addition, upper bound expressions for forces causing negative damping and static divergences are given; these forces are confined to regions of the annulus where area changes occur.

9. ACKNOWLEDGEMENTS

This paper is published with the permission of PowerGen.

The contribution of Mr M Dolding who helped to carry out the experimental work is gratefully acknowledged.

REFERENCES

1. PAIDOUSSIS, M.P., AU-YANG, M.K., CHEN,S.S, (Editors). Flow-Induced Vibrations Due to Internal and Annular Flows. International Symposium on Flow-Induced Vibration and Noise, ASME, 1988.

2. HOBSON, D.E. Fluid elastic instabilities caused by flow in an annulus, Third International Conference on Flow Induced Vibrations. Keswick, 1982.

3. HOBSON, D.E. & Spurr, A. Forces on the vibrating centrebody of an annular diffuser. ASME Symposium on Flow Induced Vibrations, New Orleans, 1984.

4. PARKIN, M.W., FOX, M.J.H., FRANCE, E.R. & HOBSON, D.E. Annular flow induced vibrations associated with on-load refuelling of Advanced Gas Cooled Reactors BHRA International Conference on Flow Induced Vibrations, Bowness-on-Windermere, UK, 1987.

5. HOBSON, D.E. & JEDWAB, M Investigations of the effect of eccentricity on the unsteady forces on the centrebody of an annular diffuser. ASME Symposium on Flow Induced Vibrations and Noise, Chicago, 1988.

6. SCHLICTING, H. Boundary Layer Theory, McGraw Hill, 1968.

APPENDIX
Expressions for $g(\lambda)$ and $\phi(\beta)$

A.1 REFERENCE CONFIGURATION

Overall pressure drop $\Delta P = \frac{1}{2}\rho U^2$ $\quad$ (A1)

Reduced frequency $\quad \lambda = \omega r/U$ $\quad$ (A2)

Force coefficient
$$g(\lambda) = (F'/h')(H/\tfrac{1}{2}\rho U^2 r^2) \quad \text{(A3)}$$

$$\mathfrak{I}(g) = -(2\pi\lambda)(1-\text{sech }\epsilon)(1 + \lambda^2(1 - \text{sech }\epsilon))/(1 + \lambda^2\tanh^2\epsilon) \quad \text{(A4)}$$

$$= -2\pi\lambda \text{ as } \epsilon \to \infty \quad \text{(A5)}$$

A.2 UPSTREAM AND DOWNSTREAM SEALS

Throat velocity in seal U_t $\quad$ (A6)

Effective area ratio $\quad \mu = U/U_t$ $\quad$ (A7)

Overall pressure drop $\Delta P = \frac{1}{2}\rho U_t^2$ $\quad$ (A8)

Reduced frequency $\quad \lambda_t = \omega r/U_t$ $\quad$ (A9)

Force coefficient
$$g(\lambda_t) = (F'/h')(H/\tfrac{1}{2}\rho U_t^2 r^2) \quad \text{(A10)}$$

A.2.1 Upstream seal

$$\mathfrak{I}(g) = -(2\pi\lambda)(1-\text{sech }\epsilon)(2\nu-1+\nu\lambda^2(1-\text{sech }\epsilon))/(1 + \nu^2\lambda_t^2 \tanh^2 \epsilon) \quad \text{(A11)}$$

$$= + 2\pi\lambda_t, \; \nu \to 0, \; \epsilon \to \infty \quad \text{(A12)}$$

A.2.2 Downstream seal

$$\mathfrak{I}(g) = -(2\pi\lambda_t)(1-\text{sech }\epsilon)(\nu\lambda_t^2(1-\text{sech }\epsilon)-\nu^2(1-\nu)(1+\text{sech }\epsilon) + 1)/(1 + \nu^2\lambda_t^2 \tanh^2 \epsilon) \quad \text{(A13)}$$

$$= -2\pi\lambda_t, \quad \nu \to 0, \quad \epsilon \to \infty \qquad \text{(A14)}$$

A3 Unsteady flow parameter $\phi(\beta)$

$$1/\phi(\beta) = 1 + \{(\cos \beta - \cosh \beta) \times ((\sinh \beta + \sin \beta) - j(\sinh \beta - \sin \beta))\}/(\beta(\sinh^2\beta + \sin^2\beta)) \qquad \text{(A15)}$$

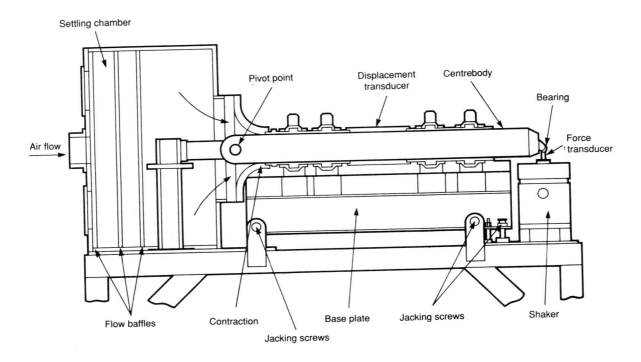

Fig. 1. Annular flow rig

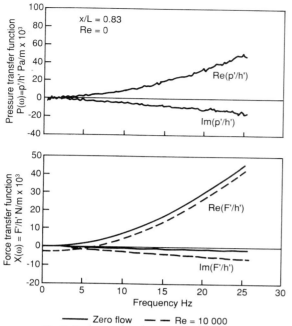

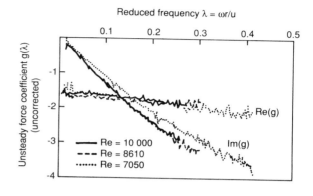

Fig. 3. Measurements of unsteady force coefficient at three turbulent Reynolds numbers

Fig. 2. Pressure and force transfer functions

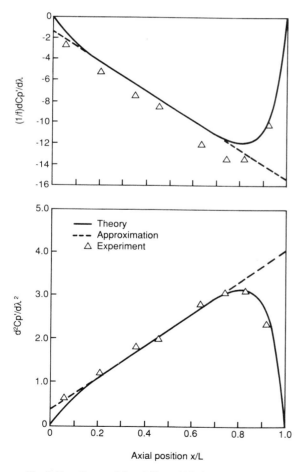

Fig. 4. Zero flow; axial variation of frictional and inertial pressures

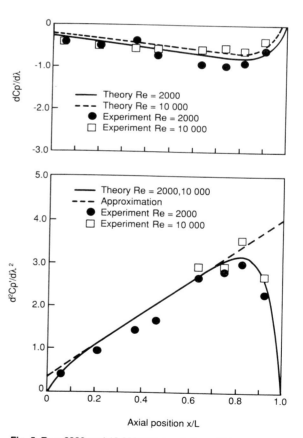

Fig. 5. Re = 2000 and 10 000; axial variation of frictional and inertial pressures

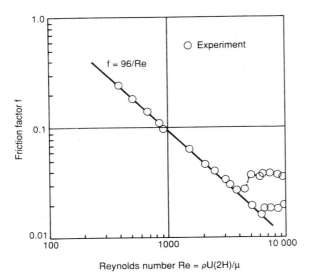

Fig. 6. Measured variation of friction factor with Reynolds number - smooth centrebody

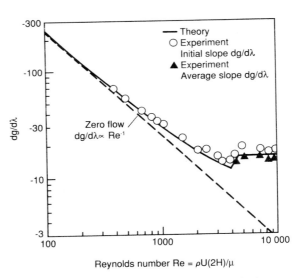

Fig. 7. Damping forces on the smooth centrebody

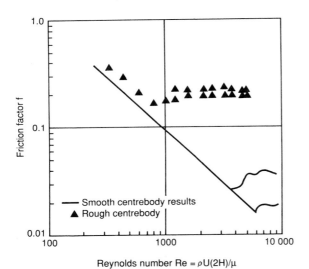

Fig. 8. Friction factor in the annulus with the rough centrebody

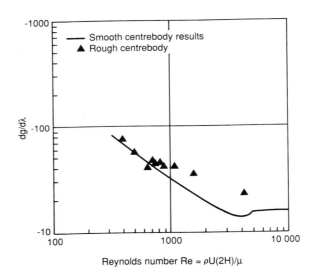

Fig. 9. Damping forces on the grooved centrebody

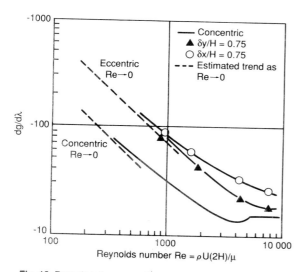

Fig. 10. Damping forces on the smooth centrebody - effect
of eccentricity

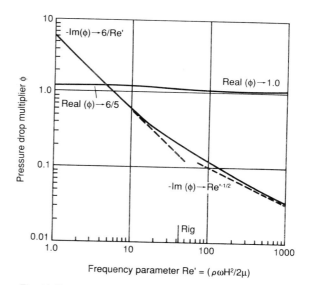

Fig. 11. Unsteady pressure drop at high frequencies: effect
of frequency parameter Re' on pressure drop multiplier φ

C416/050

Experimental investigations of the unsteady annular flow between concentric and eccentric oscillating cylinders

M P PAIDOUSSIS, PhD, CEng, FIMechE, FRSC, FASME, FCSME, MIAHR,
D MATEESCU, PhD, MAIAA, W-G SIM, ME and F BELANGER
Department of Mechanical Engineering, McGill University, Montreal, Quebec, Canada

SYNOPSIS Experiments have been conducted on two apparata involving a cylindrical 'centre–body' and a containing pipe with airflow in the annular passage. In the first apparatus, the inner cylindrical body was oscillated by a shaker in rocking motion about a hinge–point. The unsteady pressure generated by the oscillations was measured on the wall of the oscillating cylinder and on the immobile containing pipe, at various axial and azimuthal locations. Both amplitude and phase, with respect to the oscillations, were measured and compared with theoretical predictions, and agreement was found to be within 10%. In the second apparatus, the outer pipe is oscillated, while measurements of pressure are taken on the inner cylinder. Either lateral translational or rocking motion was imposed. In the equilibrium configuration the two bodies are either concentric or eccentric, in the plane of oscillation or normal to it. Experiments with translational oscillation have shown that the effect of flow velocity on the unsteady pressure is minimal, for low flow velocities (Re $\simeq$ 3 000) and low amplitudes (displacement/radius $\simeq$ 0.04). Agreement between theory and experiment is reasonably good (within 10%).

1 INTRODUCTION

Cylindrical structures subjected to annular flow are widely used in many engineering systems. For sufficiently high flow velocities the structural components in such arrangements have frequently developed self–excited oscillations, sometimes severe and occasionally destructive (1–12). It was therefore natural that this topic would come to be intensively studied by an increasing number of researchers (1–15).

The dynamics of a flexibly–mounted rigid cylinder, or "centre–body", in a co–axial duct of variable cross–section, with flow in the narrow annular passage was first investigated by Hobson and co–workers (6, 13), both theoretically and experimentally. It was shown that, for sufficiently high flow velocities, oscillatory instabilities of the centre–body developed; with some empirical input, the theoretical model was capable of predicting the observed behaviour quite well.

The two leading authors have initiated an integrated theoretical–experimental research programme in this subject as of 1983. The analytical model they have developed for narrow annular passages was initially for purely potential flow (14); then, unsteady viscous effects were taken into account approximately (15); subsequently, the analysis was further extended to deal, again approximately, with unsteady turbulent flows (16). In these studies, the centre–body was considered to be rigid and flexibly mounted about a hinge, so that it could undergo rocking motions in the annular passage; however, the dynamics and stability of a flexible centre–body (a cylindrical beam) have also been studied (17). More recently, computational fluid–dynamic (CFD) techniques have been applied to this task (18), the intention being that, eventually, the fluid dynamics of the problem would be formulated via full unsteady solutions of the Navier-Stokes equations.

In parallel to the foregoing, the problem has been studied experimentally (16, 19, 20). In the experiments, a rigid, cylindrical centre–body was forced to oscillate in a rocking mode with respect to the outer conduit which was rigid and immobile, with air–flow in the annulus. Provided that the theory with which the experiments were compared was sufficiently refined, agreement between the two was very close — see, for example, Ref. (16). Some of these experimental results will be re–examined, together with those of a new set of experiments. Hence, further discussion of the experiments, measurement techniques, and comparison with theory will be presented in subsequent sections of this paper.

2 EXPERIMENTAL APPARATA

2.1 The first apparatus

The experiments to–date have been performed on two apparata; the earlier of the two, already referred to in the foregoing, is shown diagrammatically in Fig. 1. The meshes, honeycomb and upstream ogive help to render the approach flow to the hinged centre–body as uniform as possible. The centre–body was a rigid hollow cylinder with rounded end–caps, which was forced to oscillate about one of three possible locations of a hinge by an electrodynamic shaker (B & K 4801 and 4812). The shaker was connected to the centre–body through the hinge, via a set of linkages. Details of this apparatus may be found in Ref. (19).

The measurements taken were of (i) the unsteady pressure on the surface of the oscillating centre–body and, across the annular gap, on the outer fixed pipe, and (ii) the oscillation of the centre–body by an accelerometer (B & K 4381) mounted within the centre–body. The pressure measurements were made via semiconductor differential pressure transducers (Kulite PTQH–360–1D), with sensitivity of 8.7 mV/kPa (60 mV/psi) for pressures up to 6.9 kPa (1 psi); these transducers were found to have good linearity and repeatability both for steady and unsteady measurements and, when mounted within the oscillating centre–body, negligible acceleration sensitivity. The air–flow velocity was measured by obvious means (Fig. 1).

The following parameters were varied in the experiments: (a) oscillation frequency, (b) oscillation amplitude, (c) flow velocity, (d) hinge position, (e) axial location of the pressure transducer on the centre–body, and (f) azimuthal location of the transducer. The centre-body radius, a, was 44.5 mm and the annular gap, H, was 4.85 mm in all tests, so that the ratio $h \equiv H/a = 0.109$ was constant throughout. The possible ranges of oscillation frequency and amplitude were limited by shaker characteristics (20); thus, although at low frequencies absolute amplitude control was possible, at higher frequencies the shaker operated in a constant-acceleration mode — resulting in peculiar pressure-amplitude versus frequency results (see, for example, Figs. 3 and 4 to be discussed later), entirely due to this peculiarity of the shaker system. Most of these measurements have been presented in earlier papers (16, 19), but some typical results will nevertheless be discussed in Section 3, together with those obtained from the newer apparatus.

2.2 The newer apparatus

In the older apparatus, only rocking motion of the centre–body was possible. It was therefore considered desirable to construct a new apparatus in which rocking and lateral motion would be equally feasible — where "lateral motion" is understood to mean motion transverse to the flow, such that the sides of the two cylindrical bodies remain parallel to each other. At the same time, several other, equally important modifications were introduced in the design, as follows: (a) the possibility of having axial variations in the annular passage, either smooth or abrupt; (b) the possibility of conducting experiments with eccentric arrangements, with oscillation either in the plane of eccentricity or normal to it; (c) the facility of having very low flow velocities, so that flow in the annulus would be laminar rather than turbulent.

To accommodate all these possibilities it was found convenient, in this new apparatus, to oscillate part of the *outer* cylindrical conduit, while the centre–body remains immobile, as shown diagrammatically in Fig. 2. So far, experiments have been conducted only with the cylindrical annular passage, as depicted in Fig. 2, in which the centre–body outer radius and outer-pipe inner radius, were $a = 44.5$ mm and $b = 53.8$ mm, respectively. The oscillation of the outer cylinder could be purely transverse or of the rocking type, in which case oscillation was about a hinge. Obviously, there is relative motion between the oscillating part of the outer cylinder and the immobile one. The "obvious" solution of utilizing flexible rubber seals was found unsatisfactory, because locked–in stresses in the rubber seals combined with the slight flexibility in the shaker actuator to give rise to small but important asymmetries to the desired motion. For sufficiently low flow velocities, and relatively low annular pressure differences vis–à–vis the ambient one, the arrangement shown in Fig. 2(b) was found to be a superior solution to the sealing problem, although not achieving a total seal; the closed arrangement of Fig. 2(c) was occasionally used, but only with zero mean flow in the annulus.

The oscillation of the outer cylinder was measured by an accelerometer (B & K 4381) on the yoke supporting the movable part of the outer pipe. The unsteady pressure was measured simultaneously at six locations along the immobile centre–body by internally mounted piezoelectric pressure transducers (PCB 112A22).

In addition to the blower that was used in the previous experiments for high flows, a small vacuum–cleaner blower was used, either in the blow– or suction–mode, to generate laminar, or low–velocity turbulent flows in the test section.

2.3 Signal processing

The signals from the pressure transducers and accelerometers were processed through a dual–channel FFT digital signal analyzer (H–P 3582A). The amplitude of either signal could be obtained from the power spectrum, while the phase difference between pressure and acceleration could similarly be obtained from the cross–spectrum of these two quantities. This instrument could accept signals of very low level without special conditioning, a distinct advantage, since in some of the experiments the pressure signal was as low as 2 mV.

3 EXPERIMENTAL RESULTS AND COMPARISON WITH THEORY

3.1 Experiments with rocking motion

Typical results for rocking motion of the centre–body, obtained with the earlier apparatus, are shown in Figs. 3 and 4.

For the experiments of Fig. 3 the hinge was at $L_o = 115$ mm, while the centre–body length was $L = 421$ mm, so that $L_o/L = 0.273$. The pressure transducer was located at $x/L = 0.591$ at various azimuthal orientations, θ — where $\theta = 0$ corresponds to the plane of oscillation. ΔP is the differential pressure across a diameter of the centre–body, and ψ is the phase angle of this pressure measured with respect to centre–body acceleration. The results shown are for two flow velocities, $U = 52.4$ and 73.0 m/s in the annulus, which corresponds to Reynolds numbers, Re = 34 980 and 48 730, clearly in the turbulent regime.

Several features of the experimental results should be commented upon, as follows.

(a) The peculiar shape of the ΔP versus f curve has already been touched upon; no special significance should be placed on it, as it is entirely a function of the shaker–head vibration amplitude, Δz. This amplitude (19) was virtually constant up to $f \simeq 35$ Hz; hence, in this case, the increase in ΔP with f is real. For $f > 35$ Hz, the vibration amplitude Δz decreased more–or–less linearly with f, so that, at maximum f, it was only about 15% the value at $f < 35$ Hz. Thus, the decrease in ΔP beyond $f \simeq 35$ Hz simply reflects the sharply decreasing Δz. Had the ratio $\Delta P/\Delta z$ been plotted versus f, one would have seen a nearly quadratically increasing curve with increasing f. This, in turn, reflects the dependence of ΔP on body velocity (and acceleration) as predicted by theory — even potential theory (14).

(b) The values of ΔP decrease with increasing θ. This is physically reasonable. One would expect the pressure to be maximum in the plane of oscillation, $\theta = 0$, and to steadily decrease to zero at $\theta = 90°$. This latter point could not be confirmed, as for $\theta > 75°$ the pressure levels became of the order of the resolution of the transducer.

(c) The phase is a function of frequency, being largest (in the absolute sense) at low frequencies and smallest at the high frequencies. (The scale of the ordinate is very compact; the variation of ψ versus θ is quite substantial.) The results suggest that as f is increased, the value of ψ appears to tend towards some asymptote, of the order of $-80°$.[1]

(d) The phase angle is a weak function of θ. This is consistent with the global character of the flow as the centre–body undergoes oscillation, which, incidentally, was successfully utilized in the theory to obtain an approximation to the unsteady viscous forces (15). This is the reason why only one theoretical line for ψ is given. (Obviously, if the flow had been more "local" in character, ψ would display a larger variation with θ, and hence a larger discrepancy with theory.)

Similar results are shown in Fig. 4, in this case with the hinge at $L_o/L = 0.499$ and the pressure transducer at $x/L = 0.658$. Similar comments as for Fig. 3 may be made on the experimental results. However, in this case the theoretical values for both the inviscid (14) and the viscous theory with turbulence taken into account (16) are given.

It is clear from Figs. 3 and 4 that if the viscous theory, with turbulent stresses taken into account, is used, then agreement between theory and experiment, both in terms of amplitude and phase of ΔP is excellent. If potential flow theory is used instead, then agreement with experimental amplitudes is still quite good; however, the discrepancy in the phase becomes unacceptablly large.

Another region of disagreement between theory and experiment is for pressure measurements near the extremities of the oscillating centre–body (e.g., for $x/L = 0.824$). It is obvious that in the course of the oscillation, the extremities of the body protrude into the flow, creating a discontinuity at that point which could not properly be accounted for by the theory (19).

The ultimate objective of the analytical effort is to develop theoretical models for accurately predicting the flow field about oscillating bodies in annular flow, either turbulent or laminar. The latter situation is especially important in applications involving very narrow annuli.

It was therefore important to have experimental data for systems in *laminar* annular flow, or low–intensity turbulent flow. Preliminary results with the new apparatus are shown in Fig. 5, in which $L_o/L = 0.237$ ($L = 965$ mm); it is recalled that in this case the outer pipe oscillates in rocking motion, while the centre–body remains put.

Since, several pressure transducers are available, in this case one can look at the axial variation of the signal with distance away from the hinge, along the centre–body. The flow velocity in this case was very low, just beyond transition to turbulence (Re $\simeq$ 3 000). The amplitude of oscillation was 1.00 mm for the results of Fig. 5(a) and 0.75 mm for those of Fig. 5(b) at the point of shaking, 558.8 mm from the hinge.

As may be seen in Fig. 5 the pressure increases more or less linearly with distance away from the hinge–point. In the case of the higher frequency, Fig. 5(b), agreement with this linearity condition is better; this is, at least partially, due to the slightly higher pressure readings, and hence better signal–to–noise ratios. This is further supported by the large discrepancy (in terms of percent) at low x/L: although this may be partly due to 'end effects', it is undoubtedly also related to low signal levels close to the hinge–point.

The theoretical results have been obtained by means of 2–D potential flow theory (18), in which the pressure is taken to be linearly proportional to amplitude of motion — which explains the perfectly linear theoretical result. This approximation is valid for high enough frequencies (or, more precisely, high enough S — see Section 3.2). Agreement between theory and experiment is seen to be very good, excepting the two readings in of the low-frequency test, Fig. 5(a), close to the ends of the moving pipe, which were probably affected by end effects due to local discontinuities in the flow, as well as low signal–to–noise ratios in the case of small x/L.

3.2 Experiments with lateral translation motion

All these experiments were conducted in the new apparatus, where it is recalled yet again that the outer pipe oscillates, while the centre–body on which the pressure measurements are taken remains immobile. Experiments have been conducted with the following arrangements: (i) with the centre–body concentrically mounted vis-à-vis the outer pipe; (ii) with the centre–body eccentrically mounted and motion in the plane of eccentricity; (iii) in the same eccentric arrangement as for (ii) but with motion normal to the plane of eccentricity.

The experimental results for these three cases are shown, respectively, in Figs. 6, 7 and 8. It is recalled that $a = 44.5$ mm and $b = 53.8$ mm (Section 2.2). Thus, for the concentric arrangement (Fig. 6), the gap/radius ratio was $h = 0.21$. For the eccentric arrangement (Figs. 7 and 8), the dimensionless eccentricity $e = $ (eccentricity) $/ (b - a) = 0.50$. In the experiments involving flow, the arrangement of Fig. 2(b) was used between the moving and stationary parts of the outer pipe. This arrangement, as mentioned in Section 2, achieves acceptable sealing and gives pressure readings along the centre–body relatively free of three–dimensional effects — see Ref. (21); the gap between the two blocks shown in the figure was less than 1 mm. In the case of zero flow, the arrangement of Fig. 2(c) was used.

In the experiments with axial flow, the flow velocity in all three cases was low ($U \simeq 2.2$ m/s), so that Re $\simeq 2$ 900. Although this is not low enough for laminar flow, it nevertheless represents a low turbulence–level flow. The data points shown in each case represent the average

---

[1]For a mathematical oscillator the phase difference of velocity to acceleration is $-90°$; hence, if the real part of the pressure signal were totally dominated by acceleration at high frequencies and the imaginary part by velocity, since $\psi = \text{Im}(\Delta P)/\text{Re}(\Delta P)$ one would expect something similar. However, the system is much more complex than that.

obtained by the six pressure transducers in the plane of the θ concerned.[2]

A final remark concerns the presentation of the results. Because of the different transducers utilized in this case (as compared to the earlier apparatus) the pressures here (and in Fig. 5) are the point rather than differential pressures. Moreover, unlike previous results, in this case P was plotted versus θ with f as a parameter, rather than the other way around as in the foregoing. In fact, because there were small variations in amplitude of motion for the tests as θ was varied, the ordinate is a dimensionless pressure defined by

$$\hat{p} = \frac{P}{\rho \omega^2 a^2 \epsilon}, \tag{1}$$

where P is the measured pressure, ρ the fluid density, a the radius of the centrebody, and ϵ is the dimensionless lateral amplitude of motion (non-dimensionalized with respect to a).

The following observations may be made with regard to the experimental results in Figs 6–8.

(a) The measured unsteady pressure distributions are symmetric or skew-symmetric about $\theta = 90^o$, as expected.

(b) The pressure readings increase with frequency. Shaker and apparatus limitations forced the experimenters to diminish the vibration amplitude as the frequency was increased; because of the non-dimensional plotting in this case, involving both the frequency ω and the amplitude ϵ, this is not obvious. Hence, it is instructive to consider the *dimensional* pressure P. If it is assumed that P is linearly proportional to vibration amplitude, then *the adjusted* (mean) amplitude goes from 23.1 Pa to 36.1 and 58.9 Pa, as f goes from 41.6 to 52 and 66.4 Hz, respectively (the three panels of Fig. 6). Similar conclusions may be reached with regard to Figs. 7 and 8.

(c) At these low flow velocities and for this type of motion, there is very little difference in the readings at zero and non-zero annular flow velocity. This means that the unsteady pressure field for purely transverse flow is dominated by the oscillation-induced cross-flow.

The experimental results are compared with the theoretical ones obtained by the method of Ref. (18) for potential flow theory. As discussed by Chen et al. (22) for sufficiently high values of S ($= \omega a^2 / \nu$, ω being the oscillation frequency, a the radius and ν the kinematic viscosity), $S > 15\,000$ approximately, it is possible to neglect viscous effects with little loss of accuracy. For the case of these experiments, $35\,620 < S < 56\,860$ is clearly sufficiently large. It is seen in Figures 6–8 that agreement between theory and experiment is good.

For these experiments, the reader will have noticed that no results are presented of the phase difference between motion and no comparisons with theory have been made.

The reason for this is twofold: (i) for the high values of S involved, the theoretical phase difference was $|\psi| < 7^o$ throughout; (ii) in the experiments, an accurate reading of ψ was difficult. The cause of this latter difficulty is related to the fact that pressure levels were generally rather low, and hence signal-to-noise ratios were not as high as desired.

4 CONCLUSION

A set of experiments was described, designed to test the analytical tools developed concurrently for the motion-related unsteady pressure in annular passages.

Two experimental apparata were utilized: in the first, the motion involved rocking of the centre-body in the annulus; in the second, the outer channel was oscillated, either transversely to the flow or in the rocking mode. Experiments were conducted mainly in the concentric arrangement of outer channel and centre-body, but some experiments were also performed in eccentric arrangements. The amplitude and frequency of oscillation were varied, as well as the flow velocity.

Throughout, the experimental unsteady pressure measurements were compared to the theoretical ones. For experiments in high Re flow, the theory developed in which the viscous forces and turbulent stresses have been taken into account (16) was found to be in excellent agreement with experiment. For turbulent flow of relatively low Reynolds number, potential flow theory was found to be adequate (14, 18).

One aspect of the experimental results which, by its nature, is difficult to report in detail, but which should nevertheless be stressed here, is the importance of 'end effects'. In the rocking-mode experiments in the first apparatus, the inevitable time-dependent protrusion of the ends of the oscillating centre-body into the flow generated pressure readings which were quite different from the rest (and from the theoretical predictions). Similarly, in 'lateral', transverse motion of the outer channel in the second apparatus, the local discontinuities at the two ends of the moving part could make a great deal of difference to the pressure readings, mainly in the vicinity of these discontinuities, but sometimes considerably further in. Of course, the theory is for uniform or at least smooth flow and cannot adequately account for these effects. Nevertheless, these experimental results highlight the importance of these effects, which are also present in engineering systems; hence, the importance of the next phase of our work, which deals with nonuniform and/or discontinuous annular flow passages becomes self-evident. A recent paper of Hobson and Jedwab (23) shows how intricate and challenging the flow can be in non-uniform annular passages.

In all these experiments, interest has been focussed on measurements of the unsteady pressure. This was found to be a reliable and convenient way of testing the theory. Once the motion-related unsteady pressure is known, the forces acting on the moving parts of the annular flow passage may easily be calculated; hence, the stability of the centre-body may then be evaluated — see also Refs. (15, 17).

---

[2]The range of uncertainty in the results, i.e. the maximum variation between pressure measurements from the six transducers, was less than ± 0.4 nondimensional units of $\hat{p}$, defined by equation (1).

REFERENCES

(1) PAÏDOUSSIS, M.P. Flow–induced vibrations in nuclear reactors and heat exchangers: Practical experiences and state of knowledge. In *Practical Experiences with Flow-Induced Vibration* (eds E. Naudascher and D. Rockwell), 1980, 1–81. Berlin: Springer–Verlag.

(2) PAÏDOUSSIS, M.P. Flow–induced instabilities of cylindrical structures. *Applied Mechanics Reviews*, 1987, 40, 163–175.

(3) MILLER, D.R. Generation of positive and negative damping with a flow restrictor in axial flow. In *Proceedings of Conference on Flow–Induced Vibrations in Reactor System Components*. Argonne National Laboratory Report ANL-7685, 1970, pp. 304–307. Argonne, Illinois, U.S.A.

(4) PARKIN, M.W. A review of basic studies and modelling applied to annular flow. In *Proceedings UKAEA/NPL International Symposium on Vibration Problems in Industry*, 1973, Paper No. 628. Keswick, U.K.

(5) ROBERTS, G.P., HALLAM, M.G., DEAN, R.B. and PARKIN, M.W. A theoretical study of Hartlepool AGR stringer vibration during refuelling at power. In *Proceedings 3rd International Conference on Vibration of Nuclear Plant*, 1982, pp. 624–648. Keswick, U.K.

(6) HOBSON, D.E. Fluid–elastic instabilities caused by flow in an annulus. In *Proceedings 3rd International Conference on Vibration of Nuclear Plant*, 1982, pp. 440–463. Keswick, U.K.

(7) TORRES, M.R. Flow–induced vibration of BWR feedwater spargers. In *Flow–induced vibrations of Power Plant Components* (ed. M.K. Au–Yang), 1980, pp. 159–176. New York: ASME.

(8) MULCAHY, T.M. A review of leakage–flow–induced vibrations of reactor components. Argonne National Laboratory Report ANL–83–43, 1983. Argonne, Illinois, U.S.A.

(9) SAVKAR, S.D. Fluid–elastic vibrations of a slip joint — a model problem. In *Flow–induced Vibration Design Guidelines* (ed. P.Y. Chen), 1981, pp. 127–133. New York: ASME.

(10) LACROIX, L.V. Flow–induced vibration characteristics of BWR/5201 jet pump. General Electric Nuclear Engineering Division Report GEAP 22211, 1982.

(11) PAÏDOUSSIS, M.P. and AU–YANG, M.K. (eds) *ASME Symposium on Flow-Induced Vibration; Vol. 4: Vibration Induced by Axial and Annular Flows*, 1984. New York: ASME.

(12) PAÏDOUSSIS, M.P., AU–YANG, M.K. and CHEN, S.S. (eds) *ASME/CSME/IMechE/IAHR Int'l Symposium on Flow-Induced Vibration and Noise; Vol. 4: Flow-Induced Vibrations due to Internal and Annular Flows, and Special Topics in Fluidelasticity*, 1988. New York: ASME.

(13) SPUR, A. and HOBSON, D.E. Forces on the vibrating centrebody of an annular diffuser. In Ref. (11), 1988, pp. 41–52.

(14) MATEESCU, D. and PAÏDOUSSIS, M.P. The unsteady potential flow in an axially variable annulus and its effect on the dynamics of the oscillating rigid center–body. *ASME Journal of Fluids Engineering*, 1985, 107, 421–427.

(15) MATEESCU, D. and PAÏDOUSSIS, M.P. Unsteady viscous effects on the annular–flow–induced instabilities of a rigid cylindrical body in a narrow duct. *Journal of Fluids and Structures*, 1987, 1, 197–215.

(16) MATEESCU, D., PAÏDOUSSIS, M.P. and BELANGER, F. A theoretical model compared with experiments for the unsteady pressure on a cylinder oscillating in turbulent annular flow. *Journal of Sound and Vibration*, 1989, 135, 487–498.

(17) PAÏDOUSSIS, M.P., MATEESCU, D. and SIM, W.–G. Dynamics and stability of a flexible cylinder in a narrow coaxial cylindrical duct subjected to annular flow. *Journal of Applied Mechanics*, 1990, 57, 232–240.

(18) MATEESCU, D., PAÏDOUSSIS, M.P. and SIM, W.–G. CFD solutions for steady viscous and unsteady potential flow between eccentric cylinders. In *Proceedings of Int'l Symposium on Nonsteady Fluid Dynamics* (eds J.A. Miller and D.P. Telionis), 1990, pp. 235–242. New York: ASME.

(19) MATEESCU, D., PAÏDOUSSIS, M.P. and BELANGER, F. Unsteady pressure measurements on an oscillating cylinder in a narrow annular flow. *Journal of Fluids and Structures*, 1988, 2, 615–628.

(20) MATEESCU, D., PAÏDOUSSIS, M.P. and BELANGER, F. Experiments on the unsteady flow around an oscillating cylinder. *AIAA 15th Aerodynamic Testing Conference*, San Diego, Calif., May 1988, Paper AIAA 880–2031.

(21) MULCAHY, T.M. Fluid forces on rods vibrating in finite length annular regions. *Journal of Applied Mechanics*, 1980, 47, 234–240.

(22) CHEN, S.S., WAMBSGANSS, M.W. and JENDRZEJCZYK, J.A. Added mass and damping of a vibrating rod in confined viscous fluid. *Journal of Applied Mechanics*, 1976, 43, 325–329.

(23) HOBSON, D.E. and JEDWAB, M. Investigations of the effect of eccentricity on the unsteady fluid forces on the centrebody of an annular diffuser. *Journal of Fluids and Structures*, 1990, 4, 155–169.

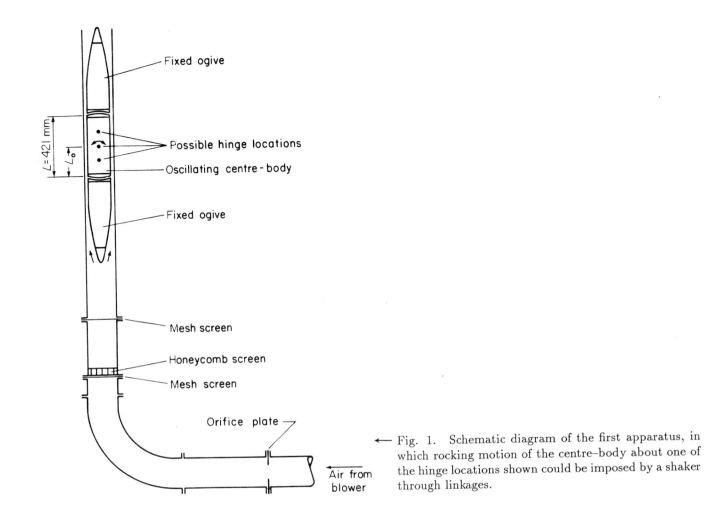

$\leftarrow$ Fig. 1. Schematic diagram of the first apparatus, in which rocking motion of the centre–body about one of the hinge locations shown could be imposed by a shaker through linkages.

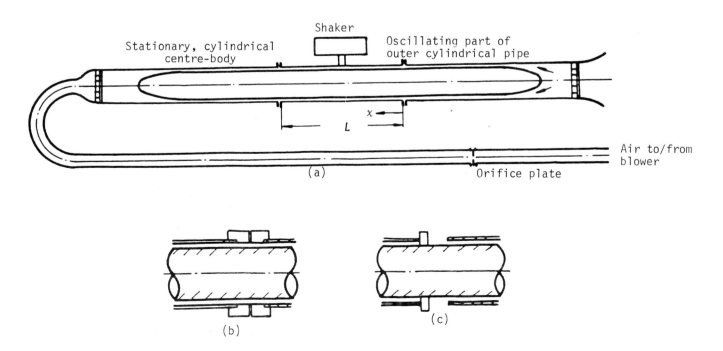

Fig. 2. (a) Schematic diagram of the newer apparatus in which either transverse or rocking motion of the central portion of the outer pipe could be imposed by the shaker. Sealing between the moving and stationary parts of the outer pipe was (b) through close–fitting rings, (c) through a positive, rubbing ring seal.

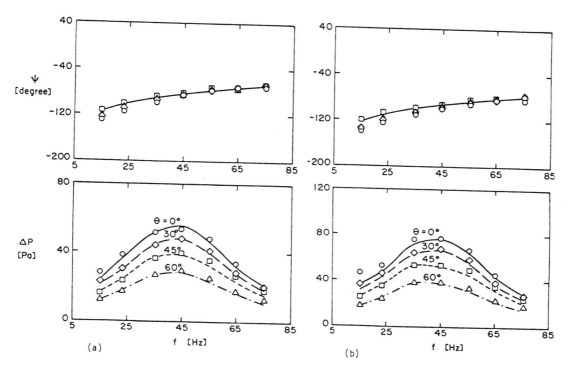

Fig. 3. Unsteady pressure measurements (amplitude ΔP and phase ψ) versus oscillation frequency, f, obtained with the earlier apparatus (Fig. 1), showing the influence of the circumferential position for $\theta = 0°, 30°, 45°$ and $60°$. Lines: unsteady viscous theory of Ref. (16); the theoretical phase does not depend on θ. Experiments: $\circ$, $\theta = 0°$; $\diamond$, $\theta = 30°$; $\square$, $\theta = 45°$; $\triangle$, $\theta = 60°$. (a) $U = 52.4$ m/s ; (b) $U = 73.0$ m/s.

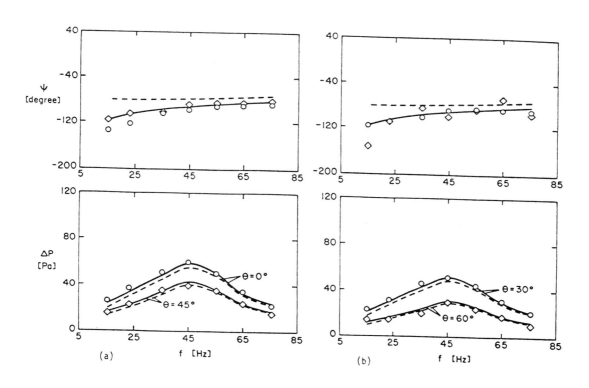

Fig. 4. Unsteady pressure measurements (amplitude ΔP and phase ψ) versus oscillation frequency, f, obtained with the earlier apparatus (Fig. 1), showing the effect of circumferential location θ for $L_0 = 210$ mm, $ax = 277$ mm and $U = 52.4$ m/s. - - - potential theory of Ref. (14) and ——— unsteady viscous theory of Ref. (16). Experiments: (a) $\circ$, $\theta = 0°$; $\diamond$, $\theta = 45°$; (b) $\circ$, $\theta = 30°$; $\triangle$, $\theta = 60°$.

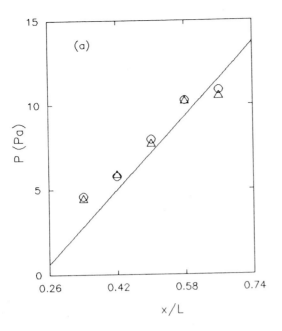

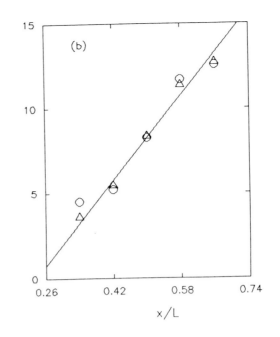

Fig. 5. Measured unsteady pressure amplitude, P, versus position along the centre–body, obtained with the newer apparatus (Fig. 2) in rocking motion, for $L_o = 229$ mm ($L = 965$ mm) and for frequency of oscillation (a) $f = 34.4$ Hz ($S = 29\,460$) and (b) $f = 42.6$ Hz ($S = 36\,480$). ———, potential flow theory; ○, experimental, with no axial flow; △, experimental with axial flow (Re $\simeq 3\,000$).

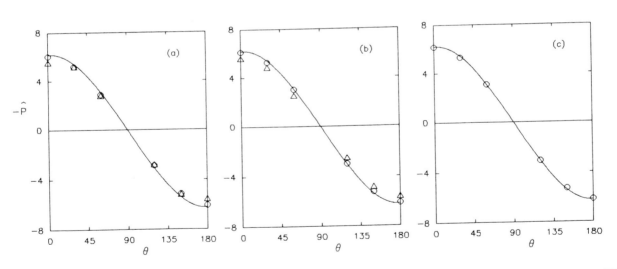

Fig. 6. Unsteady dimensionless pressures versus the azimuthal angle θ, obtained with the newer apparatus (Fig. 2) in translational lateral motion for a concentric arrangement. Oscillation frequency: (a) $f = 41.6$ Hz, (b) $f = 52.0$ Hz, (c) $f = 66.4$ Hz. ———, Potential flow theory; ○, experimental without axial flow; △, experimental with axial flow.

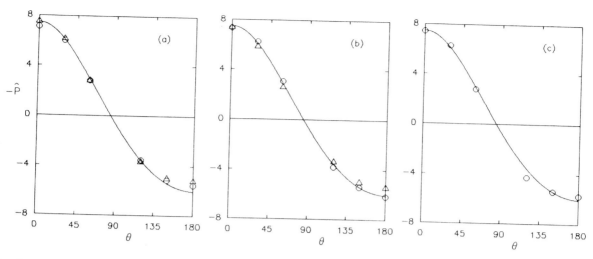

Fig. 7. Unsteady dimensionless pressures versus the azimuthal angle θ, obtained with the newer apparatus (Fig. 2) in translational lateral motion for an eccentric arrangement with oscillation in the plane of eccentricity; nondimensional eccentricity = 0.5. Oscillation frequency: (a) $f = 41.6$ Hz, (b) $f = 52.0$ Hz, (c) $f = 66.4$ Hz. _____ , Potential flow theory; o, experimental without axial flow; $\triangle$, experimental with axial flow.

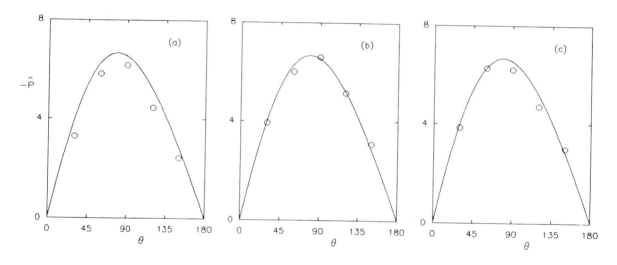

Fig. 8. Unsteady dimensionless pressures versus the azimuthal angle θ, obtained with the newer apparatus (Fig. 2) in translational lateral motion for an eccentric arrangement with oscillation normal to the plane of eccentricity; nondimensional eccentricity = 0.5. Oscillation frequency: (a) $f = 41.6$ Hz, (b) $f = 52.0$ Hz, (c) $f = 66.4$ Hz. _____ , Potential flow theory; o, experimental without axial flow; $\triangle$, experimental with axial flow.

C416/067

Heat exchanger fin failures caused by flow induced vibration

D S WEAVER, PhD and X Y HUANG, PhD
Department of Mechanical Engineering, McMaster University, Hamilton, Ontario, Canada

SYNOPSIS The failure of a number of fins of a large reciprocating compressor intercooler was studied. It appeared that leakage flow across the ends of the fins excited vibrations and eventually caused fatigue failures. Simple laboratory tests confirmed this excitation mechanism and the problem was cured by using sealing strips to prevent the leakage flow.

1. INTRODUCTION

The intercooler of a large two-stage reciprocating air compressor was found to have suffered severe damage to a number of its fins. While heat exchangers are known to be subject to flow induced vibration problems (1), the excitation mechanisms are generally associated with interaction of the cross-flow and the tubes (2,3). In the present case, the tubes were essentially rigid and the mean flow through the three pass intercooler was parallel to the damaged fins. The authors know of no similar heat exchanger problem which has been reported in the open literature.

This paper outlines the case history of these intercooler fin failures. The excitation mechanism and a method of prevention are then proposed. A simple laboratory experiment designed to confirm the proposed excitation mechanism is then described.

2. CASE HISTORY

The intercooler in question is between stages of a two-stage reciprocating compressor which is rated at 3000 cfm. The configuration is shown schematically in Figure 1. The tubes are 15.9mm o.d., 0.9m long, and arranged in a square pattern with a pitch ratio of 2.4. The array is 8 tubes wide by 8 tubes deep and there are 3 passes of somewhat different lengths between baffles. The nominal inlet and outlet temperatures of the air flowing across the tubes are 130°C and 40°C respectively, and the nominal outlet pressure is 220 kPa gauge. Unfortunately, the inlet pressure and the temperatures and pressures at locations between the passes were unknown. Rough calculations suggest that the mean velocity across the tubes is in excess of 15 m/s.

Each flow pass contains fins made of a copper-nickel alloy which are soldered to the tubes. These fins are 0.38mm thick, are spaced approximately 1.93 mm apart and are corrugated as shown in the schematic detail of Figure 2. In this configuration, the heat is transferred by the turbulent air passing parallel to the very large surface area of the fins and thence to the tubes.

An examination of the heat exchanger after some period of service showed severe damage to the fins adjacent to the baffles as indicated by the circled numbers in Figure 1. At location 1, there were 3 rows of fins with cracks and small sections missing adjacent to the baffle in pass 1. On the other side of the baffle in pass 2, there were 11 rows of fins which were either badly damaged or apparently missing altogether. Fins which were still intact had broken their joints with the tubes and could slide rather freely along the tubes. The second area of significant damage was adjacent to the baffle/support plate in pass 3 as noted by the circled 2 in Figure 1. In both locations, the damage was most severe immediately adjacent to the baffle/support plates. The large number of broken pieces of fin were swept downstream and either partially plugged the flow area of the next heat exchanger pass or carried on to the second compressor stage.

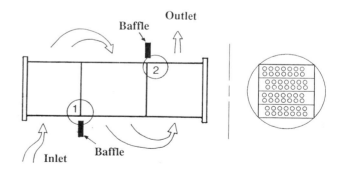

Fig. 1 Schematic of intercooler showing areas of damage.

2.1 Proposed Excitation Mechanism

It is clear that the excitation mechanism causing the fin failures is not one of the standard mechanisms associated with heat exchangers. The effect of the closely spaced fins is to make the tubes relatively rigid and certainly incapable of moving relative to one another. One candidate mechanism might be a type of fin flutter induced by parallel flow. However, this seems rather unlikely since the damaged fins are in areas in which the parallel flow velocity is expected to be the least. The turning of the flow in the baffle windows between passes will produce separation regions near the baffle/support plates and a non-uniform flow distribution across each pass. Fin damage due to flutter would be expected in regions of highest flow velocity, away from the baffle/support plates.

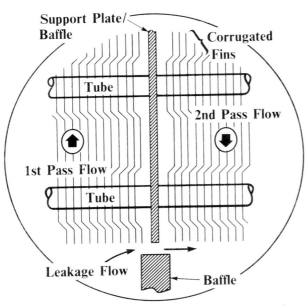

Fig. 2   Enlarged view of damage area 1 in Fig. 1.

Careful examination of figure 2 shows that the 2.5mm gap between the baffles and the tube support plate/baffle provides a leakage flow path between heat exchanger passes. The resulting jet will pass across the ends of the fins which form a succession of deep cavities as shown in Figure 3. It is well known that oscillations of a shear layer across a cavity exhibit selective amplification of certain frequencies and can be self-sustaining in the presence of a suitable feedback mechanism (4-7). In this case, the feedback mechanism could be the oscillations of the fins at their natural frequency. While shear layer excitation with fluidelastic feedback has not been reported previously for such a configuration, it has been reported for metal bellows (8). Given the location of the fin damage adjacent to the baffle/support plates, this excitation mechanism would appear to be the most likely candidate.

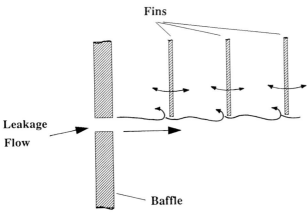

Fig. 3   Leakage flow across ends of fins.

2.2   Feasibility Study and Recommended Fix

It remains to do some simple calculations to determine if the proposed excitation mechanism is a feasible explanation. The shear layer oscillations past a cavity are usually characterized using an empirically determined dimensionless Strouhal number, S.

$$S = \frac{f\ell}{V} \qquad (1)$$

where f is the frequency of the shear layer oscillation in Hertz, ℓ is the characteristic shear layer length and V is the free stream flow velocity across the cavity. For a deep cavity, the Strouhal number is about 0.45 or an integer multiple of this for shear layer frequency harmonics. Self-sustaining oscillations will occur in this case when the frequency, f, is equal to one of the fin natural frequencies.

An estimate of the lowest fin natural frequency can be made by assuming that the extension of the fin past the last bend is a cantilevered plate, 9.5mm long by 0.38mm thick. This gives a fundamental frequency of about 2800 Hz. Using the spacing between fins as the shear layer length, $\ell = 1.93$mm, and a Strouhal number of 0.45, equation 1 gives a resonance flow velocity of approximately 12 m/s. Even the most conservative estimate of the pressure drop between intercooler passes would produce leakage flow velocities in excess of this.

The rough calculations suggest that impinging shear layer flow across the ends of the fins could very well have caused the severe fin damage experienced by this intercooler. Thus, the vibration problem can be eliminated simply by preventing the leakage flow across the ends of the fins. It was recommended that sealing strips be placed on the upstream side of the leakage gap so that the pressure drop across the strip would tend to increase the effectiveness of the seal.

3.   LABORATORY STUDY

The evidence outlined in the previous section suggests that the intercooler fin failures were caused by leakage flow shear layer oscillations with fluidelastic feedback. However, the calculations were based on engineering approximations and such multiple fin oscillations have apparently not been studied before. Therefore, it was thought desirable to conduct a confirmatory laboratory test. As the intent of the experiments was to demonstrate the existence of the phenomenon, no attempt was made to model the intercooler fins precisely. Rather, they were represented as a series of 3 cantilevered plates downstream of a rectangular slit as shown in Figure 4.

The model fins were made from 0.7mm thick steel sheet, were 100mm wide and cantilevered 50mm from a solid base. The base permitted the spacing between fins to be varied. The slit was 6mm wide and 110mm long in a 25mm thick plate and was arranged such that the jet flow through the slit passed across the ends of the fins. This test section was placed between two acrylic pipes upstream of a roots-type blower. The "wind-tunnel" pipes were kept short so that any organ pipe acoustic frequencies in the pipe were well separated from the fin natural frequencies.

Additionally, the blower was separated from the "wind-tunnel" by an acoustic absorption plenum so that no blower noise contaminated the test section flow. Flow velocity control was achieved by adjusting the rotational speed of the blower.

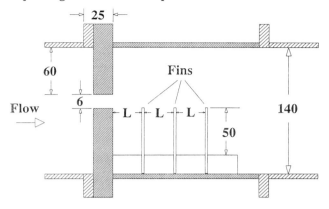

Fig. 4   Laboratory model of fins with flow across ends.

3.1   Experimental Procedure

Preliminary tests were conducted using 1 to 5 fins and it was found that 3 fins provided representative results. Thus, the experiments reported here are for 3 fins as shown in Figure 4. The velocity used to report the data was that measured by a carefully calibrated hot wire located in the centre of the jet and 2mm downstream of the slit exit plane. Shear layer oscillations were measured using a hot wire probe located in the gap between the slit and the first fin. The probe could be moved around in the gap so that very clear oscillation signals were obtained. Fin vibration response was measured using a strain gauge mounted near the base of the first fin downstream of the slit. All signals were processed using a Fourier analyzer. The shear layer fin oscillation frequencies and magnitudes were obtained from the peaks of spectra obtained from 40 sample averages. Data were obtained starting at some low flow velocity. The velocity was then incremented and the data collection repeated after a steady state had been achieved.

3.2   Experimental Results and Discussion

The experiments were repeated for fin spacings of 9.5mm and 15mm and the results are shown in Figures 5 and 6 respectively. Figure 5(a) shows that the shear layer oscillation frequency increases nearly linearly with flow velocity up to about 9.5m/s whereupon it jumps to a new line with a larger slope. Figure 5(b) indicates that when the shear layer oscillation frequency matches the fin natural frequencies, 218Hz and 685Hz, a large resonant fin response is produced. During this resonance, the shear layer oscillation frequency "locks-on" to the fin natural frequency and deviates from the natural linear relationship with flow velocity.

Figures 6(a) and (b) show essentially the same behaviour as described above. However, in this case, (a) jumps in the linear shear layer oscillation frequency vs. flow velocity relationship occur at 5.3m/s and 9.7m/s. Fin resonance peaks are seen in the first three fin modes, 218Hz, 685Hz and 1405Hz.

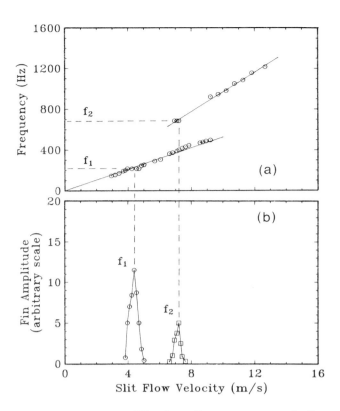

Fig. 5   Flow oscillation frequency and fin amplitude response, fin spacing 9.5mm.

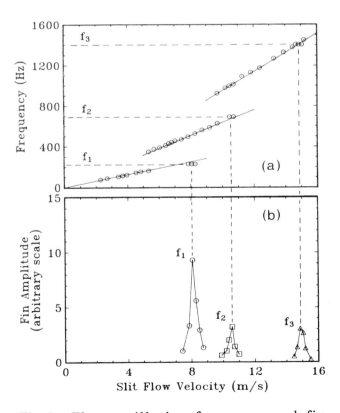

Fig. 6   Flow oscillation frequency and fin amplitude response, fin spacing 15mm.

These data can be better understood by plotting dimensionless frequency against flow velocity as shown in Figure 7. In this figure, the characteristic length, ℓ, is taken as the spacing between the fins. this dimensionless frequency is called the Strouhal number which is seen to be essentially constant over the flow velocity range tested. The Reynolds number based on the maximum slit velocity and the width of the slit is about 10^5. The Strouhal numbers in Figure 7 are about 0.48, 0.95 and 1.43, almost exactly in the ratios 1:2:3.

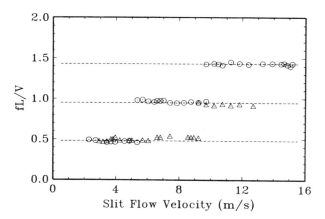

Fig. 7   Strouhal number vs. flow velocity;
Δ 9.5mm fin spacing, **O** 15mm spacing.

This behaviour of constant Strouhal numbers and frequency jumps to integer multiple Strouhal numbers with increasing flow velocity are characteristic of impinging shear layer oscillations (see, for example, Rockwell and Naudascher (5)). The lowest Strouhal number is associated with one vortex or wave on the shear layer between points of flow separation and reattachment. Each successive Strouhal number is associated with another vortex or wave, which gives rise to their integer multiple relationship. Such behaviour is clearly shown in the flow visualization photographs by Weaver and Huang (9) of shear layer oscillations between two orifice plates. The Strouhal number of 0.48 is in the range expected for flow over a single deep cavity (6) and is close to that used in the calculations of the previous section.

The model fins used in this experiment are simple cantilevered plates with well separated natural frequencies. Thus, their flow induced resonances appear as distinct peaks with regions of flow velocity where no significant vibrations occur. The actual intercooler fins are quite complicated and probably have a large number of relatively closely spaced natural frequencies. Therefore, it would be reasonable to expect that significant fin vibration response would occur at all flow velocities beyond that required to induce resonance in the first mode. This type of behaviour is observed for bellows (8).

These simple experiments show that significant resonant fin vibration can be caused by their interaction with an impinging shear layer and provide support for the proposal that this mechanism was responsible for the intercooler fin damage described in the above case history.

4.   CONCLUSIONS

A case history of severe fin damage in a compressor intercooler has been examined. Physical evidence and simple calculations suggest that the damage was due to leakage flow across the ends of the fins. The excitation mechanism is shear layer oscillations across the multiple cavities formed by the fins with fluidelastic feedback from the fin oscillations. Laboratory tests confirmed that such a phenomenon can produce significant fin resonant at a Strouhal number of 0.48 or an integer multiple of 0.48. It is concluded that fin damage can be prevented by introducing seals which eliminate the leakage flow.

ACKNOWLEDGEMENTS

The authors are grateful to the Natural Sciences and Engineering Research Council of Canada for its support of the laboratory research.

REFERENCES

(1)   PAIDOUSSIS, M.P., "Flow-induced vibrations in nuclear reactors and heat exchangers: practical experiences and state of knowledge", In Proceedings IAHR/IUTAM Symposium on Practical Experiences with Flow-Induced Vibration, eds. E. Naudascher, D. Rockwell, Springer-Verlag, Berlin, 1980, pp. 1-81.

(2)   PAIDOUSSIS, M.P., "A review of flow-induced vibrations in reactors and reactor components", Nuclear Engineering and Design, 1983 (74), pp. 31-60.

(3)   WEAVER, D.S. and FITZPATRICK, J.A., "A review of cross-flow induced vibrations in heat exchanger tube arrays", J. of Fluids and Structures, 1988 (2), pp. 73-93.

(4)   ROCKWELL, D., "Prediction of Oscillation Frequency for Unstable Flow Past Cavities", ASME J. of Fluids Engineering, 1978 (100), pp. 152-165.

(5)   ROCKWELL, D., and NAUDASCHER, E., "Reviw - Self-sustaining oscillations of flow past cavities", ASME J. of Fluids Engineering, 1978 (100), pp. 152-165.

(6)   ROCKWELL, D., and NAUDASCHER, E., "Self-sustaining oscillations of impinging free shear layers", Annual Review Fluid Mech. 1979 (11), pp. 67-94.

(7)   ZIADA, S., BUHLMANN, E.T., and BOLLETER, U., "Flow impingement as an excitation source in control valves", J. Fluids and Structures, 1989 (3), pp. 529-549.

(8)   WEAVER, D.S., and AINSWORTH, P., "Flow-induced vibrations in Bellows", ASME J. Pressure Vessel Technology, 1989 (11), pp. 402-406.

(9)   HUANG, X.Y., and WEAVER, D.S., "A Flow Visualization Study of the Active Control of Free Shear Layer Oscillation", Flow-Induced Vibration - 1990, eds. S.S. Chen, K. Fujita and M.K. Au-Yang, ASME Conference, Nashville, Tennessee, PVP-Vol. 189, 1990, pp. 31-37.

Flow induced vibrations in the tube banks of fossil fired boilers

G ALLEN, BSc, CEng, MInstE
NEI International Combustion Limited, Derby

SYNOPSIS   Research was undertaken at NEI International Combustion Limited to develop correlations for predicting vortex shedding and fluidelastic vibration thresholds for the in-line tube banks generic to fossil fuel fired boilers.   Full parametric studies were made by testing one fifth scale ten-row and two-row model tube banks in a pressurised wind tunnel.

Vortex shedding was undetectable in ten-row tube banks which had longitudinal (X_L) and transverse (X_T) pitch to diameter ratios less than 2.   The only bank which demonstrated vortex shedding had a square pitch of $X_L = X_T = 2$, and produced a Strouhal number of 0.15.

Conversely all the two row tube banks demonstrated vortex shedding.   Strouhal numbers between 0.15 – 0.19 and 0.12 – 0.13 were measured for banks with small and large transverse tube spacings.

Fluidelastic instability of the ten-row tube banks commenced at lower critical velocities than were expected from published data.   Tightly spaced tube banks, which had X_L and X_T values less than 2.0, produced instability factors K of 1.5 and 3.3.   Work on the two-row tube banks showed vibration to be independent of air pressure and density.   This indicated an excitation mechanism other than fluidelasticity.

NOTATION

D	tube outside diameter (m)
f_n	tube natural frequency (Hz)
f_v	vortex shedding frequency (Hz)
L	longitudinal tube pitch (m)
M	tube mass per unit length (Kg/m)
Q	tube dynamic magnification factor (π/δ)
Re	Reynolds number $(\rho UD/\mu)$
S	Strouhal number $(f_v D/U)$
T	transverse tube pitch (m)
L	longitudinal tube pitch (m)
U	tube gap velocity for tube banks, approach velocity for a single tube (m/s)
U_c	critical tube gap velocity at the onset of fluidelastic vibrations (m/s)
X_L	dimensionless longitudinal pitch (L/D)
X_T	dimensionless transverse pitch (T/D)
K	fluidelastic instability factor (–)
δ	tube logarithmic decrement $(\approx 2\pi\varsigma)$
ς	tube damping ratio (–)
μ	gas dynamic viscosity (Ns/m²)
ρ	gas density (kg/m³)

1   INTRODUCTION

Flow induced vibrations of tube banks in cross-flow have been a problem to designers in the power industry for many years, and a number of incidents of fatigue failure have been experienced [1].   Consequently research was performed between 1979–86 to develop reliable design correlations for the avoidance of both vortex and fluidelastically induced vibration in the in-line tube banks specific to industrial and utility water tube boilers.

Detailed vibration studies were conducted on one fifth scale model tube banks in a 0–7 barg pressurised wind tunnel.   Eleven representative in-line tube bank patterns, as shown in Figure 1, were selected and individually tested.   Table 1 summarises the geometry and dynamic characteristics of these tube arrays.

This paper details the studies made, and identifies the principal findings.

2   BACKGROUND

2.1   Vortex shedding

The phenomenon of vortex shedding behind tubes in cross-flow is well documented [2].   The frequency with which vortices are shed is characterised by a Strouhal number:-

$$S = \frac{f_v D}{U} \qquad (1)$$

For an isolated circular cylinder S remains constant at 0.2 over a wide range of Reynolds numbers. When the vortex shedding frequency coincides with the tube natural frequency, resonance occurs, causing large and potentially damaging tube vibrations.

In tube banks vortex shedding still occurs, however there is insufficient space for the vortices to form in the same way they do behind a single tube. Accordingly different tube vibration excitation processes take place which are not fully understood. For design predictions the correlations of Chen (3) and Fitz-Hugh (4) have traditionally been adopted to avoid vortex induced tube vibration. More recently the work of Rae & Wharmby (5) has identified the unreliability of these correlations, specifically for in-line tube arrays.

2.2 Fluidelastic instability

As a fluid flows through a tube bank a change in the relative position of adjacent tubes causes a perturbation in the pressure field. If the tubes are free to vibrate the perturbation occurs at the tube natural frequency. With large fluid velocities and/or small tube spacings the fluid forces can be significant. Providing the force is in phase with the fluid velocity, power is absorbed by the tubes from the flowing fluid. At a critical value of velocity the energy absorbed from the fluid equals that dissipated by tube damping, and further increases result in divergent tube vibrations which can cause failure in a relatively small number of cycles.

Initial pioneers, notably Connors (6), found that the critical velocity may be determined in terms of two non-dimensional groups:-

$$\frac{U_c}{f_n D} = K \left[\frac{M\delta}{e D^2} \right]^{0.5} \qquad (2)$$

where K is the fluidelastic instability factor

The validity of this expression was later confirmed by the mathematical models proposed by Blevins (7&8). These deduced the theoretical variations of the fluidelastic instability factor with transverse tube spacing illustrated in Figures 2 and 3. Experimental values of the instability factor derived by other workers (9-17) are superimposed on these figures showing reasonable agreement with Blevins theory.

Initially in heat exchanger design Connors (6) K value of 9.9 was adopted. This value was obtained from experiments on a single tube row. Later experimentation conducted during the 1970's (9-17) proved tube banks to be inherently less stable than single tube rows. Accordingly the rock bottom safe K

value of 3.3, as proposed by Pettigrew (18), became much used. Recently a state of the art review by Weaver and Fitzpatrick (19) has proposed more comprehensive correlations for various tube array patterns: for square in-line tube banks a lower K value of 2.5 is cited, with a revised index of 0.48, rather than 0.5, to Equation 2.

3 TEST RIG SELECTION

3.1 Tube geometries selected for test

A study was made of the tube banks used in U.K. fossil fuel fired boilers to establish the range of sizes in current use.

Geometry was found to be dependent upon a number of factors other than heat transfer and pressure drop. These included, standardisation of tube pitching, clearance to prevent ash fouling and metrication. However, all tube banks fell into two basic categories, multi-row and two-row tube arrays.

Accordingly the eleven tube bank geometries listed in Table 1 were selected for testing. These were considered to be fully representative of boiler design practice. The ten-row arrays were considered deep enough to simulate the multi-row tube banks used in the power industry.

3.2 Test rig scaling

To allow comprehensive flow induced vibration studies it was decided to test scale model tube banks in an existing pressurised wind tunnel. To select a suitable model scale the following parameters were considered:-

$$\text{Reynold number Re} = \frac{e UD}{\mu} \qquad (3)$$

$$\text{Strouhal number S} = \frac{f_v D}{U} \qquad (4)$$

After considering boiler and model operating conditions in conjunction with these parameters a one fifth model scale was selected as being the best compromise.

4 TEST RIG

To perform flow induced vibration studies over a wide range of fluid parameters, an existing pressurised wind tunnel was utilised. The tunnel was capable of accommodating test rigs up to 1.1 metre diameter by 3.5 metres long. The air prime mover was a 70 kW blower. This used a variable speed drive and butterfly damper combination to control air flow rate, which was measured by a conventional orifice plate calibrated in accordance with BS 1042.

Wind tunnel air temperature measurement was accomplished by using a platinum resistance thermometer. A Bourdon tube pressure gauge was utilised to record the wind tunnel operating pressure.

A photograph showing the installation of a two-row model tube bank into the pressurised wind tunnel is shown in Figure 4. Model tubes of 14 mm diameter were chosen in accordance with the one fifth scaling selected. These were manufactured from heavy gauge tube, fitted with 4 mm diameter flexible end support pins as illustrated in Figure 5. The tubes were retained by special collets purposely designed to allow tube vibration frequency to be finely tuned, whilst ensuring it had a constant value in all directions in the first bending mode. Provision to vary the span distance between tube collet support plates was incorporated to allow tube frequency to be varied between 30 and 90 Hz. Initially tube frequency was set to 30 Hz, later tests were made at 60 and 90 Hz.

To ensure a reasonable intertube velocity of up to 30 m/s a rectangular flow duct having dimensions of 493.2 mm by 450 mm was chosen. The model tubes passed through clearance holes in the side of this duct.

The test rig was designed with a variable construction to purposely accommodate the various model tube bank configurations selected for test, see Table 1.

Ten tubes were instrumented with horizontally and vertically mounted accelerometers, sited midway along the tube, see Figure 5. A mixture of principally Endevco 2222B and Birchall A/25/E piezo-electric accelerometers were used. Six instrumented tubes were used during the two-row model tube bank tests, and ten during the ten-row tube bank tests.

Fylde 128CA charge amplifiers were utilised to condition the accelerometer vibration signals, which were processed and analysed by a Nicolet 446A fast fourier transform computing spectrum analyser and plotter.

5 TEST PROCEDURE

5.1 Tube natural frequency and damping measurements

During test rig assembly the tubes were tested to establish their dynamic characteristics under no-flow conditions. The tests were performed for two reasons, firstly to ensure that all tubes had identical natural frequencies, and secondly to measure the mechanical damping of the tubes.

Tube natural frequencies in the first bending mode were determined by performing impulse tests. Tube vibration response to light hammer blows was recorded and processed using an accelerometer connected to a Nicolet 446A FFT spectrum analyser. By adjusting the tube retaining collets illustrated in Figure 5 individual tube frequencies were tuned to a ±0.5 Hz tolerance about the nominal frequency selected for each tube bank test geometry. This was either 30, 60 or 90 Hz.

The mechanical damping of each instrumented tube, together with a sample of the non-instrumented tubes, was measured by recording the tube vibration responses to impulsive blows. The rate of free tube vibration decay was used to calculate the dynamic magnification factor by the usual analytical method (20).

In later correlation and data analysis work both average tube bank frequency and damping values were used.

5.2 Flow induced vibration tests

Following the assembly of each model tube bank the test rig was installed within the pressurised wind tunnel ready for flow induced vibration trials.

Initial testing was conducted under ambient atmospheric pressure conditions. The vibration response of each instrumented tube was monitored by the Nicolet analyser as test rig air flow rate was increased. Summation averaged 0-200 Hz tube acceleration spectra were computed and plotted out for later reference. The discrete acceleration level over a ±7 Hz bandwidth about the tube vibration frequency was recorded. This value was plotted against tube gap velocity to identify the incipient point of fluidelastic tube vibration onset. This procedure was repeated at other test rig operating pressures up to a maximum of 4.14 barg.

Whenever vortex shedding excitation was evident its frequency was noted. Eventually graphs of vortex shedding frequency against tube gap velocity were constructed and Strouhal number calculated.

Different methods for selecting representative critical velocity values were examined. The best technique was one which adjudged the critical velocity to occur when the tube vibration response first deviated markedly from the turbulence square law response. Log-log graphs of tube vibration against tube gap velocity were drawn to identify this transition point. The velocity at which the slope of the curve changed from the square law was taken to be the onset of fluidelastic instability.

6 DISCUSSION OF TEST RESULTS

6.1 Vortex shedding results

These test results are summarised in Table 2, which presents values of the experimentally derived Strouhal numbers for each in-line model tube bank geometry tested. These values are also compared with the Strouhal numbers projected by other workers (3, 4 & 5).

The closely pitched two-row tube arrays, $X_L = 1.5/2.0$ and $X_T = 2.0$, produced Strouhal numbers which varied between 0.15 and 0.19 experimentally. Conversely the two-row tube banks which have wide transverse spacings, $X_L = 1.5$ and $X_T = 3.4/4.0$, gave lower Strouhal numbers of 0.12 and 0.13.

Vortex shedding proved undetectable in the ten-row tube banks tested which had X_L values lower than 2.0. The Strouhal number for the $X_L = X_T = 2.0$ ten-row tube bank was 0.15.

Table 2 illustrates how the experimental results significantly deviate from the traditionally used design correlations developed by Chen (3) and Fitz-Hugh (4). The results compare more favourably with the recent work of Rea & Wharmby (5).

A final test was conducted to validate the accuracy of the experimental technique. Vortex shedding behind a single test rig tube was observed in order to compare its Strouhal number with the expected text book value of 0.2. The experimental result of 0.19 validated the technique.

6.2 In-line ten-row tube bank vibration results

These results are presented non-dimensionally in Figure 6. This is a log-log graph of the critical velocity factor against the tube mass and damping parameter. As shown the test results have been correlated assuming the traditionally adopted fluidelastic vibration criteria set down in equation (2). This indicates that if the critical velocity and tube mass and damping factors are plotted logarithmically against one another then a straight line relationship, of slope 0.5, can be expected for the test data. As shown good correlation exists which confirms that all the model ten-row tube banks exhibited genuine fluidelastic vibration behaviour.

The experimental instability factors of 1.5 to 4.5 are quite low in comparison to the values determined by other workers, see Figure 2. However, both Connors (12) and Lockey et al (14), who performed experiments with air, deduced similar values of 2-4 for the fluidelastic instability factor. Additionally the more recent square tube array correlation developed by Weaver & Fitzpatrick (19) agrees well with the experimental results, see Figure 6. Accordingly designers should be aware that in closely pitched tube banks they may have to use very conservative design parameters to avoid fluidelastic vibration problems.

6.3 In-line two-row tube bank vibration results

These results are presented non-dimensionally in Figure 7. The results appear independent of the tube mass and damping parameter, which suggests a wake driven vibration mechanism rather than true fluidelastic excitation.

A possible mechanism is a tube gap flow switch phenomenon which has been observed by other workers (21&22). This occurs between tubes which have small longitudinal pitches, at values of the critical velocity factor in excess of 7.

7 CONCLUSIONS

The results of one fifth scale model test on both two and ten-row in-line tube banks

identified the following features:-

7.1 All the two-row tube banks produced vortex shedding. The closely pitched banks, $X_L = 1.5/2.0$ and $X_T = 2$, produced Strouhal numbers of 0.15 and 0.19. Conversely the banks with wide transverse tube spacings, $X_L = 1.5$ and $X_T = 3.4/4.0$, gave lower Strouhal numbers of 0.12 and 0.13

7.2 The two-row tube bank vibration results appeared to be independent of the tube mass and damping parameter, suggesting an excitation mechanism other than fluidelasticity.

7.3 Vortex shedding proved undetectable in ten-row tube arrays which had X_L and X_T values less than 2.0. The only ten-row array which demonstrated true vortex shedding had a square geometry with X_L and $X_T = 2$. This produced a Strouhal number of 0.15.

7.4 The ten-row tube banks exhibited true fluidelastic vibration behaviour. Instability factors ranged from 1.5 to 4.5.

8 REFERENCES

(1) Smeaton, E. J., Welbourne, M. C. Gas side flow excitation problems in boiler plant. International Symposium on Vibration Problems in Industry, Keswick, England, 1973, paper 425 (UKAEA/NPL).

(2) Blevins, R. D. Flow induced vibration, 1977, pp. 11-54, (Van Nostrand Reinhold).

(3) Chen, Y. N. Flow induced vibration and noise in tube bank heat exchangers due to Von Karmen Streets. ASME Journal of Engineering for Industry, 1968, vol. 90, pp. 134-146.

(4) Fitz-Hugh, J. S. Flow induced vibration in heat exchangers. International Symposium on Vibration Problems in Industry, Keswick, England, 1973, paper 427 (UKAEA/NPL).

(5) Rae, G. J., Wharmby, J. S. Strouhal numbers for in-line tube arrays. First International Conference on Flow Induced Vibrations, Bowness-on-Windermere, England, 1987, paper E4 (BNES/UKAEA/IAHR/BHRA).

(6) Connors, H. J. Fluidelastic vibration of tube arrays excited by cross flow. Proceedings of the Symposium on Flow Induced Vibrations in Heat Exchangers, New York, 1970, pp. 42-56 (ASME).

(7) Blevins, R. D. Fluidelastic whirling of a tube row. ASME Journal of Pressure Vessel Technology, 1974, vol. 96, pp. 263-267.

(8) Blevins, R. D. Fluidelastic whirling of tube rows and tube arrays. ASME Journal of Fluids Engineering, Sept. 1977, pp. 457-461.

© IMechE 1991 C416/104

(9) Ishigai, Nishikawa, E., Yagi, E. Structure of gas flow and vibration in tube banks with axes normal to flow. ISME, Tokyo, Nov. 1972.

(10) Gibert, R. J., Chabrerir, J., Sagner, M. Tube bundle vibration in transversal flow. International Conference on Vibration in Nuclear Plant, Keswick, England, 1978, paper 2.2 (BNES/UKAEA).

(11) Soper, B. M. H., Lockey, I. M. Fluid-elastic instability of tube bundles in water-preliminary report. HTFS Report No. RS315 (AERE R9876), July 1980.

(12) Connors, H. J. Fluidelastic vibration of heat exchanger tube arrays. ASME Journal of Mechanical Design, 1978, vol. 100, pp. 347-353.

(13) Hartlen, R. T. Wind tunnel determination of fluidelastic vibration thresholds for typical heat exchanger tube patterns. Ontario Hydro Report No. 74-309-K, 1974.

(14) Lockey, I. M., Soper, B. M. H., Whittle, R.H. The effect of tube layout on the susceptibility of tube banks to self excited vibrations. HTFS Report No. RS193 (AERE R8772), 1977.

(15) Pettigrew, M. J., Sylvestre, Y., Campagna, A. O. Flow induced vibration analysis of heat exchanger and steam generator designs. Fourth International Conference on Structural Mechanics in Reactor Technology, San Francisco, U.S.A., 1977, paper F6/1.

(16) Gross, H. J. Investigation in aero-elastic vibration mechanisms and their application in design of tubular heat exchangers. Dissertation, Technical University of Hannover, 1975.

(17) Gorman, D. J. Experimental development of design criteria to limit liquid cross flow induced vibrations of heat exchanger equipment. Nuclear Science & Engineering, 1976, vol. 61, pp 324-336.

(18) Pettigrew, M. J., Gorman, D. J. Vibration of heat exchanger components in liquid and two phase cross-flow. International Conference on Vibration in Nuclear Plant, Keswick, England, 1978, paper 2.3 (BNES/UKAEA).

(19) Weaver, D. S., Fitzpatrick, J. A. A review of flow induced vibrations in heat exchangers. First International Conference on Flow Induced Vibration, Bowness-on-Windermere, England, 1987, Paper A1 (BNES/UKAEA/IAHR/BHRA).

(20) Thomson, W. T. Theory of vibration, 1981, pp. 30 and 77 (George Allen & Unwin).

(21) Chen, S. S. A review of flow induced vibration of two circular cylinders in cross flow. ASME Journal of Pressure Vessel Technology, 1986, Vol. 108, pp. 382-393.

(22) Lakshmana Gowda, B. H., Prabhu, D. R. Interference effects on the flow induced vibrations of a circular cylinder. Journal of Sound and Vibration, 1987, Vol. 112, pp. 487-500.

Table 1 In-line model banks tested.

Test arrangement number	Tube bank type	Number of tube rows deep x wide	$X_L(-)$	$X_T(-)$	f_n(Hz)	Q (-) mean	Q (-) variation
1	Two-row	2 x 18	1.5	2.0	30	190	63 – 311
2	" "	2 x 18	1.5	2.0	30	61	26 – 136
3	" "	2 x 18	1.5	2.0	60	415	200 – 611
4	" "	2 x 18	1.5	2.0	90	674	167 – 1167
5	" "	2 x 18	2.0	2.0	60	288	135 – 509
6	" "	2 x 10	1.5	3.4	60	232	67 – 384
7	" "	2 x 9	1.5	4.0	60	426	59 – 616
8	Ten-row	10 x 21	1.5	1.7	60	461	169 – 964
9	" "	10 x 18	1.5	2.0	30	256	46 – 818
10	" "	10 x 18	1.5	2.0	30	74	21 – 208
11	" "	10 x 18	2.0	2.0	60	365	227 – 729

Table 2 Comparison of vortex shedding results.

Test arrangement number	Tube bank type	$X_L(-)$	$X_T(-)$	Strouhal numbers Experimental	Chen (3)	Fitz-Hugh (4)	Rae et al (5)
3	Two-row	1.5	2.0	0.19	0.37	0.26	0.15
4	" "	1.5	2.0	0.15	0.37	0.26	0.15
5	" "	2.0	2.0	0.15	0.27	0.26	0.15
6	" "	1.5	3.4	0.12	–	0.18	0.13
7	" "	1.5	4.0	0.13	–	0.18	0.13
8	Ten-row	1.5	1.7	*	0.33	0.31	0.12
9	" "	1.5	2.0	*	0.37	0.26	0.13
10	" "	1.5	2.0	*	0.37	0.26	0.13
11	" "	2.0	2.0	0.15	0.27	0.26	0.15
–	Single tube	–	–	0.19	–	–	–

Notes

i) * Denotes that vortex shedding proved undetectable.

ii) No vortex shedding measurements were taken with test arrangements 1 and 2.

© IMechE 1991 C416/104

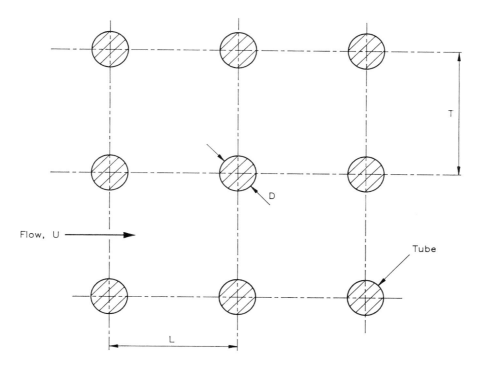

Fig 1 In—line tube bank pattern.

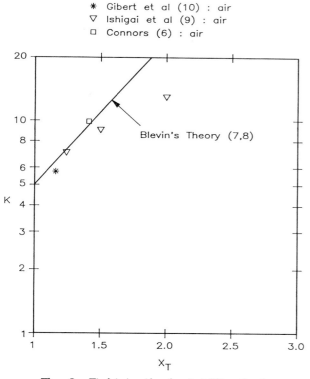

Fig 2 Fluidelastic instability factors
for a single tube row.

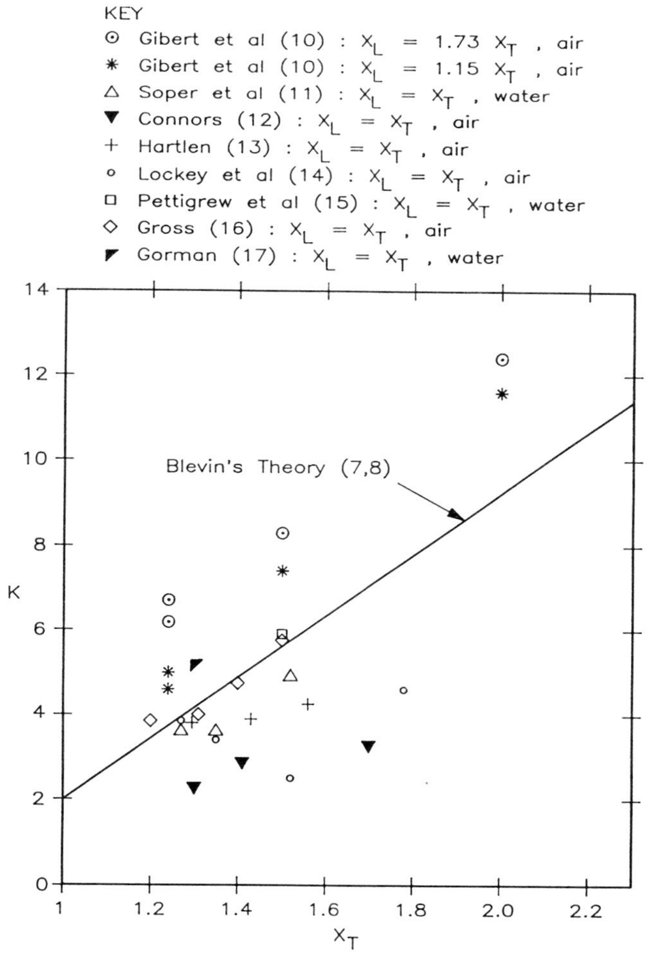

Fig 3 Fluidelastic instability factors for
in—line tube banks.

Fig 4 The test rig

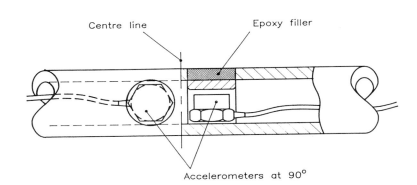

ENLARGED PART SECTION AT A

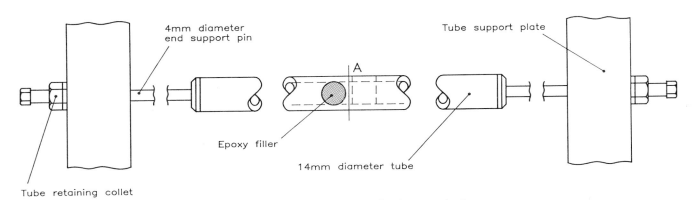

Fig 5 Details of an instrumented
test rig tube.

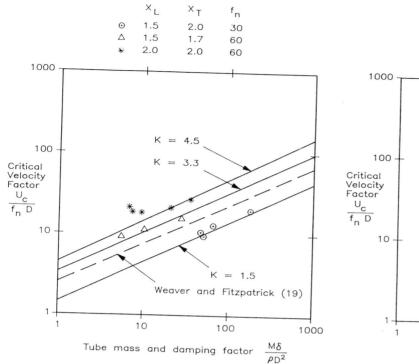

Fig 6 Fluidelastic vibration results : ten—row in—line tube banks.

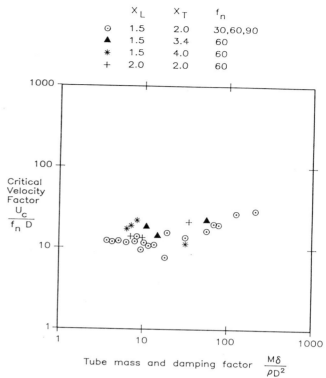

Fig 7 Fluidelastic vibration results : two—row in—line tube banks.

Vorticity shedding and acoustic resonance in an in-line tube bundle. Part one: vorticity shedding

S ZIADA, MEng, PhD, MASME and A OENGOEREN, PhD
Laboratory for Vibrations and Acoustics, Sulzer Innotec, Winterthur, Switzerland

SYNOPSIS   An in-line tube array with intermediate tube spacings is tested in a wind tunnel and a water channel. Extensive flow visualization and correlation measurements are carried out to reveal the nature of the vorticity shedding excitation. The instability of the jet issuing between the tubes is found to be the source of the vorticity shedding excitation. The jet instability occurs at its symmetric mode, whereupon large scale vortices are formed symmetrically on both sides of each flow lane. Since the jet instability in each flow lane is 180° out of phase with that in the neighbouring lanes, vortices are formed anti-symmetrically in the tube wakes.

NOTATION

C_{PV}	coherence between pressure and velocity fluctiations
C_{PP}	coherence of pressure fluctuations
d	tube diameter
f_v	frequency of vorticity shedding
L	streamwise tube spacing
p_v	rms amplitude of pressure fluctuation at the vorticity shedding frequency, f_v.
p_T	total rms amplitude of pressure fluctuations
Re	Reynolds number, $Re = V_t d / \nu$
S	Strouhal number, $S = f_v d / V_t$
T	transverse tube spacing
V_t	gap velocity
$\tilde{v}$	rms amplitude of velocity fluctuation at the vorticity shedding frequency, fv.
X_L	streamwise spacing ratio, $X_L = L/d$
X_T	transverse spacing ratio, $X_T = T/d$
x,y	system coordinates
ϕ_p, ϕ_v	phase of p_v and $\tilde{v}$, respectively
ρ	flow density
ν	kinematic viscosity

1   INTRODUCTION

It is now generally accepted that flow induced vibrations of tube arrays in crossflow are excited by four basic mechanisms. These are: (a) turbulent buffeting, (b) vorticity shedding, (c) fluidelastic instability and (d) acoustic resonance. Excellent reviews by Paidoussis (1-3) and Weaver and Fitzpatrick (4) summarize recent advances and the state of knowledge in this field. This two-part paper focuses on two of these basic mechanisms; namely, the vorticity shedding and the acoustic resonance mechanisms.

Tube arrays in crossflow are excited, to varying degrees, by periodic fluid forces, the frequency of which varies linearly with the flow velocity. In the literature, this periodic excitation is variously known as: flow periodicity, Strouhal periodicity, or vorticity shedding. Although this type of excitation has been recognized since the 1950's, its nature still remains far from being well understood (see Refs. (3,4)).

Early studies (5-9) attributed the vorticity shedding excitation to vortex shedding from the tubes, arguing by analogy to the classical vortex shedding from isolated cylinders. In 1960, Owen (10) disputed the possibility of coherent vortex shedding deeply inside closely spaced arrays. Instead, he argued that the rather turbulent flow within the array contains a dominant turbulence length scale. Because the tubes are only lightly damped, they will show a resonance peak corresponding to the frequency range associated with the dominant turbulence length scale. Although this argument did not recieve widespread acceptance, it underlined the need for an alternative reasoning which is more convincing than the classical vortex shedding model. It is to that end that Y.N. Chen (11) suggested various mechanisms and sketched several patterns of flow structures which could give rise to the vorticity shedding excitation. However, these mechanisms and patterns have not been confirmed experimentally to date.

Flow visualization studies have been carried out to resolve the dispute about vortex shedding. The studies carried out by Funakawa and Umakoshi (12) and Weaver and Abd-Rabbo (13) indicated that vortices can be formed inside tube arrays. These studies, however, were somewhat inconclusive because vortex shedding occurred _only_ when the system was at resonance (free surface waves in Ref. (12) and tube vibrations in Ref. (13)). Abd-Rabbo and Weaver (14) observed laminar vortex formation at low Reynolds numbers inside a staggered tube array. More recently, Ziada et al.(15) visualized the flow inside an in-line array in the absence of resonance effects and well into the turbulent regime. This study left no doubt that vortices can be formed inside tube arrays with streamwise spacing ratios as small as 1.4. For smaller spacing ratios, however, the possibility of vortex formation is still open.

Much more important is the nature of the flow instability which gives rise to the vorticity shedding excitation, irrespective of whether this instability is associated with vortex formation or not. This aspect is particularly important for in-line tube arrays because their acoustic response in relation to the vorticity shedding excitation is very peculiar. Many authors (15-19) have reported that the occurrence of resonance of in-line arrays does not seem to be related to the vorticity shedding excitation which is active at off-resonance conditions. The recent flow visualization study by Ziada et al. (15) has shed some light on this phenomenon. They found the flow periodicity to be dominated by a symmetric instability mode of the jet issuing between the tubes. Since the particle velocity of the acoustic modes has an anti-symmetric phase distribution and the jet instability has a symmetric phase distribution, coupling between the jet instability and the acoustic modes is not possible. Ziada et al. argued further that it must be that acoustic resonances of in-line arrays are excited by an anti-symmetric jet mode which is usually (i.e. at off resonance conditions) suppressed because of the kinematic constraints imposed by the in-line geometry. This argument, however, was based on very limited flow visualization results and was not supported by detailed correlation measurements which could allow definite conclusions to be made.

The object of this study is to reveal the nature of the flow instability which generates the vorticity shedding excitation inside in-line arrays. Since an earlier study dealt with a closely packed array (15), we consider here a geometry of intermediate spacings. This geometry is tested in air and water flows. Flow visualization and simultaneous hot film measurements are conducted to reconstruct the flow structure at any location of the array at the same instant of time. Moreover, extensive correlation measurements using a hot wire and two microphones are carried out to obtain distributions of the amplitude, the phase and the coherence of the velocity fluctuation across the flow lanes and the tube wakes at different

locations within the bundle. The water and air tests complemented one another and provided a clear picture of the periodic flow evolution from the first row inwards into the array.

The second part of this paper deals with the mechanism by which acoustic resonances are excited and the relationship of this mechanism to the vorticity shedding excitation which is fully characterized in the first part of the paper.

2 EXPERIMENTAL FACILITY AND INSTRUMENTATION

2.1 Wind tunnel facility

The tested array had an in-line configuration with spacing ratios of $X_L / X_T = 1.75/2.25$. It consisted of 10 rows with 11 tubes per row (ten full tubes and two halves). The tubes were 20 mm in diameter and 200 mm in length, and were manufactured of acrylic rods. They were rigidly fixed at both ends to the side walls of the test section. The test section had a cross-section of 200 x 495 mm and was fabricated of 10 mm thick aluminium plates. The upstream turbulence level was less than 1 %.

The wind tunnel test section is shown schematically in Fig. 1 (a). Note that the streamwise coordinate, x, is measured from the centers of the tubes in the first row, and the transverse coordinate, y, is measured from the top wall. Fig. 1 (c) shows the method used to number the tube wakes and the flow lanes between the tubes (thereafter for brevity, the flow lanes are sometimes referred to as jets).

2.2 Water channel facility

The array tested in water had the same spacing ratios as those used in the air tests. The tubes were 25 mm in diameter and 400 mm in length, and were made of acrylic rods. The array consisted of 10 rows and 5 full tubes per row. No half tubes were used on the side walls, but the side gaps were made equal to half the transverse spacing, see Fig. 1(b). The tubes were placed vertically in the channel by mounting them rigidly to the top and bottom walls of an insert test section which was placed inside the channel test section. Both test sections were fabricated from plexiglas to enable flow visualization. The upstream turbulence level was less than 0.1 %.

Dye injection technique was used to visualize the flow inside the tube bundle. The dye was mixed with water and injected into the tube wakes via ejector pipes which were mounted in special grooves along the front stagnation lines of the tubes. With this arrangement it was possible to place the ejector pipes at any vertical location along the tubes. The ejector pipes had an outlet diameter of 1.0 mm.

2.3 Instrumentation

The sound pressure level (SPL) was measured by means of Brüel and Kjaer 1/4" condenser microphones. Disa anemometers and linearizers were used to measure the mean and the fluctuating velocity inside the arrays. In the air tests, miniature hot wire probes, and in the water tests, hot film probes were used. The probes could be moved to any location within the arrays to measure the fluctuating velocity distributions across the jets and the tube wakes. It was also possible to mount the microphones at many locations on the top or the side walls of the test section. Fig. 1 (d) shows these locations with respect to the array lattice.

Frequency analysis was carried out by means of a Nicolet 444A FFT spectrum analyser. A Hewlett Packard two channel analyser type 3562A was used to carry out the phase and coherence measurements. In general, the measuring ranges were 0-10 Hz and 0-1 kHz during the water and the air tests, respectively. At least 16 spectra in the water tests and 64 spectra in the air tests were averaged for each measurement.

The visualized flow field was recorded by means of a video system which consisted of two cameras, a video mixer and a high resolution monitor. The camera used to view the flow was equipped with a high speed shutter (1/1000 sec.). The other camera was used to monitor the hot film signal. The video mixer allowed the recording of the visualized field and the signal of the hot film simultaneously. Recording of the hot film signal served as a time reference for the photos and helped analysing various flow mechanisms. The photos presented in this paper were taken from the video screen using a Canon camera and 35 mm films.

3 TEST RESULTS
3.1 Strouhal number

Fig. 2 shows the development of the frequency spectrum of the fluctuating velocity as the gap velocity, V_t, is increased. In both air and water tests, the hot wire/film was diagonally centered between the tubes of the second and the third rows. The velocity fluctuations are seen to occur at a well defined (single) frequency, f_v, which increases as the flow velocity is increased. In the air tests, a higher harmonic component at the frequency $2f_v$ is also present. The occurrence of this higher harmonic is an inherent feature of separated flows. According to the nonlinear hydrodynamic instability theory and the experimental findings (20, 21), higher harmonics are generated when the amplitude of the fundamental component exceeds about 4 % of the mean flow. Since the amplitude of the fundamental component is substantially higher in the air tests (as will be seen later), the harmonic $2f_v$ is well established in the air tests, but not in the water tests.

The frequency of the flow periodicity, f_v, is plotted as a function of the gap flow velocity in Figs. 3 (a_1) and 3 (b_1) for the air and the water tests, respectively. The Strouhal number of the flow periodicity in both cases is similar, and is equal to $S = f_v d/V_t = 0.15 \pm 0.005$. This leads to the conclusion that the nature of the flow instability must be the same in both cases.

The measured Strouhal number (0.15) is substantially lower than those given in the charts constructed by Fitz-hugh (22) and Chen (23). These charts give the values 0.24 and 0.28, respectively. The Chen chart gives an additional subharmonic component of 0.14, which is close to the measured value. This disagreement of Strouhal numbers is hardly surprising since the earlier data used to construct the above mentioned charts are obtained from acoustic resonance cases. As will be shown clearly in the second part of this paper, the Strouhal number of the flow periodicity is different from that at which acoustic resonances occur. Rae and Wharmby (24) constructed a Strouhal number chart based on non-resonant data only. This chart gives a value of 0.15 which agrees with the present value.

The Strouhal number charts constructed by Weaver et al. (25) are valid only for the standard geometries (e.g. square in-line arrays). Since the present case is not a standard geometry, direct comparison with these charts is not possible.

The effect of the flow velocity on the rms amplitude of the fluctuating velocity, $\tilde{v}$, is shown in Figs. 3(a_2) and 3(b_2) for the air and the water tests, respectively. The hot wire was located behind the second row in the air tests. In the water tests however, the hot film was moved further downstream, behind the fourth row, to allow measurements of the saturation amplitude which was still not reached behind the second row at the maximum flow velocity. As the flow velocity is increased, the rms amplitude of the fluctuating velocity is seen to increase until it reaches a saturation value of 10 to 12 percent of the gap velocity. At relatively high velocities, the saturation value of $\tilde{v}/V_t$ decreases slightly, possibly owing to the saturation of $\tilde{v}$. It is important to point out that increasing the flow velocity causes the ratio $\tilde{v}/V_t$, and not only $\tilde{v}$, to increase.

Since the ratio $\tilde{v}/V_t$ represents the degree of "maturity" of the flow instability, the results of Figs. 3 (a_2) and (b_2) indicate that the flow instability behind a certain row becomes more mature as the flow velocity (or the Reynolds number) is increased. This implies that the position at which the flow instability becomes fully developed, i.e. the location at which $\tilde{v}/V_t$ saturates, moves upstream as the Reynolds number is increased. This general feature is in accordance with the flow visualization results reported by Ziada et al.(15). They found that the position at which vortices start to appear in a closely spaced array moves upstream as the Reynolds number is increased.

It should be noted that the number of tube rows in the air tests was reduced to 6 rows in order to obtain the results given in Figs. 2 (a) and 3 (a). This reduction in the number of rows was necessary to avoid the occurrence of acoustic resonance which would otherwise be initiated at $V_t \approx 35$ m/s. All other measurements given in this paper were obtained from tests with 10 rows.

3.2 Streamwise development of flow instability

The rms amplitude of the streamwise velocity fluctuation was measured along a line centered between two tube columns of the array tested in water. The flow velocity during these tests was 0.26 m/s (Re = $6 \cdot 8 \times 10^3$). As shown in Fig. 4, the dimensionless amplitude increases in the downstream direction until the fifth row, where it reaches a saturation amplitude of about 13 %. Behind each row, the fluctuating velocity grows rapidly, but this rapid growth is impeded by the presence of the tubes of the subsequent rows, resulting in the amplitude plateaux at $x/L \approx 1, 2$ and 3. These plateaux make the evaluation of the disturbance growth rate within the array rather difficult. Detailed measurements were therefore carried out between the first two rows to gain more insight into the initial stage of the disturbance growth. As shown in Fig. 5, the fluctuating velocity grows exponentially in the downstream direction before it is hindered by the tubes of the second row. This exponential growth of disturbance accords with the prediction of the hydrodynamic stability theory for separated flows, i.e. shear layers, jets and wakes (26, 27).

The air test facility was used to measure the distributions of the fluctuating velocity amplitude behind the first, the second and the fourth rows. The measurements were carried out along the lines centered between the tube rows, and at a flow velocity of 30.6 m/s (Re = 3.8×10^4). Fig. 6 depicts the distributions across the sixth and the seventh jets. The distributions across the fourth and fifth jets were also measured and were found to be similar to those given in Fig. 6, they are not presented here for the sake of brevity.

As shown in Fig. 6, the velocity fluctuations behind the first row are much stronger at the edges of the jet than in its core. This distribution indicates that the flow instability is initiated by the inducement of small velocity perturbations into the shear layers which separate from the tubes of the first row. These velocity perturbations are amplified exponentially in the downstream direction, as has been shown already in Fig. 5. Because the Reynolds number is relatively high, the fluctuation amplitude reaches 13 % of the gap velocity already behind the second row. Interestingly, the fluctuation amplitude in the middle of the jet becomes comparable to that at the jet edges. Further downstream, behind the fourth row, the fluctuation amplitude in the middle of the jet becomes substantially higher than that at the jet edges. This gradual change in the shape of the amplitude distributions will be discussed later in conjunction with the phase measurements and the flow visualization study.

3.3 Phase distributions

The phase of the velocity fluctuations was measured in detail behind the fourth row during the air tests. The phase was obtained by computing the cross spectrum (magnitude and phase) between the signals of a microphone, which constituted the reference transducer, and a hot wire, which was traversed across the flow. Both the microphone and the hot wire, were centered between the fourth and the fifth rows. All phase measurements were carried out at a flow velocity of 30.6 m/s, which corresponds to the amplitude distributions given in Fig. 6.

Before dealing with the phase distributions, it is helpful to discuss the relationship between the signal of a microphone, attached to the side wall of the wind tunnel, and that of a hot wire, positioned in the mid-span of the wind tunnel. Typical spectra of such a case are given in Fig. 7. While the microphone is sensitive to the response of the acoustical modes (f_1 and f_2 in Fig. 7 (b)), the hot wire is not because the acoustical particle velocity is perpendicular to the main flow dominating the hot wire response. The microphone is also sensitive to the flow periodicity within the array, see the peak at the frequency f_v in Fig. 7 (b). The broad band peak at f_t is caused by the turbulent boundary layer on the side wall of the wind tunnel.

Figs. 7 (c) and 7 (d) show the coherence function, C_{pv}, and the phase difference, ϕ_{pv}, between the microphone and the hot wire signals. At the frequency f_v, the coherence is relatively high, $C_{pv} = 0.9$, indicating that the microphone and the hot wire signals are well correlated despite the large span-

© IMechE 1991 C416/047

wise distance between them (about 5d). The phase measured from Fig. 7 (d) was therefore not only repeatable, but also meaningful.

The value of the coherence function at the frequency f_v is given in Fig. 8 as a function of the hot wire position. The solid data point indicates the position of the microphone. The value of C_{pv} remained in the range of 0.75 to 0.9, even when the microphone and the hot wire were positioned in different jets.

The phase distribution of the velocity fluctuation behind the fourth row is given in Fig. 9. The round data points in Figs. 9 (a) and 9 (b) represent the phase variations across jets 4 and 6, respectively. The triangular data points correspond to the phase across jets 5 and 7, but after adding a value of π. The phase distribution across any one jet is seen to be symmetric, i.e. the velocity fluctuations occurring at one edge of a jet is in phase with that at the other edge. Moreover, the velocity fluctuation in any jet as a whole is 180° out of phase with that in the neighbouring jet. The phase distributions across the four jets 4 to 7 are presented together in Fig. 9 (c). This figure emphasises the remarkable organised nature of the flow activities. Jet 5, for example, is in phase with jet 7, but is 180° out of phase with jets 4 and 6.

Two microphones attached to the side wall of the wind tunnel were used to survey the amplitude and the phase of the flow periodicity within the array. This was possible because the flow periodicity was well represented in the microphone signal. As shown in Fig. 10(a), the rms amplitude of the pressure fluctuation associated with the flow periodicity, p_v, is about 30 % of the total rms amplitude, p_T. Moreover, the streamwise development of the pressure fluctuation amplitude, p_v, is seen to be similar to that obtained by measuring the amplitude of the velocity fluctuation; compare Figs. 4 and 10 (a).

The phase difference between the pressure fluctuations at both sides of a jet was measured by mounting the microphones at the locations numbered 1 and 2 in Fig.1(d). By positioning the microphones at locations 2 and 3, the phase difference across the tube wake was obtained. This procedure was used to measure the phase difference across jet 5 and that across wake 4. The results of these measurements are given in Figs. 10(b) and 10(c).

The coherence of the pressure pulsations across the jet is always higher than that across the wake, see Fig.10(c). This difference may be due to the shorter distance between the microphones while measuring the phase across the jet. The coherence across the wake, however, was sufficiently high to yield repeatable phase measurements.

As shown in Fig.10(b), the phase difference across the jet is approximately zero, and that across the wake is approximately π. These phase differences are seen to be persistent up to the sixth row. Thus, the phase distribution behind any tube row, or at least behind any of the first six, can be expected to be generally similar to that behind the fourth row, which is detailed in Fig. 9.

4   FLOW VISUALIZATION

4.1   Effect of the Reynolds number

The development of the flow structure behind the second and the third rows as the Reynolds number is increased from 0.7×10^4 to 2×10^4 is shown in Fig. 11. At the lowest Reynolds number, Fig. 11(a), small scale vortices are formed in the shear layers behind the second row. These vortices are not related to the vorticity shedding excitation because the frequency of their formation is about 10 times higher than that of the vorticity shedding. In spite of this small scale vortex formation, the shear layers at both sides of the jet do not undergo any noticeable sideways (i.e. transverse) oscillations. The thickness of the jet therefore, remains uniform from the first to the fourth row, Fig. 11 (a). Downstream of the fourth row, the shear layers start to exhibit appreciable sideways oscillations.

At a Reynolds number of 1.5×10^4, Fig. 11 (b), the flow pattern which was observed behind the fourth row at the lowest Reynolds number moves upstream to behind the third row. The formation of the small scale vortices also moves upstream, it occurs behind the first row instead of the second. As shown in Fig. 11 (b), the shear layers oscillate sideways in a symmetric pattern with respect to the jet centerline. This produces periodic narrowing and widening of the jet issuing between the tubes of the third row. This is the oscillation pattern which is associated with the vorticity shedding excitation.

The shear layer sideways oscillations and the resultant periodic variations in the jet thickness become more intense when the Reynolds number is increased further to 2×10^4, Fig.11(c). This can be seen by comparing the deflection of the dye injection jets which are marked by the broken white lines. Since all the photos given in Fig. 11 correspond to the same time instant of the oscillation cycle, the relative intensity of oscillation is proportional to the deflection angle of the dye injection jets. This angle is seen to be larger the higher the Reynolds number is.

4.2 Flow structure in the tube wakes and the flow lanes

Flow visualization photos showing the formation of vortices in the tube wakes are given in Fig. 12. The vortices are seen to form symmetrically on both sides of the jet, Fig. 12(a), and anti-symmetrically in the tube wake, Fig. 12(b). This pattern of vortex formation agrees fully with the results of the phase measurements addressed earlier, Fig. 9.

The visualized flow structure was very organized and repeated itself consistently. This is demonstrated in Fig. 13 which shows an oscillation cycle of the flow pattern behind the fourth row. At t = 0, vortices are being formed at the outer edges of the tube wakes. At the same time, the vortices which were formed at the inner side of the wakes are being shed into the gap between the tubes of the fifth row. This shedding of vortices increases the flow velocity between the tubes in the fifth row. A hot film positioned at the fifth row recorded the maximum flow velocity at this instant.

One quarter of the cycle later, the jet thickness is enlarged and the vortices at the outer edges of the wakes become fully developed. At t=P/2, these vortices are shed into the outer flow lanes and new vortices are forming at the inner edges of the wakes. At this instant, the jet reaches its maximum thickness and the flow velocity at the fifth row becomes minimal. At t = 3P/4, the jet thickness starts to become smaller, the mean flow velocity starts to increase, and the inner vortices become fully developed. At the end of the cycle, t = P, the flow structure regains its original pattern; the inner vortices are shed into the gap between the downstream tubes and the outer vortices are forming.

Scrutiny of the photos in Fig. 13 reveals that there is a substantial amount of mass transfer between the flow lanes. At t=0 and t=P for example, there is a mass transfer from the outer flow lanes into the middle one. When this occurs, the flow velocity in the middle lane reaches its maximum value. At t=P/2, the mass transfer occurs in the other direction and the flow velocity in the middle lane becomes minimal.

Another feature which is exemplified in Figs. 12 and 13 is that despite the large size of the observed vortices, they are formed totally inside the tube wakes. They do not intrude into the flow lanes until they are fully formed.

4.3 Global structure of the flow instability

Flow visualization pictures taken at different locations within the array, but at the same time instant of the cycle, were pieced together to construct

the development of the flow structure within the first five rows. The signal of the hot film, which was kept in a fixed location, was used as a time reference. The result of this piece-wise method of flow visualization is shown in Fig. 14. The flow structure in the flow lane, Fig. 14(a), displays, very clearly, a symmetric mode of an unstable jet. The symmetry with respect to the jet centerline and the clarity of the jet structure are rather remarkable. In the tube wakes, Fig. 14(b), the vortices form in an anti-symmetric pattern. It should be mentioned here that this anti-symmetric pattern in the tube wakes is, in principle, not related in any way to the alternating vortex shedding from isolated cylinders.

In a recent flow visualization study of a closely packed, in-line tube array (15), the present authors suggested that the flow periodicity is dominated by the instability of the jets which issue between the tubes; further, it was argued that this jet instability must occur at the symmetric mode because of the influence of the downstream tubes, which are positionend symmetrically at both sides of the jet. These suppositions, which were based on very little evidence, are substantiated beyond doubt by the present experiments. A detailed discussion of the kinematic constraints associated with the in-line geometry and why these constraints impose the symmetric mode of the jet instability can be found in Ref. (15).

There is a major difference between the present results and those of the closely packed array (15). Whereas the vortex pattern in the tube wakes of the closely packed array was found to be symmetric, an anti-symmetric pattern occurred in the present tests. This is due to the difference in vortex size which is related to the streamwise spacing in both cases. In the closely packed array, the formed vortices were very small and there was no mass transfer across the tube wakes. This allowed the wake vortices to form symmetrically and therefore adjacent jets oscillated in phase with one another. In the present case of intermediate tube spacings, the formed vortices are larger and they occupy a large portion of the confined tube wakes. There is also a substantial mass transfer across the wakes. This necessitates anti-symmetric vortex formation in the wakes. Since these wake vortices are generated by the instability of the jets in the adjacent lanes, it follows that the jet instability occurring in a flow lane must be 180° out of phase with that occurring in the adjacent lanes.

The wavelength of the jet instability pattern is not twice the streamwise spacing (2L) as may appear from Fig. 14. Careful study of Fig. 14 (b) indicates that the vortex formed behind the fourth row is less developed than that formed behind the third row which, in turn, is less developed than that formed behind the second row. This observation agrees with the results of the phase measurements carried out by means of two microphones attached to the wind tunnel side wall.

5 DESCRIPTION OF THE VORTICITY SHEDDING EXCITATION

When the tubes are arranged in an in-line pattern, they form free flow lanes and confined tube wakes. As the flow proceeds into the array, a jet-like profile develops continuously along the flow lanes, but a wake profile never develops in the tube wakes. Thus, the flow dynamics in the flow lanes would be expected to dominate the development of the velocity fluctuations within the array. The present results accord with this expectation; the vorticity shedding excitation is shown to be caused by the instability of the jets which proceed along the flow lanes.

The jet instability is initiated at the locations of flow separation from the tubes in the first row. In this initial region, the velocity fluctuation is still small and is manifested primarily in the thin shear layers of the jet. Between the first and the second rows, the velocity fluctuation undergoes a spatial exponential growth, which is in accordance with the linear theory of hydrodynamic stability. Furthermore, the amplitude and the phase of the initial velocity fluctuation have symmetric distributions with respect to the jet centerline.

As the flow proceeds downstream, or as the Reynolds number is increased, the amplitude of the velocity fluctuation grows until it reaches the non-linear saturation amplitude, typically about 15% of the gap flow velocity. Further downstream, the increase in the turbulence level reduces the saturation amplitude slightly.

The jet instability occurs at a preferred symmetric mode (for reasons which are discussed in detail in Ref. (15)). This is shown by measuring the distributions of the phase and the amplitude of the velocity fluctuations behind the first, the second and the fourth rows, and also by visualizing the flow structure. Large scale vortices are formed symmetrically at both sides of each flow lane. Because of the kinematic constraints imposed by the large size of the formed vortices and the associated mass transfer across the wakes, vortices are forced to form anti-symmetrically in the tube wakes. This dictates the phase difference between the flow activities in adjacent flow lanes. The flow visualization results and the measured phase distribution show that the jet instability occurring in each flow lane is 180° out of phase with that occurring in the neighbouring lanes.

More insight into the flow activities downstream of the jet developing region can be gained by further study of the present data. The amplitude distributions given in Fig. 6 exhibit rapid changes as the flow proceeds downstream. The fluctuation amplitude at the jet centerline, in comparison with that at the jet edges, increases rapidly from a negligible value behind the first row to being significantly larger behind the fourth row. The phase distribution behind the fourth row, Fig. 9, is relatively flat across the jet and undergoes a sudden jump of about 180° at the wake centerline. These findings suggest the existence of a rather pulsating flow downstream of the jet developing region, i.e. behind the fourth row. Indeed, the ejection of the fully developed jet vortices into the small gap between the tubes may well generate such a pulsating flow. Moreover, the existence of pulsating flows with a phase shift of 180° at both sides of a tube column can generate vortices which are totally confined to the tube wakes until they are ejected into the flow lanes when the pulsating flow changes direction. Such features have also been observed in the visualized flow structure.

6 CONCLUSIONS

An in-line tube bundle with spacing ratios of $X_L/X_T = 1.75/2.25$ has been tested in air and water flows to investigate the nature of the vorticity shedding excitation and the flow structure associated with it. Correlation measurements, by means of a hot wire and two microphones, have been carried out during the air tests to construct the distributions of the amplitude, the phase and the coherence of the fluctuating velocity, behind several tube rows. These distributions together with the hot film measurements and the flow visualization, carried out during the water tests, revealed a clear picture of the type and the evolution of vorticity shedding excitation.

The instability of the jet issuing between the tubes is found to be the source of the vorticity shedding excitation. The jet instability occurs at the symmetric mode. Large scale vortices are formed on both sides of the flow lanes. The measured distributions and the flow visualization photos depict very clearly a developing jet instability pattern within the first few rows. Downstream of this development region, the flow in the lanes between the tubes resembles a pulsating flow pattern, which is caused by the flow blockage as the symmetric vortices are shed into the small gap between the tubes.

Due to the kinematic constraints imposed by the large size of the formed vortices, the flow blockage and the mass transfer between adjacent flow lanes, the jet instability in any flow lane is 180° out of phase with those in the neighbouring lanes. Thus, the vortices in the tube wakes are forced to form anti-symmetrically, i.e. similar, but in principle not related, to the alternating vortex shedding from isolated cylinders.

The jet instability is expected to dominate the vorticity shedding excitation for a wide range of in-line tube spacings, as long as the tubes do not become too far from one another. In a recent work by the authors (15), the jet instability was found to be dominant in a closely packed array (X_L/X_T = 1.4/1.5). Current tests with larger spacing ratios suggest that the present findings are still valid for tube spacings as large as X_L/X_T = 2.6/3.0. For relatively large tube spacings however, X_L/X_T = 3.25/3.75, the coherence between both sides of the flow lanes becomes very weak, although the vortices still form symmetrically.

ACKNOWLEDGEMENT

This work is jointly supported by "Schweizerisches Bundesamt für Energiewirtschaft BEW" (The swiss federal office for energy) and the Thermal Energy Department of Sulzer Brothers Limited. The financial support and permission for publication are gratefully acknowledged. The authors are grateful to Mr. R. Qian for his help during the initial period of this research.

REFERENCES

(1) PAIDOUSSIS, M.P. Flow induced vibration in nuclear reactors and heat exchangers: practical experiences and state of knowledge. IUTAM-IAHR Symposium on *Practical Experiences with Flow Induced Vibrations* (eds. E. Naudascher and D. Rockwell), 1979, 1-81, Springer-Verlag.

(2) PAIDOUSSIS, M.P. Fluidelastic vibration of cylinder arrays in axial and cross flow: state of the art. *Journal of Sound and Vibrations*, 1981, 76, 329-360.

(3) PAIDOUSSIS, M.P. A review of flow-induced vibrations in reactors and reactor components. *Nuclear Engineering and Design*, 1982, 74, 31-60.

(4) WEAVER, D.S. and FITZPATRICK, J.A. A review of cross-flow induced vibrations in heat exchanger tube arrays. *Journal of Fluids and Structures*, 1988, 2, 73-93.

(5) BAIRD, R.C. Pulsation-induced vibration in utility steam generation units. *Combustion*, 1954, 25, 38-44.

(6) Grotz, B.J. and Arnold, F.R. Flow induced vibration in heat exchangers. Dept. of Mech. Eng., Stanford University, 1956, Report No. 31.

(7) CHEN, Y.N. Flow induced vibration and noise in tube-banks of heat exchangers due to von Karman streets. *Journal of Engineering for Industry*, 1968, 90, 134-146.

(8) HALLIDAY, J. Boiler vibration caused by combustion gas flow. ASME Paper 56-A-216, 1956.

(9) PUTNAM, A.A. Flow induced noise in heat exchangers. *Journal of Engineering for Power*, 1959, 81, 417-422.

(10) OWEN, R.R. Buffeting excitation of boiler tube vibration. *Journal of Mechanical Engineering Science*, 1965, 7, 431-439.

(11) CHEN, Y.N. The sensitive tube spacing region of tube bank heat exchangers for fluid-elastic coupling in cross flow. ASME Symposium, *Fluid-Structure Interaction Phenomena in Pressure Vessel and Piping Systems* (eds. M.M. Au Yang, S.J. Brown), 1977, 1-18.

(12) FUNAKAWA, M. and UMAKOSHI, R. The acoustic resonance in a tube bank. *Journal of the Japan Society of Mechanical Engineers*, 1970, 13, 348-355.

(13) WEAVER, D.S. and ABD-RABBO, A. A flow visualization study of a square array of tubes in water crossflow. *Journal of Fluids Engineering*, 1985, 107, 354-363.

(14) ABD-RABBO, A. and WEAVER, D.S. A flow visualization study of flow development in a staggered tube array. *Journal of Sound and Vibration*, 1986, 106, 241-256.

(15) ZIADA, S., OENGOEREN, A. and BUEHLMANN, E.T. On acoustical resonance in tube arrays - Part I: experiments. *Journal of Fluids and Structures*, 1989, 3, 293-314.

(16) FITZPATRICK, J.A. and DONALDSON, I.S. A preliminary study of flow and acoustic phenomena in tube banks. *Journal of Fluids Engineering*, 1977, 99, 681-686.

(17) FITZPATRICK, J.A. A design guide proposal for avoidance of acoustic resonances in in-line heat exchangers. *Journal of Vibrations, Acoustics, Stress, and Reliability in Design*, 1986, 108, 296-300.

(18) RAE, G.J. and MURRAY, B.G. Flow induced acoustic resonances in heat exchangers. International Conference on Flow-Induced Vibrations, Bowness-on-Windermere, England, 1987, 221-231.

(19) DONALDSON, I.S. and McKNIGHT, W. Turbulence and acoustic signals in a cross-flow heat exchanger model. *Flow induced vibrations*, ASME Third National Congress on Pressure Vessel and piping Technology, California, 1979, 123-128.

(20) ZIADA, S. and ROCKWELL, D. Generation of higher harmonics in a self-oscillating mixing layer-edge system. *A.I.A.A.J.*, 1982, 20, 196-202.

(21) Robinson, J.L. The inviscid non-linear instability of parallel shear flows. *Journal of Fluid Mechanics*, 1974, 63, 723-752.

(22) FITZ-HUGH, J.S. Flow-induced vibration in heat exchangers. UKAEA/NPL International Symposium on Vibration Problems in Industry, Keswick, Paper No. 427.

(23) CHEN, Y.N. Flow-induced vibrations of in-line heat exchangers. Symposium on Flow Induced vibrations, 3 (eds. M.P. Paidoussis, J.M. Chenowth, J.M. Bernstein), New Orleans, 1984, 163-170.

(24) RAE, G.J. and WHARMBY, J.S. Strouhal numbers for in-line tube arrays. International Conference on Flow-Induced Vibrations, Bowness-on-Windermere, England, 1987, 233-242.

(25) WEAVER, D.S., FITZPATRICK, J.A. and ELKASHLAN, M. Strouhal numbers for heat exchanger tube arrays in cross flow. *Flow-Induced Vibrations*, ASME Publication PVP-104, 1986, 193-200.

(26) MICHALKE, A. On spatially growing disturbances in an inviscid shear layer. *Journal of Fluid Mechanics*, 1965, 23, 521-544.

(27) BAJAJ, A.K. and GARG, V.K. Linear stability of jet flows. *Journal of Applied Mechanics*, 1977, 44, 378-384.

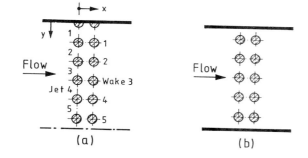

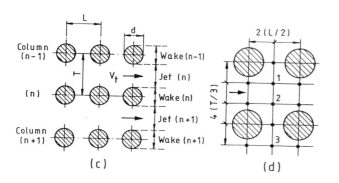

Fig 1 Schematic presentation of the tested tube array. (a) wind tunnel test section, (b) water channel test section, (c) system parameters, (d) possible locations of pressure measurements with respect to the array lattice.

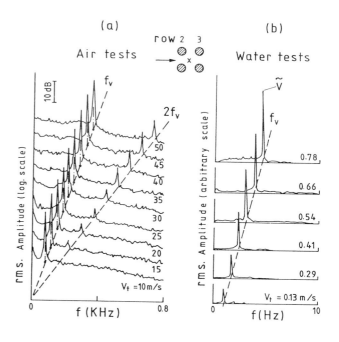

Fig 2 Typical spectra of the streamwise fluctuating velocity measured behind the second row in (a) the air tests and (b) the water tests.

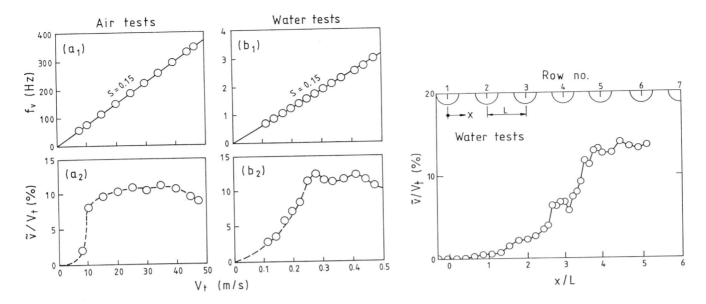

Fig 3 Frequency and dimensionless amplitude of the periodic velocity fluctuation as functions of the gap velocity (a) behind row 2 - air tests, (b) behind row 4 - water tests.

Fig 4 Development of the streamwise velocity fluctuation along the center-line of a flow lane. Water tests, $V_t=0.27$ m/s, Re=6.8 x 10^3, $f_v=1.65$ Hz.

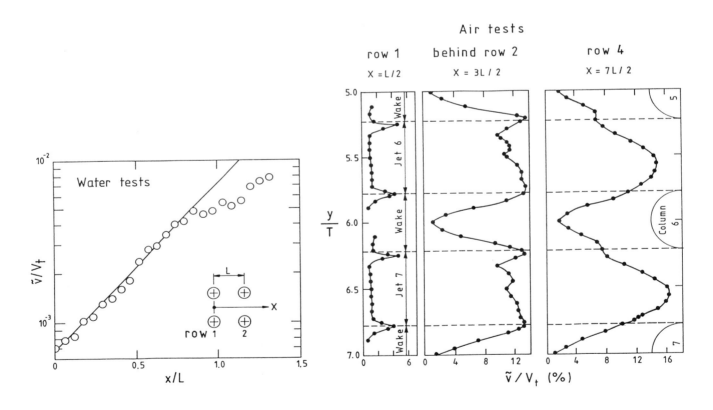

Fig 5 Initial exponential growth of the streamwise velocity fluctuation. Water tests, $V_t=0.27$ m/s, Re=6.8 x 10^3, $f_v=1.65$ Hz.

Fig 6 Distributions of the dimen-sionless amplitude of the velocity fluc-tuation behind the first, the second and the fourth rows. Air tests, $V_t=30.6$ m/s, Re=3.8 x 10^4, $f_v=230$ Hz.

506

© IMechE 1991 C416/047

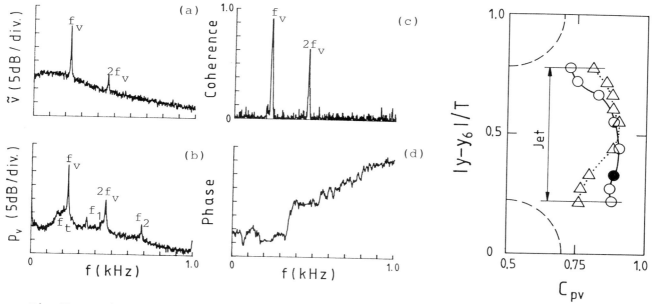

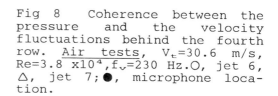

Fig 7 Typical results of correlation measurements during the <u>air tests</u>. (a) spectrum of a hot wire positioned in jet 6 behind row 4, (b) spectrum of a microphone positioned on the side wall in jet 6 behind row 4, (c) coherence and (d) phase between the hot wire and the microphone signals. V_t = 30.6 m/s.

Fig 8 Coherence between the pressure and the velocity fluctuations behind the fourth row. <u>Air tests</u>, V_t=30.6 m/s, Re=3.8 x10⁴, f_v=230 Hz. O, jet 6, △, jet 7; ●, microphone location.

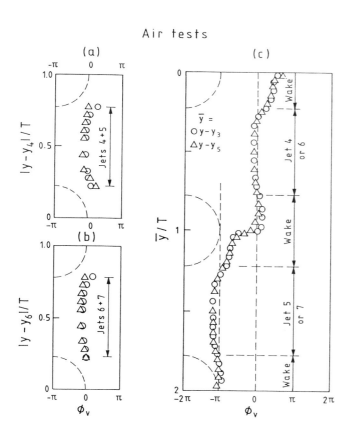

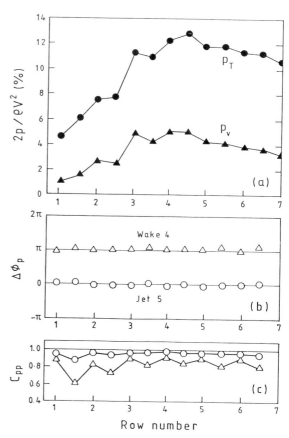

Fig 9 Phase distributions of the velocity fluctuation behind the fourth row at x=7L/2. <u>Air tests</u>, V_t=30.6 m/s, Re=3.8 x 10⁴, f_v=230 Hz. (a) O, ϕ_{v4};△, ϕ_{v5} + π; (b) O, ϕ_{v6}; △, ϕ_{v7} + π ; (c) O, ϕ_{v4} and ϕ_{v5}; △, ϕ_{v6} and ϕ_{v7}.

Fig 10 Streamwise distributions of (a) amplitude, (b) phase and (c) coherence of pressure fluctuation on the side wall of the wind tunnel. <u>Air tests</u>, f_v=230 Hz, V_t = 30.6 m/s. ●, total rms amplitude, (p_T);▲, rms amplitude at frequency f_v, (p_v); O,△, phase and coherence across, O, jet 5 and,△, wake 4.

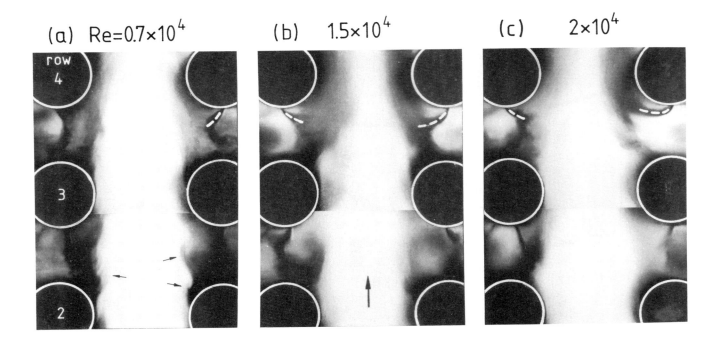

Fig 11   Effect of Reynolds number on the flow development. (a) Re=0.73 x 10⁴, (b) 1.5x10⁴, (c) 2x10⁴. The arrows in Fig. (a) indicate small scale vortices behind the second row.

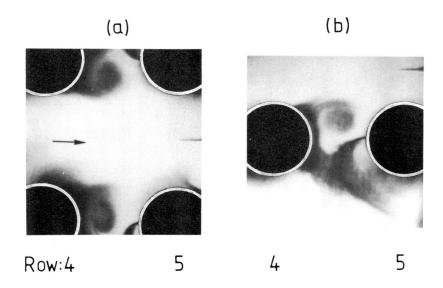

Row:4   5   4   5

Fig 12   Flow visualization photos showing (a) symmetric vortex formation in a flow lane and (b) anti-symmetric vortex formation in a tube wake. Re=1.5 x 10⁴.

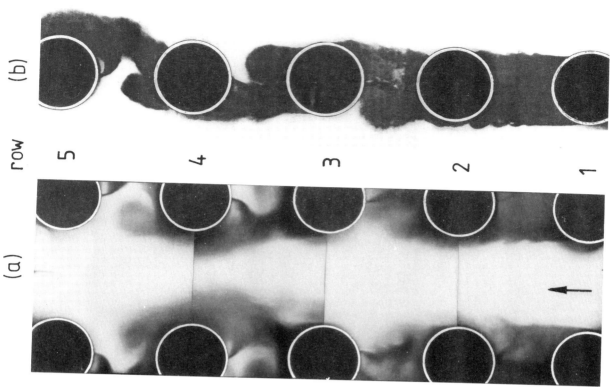

row 5 4 3 2 1

(b)

(a)

Fig 14 Flow visualization photos showing the global flow structure in (a) a flow lane and (b) several tube wakes. Re = 1.5 x 10⁴.

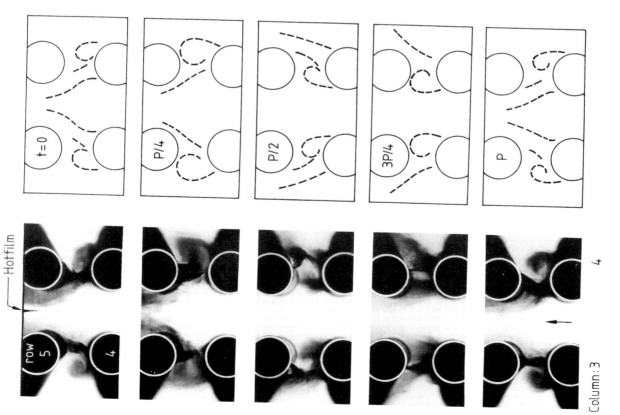

Hotfilm

row 5 4

Column:3

t=0   P/4   P/2   3P/4   P

Fig 13 Time series showing the flow activities during one period, P, of oscillations. Re=1.0 x 10⁴.

509

C416/091

A study of vortex shedding in a normal triangular tube array

D S WEAVER, PhD, H Y LIAN and X Y HUANG, PhD
Department of Mechanical Engineering, McMaster University, Hamilton, Ontario, Canada

SYNOPSIS A fundamental experimental study was conducted to determine the nature of the constant Strouhal number excitation phenomenon in a normal triangular array of tubes in cross flow. A special wind tunnel test section was designed with large tubes arranged in a normal triangular pattern with pitch ratio of 1.71 so that the interstitial flow could be studied. Flow visualization showed clear alternate vortex shedding in the first three tube rows.

1   INTRODUCTION

Flow-induced vibrations in heat exchanger tube arrays have caused numerous tube failures in a variety of heat exchange equipment (1). An extensive literature has developed and several thorough reviews have been published (2-4). It is now generally accepted that the fluid excitation mechanisms can be lumped into 4 categories: (a) turbulence, (b) vortex shedding, (c) fluid-elastic instability and (d) acoustic resonance. The vortex shedding mechanism is the subject of this paper.

Significant data in the literature show that some constant Strouhal number periodicity exists in tube arrays. This phenomenon may excite tube vibration in liquid flows or acoustic resonance in gas flows. In order to predict the onset of resonance, the Strouhal number for a particular array must be known. Unfortunately, this is rather difficult because of the enormous scatter in the data (5-7). While some of this scatter may be attributed to experimental error, it is now recognized that the Strouhal number for a given array may be Reynolds number and row depth dependent and there may even be multiple Strouhal numbers at a given Reynolds number (see, for example, reference 7).

Confusion has been added by the controversy regarding the basic nature of this excitation mechanism. Owen (8) believed that discrete vortex shedding was impossible in closely spaced tube arrays and attributed tube excitation to a peak in the turbulence spectrum. As a result, this mechanism has been called a variety of names including turbulence, vorticity shedding, and periodic wake shedding. While it is certain that this mechanism is distinct from turbulence, its precise nature has remained a mystery. Indeed, there may well be more than one constant Strouhal number excitation mechanism. Weaver and Abd-Rabbo (9) observed symmetric vortex shedding in an in-line tube array but this was associated with large amplitude streamwise tube motion. No flow periodicity was observed in the absence of tube motion. On the other hand, Abd-Rabbo and Weaver (10) reported clear alternate vortex shedding in the early tube rows of a rotated square array. However, the flow was laminar and the Reynolds number was too low to be of practical significance. No observations of actual vortex shedding have been reported for tube arrays with flow velocities in the turbulence range. Thus, this appelation is based on circumstantial evidence and the true mechanism(s) remains unknown.

The purpose of the research presented in this paper was to study the interstitial flow in a normal triangular tube array and, thereby, to elucidate the nature of the constant Strouhal number excitation mechanism. A special wind tunnel test section was designed to permit interstitial flow measurements and visualization. Flow periodicity data and flow visualization photographs showing alternate vortex shedding in the first two tube rows will be presented.

2   EXPERIMENTAL FACILITY AND PROCEDURE

As a result of all of the confusion and controversy regarding the constant Strouhal number mechanism, it was decided to chose an array of tubes which was most likely to yield clear results. Weaver and Yeung (11) found that a normal triangular array of tubes in a water flow showed clear off-resonance tube response and a well defined resonance peak which was well separated from fluid-elastic instability. Thus, the normal triangular geometry exhibits measurable flow periodicity which does not depend on tube motion or acoustic feedback and is readily distinguishable from other excitation mechanisms. A pitch ratio of 1.71 was chosen together with large diameter acrylic tubes (88.9 mm OD) to facilitate interstitial flow measurement and flow visualization. As this excitation mechanism is apparently dominant in the early tube rows, the array was made only four rows deep. A cross-section of the array is shown in figure 1. Half-tubes were placed on the side walls to minimize boundary effects. The tubes were cantilevered rigidly from the bottom of the test section and two top plates were used, one perforated for hot-wire probe traverses and one completely clear for unobstructed viewing of the flow.

This test section was placed in a low turbulence wind tunnel (turbulence intensity less than 0.2%) with a flat velocity profile (within 1%)

upstream of the tube array. The test section was 0.305 m square.

The upstream velocity was measured using a pitot static probe and a Betz micromanometer. The velocities and turbulence spectra within the array were obtained using a calibrated DISA 90-degree miniature hot-wire probe in conjunction with a DISA constant temperature anemometer. The output was displayed on a digital voltmeter and turbulence spectra were obtained from 100 sample averages using a Spectral Dynamics Fourier Analyzer. Measurements were taken at various upstream velocities up to about 3 m/s which corresponds to a Reynolds number of 1.77×10^4 based on upstream velocity and tube diameter.

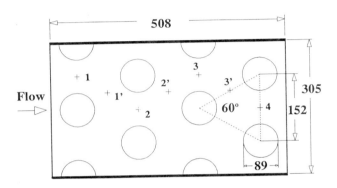

Fig. 1   Schematic cross-section of tube array

3   EXPERIMENTAL RESULTS AND DISCUSSION

Turbulence spectra were observed at a number of locations in the array over a range of flow velocities up to 3 m/s. Typical spectra are shown in figures 2(a) and (b) which correspond to location 2' behind the second row at an upstream velocity of 0.14 m/s and to location 1' behind the first row at an upstream velocity of 0.30 m/s, respectively. Both spectra are the result of 100 sample averages and show discrete periodicity in the flow.

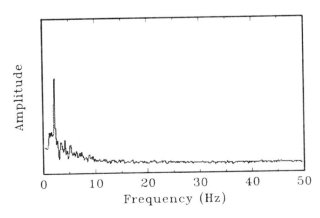

Fig. 2(a)   Frequency spectrum behind second tube row, $V_u = 0.14$ m/s.

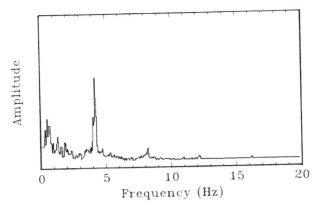

Fig. 2(b)   Frequency spectrum behind first tube row, $V_u = 0.30$ m/s.

The frequency data from such spectra are plotted against upstream flow velocity in figure 3. It is seen that the discrete periodicity is a linear function of flow velocity and gives a Strouhal number, S_u, based on upstream flow velocity, V_u, and tube diameter, d, of 1.20

$$S_u = \frac{fd}{V_u} = 1.20 \qquad (1)$$

Zukauskas and Katinas (12) developed an empirical formula for Strouhal numbers in normal triangular arrays. Their Strouhal number, S_g, is based on the mean velocity in the gap between tubes in a row, V_g, and is given by:

$$S_g = 0.2 + \exp\left(\frac{-X_p^{1.8}}{2.3}\right) \qquad (2)$$

where X_p is the array pitch ratio, $X_p = p/d$. For the present array, the pitch ratio is 1.71 and the Strouhal number predicted by equation 2 is $S_g = 0.52$. For a normal triangular array, the mean gap velocity is related to the upstream velocity by simple continuity

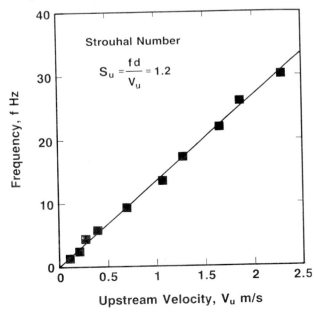

Fig. 3   Frequency vs. upstream flow velocity

$$V_g = \left(\frac{X_p}{X_p - 1}\right) V_u \qquad (3)$$

Using a pitch ratio of 1.71 in equation 3 gives $V_g = 2.41 V_u$. Thus, the Strouhal number for the present array based on gap velocity is $S_g = 0.50$. This agrees very well with the empirical prediction of Zukauskas and Katinas. It is reasonable to assume, therefore, that the flow periodicity measured in this rigid array is caused by the same phenomenon as observed by Zukauskas and Katinas in arrays with the same geometry but different pitch ratios. It remains to discover what this phenomenon is.

Spectra similar to those illustrated above were obtained at a variety of locations through the array at several flow velocities. The averaged discrete frequency peak was found to be largest at row 2, location 2 in figure 1, and the data from other locations were normalized with respect to this largest value and plotted against row depth location in figure 4. It is seen that negligible periodicity was measured at location 1, midway between the tubes in row 1. More surprisingly, the discrete periodicity has reduced to negligible levels by location 3, midway between tubes in row 3. These data were obtained over the flow velocity range 0.22 m/s $\leq V_u \leq 1.57$ m/s corresponding to a Reynolds number range $1300 \leq R_u \leq 9300$. It would appear that the discrete periodicity is created in the first two tube rows in this array and is very rapidly dissipated by turbulence. It must be stated, however, that if the tube were excited to vibrate or in the presence of acoustic resonance, the flow periodicity would undoubtedly be sustained much deeper into the tube bank. Although not so clear in figure 4, the maximum periodicity strength occurred at an upstream flow velocity just over 1 m/s, which corresponds to a Reynolds number of the order of 6000. By a flow velocity $V_u \simeq 1.6$ m/s ($R_u \simeq 9450$), the periodicity is becoming somewhat unsteady and the spectra show several smaller peaks around the dominant one. For flow velocities above about 2.5 m/s ($R_u \simeq 1.5 \times 10^4$), the periodicity becomes submerged in the background broad band turbulence.

4 FLOW VISUALIZATION

The research to this point has simply served to show that the periodicity in the flow of the present rigid array is the same phenomenon as reported earlier by numerous authors for geometrically similar arrays. A flow visualization study was conducted to determine as far as possible the basic nature of the flow periodicity.

The flow was seeded using a mixture of ammonia and sulphur dioxide gases. This produces a dense white precipitate which is ideal for photography. A 10 mm thick sheet of light was shone through the tube bundle at right angles to the axis of the tubes and at a distance 70 mm below the top of the test section. This provided illumination for the tracer while eliminating any boundary layer effects. The light source was a high intensity strobe which was triggered by a miniature hot-wire probe inserted between the tubes where significant velocity fluctuations were observed. The flow was observed and photographed from above the test section, looking at the ends of the tubes.

Figures 5(a) and (b) show still photographs of the flow downstream of a 2nd row tube at a flow velocity, $V_u = 0.14$ m/s. These pictures correspond to the frequency spectrum given in figure 2(a). The flow is from left to right. Figure 5(a) shows a vortex just forming in the shear layer separating from the top edge of the tube and a fully formed vortex in the shear layer separating from the bottom edge. A previous vortex from the top edge has been stretched out as it passes between the 3rd row tubes. Figure 5(b) shows the same alternate vortex shedding process about 1/2 a cycle later. The triggering hot-wire probe appears as a white line slanting downwards from above the tube in both photographs. At higher flow velocities, turbulence obscures the flow pattern and clear alternate vortex shedding could not be seen. However, the hot-wire spectra showed the same periodicity and, importantly, the Strouhal number remains essentially the same at higher flow velocities.

Figures 6(a) and (b) show flow visualization photographs behind the 1st row tube at a flow velocity, $V_u = 0.30$ m/s. These correspond to the frequency spectrum of figure 2(b). Figure 6(a) shows vortex formation at about the same point in the cycle as figure 5(a). Note the stretched out vortex which has been shed from the upper edge between the 2nd row tubes. Figure 6(b) shows the vortex shedding process at a slightly later point in the cycle. The previously shed vortex has essentially disappeared and the vortex in the lower shear layer is about to separate.

The fact that essentially laminar vortex shedding is sustained at higher velocities behind the first row tubes than behind the second row tubes is not surprising. Similar behaviour was observed by Abd-Rabbo and Weaver (10) in their water-tunnel study of flow development in a rotated square tube array. The transition to turbulence occurs first behind the third tube row and moves upstream in the bundle as the flow velocity is increased. Thus, laminar vortex shedding is observed behind the 1st row tube long after such behaviour has disappeared behind the second row tubes. Again, it is important to note that the flow periodicity behind the first row tube

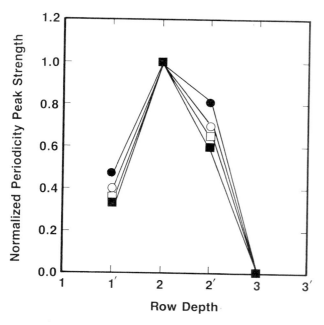

Fig. 4   Vorticity strength vs. row depth

remains at essentially the same Strouhal number for velocities well beyond those for which laminar vortex shedding is observed. It seems reasonable to conclude that the periodicity in the flow at these higher flow velocities is turbulent alternative vortex shedding.

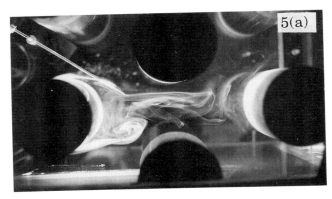

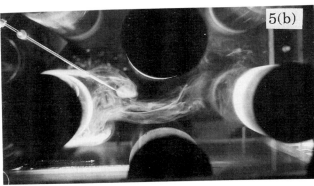

Fig. 5   Flow visualization behind second row, $V_u = 0.14$ m/s.

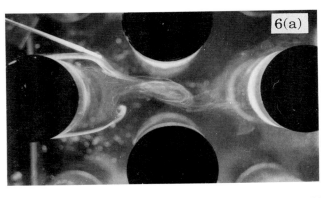

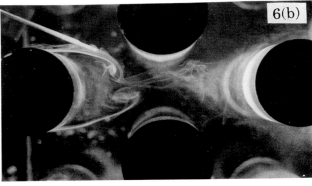

Fig. 6   Flow visualization behind first row, $V_u = 0.30$ m/s.

5   CONCLUSIONS

An experimental wind tunnel study has been conducted on a rigid array of tubes of normal triangular geometry with a pitch ratio of 1.71. Interstitial turbulence spectra were obtained using a miniature hot wire probe at a variety of locations in the array and over a range of flow velocities up to 3 m/s (Reynolds number of 1.8×10^4 based on upstream velocity and tube diameter). Flow visualization was used to study the fluid mechanics. The principal conclusions drawn are as follows:

1.   Turbulence spectra show discrete periodicity at a Strouhal number based on upstream velocity of 1.20 over a range of Reynolds numbers $830 \leq R_u \leq 1.5 \times 10^4$.

2.   Flow visualization at the low end of the Reynolds number range $830 \leq R_u \leq 1800$ showed that the discrete periodicity is due to alternate vortex shedding. Since the Strouhal number of the flow periodicity over the entire Reynolds number range is the same, it is concluded that turbulent alternate vortex shedding is the mechanism causing the periodicity.

3.   Alternate vortex shedding occurs only in the first two rows of this normal triangular array and, in the absence of tube motion or acoustic resonance, the vorticity is stretched out and submerged in the turbulence of the further downstream tube rows.

4.   Since the Strouhal number obtained for the present array agrees with the empirical prediction of Zukauskas and Katinas (12) obtained for arrays of the same geometry but different pitch ratios, it is reasonable to assume that the dominant periodic flow excitation mechanism in normal triangular arrays is alternate vortex shedding.

ACKNOWLEDGEMENTS

The authors gratefully acknowledge the financial support of the Natural Sciences and Engineering Research Council of Canada.

REFERENCES

(1)   PAIDOUSSIS, M.P., "Flow-induced vibrations in nuclear reactors and heat exchangers: practical experiences and state of knowledge", In Proceedings IAHR/IUTAM Symposium on Practical Experiences with Flow-Induced Vibration, eds. E. Naudascher, D. Rockwell, Springer-Verlag, Berlin, 1980, pp. 1-81.

(2)   PAIDOUSSIS, M.P., "A review of flow-induced vibrations in reactors and reactor components", Nuclear Engineering and Design, 1983 (74), pp. 31-60.

(3)   WEAVER, D.S. and FITZPATRICK, J.A., "A review of cross-flow induced vibrations in heat exchanger tube arrays", J. of Fluids and Structures, 1988 (2), pp. 73-93.

(4) CHEN, S.S., *Flow-Induced Vibration of Circular Cylindrical Structures*, Hemisphere Publishing Corp., 1987.

(5) FITZ-HUGH, J.S., "Flow-induced vibration in heat exchangers", Proceedings of the International Symposium on Vibration Problems in Industry", paper 427, Keswick, U.K., 1973.

(6) CHEN, Y.N., "Flow induced vibration and noise in tube banks due to von Karman streets", *ASME J. of Engineering for Industry*, 1968 (90), pp. 134-146.

(7) WEAVER, D.S., FITZPATRICK, J.A. and ELKASHLAN, M., "Strouhal numbers for heat exchanger tube arrays in cross flow", *ASME J. Pressure Vessel Technology*, 1987 (109), pp. 219-223.

(8) OWEN, P.R., "Buffeting excitation of boiler tube vibration", *J. of Mechanical Engineering Science*, 1965, vol. 7(4), pp. 431-439.

(9) WEAVER, D.S. and ABD-RABBO, A., "A flow visualization study of a square array of tubes in water cross-flow", *ASME J. of Fluids Engineering*, 1985 (107), pp. 354-363.

(10) ABD-RABBO, A. and WEAVER, D.S., "A flow visualization study of flow development in a staggered tube array", *J. of Sound and Vibration*, 1986 vol. 106 (2), pp. 241-256.

(11) WEAVER, D.S. and YEUNG, H.C., "The effect of tube mass on the flow induced response of various tube arrays in water", *J. of Sound and Vibration*, 1984, Vol. 93(3), pp. 409-425.

(12) ZUKAUSKAS, A. and KATINAS, V., "Flow induced vibration in heat exchanger tube banks", Proceedings IAHR/IUTAM Symposium on Practical Experiences with Flow Induced Vibration, Karlsruhe 1979, eds. E. Naudascher and D. Rockwell, Springer-Verlag, Berlin, 1980, pp. 188-196.

C416/062

Wall pressure distribution on an in-line tube bundle in cross-flow

L R LJUNGKRONA, MSc(Eng) and B A SUNDEN, MSc(Eng), PhD
Department of Thermo-and Fluid Dynamics, Goteborg, Sweden
H G D GOYDER, BSc, MA, PhD and C E TEH, BSc, PhD
AEA Industrial Technology, Harwell Laboratory, Oxfordshire

SYNOPSIS
Experimental results of mean and fluctuating pressures on tube surfaces in an in-line square tube bundle having a pitch to diameter ratio of 1.26:1 are presented. The measurements were carried out in an open-circuit wind tunnel at Harwell Laboratory. Data were taken for the first, second and mid tube rows. The fluctuating pressures were recorded by a microphone placed in a pin-hole configuration. The r.m.s. fluctuating pressure coefficients are low on the first tube row but much higher on the second and mid tube rows. A velocity dependent frequency with low corresponding Strouhal numbers was detected.

NOTATION

C_p	mean pressure coefficient
$C_{p'}$	r.m.s. pressure coefficient
$C_{p'_{ac}}$	r.m.s. pressure coefficient of the acoustical disturbances (based on the approach velocity)
D	tube diameter
f_s	Strouhal frequency
G_{pp}	pressure energy spectra or velocity energy spectra
p	mean pressure
p'	fluctuating pressure
$P'_{r.m.s.}$	r.m.s. - value of fluctuating pressure
Re	Reynolds number ($= u_{max}D/\nu$)
u_{max}	maximum velocity = gap velocity
U_o	$= u_{max}$ (used in Figs. 4 and 5)
y	coordinate in the transverse direction

Greek symbols

ν	kinematic viscosity
ρ	density
φ	angle from forward stagnation point

1. INTRODUCTION

The vibration of tubes in heat exchangers can be excited by high wall pressure fluctuations around initially stationary tubes. However, only a few studies (1,2) have dealt with the wall pressure distributions (mean, r.m.s. and related quantities) in tube bundles.

Batham (1) measured mean and fluctuating pressures on tubes in in-line square bundles having pitch to diameter ratios of 2:1 and 1.25:1. Tests were carried out at Reynolds numbers in the range of $2.8 \cdot 10^4$ to 10^5 and he found that the Reynolds number had a negligible effect on the mean and r.m.s. fluctuating pressure coefficients within this range.

Incident turbulence was found to have a large effect for the widely spaced bundle, but no effect for the closely spaced bundle. For the closely spaced bundle, the mean pressure distribution on the 7th row tubes (10 rows in the flow direction) was highly three-dimensional and small movements of the upstream tubes caused strong changes in the distribution. This latter fact suggests that the flow in closely spaced bundles is governed by a Coanda switching phenomenon. See also Cheng and Moretti (3), who recently investigated flow patterns in some tube bundles. As an effect, the pressure distribution is not necessarily symmetric around the tube surface. For the widely spaced bundle, coherent peaks corresponding to vortex shedding and wake oscillation were observed in the spectra of the pressures. The number of peaks (and associated Strouhal numbers) were found to be a function of the Reynolds number but agreed poorly with the work by Chen (in the paper by Chenoweth (4)). Turbulence in the incident flow suppressed the coherent peaks from the first few tube rows. For the closely spaced bundle no peaks corresponding to vortex shedding were identified.

Zdravkovich and Namork (2) measured pressure distributions (mean and r.m.s.) in a triangularly staggered tube bundle. The transverse pitch to diameter ratio was 1.375:1 while the longitudinal one was 1.875:1. The bundle was six row deep and measurements were taken at a Reynolds number of $1.1 \cdot 10^5$. It was found that the pressure distributions in the first two tube rows were quite different from those in the rest of the bundle. The reason for this is the different structure of the flow at various positions in the bundle. To confirm the conclusion concerning susceptibility of tubes in the second row to flow vibration, tests with the same tube bundle with one end of the tubes free to move were conducted.

A recent investigation (5) concerning the flow behind a single row and two rows of tubes showed flow regions with great nonuniformities at small transverse pitch to diameter ratios. These flow nonuniformities resulted in non-symmetric mean pressure distribuions on the tube surfaces.

Mean pressure distributions on tubes in various bundle configurations are available in (6,7).

The present collaborative work concerns an experimental investigation of mean and fluctuating pressures on the tube surfaces in an in-line square tube bundle having a pitch to diameter ratio of 1.26:1. Data were taken for the first, second and mid tube rows. Most of the measurements were taken at two Reynolds numbers ($5.1 \cdot 10^4$ and $6.8 \cdot 10^4$) and were repeated a couple of times. Due to the limited available knowledge on fluctuating wall pressures in tube bundles, the present paper, which is a brief account of a comprehensive investigation, will provide new and additional knowledge in this field.

2. TEST EQUIPMENT

2.1 Wind tunnel

The Harwell wind tunnel shown in Fig. 1 was used in the measurements. The working section has a cross section of 0.457 x 0.457 m and the contraction ratio of the air intake is 3.2:1. Air is forced through the wind tunnel by a centrifugal fan which is capable of giving a maximum empty tunnel velocity of 30 m/s. The fan is run at constant speed and control of the flow through the test section is achieved by bleeding air into the tunnel, downstream of the test section.

Flow measurements (pitot static tube) in the empty tunnel showed that the mean velocity was reasonable uniform (within 2 %).

During the measurements, the approach air velocity was determined from the pressure drop across the intake contraction measured using a micromanometer.

The background acoustical disturbances in the wind tunnel were measured by a wall-mounted microphone. At the lowest approach velocity (3.6 m/s), the r.m.s. - value of the acoustical pressure coefficient $C_{p'}{}_{ac}$ was 2.1. By increasing approach velocity, this value decreased and at an approach velocity of 15.2 m/s $C_{p'}{}_{ac}$ was 0.17.

2.2 Tube bundle

The tube bundle comprises 10 rows in the flow direction and 14 rows in the transverse direction. The tubes of perspex have an outer diameter of 25.4 mm. This bundle has previously been used in experiments concerning the critical flow velocity for fluid-elastic instability, see (8). Originally, the tubes had one end cantilevered into a thick perspex wall, while the other end was free to move. In the present investigation, the bundle was rigidized so that both ends were fixed to the walls of the test section. An instrumented tube was placed sequentially in various rows to enable the measurements. The results from measurements on rigid tubes provide insight in the susceptibility of various tubes to vibrate and the fluid mechanics involved. This matter may be

confirmed by complementing measurements with flexible tubes.

2.3 Instrumented tube

The instrumented tube was equipped with a 1/4" microphone (B & K 4135) in a pinhole arrangement in order to measure the fluctuating wall pressure. The mean pressure was recorded by a pressure tap placed 0.18 m from the pinhole. Details of the pressure measurement technique is provided in (9) and (10).

2.4 Hot wire measurements

A hot wire was used to measure the turbulence structure in the empty wind tunnel and to measure the turbulence level and in particular the frequencies of the velocity fluctuations in the bundle. A Dantec P01 hot wire was traversed behind the first, second and mid tube rows.

2.5 Data acquisition system

The digital data acquisition systems of Harwell and Chalmers University were employed in the measurements and evaluations. Data were also recorded on a tape recorder (Tandberg TIR 115) and diskettes for later evaluation.

In the pressure measurements typically 256 ksamples at a sampling frequency of 5 kHz were taken. In the hot wire measurements 256 ksamples with a sampling frequency of 10 kHz were taken.

2.6 Experimental uncertainties

The uncertainties in the determination of the r.m.s. coefficients are estimated to be less than 3 %.

3. RESULTS AND DISCUSSION

3.1 Mean pressure distributions

Figure 2 shows measured distributions of the mean pressure coefficient on the first, second and fifth tube rows. C_p is defined as

$$C_p = 1 - \frac{p(\varphi=0) - p(\varphi)}{\rho u_{max}^2/2} \qquad (1)$$

where u_{max} is the gap velocity.

It is evident that the C_p - distribution on the first tube row is different from those on the second and fifth rows. This fact is the result of changes in the flow structure as the fluid penetrates deeper into the bundle. The distribution on the first tube row is similar to that on a single tube. The C_p - distribution on the second tube row is not symmetric around the surface. This might be caused by small imperfections in the in-line arrangement. It is known from (1), (3) and (5) that the flow patterns in closely spaced bundles are very sensitive to disturbances and various patterns may occur. The pressure distribution is then affected accordingly. Unsymmetric pressure distributions have also been found in (9) for two tubes in in-line arrangements if the

© IMechE 1991 C416/062

dimensionless tube spacing is ≤ 1.5. The C_p-distribution (second tube row) in Fig. 2 shows a minimum at the forward stagnation point. At $\varphi \approx$ 50-55 ^{o} on the upper side (φ positive) and $\varphi \approx$ 35 ^{o} on the lower side maxima occur probably due to reattachment of shear layers separated from the tubes in the first row. A minimum appears at $\varphi \approx$ 90 ^{o} on both sides and then a relatively flat maximum shows up. These maxima may be due to flow separation from the second tube row. It is also found that for the rear part of the tubes, in the second row, the C_p - distribution is rather symmetric.

The C_p - distribution on the fifth row looks similar to that on the second row but the levels of C_p is lower except around $\varphi = 0$ ^{o}. Also the first maximum appears at a lower φ - value than on the second tube row. After the appearance of the minimum, the distribution gradually approaches a constant value at the rear part. The results on the fifth row agree with those in (6) and (7) for a tube deep in the bundle despite that the Reynolds number in (6) and (7) is higher. Distributions on the first and second rows for a 1.26 x 1.26 in-line bundle have not been reported in the literature previously.

3.2 R.m.s. pressure coefficients

In the evaluation of the fluctuating pressure signals on the tube surfaces, the signals from the wall-mounted microphone were subtracted. No acoustic resonance was found in this case.

The r.m.s. pressure coefficients on the first, second and fifth rows are provided in Fig. 3. $C_{p'}$ is defined as

$$C_{p'} = \frac{p'_{r.m.s.}}{\rho u_{max}^2 / 2} \qquad (2)$$

It is obvious that the level of $C_{p'}$ is very low on the first tube row. This distribution is almost increasing monotonically with increasing (and decreasing) φ - values but a maximum seems to appear at $\varphi \approx \pm 90$ ^{o}, which is in accord with the minima appearing at $\varphi \approx \pm 90$ ^{o} in the distribution of the mean pressure coefficient.

The distributions on the second and fifth rows show high values of $C_{p'}$ and the distributions are not symmetric around the tube surfaces. Again this might be due to imperfections in the in-line arrangement. The disturbances in the flow pattern may be strongly reflected in the fluctuating pressure and as an effect non-symmetrical distributions are achieved. The peaks in the $C_{p'}$ - distributions appear at positions corresponding to those in the C_p - distributions. The lower side on the tube in the second tube row shows however a bumpy behaviour.

It should be pointed out that we attemped

to get rid off the unsymmetric distributions by lining up the bundle as perfect as possible several times. However, we were not successful and presently we believe that the unexpected non-symmetrical distributions are due to flow instabilities. Measurements at two other Reynolds numbers also showed non-symmetrical distributions. A preliminary investigation for a 1.75 x 1.75 in-line bundle indicates much better symmetry in the distributions.

3.3 Spectral distributions

Some spectral distributions are shown in Fig. 4. In the spectra evaluations, the acoustic signals were not subtracted and thus some of the peaks appearing in the spectras are from the acoustical disturbances. However by studying the results on the first tube row at two Reynolds numbers, a velocity dependent frequency is identified. The corresponding Strouhal number is low, Sr ≈ 0.04 at the lower Reynolds number and Sr ≈ 0.03 at the higher. Multiple values of Strouhal number were not found. It should be mentioned that additional measurements did not verify this and the existence of this velocity dependent frequency is uncertain. However, vortex shedding in an in-line bundle (pitch to diameter ratio = 1.5) with low Strouhal numbers has been reported by Price and Paidoussis (11).

The spectral distributions of the velocity fluctuations, see Fig. 5, do not indicate any particular peaks. (The Reynolds number in Fig. 5 is slightly less than those in Fig. 4). The acoustical disturbances seem not to be reflected either. (In Fig. 5, y = 0 is at the middle of the gap between two tubes).

4. CONCLUSIONS

An experimental investigation of mean and r.m.s. pressure distributions on tubes in an in-line bundle (pitch to diameter ratio 1.26:1) has been performed.

The mean pressure distribution on the second tube row and the r.m.s pressure distributions on the second and fifth tube rows were not symmetric. These results are believed to be associated with flow instabilities and not with tube surface imperfections. The r.m.s. pressure coefficients were low on the first tube row but much higher on the second and fifth tube rows.

A velocity dependent frequency with low corresponding Strouhal numbers was detected. However, additional measurements did not verify this conclusion.

5. REFERENCES

(1) BATHAM, J.P. Pressure distributions on in-line tube arrays in cross flow, Int. Symp. Vibr. Prob. Industry, Keswick, 1973, Paper No 411, 1-24.

(2) ZDRAVKOVICH, M.M., NAMORK, J.E. Excitation, amplification and suppression of flow-induced vibrations in heat exchangers, Proc. Practical Experiences with Flow Induced Vibration, Berlin, 1980, Paper A5, 109-117.

(3) CHENG, M., MORETTI, P.M. Flow instabilities in tube bundles, The 1989 ASME Pressure Vessels and Piping Conference, 1989, PVP-Vol. 154, 11-15.

(4) CHENOWETH J.M. Design of shell and tube heat exchangers to avoid flow induced vibration, Proc. VIIth Int. Heat Transfer Conference, Munich, 1982, Vol. 6, 173-178 (Hemisphere Publ. Corp)

(5) ZDRAVKOVICH, M.M., STONEBANKS, K.L. Intrinsically nonuniform and metastable flow in and behind tube arrays, J. Fluids and Structures, 1990, Vol. 4, 305-319.

(6) ZUKAUSKAS, A.A., ULINSKAS, R., KATINAS, V. Fluid dynamics and flow-induced vibrations of tube banks, 1988, Hemisphere Publ. Corp.

(7) ZUKAUSKAS, A.A. Convective heat transfer in cross flow, Handbook of Single-Phase Convective Heat Transfer, 1987, Ch. 6, 6.1-6.45.

(8) SOPER, B.M.H. Experimental studies of fluid elastic whirling of cantilevered elements, 1982, Final report on IEA-work 1977-1980.

(9) LJUNGKRONA, L. Influence of freestream turbulence and tube spacing on wall pressures for two tubes in an in-line arrangement, Thesis, 1990, Dept. of Applied Thermodynamics and Fluid Mechanics, Chalmers University of Technology, Göteborg.

(10) NORBERG, C., SUNDEN, B. Turbulence and Reynolds number effects on the flow and fluid forces on a single cylinder in cross flow, J. Fluids and Structures, 1987, Vol. 1, 337-357.

(11) PRICE S.J., PAIDOUSSIS, M.P. The flow-induced response of a single flexible cylinder in an in-line array of rigid cylinders, J. Fluids and Structures, 1989, Vol. 3, 61-82.

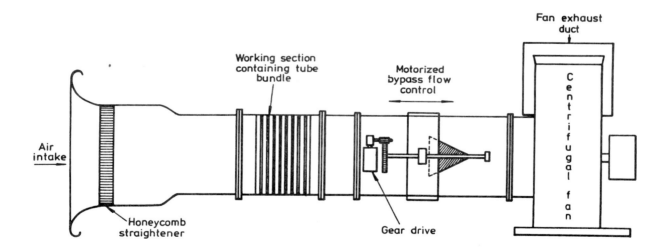

Figure 1. General arrangement of the Harwell wind tunnel.

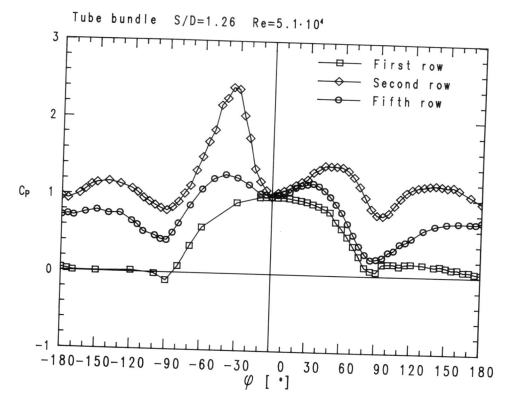

Figure 2. Distributions of mean pressure coefficient on the first, second and fifth tube rows.

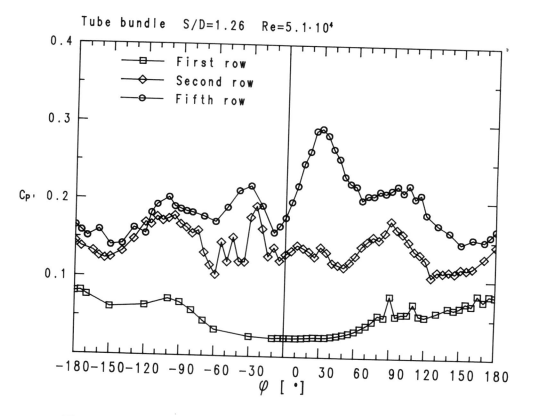

Figure 3. Distribution of r.m.s. pressure coefficient on the first, second and fifth tube rows.

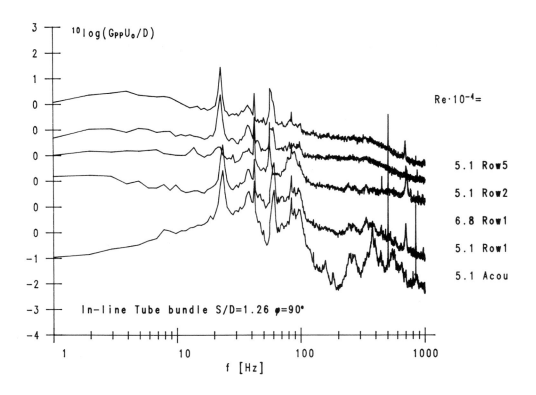

Figure 4. Spectral distributions of the pressure fluctuations.

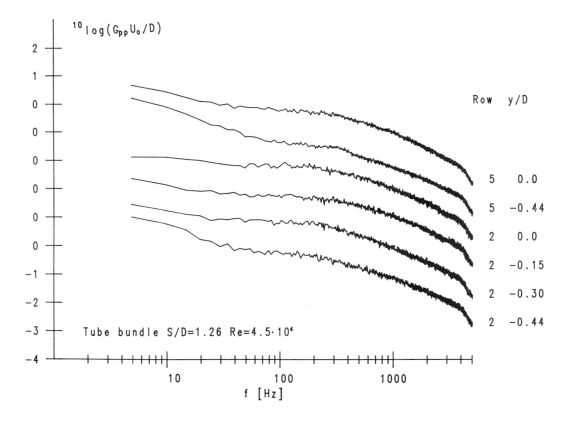

Figure 5. Spectral distributions of the velocity fluctuations.

C416/069

Flow-excited acoustic resonance in a duct: the feedback mechanism

J WU, MSc, J SORIA, PhD, K HOURIGAN, PhD, M C WELSH, BE
and L W WELCH, DipEng
CSIRO Division of Building, Construction and Engineering, Highett, Victoria, Australia

SYNOPSIS The feedback effect of sound and velocity perturbations on shear layers separating from plates and aerofoils is reported. The feedback effect leads to the formation of discrete vortices in the shear layers by a number of different processes. The particular process depends on the state of the boundary layers prior to separation and whether or not the plates or aerofoils are located in a duct flow or an open jet.

NOTATION

U   freestream velocity (mm/s)

$\tilde{u}$ fluctuating flow velocity (R.M.S.) imposed by oscillating side walls (mm/s)

Δz spanwise distance across the aerofoils or plates (m)

1 INTRODUCTION

Flow-excited acoustic resonances were examined in detail by Parker (1,2) using a cascade of plates in a duct. He found that higher order duct acoustic modes were excited in the space surrounding the plates and defined these two-dimensional modes as the α, β, γ and δ modes (2). Similarly, the resonant acoustic modes excited by flow in multi-tube heat exchangers were higher order modes which vibrated in a plane transverse to the mean flow direction (3).

Since the late 1970s, Welsh and his colleagues (4–9) have examined the fluid dynamics of the flow-excited acoustic resonant process. Their initial experiments (4), using a single plate located in a duct with the longer sides parallel to the flow, showed that the major variables in the excitation process were the vorticity shed from the plate and the particle velocity of the excited acoustic mode. The dominant acoustic mode always had an acoustic particle velocity antinodal line along the vortex street. Further experiments were undertaken to establish the phase relationship between the acoustic particle velocities and the vortex shedding. It was found that a vortex always commenced growth when the acoustic particle velocities changed direction and were in the same direction as that of the mean flow at the point where the flow separated from the plate.

From their observations, Welsh et al. (5) developed a model of the acoustic resonant process which had three fundamental components: (a) an acoustic source (vortex street), (b) a feedback effect of the resonant sound on the development of the vortex street, and (c) a damping process whereby the acoustic energy generated by the source was transferred out of the duct. Using their model and the empirical phase relationship data, Welsh et al. (5) were able to use Howe's theory (10) of aerodynamic sound to predict the flow velocities at which net acoustic energy was available to excite

a resonant acoustic field. The model gave good agreement with the experimental flow velocities corresponding to when resonances were observed. Recently, Hourigan et al. (9) improved the model of acoustic resonance using more sophisticated mathematical models of the flow to predict the experimentally observed results. This model also correctly predicted the phase relationship between the acoustic field and the vortex shedding process when a resonance was excited.

There were two key assumptions associated with the feedback mechanism in the mathematical models discussed above, namely, (a) that when the resonant acoustic particle velocity was greater than a particular threshold, the vortex shedding was in phase along the trailing edge of the plate leading to an efficient sound source, and (b) that the frequency of the oscillating resonant acoustic particle velocity at the point where the flow separated from the plate determined the rate of vortex shedding during resonance.

Although the mathematical models described above predicted the overall acoustic resonant process well, the two assumptions described in (a) and (b) above have not been explicitly validated. The aim of this paper is to describe experiments which provide more evidence of the validity of these assumptions. It will be shown that when a two-dimensional oscillating velocity field exceeds a particular threshold amplitude, the vortices shed in phase along the trailing edge of a plate and remain in phase for more than four plate thicknesses downstream in the wake. Furthermore, it will be shown that for a laminar wake, an oscillating velocity field overrides the instability excited by vortex impingement and causes vortices to shed at the frequency of the oscillating field.

2 BACKGROUND

For two aerofoils or plates (aerofoils/plates) located in tandem in a duct, flow-induced oscillations in the wake from the upstream aerofoil can be generated in a number of different ways. The geometries of the objects in the flow, the ducting surrounding the flow and whether or not the flow in the wake is laminar or turbulent all determine which mechanism is responsible for flow-induced unsteadiness in wake flows.

Johnson and Loehrke (11) examine the fluid dynamics of the generation of sound by the flow around two aerofoils/plates located in tandem in an open jet. They show that the vortex impingement feedback mechanism, as described by Rockwell and Naudascher (12) and Rockwell (13), is responsible for the unsteadiness in the wake when the aerofoils shed a laminar boundary layer. The frequency of the unsteadiness is a function of the flow velocity and the gap between the aerofoils. Johnson and Loehrke (11) also show that when the trailing edge of the leading aerofoil is thickened, a turbulent separated wake is shed. The frequency of the unsteadiness in the wake is then independent of the downstream aerofoil when the gap between the aerofoils is greater than three trailing edge thicknesses. There is an acoustic source at the trailing edge of the leading aerofoil and, depending on the spacing between the aerofoils, an acoustic sink or an acoustic source at the leading edge of the downstream aerofoil. In this case the vortex impingement feedback mechanism is overridden by the formation of a normal asymmetric vortex street shed within the context of an absolute instability in the near wake (14).

The results described by Stoneman et al. (7) show that when two plates are shedding a turbulent wake in a hard walled duct, a resonant acoustic standing wave is excited by the flow. The velocity perturbation due to the resonant acoustic field can be as high as 25% of the mean flow velocity. In this case, the oscillating perturbation velocity field due to a resonant acoustic standing wave overrides the formation of a normal asymmetric vortex street even when the flow is turbulent. Vortices form in the shear layers shed from each side of a thick plate at the sound frequency close to the trailing edge. When the downstream plate is positioned in the preformation region (15), that is, within two plate thicknesses of the upstream plate, the formation of the vortex street would normally be suppressed but with the resonant acoustic field present, the vortices are generated at the acoustic frequency and form an asymmetric vortex street which passes around the downstream plate (M.C. Welsh, pers. comm.).

In summary, the cases of a laminar wake and a turbulent wake with two aerofoils/plates located in tandem in an open jet (11), and the case of a turbulent wake inside a hard walled duct surrounded by a resonant sound field, have been investigated (7; and M.C. Welsh, pers. comm.).

3 EXPERIMENTAL EQUIPMENT & PROCEDURE

3.1 Water tunnel

The return circuit water tunnel, schematic shown in Fig. 1, is designed for low levels of freestream turbulence in the square working section and is described in detail in (8). Water is pumped through a diffuser incorporating screens into a settling chamber containing filter material and a honeycomb section. The water then passes through a two-dimensional four-to-one contraction with an outlet dimension of 244 mm x 244 mm into ducting having the same dimensions. This duct consists of three sections, a 660 mm length followed by a 770 mm long working section and a further length of 440 mm which is connected to an outlet reservoir. The duct sections are constructed from 20 mm thick acrylic sheet supported and joined by aluminium flanges.

The mean volume flow through the tunnel is monitored with an orifice plate installed in accordance with the British Standard and the mean velocity can be varied up to a maximum of 400 mm/s. The mean velocity profile, 1030 mm downstream of the contraction outlet between the wall boundary layers, is uniform within 0.5% and the longitudinal turbulence level is typically 0.1% when band-pass filtered between 0.08 Hz and 20 Hz. The spectra of the fluctuating longitudinal velocity is free of sharp peaks and decreases in amplitude by 20 dB/Hz from 0.08 Hz.

A major feature of the water tunnel is the flexibly mounted, full width, 400 mm long panels in the centre of the working section (see enlargement detail Fig. 1). These could be oscillated in unison to superimpose a transverse flow velocity perturbation on the mean flow similar to that imposed by a resonant acoustic β-mode (2). An eccentric cam generates an essentially sinusoidal oscillation with the velocity amplitude of the second harmonic 10 dB below the fundamental and other harmonics at least 20 dB below. The oscillation could be adjusted in amplitude over the range 0 to 5 mm and in frequency from 0 to 6 Hz.

3.2 Test models

All of the test models are manufactured from acrylic and two test model configurations are used in these experiments. The first consists of two aerofoils in tandem with the leading aerofoil being a C4 type (16) having a maximum thickness of 12.4 mm, zero camber and a chord of 130 mm (Fig. 2a). This aerofoil is mounted vertically on the centre-line of the working section at zero angle of attack. A second aerofoil, shaped like the leading edge of the first aerofoil, is located in tandem 32 mm downstream (Fig. 2a). The second model arrangement, a single plate (Fig. 2b), again utilised a C4 aerofoil leading edge which is connected to a constant thickness flat plate to form a model with a chord of 130 mm and a maximum thickness of 12.2 mm. This plate is also mounted vertically on the centre-line of the working section at zero angle of attack.

Based on the chord of the leading aerofoil, and the chord of the single plate, the Reynolds number for the experiments described in this paper is typically 1×10^3. All of the experiments are carried out with a water temperature of approximately 15°C.

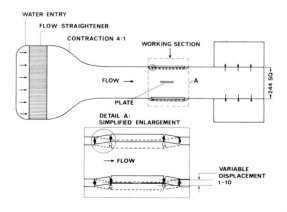

Fig. 1. Schematic of return circuit water tunnel showing the oscillating side walls of the working section.

© IMechE 1991 C416/069

3.3 Flow visualisation

The hydrogen bubble technique (17) is used for flow visualisation where the hydrogen bubbles are generated by electrolysis from a nicrome wire cathode. The light is generated by a continuous 4 W A-Ion laser spread into a thin sheet and passed through a side wall of the working section. Scotchlight 7516 material is placed on the opposite side of the working section to reflect the laser light exactly back over itself and thereby increase the light intensity.

The flow is viewed in two different planes. For both model configurations (Figs 2a and 2b) the aerofoils and the plate are mounted vertically and the sheet of laser light and the hydrogen bubbles are horizontal; the flow is then viewed from above the models. The flow near the plate in the second configuration (Fig. 2b) is also viewed in another plane. The model, the sheet of hydrogen bubbles and the sheet of laser light are all vertical with the hydrogen bubbles positioned 24 mm upstream of the model. The sheet of laser light is located 48 mm downstream of the plate at right angles to the flow direction in a plane parallel with the trailing edge. The flow is viewed by looking upstream through a window in the outlet reservoir at the oncoming flow.

3.4 Calibration of the velocity perturbation imposed by the oscillating side walls

The amplitude and frequency of the oscillation of the side walls are measured by a displacement transducer when the flow velocity is 207 mm/s. The vortex shedding frequency is 4.69 Hz and the side walls of the working section are oscillated at this frequency. The fluctuating velocities are measured at a reference point 1 mm from the surface of the plate and 3 mm upstream from the trailing edge using a 'TSI' single channel He-Ne Laser Doppler Anemometer (LDA) in back scatter mode. Hydrogen bubbles introduced from the surface of the model are used for seeding giving sampling rates of typically 20 Hz. The calibration data are shown in Fig. 3.

Since the flow can only be seeded with a mean flow, the LDA measures the total velocity perturbation which includes the effects of boundary layer turbulence, vortex shedding, etc. To determine the velocity perturbation imposed by oscillating the side walls in the absence of mean flow, the total velocity perturbation is measured with the walls oscillating at amplitudes greater than 0.08 mm peak to peak (the vortex shedding becomes virtually two-dimensional at these amplitudes; see Section 4.2). These data are then extrapolated linearly back to zero wall oscillation to determine the effect due to turbulence, etc.

3.5 Measurement of the instantaneous flow velocities

The instantaneous flow velocities surrounding the two aerofoils in tandem (Fig. 2a) are obtained using a particle image velocimetry (PIV) technique (18). The flow is seeded with hydrogen bubbles similar to that used for the flow visualisation. This technique permits the measurement of the instantaneous flow velocities in a plane surrounding the aerofoils. It has a major advantage over particle tracking techniques in that it avoids the extremely difficult task of individually tracking dots on a film.

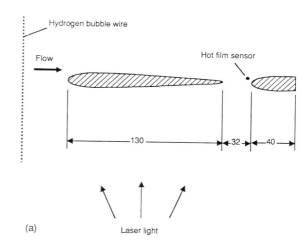

(a)

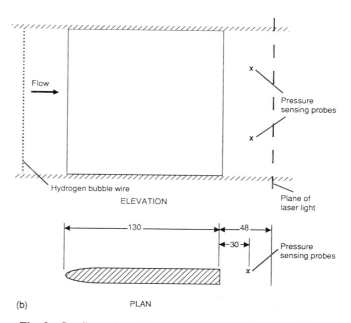

(b)

Fig. 2. Configuration of test models: (a) tandem aerofoils; (b) single plate.

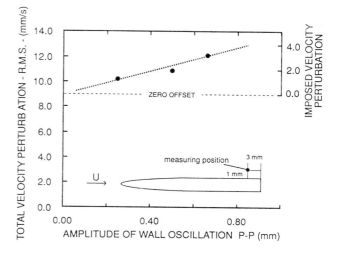

Fig. 3. Calibration of perturbation velocity imposed on flow around plate with oscillation of side walls at 4.69 Hz for a flow velocity of 207 mm/s.

Conditionally averaged data are obtained using the PIV technique by locating a miniature hot film sensor (TSI 1260-10W in conjunction with a TSI-IFA 100 anemometer) 32 mm downstream of the trailing edge of the leading aerofoil and 2 mm from the surface of the second aerofoil (Fig. 2a) in a plane 9.6 mm below the plane of the bubbles. The positive going zero crossing of the hot film signal is used to trigger the photographs for the PIV at the same point in the oscillation cycle. A total of 36 photographs are used to produce the conditional ensemble averaged data which are used to produce the instantaneous streamline patterns of the flow.

3.6 Measurement of coherence, cross-correlation and spectra

The low-frequency pressure fluctuations associated with the wakes are measured using two solid state pressure transducers ('Micro Switch' 163PC01D36) connected by PVC tubing to probes made from short lengths of 1.6 mm OD hypodermic tubing. The total length from probe tip to pressure transducer is less than 140 mm for both probes. The resulting signals are amplified by 40 dB and bandpassed between 0.01 and 10.0 Hz. The sensing tip of each tube is placed 5.3 mm from the centreline of the plate and 30 mm downstream of the trailing edge where the pressure fluctuations due to the oscillating velocity field are 20 dB less than those due to the vortex shedding (Fig. 2b). All the measurements are made with a flow velocity of 171 mm/s where the vortex shedding frequency is 3.75 Hz.

The fluctuating signals are recorded and processed on a 'DEC' PDP 11/44 computer with two analog-to-digital convertors operating through a Laboratory Peripheral Accelerator. The fluctuating signals are typically sampled at 40 Hz for 320 s. Subsequent data processing to determine cross-correlation, coherence and power spectra is carried out using the 'Signal Technology' signal processing software package ILS. FFT calculations are averaged over 50 frames using 256 data points per frame. A 'Data Precision' four-channel Data 6000–Universal Waveform Analyzer is used for signal monitoring and real time statistical processing.

4 RESULTS

4.1 Two aerofoils in tandem

Figure 4a shows a PIV photograph of the laminar flow past the two aerofoils located in tandem. An oscillation in the wake is clearly evident (1.66 Hz) when the flow velocity is 74 mm/s. When the downstream aerofoil is removed, there is no significant oscillation in the wake and no discrete vortices are formed.

The data depicted in the PIV photograph in Fig. 5a correspond to exactly the same geometry and flow approaching the aerofoils as that shown in Fig. 4. However, the side walls of the water tunnel are oscillating at 2.5 Hz and generate a fluctuation velocity perturbation at the trailing edge of the upstream aerofoil of 3.6% of the freestream velocity. Under

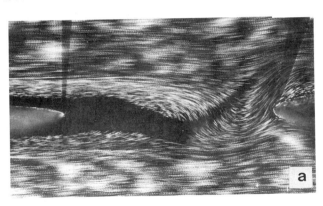

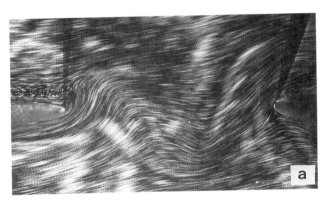

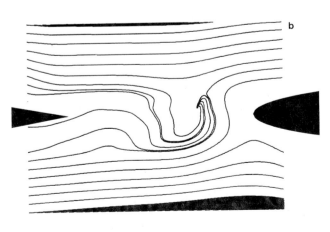

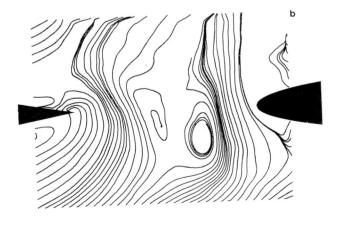

Fig. 4. Flow around aerofoils in tandem without side walls oscillating, U = 74 mm/s: (a) particle image velocimetry photograph; (b) instantaneous streamlines calculated from conditional ensemble averaged data in a frame of reference moving at 20.9 mm/s.

Fig. 5. Flow around aerofoils in tandem with side walls oscillating to give a velocity perturbation of 3.6% of the freestream velocity, U = 74 mm/s: (a) particle image velocimetry photograph; (b) instantaneous streamlines calculated from conditional ensemble averaged data in a frame of reference moving at 57.7 mm/s.

© IMechE 1991 C416/069

these circumstances, the vortices are shed at the same frequency as the frequency of the perturbation velocity.

The instantaneous streamlines corresponding to the flows shown in Figs 4a and 5a are shown in Figs 4b and 5b respectively. In Fig. 4b, the streamlines are in a reference frame moving with the convection velocity (20.9 mm/s) of the vortex nearest the downstream aerofoil; the data in Fig. 5b are for an observer moving with a velocity of 57.7 mm/s. These data can be interpreted using critical point theory (19). There is a marked difference between the topologies of the flows and in particular the difference between the foci just upstream of the downstream aerofoil. The flow without the side walls oscillating (Fig. 4) is much more three-dimensional.

4.2 Single plate

With the single plate (Fig. 2b), the influence of oscillating the side walls at the natural Strouhal vortex shedding frequency on the coherence and the cross-correlation of the pressure

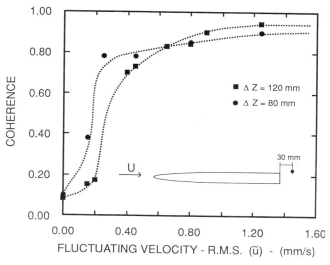

Fig. 6. Variation of the coherence at 3.75 Hz of the pressure signals 30 mm downstream of the single plate with perturbation velocity amplitude for a freestream velocity of 171 mm/s.

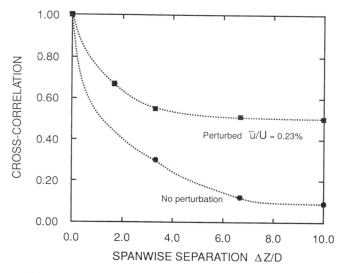

Fig. 7. Influence of perturbation velocity on the cross-correlation of the pressure signals 30 mm downstream of the single plate for a range of spanwise locations of the sensors at a freestream velocity of 171 mm/s.

signals near the trailing edge of the plate is shown in Figs 6 and 7. There is a significant increase in the coherence of the pressure signals at the vortex shedding frequency when the perturbation velocity is greater than a very small velocity perturbation (0.2% of the freestream velocity).

Without an ocillation superimposed on the flow, the autocorrelation of the pressure signals oscillates at the Strouhal vortex shedding frequency at all positions along the span of the plate, while the cross-correlation decreases rapidly to almost zero with a transverse spacing of approximately six plate thicknesses (Fig. 7). However, when a transverse velocity perturbation is imposed on the flow at the natural Strouhal vortex shedding frequency, the cross-correlation is sensitive to the perturbation and remains relatively high over the span of the plate.

Typical photographs of the flow downstream of the plate without and with the transverse velocity perturbation superimposed on the flow at the natural Strouhal vortex shedding frequency are shown in Figs 8a and 8b. The vortices are seen to be more compact when the forced oscillation is present; the convection velocity of the vortices is also reduced indicating a higher circulation in the vortices.

The alternative view of the flow around the plate without and with the forced velocity perturbation superimposed on the flow is depicted in Figs 9a and 9b. Without the walls oscillating the vortex wake is clearly passing through the sheet of laser light with varying phase (Fig. 9a). However, when the two-dimensional transverse velocity perturbation is superimposed on the flow, the wake has the same phase across the span of the plate (Fig. 9b).

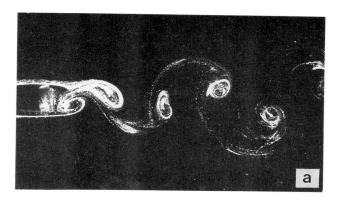

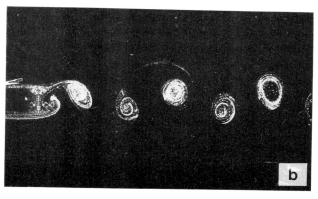

Fig. 8. Flow downstream of a single plate, U = 81 mm/s: (a) no flow perturbation imposed on flow; (b) with a flow perturbation of 0.5% of the freestream velocity imposed on the flow at the natural Strouhal vortex shedding frequency (1.55 Hz).

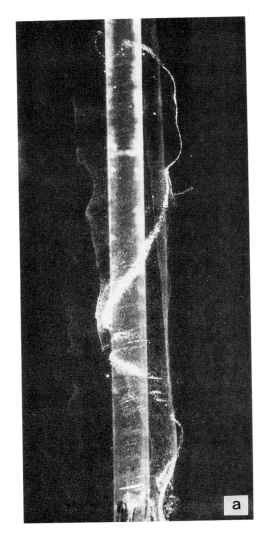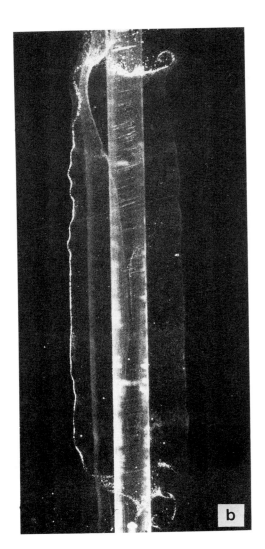

Fig. 9. Flow passing through a plane 48 mm downstream of a single plate and parallel to the trailing edge, U = 81 mm/s: (a) no flow perturbation imposed on flow; (b) with a flow perturbation of 0.5% of the freestream velocity imposed on the flow at the natural vortex shedding frequency (1.55 Hz).

5   DISCUSSION OF RESULTS

5.1   Two aerofoils in tandem

The flow visualisation and the streamlines shown in Figs 4a and 4b confirm the results of Johnson and Loehrke (11) where the unsteadiness in the wake arises from the vortex impingement mechanism in a laminar wake. However, similar information shown in Figs. 5a and 5b clearly show that an oscillating velocity perturbation imposed on the flow at the trailing edge of the leading aerofoil overrides the vortex impingement mechanism when the boundary layer shed from the aerofoil is laminar; vortices form at the frequency of the imposed oscillation. It is hypothesised that this result is similar to that found when a resonant acoustic standing wave surrounds a pair of tandem aerofoils shedding a laminar wake in a duct.

5.2   Single plate

The results depicted in Figs 6 and 7 and the photographic evidence in Figs 8a, 8b, 9a and 9b undoubtedly illustrate that a transverse velocity perturbation increases the correlation of the vortex shedding from the trailing edge of a plate. The increase in correlation is due to the vortices shedding in phase; the level of velocity perturbation needed to cause the change is very small (0.2% of the freestream velocity). This

process is analogous to that observed when a vibrating body sheds a wake in a flow (20), and is a necessary requirement for vortex shedding to act as an efficient sound source in the acoustic resonant process.

6   SUMMARY

Unsteadiness in the wake between two colinear aerofoils/ plates can be generated by the following mechanisms.

(a)   In a open jet, unsteadiness is generated by a feedback mechanism due to vortex impingement when the wake shed from the upstream aerofoil is laminar (11). The frequency of the unsteadiness depends on the spacing between the aerofoils and the mean flow velocity.

(b)   If a turbulent wake is shed from a similar aerofoil configuration with thick trailing edges in an open jet, then a normal asymmetric vortex street is generated in the context of the absolute instability in the near wake (11). The frequency of the vortex shedding is independent of the plate spacing except when the downstream plate is moved up close to the trailing edge of the leading plate when the formation of the vortex street is suppressed (14).

(c) In a hard walled duct, when a laminar wake between the aerofoils is perturbed by an imposed transverse flow velocity oscillation, the vortex impingement mechanism is overridden and the vortex shedding process becomes 'locked' to the frequency of the perturbation.

(d) If a turbulent wake is shed in a hard walled duct from a similar aerofoil/plate configuration in the presence of a transverse flow velocity perturbation due to a resonant acoustic field, then an asymmetric vortex street is shed even when the downstream plate is close to the upstream plate (M.C. Welsh, pers. comm.).

7 CONCLUSIONS

It is concluded that a velocity field oscillating transverse to the mean flow direction can:

(a) override oscillations in a laminar wake due to other mechanisms such as vortex impingement and cause vortices to shed at the imposed oscillation frequency, and

(b) cause vortices to shed in phase in the near wake and therefore act as a strong acoustic source.

ACKNOWLEDGEMENTS

The authors wish to thank Mr N. Hamilton for photographing the flows shown in this paper. Dr J. Soria wishes to acknowledge the support of a CSIRO Post-Doctoral Fellowship.

REFERENCES

(1) PARKER, R. Resonance effects in wake shedding from parallel plates: Experimental observations, *Journal of Sound and Vibration*, 1966, **4**, 62–72.

(2) PARKER, R. Resonance effects in wake shedding from parallel plates: Calculation of resonant frequencies, *Journal of Sound and Vibration*, 1967, **5**, 330–343.

(3) ZIADA, S., OENGÖREN, A. and BUHLMANN, E.T. On acoustical resonance in tube arrays, Part I: Experiments, *Journal of Fluids and Structures*, 1989, **3**, 293–314.

(4) WELSH, M.C. and GIBSON, D.C. Interaction of induced sound with flow past a square leading edged plate in a duct, *Journal of Sound and Vibration*, 1979, **67**, 501–511.

(5) WELSH, M.C., STOKES, A.N. and PARKER, R. Flow-resonant sound interaction in a duct containing a plate, Part I: Semi-circular leading edge, *Journal of Sound and Vibration*, 1984, **95**, 305–323.

(6) STOKES, A.N. and WELSH, M.C. Flow-resonant sound interaction in a duct containing a plate, Part II: Square leading edge, *Journal of Sound and Vibration*, 1986, **104**, 55–73.

(7) STONEMAN, S.A.T., HOURIGAN, K., STOKES, A.N. and WELSH, M.C. Resonant sound caused by flow past two plates in tandem in a duct, *Journal of Fluid Mechanics*, 1988, **192**, 455–484.

(8) WELSH, M.C, HOURIGAN, K., WELCH, L.W., DOWNIE, R.J., THOMPSON, M.C. and STOKES, A.N. Acoustics and experimental methods: The influence of sound on flow and heat transfer, *Experimental Thermal and Fluid Science*, 1990, **3**, 138–152.

(9) HOURIGAN, K., WELSH, M.C., THOMPSON, M.C. and STOKES, A.N. Aerodynamic sources of acoustic resonances in a duct with baffles, *Journal of Fluids and Structures*, in press.

(10) HOWE, M.S. On the absorption of sound by turbulence, *Institute of Mathematics and its Applications, Journal of Applied Mathematics*, 1984, **32**, 187–209.

(11) JOHNSON, C.O. and LOEHRKE, R.I. An experimental investigation of wake edge tones, *American Institute of Astronautics and Aeronautics Journal*, 1984, **22**, 1249–1253.

(12) ROCKWELL, D. and NAUDASCHER, E. Self-sustained oscillations of impinging free shear layers, *Ann. Rev. Fluid Mech.*, 1979, **11**, 67–94.

(13) ROCKWELL, D. Oscillations of impinging shear layers, *American Institute of Astronautics and Aeronautics Journal*, 1983, **21**, 645–664.

(14) UNAL, M.F. and ROCKWELL, D. On vortex formation from a cylinder, Part 1: The initial instability, *Journal of Fluid Mechanics*, 1988, **190**, 491–512.

(15) UNAL, M.F. and ROCKWELL, D. On vortex formation from a cylinder, Part 2: Control by splitter-plate interference, *Journal of Fluid Mechanics*, 1988, **190**, 513–529.

(16) HOWELL, A.R. Fluid dynamics of axial compressors, *Proc. Institute of Mechanical Engineering*, 1945, 153.

(17) SCHRAUB, F.A., KLINE, S.J., HENRY, J., RUNSTADLER, P.W. and LITTELL, A. Use of hydrogen bubbles for quantitative determination of time-dependent velocity fields in low-speed water flows, *Journal of Basic Engineering, ASME*, 1965, **87**, 429–444.

(18) SHEPHERD, I.C., LaFONTAINE, R.F., WELCH, L.W., SORIA, J. and PEARSON, I.G. Measurement of instantaneous flows using particle image velocimetry, 2nd World Conference on Heat Transfer, Fluid Mechanics and Thermodynamics, 23–28 June 1991, Dubrovnik, Yugoslavia.

(19) PERRY, A.E. and STEINER, T.R. Large-scale vortex structures in turbulent wakes behind bluff bodies. Part 1 – Vortex formation. *Journal of Fluid Mechanics*, 1987, **174**, 233–270.

(20) TOEBES, G.H. The unsteady flow and wake near an oscillating cylinder, *Journal of Basic Engineering, ASME*, 1969, **91**(3), 493–505.

C416/068

Active control of flow-excited acoustic resonance: higher order acoustic modes

M C WELSH, BE and K HOURIGAN, PhD
CSIRO Division of Building, Construction and Engineering, Highett, Victoria, Australia
R J ALFREDSON, BE ME, PhD, MIEAust, MAAS
Department of Mechanical Engineering, Monash University, Clayton, Victoria, Australia
PAN DI LIN, Department of Mechanical Engineering, Huainan Mining Institute, Anhui　　/ince, Province, People's Republic of China

SYNOPSIS The active control and attenuation of an acoustic resonance excited by the flow around a plate in a duct is described. The acoustic mode is an evanescent first-cross mode of the duct upstream and downstream of the plate and is known as a Parker-β mode. It is shown that the minimum gain setting on the power amplifier which generates maximum attenuation is obtained when the sound pressure is fed back into the duct 180° out of phase with the flow-excited sound pressure field. It is also shown that the resonant sound is attenuated at four distinctly different rates as the gain on the power amplifier increases. Initially there is a low rate, followed by a high rate and then a low rate again before the system becomes unstable and rapidly amplifies the sound.

It is hypothesised that the higher rate of attenuation is due to the vortex shedding becoming uncorrelated along the trailing edge of the plate. The feedback system initially reduces the amplitude of the acoustic field approximately linearly with gain setting on the power amplifier. When the acoustic particle velocity is less than the threshold necessary to ensure that the vortices are shed in phase from the trailing edge of the plate, the vortex street no longer acts as a strong acoustic source and the resonant sound is rapidly attenuated. This feature of active control systems influencing the source of the sound is distinctly different from the active noise attenuators investigated during the past decade.

Using a simple *non-adaptive active feedback control* system, the resonant acoustic field at the fundamental frequency is attenuated 24 dB, while the first and second harmonics are attenuated by 38 and 12 dB respectively.

NOTATION

P	acoustic power (W)
u	acoustic particle velocity (m/s)
v	total fluid velocity (m/s)
V	volume (m³)
ω	vorticity (s⁻¹)

1 INTRODUCTION

Recently, Ffowcs Williams and Zhao (1) showed that the vortex shedding from a cylinder could be suppressed using an active control system to feed back sound onto the vortex street. Similarly, Ffowcs Williams and Huang (2) used an active control system to stabilise the operation of a compressor in a flow regime where surging normally occurred. More recently, Huang and Weaver (3) showed that an active control system could suppress the longitudinal acoustic resonance generated by the flow through a pipe containing two orifice plates located close together.

On the other hand, during the past decade there has been much research into active noise attenuators (4 and others). These systems are distinctly different from the active control systems referred to above and that described in this paper. They rely on the continuous superposition of a sound field identical to that which already exists in the duct but 180° out of phase. In contrast, the active control systems interact with the acoustic source in the flow causing it to become less efficient and therefore unable to excite loud resonant sound.

The aim of this paper is to describe the results of a simple *non-adaptive active control* system attenuating a higher order duct acoustic mode (Parker-β mode) which is sustained by vortex shedding from a plate. These higher order modes are those most commonly observed in turbomachinery and heat exchangers (5,6). A further aim of this paper is to present hypotheses which explain the fluid dynamics of the attenuation of the sound due to active control in terms of the linear superposition of two sound fields, one being excited by the flow and the other by the speakers.

2 BACKGROUND

2.1 General

The excitation of acoustic resonances by flow has been known for many years (7). Parker and his colleagues were the first to undertake a comprehensive study of the subject (8–10) where they identified and defined the resonant acoustic modes in ducts as the α, β, γ and δ modes. They also established that the excitation of the resonant sound was due to vortex shedding and not structural vibration.

2.2 Flow-excited acoustic resonance

In the 1980s, Welsh and his colleagues commenced detailed studies of the fluid dynamic processes which sustain an acoustic resonance (11–15). These studies involved both carefully controlled experiments and mathematical modelling of the process which produces a net supply of energy to sustain the resonance. It was shown that the acoustic resonant process could be described in terms of an interchange of energy between the flow and the acoustic fields and had three basic components: (a) a sound source (vortex street), (b) a feedback effect of the sound on to the vortex shedding, and (c) a damping process whereby acoustic energy was transferred out of the duct system.

The feedback effect of the sound was to correlate the vortex shedding along the trailing edge of the plate when the sound level was greater than approximately 112 dB (11). The mathematical modelling of the acoustic source used the aerodynamic theory due to Howe (16) who showed that when an acoustic oscillation occurred in an inviscid, isentropic but rotational flow, an acoustic power P was generated in a volume V given by:

$$P \ \alpha \int \omega \times \mathbf{v} . \mathbf{u} \ dV \tag{1}$$

where $\mathbf{v}$ represents the total fluid velocity, ω the vorticity and $\mathbf{u}$ the acoustic particle velocity.

The flow was modelled by a two-dimensional inviscid incompressible flow, irrotational everywhere except at the centres of elemental vortices. The assumption of two-dimensionality was justified because of the presence of the two-dimensional sound field surrounding the plate. The vortex shedding was modelled by the creation of elemental vortices convected under the influence of the other vortices and the irrotational flow. A detailed description of the flow modelling processs is given in (13).

By applying Howe's theory using mathematical models of both the flow and the sound field, the net energy transferred from the flow to the resonant sound field was calculated. This was done for two plates located in tandem in a duct (13) and two orifice plates located close together in a duct (15). The mathematical modelling provided an understanding of the necessary phase relationships between the acoustic field and the flow for the transfer of a net supply of acoustic energy to sustain the resonances. It also correctly predicted the feedback effect of the sound on the vortex shedding, i.e. it correctly predicted the time in the acoustic cycle when vortices commenced growth and showed the vortex shedding 'locked' to the acoustic standing wave.

2.3 Vortex impingement or acoustic standing wave

Very recent publications (e.g. 6) and verbal communication with many researchers, indicate the general acceptance of the vortex impingement mechanism (17) being responsible for sustaining acoustic resonances in duct systems, heat exchangers and turbomachinery. This mechanism is often responsible for sustaining resonant sound when laminar boundary layers are shed from a body on to a body located in tandem downstream (18). However, it does not apply to the case of a single body shedding a vortex street from its trailing edge and exciting a resonant sound field in a duct because of the lack of an impingement surface (11). As shown by Stoneman et al. (13) for two plates located in tandem in a duct, the vortex shedding frequency during resonance is determined by the resonant acoustic frequency of the space surrounding the plates and is unrelated to the vortices impinging on the downstream plate. Furthermore, when the vortex impingement mechanism is present, it exhibits an increase in the oscillation frequency as the flow velocity increases. This

is not the case when a turbulent flow excites a resonant acoustic standing wave in the duct where the frequency of the sound remains virtually constant over a range of flow velocity when a particular duct cross mode is being excited.

2.4 Multiple Strouhal numbers

A phenomenon observed in both heat exchangers and turbomachinery is that acoustic resonances occur over a number of different Strouhal number ranges. Recent work at the CSIRO (12,19) showed that for plates and tubes, this phenomenon was due to multiple sets of vortices existing between the point of flow separation and the acoustic source region, while for aerofoils it was due to different instabilities in the wakes (14,16,20).

3 ACOUSTIC FIELD

The acoustic fields excited in a wide range of industrial equipment are higher order transverse modes at frequencies less than their cut-on frequency. The acoustic resonance described in this paper, a Parker-β mode (8), corresponds to the first-cross mode of the duct upstream and downstream of the plate. Although it is the first-cross mode of the duct, it reveals the same flow/acoustic interaction processes as those observed when higher order acoustic modes are excited by the flow.

For the Parker-β mode, the acoustic pressure field is in phase along the lower half of the duct below the plate and 180° out of phase with the field above the plate in the upper half of the duct. Due to the presence of the plate, the resonant frequency is less than the cut-on frequency of the empty duct by an amount depending on the ratio of the chord of the plate to the duct dimension (9). Consequently, the acoustic amplitudes reduce exponentially both upstream and downstream of the plate when excited by the flow, and similarly upstream and downstream of the speakers when excited by the speakers. This leads to the speakers having to be located relatively close to the acoustic source in the flow for the active control system to operate successfully.

In the flows of interest here, the Mach number is low and the acoustic pressure satisfies the non-convective wave equation. A detailed description of a solution method of the wave equation is given in (13).

4 EXPERIMENTAL EQUIPMENT

4.1 Wind tunnel and instrumentation

The suck-down wind tunnel used to study the attenuation of flow-excited acoustic resonances was described in detail in (14). The working section was slightly reconfigured from that described previously and was 2820 mm long with a 244 mm square cross-section (Fig. 1). Without a plate installed, the mean velocity profile in the working section was uniform within ±0.5%, while the longitudinal turbulence level was 0.04% with the major spectral content (40 dB down) at frequencies less than 300 Hz; there were no sharp spectral peaks in the turbulence spectrum. Care was taken in the design of this wind tunnel to maintain stable flow through the working section as the active control system used in these experiments was extremely simple and not self-adapting.

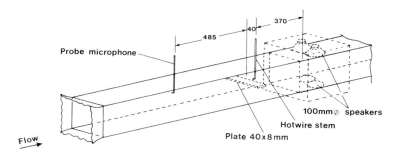

Fig. 1 Schematic of working section in wind tunnel

Two test plates, 8 mm thick, were chosen with short chords (40 mm) relative to the dimension of the duct cross-section so that the resonant frequency was approximately 1 Hz less than the cut-on frequency of the (1,0) mode of the empty duct. As a consequence, the rate of decay of the acoustic amplitudes with distance from the speakers was small. This permitted the speakers to be positioned 370 mm from the trailing edge of the plate and still be able to impose a high enough perturbation at the trailing edge to control the vortex shedding.

A preliminary experiment was undertaken with a plate having a chord of 40 mm and semicircular leading and trailing edges. This plate was 8 mm thick and was located on the centre-line of the duct with the leading edge located 1043 mm downstream of the contraction outlet with the longer sides parallel to the mean flow direction (Fig. 1). The majority of the tests described here were undertaken with a similar test plate except that it had a *square* trailing edge.

A probe microphone, with a 1 mm outside diameter and a nose shaped similar to an elliptical pitot-static tube, was used to record the sound pressure level (SPL) 485 mm upstream of the trailing edge of the plate and 33 mm below the upper surface of the duct. The frequency of the vortex shedding from the trailing edge of the plate was measured with a hot-wire sensor located 30 mm downstream of the trailing edge in a plane level with the upper surface of the plate (Fig. 1).

The cross-correlation coefficient of the vortex shedding from the trailing edge of the plate was obtained using two additional microphones fitted with straight probes. The tips of the probes were located 40 mm downstream of the plate trailing edge and 100 mm apart (≈ 12 plate thicknesses) in a spanwise direction on the centre-line of the duct. The microphone signals were band-pass filtered between 200 and 800 Hz.

In addition to the sound generated by the flow, sound could also be generated in the duct using two 100 mm diameter speakers located in the upper wall of the working section and two similar speakers located opposite in the lower wall (Fig. 1). The speakers were 370 mm downstream of the trailing edge of the plate and those speakers in each wall were connected in series. The speakers in the upper wall were connected in antiphase with those in the lower wall and therefore strongly excited the same acoustic mode as that generated by the flow. The speaker module was capable of generating SPLs of ≈ 131 dB at the resonant frequency.

The microphone and hot-wire signals, together with the signal driving the speakers, were recorded and processed using a high-speed LPA-11 analog-to-digital convertor connected to a PDP-11/44 computer using Interactive Laboratory Systems software.

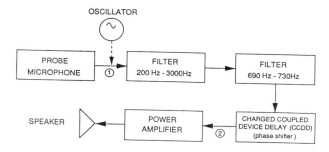

Fig. 2 Active control system for attenuating acoustic resonances

4.2 Feedback non-adaptive control system

A simple non-adaptive control system was used to attenuate the flow-induced sound (Fig. 2). It consisted of the probe microphone located upstream of the plate, analog filters, a charged coupled device delay (CCDD, phase shifter), power amplifier and speakers. The signal from the probe microphone was band-pass filtered between 200 Hz and 3 kHz for recording and processing purposes before being band-pass filtered again between 690 and 730 Hz (flow-induced resonant sound ≈ 705 Hz). This filtered signal was then passed through a CCDD which permitted it to be phase-shifted relative to the input signal over one complete cycle. The phase-shifted signal was then passed through a power amplifier to the speakers described above.

5 EXPERIMENTAL PROCEDURE

5.1 Calibration of probe microphone

The calibration of the probe microphone upstream of the plate was undertaken in two stages. First, a 12.7 mm diameter microphone was calibrated using a standard Bruel and Kjaer piston phone. This microphone and the probe microphone were then located close to each other near a white noise sound source to obtain the transfer function between the two microphones. After adding the calibration in dB of the 12.7 mm diameter microphone to the transfer function in dB, the probe microphone was then used to accurately measure the SPL with an order of magnitude greater spatial resolution than was possible using a standard 12.7 mm diameter microphone due to the small size of the probe.

5.2 Measurement of the resonant SPL and the vortex shedding frequency

The SPL at the resonant frequency and the vortex shedding frequency were determined from spectra of the probe microphone (located upstream of the plate) signal and the signal from the hot wire located in the wake. These spectra were computed using a ninth-order FFT with 50 averages. Both signals were sampled at 6 kHz with the probe microphone signal band passed between 200 Hz and 3 kHz and the hot-wire signal band passed between 10 Hz and 3 kHz. The bin width of the spectra was 13.3 Hz.

5.3 Determination of the delay between flow-generated and speaker-generated sound fields

The delay between the acoustic pressure field at the probe microphone upstream of the plate due to the flow and the acoustic pressure fed back via the active control system through the speakers was measured in the following way: since the time delay between these fields depended on flow velocity, it was necessary to have the tunnel operating at the flow velocity corresponding to resonance (24.5 m/s) but with the resonance suppressed by slightly inclining the plate to the flow. A resonant sound field was then excited by the speakers with an oscillator signal connected to the filters (position 1 in Fig. 2). The delay between the output signal from the CCDD or phase shifter (position 2 in Fig. 2) and the signal from the probe microphone upstream of the plate, was then measured for a range of ambient temperatures and frequencies for a constant flow velocity of 24.5 m/s.

With the plate reset to zero incidence, the acoustic resonance was again excited by the flow at 24.5 m/s. The probe microphone signal was connected to the filter input (position 1 in Fig. 2) and the gain on the power amplifier was reduced so that no signal existed at the speakers. The delay between the signal from the probe microphone (position 1) and the output signal from the CCDD (position 2) was then measured and adjusted to give a range of delays between the sound field recorded by the probe microphone and the sound field being fed back into the duct via the speakers.

A phase difference of 180° between the sound pressure field recorded at the probe microphone and that due to the control system and speakers corresponds to the sound being fed back into the duct 180° out of phase with the original sound. It should be noted that for the acoustic modes excited by both the flow and the active control system, the acoustic pressures have constant phase along the duct.

5.4 Measurement of the cross-correlation coefficient of the vortex shedding from the plate

Hot wires could not be used to determine the correlation of the vortex shedding along the span of the plate in the presence of a resonant sound field since they recorded the acoustic particle velocities as well as the velocity perturbations due to the vortex street. Instead, probe microphones with their sensing end located on the centre-line of the duct at an acoustic pressure node for the β-mode were used to measure the correlation of the vortex shedding; the probe microphone signals were band-pass filtered between 200 and 800 Hz.

Tests were made to establish the reliability of the method described above for recording the correlation coefficient of the vortex shedding. The flow velocity was reduced to 21.4 m/s where resonant sound was not excited by the flow and vortices were shed at 615 Hz. The autocorrelation coefficients of each probe microphone signal oscillated sinusoidally at 615 Hz with a maximum value after two cycles of 0.6, indicating that the vortex shedding was regular at each probe microphone. However, since the cross-correlation coefficient of the signals from the probe microphones also oscillated sinusoidally at 615 Hz with a maximum value of only 0.09 (Fig. 3), the vortices were not being shed in phase along the trailing edge of the plate.

Without changing the flow velocity, sound was then applied by the speakers using an oscillator at the resonant acoustic frequency (705 Hz) and at the same measured SPL (131 dB) as the flow-induced sound. The autocorrelation coefficients of each probe microphone signal again oscillated at 615 Hz with a maximum value after one cycle of typically 0.4. However, the cross-correlation coefficient of the probe microphone signals oscillated at the sound frequency of 705 Hz with a maximum value of 0.13, indicating that the component of the signal due to the sound pressure field was very small (Fig. 3). Consequently, a significantly higher cross-correlation coefficient than 0.13 when the flow was exciting the resonant sound field would indicate that the vortices were shedding in phase from the trailing edge of the plate.

The cross-correlation coefficients were determined using an eighth-order FFT with 64 averages and a sampling rate of 9 kHz on each channel.

6 RESULTS

6.1 Preliminary experiments

The results of the preliminary experiments using the plate with semicircular leading and trailing edges show that a β-mode resonance is generated by the flow. However, when the active control system is adjusted to give maximum attenuation, the resonant β-mode is eliminated entirely but is replaced with another resonance of slightly higher frequency. When this plate is replaced with a plate of the same thickness and chord but with a *square* trailing edge, the β-mode is again generated by the flow. However, when the resonance is attenuated using the active control system it is not replaced by another resonance. Consequently, this latter plate with the square trailing edge is used for all of the experimental results described below.

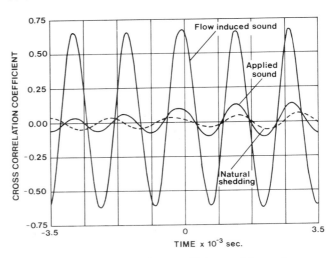

Fig. 3 Cross-correlation coefficients of the probe microphones downstream of the trailing edge of the plate on the duct centre-line

6.2 Without active control

Spectra of the signals from the probe microphone located upstream of the plate are shown in Fig. 4 at flow velocities ranging between 0 and 30 m/s. The gradual increase in the amplitude of the resonant sound at 705 Hz is clear. At the maximum level, harmonics of the fundamental are also present.

The SPL at the resonant acoustic frequency and the vortex shedding frequencies for flow velocities ranging between 7 and 28 m/s are depicted in Fig. 5. These data show that the vortex shedding from the trailing edge of the plate first 'locks up' to the acoustic resonant frequency of ≈ 705 Hz at ≈ 24.5 m/s and then unlocks at 25.9 m/s. The maximum SPL reached is ≈ 131 dB.

6.3 With active control

Data analogous to that in Fig. 4, but with active control operating, are shown in Fig. 6. The active control system is set for maximum SPL attenuation (14 dB amplifier gain/180° phase setting) at a flow velocity of 24.5 m/s. These data show that this gain setting is not as effective at higher flow velocities. However, further adjustment of the active control system for these higher flow velocities leads to similar attenuations except when the natural vortex shedding frequency is equal to the acoustic resonant frequency.

A comparison of spectra of the signal from the probe microphone located upstream of the plate at 24.5 m/s, with and without the active control (14 dB gain/180° phase setting), is illustrated in Fig. 7. The attenuation is 24 dB for the fundamental, 38 dB for the first harmonic and 12 dB for the second harmonic with the same gain/phase settings.

Figure 8 shows the variation in the SPL at the acoustic resonant frequency with gain setting on the power amplifier for a range of phase angles. At a constant phase angle of 180°, which corresponds to the sound being fed back into the duct 180° out of phase with the sound field at the probe

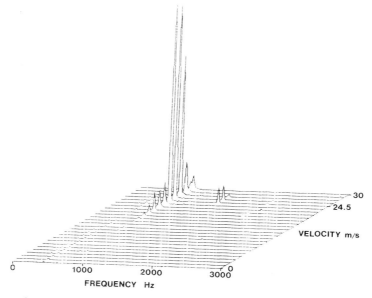

Fig. 4 Variation of the probe microphone spectra with flow velocity upstream of the plate without active control

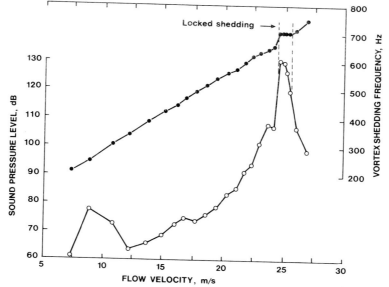

Fig. 5 Variation of the resonant SPL at ≈ 705 Hz and the vortex shedding frequency with flow velocity approaching the plate without active control: •——•, vortex shedding frequency; ○——○, SPL at resonant sound frequency (≈ 705 Hz)

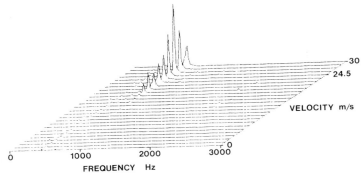

FREQUENCY Hz

Fig. 6 Variation of the probe microphone spectra with flow velocity upstream of the plate using active control: phase setting = 180°; amplifier gain of 14 dB

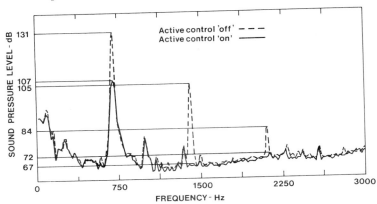

FREQUENCY - Hz

Fig. 7 Probe microphone spectra with and without active control: flow velocity = 24.5 m/s; phase angle = 180°; gain of 14 dB

microphone, a minimum gain of ≈ –10 dB is required to produce a sudden reduction in the SPL. At other phase angles, a higher gain setting is required to achieve the sudden attenuation of the SPL. With a further increase in the gain up to ≈ 14 dB following the sudden attenuation, the SPL gradually reduces to 107 dB, and when the gain is increased beyond 14 dB the SPL increases rapidly (not shown on Fig. 8). When the wind tunnel is shut down and the gain setting on the power amplifier is again increased beyond 14 dB, a resonant sound field at 705 Hz is excited by the active control system.

At all of the phase angles shown in Fig. 8, the SPL reduces as the gain setting increases. However, when the gain is gradually increased for phase angles ≥150° and ≤240° there is a setting where sudden attenuation of the SPL occurs.

When the flow excites resonant sound at 24.5 m/s, the cross-correlation coefficient of the signals from the probe microphones located at the trailing edge of the plate increases from 0.13 to 0.68 (Fig. 3). This is consistent with the resonant acoustic field causing the vortex shedding to be correlated across the trailing edge of the plate, as shown by Parker (10).

Figure 9 illustrates the variation of the cross-correlation coefficient with the gain setting on the power amplifier. At gain settings ≤–10 dB, when the SPL is ≈ 131 dB, the cross-correlation coefficient is 0.67 and the vortex shedding is correlated along the trailing edge of the plate. However, after the sudden attenuation of the SPL, the cross-correlation coefficient is 0.16 and therefore the vortex shedding is no longer correlated.

7   DISCUSSION OF RESULTS

Figure 8 shows that the attenuation of the flow-induced resonant sound always occurs when the sound is fed back to produce a sound field in the duct which has a component out of phase with the original flow-induced sound. Furthermore, the minimum gain setting on the power amplifier capable of generating maximum attenuation of the resonant sound occurs when sound is fed back 180° out of phase with the original flow-induced sound.

Figure 8 also shows that the attenuation of the flow-induced resonant sound with increasing gain occurs in three distinct regimes for phase angles between 150° and 240° inclusive, while additional data not illustrated on Fig. 8 due to the instability of the system, show there is a fourth regime where the resonant sound is amplified rapidly as the gain setting increases beyond 14 dB. The experimental data also indicate that the sound field fed back into the duct at a phase angle of 180°, just prior to the sudden attenuation, is typically of the same order of magnitude as the flow-induced resonant sound field. It is therefore hypothesised that the gradual reduction in the SPL as the gain is increased from –17 to –10 dB and from ≈ –5 to ≈ 14 dB is due to the linear superposition of two sound fields having identical frequencies but opposing phases.

The pronounced dip in the SPL over a range of gains (Fig. 8) is a characteristic of active control systems which is different from active noise attenuators; active noise attenuators only have the pronounced dip at one gain setting.

Figure 9 demonstrates that the vortex shedding is strongly correlated when the resonant sound field of ≈ 131 dB is present at ≤ –10 dB gain setting. This is consistent with the results of Parker (10) who also found that resonant sound fields are associated with correlated vortex shedding from the trailing edge of a plate. Welsh et al. (11) found that when the SPL reduced below ≈ 112 dB, the acoustic particle velocity is

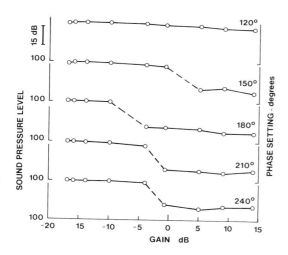

Fig. 8 Variation of SPL with gain on the power amplifier at various phase settings: flow velocity = 24.5 m/s

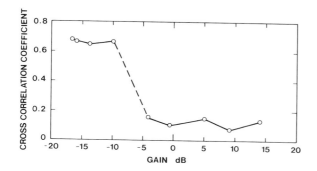

Fig. 9 Variation of the cross-correlation coefficient of the signals from the probe microphones located on the duct centre-line downstream of the plate with gain setting on the power amplifier: flow velocity = 24.5 m/s; phase setting = 180°

less than the threshold level necessary to correlate the vortex shedding. This is also consistent with the data in Fig. 9 which demonstrate the vortex shedding is no longer highly correlated at a SPL of 107 dB, i.e. the vortices are shedding out of phase along the trailing edge of the plate, and therefore can no longer act as a strong acoustic source (equation 1).

It is therefore hypothesised that the sudden attenuation of the SPL at a gain setting of ≈ −10 dB and 180° phase setting is due to the reduction of the acoustic particle velocities at the trailing edge of the plate to a level less than the threshold necessary to correlate the vortex shedding. Consequently, the vortex street is no longer a strong acoustic source. It is further hypothesised that the sudden amplification of the resonant sound field as the gain on the power amplifier increases beyond 14 dB is not due to a change in the flow. Instead it is due to an acoustic feedback between the probe microphone and loudspeakers and occurs without flow.

It should also be noted that when the active control system is operating, the signal fed to the speakers is sourced by the probe microphone. Since this signal reduces as the SPL reduces, then at maximum attenuation of the sound field, the power driving the speakers is very small. While the resonance remains attenuated, the resonant system is in a state of dynamic equilibrium. This feature is distinctly different from the

active noise attenuators researched during the past decade (4), where SPLs of the same amplitude as in duct noise are continuously generated by the speakers to achieve attenuation. The major practical implication of this difference between the two systems is that the speakers, or the equivalent, do not require large power input as is often the case for active noise attenuators.

8 RECOMMENDATIONS

It is recommended that:

(a) An adaptive phase-locked control system be developed to attenuate flow-induced acoustic resonances. These systems should be capable of adapting both the gain and phase settings to attenuate the resonances over a range of frequencies and flow velocities, i.e. the control system must be capable of simultaneously attenuating a number of coexisting acoustic modes.

(b) A robust speaker or equivalent acoustic driver should be developed for application of active control systems to industrial vibration problems.

9 CONCLUSIONS

The following are concluded from a study of the attenuation of a higher order transverse acoustic mode resonance by a non-adaptive active control system.

(a) The resonant sound field is associated with vortices shedding at the sound frequency in phase along the trailing edge of the plate.

(b) The active control system significantly attenuates a resonant sound field by superimposing a sound field of identical frequency but of opposite phase. This reduces the acoustic particle velocities below the threshold necessary to correlate the vortex shedding along the trailing edge. Since the vortex shedding has varying phase, it is no longer a strong acoustic source and leads to significant attenuation of the resonant sound.

(c) The signal being fed to the active control system comes from a probe microphone which is measuring the SPL in the duct. Since the SPL is reduced using the active control system, the system is eventually in a state of dynamic equilibrium with only a relatively small amount of power activating the speakers. This is distinctly different from the active noise attenuators developed during the last decade which require the speakers to continuously generate the same sound levels as the original in duct noise. This difference has practical implications since the speakers do not need to be as powerful in the case of the active control systems.

(d) Resonant sound at the fundamental frequency is attenuated by 24 dB while the first and second harmonics are reduced by 38 and 12 dB respectively.

(e) A self-adapting active control system should be developed to automatically adjust the gain and phase settings to simultaneously attenuate coexisting resonant sound fields over a range of frequencies and flow velocities since the attenuation of one particular resonance often leads to another being excited.

REFERENCES

(1) FFOWCS WILLIAMS, J.E. and SHAH, B.C. The active control of vortex shedding. *Journal of Fluids and Structures*, 1989, **3**, 115–122.

(2) FFOWCS WILLIAMS, J.E. and HUANG, X.Y. Active stabilisation of compressor surge. *Journal of Fluid Mechanics*, 1989, **204**, 245–262.

(3) HUANG, X.Y. and WEAVER, D.S. A flow visualization study of shear layer oscillations past a cavity and their control. ASME PVP Conference, Nashville, USA, 1990.

(4) SHEPHERD, I.C., LA FONTAINE, R.F. and CABELLI, A. Active attenuation in flow ducts: Assessment of potential applications. Proc. ASME Winter Annual Meeting, Anaheim, Ca, USA, 1986, Paper No. 86-WA/NCA-26.

(5) PARKER, R. and STONEMAN, S.A.T. An experimental investigation of the generation and consequences of acoustic waves in an axial-flow compressor: Large axial spacings between blade rows. *Journal of Sound and Vibration*, 1987, **116**, 509–525.

(6) ZIADA, S., OENGÖREN, A. and BUHLMANN, E.T. On acoustical resonance in tube arrays, Part I: Experiments. *Journal of Fluids and Structures*, 1989, **3**, 293–314.

(7) BATCHELOR, G.K. and TOWNSEND, A.A. Singing corner vanes: A note on a peculiar double resonant sustained oscillation occurring in a wind tunnel. Council for Scientific and Industrial Research, Division of Aerodynamics, Note 62, 1945.

(8) PARKER, R. Resonance effects in wake shedding from parallel plates: experimental observations. *Journal of Sound and Vibration*, 1966, **4**, 62–72.

(9) PARKER, R. Resonance effects in wake shedding from parallel plates: Calculation of resonant frequencies. *Journal of Sound and Vibration*, 1967, **5**, 330–343.

(10) PARKER, R. Discrete frequency noise generation due to fluid flow over blades, supporting spokes and similar bodies. ASME, 1969, 69-WA/GT-13.

(11) WELSH, M.C., STOKES, A.N. and PARKER, R. Flow-resonant sound interaction in a duct containing a plate, Part I: Semi-circular leading edge. *Journal of Sound and Vibration*, 1984, **95**, 305–323.

(12) STOKES, A.N. and WELSH, M.C. Flow-resonant sound interaction in a duct containing a plate, Part II: Square leading edge. *Journal of Sound and Vibration*, 1986, **104**, 55–73.

(13) STONEMAN, S.A.T., HOURIGAN, K., STOKES, A.N. and WELSH, M.C. Resonant sound caused by flow past two plates in tandem in a duct. *Journal of Fluid Mechanics*, 1988, **192**, 455–484.

(14) WELSH, M.C, HOURIGAN, K., WELCH, L.W., DOWNIE, R.J., THOMPSON, M.C. and STOKES, A.N. Acoustics and experimental methods: The influence of sound on flow and heat transfer. *Experimental Thermal and Fluid Science*, 1990, **3**, 138–152.

(15) HOURIGAN, K., WELSH, M.C., THOMPSON, M.C. and STOKES, A.N. Aerodynamic sources of acoustic resonances in a duct with baffles. *Journal of Fluids and Structures*, 1990, **4**, 345–370.

(16) HOWE, M.S. On the absorption of sound by turbulence. *Journal of Applied Mathematics*, 1984, **32**, 187–209.

(17) ROCKWELL, D. Oscillations of impinging shear layers. *American Institute of Astronautics and Aeronautics Journal*, 1983, **21**, 645–664.

(18) JOHNSON, K.O. and LOEHRKE, R.I. An experimental investigation of wake edge tones. *American Institute of Astronautics and Aeronautics Journal*, 1984, **22**, 1249–1253.

(19) HOURIGAN, K., WELSH, M.C., THOMPSON, M.C., WELCH, L.W., DOWNIE, R.J. and STOKES, A.N. Unsteady separated flows and acoustic feedback effects – prediction and observation. American Institute of Astronautics and Aeronautics Paper No. 88–3520–CP.

(20) MATHIAS, M., STOKES, A.N., HOURIGAN, K. and WELSH, M.C. Low-level flow-induced acoustic resonances in ducts. *Fluid Dynamics Research*, 1988, **3**, 353–356.

C416/092

Self-induced oscillation of free surface in a tank with circulating flow

K OKAMOTO, MJSME, H MADARAME, PhD MJSME and T HAGIWARA, MJSME
Nuclear Engineering Research Laboratory, Faculty of Engineering, University of Tokyo, Japan

SYNOPSIS A self-induced free surface oscillation was observed in a thin rectangular tank having circulating flow which supplied the energy for oscillations to occur.

Water flowed horizontally into the tank and flowed out through a bottom outlet. Oscillations grew at a specific range of inlet velocities and water levels, with its frequency being measured to be equal to the first order eigenvalue of liquid in the tank. An oscillation energy supply model is proposed which successfully explains the experimental results.

NOTATION

A	perturbation amplitude
B	inlet height
D	test section thickness
E	wave energy
f	frequency
f^+	global nondimensional frequency (fh/V)
f^*	local nondimensional frequency (fL/u)
Fr	Froude Number $(V/\sqrt{gh})$
H	water level from the inlet center
h	water level from test section base
L	coordinate system test section width
t	time
u	velocity under the surface
V	inlet velocity
W	test section width
x	longitudinal coordinate
α	$\partial\delta/\partial h$
δ	water level difference between the right side and the lowest position
ΔE	energy supplied in one cycle
ζ	logarithmic growing rate
η	wave height
κ	nondimensional geometry number
ρ	density
τ	time lag
ω	angular velocity

1. Introduction

A Fast Breeder Reactor (FBR) consists of a reactor vessel containing liquid sodium coolant. The liquid sodium in the vessel has a free surface and a circulating flow. Recently, a small size reactor vessel design has been proposed in order to reduce the initial cost of an FBR plant (1). For example, the reactor vessel was about 10m diameter and about 16m height, and the flow rate is about 50×10^3 ton/hour. In these designs the liquid sodium circulating velocity is increased when compared to larger designs, causing undesirable surface phenomena to occur, i.e., surface waves and bubble entrainment (2). Surface waves induce a high thermal stress at the vessel wall due to the sodium's high thermal conductivity, and bubble entrainment should be avoided because the FBR core has a positive void factor.

The flow characteristics in a tank with free surface should therefore be investigated, and although many studies have already been conducted which consider oceans, rivers, and large petroleum tank free surface flows, the vessel size is relatively too large or flow velocity relatively too low to use the results to analyze small size FBR reactor vessels having high velocity flow.

In the presented study, the basic characteristics of a tank's flow with free surface is experimentally investigated using a simple thin rectangular tank having a circulating flow.

The shape of the free surface was usually stablized by the balance between gravity and flow, yet under certain conditions self-induced wavy surface oscillations were observed. The characteristics of these oscillations were investigated, and a theoretical model to explain oscillation growth is proposed.

2. Experimental Apparatus

In order to determine basic flow characteristics with a free surface, a simple thin rectangular tank was used as a test section. Figure 1 shows the schematic view of the test section, though its geometry could be changed by placing solid blocks into it.

Four types of test sections were used, with Table 1 listing their dimensions. Type A was the standard case, and in the rest of the cases one dimension parameter was changed, i.e., the width in Type B, the inlet height in Type C, and the thickness in Type D.

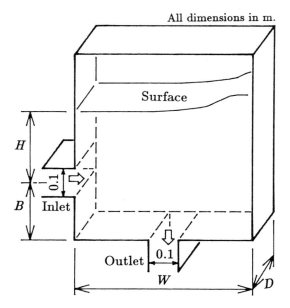

All dimensions in m.

Fig.1 Test section

Table 1 Test section geometries

	W	B	D
	m	m	m
Type A	1.00	0.25	0.10
Type B	0.75	0.25	0.10
Type C	1.00	0.45	0.10
Type D	1.00	0.25	0.20

Inlet flow was supplied by a head tank ($\sim$ 6m above test section) which was continuously pump filled from a dump tank. The head tank water level was maintained stable by overflow, therefore pump vibrations were not observed in the test section inlet flow. The inlet velocity was valve controlled, and measured by a floating-type flow meter. The mean water level of the test section was controlled by an overflow tank gate which was directly connected to the test section. The water surface was not completely horizontal, thus the water level, h, was measured at the left side wall from the base of the test section.

The water level was measured by a condenser type level meter that was made from a 7 mm diameter glass tube containing a thin copper wire, thus allowing the electric capacity between the wire and water to be measured.

The water levels were also measured by a TV camera and VTR recorded to show the surface profiles. The velocity distributions in the test section were measured from the VTR data, and velocity profiles were obtained by following tracer particles using an image processing technique.

3. Experimental Results

3.1 Typical Flow Pattern

Figure 2 shows a typical experimental flow pattern which was obtained from the VTR data after using an image processing technique (3). Water flowed

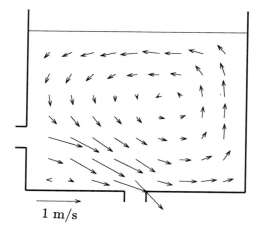

Fig.2 Typical flow pattern
(Type A, V=1.0 m/s, h=0.75 m)

horizontally into the test section and flowed out at a bottom centered vertical outlet. A large circulating flow was present at the test section's right region, and an under water surface stream flowed from the right to the left, appearing to flow downwards at the tank's center and left regions.

3.2 Self-induced Oscillation

Self-induced surface oscillations were observed in the test section. Figure 3(a) shows these oscillation for the Type A geometry at a inlet flow velocity of 0.67 m/s as the inlet side water level was changed from 650 mm to 630 mm. At 650 mm the fluctuations were small, although when the level was changed to 630 mm they increased to 80 mm. It took 5 minutes for this oscillation to occur (at an

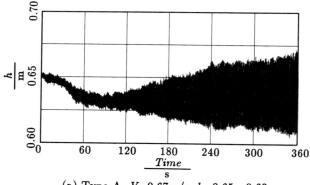

(a) Type A, V=0.67m/s, h=0.65→0.63 m

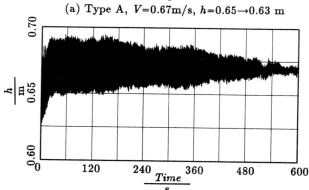

(b) Type A, V=0.67m/s, h=0.65→0.67 m

Fig.3 Self-induced oscillation

approximate period of 1.2s), indicating that the energy input was small in this case. The oscillation amplitude was about 80 mm, and is quite large when comparing it to the water level (630mm) and the test section width (1000mm). Figure 3(b) shows the inverse case, with the water level being changed from 650 mm to 670 mm. The oscillation amplitude in this case was reduced and diminished after 10 minutes.

Figure 4(a) shows the oscillating surface shapes for the Type A case with an inlet velocity of 0.75 m/s, and a water level of 550 mm. Figure 4(b) shows water levels with respect to time at three positions, i.e., left (inlet side), center, and right side. Figure 4 was obtained from the VTR images. The difference between maximum and mean level was greater than that between minimum and mean level, because of the non-linearity. The phase difference between the left and right side water levels was $\sim 180°$. At the left side, it took ~ 0.7 s from the maximum to the minimum level but only ~ 0.5 s from this minimum to the next maximum

level, whereas contrastingly, at the right side the times were the same (0.6 s). The center water level reached its maximum level ~ 0.2 s after the left side maximum level was reached, thus indicating upward force was added to the surface by the circulating flow, when the left side surface was rising. Similar oscillations were observed in all test section cases.

3.3 Oscillation Frequency

The oscillation frequency was calculated using the water level meter data. If this oscillation was the resonance of the tank fluid, the frequency was related to the eigenvalue. If no flow exists in the test section the eigenvalue of liquid in a tank is theoretically obtained as follows[6],

$$f = \frac{1}{2\pi}\sqrt{n\frac{g\pi}{W}\tanh(n\frac{h}{W}\pi)} \tag{1}$$

where W is the width of the tank, h is the water level, and n is a positive integer. In Eq.(1), the first order theoretical eigenvalue is obtained when $n = 1$, and can be nondimensionalized by the inlet velocity V and the water level h as follows,

$$f^+ = \frac{fh}{V} = \frac{1}{2\pi}(\kappa Fr)^{-1} \tag{2}$$

$$Fr = \frac{V}{\sqrt{gh}} \tag{3}$$

$$\kappa = (\frac{h}{W}\pi\tanh(\frac{h}{W}\pi))^{-\frac{1}{2}} \tag{4}$$

Equation (2) shows that the nondimensionalized eigenvalue f^+ is inversely proportional to the Froude Number (Fr).

Figure 5 compares experimental frequencies and the theoretical eigenvalues, with the theoretical first order eigenvalue line being denoted. All experimental results were plotted, and since the experimental frequencies are nearly equal to the theoreti-

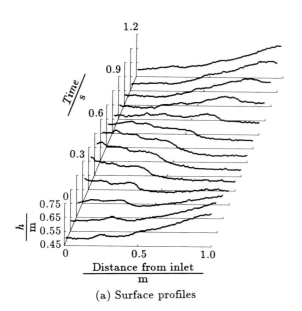

(a) Surface profiles

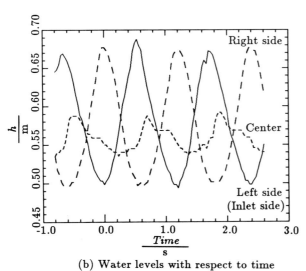

(b) Water levels with respect to time

Fig.4 Oscillating surface shapes
(Type A, $V=0.75$ m/s, $h=0.55$ m)

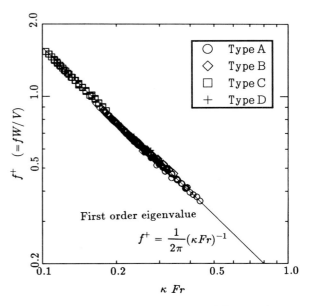

Fig.5 Comparison of experimental frequencies and theoretical eigenvalues

cal values, the oscillation frequency is considered equal to the theoretical first order eigenvalue of liquid in a tank without circulating flow.

3.4 Oscillation Map

Figure 6 summarizes the oscillating region by showing in map form the inlet velocity, water level, and geometry. The x-axis is the inlet velocity, nondimensionalized by the theoretical eigenvalue and the test section width. The y-axis shows surface water level from the inlet center, H, nondimensionalized by the width. For each geometry, using constant velocity the oscillating water levels were found by decreasing the water level. Then at the same velocity, by increasing the water level the non-oscillating water levels were found. The plotted points denote the oscillating water levels for each velocity, i.e., oscillating region, which was obtained by either increasing or decreasing the water level.

Figure 6 shows, in all cases, if the velocity was less than a specific value the oscillations did not occur, yet they did occur if the velocity exceed this value. However, if the water level was either too low or too high the oscillations did not occur. Additionally, as the inlet velocity increased, the oscillating water level region became smaller, until the oscillation did not occur at any water level.

Figure 6 shows that the oscillating region of Type A and B is very similar. There was a difference in width between A and B, causing the eigenvalues to be different, but in the oscillating region the value of V/fW is nearly unity for both cases. Therefore oscillations occur when the width, W, is equal to the length, V/f, i.e., the distance traveled in one cycle at the inlet velocity, V.

In Type C the water inlet height was higher than in Type A, and the resulting oscillating region was very different from that in either Type A or B. The V/fW of the oscillating region was smaller than in Type A, yet the H/W of this oscillating region was similar to both Type A and B. If the

y-axis is changed from H/W to h/W, the value of the region is now different from Type A and B, i.e. the region is $0.3 < h/W < 0.6$ for Type A, and $0.6 < h/W < 0.9$ for Type C. This indicates that in the oscillating region the effects of the water level from the inlet center, H, is greater than that of water level from the bottom, h.

In Type D the test section thickness was changed from type A, and if the test section were perfectly two-dimensional, then the oscillating region should be same as Type A, however it was found to be very different, especially at high water levels. This difference is believed to be mainly caused by three dimensional effects.

It is concluded that the oscillations occurred only at certain water levels and inlet flow velocities, and since the oscillations could not occur without circulating flow, some energy mechanism must be supplied from the circulating flow. The oscillation changes the flow, and this change then effects the oscillation by causing it to increase.

4. Steady State Surface Shapes and Flow Patterns

4.1 Flow Pattern Transformation

A two dimensional model was used as shown in Fig.7 because of the tank's narrow width. The origin of the coordinate system is located at the

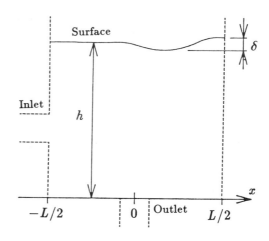

Fig.7 Model coordinate system

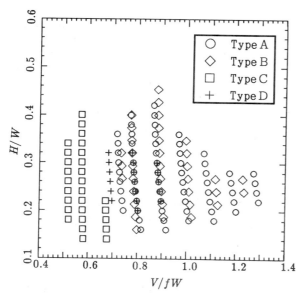

Fig.6 Oscillation Map
(marks denote oscillating condition)

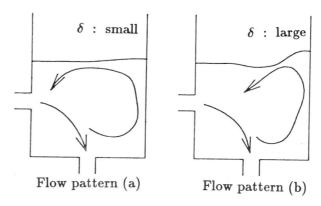

Fig.8 Flow pattern classifications

center of the bottom, with the right side at $L/2$ and the left side at $-L/2$.

The value δ is defined as the difference between the right side water level and the lowest level, whereas h is redefined as the mean water level.

Figure 8 shows two different observed flow patterns. The velocity distributions appear to be similar in both flow patterns, but pattern (b) has distorted circulating flow in the right region, and also their surfaces are very different from each other. In pattern (a) the shape is smooth and δ is small, however in pattern (b) the right side water level is higher and δ is larger. These flow patterns are related to the inlet flow velocity and the water level.

Pattern (a) occurs when the water level is high, and as it decreases the circulating flow is distorted in the right region due to the circulating flow which has a circular tendency, thus resulting in pattern (b). If the water level decreases further, the circulating flow space is narrowed and forms an ellipse, resulting in a flow pattern similar to pattern (a). In this flow pattern transformation, δ has a maximum value for a specific h, i.e., if h is decreased δ becomes larger (pattern (b)), and therefore the next δ becomes smaller causing $\partial\delta/\partial h$ to be positive at low water levels.

This transformation seems have occurred at a specific inlet velocity, because to if the velocity was too low, pattern (b) was not observed, and if it was too high the circulating flow in pattern (b) did not change to elliptical shape. Therefore in these conditions $\partial\delta/\partial h$ is always negative.

4.2 Measurement and Calculation of δ

During the experiment surface oscillations occurred which prevented the establishment of a steady state relationship between h and δ, therefore δ was obtained using two different methods.

4.2.1 Measurement to forcibly diminish the oscillation.

In flow pattern (b) the circulating flow was distorted in the right region, causing the left region velocity to decrease. To reduce the oscillation, a 200 mm length board was placed horizontally at the surface of the left region, and then the surface shape was studied. Although the oscillation was not completely stopped and the flow pattern was a little changed by the board, a semi-steady state flow pattern was obtained.

The relation between h and δ is shown in Fig.9, and the flow did not significantly change by the addition of the board, but when $h < 0.55$, $\partial\delta/\partial h$ becomes positive.

4.2.2 Numerical simulation calculation

Since the board must effect the flow patterns, δ was calculated using a two dimensional numerical

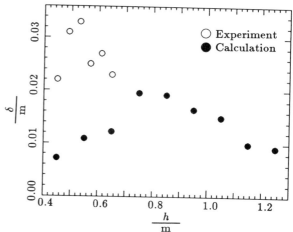

Fig.9 Relation between the water level and δ (Type A, V=1.0 m/s)

simulation code based on SOLA-VOF code (5), and included k-ε turbulence model and surface turbulent energy dissipation model (4). This code correctly simulated both the steady-state flow patterns and the surface shapes (4).

Figure 9 shows the numerically simulated δ values which are always in a steady state conditions with no oscillations occurring, even when there were experimental oscillations. The oscillating force is damped by the numerical viscosity, yet this had only a small effect on the resulting flow patterns and the surface shapes. The calculated results therefore adequately simulate non oscillating conditions, and showed that when $h < 0.75$, $\partial\delta/\partial h$ is positive. The difference between calculation and experiment was caused by the surface modeling and the experimental uncertainties, nevertheless these results indicated that in certain conditions the $\partial\delta/\partial h$ become positive.

5. Oscillation Mechanism

When $\partial\delta/\partial h$ becomes positive and h increases, δ also increases. This indicates that if the right side water level ($x=L/2$) increases due to some perturbations, the water level will increase much more because δ must increase in order to be stable. The water level increase, i.e., the level increases at $x=L/2$, does not immediately occur because of a time lag that can be approximated as a first order lag, with its time constant being related to the circulating velocity. The flow under the surface transfers this perturbation in the $x=L/2$ to $x=0$ direction.

In order to develop a mathematical model of this phenomena, η_0 is defined as the initial surface perturbation in a stable condition, and is approximated as follows,

$$\eta_0 = A\sin(kx)e^{i\omega t} \qquad (5)$$

where $k=\pi/L$ is wave number and $\omega=2\pi f$ is angular velocity. If energy is supplied to the perturbation η_0, the oscillation will increase.

When $\partial\delta/\partial h$ is positive the flow pattern is similar to pattern (b), where the circulating flow is distorted in the right region ($x>0$), therefore the left region ($x<0$) is neglected in this model. An additional perturbation caused by the initial perturbation η_0, increases δ and is defined as follows,

$$\eta_1 = A\sum_{j=1}^{\infty} a_j\cos(2jkx)e^{i\omega t} \qquad (6)$$

In Eq. (6) higher orders ($j>2$) are neglected for simplicity, and η_1 is approximated as the first order lag of η_0, thus the phase lag is defined as $\omega\tau$. Equation (6) is modified as follows,

$$\eta_1 = -A\alpha\cos(2kx)e^{i\omega(t-\tau)} \qquad (7)$$

where $\partial\delta/\partial h$ is redefined as α. The additional perturbation η_1 travels to the center by the constant velocity $u<0$, and so η_2 is defined below as the integrated traveling perturbation.

$$\eta_2 = \frac{1}{L/2-x}\int_x^{L/2}\eta_1\left(s,t-\frac{x-s}{u}\right)ds \qquad (8)$$

$$= A\alpha\frac{1}{1-f^{*2}}\frac{1}{\pi(1-2x/L)}$$
$$\times\left[if^*e^{i\omega(t-\frac{x}{u}-\tau)+i\pi f^*}+\left[if^*\cos(2kx)+\sin(2kx)\right]e^{i\omega(t-\tau)}\right]$$

$$f^* = \frac{fL}{u} \qquad (9)$$

If the surface shape becomes $\eta_0+\eta_2$, the added energy in one cycle is calculated as follows,

$$\Delta E = \rho g\oint\int_0^{L/2}-\eta_2\frac{\partial\eta_0}{\partial t}dx\,dt \qquad (10)$$

If nondimensionalized by the total energy in one cycle then,

$$\frac{\Delta E}{E} = 8\alpha\frac{1}{2(1-f^{*2})}G \qquad (11)$$

$$E = \frac{1}{8}\rho g A^2 L \qquad (12)$$

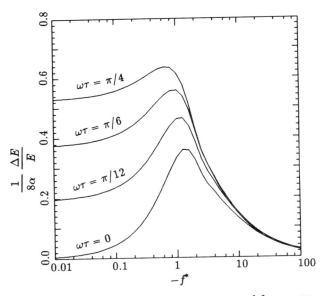

Fig.10 Relation between local nondimensional frequency and the energy input rate

$$G=\int_0^{\frac{\pi}{2}}\left(-f^*\frac{\cos(\theta)\cos(2f^*\theta-\omega\tau)}{\theta}+f^*\cos(\omega\tau)\frac{\cos(2\theta)\cos(\theta)}{\theta}\right.$$
$$\left.+\sin(\omega\tau)\frac{\sin(2\theta)\cos(\theta)}{\theta}\right)d\theta \qquad (13)$$

Figure 10 shows the relation between the local nondimensional frequency f^* and energy input rate $(\Delta E/E)/8\alpha$. The phase lag, $\omega\tau$, is related to both the perturbation amplitude, $A\alpha$, and to the circulating flow velocity, and is very small at the beginning of the oscillation. If the velocity becomes 0, i.e., $-f^*\to\infty$, and $\Delta E/E$ becomes 0, the velocity decreases, the traveling perturbation remains for a long time period, and the added energy, ΔE, decreases. However, if the velocity approaches $-\infty$, i.e. $-f^*\to 0$, then $\Delta E/E$ has a positive value. For all phase lags, $\Delta E/E$ has a positive maximum value at $-f^*\approx 1$. These results show that when $\partial\delta/\partial h>0$ and $-f^*\approx 1$, the perturbation supplies enough energy for oscillation growth.

6. Discussion

Figure 9 shows that $\partial\delta/\partial h$ becomes positive at $h<0.55$, and since the experiment oscillation also occurred at $h<0.55$, this shows that the oscillating region determined using the proposed energy supply mechanism agrees well with the experimental results.

The velocity under the surface as measured by the VTR data was ~ 0.4 m/s, and if this velocity represents the velocity u, then the nondimensional frequency $f^*\approx 2$, with Fig.10 showing that $\Delta E/E$ is large and positive. Figure 9 additionally shows $\partial\delta/\partial h\approx 0.05$, leading to $\Delta E/E\approx 0.08$ (in Fig.10 if $\omega\tau = 0$). The oscillation growth rate with no damping is as follows,

$$\zeta = \frac{1}{2}\log(1+\frac{\Delta E}{E}) \qquad (14)$$

where ζ is the oscillation logarithmic growing rate, with $\zeta\approx 0.038$ using this model. Again the experimental results agree well because a $\zeta\approx 0.03$ was obtained experimentally.

Figure 6 shows the experimental oscillating regions. For both the Type A and B cases the oscillation occurred when $V/fW\approx 1$, causing this relation to be modified as follows,

$$\frac{V}{fW} = \frac{V}{u}\cdot\frac{1}{f^*}\approx 1 \qquad (15)$$

Equation (15) shows that the oscillation occurs at $f^*\approx V/u$. In Type A the ratio between the inlet velocity and the velocity under the surface, V/u, becomes $1.5\sim 3.0$. And in the region $f^*\approx 1.5\sim 3.0$, the value $\Delta E/E$ is large and positive, indicating that the presented model explains the experimental results well. However, when the inlet velocity increased the oscillation did not occur. In this particular region $f^*\approx 0.5\sim 1.0$, and the value $\Delta E/E$ is also large and positive, yet the increased velocity makes the $\partial\delta/\partial h$ negative, so as to dampen the oscillation.

By these results the presented model can be

used to explain well oscillation growth, although it should be noted that this model contains an unknown phase lag factor $\omega\tau$, and the surface perturbation modeling region is only on right side at $0 < x < L/2$. Some experimental results can not be explained, i.e., the difference in the oscillating regions between Type A and D, and Type A and C. These differences are believed to be caused by the differences in the flow pattern transformation, thus requiring a more detailed theoretical model to explain these differences.

7. Conclusion

A self-induced free surface oscillation was observed in a thin rectangular tank having circulating flow. The characteristics of this oscillation were investigated, and an oscillation energy supply mechanism was proposed. This model was based on the flow pattern transformation and successfully explained the experimental results. Using the experiment and the theoretical model the following results were obtained

(a) The oscillation frequency was equal to the first order eigenvalue of liquid in a tank without flow.

(b) The oscillating region was summarized by showing in a map form the inlet velocity, water level and test section geometries.

(c) Due to the flow pattern transformations, $\partial\delta/\partial h$ is found to be positive at specific inlet velocities and water levels.

(d) When $\partial\delta/\partial h > 0$ and $-f^* \approx 1$, oscillations occurred.

REFERENCES

1 **Nakagawa,H.,** Current Status of Design and Development of DFBR in Japan , *Journal of the Atomic Energy Society of Japan,* 1988, **30** - 11, 963-970. (In Japanese)

2 **Laithwaite,J.M. and Taylor,A.F.,** Hydraulic problems in the PFR coolant circuit, *Proc. IAEA Symp. on Sodium Cooled Fast Reactor Eng.,* Monaco,1970,pp. 75-

3 **Hagiwara,T., Okamoto,K. and Madarame,H. ,** The flow pattern of the circulating flow with surface in a tank, *J. Nucl. Sci. Technol.,* to be submitted.

4 **Hagiwara,T.,** A numerical analysis of two-dimensional turbulent flow in a tank with a free surface, *Proc. 4th Int.Symp. on Refined Flow Modeling and Turbulence Measurements,* Wuhan,1990

5 **Nichols,B.D. et.al.** SOLA-VOF, A solution algorithm for transient fluid flows with multiple free boundaries, *LA-8355,* 1980

6 **Lamb,H.** *Hydrodynamics,* 6th edition, 1932(Cambridge)

C416/002

Propulsor blade singing — an experimental investigation of its generation and control

R L POWELL, IEng and N A SHELLEY, BA, MSc, GIMA
Marconi Underwater Systems Limited, Waterlooville, Hampshire

SYNOPSIS Propulsor blades sometimes produce loud discrete tones due to a phenomenon known as singing, which is caused by the interaction of trailing-edge vortex shedding with structural vibration of the blade, leading to a self-excited vibration. This paper describes a research programme aimed at understanding the phenomenon. It includes studies of the modal behaviour of blades which are used to predict the onset of singing by correlation with vortex shedding frequencies and blade dimensions. The search for a robust control technique encompassing both hydrodynamic and structural solutions is also described. A new trailing edge modification has been identified which has been found to eliminate singing on a wide range of blades.

NOTATION

S	Strouhal Number
f_s	vortex shedding frequency (singing frequency)
$d(t)$	trailing edge thickness
V_∞	fluid flow velocity
f_n	natural frequency of blade in water

1 INTRODUCTION

At the trailing edge of lifting surfaces the boundary layer separates and the flow tends to form a pattern of discrete swirling vortices. These vortices shed alternately from either side of the body forming a regular pattern, the well known Karman vortex streets (1). This vortex shedding generates periodic forces on the structure and, if the shedding frequency coincides, "locks-in" with a structural natural frequency, resonance occurs. This form of excitation can produce considerable acoustic energy known as singing when associated with propeller blades in water. Such a source of noise is unacceptable for military underwater vehicles.

There is an extensive bibliography covering experimental work on singing (e.g. 2, 3). Examination of that bibliography highlighted not only the complexity of the problem but also the importance of conducting model experiments at or very close to the full-scale Reynolds Number to minimise complex scaling effects. This examination further revealed that very little data has been gathered on three dimensional hydrofoils at high Reynolds Numbers (>3 x 10⁵) although extensive vortex shedding data exists on the study of simple flat plates and circular cylinders over a wide range of Reynolds Numbers.

2 RESEARCH PROGRAMME

The overall objective of the research programme was to explore means of eliminating or avoiding singing on both fixed and rotating blades.

The programme was broken down into three distinct phases.

Phase 1: Identify a facility where singing could be studied experimentally in a laboratory. Prove the facility, i.e. demonstrate that singing occurs and is representative of in-water trials.

Phase 2: Explore and understand the mechanism of singing and identify methods for control and elimination.

Phase 3: Explore manufacturing aspects.

Phases 1 and 2 have been completed but the final phase, proving that the control techniques identified experimentally are viable from a practical/manufacturing point of view, is not yet complete.

3 DEVELOPMENT OF HIGH SPEED TEST FACILITY AT NEL EAST KILBRIDE

Early in 1985 it was decided to study this phenomenon under laboratory conditions. A survey was undertaken of all UK facilities, presently available. This showed that none were suitable as they were unable to provide the flow speeds and working area sufficient to enable singing to be studied at conditions of interest to MUSL. Although possible facilities were identified elsewhere in Europe and the USA, the cost and inconvenience precluded their use.

However, a visit to the National Engineering Laboratory (NEL), East Kilbride, Scotland (4) showed promise of providing the required speeds with modifications to the Variable Pressure Water Tunnel (VPWT). A new working section, along with its associated inlet and outlet pipework, was designed and manufactured to MUSL's requirements.

The rig was installed in the NEL VPWT as shown in Fig 1. The working section (see Fig 2) is capable, by interchanging components, of holding blades fixed at both ends (fixed-fixed) or those fixed at only one end (fixed-free) (see for example Fig 3). The blades are installed in a turn-table which can be used to vary the angle of attack. The working section is 500 mm in length with a width and height of 250 and 100 mm respectively. Acrylic windows have been incorporated on two sides of the working section to aid viewing, photographic and video work. The air content and tunnel pressure can be varied to suit test requirements.

Calibration of the working section velocity profile was undertaken using a pitôt rake arm. This provided a correlation between tunnel pump speed (the main control parameter) and the mean velocity in the working section. Flow speeds up to 35 m/s can be achieved in the working section.

4 MODAL BEHAVIOUR OF PROPULSOR BLADES

Singing depends critically on the natural frequencies and damping of the blades. In order to be able to correlate the acoustic effects of singing with the structural vibration of the blades the modal behaviour of the blade was examined. The blades were tested by attaching an accelerometer to the blade and then exciting the blade with a force hammer. Analysis of the frequency response functions obtained enabled natural frequency, mode shape and damping levels to be calculated. The blades tested include both fixed-fixed and fixed-free. The test rig used for the modal analysis represents the configuration at NEL, i.e. the fittings are representative and the test piece is under water.

Both bending and torsional modes were encountered. As a result of the shape of the blades some modes were more complex, being apparently combinations of bending and torsional modes. Fig 4 illustrates the shapes of the more common modes encountered.

5 TESTING OF PROPULSOR BLADES AND CORRELATION WITH MODAL DATA

5.1 Testing

Each different type of blade, both fixed-fixed and fixed-free, was tested extensively in the working section.

Prior to the tests, the modal pattern of each blade was obtained by Modal Analysis techniques. In-water damping and natural frequencies were established along with nodal lines. This information was then used to determine the position on each blade where strain gauges were to be applied. It was not possible to attach accelerometers to the blade in the working section as they either disturbed the flow or affected the vibration performance of the blade. The piezo electric gauges have a frequency response sufficient to enable measurement of any singing frequency encountered. The response of the gauges thus enabled frequency and mode shape to be determined.

Direct measurements of radiated noise from a singing blade were not possible as hydrophones could not be placed in the water tunnel. It was found, however, that an accelerometer attached to the side window of the working section was sufficiently isolated from the blade for its output to be dominated by radiated noise.

Both strain gauge and accelerometer channels were connected, as shown in Fig 5, and their outputs recorded on magnetic tape. Each blade was tested, at zero incidence, over the velocity range 0-35 m/s by increasing the pump speed, in 50 rpm increments, from zero to 900 rpm.

Analysis of the vibration data over the 0-10 kHz frequency range was undertaken and any 'singing' noted. Tests were then conducted to establish the onset and offset of singing at each discrete frequency. A method of testing was established which involved increasing the pump speed from 100 rpm to the maximum in approximately 90 seconds.

This test procedure enabled a waterfall plot (time history spectrogram) to be made which gave a rough guide to the response of the blade.

The tests on each blade included testing at various tunnel pressures to simulate depth and also the effect of the angle of blade incidence to the flow.

5.2 Correlation of Testing with Modal Analysis and Blade Geometry

The singing frequencies encountered were compared with the frequencies obtained during modal analysis. In all cases the singing frequencies coincided with a natural frequency. In the case of fixed-free blades the most severe singing was associated with the first bending and first torsional modes of vibration. The mode shapes in these cases both have large movements of the trailing edge, particularly at the tip. For fixed-fixed blades the most severe singing again correlated with the first bending and torsional modes although in this case maximum movement occurred mid span of the trailing edge. It should be noted that although singing always occurred at a natural frequency it did not occur at every natural frequency. Singing only occurred at frequencies with mode shapes where the trailing edge movement resembled that of the first bending mode.

In order to be able to predict the likelihood of singing at the design stage two basic factors need to be known. These are firstly the natural frequencies of the blade, which can be predicted from finite-element analysis, and secondly the vortex shedding frequency. Measurements of singing from flat plates and cylinders, (5), have shown that at high Reynolds Number, the vortex shedding frequency can be predicted using the formula

$$S = \frac{f_s d(t)}{V_\infty}$$

Strouhal numbers (6) of 0.18 and 0.22 have been found, by other researchers, for flat plates and cylinders respectively. Averaging many results for propulsor blades in the test facility at NEL yields a Strouhal Number of 0.12 and this is the value to be used in prediction work.

Conversely the flow velocity past the blade, needed to induce singing, can be predicted from the natural frequencies obtained during modal analysis by rewriting the above equation as:

$$V_\infty = \frac{f_n d(t)}{S}$$

Fig 6 illustrates the correlation between singing frequencies obtained during testing and the natural frequencies.

6 STUDYING THE PHENOMENON

Once it had been established that singing occurred in the facility, several blades, both fixed-fixed and fixed-free, were produced to enable studies of the generation and control to be undertaken. The blades were produced from a variety of materials including aluminium and stainless steel.

6.1 High Speed Videography

Attempts were made to capture visually the vortex shedding, from a singing blade, using High Speed Videography (HSV). The NEL Kodak EKTAPRO 1000 motion analyser system was commissioned for this task. Biodegradable dyes (identified and supplied by ICI) of various colours and strengths were injected into the flow utilising the wall static holes and a compressed air supply. This was only partially successful for a number of reasons which include heat generation of high intensity lighting (which would have affected the structural integrity of acrylic windows) and frame limitation of the system. These tests were therefore curtailed.

© IMechE 1991 C416/002

6.2 Standard Video

Tests were conducted with a standard video system (VHS). In this instance air was injected into the working section. This was more successful than the HSV in that the boundaries of the vorticity were captured on film when the blade (a stainless steel rotor blade) was in singing (1st torsional-chosen as the most responsive frequency) and non-singing conditions. These films were studied in the NEL film studios and showed that at the condition of singing the separation of the cores was approximately 1.5 mm with the vortex core being approximately 1 mm in diameter.

6.3 Laser Doppler Anemometry (LDA)

As a result of the above findings the NEL Laser Group was commissioned to help with our studies making use of one of their in-house LDA systems. This work involved constructing an enclosure around the working section with the laser units isolated from tunnel vibration by a suspension system.

A 5 watt argon-ion laser was installed and the dual laser beams were directed by a series of mirrors through the lower window, close to the trailing edge of the blade.

The LDA velocity traverses produced information on the wake of the blade, vortex size and vortex shedding frequencies for both singing and non-singing conditions (7). A software auto-correlation technique was used to obtain vortex frequencies from the analysed data.

This work has been presented separately (8) at the Third International Conference on Laser Anemometry Advances and Applications held at the University College of Swansea, Wales 26-28 September 1989.

6.4 Flow Visualisation

Further attempts were made to study the phenomenon by utilising a stroboscopic lamp in conjunction with a video camera. Air was injected into the flow, the frequency of the illumination was set to the singing frequency and the blade and flow recorded on video tape. This technique, which has been limited to speeds less than 10 m/s has been extremely successful in revealing individual vortices.

7 CONTROL OF SINGING

The research now centred on finding methods of controlling singing. This was approached by looking at different means of control which fell into three main areas. These were internal damping (different materials), additional structural damping and trailing edge treatments.

7.1 Internal Damping

Identical fixed-free blades were manufactured from aluminium, stainless steel, metal matrix composite (MMC) and carbon fibre reinforced plastic (CFRP) to assess the effect of material damping on singing. Each was subjected to modal analysis and fully tested in the facility.

The latter two, despite having the highest damping levels, displayed the most intense noise levels encountered and so, clearly, material damping alone was not going to be the solution.

7.2 Additional Structural Damping

As changes to the material of the blade had not proved sufficient to eliminate singing alternative means of increasing the damping were selected for testing. Two methods of increasing the damping were selected for testing. The first was a MUSL proprietary damping device inserted into the blade whilst the second involved mounting the blade resiliently into the base.

For ease of testing and to utilise the tunnel time effectively fixed-fixed blades were used for this investigation. The damped blades were tested in the rig with varying degrees of success. In all cases the proprietary dampers applied to the blades reduced the singing significantly but did not completely remove the effect at the most severe frequency.

The resiliently-mounted blade also reduced noise levels significantly and in some cases eliminated singing altogether. However, at some speeds high-amplitude, low-frequency vibration was observed. If this concept is to be pursued further the flexibility of the mount will need to be taken into account. Clearly resiliently mounting blades can be a very complex engineering solution so the concept was not pursued further in this research programme.

7.3 Blade Trailing Edge Treatment

A wide variety of trailing edge (TE) treatments was tried. In addition a blade with the machining marks left to form grooves across the surfaces but with a polished leading edge to avoid cavitation effects was tested.

The variations tried were as follows:

(a) Blade was cropped back, from its radiused form, to give a 'square' TE.

(b) Trip wire fitted near TE.

(c) Small holes drilled through blade adjacent to TE.

(d) Anti-singing bevel angles applied to one side of the TE (9).

(e) Trailing edge roughness strips applied in conjunction with the MUSL proprietary dampers fitted to the blade.

None of the treatments succeeded in controlling the singing. Despite the lack of success some interesting results were obtained. For example, the blade fitted with the trip wire only sang at one frequency but over a much greater speed range and the anti-singing bevel angles, the traditional control method, were found to be effective at low speeds but ineffective at higher speeds.

The final treatment tried was a notched edge which has proved successful at eliminating singing on a wide range of blades.

8 NOTCHED EDGE

The visualisation work suggested that singing was associated with spanwise correlation of the vortex shedding with the blade natural frequency. The notching treatment was designed to break that spanwise correlation.

The notched edge treatment was applied to all the blade types previously tested. The notches, essentially dihedra which do not remove any of the chord length, are applied alternately on each side of the blade near the trailing edge. The effect of this treatment even on the 'noisiest' blades i.e. MMC and CFRP, was to eliminate the singing. In some instances the reduction in the noise level was some 50 dB but was typically 30-40 dB.

Further research was carried out, with this modification applied, to study the influence of the modification on the flow at the trailing edge.

Experiments utilising the strobe and seeding the flow with air showed that the notching was breaking up the large vortex sheet into small 'string' vortices emanating from each notch. The reduced energy levels and the lack of spanwise correlation of these vortices meant 'lock-in' could not occur at blade natural frequencies as the fluid flow was increased.

Further tests were carried out with variations of this notching applied until an optimum geometry was established. Further research aimed at identifying cost effective manufacturing techniques is in hand.

Following the success of the notching treatment the concept was submitted for patent.

9 CONCLUSIONS

The research programme undertaken over the last five years has provided a greater understanding of the phenomenon of singing. A test facility has been established which can be used to examine blades at high Reynolds Numbers early in a project to ensure that singing is not encountered. After extensive testing of possible control methods a trailing edge treatment has been identified which shows great promise for a wide range of applications.

REFERENCES

1   Von Kármán, Th "Uber den Mechanisms des Widerstandes, den ein bewegter Körper in einer Flüssigbeit erzeught". Nachr. Ges. Wiss. Göttingen, Math. Phys. Klasse 509-517 (1911) and 547-556 (1912).

2   Blake W K et al "Hydroelastic Variables Influencing Propeller and Hydrofoil Singing" - Proceedings ASMESymposium - Noise Fluids Eng, Atlanta, Ga 191-200 (1977).

3   Gongwer CA "A Study of Vanes Singing in Water" Journal Applied Mechanics 19, 532-538 (1952).

4   G Scobie and J D Leithhead "The NEL Variable Pressure Water Tunnel" Fluid Mechanics Division NEL East Kilbride Glasgow. November 1977.

5   Schlichting H "Boundary Layer Theory" Seventh Edition.

6   Strouhal V "Uber eine besondere Art der Touereging" Ann Physik (Leipzig 1878).

7   Dupont Ph, et al "Wake Flow Analysis for a Hydrofoil with and without Hydroelastic Lock-In". Paper J4 presented at the International Conference of Flow Induced Vibrations, Bowness-on-Windermere, England, 12-14 May 1987.

8   R L Powell (MUSL), Mrs J A Sattary (NEL), E P Spearman (NEL) and Dr M J Reader-Harris (NEL) "The Study of Vortices Downstream of a Hydrofoil using LDA and Correlation Techniques". A paper presented at the Third International Conference on Laser Anemometry Advances and Applications. University College of Swansea, Wales - 26-28 September 1989.

9   Ippen A T et al "The Hydroelastic Behaviour of Flat Plates as Influenced by Trailing Edge Geometry" MIT Hydrodynamics Laboratory Report 1960.

ACKNOWLEDGEMENTS

The authors wish to thank the many people both at MUSL and NEL, who have been involved in this extensive research programme.

The authors would also like to thank the Directors of Marconi Underwater Systems Limited for permission to publish this paper and NEL for permission to use the photographs.

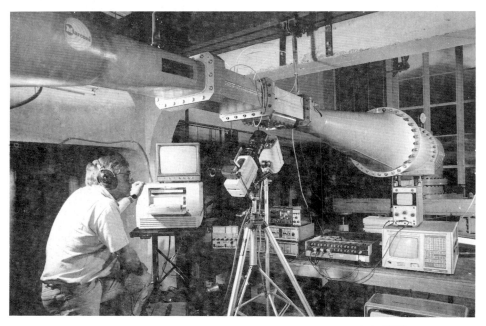

Fig 1   The NEL variable pressure water tunnel with MUSL high speed test sections installed

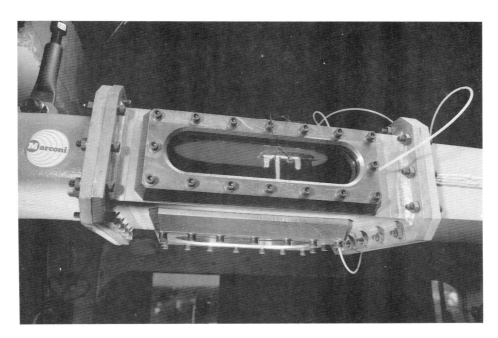

Fig 2   Working section

Fig 3   Fixed-free blade installed in
working section

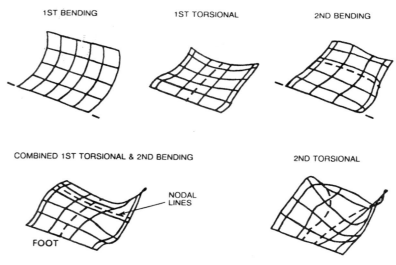

1ST BENDING   1ST TORSIONAL   2ND BENDING

COMBINED 1ST TORSIONAL & 2ND BENDING   2ND TORSIONAL

NODAL
LINES

FOOT

Fig 4   Typical mode shapes for fixed-free
blade

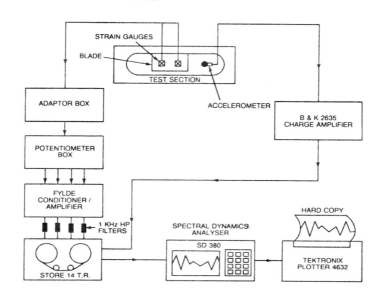

Fig 5   Instrumentation layout

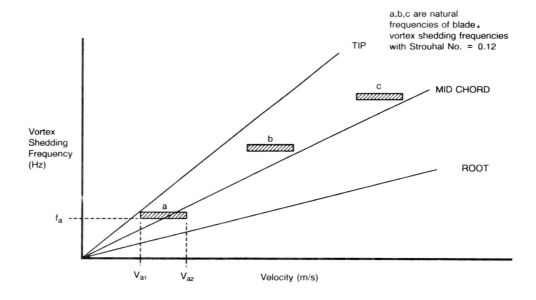

a,b,c are natural
frequencies of blade.
vortex shedding frequencies
with Strouhal No. = 0.12

TIP

MID CHORD

ROOT

Vortex
Shedding
Frequency
(Hz)

f_a

V_{a1} V_{a2} Velocity (m/s)

Blade sings at frequency f_a at velocities V_{a1} to V_{a2}

Fig 6   Correlation between measured natural frequencies, predicted
vortex shedding frequencies and occurrence of singing